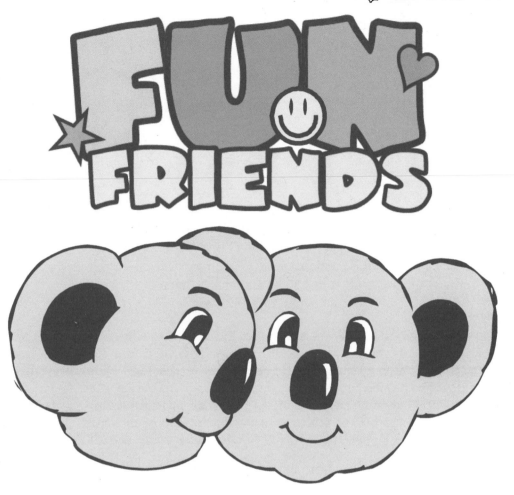

FUN FRIENDS

FUN FRIENDS Workbook for Children:
A Family Guide for Building Resilience with
4 to 7 year-old Children through Play

DR PAULA BARRETT

www.pathwayshrc.com.au

FUN FRIENDS:
A Family's Guide to Building Resilience with 4 to 7 year-old Children through Play

FUN FRIENDS (2nd Ed) 2009
First published in 2007
Barrett Research Resources
PO Box 5699
WEST END QLD 4101
Australia

Canadian version first released in 2009
Reprinted March 2012

ISBN: 978-0-9804571-2-4

All text copyright © 2008 Barrett Research Resources Pty Ltd
Cover design with the support of Gemma O'Brien and Eva Fritz
Typesetting by Cheryll Beaumont
Book content images by Eva Fritz and Gemma O'Brien

DISCLAIMER:
During the preparation of this work, all possible efforts have been made to provide information based on quality standards and acceptable practice at the time of publication. The publisher, however, makes no warranties of any kind in terms of psychological outcome relating to the use of this work and disclaims all responsibility or liability for direct or consequential damages resulting from any use of the material that is contained in this book.

ACKNOWLEDGEMENT:
We would like to gratefully acknowledge the invaluable contribution of Cathy Austin, Director of Austin Resilience Development Inc., for her consultation and conversion to Canadian content of the FUN FRIENDS educational materials.

In British Columbia, funding for these materials <u>for use in schools</u> is provided by the Ministry of Children and Family Development, upon completion of training.

British Columbia schools can order additional copies through a district FRIENDS liaison or e-mail: mcf.cmyhfriends@gov.bc.ca.

iii

CONTENTS

Foreword by Tony Ryan — v

FUN FRIENDS Acronym — vi

Introduction — 1

Session 1: My family and I — 2
    Home Play — 10

Session 2: Understanding feelings in ourselves — 11
    Home Play — 20

Session 3: Understanding feelings in other people — 21
    Home Play — 30

Session 4: Understanding body clues — 31
    Home Play — 40

Session 5: Learning about "red" (unhelpful) and "green" (helpful) thoughts — 41
    Home Play — 47

Session 6: Learning more about "red" (unhelpful) and "green" (helpful) thoughts — 48
    Home Play — 57

Session 7: Learning to set goals and trying to do new things — 59
    Home Play — 67

Session 8: Learning how to be a good friend — 68
    Home Play — 74

Session 9: Learning about rewarding ourselves — 75
    Home Play — 86

Session 10: Learning about role models in our lives — 87
    Home Play — 92

Session 11: Learning about support teams in our lives — 93
    Home Play — 100

Session 12: Learning to be happy with our efforts — 101
    Home Play — 106

Appendix 1: (Sessions 5 & 6) "Green" Thoughts vs "Red" Thoughts — 108

Appendix 2: (Sessions 5 & 6) Thought Bubbles — 110

Appendix 3: (Sessions 5 & 6) Hand Puppet and Finger Puppets — 111

Appendix 4: (Session 8) Friend Chart — 112

Appendix 5: (Sessions 10 & 12)
Someone Special I Know Who is Brave and Kind!!! — 120

Appendix 6: (Session 10) Who is...? — 121

Appendix 7: (Session 12) Pass the Parcel — 122

Graduation Certificate for the FUN FRIENDS Program — 124

FUN FRIENDS: A Family Guide to Building Resilience with 4 to 7 year-old Children through Play
www.ourfunfriends.com www.pathwayshrc.com.au

Copyright © 2008 Paula Barrett
This page is printed in blue on white paper. Any other version is unauthorised.

"I dedicate this book to my children, Ana and Tom, and all the children I have worked with over the years – thank you for everything you have taught me.

Paula Barrett doing the Fun Friends Program for the Pathways to Resilience Charitable Trust with Australian Indigenous Children

> "An important lesson to draw from the entire literature on successful early interventions is that it is the social skills and motivation of the child that are more easily altered—not IQ. These social and emotional skills affect performance in school and in the workplace. We too often have a bias toward believing that only cognitive skills are of fundamental importance to success in life."
>
> James J Heckman, PhD
> Nobel Laureate in Economic Sciences (2000)

FOREWORD

What do teachers most want for their students? Well, they want lots of things, but in my 30 years of working with thousands of brilliant educators all over the world, I hear the same thing over and over; they want support for developing emotional resilience in young people.

The research is indisputable. Prevention is much better than a cure. When children are encouraged to develop their self-worth and resilience, they are more likely to become happy and successful people in their later years. And teachers know this.

The FRIENDS program is already strongly supported by the World Health Organization. This new FUN FRIENDS framework is simply brilliant. It has been scientifically validated through many years of clinical and practical analysis. And it will make a powerful and life-changing difference in the lives of your children.

Tony Ryan
Educational Consultant

ARHRF Acknowledgement

The author, Paula Barrett, wishes to thank the Australian Rotary Health Research Fund for their support with research funding for the Fun Friends Program.

FUN FRIENDS: A Family Guide to Building Resilience with 4 to 7 year-old Children through Play
www.ourfunfriends.com www.pathwayshrc.com.au

Copyright © 2008 Paula Barrett
This page is printed in blue on white paper. Any other version is unauthorised.

Families and School Communities Nurturing Children's Emotional and Social Learning

Acronym of FUN FRIENDS

 F Ü N

Feelings (Talk about your feelings and care about other people's feelings)

Relax (Do 'milkshake' breathing. Have some quiet time)

I can try (Try your best)

Encourage (Be a good friend; Make Step Plans to the "Brave Happy Home")

Nurture (Do fun activities with teachers, family and friends)

Dare to be brave (Practise the skills every day with family and friends)

Stay

www.ourfunfriends.com

The FUN FRIENDS program is designed to teach young children practical, useful strategies for coping with stress, worry, fear and sadness (e.g. how to be brave, solve problems, think positively, relax and face challenges). It helps young children to become more resilient and "bounce back" from challenging or stressful situations they may face. FUN FRIENDS also helps children learn important emotional and social skills that will help them excel during their school years.

The FUN FRIENDS Program has twelve sets of activities (sessions), which take approximately 30 minutes to 1 hour to complete. The program works best if you follow the sessions from 1 to 12, as the social emotional skills taught follow a logical sequence that must be maintained. It is important to complete the activities for each session in the order they appear as they are designed to build on each other.

We suggest that you and your child work on 1 session a week for 12 consecutive weeks. The activities in each session can be worked on throughout the week, not all at once. Please do not expect your child to pay attention for longer than 15 minutes at a time. She/he may need a little break to have a drink, get a hug, move around, or have something to eat! The activities are designed to provide fun, bonding activities between your family members that your child will remember with fondness later in life.

It is helpful to schedule a special time each day or week to work on the FUN FRIENDS activities with your child. It might be in the evenings before bedtime, after dinner, or after breakfast on the weekends. You can include other family members in the discussions and activities. One of the best ways of helping your child learn ways to cope with challenging situations is by talking about how "we as a family" can cope. Remember that you, as parents, are powerful role models for your children. If you model positive coping skills in times of stress, you'll learn as a family and your child will also learn more effectively of course!

Your involvement is important to the success of the program and your child will benefit from lots of opportunities to practise the new skills he/she is learning in every part of his/her life: at home, at school, at play, with extended family, and caregivers. Just like when learning a sport, or learning to riding a bike, practice is the key to really learning the skills. When the FUN FRIENDS program sessions have ended, your child can keep the FUN FRIENDS Family Guide workbook as a reminder on the bedside table and re-visit any relevant session when faced with a challenging situation.

As your child gets older, there are two other versions of the Friends Program that your child may participate in: Friends for Life for elementary school children and a youth version for middle and high school adolescents. The skills taught in each one of these courses, are designed to match the developmental needs and challenges faced in that age group. At both of these two older age levels, there is still parental involvement, but the course must be run by trained teachers in school settings, or by trained mental health professionals. This is to ensure that the Friends Program will be used properly, at an age where some children may have other challenges which must be handled by an independent, unbiased professional.

FUN FRIENDS: A Family Guide to Building Resilience with 4 to 7 year-old Children through Play
www.ourfunfriends.com www.pathwayshrc.com.au

Copyright © 2008 Paula Barrett
This page is printed in blue on white paper. Any other version is unauthorised.

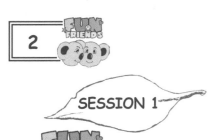

SESSION 1

My Family and I

Learning Components:

- Building a sense of identity
- Feeling scared is OK; we can all learn to be brave
- Being brave: looking people in the eye, smiling, saying hello with a brave voice, trying your best, trying something for the first time, sharing, trying and then coming last and staying happy
- Understanding that we all share similarities and differences
- Learning social skills

First, let's teach our children about being able to describe who they are by sharing information about themselves. This information can include: where they live, their family composition, their home, what they like to do, their pets, their favourite toys or games, and where they go to school. Please ask your children to look you in the eye (and also look other people in the eye), smile and speak with a brave, clear, big voice when sharing this information.

Your children can practise speaking with a brave voice in front of the mirror if necessary. Encourage your children to practise smiling at family members, teachers, and other children. Prompt children to notice how other people seem happy when they smile at them and how most people smile back!

You can help your children learn to talk about themselves with confidence, and also to have a clear sense of identity. They will be able to answer the following questions:

- Who am I?
- What is my name?
- How old am I?
- When is my birthday?
- Who is in my family?
- What pets do I have?
- Where is my home?
- What is my country?
- What is my language?
- What are my favourite foods?
- What are my favourite colours?

- What are my favourite activities?
- What are my favourite sports?
- What are my favourite holidays?

This information helps children develop a strong sense of self and their place in the world.

Talking with a brave voice, looking people in the eye, and smiling more often are basic, easy-to-do social skills which will make friends, family and teachers alike respond favourably to your child. Remember, throughout the family activities book there are **no right or wrong answers or suggestions**, just try your best and encourage your child to give each activity a try.

Picture 1a

ANA, a koala girl, and TOM, a koala boy, and pet dogs POPPY and LILLY

While looking at the picture together, ask your children:

What are the koalas doing?

Where are they playing: in the garden, park, beach, or rainforest?

Where might they live?

What foods do they like to eat most?

What are their favourite games?

What are their favourite colours?

Ask your children to draw themselves first. Help your children to describe the drawing and each detail in it. What colours do they choose? Why? You can also draw yourself as an example for your children, and describe the same things about yourself!

Picture 1a – ANA, a koala girl, and TOM, a koala boy, and pet dogs POPPY and LILLY

FUN FRIENDS: A Family Guide to Building Resilience with 4 to 7 year-old Children through Play
www.ourfunfriends.com www.pathwayshrc.com.au

Picture 1b

A Koala family

Ask your children to draw their families and encourage them to describe each detail.

Draw yourself with your family of origin when you were a young girl or young boy. Describe each detail to your children. Tell your children about some happy, positive memories from your childhood and your own family life when you were a child.

Picture 1b – A Koala family

Picture 1c

A Koala home in the eucalyptus tree

Ask your children to draw their home and encourage them to describe all the details of the home. Ask them to remember some happy times they spent in their home, what happened, and who was with them.

Draw yourself in your home(s) when you were a child. Describe each detail/memory of your own happy home experiences to your child.

People and homes around the world

Get a good illustrated children's Atlas from the local library. Encourage your children to find out about people and homes in different parts of the world such as: the North Pole, Africa, different countries in Europe, different countries in Asia, and Latin America. Why are the houses built so differently? What language do the people speak? What foods do they eat? What type of clothes do they wear?

Discuss with your children some of the similarities we all share. For example, we all have people who love us, we all have homes, we all laugh, we all cry, we all love yummy food, birthdays and parties. We all love hugs, playing fun games, going to the park and cuddling our pets or soft toys. We all cry and we all have hearts! We all have the same colour blood when we fall and hurt our knees!

Go on to discuss how we are also different from one another. Make sure that you reinforce that these differences are exciting and great! We all have different types of families, houses, clothing, languages, names, and sometimes different foods we like too. We are born in different places, and some of us come from different countries.

Make sure you point out that it is great and OK that we are all the same and all different! It would be so boring if we were all exactly the same! There would be no new fun things to learn and no new yummy things to eat!

Animals, birds, reptiles, fish and insect homes

Encourage your children to also find out about different animals, birds, reptiles, fish and insect homes. You will find excellent illustrated books in your local libraries. Which animals live where in the world? What type of home do they make for their babies? Why? Is it the Dad or the Mom who looks after their babies? Or do they take turns?

Picture 1c – A Koala home in the eucalyptus tree

SESSION 1

HOME PLAY

1. Each night (e.g. around the dinner table), ask each member of the family to share at least one positive/ happy thing that happened that day (it can be as small as a hug from Mom!).

2. Help your child practise being BRAVE! Try to reward your child for doing this as much as possible.
   a. Looking people in the eye
   b. Smiling
   c. Using a brave voice
   d. Standing up tall
   e. Trying your best and giving new things a try.

Feelings
(Talk about your feelings and care about other people's feelings)

SESSION 2

 ## Understanding Feelings in Ourselves

Learning Components:

- Identifying feelings in ourselves and others
- Role-playing feelings
- Normalizing all feelings
- Making happy feelings grow

We want to help our children to be able to channel certain feelings into positive behaviours. For example, when feeling angry they can try jumping on the trampoline or running, instead of yelling and punching.

Helpful Hint:

It may be helpful to refer to the unhelpful things our children do as "thumbs down" ideas (e.g. kicking or breaking things) and the helpful things as "thumbs up" ideas. Your family can enjoy playing games where each of you can come up with ideas of what you could do with certain feelings and then put your thumbs up or down!

Picture 2a

4 basic feelings

Ask your children to identify the four basic feelings on the page: happy, sad, worried, and angry.

Play a feelings charade game with your children. Make certain facial expressions and actions and have your children try to guess what feeling it is. Then ask your children to role play certain feelings and you try to guess them.

Explain to your children how you feel in different situations in your life. Explain that everyone feels happy, sad, angry or worried sometimes and that is normal and OK! What counts is what we CHOOSE to do with our feelings.

We can choose to do very unhelpful things that hurt other people's feelings such as yelling, throwing a temper tantrum, running away, breaking things, kicking, or punching. We can also choose to do more helpful things such as drinking water to calm down, taking deep breaths, cuddling our pet or soft toy, hugging our Mom or Dad, or talking about our feelings with a calm voice. We can all try to do this. Sometimes it is easy; sometimes it is not!

 ### Additional Activities

Popsicle stick/paper plate faces or koala feeling faces

Make paper puppets (e.g. with Popsicle sticks and paper plates) with different feeling faces on them and perform a little play.

Feelings Scenarios

Read some scenarios aloud, and have your children point to the appropriate feeling face using the koala pictures or paper plate faces (happy, angry, sad or scared). Some example scenarios you could read aloud might include:

- You lost your favourite toy.
- It's your birthday.
- You fell and skinned your knee.
- You have to do "show and tell".
- You have no one to play with.
- You got a new pet.
- You dropped your ice-cream cone.
- You are going swimming with your family.
- Your little brother/sister knocked over your blocks.
- You are alone in your bed in the dark.
- Your Mom dropped you off at school.

Copyright © 2008 Paula Barrett
This page is printed in blue on white paper. Any other version is unauthorised.

FUN FRIENDS: A Family Guide to Building Resilience with 4 to 7 year-old Children through Play
www.ourfunfriends.com www.pathwayshrc.com.au

Picture 2a – 4 basic feelings

Picture 2b

Different life situations with respective associated feelings

Ask your children to draw a face in each circle to represent the feelings people may be having, and to use different coloured crayons for each feeling.

Picture 2b – Different life situations with respective associated feelings

Picture 2c

Different life situations with respective associated feelings

Ask your children to draw a face in each circle to represent the feelings people may be having, and to use different coloured crayons for each feeling.

Picture 2c – Different life situations with respective associated feelings

Picture 2d

A tree with feelings circles

Ask your children to draw different feelings (facial expressions) in each circle and ask them to tell a story about when they, or a friend, or family member, felt like that and why. Help them out by drawing a couple of circles and explaining when you or people you know, felt like that, and why.,

Picture 2d – A tree with feelings circles

SESSION 2

HOME PLAY

1. Encourage your child to continue identifying feelings in himself/herself and others. Model this yourself. You can share how different situations make you feel; for example, "I feel angry when my children don't do their chores," or "I feel happy when friends come to visit."

2. Discuss helpful things that he/she can do to make himself/herself feel better when he/she has unpleasant feelings (e.g. worried, sad, angry), and encourage him/her to do these things. Praise and reward them whenever he/she tries to take control of their feelings.

3. Keep encouraging your child to practise being BRAVE! Try to reward your child for doing this as much as possible. Some ways your child can practise being brave are by:
   a. Looking people in the eye
   b. Smiling
   c. Using a brave voice
   d. Standing up tall
   e. Trying his/her best and giving it a try.

Feelings

(Talk about your feelings and care about other people's feelings)

 ## Understanding Feelings in Other People

Learning Components:

- Paying attention to other people's feelings – parents, siblings, grandparents, teachers, friends
- Helping other people feel better (empathy training)
- Recognizing other's feelings

You will be helping your children to "feel what other people feel" and develop empathy skills. We want children to understand feelings in other people and help them feel better. We are helping children learn that it is important to help others feel better.

Picture 3a

One koala child is alone near the tree while other koala children are having fun playing together with a ball or climbing trees with a friend.

Allow your children to colour in the picture and talk about what the koalas in the picture are doing. Ask your children to identify the different feelings the koala children may be having in the drawing.

Ask your children what they could do to make the lonely koala feel better. Try to help your child come up with as many answers as possible, such as: talk to the koala, invite the koala to play, hug the koala, share a toy with the koala or give the koala a drawing.

Ask your children to identify the feeling that the koala climbing the tree may be experiencing. Ask questions like:

"What could the koala, already on the tree, do to help the koala who is trying to get on the tree?"

"What would the koala climbing feel once he got to the top?"

"How would the koala that helped the other feel if his friend made it to the top of the tree?"

Picture 3a – One koala child is alone near the tree while other koala children are having fun
playing together with a ball or climbing trees with a friend.

Picture 3b

Dad koala is feeling sick in bed, so his son koala is sitting next to him.

Ask your children what the Dad koala may be feeling. Encourage them to come up with many different feelings that the Dad koala may have such as feeling sore, sad, miserable, lonely, bored, unhappy, or helpless.

Ask your children what the boy koala may be feeling. Again, ask your child to come up with many ideas. He may be feeling sad for his Dad but happy he can help him feel better. He may be worried about his Dad being sick, or he may feel loving towards his Dad.

Ask your children to come up with as many ideas as possible on what they can do to help their Dad (or Mom) feel better. For example, they can: give him a drink, prepare some food for him, ask friends and family to come and visit, bring him some beautiful flowers to put on his bedside table, sing him a song, give him a hug, make him an "I love you" card, talk to him about happy things, or ask him what he would like them to do for him.

Picture 3b – Dad koala is feeling sick in bed so his son koala is sitting next to him.

Picture 3c

Grandma and Grandpa koala walking into their tree-home, with walking sticks, with the help of their grandchildren

Ask your children to describe the drawing, and say what they think their grandma and grandpa may be feeling. Encourage your children to come up with as many ideas as possible. For example, their grandma and grandpa might be feeling sore in their legs, very tired, frustrated they can't walk easily by themselves. They may feel happy to have helpful grandchildren and also each other's company, and happy that they are going home to have a rest and some yummy lunch.

Ask your children to come up with as many ideas as possible for what they can do to help their grandparents feel happy.

Picture 3c – Grandma and Grandpa koala walking into their tree-home, with walking sticks, with the help of their grandchildren

Picture 3d

Multiple family activities

Ask your children to find koalas without a facial expression in the drawing and ask them to guess what that koala may be feeling and why. Draw the feelings on the faces of the koalas you find without the face completed (in total 5 koalas!), depending on the situation they may be in. Encourage your child to tell a story about that situation. Give your child examples, such as:

"Two friend koalas were climbing up a tree and moving across one of the branches to get an especially yummy gum leaf, but the branch snapped with the weight of the heavy little koala, and 'oops', down he came with a thump!"

"What do you think the koala who fell may have been feeling?" "What do you think his friend koala who was watching him fall from up the tree may have been feeling?" "Try and guess. Remember there is no right or wrong!"

Encourage your children to find all the koalas who may need THEIR help, and ask them to draw themselves – the kind "helper me"!!

 ## Additional Activities

Look through a magazine or old picture book with your children. Have your children identify feelings demonstrated in the pictures. If possible, cut out the pictures to re-use. Discuss how the person in the picture feels by looking at the facial expression and body language. Ask your children why the person might they feel this way and what they think could have happened (e.g. Someone snatched their toy; their friend did not want to play). Most importantly, ask your children to come up with ideas on what they can do to help them feel better!

You can also practise one of the feelings songs taught in the program!

Song (sung to the tune of "Twinkle, Twinkle Little Star")

We have feelings
Yes it's true
Let's all sing about a few

I feel happy helping others
I feel scared without my mother
I feel sad when friends don't share
I feel mad when things aren't fair

All our feelings are OK
What counts is what we do and say

We have feelings
Quite a few
We can think of what to do

Picture 3d – Multiple family activities

SESSION 3

HOME PLAY

1. Encourage your child to continue identifying feelings in himself/herself and others. Model this yourself.

2. Discuss things that your children can do to make himself/herself feel better when he/she has unpleasant feelings. This is called self-soothing or self-regulation. For example, if you are sad, have a cuddle, talk to someone you love, play with a pet, have a bubble bath. If you are angry, go to a "chill out zone," have a cool drink of water, or do something physical (run/swim). If you feel worried, talk to Mom or Dad, listen to some nice music, or play a fun game. Praise them for what they tell you and for doing these things.

3. Ask your child to try and work out what other people may be feeling by looking carefully at their faces and bodies. Remind him/her to help one person every day to feel better, even if it is just giving a hug or a glass of water!

4. Keep encouraging your child to practise being BRAVE! Try to reward your child for doing this as much as possible.

Relax

(Do "milkshake" breathing. Have some quiet time)

SESSION 4

Understanding Body Clues

Learning components:
- Paying attention to what your body is telling you. "Listen"!!
- Breathing slowly/milkshake breathing!
- Playing relaxation games

You will be helping your children to understand that their body is being their friend by giving them body clues or signs (e.g. stomach ache, heart beating fast) to let them know when they need to have some quiet time and relax.

It is important to practise relaxation for 10 minutes every day, such as when you get home from work, when children get home from school or before going to sleep to help get a good night's sleep! The relaxation should occur as a group/family rather than individually.

Like brushing your teeth, practising relaxation together should become part of the family routine. By doing this you are giving a life-long gift to your children! The belief that anyone has the power to make themselves feel better by choosing to calm down, do slow, deep "milkshake" breathing and take their minds into a favourite place is quite powerful and has many practical applications.

Picture 4a

The koala has butterflies in his tummy and his heart is beating fast.

Show your children the drawing of the koala with a worried look on his face, butterflies in his tummy and his heart beating fast. Explain to your children that there are other body clues our body can give us when we are feeling worried, scared, sad or angry. For example:

"You can get a headache, tummy ache, get sweaty, have red cheeks, and get goose-bumps, tears, a sore throat, or shaky legs. It may be hard to go to sleep at night. But this does not mean you are getting sick! It only means your body is being your friend and giving you warning signs that you need to relax and calm down. You can take deep slow breaths, make your body soft like a rag doll, have a drink of water, wash your face with cold water, hug your Mom or Dad, play with a pet, play with other children, or talk about the problem with someone in your family or a teacher."

You can help your children play the "robots and jellyfish" game as a basic introduction to relaxation, i.e. tense all your muscles, go stiff like a robot, then, go limp and floppy like a jellyfish. Children usually love playing this game and it helps them get used to differentiating the feelings of tension and relaxation in their bodies.

Picture 4a – The koala has butterflies in his tummy and his heart is beating fast.

FUN FRIENDS: A Family Guide to Building Resilience with 4 to 7 year-old Children through Play
www.ourfunfriends.com www.pathwayshrc.com.au

Picture 4b

A boy and a girl have butterflies in their tummies, are sweating, have shaky arms, and their hearts are beating fast.

Ask your children to work on the drawing of their own gender. Ask them to draw inside the boy or girl picture anything that may happen to their own bodies when they are feeling nervous or scared. Talk about your own body clues. Everyone is different!

Ask your children to colour in red the body clues that they experience when they get upset or scared.

Explain to your child that **everyone feels worried and nervous when difficult things happen. It is normal and healthy.** It is what **we choose** to do with our feelings that count the most.

Picture 4b – A boy and a girl have butterflies in their tummies, are sweating, have shaky arms, and their hearts are beating fast. Help your child to write their name above the drawing that looks like them.

FUN FRIENDS: A Family Guide to Building Resilience with 4 to 7 year-old Children through Play
www.ourfunfriends.com www.pathwayshrc.com.au

Picture 4c

A koala Dad with his child resting on the hammock, two koala friends going on a bike ride and a picnic, two koalas reading a book and drawing, a koala having a rest and cuddling up with a pet, a koala relaxing in a bubble bath

Ask your children to come up with other ideas of fun and calm things to do when they are feeling nervous or upset. Examples: ask for a hug, talk to Mom or Dad, have a swim, or go for a run in the backyard.

Ask your children what other ideas they have for helping themselves feel happy and relaxed. Some ways to relax are: riding a bike, walking the pet dog, making yummy food with Mom or Dad, playing a board game with friends, skipping, singing, dancing, looking at a book, or helping to plant flowers in the garden.

Ask your children to do a drawing of themselves doing something they enjoy and that makes them happy. They can do this activity to help themselves calm down when they are feeling upset, worried or scared. Please explain that there is **no right or wrong**. They can just try!

Picture 4c – A koala Dad with his child (resting on the hammock), two koala friends going on a bike ride and a picnic, two koalas reading a book and drawing, a koala having a rest and cuddling up with a pet, a koala relaxing in a bubble bath

Picture 4d

A koala family lying on their relaxation mat with eye pillows on and doing their "milkshake" breathing (take slow breaths in through your nose and out through your mouth)

Practise "milkshake" breathing, first in a plastic glass that is 1/3 filled with water with a long straw. Teach your children to blow slowly into the glass for a long time and to make small bubbles in the water. Slow, deep breathing makes us calm down and feel relaxed!

Teach your children and yourself to do some basic relaxation exercises. Help your children lie on the floor with a pillow under their feet, or on a blanket in the backyard or park, with a soft eye pillow on their eyes.

"Take 4 very deep slow breaths in through your nose and out through your mouth. Imagine you are breathing in through your nose calm, happy feelings and breathing away angry and sad feelings out through your mouth. The wind is blowing those sad, worried and angry feelings far away from you. Now, make all your muscles as hard and stiff as possible, then relax, and shake your arms and legs gently." Repeat the tensing and relaxing again.

"Now imagine your favourite park or your favourite beach. Imagine all the fun things you can see, all the sounds you can hear, all the beautiful scents you can smell, all the tastes of all the yummy foods you can eat and drink, and how the water and sand at the beach, or grass in the park feels on your skin."

Help your children draw their favourite, peaceful place. Go through it with them and write down all the details about their place. Get your children to think of a favourite, peaceful, calm place in detail (e.g. a park, beach, holiday house, or their bedroom). You can use the details for imagery.

 Additional Activity

Before doing "milkshake" breathing, you can practise the song learned in the program about "milkshake" breathing.

Song Use the tune for "Twinkle, Twinkle Little Star".

"We can fill our lungs with air
Like we've got balloons in there
Then we breathe out soft and slow
Making bubbles as we go.
Milkshake breathing is so fun
It's for me and everyone!"

Practise "milkshake" breathing first in a plastic
glass, 1/3 filled with water with a long straw.
Teach your children to blow slowly into the
glass for a long time to make small bubbles in
the water. Slow deep breathing makes you calm
down and feel relaxed!

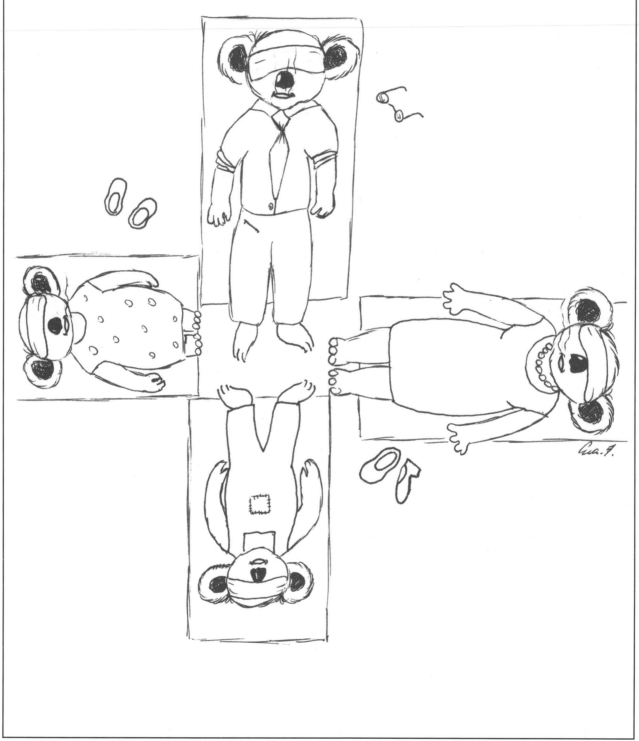

Picture 4d – A koala family is lying on relaxation mats with eye pillows on and doing their "milkshake"
breathing (take deep slow breaths in through your nose and out through your mouth).

FUN FRIENDS: A Family Guide to Building Resilience with 4 to 7 year-old Children through Play
www.ourfunfriends.com www.pathwayshrc.com.au

SESSION 4

HOME PLAY

1. Encourage your child to continue identifying feelings in himself/herself and to do things that make him/her feel better when he/she have unpleasant feelings.

2. Practise relaxation strategies every day for at least 10 minutes. Try to create a calm environment when you do this (e.g. no distractions such as TV).

3. Encourage your child to use relaxation strategies to calm down if he/she feel upset, worried or angry (e.g. use "milkshake" breathing and imagine a peaceful place). Reward him/her for using these strategies in times of stress.

4. Continue praising and rewarding your child for being BRAVE!

I can try

(Try your best)

Learning about "Red" (unhelpful) and "Green" (helpful) thoughts

Learning components:

- Choosing to make our unhelpful "RED" thoughts – STOP!
- Choosing to make our helpful "GREEN" thoughts – GO!

You will be helping your children learn about the following: "red" (unhelpful) and "green" (helpful) thoughts, the difference between the two types of thoughts, and how these thoughts make them, and other people around them feel.

Examples of "red" and "green" thoughts are provided in the Appendices section of the Family Guide (Appendix 1 & 2). You will also find hand and finger puppets to cut and colour in with your children (Appendix 3). The sad faces are to be coloured red and the happy faces are to be coloured green. Throughout this session, teach your children to raise their red hand or finger puppet when talking about sad, scared or angry thoughts. Teach your children to raise their green hand or finger puppet when talking about happy and brave thoughts.

It is not an exercise about good or bad. The emphasis should be that WE CAN be the boss of our thoughts and feelings and behaviours. WE CAN CHOOSE to make our "green" thoughts "go" and our "red" thoughts "stop". We can do it as a family and we can do it as individual people. Emphasize the idea that the more we practise as a family the better we will become at it!

Make sure the family practises every day at meal times. When it becomes easier for everyone, you can even play the game in the car on the way to school!

Picture 5a

Dad takes Ana to school and she is separated from Mom and Dad and Ana is sleeping in her bed by herself and saying goodnight to her Mom and Dad.

The top two squares show a koala family (Mom, Dad and Ana). These squares show two different scenarios of what could happen when Dad takes Ana to school and she is separated from Mom. In the left square, Mom's face and Ana's face look sad, and Dad would also feel upset to see everyone sad. Ana, being upset and scared, could make Mom and Dad also feel sad, because they don't like to see their daughter upset.

Explain to your children what Ana, the little girl koala, may be thinking thoughts such as:

• "I will miss Mom."
• "I will not like school."
• "I will not like the teacher and the other children."
• "School is boring."

This is an unhelpful way of thinking – we call it "red" thinking. We want to STOP our "red thoughts". Just like at a red traffic light when driving a car on the street, we must stop! This way of thinking, which is unhelpful and "red," makes us feel upset and sad and scared, so we try our best to stop it!

In the right square, Mom's face and Ana's face both look happy and relaxed. Dad is taking Ana to school and she is happy to go to school with her Dad because she knows she can have fun with her Mom after school that same day. By being happy and brave, Ana would make her Mom and Dad also feel happy because all parents like to see their children happy and confident and trying out new things!

Explain to your children what Ana, the little girl koala, may be thinking. For example, she may think:

• "I will learn so many new things at school."
• "I will make new friends and have many children to play with."
• "The school has so many nice playgrounds."
• "It will be much more fun than staying at home."
• "I can tell Mom and Dad all about it when I come home after school. I will have so many new things to tell them about!"

This is a helpful way of thinking that we call "green" thinking. Just like at a green traffic light when driving the car, we must GO! This way of thinking, which is helpful and "green," makes us feel brave, happy and like trying new things. We try our best to encourage this way of thinking, "GO! and GROW!" The more we think like this, the braver we become and the happier we feel!

In the bottom drawings, Dad is kissing Ana goodnight. On the left side of the page, Ana is feeling sad because she does not like sleeping in her bed by herself, without Mom and Dad. Ana is thinking she will be scared in the dark, that there may be scary shadows on the wall, and perhaps, there's someone hiding under her bed, ready to jump out! Ana is thinking in unhelpful ways, "red" thoughts – STOP! Like a red traffic light, she must stop and change her thinking. ...continued page 44

Copyright © 2008 Paula Barrett
This page is printed in blue on white paper. Any other version is unauthorised.

FUN FRIENDS: A Family Guide to Building Resilience with 4 to 7 year-old Children through Play
www.ourfunfriends.com www.pathwayshrc.com.au

Picture 5a – Mom and Ana are sad when Dad takes Ana to school, and Mom and Ana are happy when Dad takes Ana to school. Ana is sad sleeping in her bed by herself and Ana is happy saying goodnight to Dad and Mom.

Picture 5a continued

On the right side of the page Ana looks happy saying goodnight to her Dad and Mom. They all look happy! Ana can make herself feel better. She can choose to think that she is safe in her beautiful warm bedroom which is right next to her Mom and Dad's bedroom. She can also think she is going to have lovely dreams about her friends or her holidays on the beach, playing in the ocean and making sandcastles. Thinking like this is helpful because it makes Ana feel brave and happy, and makes the whole family happy too. It is "green" thinking - GO! Ana can become braver and braver!

Picture 5b

Tom is meeting his new teacher at school and standing in his classroom in front of the class for "show and tell" with his teacher.

In the top drawings, Tom is meeting his new teacher at school. On the left side of the page, Tom is feeling worried because he is thinking the teacher may be mean and not like him. Tom is also worried that he won't know where to go at school, or where to find the washrooms or lunch room. He is also worried about all the new things he is going to learn and all the new children he is going to meet. Tom is thinking in unhelpful ways which prevents him from enjoying school and meeting his nice teacher. It is "red" thinking so he must remember to STOP!

On the right side of the page, Tom is feeling happy about meeting his new teacher, and about all the fun games he is going to play with his new friends, and all the exciting things he is going to learn. Tom is now thinking in helpful ways, which make him feel happy and brave about school. This is "green" thinking - GO!

The bottom drawings are of Tom, the little boy koala, in the classroom, standing in front of the class for "show and tell" with his teacher. Explain to your children that Tom's teacher is looking forward to hearing all about what Tom has to say for his "show and tell". His class friends are also looking forward to it.

Tom is feeling very scared, his knees are all wobbly, his heart is beating fast and he is thinking unhelpful "red" thoughts; for example, "I can't do it," "I will make a mistake and everyone will laugh," "I will forget what to say," and "What I was going to say is silly anyway." These "red," "unhelpful" thoughts are making Tom feel even more nervous. He has sweaty palms and teary eyes. His heart is beating even faster than before. He has butterflies in his tummy and a headache!

Then he remembers what he is learning in the FUN FRIENDS Program. Think "helpful," "green" thoughts like "I can do it," and "I have done it before." "I just have to remember that all the other kids do "show and tell" too and it is fun. I will tell them about my holidays at the beach on Stradbroke Island, and how I saw turtles and dolphins. It's easy!" So Tom put a smile on his face, looked all the other kids in the eye, took a few deep slow breaths and spoke with a very confident voice! All the children in the class loved the "show and tell" and the teacher also thought it was excellent. She praised Tom and also gave Tom a great sticker to put on his shirt at the end of the school day!

Picture 5b – Tom is feeling scared meeting his new teacher and then feeling happy meeting his new teacher.
Tom is feeling scared about "show and tell," then he puts a smile on his face.

Help your children go back in this FUN FRIENDS Family Guide to find Picture 3d, a one page drawing of multiple family activities (like a 'Where's Wally' book). Several blank koala faces are scattered through the drawing. The children have to find them and turn them into happy, sad, angry, or worried faces, depending on the life situation that the koalas are in, and colour them in red or green. There are many koalas and families doing different things in the drawing.

Ask your children to colour all the pictures of happy koalas doing fun things **GREEN**. Ask your children to colour all the angry, sad, worried koalas **RED**.

 ### Additional Activities

You can demonstrate "red" and "green" thoughts using a traffic light! Draw a traffic light on cardboard or paper with emphasis on the "red" and "green" lights. Green means GO! Red means STOP! The green light represents "green" thoughts and the red light represents "red" thoughts. We "GO" with "green" thoughts and we "STOP" with "red" thoughts! The yellow light can be seen as a time for changing red thoughts to green thoughts.

Give examples of red and green thoughts to your children and ask them to indicate whether it's a "red" or "green" thought by pointing to the coloured traffic light or by using red and green puppets.

Some red thoughts are:
- "I can't do it. It's too hard."
- "I don't want to try."
- "I'm dumb."
- "I'm no good at drawing."
- "I give up."
- "I have no friends."

Some green thoughts are:
- "I will try."
- "I am brave."
- "I can do it."
- "My teacher or my Mom or Dad can help me."
- "I have lots of friends."
- "I am going to have a good day."

HOME PLAY

1. Explain what "red" and "green" thoughts are to all family members. Read through the list of "green" thoughts in the Appendices and come up with other "green" thoughts.

2. Practise identifying "red" and "green" thoughts as much as possible. Model turning "red" thoughts into "green" ones and assist your child in doing the same with their own "red" thoughts.

3. Practise relaxation strategies every day for at least 10 minutes. Try to create a calm environment when you do this (e.g. no distractions such as TV). Encourage your child to use relaxation strategies to calm down if he/she feels upset, worried or angry (e.g. use "milkshake" breathing and imagine a peaceful place). Reward him/her for using these strategies in times of stress.

4. Continue praising and rewarding your child for being BRAVE!

FUN FRIENDS: A Family Guide to Building Resilience with 4 to 7 year-old Children through Play
www.ourfunfriends.com www.pathwayshrc.com.au

Copyright © 2008 Paula Barrett
This page is printed in blue on white paper. Any other version is unauthorised.

SESSION 6

I can try

(Try your best)

Learning More About "Red" (unhelpful) and "Green" (helpful) Thoughts

Learning components:

• Changing red thoughts into green thoughts

• Throwing away "red" thoughts can be so easy

You will continue to help your children learn about "red" (unhelpful) and "green" (helpful) thoughts. It is important for your children to understand more about the differences between the two types of thinking and how each type of thinking makes them feel.

Explain to your children that WE CAN CHOOSE whether to think "red" or "green" thoughts in every life situation we are faced with. As in session 5, throughout this session, teach your children to raise their red koala hand puppet or finger puppet when talking about sad, scared or angry thinking. Teach your children to raise their green koala hand puppet or finger puppet when talking about happy and brave thinking.

Depending on what we choose to think, we may feel happy or sad. If we choose "red," unhelpful thinking, we will often feel sad and upset. If we choose "green," helpful thinking, we may feel brave and happy. After showing and explaining to your children the examples in the pictures below, please give your children lots of examples of your own everyday life situations. As you often have to live through difficult situations, explain to them the choices you made, what you thought, and how you felt.

You can think of the general way a person thinks about the world as being either the 'glass half full' or 'glass half empty'. We can teach children to think in 'glass half full' ways. Everyone can choose to be a helpful, positive person or the reverse. Discuss with your children which of these types of people it is more fun to be like.

You can also frequently play the "Puppets Game" with your children, so that they can have fun practising guessing "red" and "green" thoughts in a non-threatening way.

Picture 6a

Ana, the koala girl is thinking about the next time she will have to say goodbye to Mom when her Dad takes her to school.

Ana can choose the path on the left and say unhelpful, "red" thoughts in her head like, "Oh no! I have to go to school again; I will miss my Mom too much." Thinking "red" thoughts about leaving Mom and Dad for the day, not knowing everyone at school, and learning new things will make Ana will feel scared and upset.

Explain to your children that as Ana is going along the path, every time, every morning, she CAN CHOOSE the path on the right, and think "green" thoughts. She can think about all the fun things to do at school, and how she can make her Mom and Dad happy by smiling and talking about happy things. Everyone will have a good start to the day – a happy morning! Thinking "green" thoughts will make Ana feel brave and happy and good about herself.

Picture 6a – Ana the koala girl is thinking about the next time she will have to say goodbye to Mom when her Dad takes her to school.

Picture 6b

Tom, the koala boy, is going to school to meet his new teacher for the first time

Tom can CHOOSE to take the path on the left and to say unhelpful, "red" thoughts in his head like, "What if the teacher is scary? What if she does not like me? What if she is mean to me? These "red" thoughts will make Tom feel very scared and upset, and he will not like his teacher.

However, Tom can also CHOOSE to take the path on the right and to think "green" thoughts. He can say to himself that the new teacher will be kind, will help all the children, and will really like Tom if he is a good listener and finishes his work. These "green" thoughts will help Tom feel brave, confident and happy.

Picture 6b – Tom, the koala boy, is going to school to meet his new teacher for the first time.

FUN FRIENDS: A Family Guide to Building Resilience with 4 to 7 year-old Children through Play
www.ourfunfriends.com www.pathwayshrc.com.au

Picture 6c

Dad is kissing Ana goodnight

On the path to the left, Ana CHOOSES to think that she cannot sleep in her own bed because she will be too scared without Mom and Dad. These "red" thoughts make her feel sad, worried and upset.

On the path on the right, Ana CHOOSES to think that she is going to have good, happy dreams and that Mom and Dad are so proud of her for sleeping in her own room. She also thinks that she is safe in her home with her Mom and Dad. She feels happy, calm and confident because she chose to be brave and think "green" thoughts.

Picture 6c – Dad is kissing Ana goodnight

FUN FRIENDS: A Family Guide to Building Resilience with 4 to 7 year-old Children through Play
www.ourfunfriends.com www.pathwayshrc.com.au

Picture 6d

Tom is at school doing "show and tell"

On the path on the left, Tom CHOOSES to think "red" thoughts; for example, he cannot do "show and tell," he has nothing to say, the teacher and the other children do not like what he is saying, he does not like being at school anyway, and does not like all the children looking at him. These "red," unhelpful thoughts make Tom feel even more scared and embarrassed and make him want to run away and give up.

On the path on the right, Tom CHOOSES to think "green" thoughts such as how much fun it is to tell everyone in class about his "show and tell" and all the nice things that have happened. He CHOOSES to smile and speak with a confident voice. His teacher tells him that she is very proud of him, and that he did a great job with his "show and tell" and he feels happy and pleased with himself.

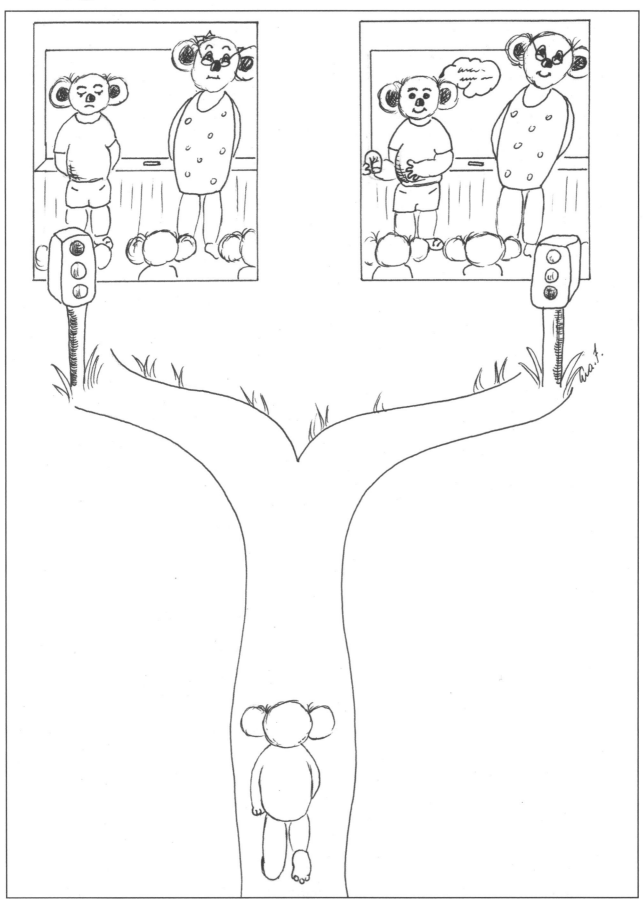

Picture 6d – Tom is at school doing "show and tell"

FUN FRIENDS: A Family Guide to Building Resilience with 4 to 7 year-old Children through Play
www.ourfunfriends.com www.pathwayshrc.com.au

HOME PLAY

1. Assist your children to identify their "red" thoughts and turn them in to "green" thoughts. Practise changing thoughts as much as possible, particularly with "red" thoughts that occur repeatedly.

2. Buy big red envelopes and big green envelopes (or colour some plain ones). After every family mealtime, start with each family member drawing or writing down "red" thoughts they may have had, then place them in the red envelope. Do the same for the "green" thoughts and place them in the green envelope. Finish on a positive note by spending extra time as a family discussing all the "green," helpful, positive thoughts and behaviours. Praise each family member for the "green" ideas shared and talk about how our "green" ideas make us feel proud. At the end of the week, place the red envelopes in the garbage and wave goodbye to them.

3. Practise relaxation strategies every day for at least 10 minutes. Try to create a calm environment when you do this (e.g. no distractions such as TV).

Encourage your child to use relaxation strategies to calm down if he/she feels upset, worried or angry (e.g. using "milkshake" breathing and imagining a peaceful place). Reward him/her for using these strategies in times of stress.

4. Continue praising and rewarding your child for being BRAVE!

Copyright © 2008 Paula Barrett
This page is printed in blue on white paper. Any other version is unauthorised.

FUN FRIENDS: A Family Guide to Building Resilience with 4 to 7 year-old Children through Play
www.ourfunfriends.com www.pathwayshrc.com.au

Encourage

(Be a good friend. Make Step Plans to the "Brave Happy Home")

SESSION 7

Learning to Set Goals and Trying to do New Things

Learning components:

- Learning to do things one step at a time
- Breaking hard things down into lots of little steps
- Learning to be brave!

You will be helping your children to learn how to set goals and try to do new or difficult things. Help your children break difficult, challenging goals into small, easy, achievable steps.

Coping Step Plans can be used to acquire any new skill or overcome a fear or something that they find challenging or difficult. Firstly explain to your child how things can become much easier if we do them one step at a time. Work together with your child on a puzzle to demonstrate. First, find the four corner pieces. Next, find all the pieces with a straight edge. Then, match up pieces of the same colour and join them together. Fill in the gaps with whichever pieces are left, and your puzzle is complete!

Choose a goal with your children, something realistic they would like to be able to do but haven't done yet. Examples of goals for children include:

- brushing their teeth without Mom or Dad asking
- putting toys in the toy box at the end of the day
- trying to swim
- riding a bike without training wheels
- being brave in the dark
- learning to draw or play a musical instrument
- being kind and sharing more with others
- writing their own name

Once you have identified a target goal, write it on the bottom step and break it in to small steps with your child (e.g. 4-5 smaller goals). Each step should be only slightly more difficult than the last one.

The children should practise each step every day, or every two days, until they reach their goal. Children should not move onto the next step until they are ready and have mastered the previous step.

Picture 7a

The "Brave Happy Home" for the child's goals

Your children will arrive at the "Brave Happy Home" when they have climbed to the top step and reached their goals.

You will arrive at the "Brave Happy Home" when your children's goals, your own personal goals (picture 7b), and your family goals (picture 7c) are reached!

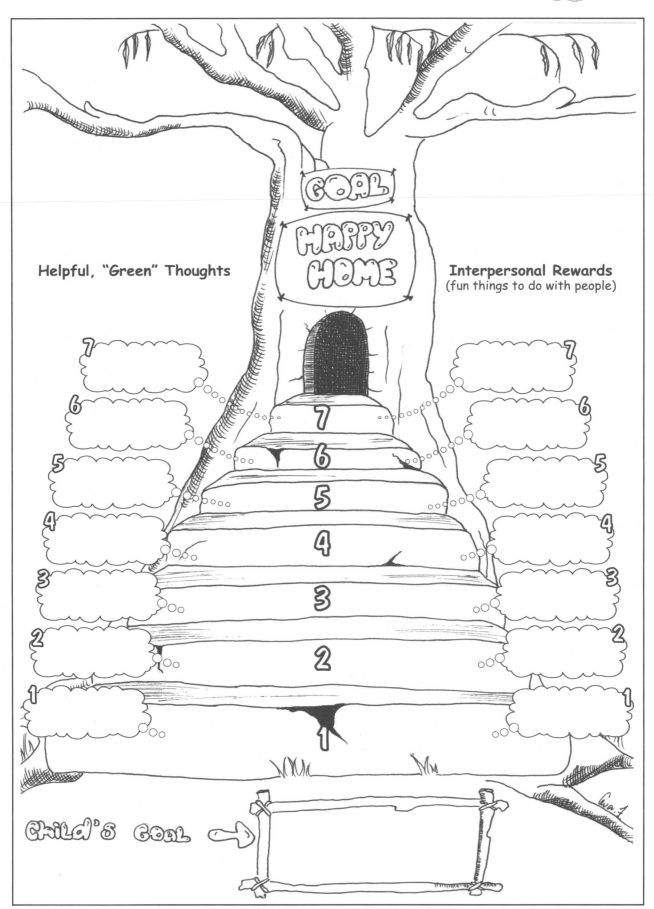

Helpful, "Green" Thoughts

Interpersonal Rewards
(fun things to do with people)

GOAL

HAPPY HOME

Child's Goal →

Picture 7a – the "Brave Happy Home" for the child's goal

Picture 7b

The "Brave Happy Home" for the parent's goal

Set a goal for yourself, such as exercising more or spending more quality time as a family having fun, and write it on the bottom of the page. Help your children do the same on another page. Break the goal into a very small, easy step for each day of the week. The easiest step starts on the bottom: step one – day one, then step two - day two, then step three – day three, until you reach the door of the "Happy Home".

At the end of the Step Plan, you and your children can celebrate by having a little party or picnic in the park. You have both achieved your goals and are in the "Brave Happy Home!"

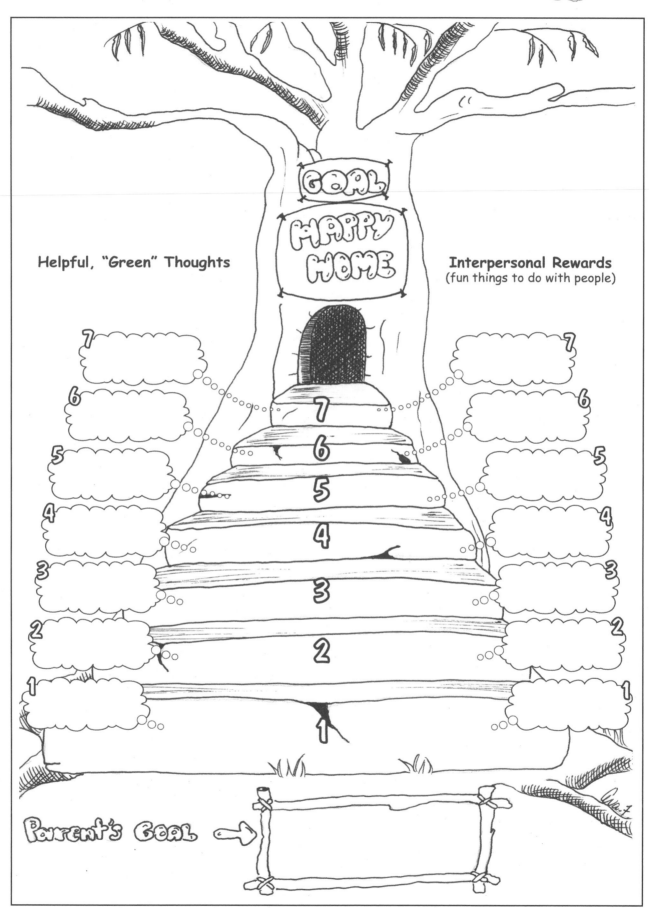

GOAL

HAPPY HOME

Helpful, "Green" Thoughts

Interpersonal Rewards
(fun things to do with people)

Parent's Goal →

Picture 7b – the "Brave Happy ome" for the parent's goal

Picture 7c

The "Brave Happy Home" for the family's goal

Remember to reach the door of the house you have to practise each step many times on that day, so it is easy the next day to climb to the next step! It is important that you reward your children for making small steps, for trying it, not just for achieving the top goal. Every time your children and yourself climb a step, give yourselves a "happy face" sticker and make the time to do something fun together (e.g. make a cake together, invite friends over, go to the park together, go bike riding together). Then you can move on to the next step. Remember that interpersonal rewards are the most powerful and long lasting in terms of positive childhood memories, not material possessions. These tend to be forgotten with time.

Goals can be about varied things your children would like to learn. Remember to always start with easy goals so your children have a sense of mastery and achievement. For example:

- smiling more
- looking people in the eye
- making new friends
- sleeping alone in their bedroom
- winning the battle against Mr. or Mrs. Angry or Mr. or Mrs. Scared
- learning to swim
- learning to ride a bike without training wheels
- learning to eat different foods like fruits and veggies
- being brave when meeting new people
- learning to get dressed in the morning
- learning to brush their teeth by themselves
- learning to put their dirty clothes in the laundry basket
- learning to put their toys away after playing
- learning to set the table and put dirty dishes in the sink, etc.
- speaking with a brave voice in front of the class (e.g. "show and tell")
- being brave when at a doctor or dentist visit

It is important that each person in the family be a positive role model for the children. We can all improve in some aspect of our lives! Goals for you and your family could be:

- exercise more/walk more/use the car less
- go for picnics/have meals together more often
- go to parks and play together more often
- smile more and say kind things to each other more often
- help one person every day, even if you just give them a glass of water

...continued page 66

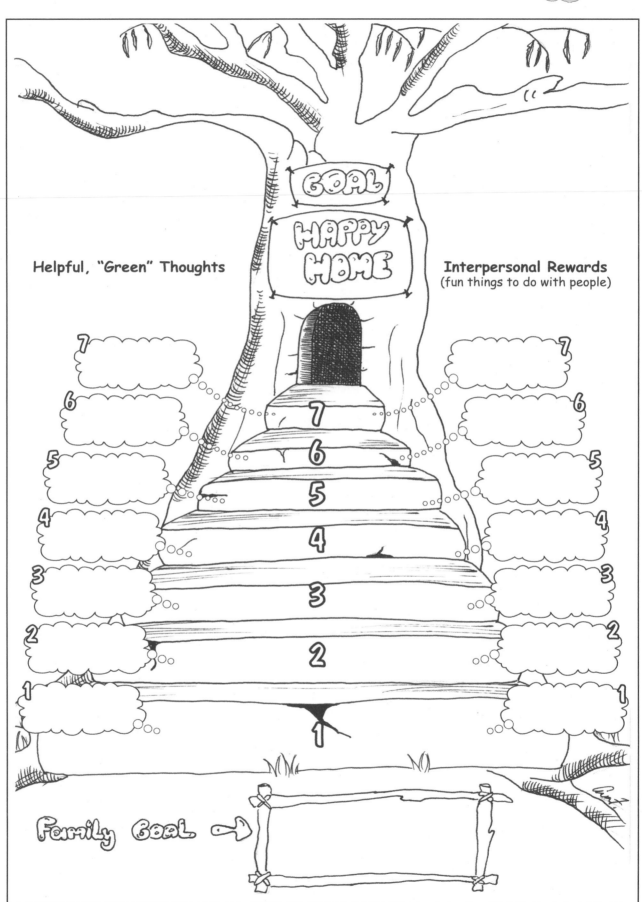

Helpful, "Green" Thoughts

Interpersonal Rewards
(fun things to do with people)

Family Goal →

Picture 7c – the "Brave Happy Home" for the family's goal

Picture 7c continued

- be a good listener to your family members
- do relaxed activities with friends more often
- dance and listen to music more often
- look after your environment every day, in every small way you can.

Together with your children draw your own "Brave Happy Home" on separate pieces of paper, and keep setting new goals every week. Try to start with a Coping Step Plan that you and your child can begin working on this week and have some success with. Once you and your child have successfully completed one coping step plan, move on to more difficult ones.

Goal setting is a lifelong process. We can all improve in kindness, tolerance, being more relaxed, and being open to learning new tasks and exploring new adventures!

It is helpful to come up with and write "green" thoughts and rewards next to each specific step. This way the children will get more motivated to climb their Step Plans!

HOME PLAY

1. Continue to develop your child's Coping Step Plan (if you have not finished it yet), and begin the first step. You may wish to gradually develop more Step Plans once your child has experienced some success with the first one.

2. Continue assisting your child and other children in the family to identify their "red" thoughts and turn them into "green" thoughts.

3. Practise relaxation strategies every day for at least 10 minutes. Try to create a calm environment when you do this (e.g. no distractions such as TV). Encourage your child to use relaxation strategies to calm down if he/she feels upset, worried or angry (e.g. use "milkshake" breathing and imagine a peaceful place). Reward him/her for using these strategies in times of stress.

4. Continue praising and rewarding your child for being BRAVE!

SESSION 8

Encourage

(Be a good friend. Make Step Plans to the "Brave Happy Home")

Learning How to be a Good Friend

Learning components:

· Learning to be friendly and make new friends

· Being a good friend: smiling, sharing, helping, and listening

You will be helping your children learn how to be a good friend by smiling, sharing, helping and listening. Encourage your children to do these things with their friends, family, and new people as well. You may wish to use the Friends chart (Appendix 4) to check off each of the behaviours (smiling, sharing, helping, listening) your child uses during the week. Reward their kind and friendly behaviour (e.g. praise, hug, sticker).

Talk to your children about the people who have been good friends to you (both now and in your childhood). What makes them good friends? And how were you good friends to them? Talk about the importance of smiling, sharing, helping and listening behaviours.

Picture 8a

Tom has fallen off his bike and hurt his knee!

Tom has just learned to ride his bike without the training wheels, with the help of his Mom, Dad and big brother! Here, we can see that poor Tom has fallen off his bike and hurt his knee! What do you think Tom is feeling? Imagine that you are there. What could you do to be a good friend to him?

Picture 8a – Tom has fallen off his bike and hurt his knee!

Picture 8b

Ana on her beach holiday building sandcastles, playing in the water, relaxing with Mom and Dad and exploring the rock pools for little sea creatures

Ana has just gotten back from a holiday with her family at the beach. Look at all the wonderful things she did: building sandcastles, playing in the water, relaxing with Mom and Dad, exploring the rock pools for little sea creatures. Ana wants to tell you all about it. What could you do to be a good friend to Ana?

Picture 8b – Ana on her beach holiday building sandcastles, playing in the water,
relaxing with Mom and Dad and exploring the rock pools for little sea creatures

Picture 8c

Ana is so hungry but she forgot to bring her lunchbox to school!

It is lunch time at school, but Ana forgot to bring her lunchbox! She is so hungry from all her playing and running around, but Ana is sad because she does not know what to do! How could you help Ana feel better?

Picture 8c – Ana is so hungry but she forgot to bring her lunchbox to school!

SESSION 8

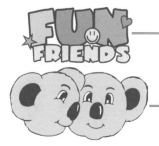

HOME PLAY

1. Continue to develop your child's Coping Step Plan (if you have not finished it yet), and begin the first step. You may wish to gradually develop more Step Plans once your child has experienced some success with the first one.

2. Praise your child when they show listening, helping, smiling and sharing behaviours throughout the week.

3. Continue assisting your child and other children in the family to identify their "red" thoughts and turn them into "green" thoughts.

4. Practise relaxation strategies every day for at least 10 minutes. Try to create a calm environment when you do this (e.g. no distractions such as TV). Encourage your child to use relaxation strategies to calm down if he/she feels upset, worried or angry (e.g. use "milkshake" breathing and imagine a peaceful place). Reward him/her for using these strategies in times of stress.

5. Continue praising and rewarding your child for being BRAVE!

Encourage

(Be a good friend. Make Step Plans to the "Brave Happy Home")

SESSION 9

Learning About Rewarding Ourselves

Learning components:

- Learning to reward ourselves when we've tried our best!
- Learning how to plan a party, step-by-step

Rewarding ourselves when we have been brave or have tried something new encourages us to keep trying and to do our best. It is important to reward ourselves for our efforts and give ourselves a pat on the back!

Review the Coping Step Plans you developed in Session 7, and see how you are doing with them, individually and as a family. Talk about rewards that your children can receive for trying their best, climbing the steps and achieving their goals!

Try to encourage rewards that involve doing things with others and not just simple, tangible rewards such as food and toys. This might be playing a favourite game, inviting a friend over to play, having their favourite meal with the family, or going on an outing with family. Remember that interpersonal rewards are the most powerful and long-lasting in terms of positive childhood memories - not material possessions, which tend to be forgotten with time.

Each parent should make steps to work towards their own goals and also set self-rewards. Parents should also model the behaviour by rewarding themselves!

It is important to remind and encourage your children to reward themselves when they are brave, when try their best, or when they do something difficult or scary.

Picture 9a

Ana is being brave: learning to rollerblade, going to the dentist and making a new koala friend

Here, we can see pictures of Ana being brave. In the first picture, she has learned to rollerblade! In the second picture, she is being brave at the dentist. In the third picture, she has made a new koala friend.

Picture 9a – Ana is being brave: learning to rollerblade, going to the dentist and making a new koala friend

FUN FRIENDS: A Family Guide to Building Resilience with 4 to 7 year-old Children through Play
www.ourfunfriends.com www.pathwayshrc.com.au

Copyright © 2008 Paula Barrett
This page is printed in blue on white paper. Any other version is unauthorised.

Picture 9b

Ana is rewarding herself for being brave by reading her favourite book with Dad, baking a cake with Mom and inviting her friends for a sleepover!

In these pictures, we can see Ana doing nice things with her friends and family. These are things she can do to reward herself for being brave at rollerblading, going to the dentist, and making new koala friends.

In the first picture, she is reading her favourite book with Dad. In the second picture, she is baking a cake with Mom. In the third picture, Ana has invited her friends for a sleepover! These things make her feel very proud for being so brave.

Picture 9b – Ana is rewarding herself for being brave by reading her favourite book with Dad, baking a cake with Mom and inviting her friends for a sleep-over!

Picture 9c

Tom is being brave by getting dressed all by himself, talking to his new teacher in a loud voice and going to bed all by himself!

Here, we can see pictures of Tom being brave. In the first picture, he has gotten dressed all by himself. He looks great and feels very proud of himself! In the second picture, he is talking to his new teacher in a loud, brave voice. In the third picture, he has gone to bed all by himself after a goodnight hug from Mom and Dad.

Picture 9c – Tom is being brave by getting dressed all by himself, talking
to his new teacher in a loud voice and going to bed all by himself!

Picture 9d

Tom is rewarding himself for being brave by eating his favourite meal with his family, playing a card game with Dad and swimming at the pool with his friends!

In these pictures, we can see Tom doing nice things with his friends and family. These are things he can do to reward himself for being brave and getting dressed, talking to his teacher, and going to bed at night.

In the first picture, he is eating his favourite meal with his family. In the second picture, he is playing a card game with Dad. In the third picture, he is swimming at the pool with his friends! These things make him feel very proud for being so brave.

Picture 9d – Tom is rewarding himself for being brave by eating his favourite meal with his family, playing a card game with Dad and swimming at the pool with his friends!

FUN FRIENDS: A Family Guide to Building Resilience with 4 to 7 year-old Children through Play
www.ourfunfriends.com www.pathwayshrc.com.au

Picture 9e

Tom and Ana are teaching their puppies, Poppy and Lilly, and their kittens, Zoe and Zac, to swim!

Tom and Ana are teaching their two Labrador puppies, Poppy and Lilly, and their two kittens, Zoe and Zac, how to swim! Poppy and Lilly are a cross between Labradors and Poodles. These dogs love water and swimming. They are very friendly and happy dogs. Zoe and Zac are Turkish Van Cats. Turkish Van Cats come from Lake Van in South-East Turkey. They love water and they are known to swim in the bath, swimming pool, or even the sea!

Picture 9e: Tom and Ana are teaching their puppies, Poppy and Lilly, and their kittens, Zoe and Zac, to swim

FUN FRIENDS: A Family Guide to Building Resilience with 4 to 7 year-old Children through Play
www.ourfunfriends.com www.pathwayshrc.com.au

SESSION 9

HOME PLAY

1. Continue to develop your child's Coping Step Plan, rewarding them as they climb each step. You may wish to gradually develop more Step Plans once your child has experienced some success with the first one.

2. Continue assisting your child and other children in the family to identify their "red" thoughts and turn them into "green" thoughts.

3. Practise relaxation strategies every day for at least 10 minutes. Try to create a calm environment when you do this (e.g. no distractions such as TV). Encourage your child to use relaxation strategies to calm down if he/she feels upset, worried or angry (e.g. use "milkshake" breathing and imagine a peaceful place). Reward him/her for using these strategies in times of stress.

4. Continue praising and rewarding your child for being BRAVE!

Nurture

(Do fun activities with teachers, family and friends)

SESSION 10

Learning About Role Models in Our Lives

Learning components:

- Think of people you really admire and respect, and people who could be there for you in both good and bad times. For example, a teacher you really like, a family member you really admire, an older sibling, or an older kid in your school who looks after you.

- Helping others - our family, friends and teachers can help us become brave and we can help them too

You will be helping your children learn about role models, people who teach us many useful things and help us learn about ourselves and life in general. Explain to your children how important it is to pay attention and listen carefully to grandparents, teachers, parents, and older brothers and sisters. They can teach us so much! There are so many new things to learn every day! Let's choose to pay attention!

 Role Models

Please explain to your children that you have role models too. Talk about your role models as a child, and now as an adult. Explain to your children what you admire in such a person, what you can learn from her/him. We can all learn new things every day, no matter how old we are!

In summary, a role model is someone who helps, who cares, who is brave, or who tries difficult things. Help your children understand that role models can be family members, extended family members, teachers, or people in the community (see Appendix 5).

Picture 10a

Dad is teaching Tom how to fish, how to tie his shoelaces, and how to make pancakes. Mom is teaching Tom how to skip.

In the top left box, we can see a parent koala teaching Tom, the boy koala, how to fish. They both seem to be having a great time and are also relaxing. There is a happy platypus smiling at them too!

In the top right box, the parent is teaching Tom how to tie his shoelaces properly and carefully, so they don't come undone and make him trip! It is a good idea for children to learn to tie their shoe laces before they go to kindergarten or grade 1.

In the bottom left box, Dad is teaching Tom the boy koala how to make yummy pancakes for breakfast! They have to use flour, eggs and sugar. It's so much fun to learn to cook and make yummy food for everybody to enjoy.

In the bottom right box, Mom is teaching Tom how to skip. It is easy and is good exercise. Once you know how to do it, you can ask other children to join in and everyone can play skipping games together. Some schools even have "skip-a-thons" to encourage all children to learn skipping, and also to make money for charity.

Picture 10a – Dad is teaching Tom how to fish, how to tie his shoelaces and how to make pancakes.
Mom is teaching Tom how to skip.

Picture 10b

Mom is teaching Ana how to swim, and how to say hello to a neighbour. Ana is learning how to plant trees and ride her bike with Dad.

In the top left box, Ana, the koala girl, is learning to swim with Mom. Swimming is easy and fun. It also feels so good to be in the water when it is hot outside! It makes us feel calm and happy.

In the top right box, Ana is learning to plant trees with Dad. She is going to give names to each one of her trees. Planting trees is a very good thing to do, because trees purify the air that we breathe every day. The more trees we have, the cleaner the air will be!

In the bottom left box, Mom is teaching Ana to say hello to the new neighbour! When we say hello, it is important we look at people in the eye, smile, and pay attention to what they say and do.

In the bottom right box, Dad is teaching Ana to ride her bike without training wheels! The bike goes much faster when she learns how to do it properly! At the beginning it seems very difficult, but as Ana keeps trying, she will be able to do it as well!

Picture 10b – Mom is teaching Ana how to swim ,and how to say hello to a neighbour.
Ana is learning how to plant trees and ride her bike with Dad.

FUN FRIENDS: A Family Guide to Building Resilience with 4 to 7 year-old Children through Play
www.ourfunfriends.com www.pathwayshrc.com.au

SESSION 10

HOME PLAY

1. Continue climbing the first Coping Step Plan and develop a new one if the last one has been completed.

2. Continue assisting your child and other children in the family to identify their "red" thoughts and turn them into "green" thoughts.

3. Practise relaxation strategies every day for at least 10 minutes. Try to create a calm environment when you do this (e.g. no distractions such as TV). Encourage your child to use relaxation strategies to calm down if he/she feels upset, worried or angry (e.g. use "milkshake" breathing and imagine a peaceful place). Reward him/her for using these strategies in times of stress.

4. Continue praising and rewarding your child for being BRAVE!

Dare to be brave

(Practise the skills every day with family and friends)

SESSION 11

Learning About Support Teams in Our Lives

Learning components:

- Helping each other; our family, friends and teachers can help us become brave and we can help them too. We can all help each other.

We all have support teams in our lives, people such as family, friends and teachers, who are there for us in good and bad times, and help us stay strong and cope well with whatever life throws our way. Support teams help us be resilient and bounce back from difficult times. It is very important that you help your children build friendship groups, spend time with extended family (e.g. grandparents, aunts, uncles, cousins, etc.), and form support networks in their school community.

Explain to your children that it is important for us to talk to our family and friends about our feelings, both happy and sad. Sharing the way we feel is wonderful, because we can get support from the people we love. They can help us find solutions for problems and also tell us about times in their lives when similar things happened to them and what they did about it. Grandfathers, grandmothers, uncles, aunts, cousins, brothers and sisters, neighbours, teachers, friends – all these people care about us, and would like to help us if we feel sad or scared. We can also help them when they feel sad or scared. When we are really happy about something it is also so nice to have people to share our happiness with! We can celebrate with a party!

Share with your children times in your life when you felt sad or very happy. Who were your support networks? What did these people do to help out? What did you do to reciprocate when they felt the same, at different times in their lives? Explain to your children that when we help other people, they also help us, so everybody will be happier. Being alone and not sharing feelings makes children and adults feel worse and feel lonely. Problems can seem very big and with no solutions. Our support networks help us to see that things are not that bad, and it is easy to find solutions when there are more people thinking!

Everybody has different skills and different jobs, so we can all help in different ways! For example, Mom may be very good at reading and swimming (so she can help people with reading and swimming), but Dad may be good at running and playing games (so he helps the children do these things!). Grandpa cooks really good cakes and Grandma is a good gardener, so Grandpa helps the children bake yummy chocolate cakes and Grandma helps them plant their own tomato bushes!

Help your children do a drawing or poster of the people in their support team, such as: grandparents, parents, siblings, neighbours, teachers, and/or pets.

You may also want to ask your children the "Who is..." questions about the family (Appendix 6).

Picture 11a

A koala pyramid

Explain to your children what a pyramid is! The bottom is big and it gets thinner as we move to the top, just like a triangle! The older, bigger people are on the bottom, giving the others support and a helping hand. We need younger people who can be lighter to go to the top, to get a better view, and do newer things!

Picture 11a – a Koala pyramid

Picture 11b

Koala families supporting each other

Explain to your children that it is important that younger and older family members get together and support each other. The older family members support and help the younger family members and the younger family members support and help the older family members.

Picture 11b – Koala families supporting each other

Picture 11c

A support group for Aussie native species

This picture shows a support group for Australian native species! Try to guess the name of each animal (clockwise the names are: cat, kangaroo, koala bear, possum, goanna lizard, kookaburra, koala bear, dog, and wombat). Some of them only exist in Australia! We all have to make sure the animals stay alive for many more generations, and that we protect their homes in our bush, rainforests, rivers and ocean waters. Then all children in the future can also enjoy learning about all these beautiful animals, birds, fish, insects and reptiles!

Talk about some of our Canadian native species! We have many wonderful animals and birds such as: beavers, moose, polar bears, wolves, seals, buffalo, snowy owls, ptarmigans, and Canada geese. Some of these are on the endangered list.

Picture 11c – a support group for Australian native species

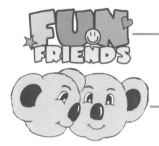

HOME PLAY

1. Encourage your child to come dressed as someone special who is brave and kind next week and bring something small and healthy to share for our celebration!! Discuss as a family the people who were brave and kind when you were young, and why.

2. Continue climbing the first Coping Step Plan and develop a new one once the first one has been completed.

3. Continue assisting your child and other children in the family to identify their "red" thoughts and turn them into "green" thoughts.

4. Practise relaxation strategies every day for at least 10 minutes. Try to create a calm environment when you do this (e.g. no distractions such as TV). Encourage your child to use relaxation strategies to calm down if he/she feels upset, worried or angry (e.g. use "milkshake" breathing and imagine a peaceful place). Reward him/her for using these strategies in times of stress.

5. Continue praising and rewarding your child for being BRAVE!

 Stay ☺

Learning to be Happy with Our Efforts!!

The FUN FRIENDS program teaches children to be happy with their efforts. The children have a party to celebrate finishing the FUN FRIENDS program and Family Guide workbook. They share happiness by spending special time doing fun things with friends and family, and eating yummy healthy food they prepare with you, their parents.

Remember to practise the skills learned for many years to come! Learning FUN FRIENDS is like getting a driver's license. If you leave the car in the garage after you've passed the exam, you will never feel comfortable to drive properly. You need to keep practising!

No one has to be perfect. What is important is to try our best and keep practising the skills, especially when difficult things happen. When difficult things happen, always wait until you and your children calm down. Take deep breaths, and have some quiet and self-regulating/self-soothing time before you begin practising the FUN FRIENDS skills. We cannot think clearly when we are feeling very upset.

Picture 12a

A party to celebrate when we achieve something

Explain to your children that the pictures are about parties and celebrations we all like to have when we achieve something, or when we try our best to learn a new task. We have finished the "FUN FRIENDS Program" and this is a very happy, exciting time that deserves a party!

Show your children the "special graduation certificate" for brave children who have learned all the skills in the FUN FRIENDS Family Guide with their families! (The certificate is on the last page of the Family Guide; fill in your child's name and frame it for their bedroom.)

Now we all have to practise every day for many, many years! Keep your FUN FRIENDS Family Guide with your children's photo albums, so they never lose it, and can always learn again and practise with the family.

You may wish to play the "Pass the Parcel" game (Appendix 7) with your children.

Copyright © 2008 Paula Barrett
This page is printed in blue on white paper. Any other version is unauthorised.

FUN FRIENDS: A Family Guide to Building Resilience with 4 to 7 year-old Children through Play
www.ourfunfriends.com www.pathwayshrc.com.au

Picture 12a – a party to celebrate when we achieve something

Picture 12b

A party to celebrate a special occasion

We also have parties to celebrate special occasions like birthdays, special holidays, or surprise parties to make someone who we care about happy. Have a picnic lunch with your family in the local park. Help your children make some of the food with you. Help them bake some muffins in colourful paper cups.

Singing, dancing, playing music, telling jokes, laughing, and sharing yummy food is so relaxing and so much fun! We can have celebration parties at home, or at the beach, at a park, or at a cottage! Ask your child to describe each drawing of the beach or forest party in detail.

Questions to ask your child:

"What are all the little things you can see in the drawing?"

"What do you prefer, the beach or the forest? "Why?"

"If you could choose, who would you like to spend more time with in the drawing?"

"Who can you be kind to and help in the drawing?"

"What would you like to bring to the party to share with the others?"

"What is your favourite activity in the drawing?"

"What could you do to keep our beautiful beaches and forests clean?"

Share with your children times in your family life (and when you were growing up), when you had fun celebrations and parties. Get your old photo albums and share the memories with your children. Tell them how you were feeling at the time.

Also, get a children's book from the local library about important anniversaries and celebrations worldwide – across different countries and different religions and cultures.

Share with your children the different ways that people have parties around the world, how the music and foods are different, and how the outfits and party clothes are also different!

Everyone, in every country, enjoys sharing parties with family and friends.

Picture 12b – a party to celebrate a special occasion

FUN FRIENDS: A Family Guide to Building Resilience with 4 to 7 year-old Children through Play
www.ourfunfriends.com www.pathwayshrc.com.au

SESSION 12

HOME PLAY

1. Continue climbing the Coping Step Plan and developing new ones once they have been completed.

2. Continue to reinforce friendship skills such as: listening, sharing, helping, and smiling.

3. Continue assisting your child and other children in the family to identify their "red" thoughts and turn them into "green" thoughts.

4. Practise relaxation strategies every day for at least 10 minutes. Try to create a calm environment when you do this (e.g. no distractions such as TV). Encourage your child to use relaxation strategies to calm down if he/she feels upset, worried or angry (e.g. use "milkshake" breathing and imagine a peaceful place). Reward him/her for using these strategies in times of stress.

5. Continue praising and rewarding your child for being BRAVE!

Appendix 1: (Sessions 5 & 6)
"Green" Thoughts vs "Red" Thoughts   **108**

Appendix 2: (Sessions 5 & 6)
Thought Bubbles   **110**

Appendix 3: (Sessions 5 & 6)
Hand Puppet and Finger Puppets   **112**

Appendix 4: (Session 5 & 6)
Friend Chart   **119**

Appendix 5: (Sessions 10 & 12)
Someone Special I Know Who is Brave and Kind!!!   **120**

Appendix 6: (Session 10)
Who is...?   **121**

Appendix 7: (Session 12)
Pass the Parcel   **122**

Graduation Certificate for the
FUN FRIENDS Program   **124**

FUN FRIENDS: *A Family Guide to Building Resilience with 4 to 7 year-old Children through Play*
www.ourfunfriends.com www.pathwayshrc.com.au

Copyright © 2008 Paula Barrett
This page is printed in blue on white paper. Any other version is unauthorised.

Appendix 1
Sessions 5 & 6

"Green" Thoughts vs "Red" Thoughts

"GREEN" thoughts are the things you say to yourself in your head that make you feel good feelings (e.g. happy, confident, brave, and calm), so they are HELPFUL thoughts.

Examples of "GREEN" thoughts:

☺ I can do it! I'll give it a try.

☺ I can try my best.

☺ I am brave.

☺ I'll help Mom/Dad/my sister.

☺ My teacher or Mom/Dad can help me.

☺ I'm good at lots of things.

☺ I'll do my best, but it doesn't matter if I make a mistake.

☺ I have lots of friends.

☺ I'm going to have a good day. I am looking forward to….

☺ I'll ignore people who tease me.

☺ I'll try this game, because it will be fun.

☺ Mommy always picks me up at the end of the day. She won't forget.

More advanced "green" thoughts (to develop over time):

☺ It doesn't matter if I make a mistake. Everyone makes mistakes and they can be a chance to learn something new.

☺ I don't have to be perfect. I just have to try my best and enjoy myself.

☺ Sport isn't all about winning. It's about having fun, getting fit, and being with friends.

☺ Just because one person is nasty to me, it doesn't mean I have no friends. I'll pay attention to the people who treat me like a friend.

☺ That person may annoy me sometimes, but there are lots of good things about them.

☺ I may feel scared at first, but it gets easier and I will have a great day at kindergarten playing with friends and doing fun activities.

☺ New things make me feel worried, but I can gradually give them a try because I know when I try new things I usually end up having fun.

"RED" thoughts are things you say to yourself that make you feel unhappy feelings (e.g. worried, sad, angry, and stressed out) or make you feel less confident, so they are UNHELPFUL thoughts.

Examples of "RED" thoughts:

☹ I can't do this.

☹ I don't want to go, because I won't have fun.

☹ No one likes me.

☹ I got something wrong, so I'm dumb.

☹ I'm silly.

☹ I'm not good at this.

☹ I have to win.

☹ People will laugh at me.

☹ I'm going to have a bad day.

☹ I don't like that person. He is awful!

☹ I want to play a computer game and not help Mom or Dad.

☹ I have the worst sister in the world!

☹ I don't want to do something new. It's too scary!

☹ I can't do it without Mom or Dad.

☹ Reading is too hard.

☹ I'll look silly if I do that!

☹ Mommy will forget to pick me up at the end of the day!

Thought Bubbles

- Read the thought bubbles to the children.
- Help them guess if these are "green" or "red" thoughts.
- Help them colour them **red** or **green**.

I can't do it!

I have no friends!

It's too hard.

People will laugh at me!

My sister is a pest!

School is fun!

Mommy will forget to pick me up!

FUN FRIENDS: A Family Guide to Building Resilience with 4 to 7 year-old Children through Play
www.ourfunfriends.com www.pathwayshrc.com.au

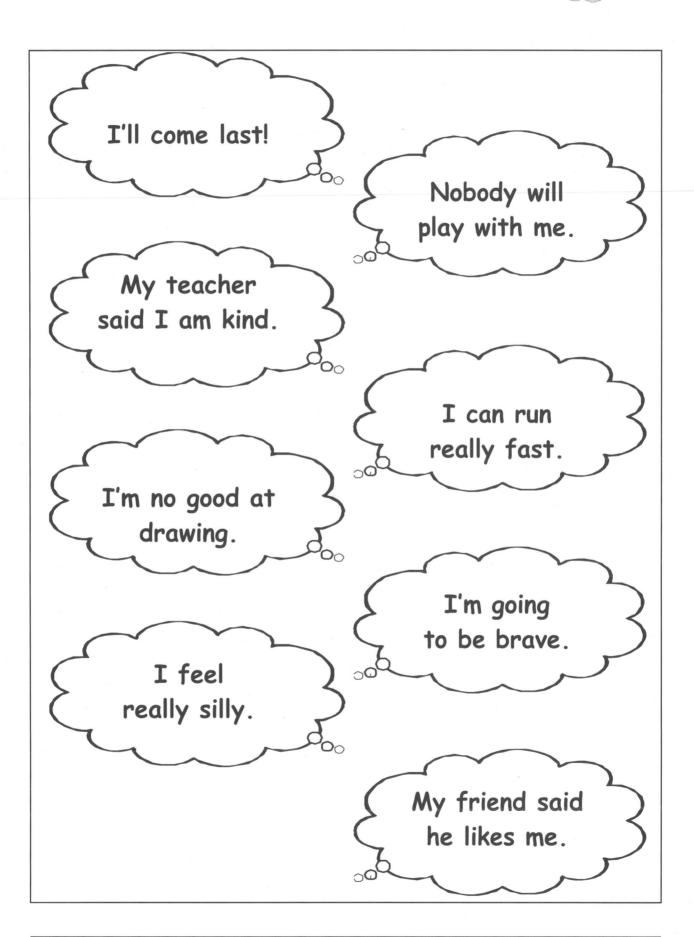

FUN FRIENDS: A Family Guide to Building Resilience with 4 to 7 year-old Children through Play
www.ourfunfriends.com www.pathwayshrc.com.au

Copyright © 2008 Paula Barrett
This page is printed in blue on white paper. Any other version is unauthorised.

Hand Puppet

Directions for paper hand puppets:

1. Cut along the straight dotted line to take out pages 113 and 115. Then colour the two puppets with crayons:

   A **Green** Face
for **HAPPY**.

   A **Red** Face
for **SAD**.

2. Use safe scissors to carefully cut along dotted lines around both sides of puppet.

3. Place sides of puppet together with coloured sides outward.

4. Staple sides of puppet together leaving the lower edge open.

Finger Puppets

Directions for paper finger puppets:

1. Cut along the straight dotted line to take out page 117. Then colour the two puppets with crayons:

   A **Green** Face
for **HAPPY**.

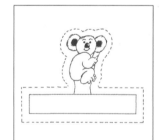   A **Red** Face
for **SAD**.

2. Use safe scissors to carefully cut along dotted lines around both puppets.

3. Wrap the puppet around a finger for size. Then sticky tape or glue the overlap together.

NOTE: Please supervise children when using scissors and staplers.

Hand Puppet – Happy Face

This page intentionally left blank

Hand Puppet – Sad Face

This page intentionally left blank

Finger Puppets

This page intentionally left blank

_____'s Being a FRIEND Chart

I can get a sticker each time I:
HELP, LISTEN, SHARE, and SMILE!

						Small Prize
						Small Prize
						Small Prize
						Small Prize
						Small Prize
						Small Prize
						Small Prize
						Small Prize
						Small Prize
						BIG PRIZE

SOMEONE SPECIAL I KNOW WHO IS BRAVE AND KIND!!!!

In my Family:

In my Neighbourhood:

At my School/Daycare:

I am BRAVE and KIND too!

In a book or movie:

Who is...?

Who in your family has the
loudest laugh?

Who is the most helpful
person in your family?

Who is the neatest person
in your family?

Who is the funniest person
in your family?

Who cooks the yummiest
food in your family?

Who is the bravest person
in your family?

Who is the best singer?

Who is...?

Who is the tallest person
in your family?

Who is a hero in your
family and why?

Who is a hero in your
neighbourhood and why?

Who is a hero in your
school and why?

Who is a hero in a book
you have read and why?

Who is a hero in a movie
you have seen and why?

Who is a hero in a TV
program and why?

Pass the Parcel!

Play the "Pass the Parcel" game during the party.

What could you do to feel brave on the first day of school?

What are some things that you can do to stay calm and relax?

Come up with a "green" thought to fight this "red" thought: "Mommy will forget to pick me up".

Come up with a "green" thought you could think if you were left out of a game.

Act brave and not brave (the group is to guess which one you are acting).

When we are brave, what should we give ourselves?

What could you do to help someone if they felt sad on their first day of school?

What can you do to be a good friend?

What can you do if you feel worried?

What can you do to make a new friend?

CERTIFICATE

Graduation Certificate for the
FUN FRIENDS Program

I've Graduated!

When your child has successfully completed the program, he/she can be given this graduation certificate - something to reward all his/her efforts.

GRADUATION CERTIFICATE
for the
FUN FRIENDS PROGRAM

Congratulations

You have learned to be
brave and happy,
to be kind to others,
and be a friend.

Date

Signature of Parent/Family Member/Teacher

To log in to MyLabsPlus (MyMathLab):
To access the online portion of your course, go to
https://mylabsplus.highline.edu/

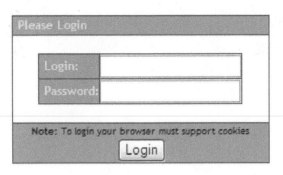

and log in using your **MyHCC** account information. If you have not activated your **MyHCC** account, you need to follow the instructions provided below.

Note: This login allows you to access your course website. To use the homework, videos, eBook, and other resources on the site, you will also be asked to enter the access code that you purchased at the bookstore (it is included with the textbook as well), or to use a credit card to purchase a code through the website when you try to use the homework for the first time.

To activate your MyHCC account:
Go to https://myinfo.highline.edu/MyInfo/Activate.php
You will see a log in screen like the one below.

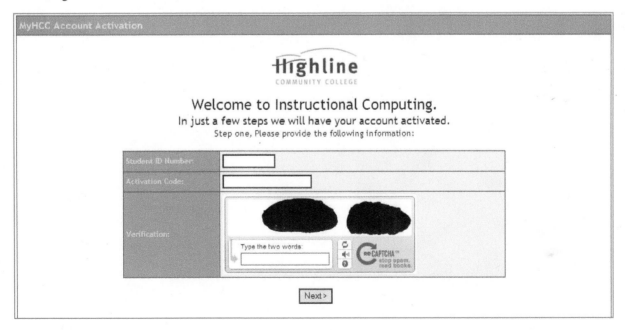

For help with this process, go to https://myinfo.highline.edu/help/ or visit the Help Desk in building 30.

To set up your Highline student email account:
Once you have activated your **MyHCC** account, you will also receive a new email account with Highline. Use your **MyHCC** login at https://students.highline.edu/ to access this email account. **All college emails will be sent to this account, so you need to check it regularly OR set this account to forward email to your preferred email address!** Information about how to set the Highline account to forward email is available at https://flightline.highline.edu/ic/ichelp/studentemail_forward.php

Beginning and Intermediate Algebra

Third Custom Edition for Highline College

Taken from:
Beginning and Intermediate Algebra with Applications & Visualization,
Third Edition
by Gary K. Rockswold and Terry A. Kreiger

Prealgebra, Seventh Edition
by Elayn Martin-Gay

Intermediate Algebra: A Graphing Approach, Fifth Edition
by Elayn Martin-Gay and Margaret Greene

Cover Art: Courtesy of Nancy Kent.

Taken from:

Beginning and Intermediate Algebra with Applications & Visualization, Third Edition
by Gary K. Rockswold and Terry A. Kreiger
Copyright © 2013, 2009, 2005 by Pearson Education, Inc.
Published by Addison-Wesley
Boston, MA 02116

Prealgebra, Seventh Edition
by Elayn Martin-Gay
Copyright © 2015, 2011, 2008 by Pearson Education, Inc.
New York, New York 10013

Intermediate Algebra: A Graphing Approach, Fifth Edition
by Elayn Martin-Gay and Margaret Greene
Copyright © 2014, 2009, 2005 by Pearson Education, Inc.
Published by Prentice Hall

Pearson Learning Solutions, 330 Hudson Street, New York, New York 10013
A Pearson Education Company
www.pearsoned.com

Printed in the United States of America

9   16

000200010271987751

SK

ISBN 10: 1-323-24600-2
ISBN 13: 978-1-323-24600-9

DETAILED CONTENTS

MAIN SECTION*

Contents xi

1 INTRODUCTION TO ALGEBRA   1

1.1 Numbers, Variables, and Expressions   2
1.2 Fractions   11
1.3 Exponents and Order of Operations   26
1.4 Real Numbers and the Number Line   34
1.5 Addition and Subtraction of Real Numbers   45
1.6 Multiplication and Division of Real Numbers   51
1.7 Properties of Real Numbers   60
1.8 Simplifying and Writing Algebraic Expressions   71

2 LINEAR EQUATIONS AND INEQUALITIES   89

2.1 Introduction to Equations   90
2.2 Linear Equations   99
2.4 Formulas   111
2.5 Linear Inequalities   124

*Main Section of this custom text is taken from *Beginning and Intermediate Algebra with Applications & Visualization*, Third Edition, by Gary K. Rockswold and Terry A. Kreiger

v

3 GRAPHING EQUATIONS   144

3.1	Introduction to Graphing	145
3.2	Linear Equations in Two Variables	154
3.3	More Graphing of Lines	164
3.4	Slope and Rates of Change	176
3.5	Slope–Intercept Form	190
3.6	Point–Slope Form	200
3.7	Introduction to Modeling	211

4 SYSTEMS OF LINEAR EQUATIONS IN TWO VARIABLES   229

4.1	Solving Systems of Linear Equations Graphically and Numerically	230
4.2	Solving Systems of Linear Equations by Substitution	241
4.3	Solving Systems of Linear Equations by Elimination	249

5 POLYNOMIALS AND EXPONENTS   267

5.1	Rules for Exponents	268
5.2	Addition and Subtraction of Polynomials	276
5.3	Multiplication of Polynomials	286
5.5	Integer Exponents and the Quotient Rule	295
5.6	Division of Polynomials	306

8 INTRODUCTION TO FUNCTIONS   320

8.1	Functions and Their Representations	321
8.2	Linear Functions	340
8.3	Compound Inequalities	358
8.4	Other Functions and Their Properties	369

10 RADICAL EXPRESSIONS AND FUNCTIONS   395

| 10.1 | Radical Expressions and Functions | 396 |

11 QUADRATIC FUNCTIONS AND EQUATIONS — 411

11.1 Quadratic Functions and Their Graphs — 412

11.2 Parabolas and Modeling — 426

11.3 Quadratic Equations — 440

11.4 The Quadratic Formula — 453

12 EXPONENTIAL AND LOGARITHMIC FUNCTIONS — 473

12.2 Exponential Functions — 474

APPENDIX A: USING THE GRAPHING CALCULATOR — AP-1

ANSWERS TO SELECTED EXERCISES — A-1

GLOSSARY — G-1

PHOTO CREDITS — G-8

BIBLIOGRAPHY — B-1

SECTION PA**

Contents 495

5 DECIMALS

5.7 Decimal Applications: Mean, Median, and Mode — 497

6 RATIO, PROPORTION, AND TRIANGLE APPLICATIONS

6.4 Square Roots and the Pythagorean Theorem — 504

8 GRAPHING AND INTRODUCTION TO STATISTICS

8.1 Reading Pictographs, Bar Graphs, Histograms, and Line Graphs — 512

8.2 Reading Circle Graphs — 525

**Section PA of this custom text is taken from *Prealgebra*, Seventh Edition, by Elayn Martin-Gay

9 GEOMETRY AND MEASUREMENT

9.2	Perimeter	532
9.3	Area, Volume, and Surface Area	542
9.4	Linear Measurement	559
9.7	Temperature and Conversions Between the U.S. and Metric Systems	572

APPENDIX D: GEOMETRIC FORMULAS	585
ANSWERS TO SELECTED EXERCISES	587
PHOTO CREDITS	591

SECTION IA***

Contents   595

2 GRAPHS AND FUNCTIONS

2.6	Interpreting Data: Linear Models	597
	Vocabulary, Readiness & Video Check	604
2.7	Graphing Piecewise-Defined Functions and Shifting and Reflecting Graphs of Functions	608
	Vocabulary, Readiness & Video Check	613

8 QUADRATIC EQUATIONS AND FUNCTIONS

8.7	Interpreting Data: Linear and Quadratic Models	616
	Vocabulary, Readiness & Video Check	622

APPENDIX E: GRAPHING STAT PLOTS AND REGRESSION EQUATIONS	626
ANSWERS TO SELECTED EXERCISES	A-1
INDEX	I-1

***Section IA of this custom text is taken from *Intermediate Algebra: A Graphing Approach*, Fifth Edition, by Elayn Martin-Gay and Margaret Greene

The reading material in the following Main Section is taken from

Beginning and Intermediate Algebra with Applications & Visualization, Third Edition,
by Gary K. Rockswold and Terry A. Kreiger

MAIN SECTION CONTENTS

1   INTRODUCTION TO ALGEBRA   1

1.1   Numbers, Variables, and Expressions   2
Natural Numbers and Whole Numbers ■ Prime Numbers and Composite Numbers
■ Variables, Algebraic Expressions, and Equations ■ Translating Words to Expressions

1.2   Fractions   11
Basic Concepts ■ Simplifying Fractions to Lowest Terms ■ Multiplication and Division
of Fractions ■ Addition and Subtraction of Fractions ■ An Application
Checking Basic Concepts: Mixed Review of Sections 1.1 and 1.2   26

1.3   Exponents and Order of Operations   26
Natural Number Exponents ■ Order of Operations ■ Translating Words to Expressions
GROUP ACTIVITY **Working with Real Data: Converting Temperatures**   34

1.4   Real Numbers and the Number Line   34
Signed Numbers ■ Integers and Rational Numbers ■ Square Roots ■ Real and Irrational
Numbers ■ The Number Line ■ Absolute Value ■ Inequality
Checking Basic Concepts: Mixed Review of Sections 1.3 and 1.4   44

1.5   Addition and Subtraction of Real Numbers   45
Addition of Real Numbers ■ Subtraction of Real Numbers ■ Applications

1.6   Multiplication and Division of Real Numbers   51
Multiplication of Real Numbers ■ Division of Real Numbers ■ Applications
Checking Basic Concepts: Mixed Review of Sections 1.5 and 1.6   60

1.7   Properties of Real Numbers   60
Commutative Properties ■ Associative Properties ■ Distributive Properties
■ Identity and Inverse Properties ■ Mental Calculations
GROUP ACTIVITY **Working with Real Data: Winning the Lottery**   71

1.8   Simplifying and Writing Algebraic Expressions   71
Terms ■ Combining Like Terms ■ Simplifying Expressions ■ Writing Expressions
Checking Basic Concepts: Mixed Review of Sections 1.7 and 1.8   79
Summary ■ Review Exercises ■ Extended and Discovery Exercises   79

2 LINEAR EQUATIONS AND INEQUALITIES   89

2.1 Introduction to Equations   90
Basic Concepts ■ Equations and Solutions ■ The Addition Property of Equality
■ The Multiplication Property of Equality

2.2 Linear Equations   99
Basic Concepts ■ Solving Linear Equations ■ Applying the Distributive Property
■ Clearing Fractions and Decimals ■ Equations with No Solutions or Infinitely Many Solutions
    Checking Basic Concepts: Mixed Review of Sections 2.1 and 2.2   111

2.4 Formulas   111
Formulas from Geometry ■ Solving for a Variable ■ Other Formulas
    Checking Basic Concepts: Review of Section 2.4   123

2.5 Linear Inequalities   124
Solutions and Number Line Graphs ■ The Addition Property of Inequalities
■ The Multiplication Property of Inequalities ■ Applications
    Checking Basic Concepts: Review of Section 2.5   137
Summary ■ Review Exercises ■ Extended and Discovery Exercises   137

3 GRAPHING EQUATIONS   144

3.1 Introduction to Graphing   145
Tables and Graphs ■ The Rectangular Coordinate System ■ Scatterplots and Line Graphs

3.2 Linear Equations in Two Variables   154
Basic Concepts ■ Tables of Solutions ■ Graphing Linear Equations in Two Variables
    Checking Basic Concepts: Mixed Review of Sections 3.1 and 3.2   164

3.3 More Graphing of Lines   164
Finding Intercepts ■ Horizontal Lines ■ Vertical Lines
    GROUP ACTIVITY **Working with Real Data: Radio Stations**   175

3.4 Slope and Rates of Change   176
Finding Slopes of Lines ■ Slope as a Rate of Change
    Checking Basic Concepts: Mixed Review of Sections 3.3 and 3.4   189

3.5 Slope-Intercept Form   190
Basic Concepts ■ Finding Slope–Intercept Form ■ Parallel and Perpendicular Lines
    GROUP ACTIVITY **Working with Real Data: College Tuition**   200

3.6   Point–Slope Form   200
Derivation of Point–Slope Form ■ Finding Point–Slope Form ■ Applications
   Checking Basic Concepts: Mixed Review of Sections 3.5 and 3.6   210

3.7   Introduction to Modeling   211
Basic Concepts ■ Modeling Linear Data
   Checking Basic Concepts: Review of Section 3.7   218
   Summary ■ Review Exercises ■ Extended and Discovery Exercises   219

4   SYSTEMS OF LINEAR EQUATIONS IN TWO VARIABLES   229

4.1   Solving Systems of Linear Equations Graphically and Numerically   230
Basic Concepts ■ Solutions to Systems of Equations

4.2   Solving Systems of Linear Equations by Substitution   241
The Method of Substitution ■ Recognizing Other Types of Systems ■ Applications
   Checking Basic Concepts: Mixed Review of Sections 4.1 and 4.2   249

4.3   Solving Systems of Linear Equations by Elimination   249
The Elimination Method ■ Recognizing Other Types of Systems ■ Applications
   GROUP ACTIVITY **Working with Real Data: Facebook Apps**   260
   Summary ■ Review Exercises ■ Extended and Discovery Exercises   260

5   POLYNOMIALS AND EXPONENTS   267

5.1   Rules for Exponents   268
Review of Bases and Exponents ■ Zero Exponents ■ The Product Rule ■ Power Rules

5.2   Addition and Subtraction of Polynomials   276
Monomials and Polynomials ■ Addition of Polynomials ■ Subtraction of Polynomials
■ Evaluating Polynomial Expressions
   Checking Basic Concepts: Mixed Review of Sections 5.1 and 5.2   286

5.3   Multiplication of Polynomials   286
Multiplying Monomials ■ Review of the Distributive Properties
■ Multiplying Monomials and Polynomials ■ Multiplying Polynomials
   GROUP ACTIVITY **Working with Real Data: Animal Biology**   294

5.5 Integer Exponents and the Quotient Rule   295
Negative Integers as Exponents ■ The Quotient Rule ■ Other Rules for Exponents
■ Scientific Notation
GROUP ACTIVITY **Working with Real Data: Water in a Lake**   306

5.6 Division of Polynomials   306
Division by a Monomial ■ Division by a Polynomial
Checking Basic Concepts: Mixed Review of Sections 5.5 and 5.6   312
Summary ■ Review Exercises ■ Test ■ Extended and Discovery Exercises   313

8 INTRODUCTION TO FUNCTIONS   320

8.1 Functions and Their Representations   321
Basic Concepts ■ Representations of a Function ■ Definition of a Function
■ Identifying a Function ■ Graphing Calculators (Optional)
GROUP ACTIVITY **Working with Real Data: U.S. Craigslist Visitors**   340

8.2 Linear Functions   340
Basic Concepts ■ Representations of Linear Functions ■ Modeling Data with Linear Functions
■ The Midpoint Formula (Optional)
Checking Basic Concepts: Mixed Review of Sections 8.1 and 8.2   358

8.3 Compound Inequalities   358
Basic Concepts ■ Symbolic Solutions and Number Lines ■ Numerical and Graphical Solutions
■ Interval Notation

8.4 Other Functions and Their Properties   369
Expressing Domain and Range in Interval Notation ■ Absolute Value Function
■ Polynomial Functions ■ Rational Functions (Optional) ■ Operations on Functions
Checking Basic Concepts: Mixed Review of Sections 8.3 and 8.4   385
Summary ■ Review Exercises ■ Extended and Discovery Exercises   386

10 RADICAL EXPRESSIONS AND FUNCTIONS   395

10.1 Radical Expressions and Functions   396
Radical Notation ■ The Square Root Function ■ The Cube Root Function
Summary ■ Review Exercises ■ Extended and Discovery Exercises   407

11 QUADRATIC FUNCTIONS AND EQUATIONS   411

11.1 Quadratic Functions and Their Graphs   412
Graphs of Quadratic Functions ■ Min–Max Applications ■ Basic Transformations of $y = ax^2$
■ Transformations of $y = ax^2 + bx + c$ (Optional)

11.2 Parabolas and Modeling   426
Vertical and Horizontal Translations ■ Vertex Form ■ Modeling with Quadratic
Functions (Optional)

Checking Basic Concepts: Mixed Review of Sections 11.1 and 11.2   440

11.3 Quadratic Equations   440
Basics of Quadratic Equations ■ The Square Root Property ■ Completing the Square
■ Solving an Equation for a Variable ■ Applications of Quadratic Equations

GROUP ACTIVITY **Working with Real Data: Personal Consumption**   453

11.4 The Quadratic Formula   453
Solving Quadratic Equations ■ The Discriminant ■ Quadratic Equations Having
Complex Solutions

Checking Basic Concepts: Mixed Review of Sections 11.3 and 11.4   465

Summary ■ **Review Exercises** ■ **Extended and Discovery Exercises**   466

12 EXPONENTIAL AND LOGARITHMIC FUNCTIONS   473

12.2 Exponential Functions   474
Basic Concepts ■ Graphs of Exponential Functions ■ Percent Change and
Exponential Functions ■ Compound Interest ■ Models Involving Exponential Functions
■ The Natural Exponential Function

Checking Basic Concepts: Review of Section 12.2   490

Summary ■ **Review Exercises** ■ **Extended and Discovery Exercises**   491

APPENDIX A: Using the Graphing Calculator AP-1

Answers to Selected Exercises*A-1

Glossary G-1

Photo Credits G-8

Bibliography B-1

1 Introduction to Algebra

1.1 Numbers, Variables, and Expressions

1.2 Fractions

1.3 Exponents and Order of Operations

1.4 Real Numbers and the Number Line

1.5 Addition and Subtraction of Real Numbers

1.6 Multiplication and Division of Real Numbers

1.7 Properties of Real Numbers

1.8 Simplifying and Writing Algebraic Expressions

Unless you try to do something beyond what you have already mastered, you will never grow.

—RONALD E. OSBORN

J ust over a century ago only about one in ten workers was in a professional, technical, or managerial occupation. Today this proportion is nearly one in three, and the study of mathematics is essential for anyone who wants to keep up with the technological changes that are occurring in nearly every occupation. Mathematics is the *language of technology*.

In the information age, mathematics is being used to describe human behavior in areas such as economics, medicine, advertising, social networks, and Internet use. For example, mathematics can help maximize the impact of advertising by analyzing social networks such as Facebook. Today's business managers need employees who not only understand human behavior but can also describe that behavior using mathematics.

It's just a matter of time before the *majority* of the workforce will need the analytic skills that are taught in mathematics classes every day. No matter what career path you choose, a solid background in mathematics will provide you with opportunities to reach your full potential in your vocation, income level, and lifestyle.

Source: A. Greenspan, "The Economic Importance of Improving Math-Science Education."

1

1.1 Numbers, Variables, and Expressions

Natural Numbers and Whole Numbers • Prime Numbers and Composite Numbers • Variables, Algebraic Expressions, and Equations • Translating Words to Expressions

A LOOK INTO MATH ▶

Numbers are an important concept in every society. A number system once used in southern Africa consisted of only the numbers from 1 to 20. Numbers larger than 20 were named by counting groups of *twenties*. For example, the number 67 was called *three twenties and seven*. This base-20 number system would not work well in today's technologically advanced world. In this section, we introduce two sets of numbers that are used extensively in the modern world: natural numbers and whole numbers.

Natural Numbers and Whole Numbers

NEW VOCABULARY

- ☐ Natural numbers
- ☐ Whole numbers
- ☐ Product
- ☐ Factors
- ☐ Prime number
- ☐ Composite number
- ☐ Prime factorization
- ☐ Variable
- ☐ Algebraic expression
- ☐ Equation
- ☐ Formula

One important set of numbers is the set of **natural numbers**. These numbers comprise the *counting numbers* and may be expressed as follows.

$$1, 2, 3, 4, 5, 6, \ldots$$

Because there are infinitely many natural numbers, three dots are used to show that the list continues without end. A second set of numbers is called the **whole numbers**, and may be expressed as follows.

$$0, 1, 2, 3, 4, 5, \ldots$$

Whole numbers include the natural numbers and the number 0.

CRITICAL THINKING

Give an example from everyday life of natural number or whole number use.

▶ **REAL-WORLD CONNECTION** Natural numbers and whole numbers can be used when data are not broken into fractional parts. For example, the bar graph in Figure 1.1 shows the number of apps on a student's iPad for the first 5 months after buying the device. Note that both natural numbers and whole numbers are appropriate to describe these data because a fraction of an app is not possible.

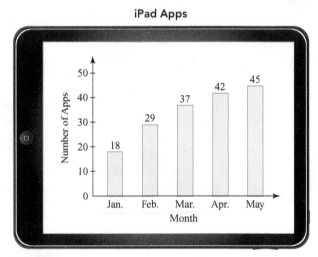

Figure 1.1

STUDY TIP

Bring your book, notebook, and a pen or pencil to every class. Write down major concepts presented by your instructor. Your notes should also include the meaning of words written in bold type in the text. Be sure that you understand the meaning of these important words.

Prime Numbers and Composite Numbers

When two natural numbers are multiplied, the result is another natural number. For example, multiplying the natural numbers 3 and 4 results in 12, a natural number. The result 12 is called the **product** and the numbers 3 and 4 are **factors** of 12.

$$3 \quad \cdot \quad 4 \quad = \quad 12$$
$$\text{factor} \quad \text{factor} \quad \quad \text{product}$$

NOTE: Products can be expressed in several ways. For example, the product $3 \cdot 4 = 12$ can also be written as $3 \times 4 = 12$ and $3(4) = 12$.

A natural number greater than 1 that has *only* itself and 1 as natural number factors is a **prime number**. The number 7 is prime because the only natural number factors of 7 are 1 and 7. The following is a partial list of prime numbers. There are infinitely many prime numbers.

$$2, \quad 3, \quad 5, \quad 7, \quad 11, \quad 13, \quad 17, \quad 19, \quad 23, \quad 29$$

A natural number greater than 1 that is not prime is a **composite number**. For example, the natural number 15 is a composite number because $3 \cdot 5 = 15$. In other words, 15 has factors other than 1 and itself.

Every composite number can be written as a product of prime numbers. For example, we can use a factor tree such as the one shown in Figure 1.2 to find the prime factors of the composite number 120. Branches of the tree are made by writing each composite number as a product that includes the smallest possible prime factor of the composite number.

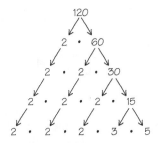

Figure 1.2 Prime Factorization of 120

Figure 1.2 shows that the **prime factorization** of 120 is

$$120 = 2 \cdot 2 \cdot 2 \cdot 3 \cdot 5.$$

Every composite number has a unique prime factorization, and it is customary to write the prime factors in order from smallest to largest.

MAKING CONNECTIONS

Factor Trees and Prime Factorization

The prime factors of 120 can also be found using the following tree. Even though this tree is different than the one used earlier, the prime factors it reveals are the same.

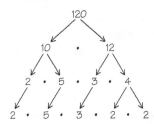

No matter what tree is used, a prime factorization is *always* unique.

READING CHECK

- How do prime numbers differ from composite numbers?

CRITICAL THINKING

Suppose that you draw a tree diagram for the prime factorization of a prime number. Describe what the tree will look like.

EXAMPLE 1   **Classifying numbers as prime or composite**

Classify each number as prime or composite, if possible. If a number is composite, write it as a product of prime numbers.
(a) 31   **(b)** 1   **(c)** 35   **(d)** 200

Solution
(a) The only factors of 31 are itself and 1, so the number 31 is prime.
(b) The number 1 is neither prime nor composite because prime and composite numbers must be greater than 1.
(c) The number 35 is composite because 5 and 7 are factors. It can be written as a product of prime numbers as $35 = 5 \cdot 7$.
(d) The number 200 is composite because 10 and 20 are factors. A factor tree can be used to write 200 as a product of prime numbers, as shown in Figure 1.3. The factor tree reveals that 200 can be factored as $200 = 2 \cdot 2 \cdot 2 \cdot 5 \cdot 5$.

Now Try Exercises 13, 15, 17, 21

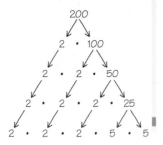

Figure 1.3 Prime Factorization of 200

Variables, Algebraic Expressions, and Equations

There are 12 inches in 1 foot, so 5 feet equal $5 \cdot 12 = 60$ inches. Similarly, in 3 feet there are $3 \cdot 12 = 36$ inches. To convert feet to inches frequently, Table 1.1 might help.

TABLE 1.1 Converting Feet to Inches

Feet	1	2	3	4	5	6	7
Inches	12	24	36	48	60	72	84

However, this table is not helpful in converting 11 feet to inches. We could expand Table 1.1 into Table 1.2 to include $11 \cdot 12 = 132$, but expanding the table to accommodate every possible value for feet would be impossible.

TABLE 1.2 Converting Feet to Inches

Feet	1	2	3	4	5	6	7	11
Inches	12	24	36	48	60	72	84	132

READING CHECK

• What is a variable?
• Give one reason for using variables in mathematics.

Variables are often used in mathematics when tables of numbers are inadequate. A **variable** is a symbol, typically an italic letter such as x, y, z, or F, used to represent an unknown quantity. In the preceding example, the number of feet could be represented by the variable F, and the corresponding number of inches could be represented by the variable I. The number of inches in F feet is given by the *algebraic expression* $12 \cdot F$. That is, to calculate the number of inches in F feet, multiply F by 12. The relationship between feet F and inches I is shown using the *equation* or *formula*

$$I = 12 \cdot F.$$

A dot ($\cdot$) is used to indicate multiplication because a multiplication sign ($\times$) can be confused with the variable x. Many times the multiplication sign is omitted altogether. Thus all three formulas

$$I = 12 \cdot F, \quad I = 12F, \quad \text{and} \quad I = 12(F)$$

represent the same relationship between feet and inches. If we wish to find the number of inches in 10 feet, for example, we can replace F in one of these formulas with the number 10. If we let $F = 10$ in the first formula,

$$I = 12 \cdot 10 = 120.$$

That is, there are 120 inches in 10 feet.

More formally, an **algebraic expression** consists of numbers, variables, operation symbols such as $+$, $-$, $\cdot$, and $\div$, and grouping symbols such as parentheses. An **equation** is a mathematical statement that two algebraic expressions are equal. Equations *always* contain an equals sign. A **formula** is a special type of equation that expresses a relationship between two or more quantities. The formula $I = 12F$ states that to calculate the number of inches in F feet, multiply F by 12.

EXAMPLE 2   **Evaluating algebraic expressions with one variable**

Evaluate each algebraic expression for $x = 4$.

(a) $x + 5$ **(b)** $5x$ **(c)** $15 - x$ **(d)** $\dfrac{x}{(x - 2)}$

Solution

(a) Replace x with 4 in the expression $x + 5$ to obtain $4 + 5 = 9$.
(b) The expression $5x$ indicates multiplication of 5 and x. Thus $5x = 5 \cdot 4 = 20$.
(c) $15 - x = 15 - 4 = 11$
(d) Perform all arithmetic operations inside parentheses first.

$$\frac{x}{(x - 2)} = \frac{4}{(4 - 2)} = \frac{4}{2} = 2$$

▌ Now Try Exercises 45, 47, 51, 53

▶ **REAL-WORLD CONNECTION** Some algebraic expressions contain more than one variable. For example, if a car travels 120 miles on 6 gallons of gasoline, then the car's *mileage* is $\frac{120}{6} = 20$ miles per gallon. In general, if a car travels M miles on G gallons of gasoline, then its mileage is given by the expression $\frac{M}{G}$. Note that $\frac{M}{G}$ contains two variables, M and G, whereas the expression $12F$ contains only one variable, F.

EXAMPLE 3   **Evaluating algebraic expressions with two variables**

Evaluate each algebraic expression for $y = 2$ and $z = 8$.

(a) $3yz$ **(b)** $z - y$ **(c)** $\dfrac{z}{y}$

Solution

(a) Replace y with 2 and z with 8 to obtain $3yz = 3 \cdot 2 \cdot 8 = 48$.
(b) $z - y = 8 - 2 = 6$

(c) $\dfrac{z}{y} = \dfrac{8}{2} = 4$

▌ Now Try Exercises 55, 57, 59

EXAMPLE 4   **Evaluating formulas**

Find the value of y for $x = 15$ and $z = 10$.

(a) $y = x - 3$ **(b)** $y = \dfrac{x}{5}$ **(c)** $y = 8xz$

Solution

(a) Substitute 15 for x and then evaluate the right side of the formula to find y.

$$
\begin{aligned}
y &= x - 3 && \text{Given formula} \\
&= 15 - 3 && \text{Replace } x \text{ with 15.} \\
&= 12 && \text{Subtract.}
\end{aligned}
$$

(b) $y = \dfrac{x}{5} = \dfrac{15}{5} = 3$

(c) $y = 8xz = 8 \cdot 15 \cdot 10 = 1200$

Now Try Exercises 61, 67, 69

Translating Words to Expressions

Many times in mathematics, algebraic expressions are not given; rather, we must write our own expressions. To accomplish this task, we often translate words to symbols. The symbols $+$, $-$, $\cdot$, and $\div$ have special mathematical words associated with them. When two numbers are added, the result is called the *sum*. When one number is subtracted from another number, the result is called the *difference*. Similarly, multiplying two numbers results in a *product* and dividing two numbers results in a *quotient*. Table 1.3 lists many of the words commonly associated with these operations.

TABLE 1.3 **Words Associated with Arithmetic Symbols**

Symbol	Associated Words
$+$	add, plus, more, sum, total
$-$	subtract, minus, less, difference, fewer
$\cdot$	multiply, times, twice, double, triple, product
$\div$	divide, divided by, quotient

EXAMPLE 5   **Translating words to expressions**

Translate each phrase to an algebraic expression. Specify what each variable represents.
(a) Four more than a number
(b) Ten less than the president's age
(c) A number plus 10, all divided by a different number
(d) The product of 6 and a number

Solution

(a) If the number were 20, then four more than the number would be $20 + 4 = 24$. If we let n represent the number, then four more than the number would be $n + 4$.
(b) If the president's age were 55, then ten less than the president's age would be $55 - 10 = 45$. If we let A represent the president's age, then ten less would be $A - 10$.

(c) Let x be the first number and y be the other number. Then the expression can be written as $(x + 10) \div y$. Note that parentheses are used around $x + 10$ because it is "all" divided by y. This expression could also be written as $\frac{x + 10}{y}$.

(d) If n represents the number, then the product of 6 and n is $6 \cdot n$ or $6n$.

▌ Now Try Exercises 73, 77, 83, 85

▶ **REAL-WORLD CONNECTION** Cities are made up of large amounts of concrete and asphalt that heat up in the daytime from sunlight but do not cool off completely at night. As a result, urban areas tend to be warmer than surrounding rural areas. This effect is called the *urban heat island* and has been documented in cities throughout the world. The next example discusses the impact of this effect in Phoenix, Arizona.

EXAMPLE 6 ▌ **Translating words to a formula**

For each year after 1970, the average nighttime temperature in Phoenix has increased by about $0.1°C$.
(a) What was the increase in the nighttime temperature after 20 years, or in 1990?
(b) Write a formula (or equation) that gives the increase T in average nighttime temperature x years after 1970.
(c) Use your formula to estimate the increase in nighttime temperature in 2000.

Solution
(a) The average nighttime temperature has increased by $0.1°C$ per year, so after 20 years the temperature increase would be $0.1 \cdot 20 = 2.0°C$.
(b) To calculate the nighttime increase in temperature, multiply the number of years past 1970 by 0.1. Thus $T = 0.1x$, where x represents the number of years after 1970.
(c) Because $2000 - 1970 = 30$, let $x = 30$ in the formula $T = 0.1x$ to get

$$T = 0.1(30) = 3.$$

The average nighttime temperature increased by $3°C$.

▌ Now Try Exercise 91

Another use of translating words to formulas is in finding the areas of various shapes.

EXAMPLE 7 ▌ **Finding the area of a rectangle**

The area A of a rectangle equals its length L times its width W, as illustrated in the accompanying figure.
(a) Write a formula that shows the relationship between these three quantities.
(b) Find the area of a standard sheet of paper that is 8.5 inches wide and 11 inches long.

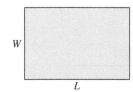

Solution
(a) The word *times* indicates that the length and width should be multiplied. The formula is given by $A = LW$.
(b) $A = 11 \cdot 8.5 = 93.5$ square inches

▌ Now Try Exercise 97

1.1   Putting It All Together

STUDY TIP

Putting It All Together gives a summary of important concepts in each section. Be sure that you have a good understanding of these concepts.

CONCEPT	COMMENTS	EXAMPLES
Natural Numbers	Sometimes referred to as the *counting numbers*	1, 2, 3, 4, 5, …
Whole Numbers	Includes the natural numbers and 0	0, 1, 2, 3, 4, …
Products and Factors	When two numbers are multiplied, the result is called the product. The numbers being multiplied are called factors.	$6 \cdot 7 = 42$ factor factor product
Prime Number	A natural number greater than 1 whose only factors are itself and 1; there are infinitely many prime numbers.	2, 3, 5, 7, 11, 13, 17, and 19 are the prime numbers less than 20.
Composite Number	A natural number greater than 1 that is *not* a prime number; there are infinitely many composite numbers.	4, 9, 25, 39, 62, 76, 87, 91, 100
Prime Factorization	Every composite number can be written as a product of prime numbers. This unique product is called the prime factorization.	$60 = 2 \cdot 2 \cdot 3 \cdot 5$, $84 = 2 \cdot 2 \cdot 3 \cdot 7$
Variable	Represents an unknown quantity	x, y, z, A, F, and T
Algebraic Expression	May consist of variables, numbers, operation symbols such as $+, -, \cdot,$ and $\div$, and grouping symbols such as parentheses	$x + 3, \frac{x}{y}, 2z + 5, 12F,$ $x + y + z,$ $x(y + 5)$
Equation	An equation is a statement that two algebraic expressions are equal. An equation always includes an equals sign.	$2 + 3 = 5, x + 5 = 7,$ $I = 12F,$ $y = 0.1x$
Formula	A formula is a special type of equation that expresses a relationship between two or more quantities.	$I = 12F, y = 0.1x,$ $A = LW,$ $F = 3Y$

1.1 Exercises

CONCEPTS AND VOCABULARY

1. The _____ numbers comprise the counting numbers.

2. A whole number is either a natural number or the number _____.

3. The factors of a prime number are itself and _____.

4. A natural number greater than 1 that is not a prime number is called a(n) _____ number.

5. Because $3 \cdot 6 = 18$, the numbers 3 and 6 are _____ of 18.

6. A(n) _____ is a special type of equation that expresses a relationship between two or more quantities.

7. A symbol or letter used to represent an unknown quantity is called a(n) _____.

8. Equations always contain a(n) _____.

9. When one number is added to another number, the result is called the _____.

10. When one number is multiplied by another number, the result is called the _____.

11. The result of dividing one number by another is called the _____.

12. The result of subtracting one number from another is called the _____.

PRIME NUMBERS AND COMPOSITE NUMBERS

Exercises 13–24: Classify the number as prime, composite, or neither. If the number is composite, write it as a product of prime numbers.

13. 4   14. 36

15. 1   16. 0

17. 29   18. 13

19. 92   20. 69

21. 225   22. 900

23. 149   24. 101

Exercises 25–36: Write the composite number as a product of prime numbers.

25. 6   26. 8

27. 12   28. 20

29. 32   30. 100

31. 39   32. 51

33. 294   34. 175

35. 300   36. 455

Exercises 37–44: State whether the given quantity could accurately be described by the whole numbers.

37. The population of a country

38. The cost of a gallon of gasoline in dollars

39. A student's grade point average

40. The Fahrenheit temperature in Antarctica

41. The number of apps on an iPad

42. The number of students in a class

43. The winning time in a 100-meter sprint

44. The number of bald eagles in the United States

ALGEBRAIC EXPRESSIONS, FORMULAS, AND EQUATIONS

Exercises 45–54: Evaluate the expression for the given value of x.

45. $3x$ $x = 5$ 46. $x + 10$ $x = 8$

47. $9 - x$ $x = 4$ 48. $13x$ $x = 0$

49. $\dfrac{x}{8}$ $x = 32$ 50. $\dfrac{5}{(x - 3)}$ $x = 8$

51. $3(x + 1)$ $x = 5$ 52. $7(6 - x)$ $x = 3$

53. $\left(\dfrac{x}{2}\right) + 1$ $x = 6$ 54. $3 - \left(\dfrac{6}{x}\right)$ $x = 2$

Exercises 55–60: Evaluate the expression for the given values of x and y.

55. $x + y$ $x = 8, \ y = 14$

56. $5xy$ $x = 2, \ y = 3$

57. $6 \cdot \dfrac{x}{y}$ $x = 8, \ y = 4$

58. $y - x$ $x = 8, \ y = 11$

59. $y(x - 2)$ $x = 5, \ y = 3$

60. $(x + y) - 5$ $x = 6, \ y = 3$

Exercises 61–64: Find the value of y for the given value of x.

61. $y = x + 5$ $x = 0$

62. $y = x \cdot x$ $x = 7$

63. $y = 4x$ $x = 7$

64. $y = 2(x - 3)$ $x = 3$

Exercises 65–68: Find the value of F for the given value of z.

65. $F = z - 5$ $z = 12$

66. $F = \dfrac{z}{4}$ $z = 40$

67. $F = \dfrac{30}{z}$ $z = 6$

68. $F = z \cdot z \cdot z$ $z = 5$

Exercises 69–72: Find the value of y for the given values of x and z.

69. $y = 3xz$ $x = 2,\ \ z = 0$

70. $y = x + z$ $x = 3,\ \ z = 15$

71. $y = \dfrac{x}{z}$ $x = 9,\ \ z = 3$

72. $y = x - z$ $x = 9,\ \ z = 1$

TRANSLATING WORDS TO EXPRESSIONS

Exercises 73–86: Translate the phrase to an algebraic expression. State what each variable represents.

73. Five more than a number

74. Four less than a number

75. Three times the cost of a soda

76. Twice the cost of a gallon of gasoline

77. The sum of a number and 5

78. The quotient of two numbers

79. Two hundred less than the population of a town

80. The total number of dogs and cats in a city

81. A number divided by six

82. A number divided by another number

83. The product of a car's speed and traveling time

84. The difference between 220 and a person's heart rate

85. A number plus seven, all divided by a different number

86. One-fourth of a number increased by one-tenth of a different number

APPLICATIONS

87. *Dollars to Pennies* Write a formula that converts D dollars to P pennies.

88. *Quarters to Nickels* Write a formula that converts Q quarters to N nickels.

89. *Yards to Feet* Make a table of values that converts y yards to F feet. Let $y = 1, 2, 3, \ldots, 7$. Write a formula that converts y yards to F feet.

90. *Gallons to Quarts* Make a table of values that converts g gallons to Q quarts. Let $g = 1, 2, 3, \ldots, 6$. Write a formula that converts g gallons to Q quarts.

91. *NASCAR Speeds* On the fastest speedways, some NASCAR drivers reach average speeds of 3 miles per minute. Write a formula that gives the number of miles M that such a driver would travel in x minutes. How far would this driver travel in 36 minutes?

92. *NASCAR Speeds* On slower speedways, some NASCAR drivers reach average speeds of 2 miles per minute. Write a formula that gives the number of miles M that such a driver would travel in x minutes. How far would this driver travel in 42 minutes?

93. Thinking Generally If there are 6 blims in every drog, is the formula that relates B blims and D drogs $D = 6B$ or $B = 6D$?

94. *Heart Beat* The resting heart beat of a person is 70 beats per minute. Write a formula that gives the number of beats B that occur in x minutes. How many beats are there in an hour?

95. *Cost of album downloads* The table lists the cost C of downloading x albums. Write an equation that relates C and x.

Albums (x)	1	2	3	4
Cost (C)	$12	$24	$36	$48

96. *Gallons of Water* The table lists the gallons G of water coming from a garden hose after m minutes. Write an equation that relates G and m.

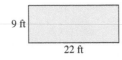

Minutes (m)	1	2	3	4
Gallons (G)	4	8	12	16

97. *Area of a Rectangle* The area of a rectangle equals its length times its width. Find the area of the rectangle shown in the figure.

9 ft

22 ft

98. *Area of a Square* A square is a rectangle whose length and width have equal measures. Find the area of a square with length 14 inches.

WRITING ABOUT MATHEMATICS

99. Give an example in which the whole numbers are not sufficient to describe a quantity in real life. Explain your reasoning.

100. Explain what a prime number is. How can you determine whether a number is prime?

101. Explain what a composite number is. How can you determine whether a number is composite?

102. When are variables used? Give an example.

1.2 Fractions

Basic Concepts ▪ Simplifying Fractions to Lowest Terms ▪ Multiplication and Division of Fractions ▪ Addition and Subtraction of Fractions ▪ An Application

A LOOK INTO MATH ▶

NEW VOCABULARY

☐ Lowest terms
☐ Greatest common factor (GCF)
☐ Basic principle of fractions
☐ Multiplicative inverse or reciprocal
☐ Least common denominator (LCD)

Historically, natural and whole numbers have not been sufficient for most societies. Early on, the concept of splitting a quantity into parts was common, and as a result, fractions were developed. Today, fractions are used in many everyday situations. For example, there are four quarters in one dollar, so each quarter represents a fourth of a dollar. In this section we discuss fractions and how to add, subtract, multiply, and divide them.

Basic Concepts

If we divide a circular pie into 6 equal slices, as shown in Figure 1.4, then each piece represents one-sixth of the pie and can be represented by the fraction $\frac{1}{6}$. Five slices of the pie would represent five-sixths of the pie and can be represented by the fraction $\frac{5}{6}$.

The parts of a fraction are named as follows.

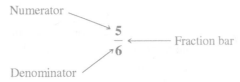

Numerator
$$\frac{5}{6}$$ ⟵ Fraction bar
Denominator

Sometimes we can represent a general fraction by using variables. The fraction $\frac{a}{b}$ can represent *any* fraction with numerator a and denominator b. However, the value of b cannot equal 0, which is denoted $b \neq 0$. (The symbol $\neq$ means "not equal to.")

NOTE: The fraction bar represents division. For example, the fraction $\frac{1}{2}$ represents the result when 1 is divided by 2, which is 0.5. We discuss this concept further in Section 1.4.

Figure 1.4

EXAMPLE 1   **Identifying numerators and denominators**

Give the numerator and denominator of each fraction.

(a) $\dfrac{6}{13}$ **(b)** $\dfrac{ac}{b}$ **(c)** $\dfrac{x-5}{y+z}$

Solution

(a) The numerator is 6, and the denominator is 13.
(b) The numerator is ac, and the denominator is b.
(c) The numerator is $x - 5$, and the denominator is $y + z$.

Now Try Exercise 2

Simplifying Fractions to Lowest Terms

Consider the amount of pizza shown in each of the three pies in Figure 1.5. The first pie is cut into sixths with three pieces remaining, the second pie is cut into fourths with two pieces remaining, and the third pie is cut into only two pieces with one piece remaining. In all three cases half a pizza remains.

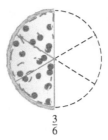 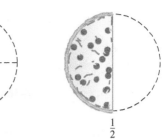

$$\frac{3}{6} \qquad \frac{2}{4} \qquad \frac{1}{2}$$

Figure 1.5

Figure 1.5 illustrates that the fractions $\frac{3}{6}, \frac{2}{4}$, and $\frac{1}{2}$ are equal. The fraction $\frac{1}{2}$ is in **lowest terms** because its numerator and denominator have no factors in common, whereas the fractions $\frac{3}{6}$ and $\frac{2}{4}$ are not in lowest terms. In the fraction $\frac{3}{6}$, the numerator and denominator have a common factor of 3, so the fraction can be simplified as follows.

$$\frac{3}{6} = \frac{1 \cdot 3}{2 \cdot 3} \qquad \text{Factor out 3.}$$

$$= \frac{1}{2} \qquad \frac{a \cdot c}{b \cdot c} = \frac{a}{b}$$

To simplify $\frac{3}{6}$, we used the *basic principle of fractions*: The value of a fraction is unchanged if the numerator and denominator of the fraction are multiplied (or divided) by the same nonzero number. We can also simplify the fraction $\frac{2}{4}$ to $\frac{1}{2}$ by using the basic principle of fractions.

$$\frac{2}{4} = \frac{1 \cdot 2}{2 \cdot 2} = \frac{1}{2}$$

When simplifying fractions, we usually factor out the *greatest common factor* of the numerator and the denominator. The **greatest common factor (GCF)** of two or more numbers is the largest factor that is common to those numbers. For example, to simplify $\frac{27}{36}$, we first find the greatest common factor of 27 and 36. The numbers 3 and 9 are *common* factors of 27 and 36 because

$$3 \cdot 9 = 27 \text{ and } 3 \cdot 12 = 36, \quad \text{and} \quad 9 \cdot 3 = 27 \text{ and } 9 \cdot 4 = 36.$$

However, the *greatest* common factor is 9 because it is the largest number that divides evenly into both 27 and 36. The fraction $\frac{27}{36}$ simplifies to lowest terms as

$$\frac{27}{36} = \frac{3 \cdot 9}{4 \cdot 9} = \frac{3}{4}.$$

SIMPLIFYING FRACTIONS

To simplify a fraction to lowest terms, factor out the greatest common factor c in the numerator and in the denominator. Then apply the **basic principle of fractions**:

$$\frac{a \cdot c}{b \cdot c} = \frac{a}{b}.$$

NOTE: This principle is true because multiplying a fraction by $\frac{c}{c}$ or 1 does not change the value of the fraction.

The greatest common factor for two numbers is not always obvious. The next example demonstrates two different methods that can be used to find the GCF.

EXAMPLE 2 **Finding the greatest common factor**

Find the greatest common factor (GCF) for each pair of numbers.
(a) 24, 60   **(b)** 36, 54

Solution
(a) One way to determine the greatest common factor is to find the prime factorization of each number using factor trees, as shown in Figure 1.6.

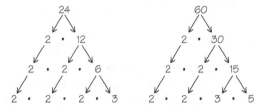

Figure 1.6 Prime Factorizations of 24 and 60

The prime factorizations have two 2s and one 3 in common.

$$24 = 2 \cdot 2 \cdot 2 \cdot 3$$
$$60 = 2 \cdot 2 \cdot 3 \cdot 5$$

Thus the GCF of 24 and 60 is $2 \cdot 2 \cdot 3 = 12$.

(b) Another way to find the greatest common factor is to create a factor step diagram. Working downward from the top, the numbers in each step are found by dividing the two numbers in the previous step by their *smallest common prime factor*. The process continues until no common prime factor can be found. A factor step diagram for 36 and 54 is shown in Figure 1.7 on the next page.

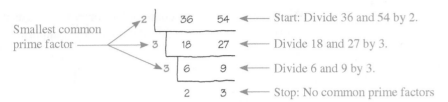

Figure 1.7 Factor Step Diagram for 36 and 54

The greatest common factor is the product of the prime numbers along the side of the diagram. So the GCF of 36 and 54 is $2 \cdot 3 \cdot 3 = 18$.

Now Try Exercises 15, 17

EXAMPLE 3

Simplifying fractions to lowest terms

Simplify each fraction to lowest terms.

(a) $\frac{24}{60}$ **(b)** $\frac{42}{105}$

Solution

(a) From Example 2(a), the GCF of 24 and 60 is 12. Thus

$$\frac{24}{60} = \frac{2 \cdot 12}{5 \cdot 12} = \frac{2}{5}.$$

(b) The prime factorizations of 42 and 105 are

$$42 = 2 \cdot 3 \cdot 7 \quad \text{and} \quad 105 = 5 \cdot 3 \cdot 7.$$

The GCF of 42 and 105 is $3 \cdot 7 = 21$. Thus

$$\frac{42}{105} = \frac{2 \cdot 21}{5 \cdot 21} = \frac{2}{5}.$$

Now Try Exercises 29, 33

CRITICAL THINKING

Describe a situation from everyday life in which fractions would be needed.

MAKING CONNECTIONS

Simplifying Fractions in Steps

Sometimes a fraction can be simplified to lowest terms in multiple steps. By using *any* common factor that is not the GCF, a new fraction in *lower* terms will result. This new fraction may then be simplified using a common factor of its numerator and denominator. If this process is continued, the result will be the given fraction simplified to lowest terms. The fraction in Example 3(b) could be simplified to lowest terms in two steps.

$$\frac{42}{105} = \frac{14 \cdot 3}{35 \cdot 3} = \frac{14}{35} = \frac{2 \cdot 7}{5 \cdot 7} = \frac{2}{5}$$

Multiplication and Division of Fractions

Suppose we cut *half* an apple into *thirds*, as illustrated in Figure 1.8. Then each piece represents one-sixth of the original apple. One-third of one-half is described by the product

$$\frac{1}{3} \cdot \frac{1}{2} = \frac{1}{6}.$$

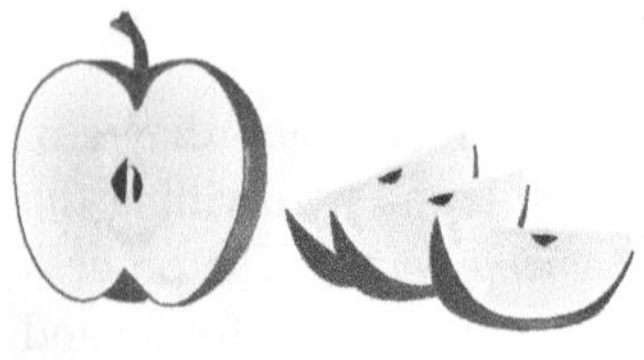

Figure 1.8

This example demonstrates that the numerator of the product of two fractions is found by multiplying the numerators of the two fractions. Similarly, the denominator of the product of two fractions is found by multiplying the denominators of the two fractions. For example, the product of $\frac{2}{3}$ and $\frac{5}{7}$ is

Multiply numerators.

$$\frac{2}{3} \cdot \frac{5}{7} = \frac{2 \cdot 5}{3 \cdot 7} = \frac{10}{21}.$$

Multiply denominators.

NOTE: The word "of" in mathematics often indicates multiplication. For example, the phrases "one-fifth of the cookies," "twenty percent of the price," and "half of the money" all suggest multiplication.

MULTIPLICATION OF FRACTIONS

The product of $\frac{a}{b}$ and $\frac{c}{d}$ is given by

$$\frac{a}{b} \cdot \frac{c}{d} = \frac{ac}{bd},$$

where b and d are not 0.

EXAMPLE 4 **Multiplying fractions**

Multiply. Simplify the result when appropriate.

(a) $\frac{4}{5} \cdot \frac{6}{7}$ **(b)** $\frac{8}{9} \cdot \frac{3}{4}$ **(c)** $3 \cdot \frac{5}{9}$ **(d)** $\frac{x}{y} \cdot \frac{z}{3}$

Solution

(a) $\frac{4}{5} \cdot \frac{6}{7} = \frac{4 \cdot 6}{5 \cdot 7} = \frac{24}{35}$

(b) $\frac{8}{9} \cdot \frac{3}{4} = \frac{8 \cdot 3}{9 \cdot 4} = \frac{24}{36}$; the GCF of 24 and 36 is 12, so

$$\frac{24}{36} = \frac{2 \cdot 12}{3 \cdot 12} = \frac{2}{3}.$$

(c) Start by writing 3 as $\frac{3}{1}$.

$$3 \cdot \frac{5}{9} = \frac{3}{1} \cdot \frac{5}{9} = \frac{3 \cdot 5}{1 \cdot 9} = \frac{15}{9}$$

The GCF of 15 and 9 is 3, so

$$\frac{15}{9} = \frac{5 \cdot 3}{3 \cdot 3} = \frac{5}{3}.$$

(d) $\frac{x}{y} \cdot \frac{z}{3} = \frac{x \cdot z}{y \cdot 3} = \frac{xz}{3y}$

When we write the product of a variable and a number, such as $y \cdot 3$, we typically write the number first, followed by the variable. That is, $y \cdot 3 = 3y$.

Now Try Exercises 35, 39, 43, 47

Multiplying and Simplifying Fractions

When multiplying fractions, sometimes it is possible to change the order of the factors to rewrite the product so that it is easier to simplify. In Example 4(b) the product could be written as

$$\frac{8}{9} \cdot \frac{3}{4} = \frac{3 \cdot 8}{9 \cdot 4} = \frac{3}{9} \cdot \frac{8}{4} = \frac{1}{3} \cdot \frac{2}{1} = \frac{2}{3}.$$

Instead of simplifying $\frac{24}{36}$, which contains larger numbers, the fractions $\frac{3}{9}$ and $\frac{8}{4}$ were simplified first.

EXAMPLE 5   **Finding fractional parts**

Find each fractional part.
(a) One-fifth of two-thirds   **(b)** Four-fifths of three-sevenths   **(c)** Three-fifths of ten

Solution
(a) The phrase "one-fifth of" indicates multiplication by one-fifth. The fractional part is

$$\frac{1}{5} \cdot \frac{2}{3} = \frac{1 \cdot 2}{5 \cdot 3} = \frac{2}{15}.$$

(b) $\frac{4}{5} \cdot \frac{3}{7} = \frac{4 \cdot 3}{5 \cdot 7} = \frac{12}{35}$

(c) $\frac{3}{5} \cdot 10 = \frac{3}{5} \cdot \frac{10}{1} = \frac{30}{5} = 6$

Now Try Exercises 49, 51, 53

▶ **REAL-WORLD CONNECTION** Fractions can be used to describe particular parts of the U.S. population. In the next application we use fractions to find the portion of the population that has completed 4 or more years of college.

EXAMPLE 6   **Estimating college completion rates**

About $\frac{17}{20}$ of the U.S. population over the age of 25 has a high school diploma. About $\frac{8}{25}$ of those people have gone on to complete 4 or more years of college. What fraction of the U.S. population over the age of 25 has completed 4 or more years of college? (*Source:* U.S. Census Bureau.)

Solution
We need to find $\frac{8}{25}$ of $\frac{17}{20}$.

$$\frac{8}{25} \cdot \frac{17}{20} = \frac{8 \cdot 17}{25 \cdot 20} = \frac{136}{500} = \frac{34 \cdot 4}{125 \cdot 4} = \frac{34}{125}.$$

About $\frac{34}{125}$ of the U.S. population over the age of 25 has completed 4 or more years of college.

Now Try Exercise 117

TABLE 1.4 Numbers and Their Reciprocals

Number	Reciprocal
3	$\frac{1}{3}$
$\frac{1}{4}$	4
$\frac{3}{2}$	$\frac{2}{3}$
$\frac{21}{37}$	$\frac{37}{21}$

The **multiplicative inverse**, or **reciprocal**, of a nonzero number a is $\frac{1}{a}$. Table 1.4 lists several numbers and their reciprocals. Note that the product of a number and its reciprocal is always 1. For example, the reciprocal of 2 is $\frac{1}{2}$, and their product is $2 \cdot \frac{1}{2} = 1$.

▶ **REAL-WORLD CONNECTION** Suppose that a group of children wants to buy gum from a gum ball machine that costs a half dollar for each gum ball. If the caregiver for the children has 4 dollars, then the number of gum balls that can be bought equals the number of half dollars that there are in 4 dollars. Thus 8 gum balls can be bought.

This calculation is given by $4 \div \frac{1}{2}$. To divide a number by a fraction, multiply the number by the reciprocal of the fraction.

$$4 \div \frac{1}{2} = 4 \cdot \frac{2}{1} \qquad \text{Multiply by the reciprocal of } \tfrac{1}{2}.$$

$$= \frac{4}{1} \cdot \frac{2}{1} \qquad \text{Write 4 as } \tfrac{4}{1}.$$

$$= \frac{8}{1} \qquad \text{Multiply the fractions.}$$

$$= 8 \qquad \tfrac{a}{1} = a \text{ for all values of } a.$$

Justification for multiplying by the reciprocal when dividing two fractions is

$$\frac{a}{b} \div \frac{c}{d} = \frac{\dfrac{a}{b}}{\dfrac{c}{d}} = \frac{\dfrac{a}{b} \cdot \dfrac{d}{c}}{\dfrac{c}{d} \cdot \dfrac{d}{c}} = \frac{\dfrac{a}{b} \cdot \dfrac{d}{c}}{1} = \frac{a}{b} \cdot \frac{d}{c}.$$

These results are summarized as follows.

DIVISION OF FRACTIONS

For real numbers a, b, c, and d, with b, c, and d not equal to 0,

$$\frac{a}{b} \div \frac{c}{d} = \frac{a}{b} \cdot \frac{d}{c}.$$

EXAMPLE 7 **Dividing fractions**

Divide. Simplify the result when appropriate.

(a) $\dfrac{1}{3} \div \dfrac{3}{5}$ **(b)** $\dfrac{4}{5} \div \dfrac{4}{5}$ **(c)** $5 \div \dfrac{10}{3}$ **(d)** $\dfrac{x}{2} \div \dfrac{y}{z}$

Solution
(a) To divide $\frac{1}{3}$ by $\frac{3}{5}$, multiply $\frac{1}{3}$ by $\frac{5}{3}$, which is the reciprocal of $\frac{3}{5}$.

$$\frac{1}{3} \div \frac{3}{5} = \frac{1}{3} \cdot \frac{5}{3} = \frac{1 \cdot 5}{3 \cdot 3} = \frac{5}{9}$$

(b) $\frac{4}{5} \div \frac{4}{5} = \frac{4}{5} \cdot \frac{5}{4} = \frac{4 \cdot 5}{5 \cdot 4} = \frac{20}{20} = 1$. Note that when we divide any nonzero number by itself, the result is 1.

(c) $5 \div \frac{10}{3} = \frac{5}{1} \cdot \frac{3}{10} = \frac{15}{10} = \frac{3}{2}$

(d) $\dfrac{x}{2} \div \dfrac{y}{z} = \dfrac{x}{2} \cdot \dfrac{z}{y} = \dfrac{xz}{2y}$

Now Try Exercises 59, 63, 67, 71

NOTE: In Example 7(c) the answer $\frac{3}{2}$ is an *improper fraction*, which could be written as the mixed number $1\frac{1}{2}$. However, in algebra, fractions are often left as improper fractions.

TECHNOLOGY NOTE

When entering a mixed number into a calculator, it is usually easiest first to convert the mixed number to an improper fraction. For example, enter $2\frac{2}{3}$ as $\frac{8}{3}$. Otherwise, enter $2\frac{2}{3}$ as $2 + \frac{2}{3}$. See the accompanying figure.

```
8/3
          2.666666667
2+2/3
          2.666666667
```

EXAMPLE 8   **Writing a problem**

Describe a problem for which the solution could be found by dividing 5 by $\frac{1}{6}$.

Solution
One possible problem could be stated as follows. If five pies are each cut into sixths, how many pieces of pie are there? See Figure 1.9.

Figure 1.9 Five Pies Cut into Sixths

Now Try Exercise 121

Addition and Subtraction of Fractions

FRACTIONS WITH LIKE DENOMINATORS Suppose that a person cuts a sheet of paper into eighths. If that person picks up two pieces and another person picks up three pieces, then together they have

$$\frac{2}{8} + \frac{3}{8} = \frac{5}{8}$$

Figure 1.10

of a sheet of paper, as illustrated in Figure 1.10. When the denominator of one fraction is the same as the denominator of a second fraction, the sum of the two fractions can be found by adding their numerators and keeping the common denominator.

Similarly, if someone picks up 5 pieces of paper and gives 2 away, then that person has

$$\frac{5}{8} - \frac{2}{8} = \frac{3}{8}$$

of a sheet of paper. To subtract two fractions with common denominators, subtract their numerators and keep the common denominator.

ADDITION AND SUBTRACTION OF FRACTIONS

To add or subtract fractions with a common denominator d, use the equations

$$\frac{a}{d} + \frac{b}{d} = \frac{a + b}{d} \quad \text{and} \quad \frac{a}{d} - \frac{b}{d} = \frac{a - b}{d},$$

where d is not 0.

EXAMPLE 9   **Adding and subtracting fractions with common denominators**

Add or subtract as indicated. Simplify your answer to lowest terms when appropriate.

(a) $\dfrac{5}{13} + \dfrac{12}{13}$ **(b)** $\dfrac{11}{8} - \dfrac{5}{8}$

Solution

(a) Because the fractions have a common denominator, add the numerators and keep the common denominator.

$$\frac{5}{13} + \frac{12}{13} = \frac{5 + 12}{13} = \frac{17}{13}$$

(b) Because the fractions have a common denominator, subtract the numerators and keep the common denominator.

$$\frac{11}{8} - \frac{5}{8} = \frac{11 - 5}{8} = \frac{6}{8}$$

The fraction $\frac{6}{8}$ can be simplified to $\frac{3}{4}$.

▌ Now Try Exercise 75

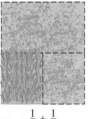

$\frac{1}{2} + \frac{1}{4}$

(a)

$\frac{2}{4} + \frac{1}{4} = \frac{3}{4}$

(b)

Figure 1.11

FRACTIONS WITH UNLIKE DENOMINATORS Suppose that one person mows half a large lawn while another person mows a fourth of the lawn. To determine how much they mowed together, we need to find the sum $\frac{1}{2} + \frac{1}{4}$. See Figure 1.11(a). Before we can add fractions with unlike denominators, we must write each fraction with a common denominator. The *least common denominator* of 2 and 4 is 4. Thus we need to write $\frac{1}{2}$ as $\frac{?}{4}$ by multiplying the numerator and denominator by the *same nonzero number*.

$$\frac{1}{2} = \frac{1}{2} \cdot \frac{2}{2} \quad \text{Multiply by 1.}$$

$$= \frac{2}{4} \quad \text{Multiply fractions.}$$

Now we can find the needed sum.

$$\frac{1}{2} + \frac{1}{4} = \frac{2}{4} + \frac{1}{4} = \frac{3}{4}$$

Together the two people mow three-fourths of the lawn, as illustrated in Figure 1.11(b).

To add or subtract fractions with unlike denominators, we first find the least common denominator for the fractions. The **least common denominator (LCD)** for two or more fractions is the smallest number that is divisible by every denominator.

READING CHECK

• What is the LCD and why is it needed?

FINDING THE LEAST COMMON DENOMINATOR (LCD)

STEP 1: Find the prime factorization for each denominator.

STEP 2: List each factor that appears in one or more of the factorizations. If a factor is repeated in any of the factorizations, list this factor the maximum number of times that it is repeated.

STEP 3: The product of this list of factors is the LCD.

The next example demonstrates two different methods that can be used to find the LCD. In part (a), the LCD is found using the three-step method shown on the previous page, and in part (b), a factor step diagram is used instead.

EXAMPLE 10 **Finding the least common denominator**

Find the LCD for each set of fractions.

(a) $\dfrac{5}{6}, \dfrac{3}{4}$ (b) $\dfrac{7}{36}, \dfrac{5}{54}$

Solution

(a) STEP 1: For the fractions $\frac{5}{6}$ and $\frac{3}{4}$ the prime factorizations of the denominators are

$$6 = 2 \cdot 3 \text{ and } 4 = 2 \cdot 2.$$

STEP 2: List the factors: 2, 2, 3. Note that, because the factor 2 appears a maximum of two times, it is listed twice.

STEP 3: The LCD is the product of this list, or $2 \cdot 2 \cdot 3 = 12$.

NOTE: Finding an LCD is equivalent to finding the smallest number that each denominator divides into evenly. Both 6 and 4 divide into 12 evenly, and 12 is the smallest such number. Thus 12 is the LCD for $\frac{5}{6}$ and $\frac{3}{4}$.

(b) The *same* factor step diagram that was used in Example 2(b) to find the GCF of 36 and 54 can be used to find the LCD for $\frac{7}{36}$ and $\frac{5}{54}$; however, the final step differs slightly. As in Example 2(b), we find the numbers in each step by dividing the two numbers in the previous step by their *smallest common prime factor*. The process continues until no common prime factor can be found, as shown in Figure 1.12.

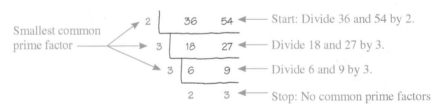

Figure 1.12 Factor Step Diagram for Finding the LCD

The process for finding the LCD differs from that used to find the GCF in that we find the LCD by multiplying not only the numbers along the side of the diagram but also the numbers at the bottom of the diagram. The LCD is $2 \cdot 3 \cdot 3 \cdot 2 \cdot 3 = 108$.

Now Try Exercises 79, 83

Once the LCD has been found, the next step in the process for adding or subtracting fractions with unlike denominators is to rewrite each fraction with the LCD.

EXAMPLE 11 **Rewriting fractions with the LCD**

Rewrite each set of fractions using the LCD.

(a) $\dfrac{5}{6}, \dfrac{3}{4}$ (b) $\dfrac{7}{12}, \dfrac{5}{18}$

Solution

(a) From Example 10(a) the LCD is 12. To write $\frac{5}{6}$ with a denominator of 12, we multiply the fraction by 1 in the form $\frac{2}{2}$.

$$\frac{5}{6} \cdot \frac{2}{2} = \frac{5 \cdot 2}{6 \cdot 2} = \frac{10}{12}$$

To write $\frac{3}{4}$ with a denominator of 12, we multiply the fraction by 1 in the form $\frac{3}{3}$.

$$\frac{3}{4} \cdot \frac{3}{3} = \frac{3 \cdot 3}{4 \cdot 3} = \frac{9}{12}$$

Thus $\frac{5}{6}$ can be rewritten as $\frac{10}{12}$ and $\frac{3}{4}$ can be rewritten as $\frac{9}{12}$.

(b) From Example 10(b) the LCD is 36. To write $\frac{7}{12}$ with a denominator of 36, multiply the fraction by $\frac{3}{3}$. To write $\frac{5}{18}$ with a denominator of 36, multiply the fraction by $\frac{2}{2}$.

$$\frac{7}{12} \cdot \frac{3}{3} = \frac{7 \cdot 3}{12 \cdot 3} = \frac{21}{36} \quad \text{and} \quad \frac{5}{18} \cdot \frac{2}{2} = \frac{5 \cdot 2}{18 \cdot 2} = \frac{10}{36}$$

Thus $\frac{7}{12}$ can be rewritten as $\frac{21}{36}$ and $\frac{5}{18}$ can be rewritten as $\frac{10}{36}$.

Now Try Exercises 89, 93

The next example demonstrates how the concepts shown in the last two examples can be used to add or subtract fractions with unlike denominators.

EXAMPLE 12   **Adding and subtracting fractions with unlike denominators**

Add or subtract as indicated. Simplify your answer to lowest terms when appropriate.

(a) $\dfrac{5}{6} + \dfrac{3}{4}$ (b) $\dfrac{7}{12} - \dfrac{5}{18}$ (c) $\dfrac{1}{4} + \dfrac{2}{5} + \dfrac{7}{10}$

Solution

(a) From Example 10(a) the LCD is 12. Begin by writing each fraction with a denominator of 12, as demonstrated in Example 11(a).

$$\frac{5}{6} + \frac{3}{4} = \frac{5}{6} \cdot \frac{2}{2} + \frac{3}{4} \cdot \frac{3}{3} \qquad \text{Change to LCD of 12.}$$

$$= \frac{10}{12} + \frac{9}{12} \qquad \text{Multiply the fractions.}$$

$$= \frac{10 + 9}{12} \qquad \text{Add the numerators.}$$

$$= \frac{19}{12} \qquad \text{Simplify.}$$

(b) Using Example 10(b) and Example 11(b), we perform the following steps.

$$\frac{7}{12} - \frac{5}{18} = \frac{7}{12} \cdot \frac{3}{3} - \frac{5}{18} \cdot \frac{2}{2} \qquad \text{Change to LCD of 36.}$$

$$= \frac{21}{36} - \frac{10}{36} \qquad \text{Multiply the fractions.}$$

$$= \frac{21 - 10}{36} \qquad \text{Subtract the numerators.}$$

$$= \frac{11}{36} \qquad \text{Simplify.}$$

(c) The LCD for 4, 5, and 10 is 20.

$$\frac{1}{4} + \frac{2}{5} + \frac{7}{10} = \frac{1}{4} \cdot \frac{5}{5} + \frac{2}{5} \cdot \frac{4}{4} + \frac{7}{10} \cdot \frac{2}{2} \qquad \text{Change to LCD of 20.}$$

$$= \frac{5}{20} + \frac{8}{20} + \frac{14}{20} \qquad \text{Multiply the fractions.}$$

$$= \frac{5 + 8 + 14}{20} \qquad \text{Add the numerators.}$$

$$= \frac{27}{20} \qquad \text{Simplify.}$$

Now Try Exercises 97, 103, 107

An Application

The next example illustrates a situation where fractions occur in a real-world application.

EXAMPLE 13 **Applying fractions to carpentry**

A board measuring $35\frac{3}{4}$ inches is cut into four equal pieces, as depicted in Figure 1.13. Find the length of each piece.

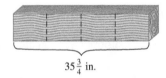

$35\frac{3}{4}$ in.

Figure 1.13

Solution
Begin by writing $35\frac{3}{4}$ as the improper fraction $\frac{143}{4}$ (because $4 \cdot 35 + 3 = 143$). Because the board is to be cut into four equal parts, the length of each piece should be

$$\frac{143}{4} \div 4 = \frac{143}{4} \cdot \frac{1}{4} = \frac{143}{16}, \quad \text{or} \quad 8\frac{15}{16} \text{ inches.}$$

Now Try Exercise 111

1.2 **Putting It All Together**

CONCEPT	COMMENTS	EXAMPLES
Fraction	The fraction $\frac{a}{b}$ has numerator a and denominator b.	The fraction $\frac{xy}{2}$ has numerator xy and denominator 2.
Lowest Terms	A fraction is in lowest terms if the numerator and denominator have no factors in common.	The fraction $\frac{3}{8}$ is in lowest terms because 3 and 8 have no factors in common.

CONCEPT	COMMENTS	EXAMPLES
Greatest Common Factor (GCF)	The GCF of two numbers equals the largest number that divides into both evenly.	The GCF of 12 and 18 is 6 because 6 is the largest number that divides into 12 and 18 evenly.
Simplifying Fractions	Use the principle $$\frac{a \cdot c}{b \cdot c} = \frac{a}{b}$$ to simplify fractions, where c is the GCF of the numerator and denominator.	The GCF of 24 and 32 is 8, so $$\frac{24}{32} = \frac{3 \cdot 8}{4 \cdot 8} = \frac{3}{4}.$$ The GCF of 20 and 8 is 4, so $$\frac{20}{8} = \frac{5 \cdot 4}{2 \cdot 4} = \frac{5}{2}.$$
Multiplicative Inverse or Reciprocal	The reciprocal of $\frac{a}{b}$ is $\frac{b}{a}$, where a and b are not zero. The product of a number and its reciprocal is 1.	The reciprocals of 5 and $\frac{3}{4}$ are $\frac{1}{5}$ and $\frac{4}{3}$, respectively, because $5 \cdot \frac{1}{5} = 1$ and $\frac{3}{4} \cdot \frac{4}{3} = 1$.
Multiplication and Division of Fractions	$$\frac{a}{b} \cdot \frac{c}{d} = \frac{ac}{bd}$$ $$\frac{a}{b} \div \frac{c}{d} = \frac{a}{b} \cdot \frac{d}{c}$$	$$\frac{3}{5} \cdot \frac{4}{9} = \frac{12}{45} = \frac{4}{15}$$ $$\frac{3}{2} \div \frac{6}{5} = \frac{3}{2} \cdot \frac{5}{6} = \frac{15}{12} = \frac{5}{4}$$
Addition and Subtraction of Fractions with Like Denominators	$$\frac{a}{d} + \frac{c}{d} = \frac{a + c}{d} \quad \text{and}$$ $$\frac{a}{d} - \frac{c}{d} = \frac{a - c}{d}$$	$$\frac{3}{5} + \frac{4}{5} = \frac{3 + 4}{5} = \frac{7}{5} \quad \text{and}$$ $$\frac{17}{12} - \frac{11}{12} = \frac{17 - 11}{12} = \frac{6}{12} = \frac{1}{2}$$
Least Common Denominator (LCD)	The LCD of two fractions equals the smallest number that both denominators divide into evenly.	The LCD of $\frac{5}{12}$ and $\frac{7}{18}$ is 36 because 36 is the smallest number that both 12 and 18 divide into evenly.
Addition and Subtraction of Fractions with Unlike Denominators	First write each fraction with the least common denominator. Then add or subtract the numerators.	The LCD of $\frac{3}{4}$ and $\frac{7}{10}$ is 20. $$\frac{3}{4} + \frac{7}{10} = \frac{3}{4} \cdot \frac{5}{5} + \frac{7}{10} \cdot \frac{2}{2}$$ $$= \frac{15}{20} + \frac{14}{20}$$ $$= \frac{29}{20}$$

1.2 Exercises

CONCEPTS AND VOCABULARY

1. A small pie is cut into 4 equal pieces. If someone eats 3 of the pieces, what fraction of the pie does the person eat? What fraction of the pie remains?

2. In the fraction $\frac{11}{21}$ the numerator is _____ and the denominator is _____.

3. In the fraction $\frac{a}{b}$, the variable b cannot equal _____.

4. The fraction $\frac{7}{12}$ is in _____ terms because 7 and 12 have no factors in common.

5. (True or False?) The numerator of the product of two fractions is found by multiplying the numerators of the two fractions.

6. (True or False?) The denominator of the sum of two fractions is found by adding the denominators of the two fractions.

7. $\frac{ac}{bc} = $ _____

8. In the phrase "two-fifths of one-third," the word *of* indicates that we _____ the fractions $\frac{2}{5}$ and $\frac{1}{3}$.

9. What is the reciprocal of a, provided $a \neq 0$?

10. To divide $\frac{3}{4}$ by 5, multiply $\frac{3}{4}$ by _____.

11. $\frac{a}{b} \cdot \frac{c}{d} = $ _____

12. $\frac{a}{b} \div \frac{c}{d} = $ _____

13. $\frac{a}{b} + \frac{c}{b} = $ _____

14. $\frac{a}{b} - \frac{c}{b} = $ _____

LOWEST TERMS

Exercises 15–20: Find the greatest common factor.

15. 4, 12

16. 3, 27

17. 50, 75

18. 45, 105

19. 100, 60, 70

20. 36, 48, 72

Exercises 21–24: Use the basic principle of fractions to simplify the expression.

21. $\frac{3 \cdot 4}{5 \cdot 4}$

22. $\frac{2 \cdot 7}{9 \cdot 7}$

23. $\frac{3 \cdot 8}{8 \cdot 5}$

24. $\frac{7 \cdot 16}{16 \cdot 3}$

Exercises 25–34: Simplify the fraction to lowest terms.

25. $\frac{4}{8}$

26. $\frac{4}{12}$

27. $\frac{10}{25}$

28. $\frac{5}{20}$

29. $\frac{12}{36}$

30. $\frac{16}{24}$

31. $\frac{12}{30}$

32. $\frac{60}{105}$

33. $\frac{19}{76}$

34. $\frac{17}{51}$

MULTIPLICATION AND DIVISION OF FRACTIONS

Exercises 35–48: Multiply and simplify to lowest terms when appropriate.

35. $\frac{3}{4} \cdot \frac{1}{5}$

36. $\frac{3}{2} \cdot \frac{5}{8}$

37. $\frac{5}{3} \cdot \frac{3}{5}$

38. $\frac{21}{32} \cdot \frac{32}{21}$

39. $\frac{5}{6} \cdot \frac{18}{25}$

40. $\frac{7}{9} \cdot \frac{3}{14}$

41. $4 \cdot \frac{3}{5}$

42. $5 \cdot \frac{7}{9}$

43. $2 \cdot \frac{3}{8}$

44. $10 \cdot \frac{1}{100}$

45. $\frac{x}{y} \cdot \frac{y}{x}$

46. $\frac{x}{y} \cdot \frac{y}{z}$

47. $\frac{a}{b} \cdot \frac{3}{2}$

48. $\frac{5}{8} \cdot \frac{4x}{5y}$

Exercises 49–54: Find the fractional part.

49. One-fourth of three-fourths

50. Three-sevenths of nine-sixteenths

51. Two-thirds of six

52. Three-fourths of seven

53. One-half of two-thirds

54. Four-elevenths of nine-eighths

Exercises 55–58: Give the reciprocal of each number.

55. (a) 5 (b) 7 (c) $\frac{4}{7}$ (d) $\frac{9}{8}$

56. (a) 3 (b) 2 (c) $\frac{6}{5}$ (d) $\frac{3}{8}$

57. (a) $\frac{1}{2}$ (b) $\frac{1}{9}$ (c) $\frac{12}{101}$ (d) $\frac{31}{17}$

58. (a) $\frac{1}{5}$ (b) $\frac{7}{3}$ (c) $\frac{23}{64}$ (d) $\frac{63}{29}$

Exercises 59–74: Divide and simplify to lowest terms when appropriate.

59. $\frac{1}{2} \div \frac{1}{3}$

60. $\frac{3}{4} \div \frac{1}{5}$

61. $\frac{3}{4} \div \frac{1}{8}$

62. $\frac{6}{7} \div \frac{3}{14}$

63. $\frac{4}{3} \div \frac{4}{3}$

64. $\frac{12}{21} \div \frac{4}{7}$

65. $\frac{32}{27} \div \frac{8}{9}$

66. $\frac{8}{15} \div \frac{2}{25}$

67. $10 \div \frac{5}{6}$

68. $8 \div \frac{4}{3}$

69. $\frac{9}{10} \div 3$

70. $\frac{32}{27} \div 16$

71. $\frac{a}{b} \div \frac{2}{b}$

72. $\frac{3a}{b} \div \frac{3}{c}$

73. $\frac{x}{y} \div \frac{x}{y}$

74. $\frac{x}{3y} \div \frac{x}{3}$

ADDITION AND SUBTRACTION OF FRACTIONS

Exercises 75–78: Add or subtract. Write each answer in lowest terms.

75. (a) $\frac{5}{12} + \frac{1}{12}$ **(b)** $\frac{5}{12} - \frac{1}{12}$

76. (a) $\frac{3}{2} + \frac{1}{2}$ **(b)** $\frac{3}{2} - \frac{1}{2}$

77. (a) $\frac{18}{29} + \frac{7}{29}$ **(b)** $\frac{18}{29} - \frac{7}{29}$

78. (a) $\frac{5}{33} + \frac{2}{33}$ **(b)** $\frac{5}{33} - \frac{2}{33}$

Exercises 79–88: Find the least common denominator.

79. $\frac{4}{9}, \frac{2}{15}$ **80.** $\frac{1}{11}, \frac{1}{2}$

81. $\frac{2}{5}, \frac{3}{15}$ **82.** $\frac{8}{21}, \frac{3}{7}$

83. $\frac{1}{6}, \frac{5}{8}$ **84.** $\frac{1}{9}, \frac{5}{12}$

85. $\frac{1}{2}, \frac{1}{3}, \frac{1}{4}$ **86.** $\frac{2}{5}, \frac{2}{3}, \frac{1}{6}$

87. $\frac{1}{4}, \frac{3}{8}, \frac{1}{12}$ **88.** $\frac{2}{15}, \frac{7}{20}, \frac{1}{30}$

Exercises 89–96: Rewrite each set of fractions with the least common denominator.

89. $\frac{1}{2}, \frac{2}{3}$ **90.** $\frac{3}{4}, \frac{1}{5}$

91. $\frac{7}{9}, \frac{5}{12}$ **92.** $\frac{5}{13}, \frac{1}{2}$

93. $\frac{1}{16}, \frac{7}{12}$ **94.** $\frac{5}{18}, \frac{1}{24}$

95. $\frac{1}{3}, \frac{3}{4}, \frac{5}{6}$ **96.** $\frac{4}{15}, \frac{2}{9}, \frac{3}{5}$

Exercises 97–108: Add or subtract. Write your answer in lowest terms.

97. $\frac{5}{8} + \frac{3}{16}$ **98.** $\frac{1}{9} + \frac{2}{15}$

99. $\frac{25}{24} - \frac{7}{8}$ **100.** $\frac{4}{5} - \frac{1}{4}$

101. $\frac{11}{14} + \frac{2}{35}$ **102.** $\frac{7}{8} + \frac{4}{15}$

103. $\frac{5}{12} - \frac{1}{18}$ **104.** $\frac{9}{20} - \frac{7}{30}$

105. $\frac{3}{100} + \frac{1}{300} - \frac{1}{200}$ **106.** $\frac{43}{36} + \frac{4}{9} + \frac{1}{4}$

107. $\frac{7}{8} - \frac{1}{6} + \frac{5}{12}$ **108.** $\frac{9}{40} - \frac{3}{50} - \frac{1}{100}$

APPLICATIONS

109. *American Flag* According to Executive Order 10834, the length of an official American flag should be $1\frac{9}{10}$ times the width. If an official flag has a width that measures $2\frac{1}{2}$ feet, find its length.

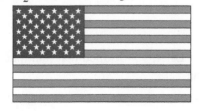

110. *American Flag* The blue rectangle containing the stars on an American flag is called the *union*. On an official American flag, the width of the union should be $\frac{7}{13}$ of the width of the flag. If an official flag has a width of $32\frac{1}{2}$ inches, what is the width of the union?

111. *Carpentry* A board measuring $64\frac{5}{8}$ inches is cut in half. Find the length of each half.

112. *Cutting Rope* A rope measures $15\frac{1}{2}$ feet and needs to be cut in four equal parts. Find the length of each piece.

113. *Geometry* Find the area of the triangle shown with base $1\frac{2}{3}$ yards and height $\frac{3}{4}$ yard. (*Hint:* The area of a triangle equals half the product of its base and height.)

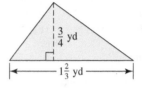

114. *Geometry* Find the area of the rectangle shown.

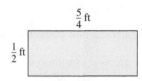

115. *Distance* Use the map to find the distance between Smalltown and Bigtown by traveling through Middletown.

116. *Distance* An athlete jogs $1\frac{3}{8}$ miles, $5\frac{3}{4}$ miles, and $3\frac{5}{8}$ miles. In all, how far does the athlete jog?

117. *Vegetarian Diets* About $\frac{4}{125}$ of U.S. adults follow a vegetarian diet. Within this part of the population, $\frac{1}{200}$ is vegan. What fraction of the adult U.S. population is vegan? (*Source: Vegetarian Times—2010.*)

118. *Women College Students* In 2010, about $\frac{29}{50}$ of all college students were women. Of these women, about $\frac{13}{20}$ were part-time students. What fraction of college students were women who were part-time students? (*Source:* National Center for Education Statistics.)

119. *Accidental Deaths* For the age group 15 to 24, motor vehicle accidents account for $\frac{31}{42}$ of all accidental deaths, and firearms account for $\frac{31}{1260}$ of all accidental deaths. What fraction of all accidental deaths do vehicle accidents *and* firearms account for? (*Source:* National Safety Council.)

120. *Illicit Drug Use* For the age group 18 to 25, the fraction of people who used illicit drugs during their lifetime was $\frac{3}{5}$, whereas the fraction who used illicit drugs during the past year was $\frac{7}{20}$. What fraction of this population has used illicit drugs but not during the past year? (*Source:* Department of Health and Human Services.)

WRITING ABOUT MATHEMATICS

121. Describe a problem in real life for which the solution could be found by multiplying 30 by $\frac{1}{4}$.

122. Describe a problem in real life for which the solution could be found by dividing $2\frac{1}{2}$ by $\frac{1}{3}$.

SECTIONS 1.1 AND 1.2

Checking Basic Concepts

1. Classify each number as prime, composite, or neither. If a number is composite, write it as a product of primes.
   (a) 19   (b) 28   (c) 1   (d) 180

2. Evaluate $\frac{10}{(x + 2)}$ for $x = 3$.

3. Find y for $x = 5$ if $y = 6x$.

4. Translate the phrase "a number x plus five" into an algebraic expression.

5. Write a formula that converts F feet to I inches.

6. Find the greatest common factor.
   (a) 3, 18   (b) 40, 72

7. Simplify each fraction to lowest terms.
   (a) $\frac{25}{35}$ (b) $\frac{26}{39}$

8. Give the reciprocal of $\frac{4}{3}$.

9. Evaluate each expression. Write each answer in lowest terms.
   (a) $\frac{2}{3} \cdot \frac{3}{4}$ (b) $\frac{5}{6} \div \frac{10}{3}$
   (c) $\frac{3}{10} + \frac{1}{10}$ (d) $\frac{3}{4} - \frac{1}{6}$

10. A recipe needs $1\frac{2}{3}$ cups of flour. How much flour should be used if the recipe is doubled?

1.3   Exponents and Order of Operations

Natural Number Exponents ▪ Order of Operations ▪ Translating Words to Expressions

A LOOK INTO MATH ▶ If there are 15 energy drinks on a store shelf and 3 boxes of 24 drinks each in the storage room, then the total number of energy drinks is given by the expression $15 + 3 \cdot 24$. How would you find the total number of energy drinks? Is the total

$$15 + 3 \cdot 24 \overset{?}{=} 18 \cdot 24 \overset{?}{=} 432, \quad \text{or} \quad 15 + 3 \cdot 24 \overset{?}{=} 15 + 72 \overset{?}{=} 87?$$

(add first, then multiply)   (multiply first, then add)

In this section, we discuss the *order of operations agreement*, which can be used to show that the expression $15 + 3 \cdot 24$ evaluates to 87.

NEW VOCABULARY

☐ Exponential expression
☐ Base
☐ Exponent

Natural Number Exponents

In elementary school you learned addition. Later, you learned that multiplication is a fast way to add. For example, rather than adding

$$3 + 3 + 3 + 3, \quad \longleftarrow \text{4 terms}$$

we can multiply $3 \cdot 4$. Similarly, exponents represent a fast way to multiply. Rather than multiplying

$$3 \cdot 3 \cdot 3 \cdot 3, \quad \longleftarrow \text{4 factors}$$

we can evaluate the *exponential expression* 3^4. We begin by discussing natural numbers as exponents.

READING CHECK

• What type of expression represents a fast way to multiply?

The area of a square equals the length of one of its sides times itself. If the square is 5 inches on a side, then its area is

$$5 \cdot 5 = 5^2 = 25 \text{ square inches.}$$

with Exponent pointing to the superscript 2 and Base pointing to the 5.

The expression 5^2 is an **exponential expression** with *base* 5 and *exponent* 2. Exponential expressions occur in a variety of applications. For example, suppose an investment doubles 3 times. Then, the calculation

$$\underbrace{2 \cdot 2 \cdot 2}_{\text{Factors}} = 2^3 = 8$$

with Exponent 3 pointing to the superscript 3.

shows that the final value is 8 times as large as the original investment. For example, if \$10 doubles 3 times, it becomes \$20, \$40, and finally \$80, which is 8 times as large as \$10. Table 1.5 contains examples of exponential expressions.

TABLE 1.5 **Exponential Expressions**

Repeated Multiplication	Exponential Expression	Base	Exponent
$2 \cdot 2 \cdot 2 \cdot 2$	2^4	2	4
$4 \cdot 4 \cdot 4$	4^3	4	3
$9 \cdot 9$	9^2	9	2
$\frac{1}{2}$	$\left(\frac{1}{2}\right)^1$	$\frac{1}{2}$	1
$b \cdot b \cdot b \cdot b \cdot b$	b^5	b	5

Read 9^2 as "9 squared," 4^3 as "4 cubed," and 2^4 as "2 to the fourth power." The terms *squared* and *cubed* come from geometry. If the length of a side of a square is 3, then its area is

$$3 \cdot 3 = 3^2 = 9$$

square units, as illustrated in Figure 1.14(a). Similarly, if the length of an edge of a cube is 3, then its volume is

$$3 \cdot 3 \cdot 3 = 3^3 = 27$$

cubic units, as shown in Figure 1.14(b).

NOTE: The expressions 3^2 and 3^3 can also be read as "3 to the second power" and "3 to the third power," respectively. In general, the expression x^n is read as "x to the nth power" or "the nth power of x."

3 Squared

(a)

3 Cubed

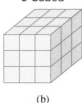

(b)

Figure 1.14

EXPONENTIAL NOTATION

The expression b^n, where n is a natural number, means

$$b^n = \underbrace{b \cdot b \cdot b \cdot \cdots \cdot b}_{n \text{ factors}}.$$

The **base** is b and the **exponent** is n.

EXAMPLE 1 **Writing products in exponential notation**

Write each product as an exponential expression.

(a) $7 \cdot 7 \cdot 7 \cdot 7$ (b) $\dfrac{1}{4} \cdot \dfrac{1}{4} \cdot \dfrac{1}{4}$ (c) $x \cdot x \cdot x \cdot x \cdot x$

Solution
(a) Because there are four factors of 7, the exponent is 4 and the base is 7. Thus $7 \cdot 7 \cdot 7 \cdot 7 = 7^4$.
(b) Because there are three factors of $\frac{1}{4}$, the exponent is 3 and the base is $\frac{1}{4}$. Thus $\frac{1}{4} \cdot \frac{1}{4} \cdot \frac{1}{4} = \left(\frac{1}{4}\right)^3$.
(c) Because there are five factors of x, the exponent is 5 and the base is x. Thus $x \cdot x \cdot x \cdot x \cdot x = x^5$.

Now Try Exercises 13, 15, 17

EXAMPLE 2 **Evaluating exponential notation**

Evaluate each expression.

(a) 3^4 (b) 10^3 (c) $\left(\dfrac{3}{4}\right)^2$

Solution
(a) The exponential expression 3^4 indicates that 3 is to be multiplied times itself 4 times.

$$3^4 = \underbrace{3 \cdot 3 \cdot 3 \cdot 3}_{4 \text{ factors}} = 81$$

CALCULATOR HELP

To evaluate an exponential expression with a calculator, see Appendix A (page AP-1).

(b) $10^3 = 10 \cdot 10 \cdot 10 = 1000$
(c) $\left(\frac{3}{4}\right)^2 = \frac{3}{4} \cdot \frac{3}{4} = \frac{9}{16}$

Now Try Exercises 25, 27

EXAMPLE 3 **Writing numbers in exponential notation**

Use the given base to write each number as an exponential expression. Check your results with a calculator, if one is available.
(a) 100 (base 10)   (b) 16 (base 2)   (c) 27 (base 3)

Solution
(a) $100 = 10 \cdot 10 = 10^2$
(b) $16 = 4 \cdot 4 = 2 \cdot 2 \cdot 2 \cdot 2 = 2^4$
(c) $27 = 3 \cdot 9 = 3 \cdot 3 \cdot 3 = 3^3$

```
10^2
                100
2^4
                 16
3^3
                 27
```

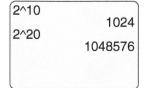

Figure 1.15

These values are supported in Figure 1.15, where exponential expressions are evaluated with a calculator by using the "^" key. (Note that some calculators may have a different key for evaluating exponential expressions.)

Now Try Exercises 29, 33, 35

▶ **REAL-WORLD CONNECTION** Computer memory is often measured in bytes, with each *byte* capable of storing one letter of the alphabet. For example, it takes four bytes to store the word "math" in a computer. Bytes of computer memory are often manufactured in amounts equal to powers of 2, as illustrated in the next example.

EXAMPLE 4

Analyzing computer memory

In computer technology 1 K (kilobyte) of memory equals 2^{10} bytes, and 1 MB (megabyte) of memory equals 2^{20} bytes. Determine whether 1 K of memory equals one thousand bytes and whether 1 MB equals one million bytes.

Solution

Figure 1.16 shows that $2^{10} = 1024$ and $2^{20} = 1{,}048{,}576$. Thus 1 K represents slightly more than one thousand bytes, and 1 MB represents more than one million bytes.

```
2^10
               1024
2^20
            1048576
```

Figure 1.16

Now Try Exercise 75

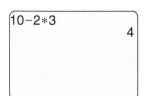

CRITICAL THINKING

One gigabyte of memory equals 2^{30} bytes and is often referred to as 1 billion bytes. If you have a calculator available, determine whether 1 gigabyte is exactly 1 billion bytes.

Order of Operations

When the expression $10 - 2 \cdot 3$ is evaluated, is the result

$$8 \cdot 3 = 24 \quad \text{or} \quad 10 - 6 = 4?$$

```
10-2*3
                  4
```

Figure 1.17

Figure 1.17 shows that a calculator gives a result of 4. The reason is that multiplication is performed before subtraction.

Because arithmetic expressions may contain parentheses, exponents, absolute values, and several operations, it is important to evaluate these expressions consistently. (Absolute value will be discussed in Section 1.4.) To ensure that we all obtain the same result when evaluating an arithmetic expression, the following rules are used.

STUDY TIP

Ideas and procedures written in boxes like the one to the right are major concepts in this section. Be sure that you understand them.

ORDER OF OPERATIONS

Use the following order of operations. First perform all calculations within parentheses and absolute values, or above and below the fraction bar.

1. Evaluate all exponential expressions.
2. Do all multiplication and division from *left to right*.
3. Do all addition and subtraction from *left to right*.

EXAMPLE 5 **Evaluating arithmetic expressions**

Evaluate each expression by hand.

(a) $10 - 4 - 3$ (b) $10 - (4 - 3)$ (c) $5 + \dfrac{12}{3}$ (d) $\dfrac{4 + 1}{2 + 8}$

Solution

(a) There are no parentheses, so we evaluate subtraction from *left to right*.

$$10 - 4 - 3 = 6 - 3 = 3$$

(b) Note the similarity between this part and part (a). The difference is the parentheses, so subtraction inside the parentheses must be performed first.

$$10 - (4 - 3) = 10 - 1 = 9$$

(c) We perform division before addition.

$$5 + \frac{12}{3} = 5 + 4 = 9$$

(d) Evaluate the expression as though both the numerator and the denominator have parentheses around them.

$$\frac{4 + 1}{2 + 8} = \frac{(4 + 1)}{(2 + 8)} = \frac{5}{10} = \frac{1}{2}$$

Now Try Exercises 43, 45, 57

EXAMPLE 6 **Evaluating arithmetic expressions**

Evaluate each expression by hand.

(a) $25 - 4 \cdot 6$ (b) $6 + 7 \cdot 2 - (4 - 1)$ (c) $\dfrac{3 + 3^2}{14 - 2}$ (d) $5 \cdot 2^3 - (3 + 2)$

Solution

(a) Multiplication is performed before subtraction, so evaluate the expression as follows.

$$25 - 4 \cdot 6 = 25 - 24 \qquad \text{Multiply.}$$
$$= 1 \qquad \text{Subtract.}$$

(b) Start by performing the subtraction within the parentheses first and then perform the multiplication. Finally, perform the addition and subtraction from left to right.

$$6 + 7 \cdot 2 - (4 - 1) = 6 + 7 \cdot 2 - 3 \quad \text{Subtract within parentheses.}$$
$$= 6 + 14 - 3 \quad \text{Multiply.}$$
$$= 20 - 3 \quad \text{Add.}$$
$$= 17 \quad \text{Subtract.}$$

(c) First note that parentheses are implied around the numerator and denominator.

$$\frac{3 + 3^2}{14 - 2} = \frac{(3 + 3^2)}{(14 - 2)} \qquad \text{Insert parentheses.}$$
$$= \frac{(3 + 9)}{(14 - 2)} \qquad \text{Evaluate the exponent first.}$$
$$= \frac{12}{12} \qquad \text{Add and subtract.}$$
$$= 1 \qquad \text{Simplify.}$$

(d) Begin by evaluating the expression inside parentheses.

$$5 \cdot 2^3 - (3 + 2) = 5 \cdot 2^3 - 5 \qquad \text{Add within parentheses.}$$
$$= 5 \cdot 8 - 5 \qquad \text{Evaluate the exponent.}$$
$$= 40 - 5 \qquad \text{Multiply.}$$
$$= 35 \qquad \text{Subtract.}$$

Now Try Exercises 59, 61, 63

Translating Words to Expressions

Sometimes before we can solve a problem we must translate words into mathematical expressions. For example, if a cell phone plan allows for 500 minutes of call time each month and 376 minutes have already been used, then "five hundred minus three hundred seventy-six," or $500 - 376 = 124$, is the number of minutes remaining for the month.

EXAMPLE 7   **Writing and evaluating expressions**

Translate each phrase into a mathematical expression and then evaluate it.
(a) Two to the fourth power plus ten
(b) Twenty decreased by five times three
(c) Ten cubed divided by five squared
(d) Sixty divided by the quantity ten minus six

Solution
(a) $2^4 + 10 = 2 \cdot 2 \cdot 2 \cdot 2 + 10 = 16 + 10 = 26$
(b) $20 - 5 \cdot 3 = 20 - 15 = 5$
(c) $\dfrac{10^3}{5^2} = \dfrac{1000}{25} = 40$
(d) Here, the word "quantity" indicates that parentheses should be used.

$$60 \div (10 - 6) = 60 \div 4 = 15$$

Now Try Exercises 67, 69, 73

1.3   Putting It All Together

CONCEPT	COMMENTS	EXAMPLES
Exponential Expression	If n is a natural number, then b^n equals $$\underbrace{b \cdot b \cdot b \cdot \cdots \cdot b}_{n \text{ factors}}$$ and is read "b to the nth power."	$5^1 = 5,$ $7^2 = 7 \cdot 7 = 49,$ $4^3 = 4 \cdot 4 \cdot 4 = 64,$ and $k^4 = k \cdot k \cdot k \cdot k$
Base and Exponent	The base in b^n is b and the exponent is n.	7^4 has base 7 and exponent 4, and x^3 has base x and exponent 3.

continued on next page

continued from previous page

CONCEPT	COMMENTS	EXAMPLES
Order of Operations	First, perform all calculations within parentheses and absolute values, or above and below a fraction bar. 1. Evaluate all exponential expressions. 2. Do all multiplication and division from *left to right*. 3. Do all addition and subtraction from *left to right*.	$10 \div 5 + 3 \cdot 7 = 2 + 21$ $= 23$ $27 \div (4 - 1)^2 = 27 \div 3^2$ $= 27 \div 9$ $= 3$

1.3 Exercises

MyMathLab    Math XL PRACTICE   WATCH   DOWNLOAD   READ   REVIEW

CONCEPTS AND VOCABULARY

1. Exponents represent a fast way to _____.

2. In the expression 2^5, there are five factors of _____ being multiplied.

3. In the expression 5^3, the number 5 is called the _____ and the number 3 is called the _____.

4. Use symbols to write "6 squared."

5. Use symbols to write "8 cubed."

6. When evaluating the expression $5 + 6 \cdot 2$, the result is _____ because _____ is performed before _____.

7. When evaluating the expression $10 - 2^3$, the result is _____ because _____ are evaluated before _____ is performed.

8. The expression $10 - 4 - 2$ equals _____ because subtraction is performed from _____ to _____.

9. (True or False?) The expressions 2^3 and 3^2 are equal.

10. (True or False?) The expression 5^2 equals $5 \cdot 2$.

NATURAL NUMBER EXPONENTS

Exercises 11–20: Write the product as an exponential expression.

11. $3 \cdot 3 \cdot 3 \cdot 3$

12. $10 \cdot 10$

13. $2 \cdot 2 \cdot 2 \cdot 2 \cdot 2$

14. $4 \cdot 4 \cdot 4$

15. $\frac{1}{2} \cdot \frac{1}{2} \cdot \frac{1}{2} \cdot \frac{1}{2}$

16. $\frac{5}{7} \cdot \frac{5}{7} \cdot \frac{5}{7} \cdot \frac{5}{7} \cdot \frac{5}{7}$

17. $a \cdot a \cdot a \cdot a \cdot a$

18. $b \cdot b \cdot b \cdot b$

19. $(x + 3) \cdot (x + 3)$

20. $(x - 4) \cdot (x - 4) \cdot (x - 4)$

Exercises 21–28: Evaluate each expression.

21. (a) 2^4 (b) 4^2 22. (a) 3^2 (b) 5^3

23. (a) 6^1 (b) 1^6 24. (a) 17^1 (b) 1^{17}

25. (a) 2^5 (b) 10^3 26. (a) 10^5 (b) 3^4

27. (a) $\left(\frac{2}{3}\right)^2$ (b) $\left(\frac{1}{2}\right)^5$

28. (a) $\left(\frac{1}{10}\right)^3$ (b) $\left(\frac{4}{3}\right)^1$

Exercises 29–40: (Refer to Example 3.) Use the given base to write the number as an exponential expression. Check your result if you have a calculator available.

29. 8   (base 2)   30. 9   (base 3)

31. 25   (base 5)   32. 32   (base 2)

33. 49   (base 7)   34. 81   (base 3)

35. 1000   (base 10)   36. 256   (base 4)

37. $\frac{1}{16}$ $\left(\text{base } \frac{1}{2}\right)$ 38. $\frac{9}{25}$ $\left(\text{base } \frac{3}{5}\right)$

39. $\frac{32}{243}$ $\left(\text{base } \frac{2}{3}\right)$ 40. $\frac{216}{343}$ $\left(\text{base } \frac{6}{7}\right)$

ORDER OF OPERATIONS

Exercises 41–64: Evaluate the expression by hand.

41. $5 + 4 \cdot 6$

42. $6 \cdot 7 - 8$

43. $6 \div 3 + 2$

44. $20 - 10 \div 5$

45. $100 - \frac{50}{5}$

46. $\frac{200}{100} + 6$

47. $10 - 6 - 1$

48. $30 - 9 - 5$

49. $20 \div 5 \div 2$

50. $500 \div 100 \div 5$

51. $3 + 2^4$

52. $10 - 3^2 + 1$

53. $4 \cdot 2^3$

54. $100 - 2 \cdot 3^3$

55. $(3 + 2)^3$

56. $5 \cdot (3 - 2)^8 - 5$

57. $\dfrac{4 + 8}{1 + 3}$

58. $5 - \dfrac{3 + 1}{3 - 1}$

59. $\dfrac{2^3}{4 - 2}$

60. $\dfrac{10 - 3^2}{2 \cdot 4^2}$

61. $10^2 - (30 - 2 \cdot 5)$

62. $5^2 + 3 \cdot 5 \div 3 - 1$

63. $\left(\dfrac{1}{2}\right)^4 + \dfrac{5 + 4}{3}$

64. $\left(\dfrac{7}{9}\right)^2 - \dfrac{6 - 5}{3}$

TRANSLATING WORDS TO EXPRESSIONS

Exercises 65–74: Translate the phrase into a mathematical expression and then evaluate it.

65. Two cubed minus eight

66. Five squared plus nine

67. Thirty decreased by four times three

68. One hundred plus five times six

69. Four squared divided by two cubed

70. Three cubed times two squared

71. Forty divided by ten, plus two

72. Thirty times ten, minus three

73. One hundred times the quantity two plus three

74. Fifty divided by the quantity eight plus two

APPLICATIONS

75. *Flash Memory* (Refer to Example 4.) Determine the number of bytes on a 512-MB memory stick.

76. *iPod Memory* Determine the number of bytes on a 60-GB video iPod. (*Hint:* One gigabyte equals 2^{30} bytes.)

77. *Population by Gender* One way to measure the gender balance in a given population is to find the number of males for every 100 females in the population. In 1900, the western region of the United States was significantly out of gender balance. In this region, there were 128 males for every 100 females. (*Source: U.S. Census Bureau.*)
   (a) Find an exponent k so that $2^k = 128$.
   (b) During this time, how many males were there for every 25 females?

78. *Solar Eclipse* In early December 2048 there will be a total solar eclipse visible in parts of Botswana. Find an exponent k so that $2^k = 2048$. (*Source: NASA.*)

79. *Rule of 72* Investors sometimes use the *rule of 72* to determine the time required to double an investment. If 72 is divided by the annual interest rate earned on an investment, the result approximates the number of years needed to double the investment. For example, an investment earning 6% annual interest will double in value approximately every $72 \div 6 = 12$ years.
   (a) Approximate the number of years required to double an investment earning 9% annual interest.
   (b) If an investment of $10,000 earns 12% annual interest, approximate the value of the investment after 18 years.

80. *Doubling Effect* Suppose that a savings account containing $1000 doubles its value every 7 years. How much money will be in the account after 28 years?

WRITING ABOUT MATHEMATICS

81. Explain how exponential expressions are related to multiplication. Give an example.

82. Explain why agreement on the order of operations is necessary.

Group Activity   Working with Real Data

Directions: Form a group of 2 to 4 people. Select someone to record the group's responses for this activity. All members of the group should work cooperatively to answer the questions. If your instructor asks for your results, each member of the group should be prepared to respond.

Converting Temperatures To convert Celsius degrees C to Fahrenheit degrees F, use the formula $F = 32 + \frac{9}{5}C$. This exercise illustrates the importance of understanding the order of operations.

(a) Complete the following table by evaluating the formula in the two ways shown.

(b) At what Celsius temperature does water freeze? At what Fahrenheit temperature does water freeze?

(c) Which column gives the correct Fahrenheit temperatures? Why?

(d) Explain why having an agreed order for operations in mathematics is necessary.

Celsius	$F = \left(32 + \frac{9}{5}\right)C$	$F = 32 + \left(\frac{9}{5}C\right)$
$-40°\,C$		
$0°\,C$		
$5°\,C$	$169°\,F$	$41°\,F$
$20°\,C$		
$30°\,C$		
$100°\,C$		

1.4   Real Numbers and the Number Line

Signed Numbers • Integers and Rational Numbers • Square Roots • Real and Irrational Numbers • The Number Line • Absolute Value • Inequality

A LOOK INTO MATH ▶

So far in this chapter, we have discussed natural numbers, whole numbers, and fractions. All of these numbers belong to a set of numbers called *real numbers*. In this section, we will see that real numbers also include *integers* and *irrational numbers*. Real-world quantities such as temperature, computer processor speed, height of a building, age of a fossil, and gas mileage are all described with real numbers.

Signed Numbers

The idea that numbers could be negative was a difficult concept for many mathematicians. As late as the eighteenth century, negative numbers were not readily accepted by everyone. After all, how could a person have -5 oranges?

However, negative numbers make more sense to someone working with money. If you owe someone 100 dollars (a debt), this amount can be thought of as -100, whereas if you have a balance of 100 dollars in your checking account (an asset), this amount can be thought of as $+100$. (The positive sign is usually omitted.)

The **opposite**, or **additive inverse**, of a number a is $-a$. For example, the opposite of 25 is -25, the opposite of -5 is $-(-5)$, or 5, and the opposite of 0 is 0 because 0 is neither positive nor negative. The following double negative rule is helpful in simplifying expressions containing negative signs.

NEW VOCABULARY

☐ Opposite (additive inverse)
☐ Integers
☐ Rational number
☐ Square root
☐ Principal square root
☐ Real number
☐ Irrational numbers
☐ Approximately equal
☐ Average
☐ Origin
☐ Absolute value
☐ Less than/Greater than
☐ Less than or equal to
☐ Greater than or equal to

DOUBLE NEGATIVE RULE

Let a be any number. Then $-(-a) = a$.

Thus $-(-8) = 8$ and $-\left(-(-10)\right) = -(10) = -10$.

READING CHECK

• How is the opposite of a number written?

EXAMPLE 1 | **Finding opposites (or additive inverses)**

Find the opposite of each expression.

(a) 13   **(b)** $-\dfrac{4}{7}$ **(c)** $-(-7)$

Solution
(a) The opposite of 13 is -13.
(b) The opposite of $-\frac{4}{7}$ is $\frac{4}{7}$.
(c) $-(-7) = 7$, so the opposite of $-(-7)$ is -7.

Now Try Exercises 17, 19, 21

NOTE: To find the opposite of an exponential expression, evaluate the exponent first. For example, the opposite of 2^4 is

$$-2^4 = -(2 \cdot 2 \cdot 2 \cdot 2) = -16.$$

EXAMPLE 2 | **Finding an additive inverse (or opposite)**

Find the additive inverse of $-t$, if $t = -\frac{2}{3}$.

Solution
The additive inverse of $-t$ is $t = -\frac{2}{3}$ because $-(-t) = t$ by the double negative rule.

Now Try Exercise 27

Integers and Rational Numbers

In the opening section of this chapter we discussed natural numbers and whole numbers. Because these sets of numbers do not include negative numbers, fractions, or decimals, other sets of numbers are needed. The **integers** include the natural numbers, zero, and the opposites of the natural numbers. The integers are given by the following.

$$\ldots, -3, -2, -1, 0, 1, 2, 3, \ldots$$

A **rational number** is any number that can be expressed as the ratio of two integers, $\frac{p}{q}$, where $q \neq 0$. Rational numbers can be written as fractions, and they include all integers. Rational numbers may be positive, negative, or zero. Some examples of rational numbers are

$$\frac{2}{3}, \quad -\frac{3}{5}, \quad \frac{-7}{2}, \quad 1.2, \quad \text{and} \quad 3.$$

The numbers 1.2 and 3 are both rational numbers because they can be written as $\frac{12}{10}$ and $\frac{3}{1}$.

STUDY TIP

The word "NOTE" is used to draw attention to important concepts that may otherwise be overlooked.

NOTE: The fraction $\frac{-7}{2}$ can also be written as $\frac{7}{-2}$ and $-\frac{7}{2}$. The position of the negative sign does not affect the value of the fraction.

The fraction bar can be thought of as a division symbol. As a result, rational numbers have decimal equivalents. For example, $\frac{1}{2}$ is equivalent to $1 \div 2$. The division

$$\begin{array}{r} 0.5 \\ 2\overline{)1.0} \end{array}$$

READING CHECK

• When a number is written in decimal form, how do we know if the number is a rational number?

shows that $\frac{1}{2} = 0.5$. In general, a rational number may be expressed in a decimal form that either *repeats* or *terminates*. The fraction $\frac{1}{3}$ may be expressed as $0.\overline{3}$, a repeating decimal, and the fraction $\frac{1}{4}$ may be expressed as 0.25, a terminating decimal. The overbar indicates that $0.\overline{3} = 0.3333333\ldots$.

▶ **REAL-WORLD CONNECTION** Integers and rational numbers are used to describe quantities such as change in population. Figure 1.18 shows the change in population from 2000 to 2009 for selected U.S. cities. Note that both positive and negative numbers are used to describe these population changes. (*Source:* U.S. Census Bureau.)

Population Change 2000–2009

Figure 1.18

EXAMPLE 3 | **Classifying numbers**

Classify each number as one or more of the following: natural number, whole number, integer, or rational number.

(a) $\frac{12}{4}$ **(b)** -3 **(c)** 0 **(d)** $-\frac{9}{5}$

Solution
(a) Because $\frac{12}{4} = 3$, the number $\frac{12}{4}$ is a natural number, whole number, integer, and rational number.
(b) The number -3 is an integer and a rational number but it is not a natural number or a whole number.
(c) The number 0 is a whole number, integer, and rational number but not a natural number.
(d) The fraction $-\frac{9}{5}$ is a rational number because it is the ratio of two integers. It is not a natural number, a whole number, or an integer.

Now Try Exercises 41, 43, 45, 47

CALCULATOR HELP

To evaluate square roots with a calculator, see Appendix A (page AP-1).

Square Roots

The number b is a **square root** of a number a if $b \cdot b = a$. Every *positive* number has one positive square root and one negative square root. For example, the positive square root of 9 is 3 because $3 \cdot 3 = 9$. The negative square root of 9 is -3. (We will show that $-3 \cdot (-3) = 9$ in Section 1.6.) If a is a positive number, then the **principal square root** of a, denoted $\sqrt{a}$, is the positive square root of a. For example, $\sqrt{25} = 5$ because $5 \cdot 5 = 25$ and the number 5 is positive. Note that the principal square root of 0 is 0. That is, $\sqrt{0} = 0$.

EXAMPLE 4   **Calculating principal square roots**

Evaluate each square root. Approximate your answer to three decimal places when appropriate.
(a) $\sqrt{36}$ **(b)** $\sqrt{100}$ **(c)** $\sqrt{5}$

Solution
(a) $\sqrt{36} = 6$ because $6 \cdot 6 = 36$ and 6 is positive.
(b) $\sqrt{100} = 10$ because $10 \cdot 10 = 100$ and 10 is positive.
(c) We can estimate the value of $\sqrt{5}$ with a calculator. Figure 1.19 reveals that $\sqrt{5}$ is *approximately* equal to 2.236. However, 2.236 does not exactly equal $\sqrt{5}$ because $2.236 \cdot 2.236 = 4.999696$, which does not equal 5.

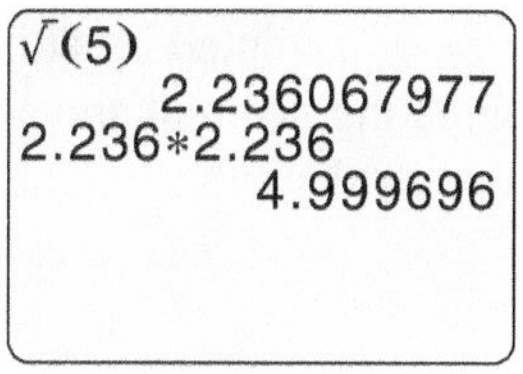

```
√(5)
          2.236067977
2.236*2.236
            4.999696
```

Figure 1.19

Now Try Exercises 49, 51, 53

Real and Irrational Numbers

If a number can be represented by a decimal number, then it is a **real number**. Every fraction has a decimal form, so real numbers include rational numbers. However, some real numbers cannot be expressed by fractions. They are called **irrational numbers**. The numbers $\sqrt{2}$, $\sqrt{15}$, and π are examples of irrational numbers. Every irrational number has a decimal representation that does not terminate or repeat.

NOTE: For any positive integer a, if $\sqrt{a}$ is not an integer then $\sqrt{a}$ is an irrational number.

Examples of real numbers include

$$-17, \quad \frac{4}{5}, \quad -\sqrt{3}, \quad 21\frac{1}{2}, \quad 57.63, \quad \text{and} \quad \sqrt{7}.$$

Any real number may be approximated by a terminating decimal. The symbol $\approx$ is used to represent **approximately equal**. Each of the following real numbers has been approximated to two *decimal places*.

$$\frac{1}{7} \approx 0.14, \quad 2\pi \approx 6.28, \quad \text{and} \quad \sqrt{60} \approx 7.75$$

Figure 1.20 on the next page shows the relationships among the different sets of numbers. Note that each real number is either a rational number or an irrational number but not both. All natural numbers, whole numbers, and integers are rational numbers.

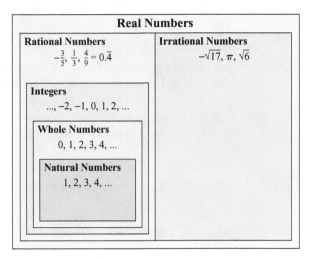

Figure 1.20 The Real Numbers

MAKING CONNECTIONS

Rational and Irrational Numbers

Both rational and irrational numbers can be written as decimals. However, rational numbers can be represented by either terminating or repeating decimals. For example, $\frac{1}{2} = 0.5$ is a terminating decimal and $\frac{1}{3} = 0.333\ldots$ is a repeating decimal. Irrational numbers are represented by decimals that neither terminate nor repeat.

EXAMPLE 5   **Classifying numbers**

Identify the natural numbers, whole numbers, integers, rational numbers, and irrational numbers in the following list.

$$-\sqrt{5}, \quad 9, \quad -3.8, \quad \sqrt{49}, \quad \frac{11}{4}, \quad \text{and} \quad -41$$

Solution

Natural numbers: 9 and $\sqrt{49} = 7$

Whole numbers: 9 and $\sqrt{49} = 7$

Integers: 9, $\sqrt{49} = 7$, and -41

Rational numbers: 9, -3.8, $\sqrt{49} = 7$, $\frac{11}{4}$, and -41

Irrational number: $-\sqrt{5}$

Now Try Exercises 55, 59, 63

▶ **REAL-WORLD CONNECTION** Even though a data set may contain only integers, we often need decimals to describe it. For example, integers are used to represent the number of wireless subscribers in the United States for various years. However, the *average* number of subscribers over a longer time period may be a decimal. Recall that the **average** of a set of numbers is found by adding the numbers and then dividing by how many numbers there are in the set.

EXAMPLE 6 **Analyzing cell phone subscriber data**

Table 1.6 lists the number of wireless subscribers, in millions, in the United States, for various years. Find the average number of subscribers for these years. Is the result a natural number, a rational number, or an irrational number?

TABLE 1.6 **U.S. Wireless Subscribers**

Year	1995	2000	2005	2010
Subscribers	28	97	194	292

Source: CTIA.

Solution
The average number of subscribers is

$$\frac{28 + 97 + 194 + 292}{4} = \frac{611}{4} = 152.75 \text{ million.}$$

The average of these four natural numbers is an integer divided by an integer, which is a rational number. However, it is neither a natural number nor an irrational number.

Now Try Exercise 105

CRITICAL THINKING

Think of an example in which the sum of two irrational numbers is a rational number.

The Number Line

The real numbers can be represented visually by using a number line, as shown in Figure 1.21. Each real number corresponds to a unique point on the number line. The point associated with the real number 0 is called the **origin**. The positive integers are equally spaced to the right of the origin, and the negative integers are equally spaced to the left of the origin. The number line extends indefinitely both to the left and to the right.

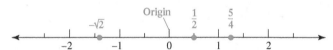

Figure 1.21 A Number Line

Other real numbers can also be located on the number line. For example, the number $\frac{1}{2}$ can be identified by placing a dot halfway between the integers 0 and 1. The numbers $-\sqrt{2} \approx -1.41$ and $\frac{5}{4} = 1.25$ can also be placed (approximately) on this number line. (See Figure 1.21.)

EXAMPLE 7 **Plotting numbers on a number line**

Plot each real number on a number line.

(a) $-\frac{3}{2}$ (b) $\sqrt{3}$ (c) π

Solution
(a) $-\frac{3}{2} = -1.5$. Place a dot halfway between -2 and -1, as shown in Figure 1.22.
(b) A calculator gives $\sqrt{3} \approx 1.73$. Place a dot between 1 and 2 so that it is about three-fourths of the way toward 2, as shown in Figure 1.22.
(c) $\pi \approx 3.14$. Place a dot just past the integer 3, as shown in Figure 1.22.

Figure 1.22 Plotting Numbers

Now Try Exercises 67, 73

Absolute Value

Figure 1.23

The **absolute value** of a real number equals its distance on the number line from the origin. Because distance is never negative, the absolute value of a real number is *never negative*. The absolute value of a real number a is denoted $|a|$ and is read "the absolute value of a." Figure 1.23 shows that the absolute values of -3 and 3 are both equal to 3 because both have distance 3 from the origin. That is, $|-3| = 3$ and $|3| = 3$.

> **EXAMPLE 8**   **Finding the absolute value of a real number**
>
> Evaluate each expression.
> **(a)** $|3.1|$ **(b)** $|-7|$ **(c)** $|0|$
>
> Solution
> **(a)** $|3.1| = 3.1$ because the distance between the origin and 3.1 is 3.1.
> **(b)** $|-7| = 7$ because the distance between the origin and -7 is 7.
> **(c)** $|0| = 0$ because the distance is 0 between the origin and 0.
>
> Now Try Exercises 75, 77, 79

Our results about absolute value can be summarized as follows.

$$|a| = a, \quad \text{if } a \text{ is positive or 0.}$$
$$|a| = -a, \quad \text{if } a \text{ is negative.}$$

Inequality

If a real number a is located to the left of a real number b on the number line, we say that a is **less than** b and write $a < b$. Similarly, if a real number b is located to the right of a real number a, we say that b is **greater than** a and write $b > a$. For example, $-3 < 2$ because -3 is located to the left of 2, and $2 > -3$ because 2 is located to the right of -3. See Figure 1.24.

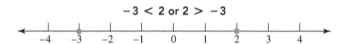

Figure 1.24

NOTE: Any negative number is always less than any positive number, and any positive number is always greater than any negative number.

We say that a is **less than or equal to** b, denoted $a \leq b$, if either $a < b$ or $a = b$ is true. Similarly, a is **greater than or equal to** b, denoted $a \geq b$, if either $a > b$ or $a = b$ is true.

Inequalities are often used to compare the relative sizes of two quantities. This can be illustrated visually as shown in the figure below.

Visualizing Inequality by Relative Size

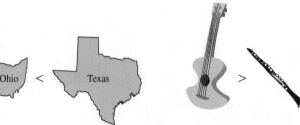

READING CHECK

• Which math symbols are used to express inequality?

EXAMPLE 9   **Ordering real numbers**

List the following numbers from least to greatest. Then plot these numbers on a number line.

$$-2, \quad -\pi, \quad \sqrt{2}, \quad 0, \quad \text{and} \quad 2.5$$

Solution

First note that $-\pi \approx -3.14 < -2$. The two negative numbers are less than 0, and the two positive numbers are greater than 0. Also, $\sqrt{2} \approx 1.41$, so $\sqrt{2} < 2.5$. Listing the numbers from least to greatest results in

$$-\pi, \quad -2, \quad 0, \quad \sqrt{2}, \quad \text{and} \quad 2.5.$$

These numbers are plotted on the number line shown in Figure 1.25. Note that these numbers increase from left to right on the number line.

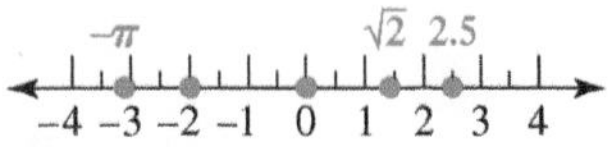

Figure 1.25

Now Try Exercise 103

1.4	**Putting It All Together**

CONCEPT	COMMENTS	EXAMPLES
Integers	Include the natural numbers, their opposites, and 0	$\ldots, -2, -1, 0, 1, 2, \ldots$
Rational Numbers	Include integers, all fractions $\frac{p}{q}$, where p and $q \neq 0$ are integers, and all repeating and terminating decimals	$\frac{1}{2}, -3, \frac{128}{6}, -0.335, 0, 0.25 = \frac{1}{4}$, and $0.\overline{3} = \frac{1}{3}$
Irrational Numbers	Any decimal numbers that neither terminate nor repeat; real numbers that are not rational	$\pi, \sqrt{3}$, and $\sqrt{15}$
Real Numbers	Any numbers that can be expressed in decimal form; include the rational and irrational numbers	$\pi, \sqrt{3}, -\frac{4}{7}, 0, -10, 0.\overline{6} = \frac{2}{3}, 1000$, and $\sqrt{15}$
Average	To find the average of a set of numbers, find the sum of the numbers and then divide the sum by how many numbers there are in the set.	The average of 2, 6, and 10 is $$\frac{2 + 6 + 10}{3} = \frac{18}{3} = 6.$$
Number Line	A number line can be used to visualize the real number system. The point associated with the number 0 is called the origin.	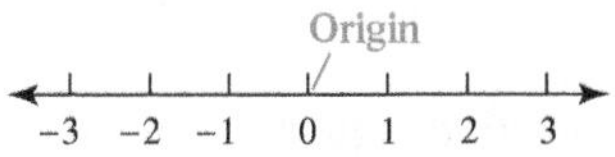

continued on next page

continued from previous page

CONCEPT	COMMENTS	EXAMPLES
Absolute Value	The absolute value of a number a equals its distance on the number line from the origin. If $a \geq 0$, then $|a| = a$. If $a < 0$, then $|a| = -a$. $|a|$ is *never* negative.	$\|17\| = 17$ $\|-12\| = 12$ $\|0\| = 0$
Inequality	If a number a is located to the left of a number b on a number line, then a is less than b (written $a < b$). If a is located to the right of b, then a is greater than b (written $a > b$). Symbols of inequality include: $<, >, \leq, \geq,$ and $\neq$.	$-3 < -2$ less than $6 > 4$ greater than $-5 \leq -5$ less than or equal $18 \geq 0$ greater than or equal $7 \neq 8$ not equal

1.4   Exercises

CONCEPTS AND VOCABULARY

1. The opposite of the number b is _____.

2. The integers include the natural numbers, zero, and the opposites of the _____ numbers.

3. A number that can be written as $\frac{p}{q}$, where p and q are integers with $q \neq 0$, is a(n) _____ number.

4. If a number can be written in decimal form, then it is a(n) _____ number.

5. If a real number is not a rational number, then it is a(n) _____ number.

6. (True or False?) A rational number can be written as a repeating or terminating decimal.

7. (True or False?) An irrational number cannot be written as a repeating or terminating decimal.

8. Write 0.272727... using an overbar.

9. The decimal equivalent for $\frac{1}{4}$ can be found by dividing _____ by _____.

10. The equation $4 \cdot 4 = 16$ indicates that $\sqrt{16} =$ _____.

11. The positive square root of a positive number is called the _____ square root.

12. The symbol $\neq$ is used to indicate that two numbers are _____.

13. The symbol $\approx$ is used to indicate that two numbers are _____.

14. The origin on the number line corresponds to the number _____.

15. Negative numbers are located to the (left/right) of the origin on the number line.

16. The absolute value of a number a gives its distance on the number line from the _____.

SIGNED NUMBERS

Exercises 17–24: Find the opposite of each expression.

17. **(a)** 9 **(b)** -9

18. **(a)** -6 **(b)** 6

19. **(a)** $\frac{2}{3}$ **(b)** $-\frac{2}{3}$

20. **(a)** $-\left(\frac{-4}{5}\right)$ **(b)** $-\left(\frac{-4}{-5}\right)$

21. **(a)** $-(-8)$ **(b)** $-\left(-(-8)\right)$

22. **(a)** $-\left(-(-2)\right)$ **(b)** $-(-2)$

23. **(a)** a **(b)** $-a$

24. **(a)** $-b$ **(b)** $-(-b)$

25. Find the additive inverse of t, if $-t = 6$.

26. Find the additive inverse of $-t$, if $t = -\frac{4}{5}$.

27. Find the additive inverse of $-b$, if $b = \frac{1}{2}$.

28. Find the additive inverse of b, if $-b = \frac{5}{-6}$.

NUMBERS AND THE NUMBER LINE

Exercises 29–40: Find the decimal equivalent for the rational number.

29. $\frac{1}{4}$ **30.** $\frac{3}{5}$

31. $\frac{7}{8}$ **32.** $\frac{3}{10}$

33. $\frac{3}{2}$ **34.** $\frac{3}{50}$

35. $\frac{1}{20}$ **36.** $\frac{3}{16}$

37. $\frac{2}{3}$ **38.** $\frac{2}{9}$

39. $\frac{7}{9}$ **40.** $\frac{5}{11}$

Exercises 41–48: Classify the number as one or more of the following: natural number, whole number, integer, or rational number.

41. 8   **42.** -8

43. $\frac{16}{4}$ **44.** $\frac{5}{7}$

45. 0   **46.** $-\frac{15}{31}$

47. $-\frac{7}{6}$ **48.** $-\frac{10}{5}$

Exercises 49–54: Evaluate the square root. Approximate your answer to three decimal places when appropriate.

49. $\sqrt{25}$ **50.** $\sqrt{81}$

51. $\sqrt{49}$ **52.** $\sqrt{64}$

53. $\sqrt{7}$ **54.** $\sqrt{11}$

Exercises 55–66: Classify the number as one or more of the following: natural number, integer, rational number, or irrational number.

55. -4.5 **56.** π

57. $\frac{3}{7}$ **58.** $\sqrt{25}$

59. $\sqrt{11}$ **60.** $-\sqrt{3}$

61. $\frac{8}{4}$ **62.** -5

63. $\sqrt{49}$ **64.** $3.\overline{3}$

65. $1.\overline{8}$ **66.** $\frac{9}{3}$

Exercises 67–74: Plot each number on a number line.

67. (a) 0   (b) -2 (c) 3

68. (a) $-\frac{3}{2}$ (b) $\frac{3}{2}$ (c) 0

69. (a) $\frac{1}{2}$ (b) $-\frac{1}{2}$ (c) 2

70. (a) 1.3   (b) -2.5 (c) 0.7

71. (a) -10 (b) -20 (c) 30

72. (a) 5   (b) 10   (c) -10

73. (a) π (b) $\sqrt{2}$ (c) $-\sqrt{3}$

74. (a) $\sqrt{11}$ (b) $-\sqrt{5}$ (c) $\sqrt{4}$

ABSOLUTE VALUE

Exercises 75–82: Evaluate the expression.

75. $|5.23|$ **76.** $|\pi|$

77. $|-8|$ **78.** $|-\sqrt{2}|$

79. $|2-2|$ **80.** $|\frac{2}{3} - \frac{1}{3}|$

81. $|\pi - 3|$ **82.** $|3 - \pi|$

83. Thinking Generally Find $|b|$, if b is negative.

84. Thinking Generally Find $|-b|$, if b is positive.

INEQUALITY

Exercises 85–96: Insert the symbol $>$ or $<$ to make the statement true.

85. 5 _____ 7   **86.** -5 _____ 7

87. -5 _____ -7 **88.** $\frac{3}{5}$ _____ $\frac{2}{5}$

89. $-\frac{1}{3}$ _____ $-\frac{2}{3}$ **90.** $-\frac{1}{10}$ _____ 0

91. -1.9 _____ -1.3 **92.** 5.1 _____ -6.2

93. $|-8|$ _____ 3   **94.** 4 _____ $|-1|$

95. $|-2|$ _____ $|-7|$ **96.** $|-15|$ _____ $|32|$

Exercises 97–100: **Thinking Generally** *Insert the symbol $<$, $=$, or $>$ to make the statement true.*

97. If a number a is located to the right of a number b on the number line, then a _____ b.

98. If $b > 0$ and $a < 0$, then b _____ a.

99. If $a \geq b$, then either $a > b$ or a _____ b.

100. If $a \geq b$ and $b \geq a$, then a _____ b.

Exercises 101–104: List the given numbers from least to greatest.

101. $-3, 0, 1, -9, -2^3$

102. $4, -2^3, \frac{1}{2}, -\frac{3}{2}, \frac{3}{2}$

103. $-2, \pi, \frac{1}{3}, -\frac{3}{2}, \sqrt{5}$

104. $9, 14, -\frac{1}{12}, -\frac{3}{16}, \sqrt{7}$

APPLICATIONS

105. *Marriage Age* The table lists the average age of females at first marriage during selected years.

Year	2001	2003	2005	2007
Age	25.1	25.3	25.5	25.9

Source: U.S. Census Bureau.

(a) What was this age in 2005?

(b) Mentally estimate the average marriage age for these selected years.

(c) Calculate the average marriage age. Is your mental estimate in reasonable agreement with your calculated result?

106. *Music Sales* The table lists the percentage of recorded music purchased through digital downloads during selected years.

Year	2005	2006	2007	2008
Percent	6.0	6.8	12.0	13.5

Source: Recording Industry Association of America.

(a) What was this percentage in 2006?

(b) Mentally estimate the average percentage for this 4-year period.

(c) Calculate the average percentage. Is your mental estimate in reasonable agreement with your calculated result?

WRITING ABOUT MATHEMATICS

107. What is a rational number? Is every integer a rational number? Why or why not?

108. Explain why $\frac{3}{7} > \frac{1}{3}$. Now explain in general how to determine whether $\frac{a}{b} > \frac{c}{d}$. Assume that a, b, c, and d are natural numbers.

SECTIONS 1.3 AND 1.4 — Checking Basic Concepts

1. Write each product as an exponential expression.
   (a) $5 \cdot 5 \cdot 5 \cdot 5$ (b) $7 \cdot 7 \cdot 7 \cdot 7 \cdot 7$

2. Evaluate each expression.
   (a) 2^3 (b) 10^4 (c) $\left(\frac{2}{3}\right)^3$

3. Use the given base to write the number as an exponential expression.
   (a) 64 (base 4)   (b) 64 (base 2)

4. Evaluate each expression without a calculator.
   (a) $6 + 5 \cdot 4$ (b) $6 + 6 \div 2$
   (c) $5 - 2 - 1$ (d) $\frac{6 - 3}{2 + 4}$
   (e) $12 \div (6 \div 2)$ (f) $2^3 - 2\left(2 + \frac{4}{2}\right)$

5. Translate the phrase "five cubed divided by three" to an algebraic expression.

6. Find the opposite of each expression.
   (a) -17 (b) a

7. Find the decimal equivalent for the rational number.
   (a) $\frac{3}{20}$ (b) $\frac{5}{8}$

8. Classify each number as one or more of the following: natural number, integer, rational number, or irrational number.
   (a) $\frac{10}{2}$ (b) -5 (c) $\sqrt{5}$ (d) $-\frac{5}{6}$

9. Plot each number on the same number line.
   (a) 0   (b) -3 (c) 2
   (d) $\frac{3}{4}$ (e) $-\sqrt{2}$

10. Evaluate each expression.
   (a) $|-12|$ (b) $|6 - 6|$

11. Insert the symbol $>$ or $<$ to make the statement true.
   (a) 4 _____ 9 (b) -1.3 _____ -0.5
   (c) $|-3|$ _____ $|-5|$

12. List the following numbers from least to greatest.

$$\sqrt{3}, \quad -7, \quad 0, \quad \frac{1}{3}, \quad -1.6, \quad 3^2$$

1.5 Addition and Subtraction of Real Numbers

Addition of Real Numbers • Subtraction of Real Numbers • Applications

A LOOK INTO MATH ▶

Addition and subtraction of real numbers occur every day at grocery stores, where the prices of various items are added to the total and discounts from coupons are subtracted. Even though prices are usually expressed in decimal form, the rules for adding and subtracting real numbers are the same no matter how the real numbers are expressed.

Addition of Real Numbers

NEW VOCABULARY

☐ Addends
☐ Sum
☐ Difference

In an addition problem the two numbers added are called **addends**, and the answer is called the **sum**. For example, in the following addition problem the numbers 3 and 5 are the addends and the number 8 is the sum.

$$3 \quad + \quad 5 \quad = \quad 8$$
$$\text{Addend} \quad \text{Addend} \quad \text{Sum}$$

READING CHECK

• What is the answer to an addition problem called?

The *opposite* (or *additive inverse*) of a real number a is $-a$. When we add opposites, the result is 0. For example, $4 + (-4) = 0$. In general, the equation $a + (-a) = 0$ is true for every real number a.

EXAMPLE 1 **Adding opposites**

Find the opposite of each number and calculate the sum of the number and its opposite.

(a) 45 (b) $\sqrt{2}$ (c) $-\dfrac{1}{2}$

Solution
(a) The opposite of 45 is -45. Their sum is $45 + (-45) = 0$.
(b) The opposite of $\sqrt{2}$ is $-\sqrt{2}$. Their sum is $\sqrt{2} + (-\sqrt{2}) = 0$.
(c) The opposite of $-\frac{1}{2}$ is $\frac{1}{2}$. Their sum is $-\frac{1}{2} + \frac{1}{2} = 0$.

▌ Now Try Exercises 11, 13, 15

▶ **REAL-WORLD CONNECTION** When adding real numbers, it may be helpful to think of money. A positive number represents income, and a negative number indicates debt. The sum $9 + (-5) = 4$ would represent being paid $9 and owing $5. In this case $4 would be left over. Similarly, the sum $-3 + (-6) = -9$ would represent debts of $3 and $6, resulting in a total debt of $9. To add two real numbers we can use the following rules.

STUDY TIP

Do you know your instructor's name? Do you know the location of his or her office and the hours when he or she is available for help? Make sure that you have the answers to these important questions so that you can get help when needed.

ADDITION OF REAL NUMBERS

To add two real numbers with *like* signs, do the following.

1. Find the sum of the absolute values of the numbers.
2. Keep the common sign of the two numbers as the sign of the sum.

To add two real numbers with *unlike* signs, do the following.

1. Find the absolute values of the numbers.
2. Subtract the smaller absolute value from the larger absolute value.
3. Keep the sign of the number with the larger absolute value as the sign of the sum.

EXAMPLE 2 **Adding real numbers**

Find each sum by hand.

(a) $-2 + (-4)$ **(b)** $-\dfrac{2}{5} + \dfrac{7}{10}$ **(c)** $6.2 + (-8.5)$

Solution

(a) The numbers are both negative, so we add the absolute values $|-2|$ and $|-4|$ to obtain 6. The signs of the addends are both negative, so the answer is -6. That is, $-2 + (-4) = -6$. If we owe \$2 and then owe \$4, the total amount owed is \$6.

(b) The numbers have opposite signs, so we subtract their absolute values to obtain

$$\frac{7}{10} - \frac{2}{5} = \frac{7}{10} - \frac{4}{10} = \frac{3}{10}.$$

The sum is positive because $\left|\frac{7}{10}\right|$ is greater than $\left|-\frac{2}{5}\right|$ and $\frac{7}{10}$ is positive. That is, $-\frac{2}{5} + \frac{7}{10} = \frac{3}{10}$. If we spend \$0.40 $\left(-\frac{2}{5} = -0.4\right)$ and receive \$0.70 $\left(\frac{7}{10} = 0.7\right)$, we have \$0.30 $\left(\frac{3}{10} = 0.3\right)$ left.

(c) $6.2 + (-8.5) = -2.3$ because $|-8.5|$ is 2.3 more than $|6.2|$. If we have \$6.20 and we owe \$8.50, we are short \$2.30.

Now Try Exercises 33, 39, 41

ADDING INTEGERS VISUALLY One way to add integers visually is to use the symbol ⌢ to represent a positive unit and to use the symbol ⌣ to represent a negative unit. Now adding opposites visually results in "zero," as shown.

⌢ + ⌣ = ◯　　　　$1 + (-1) = 0$

For example, to add $-3 + 5$, we draw three negative units and five positive units.

◯ ◯ ◯ ⌢ ⌢　　　$-3 + 5 = 2$

Because the "zeros" add no value, the sum is two positive units, or 2.

EXAMPLE 3 **Adding integers visually**

Add visually, using the symbols ⌢ and ⌣.

(a) $3 + 2$ **(b)** $-6 + 4$ **(c)** $2 + (-3)$ **(d)** $-5 + (-2)$

Solution

(a) Draw three positive units and then draw two more positive units.

⌢ ⌢ ⌢　　⌢ ⌢　　$3 + 2 = 5$

Because no zeros were formed, the sum is five positive units, or 5.

(b) Draw six negative units and then draw four positive units.

◯ ◯ ◯ ◯ ⌣ ⌣　　$-6 + 4 = -2$

Ignoring the zeros that were formed, the sum is two negative units, or -2.

(c) Draw two positive and three negative units.

◯ ◯ ⌣　　$2 + (-3) = -1$

The sum is -1.

(d)  ⌣ ⌣ ⌣ ⌣ ⌣　　⌣ ⌣　　$-5 + (-2) = -7$

The sum is -7.

Now Try Exercises 17, 19, 21, 23

Another way to add integers visually is to use a number line. For example, to add $4 + (-3)$ start at 0 (the origin) and draw an arrow to the right 4 units long from 0 to 4. The number -3 is a negative number, so draw an arrow 3 units long to the left, starting at the tip of the first arrow. See Figure 1.26a. The tip of the second arrow is at 1, which equals the sum of 4 and -3.

Adding Integers on a Number Line

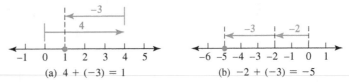

(a) $4 + (-3) = 1$ (b) $-2 + (-3) = -5$

Figure 1.26

To find the sum $-2 + (-3)$, draw an arrow 2 units long to the left, starting at the origin. Then draw an arrow 3 units long to the left, starting at the tip of the first arrow, which is located at -2. See Figure 1.26b. Because the tip of the second arrow coincides with -5 on the number line, the sum of -2 and -3 is -5.

READING CHECK

• What is the answer to a subtraction problem called?

Subtraction of Real Numbers

The answer to a subtraction problem is the **difference**. When subtracting two real numbers, changing the problem to an addition problem may be helpful.

> **SUBTRACTION OF REAL NUMBERS**
>
> For any real numbers a and b,
>
> $$a - b = a + (-b).$$
>
> To subtract b from a, add a and the opposite of b.

EXAMPLE 4   **Subtracting real numbers**

Find each difference by hand.
(a) $10 - 20$ **(b)** $-5 - 2$ **(c)** $-2.1 - (-3.2)$ **(d)** $\frac{1}{2} - \left(-\frac{3}{4}\right)$

Solution
(a) $10 - 20 = 10 + (-20) = -10$
(b) $-5 - 2 = -5 + (-2) = -7$
(c) $-2.1 - (-3.2) = -2.1 + 3.2 = 1.1$
(d) $\frac{1}{2} - \left(-\frac{3}{4}\right) = \frac{1}{2} + \frac{3}{4} = \frac{2}{4} + \frac{3}{4} = \frac{5}{4}$

Now Try Exercises 45, 47, 51, 53

In the next example, we show how to add and subtract groups of numbers.

EXAMPLE 5   **Adding and subtracting real numbers**

Evaluate each expression by hand.
(a) $5 - 4 - (-6) + 1$ **(b)** $\frac{1}{2} - \frac{3}{4} + \frac{1}{3}$ **(c)** $-6.1 + 5.6 - 10.1$

Solution
(a) Rewrite the expression in terms of addition only, and then find the sum.

$$5 - 4 - (-6) + 1 = 5 + (-4) + 6 + 1$$
$$= 1 + 6 + 1$$
$$= 8$$

(b) Begin by rewriting the fractions with the LCD of 12.

$$\frac{1}{2} - \frac{3}{4} + \frac{1}{3} = \frac{6}{12} - \frac{9}{12} + \frac{4}{12}$$
$$= \frac{6}{12} + \left(-\frac{9}{12}\right) + \frac{4}{12}$$
$$= -\frac{3}{12} + \frac{4}{12}$$
$$= \frac{1}{12}$$

CRITICAL THINKING

Explain how subtraction of real numbers can be performed on a number line.

(c) The expression can be evaluated by changing subtraction to addition.

$$-6.1 + 5.6 - 10.1 = -6.1 + 5.6 + (-10.1)$$
$$= -0.5 + (-10.1)$$
$$= -10.6$$

■ Now Try Exercises 59, 65, 67

Applications

In application problems, some words indicate that we should add, while other words indicate that we should subtract. Tables 1.7 and 1.8 show examples of such words along with sample phrases.

TABLE 1.7 Words Associated with Addition

Words	Sample Phrase
add	add the two temperatures
plus	her age plus his age
more than	5 cents more than the cost
sum	the sum of two measures
total	the total of the four prices
increased by	height increased by 3 inches

TABLE 1.8 Words Associated with Subtraction

Words	Sample Phrase
subtract	subtract dues from the price
minus	his income minus his taxes
fewer than	18 fewer flowers than shrubs
difference	the difference in their heights
less than	his age is 4 less than yours
decreased by	the weight decreased by 7

READING CHECK

- What words are associated with addition?
- What words are associated with subtraction?

▶ **REAL-WORLD CONNECTION** Sometimes temperature differences are found by subtracting positive and negative real numbers. At other times, addition of positive and negative real numbers occurs at banks if positive numbers represent deposits and negative numbers represent withdrawals. The next two examples illustrate these situations.

EXAMPLE 6   **Calculating temperature differences**

The hottest outdoor temperature ever recorded in the shade was $136°\,$F in the Sahara desert, and the coldest outside temperature ever recorded was $-129°\,$F in Antarctica. Find the difference between these two temperatures. (*Source: Guinness Book of Records.*)

Solution
The word *difference* indicates subtraction. We must subtract the two temperatures.

$$136 - (-129) = 136 + 129 = 265°\,\text{F}.$$

▪ Now Try Exercise 87

EXAMPLE 7   **Balancing a checking account**

The initial balance in a checking account is $285. Find the final balance if the following represents a list of withdrawals and deposits: $-\$15$, $-\$20$, $\$500$, and $-\$100$.

Solution
Find the sum of the five numbers.

$$285 + (-15) + (-20) + 500 + (-100) = 270 + (-20) + 500 + (-100)$$
$$= 250 + 500 + (-100)$$
$$= 750 + (-100)$$
$$= 650$$

The final balance is $650. This result may be supported with a calculator, as illustrated in Figure 1.27. Note that the expression has been evaluated two different ways.

▪ Now Try Exercise 83

```
285+(-15)+(-20)+
500+(-100)
              650
285-15-20+500-10
0
              650
```

Figure 1.27

TECHNOLOGY NOTE

Subtraction and Negation
Calculators typically have *different* keys to represent subtraction and negation. Be sure to use the correct key. Many graphing calculators have the following keys for subtraction and negation.

⊟   ⊡
Subtraction   Negation

1.5   Putting It All Together

CONCEPT	COMMENTS	EXAMPLES
Addition	To add real numbers, use a number line or follow the rules found in the box on page 45.	$-2 + 8 = 6$ $0.8 + (-0.3) = 0.5$ $-\frac{1}{7} + \left(-\frac{3}{7}\right) = \frac{-1 + (-3)}{7} = -\frac{4}{7}$ $-4 + 4 = 0$ $-3 + 4 + (-2) = -1$
Subtraction	To subtract real numbers, transform the problem to an addition problem by adding the opposite. $a - b = a + (-b)$	$6 - 8 = 6 + (-8) = -2$ $-3 - 4 = -3 + (-4) = -7$ $-\frac{1}{2} - \left(-\frac{3}{2}\right) = -\frac{1}{2} + \frac{3}{2} = \frac{2}{2} = 1$ $-5 - (-5) = -5 + 5 = 0$ $9.4 - (-1.2) = 9.4 + 1.2 = 10.6$

1.5 Exercises

 MyMathLab Math XL PRACTICE WATCH DOWNLOAD READ   REVIEW

CONCEPTS AND VOCABULARY

1. The solution to an addition problem is the _____.

2. When you add opposites, the sum is always _____.

3. (True or False?) If two positive numbers are added, the sum is always a positive number.

4. (True or False?) If two negative numbers are added, the sum is always a negative number.

5. If two numbers with opposite signs are added, the sum has the same sign as the number with the larger _____.

6. The solution to a subtraction problem is the _____.

7. When subtracting two real numbers, it may be helpful to change the problem to a(n) _____ problem.

8. To subtract b from a, add the _____ of b to a. That is, $a - b = a +$ _____.

9. The words *sum*, *more*, and *plus* indicate that _____ should be performed.

10. The words *difference*, *less than*, and *minus* indicate that _____ should be performed.

ADDITION AND SUBTRACTION OF REAL NUMBERS

Exercises 11–16: Find the opposite of the number and then calculate the sum of the number and its opposite.

11. 25

12. $-\frac{1}{2}$

13. $-\sqrt{21}$

14. $-\pi$

15. 5.63

16. -6^2

Exercises 17–24: Refer to Example 3. Find the sum visually.

17. $1 + 3$

18. $3 + 1$

19. $4 + (-2)$

20. $-4 + 6$

21. $-1 + (-2)$

22. $-2 + (-2)$

23. $-3 + 7$

24. $5 + (-6)$

Exercises 25–32: Use a number line to find the sum.

25. $-1 + 3$

26. $3 + (-1)$

27. $4 + (-5)$

28. $2 + 6$

29. $-10 + 20$

30. $15 + (-5)$

31. $-50 + (-100)$

32. $-100 + 100$

Exercises 33–44: Find the sum.

33. $5 + (-4)$

34. $-9 + 7$

35. $-1 + (-6)$

36. $-10 + (-23)$

37. $\frac{3}{4} + \left(-\frac{1}{2}\right)$

38. $-\frac{5}{12} + \left(-\frac{1}{6}\right)$

39. $-\frac{6}{7} + \frac{3}{14}$

40. $-\frac{2}{9} + \left(-\frac{1}{12}\right)$

41. $0.6 + (-1.7)$

42. $4.3 + (-2.4)$

43. $-52 + 86$

44. $-103 + (-134)$

Exercises 45–56: Find the difference.

45. $5 - 8$

46. $3 - 5$

47. $-2 - (-9)$

48. $-10 - (-19)$

49. $\frac{6}{7} - \frac{13}{14}$

50. $-\frac{5}{6} - \frac{1}{6}$

51. $-\frac{1}{10} - \left(-\frac{3}{5}\right)$

52. $-\frac{2}{11} - \left(-\frac{5}{11}\right)$

53. $0.8 - (-2.1)$

54. $-9.6 - (-5.7)$

55. $-73 - 91$

56. $201 - 502$

Exercises 57–70: Evaluate the expression.

57. $10 - 19$

58. $5 + (-9)$

59. $19 - (-22) + 1$

60. $53 + (-43) - 10$

61. $-3 + 4 - 6$

62. $-11 + 8 - 10$

63. $100 - 200 + 100 - (-50)$

64. $-50 - (-40) + (-60) + 80$

65. $1.5 - 2.3 + 9.6$

66. $10.5 - (-5.5) + (-1.5)$

67. $-\frac{1}{2} + \frac{1}{4} - \left(-\frac{3}{4}\right)$

68. $\frac{1}{4} - \left(-\frac{2}{5}\right) + \left(-\frac{3}{20}\right)$

69. $|4 - 9| - |1 - 7|$

70. $|-5 - (-3)| - |-6 + 8|$

Exercises 71–80: Write an arithmetic expression for the given phrase and then simplify it.

71. The sum of two and negative five

72. Subtract ten from negative six

73. Negative five increased by seven

74. Negative twenty decreased by eight

75. The additive inverse of the quantity two cubed

76. Five minus the quantity two cubed

77. The difference between negative six and seven (*Hint:* Write the numbers for the subtraction problem in the order given.)

78. The difference between one-half and three-fourths

79. Six plus negative ten minus five

80. Ten minus seven plus negative twenty

81. Online Exploration Use the Internet to find the highest and lowest points in the continental United States, and then find the difference in their heights.

82. Online Exploration In 1972, residents of Loma, Montana, experienced the largest 24-hour temperature swing ever recorded in the United States. Use the Internet to find the starting and ending temperatures, and then write a subtraction equation that shows the difference.

APPLICATIONS

83. *Checking Account* The initial balance in a checking account is $358. Find the final balance resulting from the following withdrawals and deposits: $-$45, $37, $120, and $-$240.

84. *Savings Account* A savings account has $1245 in it. Find the final balance resulting from the following withdrawals and deposits: $-$189, $975, $-$226, and $-$876.

85. *Football Stats* A running back carries the ball five times. Find his total yardage if the carries were 9, -2, -1, 14, and 5 yards.

86. *Tracking Weight* A person weighs himself every Monday for four weeks. He gains one pound the first week, loses three pounds the second week, gains two pounds the third week, and loses one pound the last week.
    (a) Using positive numbers to represent weight gains and negative numbers to represent weight losses, write a sum that gives the total gain or loss over this four-week period.
    (b) If he weighed 170 pounds at the beginning of this process, what was his weight at the end?

87. *Deepest and Highest* The deepest point in the ocean is the Mariana Trench, which is 35,839 feet below sea level. The highest point on Earth is Mount Everest, which is 29,029 feet above sea level. What is the difference in height between Mount Everest and the Mariana Trench? (*Source: The Guinness Book of Records.*)

88. *Greatest Temperature Ranges* The greatest temperature range on Earth occurs in Siberia, where the temperature can vary between 98°F in the summer and -90°F in the winter. Find the difference between these two temperatures. (*Source: The Guinness Book of Records.*)

WRITING ABOUT MATHEMATICS

89. Explain how to add two negative numbers. Give an example.

90. Explain how to subtract a negative number from a positive number. Give an example.

1.6 Multiplication and Division of Real Numbers

Multiplication of Real Numbers ▪ Division of Real Numbers ▪ Applications

A LOOK INTO MATH ▶

Exam and quiz scores are sometimes displayed in fraction form. For example, a student who answers 17 questions correctly on a 20-question exam may see the fraction $\frac{17}{20}$ written at the top of the exam paper. If the instructor assigns grades based on percents, this fraction must be converted to a percent. Doing so involves division of real numbers. In this section, we discuss multiplication and division of real numbers.

Multiplication of Real Numbers

READING CHECK

• What is the answer to a multiplication problem called?

In a multiplication problem, the numbers multiplied are called the *factors*, and the answer is called the *product*.

$$7 \quad \cdot \quad 4 \quad = \quad 28$$
Factor Factor Product

NEW VOCABULARY

☐ Dividend
☐ Divisor
☐ Quotient
☐ Reciprocal (multiplicative inverse)

Multiplication is a fast way to perform addition. For example, $5 \cdot 2 = 10$ is equivalent to finding the sum of five 2s, or

$$2 + 2 + 2 + 2 + 2 = 10.$$

Similarly, the product $5 \cdot (-2)$ is equivalent to finding the sum of five -2s, or

$$(-2) + (-2) + (-2) + (-2) + (-2) = -10.$$

Thus $5 \cdot (-2) = -10$. In general, the product of a positive number and a negative number is a negative number.

What sign should the product of two negative numbers have? To answer this question, consider the following patterns.

What values should replace the question marks to continue the pattern?

Continuing the pattern results in $-4 \cdot (-1) = 4$ and $-4 \cdot (-2) = 8$. This pattern suggests that if we multiply two negative real numbers, the product is positive.

SIGNS OF PRODUCTS

The product of two numbers with *like* signs is positive. The product of two numbers with *unlike* signs is negative.

NOTE: Multiplying a number by -1 results in the additive inverse (opposite) of the number. For example, $-1 \cdot 4 = -4$, and -4 is the additive inverse of 4. Similarly, $-1 \cdot (-3) = 3$, and 3 is the additive inverse of -3. In general, $-1 \cdot a = -a$.

| EXAMPLE 1 | **Multiplying real numbers** |

Find each product by hand.
(a) $-9 \cdot 7$ **(b)** $\frac{2}{3} \cdot \frac{5}{9}$ **(c)** $-2.1(-40)$ **(d)** $(-2.5)(4)(-9)(-2)$

Solution
(a) The resulting product is negative because the factors -9 and 7 have unlike signs. Thus $-9 \cdot 7 = -63$.
(b) The product is positive because both factors are positive.

$$\frac{2}{3} \cdot \frac{5}{9} = \frac{2 \cdot 5}{3 \cdot 9} = \frac{10}{27}$$

(c) As both factors are negative, the product is positive. Thus $-2.1(-40) = 84$.
(d) $(-2.5)(4)(-9)(-2) = (-10)(-9)(-2) = (90)(-2) = -180$

Now Try Exercises 13, 23, 27, 29

READING CHECK

- How can the number of negative factors be used to decide if a product is positive or negative?

MAKING CONNECTIONS

Multiplying More Than Two Negative Factors

Because the product of two negative numbers is positive, it is possible to determine the sign of a product by counting the number of negative factors. For example, the product $-3 \cdot 4 \cdot (-5) \cdot 7 \cdot (-6)$ is negative because there are an odd number of negative factors and the product $2 \cdot (-1) \cdot (-3) \cdot (-5) \cdot (-4)$ is positive because there are an even number of negative factors.

When evaluating expressions such as

$$-5^2 \text{ (Square and then negate)} \quad \text{and} \quad (-5)^2 \text{ (Negate and then square)},$$

it is important to note that the first represents the opposite of five squared, while the second indicates that negative five should be squared. The next example illustrates the difference between the opposite of an exponential expression and a power of a negative number.

EXAMPLE 2 **Evaluating real numbers with exponents**

Evaluate each expression by hand.
(a) $(-4)^2$ (b) -4^2 (c) $(-2)^3$ (d) -2^3

Solution
(a) Because the exponent is outside of parentheses, the base of the exponential expression is -4. The expression is evaluated as
$$(-4)^2 = (-4)(-4) = 16.$$
(b) This is the negation of an exponential expression with base 4. Evaluating the exponent before negating results in $-4^2 = -(4)(4) = -16$.
(c) $(-2)^3 = (-2)(-2)(-2) = -8$
(d) $-2^3 = -(2)(2)(2) = -8$

Now Try Exercises 35, 37, 39, 41

MAKING CONNECTIONS

Negative Square Roots

Because the product of two negative numbers is positive, $(-3) \cdot (-3) = 9$. That is, -3 is a square root of 9. As discussed in Section 1.4, every positive number has one positive square root and one negative square root. For a positive number a, the positive square root is called the *principal square root* and is denoted $\sqrt{a}$. The negative square root is denoted $-\sqrt{a}$. For example, $\sqrt{4} = 2$ and $-\sqrt{4} = -2$.

Division of Real Numbers

READING CHECK

- What is the answer to a division problem called?

In a division problem, the **dividend** is divided by the **divisor**, and the result is the **quotient**.

$$\underset{\text{Dividend}}{20} \; \div \; \underset{\text{Divisor}}{4} \; = \; \underset{\text{Quotient}}{5}$$

This division problem can also be written in fraction form as $\frac{20}{4} = 5$. Division of real numbers can be defined in terms of multiplication and reciprocals. The **reciprocal**, or **multiplicative inverse**, of a real number a is $\frac{1}{a}$. The number 0 has *no reciprocal*.

TECHNOLOGY NOTE

Try dividing 5 by 0 with a calculator. On most calculators, dividing a number by 0 results in an error message.

DIVIDING REAL NUMBERS

For real numbers a and b with $b \neq 0$,

$$\frac{a}{b} = a \cdot \frac{1}{b}.$$

That is, to divide a by b, multiply a by the reciprocal of b.

NOTE: Division by 0 is undefined because 0 has no reciprocal.

EXAMPLE 3 **Dividing real numbers**

Evaluate each expression by hand.

(a) $-16 \div \frac{1}{4}$ **(b)** $\dfrac{\frac{3}{5}}{-8}$ **(c)** $\frac{-8}{-36}$ **(d)** $9 \div 0$

Solution

(a) $-16 \div \frac{1}{4} = \frac{-16}{1} \cdot \frac{4}{1} = \frac{-64}{1} = -64$ The reciprocal of $\frac{1}{4}$ is $\frac{4}{1}$.

(b) $\dfrac{\frac{3}{5}}{-8} = \frac{3}{5} \div (-8) = \frac{3}{5} \cdot \left(-\frac{1}{8}\right) = -\frac{3}{40}$ The reciprocal of -8 is $-\frac{1}{8}$.

(c) $\frac{-8}{-36} = -8 \cdot \left(-\frac{1}{36}\right) = \frac{8}{36} = \frac{2}{9}$ The reciprocal of -36 is $-\frac{1}{36}$.

(d) $9 \div 0$ is undefined. The number 0 has no reciprocal.

Now Try Exercises 49, 51, 59, 63

When determining the sign of a quotient, the following rules may be helpful. Note that these rules are similar to those for signs of products.

SIGNS OF QUOTIENTS

The quotient of two numbers with *like* signs is positive. The quotient of two numbers with *unlike* signs is negative.

NOTE: To see why a negative number divided by a negative number is a positive number, remember that division is a fast way to perform subtraction. For example, because

$$20 - 4 - 4 - 4 - 4 - 4 = 0,$$

a total of five 4s can be subtracted from 20, so $\frac{20}{4} = 5$. Similarly, because

$$-20 - (-4) - (-4) - (-4) - (-4) - (-4) = 0,$$

a total of five -4s can be subtracted from -20, so $\frac{-20}{-4} = 5$.

▶ **REAL-WORLD CONNECTION** In business, employees may need to convert fractions and mixed numbers to decimal numbers. The next example illustrates this process.

EXAMPLE 4   **Converting fractions to decimals**

Convert each measurement to a decimal number.
(a) $2\frac{3}{8}$-inch bolt   (b) $\frac{15}{16}$-inch diameter   (c) $1\frac{1}{3}$-cup flour

Solution
(a) First divide 3 by 8.

$$\begin{array}{r} 0.375 \\ 8\overline{)3.000} \\ \underline{24} \\ 60 \\ \underline{56} \\ 40 \\ \underline{40} \\ 0 \end{array}$$

So, $2\frac{3}{8} = 2.375$.

(b) Divide 15 by 16.

$$\begin{array}{r} 0.9375 \\ 16\overline{)15.0000} \\ \underline{144} \\ 60 \\ \underline{48} \\ 120 \\ \underline{112} \\ 80 \\ \underline{80} \\ 0 \end{array}$$

So, $\frac{15}{16} = 0.9375$.

(c) First divide 1 by 3.

$$\begin{array}{r} 0.333\ldots \\ 3\overline{)1.000} \\ \underline{9} \\ 10 \\ \underline{9} \\ 10 \\ \underline{9} \\ 1 \end{array}$$

So, $1\frac{1}{3} = 1.\overline{3}$.

Now Try Exercises 69, 71, 75

In the next example, numbers that are expressed as terminating decimals are converted to fractions.

EXAMPLE 5   **Converting decimals to fractions**

Convert each decimal number to a fraction in lowest terms.
(a) 0.06   (b) 0.375   (c) 0.0025

Solution
(a) The decimal 0.06 equals six hundredths, or $\frac{6}{100}$. Simplifying this fraction gives

$$\frac{6}{100} = \frac{3 \cdot 2}{50 \cdot 2} = \frac{3}{50}.$$

(b) The decimal 0.375 equals three hundred seventy-five thousandths, or $\frac{375}{1000}$. Simplifying this fraction gives

$$\frac{375}{1000} = \frac{3 \cdot 125}{8 \cdot 125} = \frac{3}{8}.$$

(c) The decimal 0.0025 equals twenty-five ten thousandths, or $\frac{25}{10,000}$. Simplifying this fraction gives

$$\frac{25}{10,000} = \frac{1 \cdot 25}{400 \cdot 25} = \frac{1}{400}.$$

Now Try Exercises 81, 85, 87

FRACTIONS AND CALCULATORS (OPTIONAL) Many calculators have the capability to perform arithmetic on fractions and express the answer as either a decimal or a fraction. The next example illustrates this capability.

EXAMPLE 6

Performing arithmetic operations with technology

Use a calculator to evaluate each expression. Express your answer as a decimal and as a fraction.

(a) $\frac{1}{3} + \frac{2}{5} - \frac{4}{9}$ **(b)** $\left(\frac{4}{9} \cdot \frac{3}{8}\right) \div \frac{2}{3}$

Solution

(a) Figure 1.28(a) shows that

$$\frac{1}{3} + \frac{2}{5} - \frac{4}{9} = 0.2\overline{8}, \text{ or } \frac{13}{45}.$$

(b) Figure 1.28(b) shows that $\left(\frac{4}{9} \cdot \frac{3}{8}\right) \div \frac{2}{3} = 0.25$, or $\frac{1}{4}$.

CALCULATOR HELP

To find fraction results with a calculator, see Appendix A (pages AP-1 and AP-2).

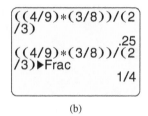

(a)   (b)

Figure 1.28

Now Try Exercises 89, 91

NOTE: Generally it is a good idea to put parentheses around fractions when you are using a calculator.

MAKING CONNECTIONS

The Four Arithmetic Operations

READING CHECK

• How are addition and subtraction related?

• How are multiplication and division related?

If you know how to add real numbers, then you also know how to subtract real numbers because subtraction is defined in terms of addition. That is,

$$a - b = a + (-b).$$

If you know how to multiply real numbers, then you also know how to divide real numbers because division is defined in terms of multiplication. That is,

$$\frac{a}{b} = a \cdot \frac{1}{b}.$$

Applications

There are many instances when we may need to multiply or divide real numbers. Two examples are provided here.

EXAMPLE 7

Comparing top-grossing movies

Even though *Avatar* (2009) was an extremely successful film that set domestic box office records, it ranks only fourteenth among top-grossing movies of all time when calculated by using estimated total admissions. The total admissions for *Avatar* are $\frac{17}{25}$ of the total admissions for *The Sound of Music* (1965), which ranks third. (*Source:* Box Office Mojo.)

(a) If *The Sound of Music* had estimated total admissions of 142 million people, find the estimated total admissions for *Avatar*.

(b) The top-grossing movie of all time is *Gone With the Wind* (1939), which had estimated total admissions of 202 million. How many more people saw *Gone With the Wind* than saw *Avatar*?

Solution

(a) To find the total admissions for *Avatar* we multiply the real numbers 142 and $\frac{17}{25}$ to obtain $142 \cdot \frac{17}{25} = \frac{2414}{25} \approx 97$.

Total admissions for *Avatar* were about 97 million people.

(b) The difference is $202 - 97 = 105$ million people.

▌ Now Try Exercise 97

EXAMPLE 8 ▶ **Analyzing the federal budget**

It is estimated that $\frac{14}{125}$ of the federal budget is used to pay interest on loans. Write this fraction as a decimal. (*Source*: U.S. Office of Management and Budget.)

Solution

One method for writing the fraction as a decimal is to divide 14 by 125, using long division. An alternative method is to multiply the fraction by $\frac{8}{8}$ so that the denominator becomes 1000. Then write the numerator in the thousandths place in the decimal.

$$\frac{14}{125} \cdot \frac{8}{8} = \frac{112}{1000} = 0.112$$

▌ Now Try Exercise 99

1.6 Putting It All Together

CONCEPT	COMMENTS	EXAMPLES
Multiplication	The product of two numbers with like signs is positive, and the product of two numbers with unlike signs is negative.	$6 \cdot 7 = 42$ Like signs $6 \cdot (-7) = -42$ Unlike signs

continued on next page

continued from previous page

CONCEPT	COMMENTS	EXAMPLES
Division	For real numbers a and b, with $b \neq 0$, $$\frac{a}{b} = a \cdot \frac{1}{b}.$$ The quotient of two numbers with like signs is positive, and the quotient of two numbers with unlike signs is negative.	$\dfrac{42}{6} = 7$ Like signs $\dfrac{-42}{6} = -7$ Unlike signs
Converting Fractions to Decimals	The fraction $\frac{a}{b}$ is equivalent to $a \div b$, where $b \neq 0$.	The fraction $\frac{2}{9}$ is equivalent to $0.\overline{2}$, because $2 \div 9 = 0.222\ldots$.
Converting Terminating Decimals to Fractions	Write the decimal as a fraction with a denominator equal to a power of 10 and then simplify this fraction.	$0.55 = \dfrac{55}{100} = \dfrac{11 \cdot 5}{20 \cdot 5} = \dfrac{11}{20}$

1.6 Exercises

MyMathLab   Math XL PRACTICE   WATCH   DOWNLOAD   READ   REVIEW

CONCEPTS AND VOCABULARY

1. The solution to a multiplication problem is the _____.

2. The product of a positive number and a negative number is a(n) _____ number.

3. The product of two negative numbers is _____.

4. The solution to a division problem is the _____.

5. The reciprocal of a nonzero number a is _____.

6. Division by zero is undefined because zero has no _____.

7. To divide a by b, multiply a by the _____ of b.

8. In general, $-1 \cdot a =$ _____.

9. $\dfrac{a}{b} = a \cdot$ _____

10. A negative number divided by a negative number is a(n) _____ number.

11. A negative number divided by a positive number is a(n) _____ number.

12. To convert $\frac{5}{8}$ to a decimal, divide _____ by _____.

MULTIPLICATION AND DIVISION OF REAL NUMBERS

Exercises 13–32: Multiply.

13. $-3 \cdot 4$

14. $-5 \cdot 7$

15. $6 \cdot (-3)$

16. $2 \cdot (-1)$

17. $0 \cdot (-2.13)$

18. $-2 \cdot (-7)$

19. $-6 \cdot (-10)$

20. $-3 \cdot (-1.7) \cdot 0$

21. $-\frac{1}{2} \cdot \left(-\frac{2}{4}\right)$

22. $-\frac{3}{4} \cdot \left(-\frac{5}{12}\right)$

23. $-\frac{3}{7} \cdot \frac{7}{3}$

24. $\frac{5}{8} \cdot \left(-\frac{4}{15}\right)$

25. $-10 \cdot (-20)$

26. $1000 \cdot (-70)$

27. $-0.5 \cdot 100$

28. $-0.5 \cdot (-0.3)$

29. $-2 \cdot 3 \cdot (-4) \cdot 5$

30. $-3 \cdot (-5) \cdot (-2) \cdot 10$

31. $-6 \cdot \frac{1}{6} \cdot \frac{7}{9} \cdot \left(-\frac{9}{7}\right) \cdot \left(-\frac{3}{2}\right)$

32. $-\frac{8}{5} \cdot \frac{1}{8} \cdot \left(-\frac{5}{7}\right) \cdot -7$

33. Thinking Generally Is the product given by the expression $a \cdot (-a) \cdot (-a) \cdot a \cdot (-a)$ positive or negative if $a > 0$?

34. Thinking Generally Is the product given by the expression $a \cdot (-a) \cdot (-a) \cdot a \cdot (-a)$ positive or negative if $a < 0$?

Exercises 35–44: Evaluate the expression.

35. $(-5)^2$ **36.** -5^2

37. $(-1)^3$ **38.** $(-6)^2$

39. -2^4 **40.** $-(-4)^2$

41. $-(-2)^3$ **42.** $3 \cdot (-3)^2$

43. $5 \cdot (-2)^3$ **44.** -1^4

Exercises 45–68: Divide.

45. $-10 \div 5$ **46.** $-8 \div 4$

47. $-20 \div (-2)$ **48.** $-15 \div (-3)$

49. $\frac{-12}{3}$ **50.** $\frac{-25}{-5}$

51. $-16 \div \frac{1}{2}$ **52.** $10 \div \left(-\frac{1}{3}\right)$

53. $0 \div 3$ **54.** $\frac{0}{-5}$

55. $\frac{-1}{0}$ **56.** $\frac{0}{-2}$

57. $\frac{1}{2} \div (-11)$ **58.** $-\frac{3}{4} \div (-6)$

59. $\frac{-\frac{4}{5}}{-3}$ **60.** $\frac{\frac{7}{8}}{-7}$

61. $\frac{5}{6} \div \left(-\frac{8}{9}\right)$ **62.** $-\frac{11}{12} \div \left(-\frac{11}{4}\right)$

63. $-\frac{1}{2} \div 0$ **64.** $-9 \div 0$

65. $-0.5 \div \frac{1}{2}$ **66.** $-0.25 \div \left(-\frac{3}{4}\right)$

67. $-\frac{2}{3} \div 0.5$ **68.** $\frac{1}{6} \div 1.5$

CONVERTING BETWEEN FRACTIONS AND DECIMALS

Exercises 69–80: Write the number as a decimal.

69. $\frac{1}{2}$ **70.** $\frac{3}{4}$

71. $\frac{3}{16}$ **72.** $\frac{1}{9}$

73. $3\frac{1}{2}$ **74.** $2\frac{1}{4}$

75. $5\frac{2}{3}$ **76.** $6\frac{7}{9}$

77. $1\frac{7}{16}$ **78.** $6\frac{1}{12}$

79. $\frac{7}{8}$ **80.** $\frac{11}{16}$

Exercises 81–88: Write the decimal number as a fraction in lowest terms.

81. 0.25   **82.** 0.8

83. 0.16   **84.** 0.35

85. 0.625   **86.** 0.0125

87. 0.6875   **88.** 0.21875

Exercises 89–96: Use a calculator to evaluate each expression. Express your answer as a decimal and as a fraction.

89. $\left(\frac{1}{3} + \frac{5}{6}\right) \div \frac{1}{2}$ **90.** $\frac{4}{9} - \frac{1}{6} + \frac{2}{3}$

91. $\frac{4}{5} \div \frac{2}{3} \cdot \frac{7}{4}$ **92.** $4 - \frac{7}{4} \cdot 2$

93. $\frac{15}{2} - 4 \cdot \frac{7}{3}$ **94.** $\frac{1}{6} - \frac{3}{5} + \frac{7}{8}$

95. $\frac{17}{40} + 3 \div 8$ **96.** $\frac{3}{4} \cdot \left(6 + \frac{1}{2}\right)$

APPLICATIONS

97. *Top-Grossing Movies* (Refer to Example 7.) *The Ten Commandments* (1956) is the fifth top-grossing movie of all time. Find the total admissions for *The Ten Commandments* if they were $\frac{13}{20}$ of the total admissions for the top-grossing movie of all time, *Gone With the Wind* (1939), which had total admissions of 202 million. (*Source:* Box Office Mojo.)

98. *Planet Climate* Saturn has an average surface temperature of -220¡ F. Neptune has an average surface temperature that is $\frac{3}{2}$ times that of Saturn. Find the average surface temperature on Neptune. (*Source:* NASA.)

99. *Uninsured Americans* In 2010, the fraction of Americans who did not have health insurance coverage was $\frac{21}{125}$. Write this fraction as a decimal. (*Source:* U.S. Census Bureau.)

100. *Uninsured Minnesotans* In 2010, the fraction of Minnesotans who did not have health insurance coverage was $\frac{23}{250}$. Write this fraction as a decimal. (*Source:* U.S. Census Bureau.)

WRITING ABOUT MATHEMATICS

101. Division is a fast way to subtract. Consider the division problem $\frac{-6}{-2}$, whose quotient represents the number of -2s in -6. Using this idea, explain why the answer is a positive number.

102. Explain how to determine whether the product of three integers is positive or negative.

Checking Basic Concepts

1. Find each sum.
   (a) $-4 + 4$ (b) $-10 + (-12) + 3$

2. Evaluate each expression.
   (a) $\frac{2}{3} - \left(-\frac{2}{9}\right)$ (b) $-1.2 - 5.1 + 3.1$

3. Write an arithmetic expression for the given phrase and then simplify it.
   (a) The sum of negative one and five
   (b) The difference between four and negative three

4. The hottest temperature ever recorded at International Falls, Minnesota, was $99°F$, and the coldest temperature ever recorded was $-46°F$. What is the difference between these two temperatures?

5. Find each product.
   (a) $-5 \cdot (-7)$ (b) $-\frac{1}{2} \cdot \frac{2}{3} \cdot \left(-\frac{4}{5}\right)$

6. Evaluate each expression.
   (a) -3^2 (b) $4 \cdot (-2)^3$ (c) $(-5)^2$

7. Evaluate each expression.
   (a) $-5 \div \frac{2}{3}$ (b) $-\frac{5}{8} \div \left(-\frac{4}{3}\right)$

8. What is the reciprocal of $-\frac{7}{6}$?

9. Simplify each expression.
   (a) $\frac{-10}{2}$ (b) $\frac{10}{-2}$ (c) $-\frac{10}{2}$ (d) $\frac{-10}{-2}$

10. Convert each fraction or mixed number to a decimal number.
    (a) $\frac{3}{5}$ (b) $3\frac{7}{8}$

1.7   Properties of Real Numbers

Commutative Properties ▪ Associative Properties ▪ Distributive Properties ▪ Identity and Inverse Properties ▪ Mental Calculations

A LOOK INTO MATH ▶ The order in which you perform actions is often important. For example, putting on your socks and then your shoes is not the same as putting on your shoes and then your socks. In mathematical terms, the action of putting on footwear is not *commutative* with respect to socks and shoes. However, the order in which you tie your shoes and put on a sweatshirt does not matter. So, these two actions are *commutative*. In mathematics some operations are commutative and others are not. In this section we discuss several properties of real numbers.

Commutative Properties

The **commutative property for addition** states that two numbers, a and b, can be added in any order and the result will be the same. That is, $a + b = b + a$. For example, if a person buys 4 DVDs and then buys 2 DVDs or first buys 2 DVDs and then buys 4 DVDs, as shown in Figure 1.29, the result is the same. Either way the person buys a total of $4 + 2 = 2 + 4 = 6$ DVDs.

Figure 1.29 Commutative Property: $4 + 2 = 2 + 4$

There is also a **commutative property for multiplication**. It states that two numbers, a and b, can be multiplied in any order and the result will be the same. That is, $a \cdot b = b \cdot a$.

NEW VOCABULARY

- ☐ Commutative property for addition
- ☐ Commutative property for multiplication
- ☐ Associative property for addition
- ☐ Associative property for multiplication
- ☐ Distributive properties
- ☐ Identity property of 0
- ☐ Additive identity
- ☐ Identity property of 1
- ☐ Multiplicative identity

For example, if one person rolls 3 dice, each resulting in 6, and another person rolls 6 dice, each resulting in 3, as shown in Figure 1.30, then each person has rolled a total of $3 \cdot 6 = 6 \cdot 3 = 18$.

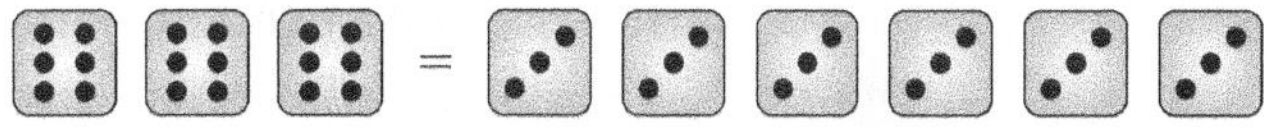

Figure 1.30 Commutative Property: $3 \cdot 6 = 6 \cdot 3$

We can summarize these results as follows.

COMMUTATIVE PROPERTIES

For any real numbers a and b,

$$a + b = b + a \quad \text{and} \quad a \cdot b = b \cdot a.$$

Addition — Multiplication

EXAMPLE 1 **Applying the commutative properties**

Use a commutative property to rewrite each expression.
(a) $15 + 100$ **(b)** $a \cdot 8$

Solution

(a) By the commutative property for addition $15 + 100$ can be written as $100 + 15$.
(b) By the commutative property for multiplication $a \cdot 8$ can be written as $8 \cdot a$ or $8a$.

Now Try Exercises 13, 19

While there are commutative properties for addition and multiplication, the operations of subtraction and division are *not* commutative. Table 1.9 shows each of the four arithmetic operations along with examples illustrating whether or not each operation is commutative.

READING CHECK

- Which of the four arithmetic operations are commutative and which are not?

TABLE 1.9 **Commutativity of Operations**

Operation	Commutative?	Example
$+$	Yes	$4 + 9 = 9 + 4$
$-$	No	$5 - 3 \neq 3 - 5$
$\cdot$	Yes	$8 \cdot 5 = 5 \cdot 8$
$\div$	No	$4 \div 2 \neq 2 \div 4$

Associative Properties

The *associative properties* allow us to change how numbers are grouped. For example, if a person buys 1, 2, and 4 energy drinks, as shown in Figure 1.31, then the total number of drinks can be calculated either as

$$(1 + 2) + 4 = 3 + 4 = 7 \quad \text{or as} \quad 1 + (2 + 4) = 1 + 6 = 7.$$

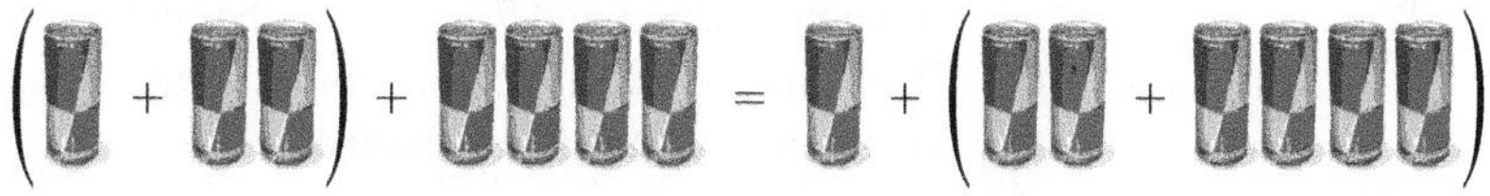

Figure 1.31 Associative Property: $(1 + 2) + 4 = 1 + (2 + 4)$

In either case we obtain the same answer, 7 drinks, which is the result of the **associative property for addition**. We did not change the order of the numbers; we only changed how the numbers were grouped. There is also an **associative property for multiplication**, which can be illustrated by considering the total number of flowers shown in Figure 1.32, where 2 shelves hold 3 pots each, and each pot contains 4 flowers. The total number of flowers can be calculated either as

$$(2 \cdot 3) \cdot 4 = 6 \cdot 4 = 24 \quad \text{or as} \quad 2 \cdot (3 \cdot 4) = 2 \cdot 12 = 24.$$

Figure 1.32

We can summarize these results as follows.

ASSOCIATIVE PROPERTIES

For any real numbers a, b, and c,

$$(a + b) + c = a + (b + c) \quad \text{and} \quad (a \cdot b) \cdot c = a \cdot (b \cdot c).$$

Addition   Multiplication

NOTE: Sometimes we omit the multiplication dot. Thus $a \cdot b = ab$ and $5 \cdot x \cdot y = 5xy$.

EXAMPLE 2   Applying the associative properties

Use an associative property to rewrite each expression.
(a) $(5 + 6) + 7$ **(b)** $x(yz)$

Solution
(a) The given expression is equivalent to $5 + (6 + 7)$.
(a) The given expression is equivalent to $(xy)z$.

Now Try Exercises 21, 23

EXAMPLE 3   Identifying properties of real numbers

State the property that each equation illustrates.
(a) $5 \cdot (8y) = (5 \cdot 8)y$ **(b)** $3 \cdot 7 = 7 \cdot 3$ **(c)** $x + yz = yz + x$

Solution
(a) This equation illustrates the associative property for multiplication because the grouping of the numbers has been changed.
(b) This equation illustrates the commutative property for multiplication because the order of the numbers 3 and 7 has been changed.
(c) This equation illustrates the commutative property for addition because the order of the terms x and yz has been changed.

Now Try Exercises 53, 55, 63

While there are associative properties for addition and multiplication, the operations of subtraction and division are *not* associative. Table 1.10 shows each of the four arithmetic operations along with examples illustrating whether or not each operation is associative.

TABLE 1.10 **Associativity of Operations**

Operation	Associative?	Example
+	Yes	$(3 + 6) + 7 = 3 + (6 + 7)$
−	No	$(10 - 3) - 1 \neq 10 - (3 - 1)$
·	Yes	$(4 \cdot 5) \cdot 3 = 4 \cdot (5 \cdot 3)$
÷	No	$(16 \div 8) \div 2 \neq 16 \div (8 \div 2)$

READING CHECK

• Which of the four arithmetic operations are associative and which are not?

STUDY TIP

The information in Making Connections ties the current concepts to those studied earlier. By reviewing your notes often, you can gain a better understanding of mathematics.

MAKING CONNECTIONS

Commutative and Associative Properties

Both the commutative and associative properties work for addition and multiplication. However, neither property works for subtraction or division.

Distributive Properties

The **distributive properties** are used frequently in algebra to simplify expressions. Arrows are often used to indicate that a distributive property is being applied.

$$4(2 + 3) = 4 \cdot 2 + 4 \cdot 3$$

The 4 must be multiplied by *both* the 2 and the 3—not just the 2.

The distributive property remains valid when addition is replaced with subtraction.

$$4(2 - 3) = 4 \cdot 2 - 4 \cdot 3$$

We illustrate a distributive property geometrically in Figure 1.33. Note that the area of one rectangle that is 4 squares by 5 squares is the same as the area of two rectangles: one that is 4 squares by 2 squares and another that is 4 squares by 3 squares. In either case the total area is 20 square units.

Distributive Property

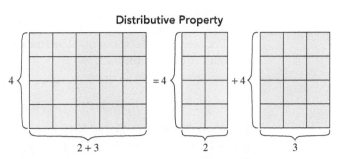

Figure 1.33 $4(2 + 3) = 4 \cdot 2 + 4 \cdot 3$

DISTRIBUTIVE PROPERTIES

For any real numbers a, b, and c,

$$a(b + c) = ab + ac \quad \text{and} \quad a(b - c) = ab - ac.$$

NOTE: Because multiplication is commutative, the distributive properties can also be written as

$$(b + c)a = ba + ca \quad \text{and} \quad (b - c)a = ba - ca.$$

EXAMPLE 4 **Applying the distributive properties**

Apply a distributive property to each expression.
(a) $3(x + 2)$ **(b)** $-6(a - 2)$ **(c)** $-(x + 7)$ **(d)** $15 - (b + 4)$

Solution
(a) Both the x and the 2 must be multiplied by 3.

$$3(x + 2) = 3 \cdot x + 3 \cdot 2 = 3x + 6$$

(b) $-6(a - 2) = -6 \cdot a - (-6) \cdot 2 = -6a + 12$

(c) $-(x + 7) = (-1)(x + 7)$ In general, $-a = -1 \cdot a$.

$\qquad\qquad\; = (-1) \cdot x + (-1) \cdot 7$ Distributive property

$\qquad\qquad\; = -x - 7$ Multiply.

(d) $15 - (b + 4) = 15 + (-1)(b + 4)$ Change subtraction to addition.

$\qquad\qquad\qquad\; = 15 + (-1) \cdot b + (-1) \cdot 4$ Distributive property

$\qquad\qquad\qquad\; = 15 - b - 4$ Multiply.

$\qquad\qquad\qquad\; = 11 - b$ Simplify.

NOTE: To simplify the expression $15 - (b + 4)$, we subtract *both* the b and the 4. Thus we can quickly simplify the given expression to

$$15 - (b + 4) = 15 - b - 4.$$

Now Try Exercises 31, 35, 37, 41

EXAMPLE 5 **Inserting parentheses using the distributive property**

Use a distributive property to insert parentheses in the expression and then simplify the result.
(a) $5a + 2a$ **(b)** $3x - 7x$ **(c)** $-4y + 5y$

Solution
(a) Because a is a factor in both $5a$ and $2a$, we use the distributive property to write the a outside of parentheses.

$$5a + 2a = (5 + 2)a \quad \text{Distributive property}$$
$$= 7a \qquad\qquad \text{Simplify.}$$

(b) $3x - 7x = (3 - 7)x = -4x$
(c) $-4y + 5y = (-4 + 5)y = 1y = y$

Now Try Exercises 45, 47, 51

EXAMPLE 6 **Identifying properties of real numbers**

State the property or properties illustrated by each equation.
(a) $4(5 - x) = 20 - 4x$ (b) $(4 + x) + 5 = x + 9$
(c) $5z + 7z = 12z$ (d) $x(y + z) = zx + yx$

Solution
(a) This equation illustrates the distributive property with subtraction.

$$4(5 - x) = 4 \cdot 5 - 4 \cdot x = 20 - 4x$$

(b) This equation illustrates the commutative and associative properties for addition.

$$
\begin{aligned}
(4 + x) + 5 &= (x + 4) + 5 && \text{Commutative property for addition} \\
&= x + (4 + 5) && \text{Associative property for addition} \\
&= x + 9 && \text{Simplify.}
\end{aligned}
$$

(c) This equation illustrates the distributive property with addition.

$$5z + 7z = (5 + 7)z = 12z$$

(d) This equation illustrates a distributive property with addition and commutative properties for addition and multiplication.

$$
\begin{aligned}
x(y + z) &= xy + xz && \text{Distributive property} \\
&= xz + xy && \text{Commutative property for addition} \\
&= zx + yx && \text{Commutative property for multiplication}
\end{aligned}
$$

Now Try Exercises 55, 57, 59, 61

Identity and Inverse Properties

The **identity property of 0** states that if 0 is added to any real number a, the result is a. The number 0 is called the **additive identity**. Examples include

$$-4 + 0 = -4 \quad \text{and} \quad 0 + 11 = 11.$$

The **identity property of 1** states that if any number a is multiplied by 1, the result is a. The number 1 is called the **multiplicative identity**. Examples include

$$-3 \cdot 1 = -3 \quad \text{and} \quad 1 \cdot 8 = 8.$$

We can summarize these results as follows.

IDENTITY PROPERTIES

For any real number a,

$$a + 0 = 0 + a = a \quad \text{and} \quad a \cdot 1 = 1 \cdot a = a.$$

Additive identity   Multiplicative identity

READING CHECK

• Restate the identity property for 0 in your own words.
• Restate the identity property for 1 in your own words.

The *additive inverse*, or *opposite*, of a number a is $-a$. The number 0 is its own opposite. The sum of a number a and its additive inverse equals the additive identity 0. Thus $-5 + 5 = 0$ and $x + (-x) = 0$.

The *multiplicative inverse*, or *reciprocal*, of a nonzero number a is $\frac{1}{a}$. The number 0 has no multiplicative inverse. The product of a number and its multiplicative inverse equals the multiplicative identity 1. Thus $-\frac{5}{4} \cdot \left(-\frac{4}{5}\right) = 1$.

INVERSE PROPERTIES

For any real number a,

$$a + (-a) = 0 \quad \text{and} \quad -a + a = 0. \quad \text{Additive inverse}$$

For any *nonzero* real number a,

$$a \cdot \frac{1}{a} = 1 \quad \text{and} \quad \frac{1}{a} \cdot a = 1. \quad \text{Multiplicative inverse}$$

EXAMPLE 7 **Identifying identity and inverse properties**

State the property or properties illustrated by each equation.

(a) $0 + xy = xy$
(b) $\frac{36}{30} = \frac{6}{5} \cdot \frac{6}{6} = \frac{6}{5}$
(c) $x + (-x) + 5 = 0 + 5 = 5$
(d) $\frac{1}{9} \cdot 9y = 1 \cdot y = y$

Solution
(a) This equation illustrates use of the identity property for 0.
(b) Because $\frac{6}{6} = 1$, these equations illustrate how a fraction can be simplified by using the identity property for 1.
(c) These equations illustrate use of the additive inverse property and the identity property for 0.
(d) These equations illustrate use of the multiplicative inverse property and the identity property for 1.

Now Try Exercises 67, 69, 71, 73

Mental Calculations

Properties of numbers can be used to simplify calculations. For example, to find the sum

$$4 + 7 + 6 + 3$$

we might apply the commutative and associative properties for addition to obtain

$$(4 + 6) + (7 + 3) = 10 + 10 = 20.$$

Suppose that we are to add $128 + 19$ mentally. One way is to add 20 to 128 and then subtract 1.

$$128 + 19 = 128 + (20 - 1) \quad 19 = 20 - 1.$$
$$= (128 + 20) - 1 \quad \text{Associative property}$$
$$= 148 - 1 \quad \text{Add.}$$
$$= 147 \quad \text{Subtract.}$$

The distributive property can be helpful when we multiply mentally. For example, to determine the number of people in a marching band with 7 columns and 23 rows we need to find the product $7 \cdot 23$. To evaluate the product mentally, think of 23 as $20 + 3$.

$$7 \cdot 23 = 7(20 + 3) \qquad 23 = 20 + 3.$$
$$= 7 \cdot 20 + 7 \cdot 3 \quad \text{Distributive property}$$
$$= 140 + 21 \qquad \text{Multiply.}$$
$$= 161 \qquad\qquad \text{Add.}$$

EXAMPLE 8   Performing calculations mentally

Use properties of real numbers to calculate each expression mentally.

(a) $21 + 15 + 9 + 5$ (b) $\frac{1}{2} \cdot \frac{2}{3} \cdot 2 \cdot \frac{3}{2}$

(c) $523 + 199$ (d) $6 \cdot 55$

Solution

(a) Use the commutative and associative properties to group numbers into pairs that sum to a multiple of 10.

$$21 + 15 + 9 + 5 = (21 + 9) + (15 + 5) = 30 + 20 = 50$$

(b) Use the commutative and associative properties to group numbers with their reciprocals.

$$\frac{1}{2} \cdot \frac{2}{3} \cdot 2 \cdot \frac{3}{2} = \left(\frac{1}{2} \cdot 2\right) \cdot \left(\frac{2}{3} \cdot \frac{3}{2}\right) = 1 \cdot 1 = 1$$

(c) Instead of adding 199, add 200 and then subtract 1.

$$523 + 200 - 1 = 723 - 1 = 722$$

(d) Think of 55 as $50 + 5$ and then apply the distributive property.

$$6 \cdot (50 + 5) = 300 + 30 = 330$$

Now Try Exercises 77, 81, 85, 91

CRITICAL THINKING

How could you quickly calculate $5283 - 198$ without a calculator?

The next example illustrates how the commutative and associative properties for multiplication can be used together to simplify a product.

EXAMPLE 9   Finding the volume of a swimming pool

An Olympic swimming pool is 50 meters long, 25 meters wide, and 2 meters deep. The volume V of the pool is found by multiplying 50, 25, and 2. Use the commutative and associative properties for multiplication to calculate the volume of the pool mentally.

Solution

Because $50 \cdot 2 = 100$ and multiplication by 100 is relatively easy, it may be convenient to order and group the multiplication as $(50 \cdot 2) \cdot 25 = 100 \cdot 25 = 2500$. Thus the pool contains 2500 cubic meters of water.

Now Try Exercise 103

1.7 Putting It All Together

PROPERTY	DEFINITION	EXAMPLES
Commutative	For any real numbers a and b, $$a + b = b + a \quad \text{and}$$ $$a \cdot b = b \cdot a.$$	$4 + 6 = 6 + 4$ $4 \cdot 6 = 6 \cdot 4$
Associative	For any real numbers a, b, and c, $$(a + b) + c = a + (b + c) \quad \text{and}$$ $$(a \cdot b) \cdot c = a \cdot (b \cdot c).$$	$(3 + 4) + 5 = 3 + (4 + 5)$ $(3 \cdot 4) \cdot 5 = 3 \cdot (4 \cdot 5)$
Distributive	For any real numbers a, b, and c, $$a(b + c) = ab + ac \quad \text{and}$$ $$a(b - c) = ab - ac.$$	$5(x + 2) = 5x + 10$ $5(x - 2) = 5x - 10$
Identity (0 and 1)	The identity for addition is 0, and the identity for multiplication is 1. For any real number a, $a + 0 = a$ and $a \cdot 1 = a$.	$5 + 0 = 5 \quad \text{and} \quad 5 \cdot 1 = 5$
Inverse	The additive inverse of a is $-a$, and $a + (-a) = 0$. The multiplicative inverse of a nonzero number a is $\frac{1}{a}$, and $a \cdot \frac{1}{a} = 1$.	$8 + (-8) = 0 \quad \text{and} \quad \frac{2}{3} \cdot \frac{3}{2} = 1$

1.7 Exercises

MyMathLab　Math XL PRACTICE　WATCH　DOWNLOAD　READ　REVIEW

CONCEPTS AND VOCABULARY

1. $a + b = b + a$ illustrates the _____ property for _____.

2. $a \cdot b = b \cdot a$ illustrates the _____ property for _____.

3. $(a + b) + c = a + (b + c)$ illustrates the _____ property for _____.

4. $(a \cdot b) \cdot c = a \cdot (b \cdot c)$ illustrates the _____ property for _____.

5. (True or False?) Addition and multiplication are commutative.

6. (True or False?) Subtraction and division are associative.

7. $a(b + c) = ab + ac$ illustrates the _____ property.

8. $a(b - c) = ab - ac$ illustrates the _____ property.

9. The equations $a + 0 = a$ and $0 + a = a$ each illustrate the _____ property for _____.

10. The equations $a \cdot 1 = a$ and $1 \cdot a = a$ each illustrate the _____ property for _____.

11. The additive inverse, or opposite, of a is _____.

12. The multiplicative inverse, or reciprocal, of a nonzero number a is _____.

PROPERTIES OF REAL NUMBERS

Exercises 13–20: Use a commutative property to rewrite the expression. Do not simplify.

13. $-6 + 10$

14. $23 + 7$

15. $-5 \cdot 6$

16. $25 \cdot (-46)$

17. $a + 10$

18. $b + c$

19. $b \cdot 7$

20. $a \cdot 23$

Exercises 21–28: Use an associative property to rewrite the expression. Do not simplify.

21. $(1 + 2) + 3$

22. $-7 + (5 + 15)$

23. $2 \cdot (3 \cdot 4)$

24. $(9 \cdot (-4)) \cdot 5$

25. $(a + 5) + c$

26. $(10 + b) + a$

27. $(x \cdot 3) \cdot 4$

28. $5 \cdot (x \cdot y)$

29. **Thinking Generally** Use the commutative and associative properties to show that $a + b + c = c + b + a$.

30. **Thinking Generally** Use the commutative and associative properties to show that $a \cdot b \cdot c = c \cdot b \cdot a$.

Exercises 31–42: Use a distributive property to rewrite the expression. Then simplify the expression.

31. $4(3 + 2)$

32. $5(6 - 9)$

33. $a(b - 8)$

34. $3(x + y)$

35. $-4(t - z)$

36. $-1(a + 6)$

37. $-(5 - a)$

38. $12 - (4u - b)$

39. $(a + 5)3$

40. $(x + y)7$

41. $12 - (a - 5)$

42. $4x - 2(3y - 5)$

43. **Thinking Generally** Use properties of real numbers to show that the distributive property can be extended as follows.

$$a \cdot (b + c + d) = ab + ac + ad.$$

44. **Thinking Generally** Use properties of real numbers to show that the distributive property can be extended as follows.

$$a \cdot (b - c - d) = ab - ac - ad.$$

Exercises 45–52: Use the distributive property to insert parentheses in the expression and then simplify the result.

45. $6x + 5x$

46. $4y - y$

47. $-4b + 3b$

48. $2b + 8b$

49. $3a - a$

50. $-2x + 5x$

51. $13w - 27w$

52. $25a - 21a$

Exercises 53–66: State the property or properties that the equation illustrates.

53. $x \cdot 5 = 5x$

54. $7 + a = a + 7$

55. $(a + 5) + 7 = a + 12$

56. $(9 + a) + 8 = a + 17$

57. $4(5 + x) = 20 + 4x$

58. $3(5 + x) = 3x + 15$

59. $x(3 - y) = 3x - xy$

60. $-(u - v) = -u + v$

61. $6x + 9x = 15x$

62. $9x - 11x = -2x$

63. $3 \cdot (4 \cdot a) = 12a$

64. $(x \cdot 3) \cdot 5 = 15x$

65. $-(t - 7) = -t + 7$

66. $z \cdot 5 - y \cdot 6 = 5z - 6y$

IDENTITY AND INVERSE PROPERTIES

Exercises 67–76: State the property or properties that are illustrated.

67. $0 + x = x$

68. $5x + 0 = 5x$

69. $1 \cdot a = a$

70. $\frac{1}{7} \cdot (7 \cdot a) = a$

71. $\frac{25}{15} = \frac{5}{3} \cdot \frac{5}{5} = \frac{5}{3}$

72. $\frac{50}{40} = \frac{5}{4} \cdot \frac{10}{10} = \frac{5}{4}$

73. $\frac{1}{xy} \cdot xy = 1$

74. $\frac{1}{a + b} \cdot (a + b) = 1$

75. $-xyz + xyz = 0$

76. $\frac{1}{y} + \left(-\frac{1}{y}\right) = 0$

MENTAL CALCULATIONS

Exercises 77–92: Use properties of real numbers to calculate the expression mentally.

77. $4 + 2 + 9 + 8 + 1 + 6$

78. $21 + 32 + 19 + 8$

79. $45 + 43 + 5 + 7$

80. $5 + 7 + 12 + 13 + 8$

81. $129 + 49$

82. $87 + 99$

83. $178 - 99$

84. $500 - 101$

85. $6 \cdot 15$

86. $4 \cdot 56$

87. $8 \cdot 102$

88. $5 \cdot 999$

89. $\frac{1}{2} \cdot \frac{1}{2} \cdot \frac{1}{2} \cdot 2 \cdot 2 \cdot 2$

90. $\frac{1}{2} \cdot \frac{4}{5} \cdot \frac{7}{3} \cdot 2 \cdot \frac{5}{4}$

91. $\frac{7}{6} \cdot \frac{1}{2} \cdot \frac{1}{2} \cdot \frac{1}{2} \cdot \frac{8}{7}$

92. $\frac{4}{11} \cdot \frac{11}{6} \cdot \frac{6}{7} \cdot \frac{7}{4}$

MULTIPLYING AND DIVIDING BY POWERS OF 10 MENTALLY

93. *Multiplying by 10* To multiply an integer by 10, attach one 0 to the number. For example, $10 \cdot 23 = 230$. Simplify each expression mentally.
(a) $10 \cdot 41$ (b) $10 \cdot 997$
(c) $-630 \cdot 10$ (d) $-14,000 \cdot 10$

94. *Multiplying by 10* To multiply a decimal number by 10, move the decimal point one place to the right. For example, $10 \cdot 23.45 = 234.5$. Simplify each expression mentally.
(a) $10 \cdot 101.68$ (b) $10 \cdot (-1.235)$
(c) $-113.4 \cdot 10$ (d) $0.567 \cdot 10$
(e) $10 \cdot 0.0045$ (f) $-0.05 \cdot 10$

95. *Multiplying by Powers of 10* To multiply an integer by a power of 10 in the form

$$10^k = \underbrace{100 \ldots 0}_{k \text{ zeros}},$$

attach k zeros to the number. Some examples of this are $100 \cdot 45 = 4500$, $1000 \cdot 235 = 235,000$, and $10,000 \cdot 12 = 120,000$. Simplify each expression mentally.
(a) $1000 \cdot 19$ (b) $100 \cdot (-451)$
(c) $10,000 \cdot 6$ (d) $-79 \cdot 100,000$

96. *Multiplying by Powers of 10* To multiply a decimal number by a power of 10 in the form

$$10^k = \underbrace{100 \ldots 0}_{k \text{ zeros}},$$

move the decimal point k places to the right. For example, $100 \cdot 1.234 = 123.4$. Simplify each given expression mentally.
(a) $1000 \cdot 1.2345$ (b) $100 \cdot (-5.1)$
(c) $45.67 \cdot 1000$ (d) $0.567 \cdot 10,000$
(e) $100 \cdot 0.0005$ (f) $-0.05 \cdot 100,000$

97. *Dividing by 10* To divide a number by 10, move the decimal point one place to the left. For example, $78.9 \div 10 = 7.89$. Simplify each expression mentally.
(a) $12.56 \div 10$ (b) $9.6 \div 10$
(c) $0.987 \div 10$ (d) $-0.056 \div 10$
(e) $1200 \div 10$ (f) $4578 \div 10$

98. *Dividing by Powers of 10* To divide a decimal number by a power of 10 in the form

$$10^k = \underbrace{100 \ldots 0}_{k \text{ zeros}},$$

move the decimal point k places to the left. For example, $123.4 \div 100 = 1.234$. Simplify each expression mentally.

(a) $78.89 \div 100$ (b) $0.05 \div 1000$
(c) $5678 \div 10,000$ (d) $-9.8 \div 1000$
(e) $-101 \div 100,000$ (f) $7.8 \div 100$

APPLICATIONS

99. *Earnings* Earning $100 one day and $75 the next day is equivalent to earning $75 the first day and $100 the second day. What property of real numbers does this example illustrate?

100. *Leasing a Car* An advertisement for a lease on a new car states that it costs $2480 down and $201 per month for 20 months. Mentally calculate the cost of the lease. Explain your reasoning.

101. *Gasoline Mileage* A car travels 198 miles on 10 gallons of gasoline. Mentally calculate the number of miles that the car travels on 1 gallon of gasoline.

102. *Gallons of Water* A wading pool is 50 feet long, 20 feet wide, and 1 foot deep.
(a) Mentally determine the number of cubic feet in the pool. (*Hint:* Volume equals length times width times height.)
(b) One cubic foot equals about 7.5 gallons. Mentally calculate the number of gallons of water in the pool.

103. *Dimensions of a Pool* A small pool of water is 13 feet long, 5 feet wide, and 2 feet deep. The volume V of the pool in cubic feet is found by multiplying 13 by 5 by 2.
(a) To do this calculation mentally, would you multiply $(13 \cdot 5) \cdot 2$ or $13 \cdot (5 \cdot 2)$? Why?
(b) What property allows you to do either calculation and still obtain the correct answer?

104. *Digital Images of Io* The accompanying picture of Jupiter's moon Io is a digital picture, created by using a rectangular pattern of small pixels. This image is 500 pixels wide and 400 pixels high, so the total number of pixels in it is $500 \cdot 400 = 200,000$ pixels. (*Source:* NASA.)

(a) Find the total number of pixels in an image 400 pixels wide and 500 pixels high.
(b) Suppose that a picture is x pixels wide and y pixels high. What property states that it has the same number of pixels as a picture y pixels wide and x pixels high?

WRITING ABOUT MATHEMATICS

105. To determine the cost of tuition, a student tries to compute $16 \cdot \$96$ with a calculator and gets $\$15,360$. How do you know that this computation is not correct?

106. A student performs the following computation by hand.

$$20 - 6 - 2 + 8 \div 4 \div 2 \stackrel{?}{=} 20 - 4 + 8 \div 2$$
$$\stackrel{?}{=} 20 - 4 + 4$$
$$\stackrel{?}{=} 20$$

Find any incorrect steps and explain what is wrong. What is the correct answer?

107. The computation $3 + 10^{20} - 10^{20}$ performed on a calculator gives a result of 0. (Try it.) What is the correct answer? Why is it important to know properties of real numbers even though you have a calculator?

108. Does the "distributive property"

$$a + (b \cdot c) \stackrel{?}{=} (a + b) \cdot (a + c)$$

hold for all numbers a, b, and c? Explain your reasoning.

Group Activity   Working with Real Data

Directions: Form a group of 2 to 4 people. Select someone to record the group's responses for this activity. All members of the group should work cooperatively to answer the questions. If your instructor asks for your results, each member of the group should be prepared to respond.

Winning the Lottery In the multistate lottery game *Powerball,* there are 120,526,770 possible number combinations, only one of which is the grand prize winner. The cost of a single ticket (one number combination) is $1. (*Source:* Powerball.com.)

Suppose that a *very* wealthy person decides to buy tickets for every possible number combination to be assured of winning a $150 million grand prize.

(a) If this individual could purchase one ticket every second, how many hours would it take to buy all of the tickets? How many years is this?

(b) If there were a way for this individual to buy all possible number combinations quickly, discuss reasons why this strategy would probably lose money.

1.8   Simplifying and Writing Algebraic Expressions

Terms • Combining Like Terms • Simplifying Expressions • Writing Expressions

A LOOK INTO MATH ▶

Filing taxes might be easier if several of the complicated tax formulas could be *combined* into a single formula. Furthermore, some of the large formulas might be easier to evaluate if they were *simplified* to be more concise. In mathematics, we *combine like terms* when we *simplify* expressions. In this section, we simplify algebraic expressions.

Terms

One way to simplify expressions is to combine like terms. A **term** is a number, a variable, or a *product* of numbers and variables raised to natural number powers. Examples include

$$4, \quad z, \quad 5x, \quad \frac{2}{5}z, \quad -4xy, \quad -x^2, \quad \text{and} \quad 6x^3y^4. \quad \text{Terms}$$

Terms do not contain addition or subtraction signs, but they can contain negative signs. The **coefficient** of a term is the number that appears in the term. If no number appears, then the coefficient is understood to be either -1 or 1. Table 1.11 on the next page shows examples of terms and their corresponding coefficients.

NEW VOCABULARY

☐ Term
☐ Coefficient
☐ Like terms

- How do you identify the coefficient in a term?

TABLE 1.11 Terms and Coefficients

Term	Coefficient
$\frac{1}{2}xy$	$\frac{1}{2}$
$-z^2$	-1
12	12
$-5w^4$	-5

EXAMPLE 1 **Identifying terms**

Determine whether each expression is a term. If it is a term, identify its coefficient.
(a) 51 **(b)** $5a$ **(c)** $2x + 3y$ **(d)** $-3x^2$

Solution
(a) A number is a term. This term's coefficient is 51.
(b) The product of a number and a variable is a term. This term's coefficient is 5.
(c) The sum (or difference) of two terms is not a term.
(d) The product of a number and a variable with an exponent is a term. This term's coefficient is -3.

Now Try Exercises 7, 9, 11, 13

One of the best ways to prepare for class is to read a section before it is covered by your instructor. Reading ahead gives you the chance to formulate any questions you might have about the concepts in the section.

MAKING CONNECTIONS

Factors and Terms

When variables and numbers are multiplied, they are called *factors*. For example, the expression $4xy$ has factors of 4, x, and y. When variables and numbers are added or subtracted, they are called *terms*. For example, the expression $x - 5xy + 1$ has three terms: x, $-5xy$, and 1.

- Which property of real numbers is used to combine like terms?

Combining Like Terms

Suppose that we have two boards with lengths $2x$ and $3x$, where the value of x could be any length such as 2 feet. See Figure 1.34. Because $2x$ and $3x$ are *like terms* we can find the total length of the two boards by applying the distributive property and *adding like terms*.

$$2x + 3x = (2 + 3)x = 5x$$

The combined length of the two boards is $5x$ units.

Visualizing Like Terms

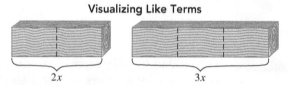

$2x$ $\quad$ $3x$

Figure 1.34 $2x + 3x = 5x$

We can also determine the difference between the lengths of the two boards by *subtracting like terms*.

$$3x - 2x = (3 - 2)x = 1x = x$$

The second board is x units longer than the first board.

If two terms contain the same variables raised to the same powers, we call them **like terms**. We can add or subtract (combine) like terms but cannot combine *unlike* terms. For example, if one board has length $2x$ and the other board has length $3y$, then we cannot determine the total length other than to say that it is $2x + 3y$. See Figure 1.35. The terms $2x$ and $3y$ are unlike terms and *cannot* be combined.

READING CHECK

• How can you tell whether two terms are like terms?

Visualizing Unlike Terms

$2x$ $3y$

Figure 1.35 $2x + 3y$

EXAMPLE 2 **Identifying like terms**

Determine whether the terms are like or unlike.
(a) $-4m, 7m$ (b) $8x^2, 8y^2$ (c) $\frac{1}{2}z, -3z^2$ (d) $5, -4n$

Solution
(a) The variable in both terms is m (with power 1), so they are like terms.
(b) The variables are different, so they are unlike terms.
(c) The term $-3z^2$ contains $z^2 = z \cdot z$, whereas the term $\frac{1}{2}z$ contains only z. Thus they are unlike terms.
(d) The term 5 has no variable, whereas the term $-4n$ contains the variable n. They are unlike terms.

Now Try Exercises 19, 21, 23, 27

EXAMPLE 3 **Combining like terms**

Combine terms in each expression, if possible.
(a) $-3x + 5x$ (b) $-x^2 + 5x^2$ (c) $\frac{1}{2}y - 3y^3$

Solution
(a) Combine terms by applying a distributive property.
$$-3x + 5x = (-3 + 5)x = 2x$$
(b) Note that $-x^2$ can be written as $-1x^2$. They are like terms and can be combined.
$$-x^2 + 5x^2 = (-1 + 5)x^2 = 4x^2$$
(c) They are unlike terms, so they cannot be combined.

Now Try Exercises 31, 39, 43

Simplifying Expressions

The area of a rectangle equals length times width. In Figure 1.36 on the next page the area of the first rectangle is $3x$, the area of the second rectangle is $2x$, and the area of the third rectangle is x. The area of the last rectangle equals the total area of the three smaller rectangles. That is,

$$3x + 2x + x = (3 + 2 + 1)x = 6x.$$

The expression $3x + 2x + x$ can be *simplified* to $6x$.

Use rectangles to explain
how to add $xy + 2xy$.

Simplifying an Expression Visually

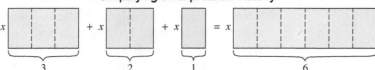

Figure 1.36 $3x + 2x + x = 6x$

EXAMPLE 4   **Simplifying expressions**

Simplify each expression.

(a) $2 + x - 6 + 5x$ **(b)** $2y - (y + 3)$ **(c)** $\dfrac{-1.5x}{-1.5}$

Solution
(a) Combine like terms by applying the properties of real numbers.

$$2 + x - 6 + 5x = 2 + (-6) + x + 5x \qquad \text{Commutative property}$$
$$= 2 + (-6) + (1 + 5)x \qquad \text{Distributive property}$$
$$= -4 + 6x \qquad \text{Add.}$$

(b)
$$2y - 1(y + 3) = 2y + (-1)y + (-1) \cdot 3 \qquad \text{Distributive property}$$
$$= 2y - 1y - 3 \qquad \text{Definition of subtraction}$$
$$= (2 - 1)y - 3 \qquad \text{Distributive property}$$
$$= y - 3 \qquad \text{Subtract.}$$

(c)
$$\frac{-1.5x}{-1.5} = \frac{-1.5}{-1.5} \cdot \frac{x}{1} \qquad \text{Multiplication of fractions}$$
$$= 1 \cdot x \qquad \text{Simplify the fractions.}$$
$$= x \qquad \text{Multiplicative identity}$$

Now Try Exercises 47, 59, 75

NOTE: The expression in Example 4(c) can be simplified directly by using the basic principle of fractions: $\frac{ac}{bc} = \frac{a}{b}$.

EXAMPLE 5   **Simplifying expressions**

Simplify each expression.

(a) $7 - 2(5x - 3)$ **(b)** $3x^3 + 2x^3 - x^3$

(c) $3y^2 - z + 4y^2 - 2z$ **(d)** $\dfrac{12x - 8}{4}$

Solution
(a)
$$7 - 2(5x - 3) = 7 + (-2)(5x + (-3)) \qquad \text{Change subtraction to addition.}$$
$$= 7 + (-2)(5x) + (-2)(-3) \qquad \text{Distributive property}$$
$$= 7 - 10x + 6 \qquad \text{Multiply.}$$
$$= 13 - 10x \qquad \text{Combine like terms.}$$

(b)
$$3x^3 + 2x^3 - x^3 = (3 + 2 - 1)x^3 \qquad \text{Distributive property}$$
$$= 4x^3 \qquad \text{Add and subtract.}$$

(c) $3y^2 - z + 4y^2 - 2z = 3y^2 + 4y^2 + (-1z) + (-2z)$ Commutative property

$\qquad\qquad\qquad\quad = (3 + 4)y^2 + (-1 + (-2))z$ Distributive property

$\qquad\qquad\qquad\quad = 7y^2 - 3z$ Add.

(d) $\qquad\qquad \dfrac{12x - 8}{4} = \dfrac{12x}{4} - \dfrac{8}{4}$ Subtraction of fractions

$\qquad\qquad\qquad = 3x - 2$ Simplify fractions.

▌ Now Try Exercises **57, 65, 71, 79**

Recall that the commutative and associative properties of addition allow us to rearrange a sum in any order. For example, if we write the expression

$$2x - 3 - 4x + 10 \quad \text{as the sum} \quad 2x + (-3) + (-4x) + 10,$$

the terms can be arranged and grouped as

$$(2x + (-4x)) + (-3 + 10).$$

Applying the distributive property and adding within each grouping results in

$$(2 + (-4))x + (-3 + 10) = -2x + 7.$$

Note that the terms in the result can be found directly by combining like (same color) terms in the given expression, where addition indicates that a term is positive and subtraction indicates that a term is negative. In the next example, we simplify an expression in this way.

EXAMPLE 6   **Simplifying an expression directly**

Simplify the expression $6x + 5 - 2x - 8$.

Solution

The like terms and their indicated signs are shown.

$$6x + 5 - 2x - 8$$

By combining like terms, the expression can be simplified as

$$4x - 3.$$

▌ Now Try Exercise **53**

Writing Expressions

▶ **REAL-WORLD CONNECTION** In real-life situations, we often have to translate words to symbols. For example, to calculate federal and state income tax we might have to multiply taxable income by 0.15 and by 0.05 and then find the sum. If we let x represent taxable income, then the total federal and state income tax is $0.15x + 0.05x$. This expression can be simplified with a distributive property.

$$0.15x + 0.05x = (0.15 + 0.05)x$$

$$= 0.20x$$

Thus the total income tax on a taxable income of $x = \$20,000$ would be

$$0.20(20,000) = \$4000.$$

EXAMPLE 7 **Writing and simplifying an expression**

A sidewalk has a constant width w and comprises several short sections with lengths 12, 6, and 5 feet, as illustrated in Figure 1.37.
(a) Write and simplify an expression that gives the number of square feet of sidewalk.
(b) Find the area of the sidewalk if its width is 3 feet.

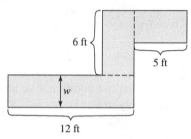

6 ft

5 ft

w

12 ft

Figure 1.37

Solution
(a) The area of each sidewalk section equals its length times its width w. The total area of the sidewalk is
$$12w + 6w + 5w = (12 + 6 + 5)w = 23w.$$

(b) When $w = 3$, the area is $23w = 23 \cdot 3 = 69$ square feet.

▌ Now Try Exercise 89

1.8 Putting It All Together

CONCEPT	COMMENTS	EXAMPLES
Term	A term is a number, variable, or product of numbers and variables raised to natural number powers.	$12, -10, x, -y$ $-3x, 5z, xy, 6x^2$ $10y^3, \frac{3}{4}x, 25xyz^2$
Coefficient of a Term	The coefficient of a term is the number that appears in the term. If no number appears, then the coefficient is either 1 or -1.	12 Coefficient is 12 x Coefficient is 1 $-xy$ Coefficient is -1 $-4x$ Coefficient is -4
Like Terms	Like terms have the same variables raised to the same powers.	$5m$ and $-6m$ x^2 and $-74x^2$ $2xy$ and $-xy$
Combining Like Terms	Like terms can be combined by using a distributive property.	$5x + 2x = (5 + 2)x = 7x$ $y - 3y = (1 - 3)y = -2y$ $8x^2 + x^2 = (8 + 1)x^2 = 9x^2$

1.8 Exercises

MyMathLab   PRACTICE   WATCH   DOWNLOAD   READ   REVIEW

CONCEPTS AND VOCABULARY

1. A(n) _____ is a number, a variable, or a product of numbers and variables raised to natural number powers.

2. The number 7 in the term $7x^2y$ is called the _____ of the term.

3. When variables and numbers are multiplied, they are called _____. When they are added or subtracted, they are called _____.

4. If two terms contain the same variables raised to the same powers, they are (like/unlike) terms.

5. We can add or subtract (like/unlike) terms.

6. We can combine like terms in an expression by applying a(n) _____ property.

LIKE TERMS

Exercises 7–16: Determine whether the expression is a term. If the expression is a term, identify its coefficient.

7. 91

8. -12

9. $-6b$

10. $9z$

11. $x + 10$

12. $20 - 2y$

13. x^2

14. $4x^3$

15. $4x - 5$

16. $5z + 6x$

Exercises 17–28: Determine whether the terms are like or unlike.

17. $6, -8$

18. $2x, 19$

19. $5x, -22x$

20. $19y, -y$

21. $14, 14a$

22. $-33b, -3b$

23. $18x, 18y$

24. $-6a, -6b$

25. $x^2, -15x^2$

26. $y, 19y$

27. $3x^2, \frac{1}{5}x$

28. $12y^2, -y^2$

29. **Thinking Generally** Are the terms $4ab$ and $-3ba$ like or unlike?

30. **Thinking Generally** Are the terms $-xyz^2$ and $3yz^2x$ like or unlike?

Exercises 31–46: Combine terms, if possible.

31. $-4x + 7x$

32. $6x - 8x$

33. $19y - 5y$

34. $22z + z$

35. $28a + 13a$

36. $41b - 17b$

37. $11z - 11z$

38. $4y + 4y$

39. $5x - 7y$

40. $3y + 3z$

41. $5 + 5y$

42. $x + x^2$

43. $5x^2 - 2x^2$

44. $25z^3 - 10z^3$

45. $8y - 10y + y$

46. $4x^2 + x^2 - 5x^2$

SIMPLIFYING AND WRITING EXPRESSIONS

Exercises 47–82: Simplify the expression.

47. $5 + x - 3 + 2x$

48. $x - 5 - 5x + 7$

49. $-\frac{3}{4} + z - 3z + \frac{5}{4}$

50. $\frac{4}{3}z - 100 + 200 - \frac{1}{3}z$

51. $4y - y + 8y$

52. $14z - 15z - z$

53. $-3 + 6z + 2 - 2z$

54. $19a - 12a + 5 - 6$

55. $-2(3z - 6y) - z$

56. $6\left(\frac{1}{2}a - \frac{1}{6}b\right) - 3b$

57. $2 - \frac{3}{4}(4x + 8)$

58. $-5 - (5x - 6)$

59. $-x - (5x + 1)$

60. $2x - 4(x + 2)$

61. $1 - \frac{1}{3}(x + 1)$

62. $-3 - 3(4 - x)$

63. $\frac{3}{5}(x + y) - \frac{1}{5}(x - 1)$

64. $-5(a + b) - (a + b)$

65. $0.2x^2 + 0.3x^2 - 0.1x^2$

66. $32z^3 - 52z^3 + 20z^3$

67. $2x^2 - 3x + 5x^2 - 4x$

68. $\frac{5}{6}y^2 - 4 + \frac{1}{12}y^2 + 3$

69. $a + 3b - a - b$

70. $2z^2 - z - z^2 + 3z$

71. $8x^3 + 7y - x^3 - 5y$

72. $4y - 6z + 2y - 3z$

73. $\dfrac{8x}{8}$

74. $\dfrac{-0.1y}{-0.1}$

75. $\dfrac{-3y}{-y}$

76. $\dfrac{2x}{7x}$

77. $\dfrac{-108z}{-108}$

78. $\dfrac{3xy}{-6xy}$

79. $\dfrac{9x - 6}{3}$

80. $\dfrac{18y + 9}{9}$

81. $\dfrac{14z + 21}{7}$

82. $\dfrac{15x - 20}{5}$

Exercises 83–88: Translate the phrase into a mathematical expression and then simplify. Use the variable x.

83. The sum of five times a number and six times the same number

84. The sum of a number and three times the same number

85. The sum of a number squared and twice the same number squared

86. One-half of a number minus three-fourths of the same number

87. Six times a number minus four times the same number

88. Two cubed times a number minus three squared times the same number

APPLICATIONS

89. *Street Dimensions* (Refer to Example 7.) A street has a constant width w and comprises several straight sections having lengths 600, 400, 350, and 220 feet.

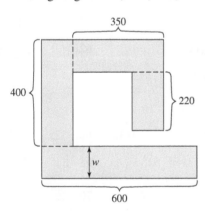

(a) Write a simplified expression that gives the square footage of the street.

(b) Find the area of the street if its width is 42 feet.

90. *Sidewalk Dimensions* A sidewalk has a constant width w and comprises several short sections having lengths 12, 14, and 10 feet.
(a) Write a simplified expression that gives the number of square feet of sidewalk.
(b) Find the area of the sidewalk if its width is 5 feet.

91. *Snowblowers* Two snowblowers are being used to clear a driveway. The first blower can remove 20 cubic feet per minute, and the second blower can remove 30 cubic feet per minute.
(a) Write a simplified expression that gives the number of cubic feet of snow removed in x minutes.
(b) Find the total number of cubic feet of snow removed in 48 minutes.
(c) How many minutes would it take to remove the snow from a driveway that measures 30 feet by 20 feet, if the snow is 2 feet deep?

92. *Winding Rope* Two motors are winding up rope. The first motor can wind up rope at 2 feet per second, and the second motor can wind up rope at 5 feet per second.
(a) Write a simplified expression that gives the length of rope wound by both motors in x seconds.
(b) Find the total length of rope wound up by the two motors in 3 minutes.
(c) How many minutes would it take to wind up 2100 feet of rope by using both motors?

WRITING ABOUT MATHEMATICS

93. The following expression was simplified *incorrectly*.

$$3(x - 5) + 5x \overset{?}{=} 3x - 5 + 5x$$
$$\overset{?}{=} 3x + 5x - 5$$
$$\overset{?}{=} (3 + 5)x - 5$$
$$\overset{?}{=} 8x - 5$$

Find the error and explain what went wrong. What should the final answer be?

94. Explain how to add like terms. What property of real numbers is used?

SECTIONS 1.7 and 1.8   Checking Basic Concepts

1. Use a commutative property to rewrite each expression.
   (a) $y \cdot 18$ (b) $10 + x$

2. Use an associative and a commutative property to simplify $5 \cdot (y \cdot 4)$.

3. Simplify each expression.
   (a) $10 - (5 + x)$ (b) $5(x - 7)$

4. State the property that the equation $5x + 3x = 8x$ illustrates.

5. Simplify $-4xy + 4xy$.

6. Mentally evaluate each expression.
   (a) $32 + 17 + 8 + 3$ (b) $\frac{5}{6} \cdot \frac{7}{8} \cdot \frac{6}{5} \cdot 8$
   (c) $567 - 199$

7. Determine whether the terms are like or unlike.
   (a) $-3x, -3z$ (b) $4x^2, -2x^2$

8. Combine like terms in each expression.
   (a) $5z + 9z$ (b) $5y - 4 - 8y + 7$

9. Simplify each expression.
   (a) $2y - (5y + 3)$
   (b) $-4(x + 3y) + 2(2x - y)$
   (c) $\frac{20x}{20}$ (d) $\frac{35x^2}{x^2}$

10. Write "the sum of three times a number and five times the same number" as a mathematical expression with the variable x and then simplify the expression.

CHAPTER 1   Summary

SECTION 1.1 ■ NUMBERS, VARIABLES, AND EXPRESSIONS

Sets of Numbers

Natural Numbers — $1, 2, 3, 4, \ldots$

Whole Numbers — $0, 1, 2, 3, \ldots$

Products and Factors — Two numbers that are multiplied are called factors and the result is called the product.

Example: $3 \quad \cdot \quad 5 \quad = \quad 15$
Factor   Factor   Product

Prime and Composite Numbers

Prime Number — A natural number greater than 1 whose only natural number factors are itself and 1

Examples: 2, 3, 5, 7, 11, 13, and 17

Composite Number and Prime Factorization — A natural number greater than 1 that is not prime; a composite number can be written as a product of two or more prime numbers.

Examples: $24 = 2 \cdot 2 \cdot 2 \cdot 3$ and $18 = 2 \cdot 3 \cdot 3$

Important Terms

Variable — A symbol or letter that represents an unknown quantity

Examples: $a, b, F, x,$ and y

Algebraic Expression — Consists of numbers, variables, arithmetic symbols, and grouping symbols

Examples: $3x + 1$ and $5(x + 2) - y$

Equation — A statement that two algebraic expressions are equal; an equation always contains an equals sign.

Examples: $1 + 2 = 3$ and $z - 7 = 8$

Formula
A special type of equation that expresses a relationship between two or more quantities.

Examples: $P = 2l + 2w$ and $A = lw$

SECTION 1.2 ■ FRACTIONS

Fractions and Lowest Terms

Fraction
A fraction has a numerator, a denominator, and a fraction bar.

Example:
Numerator $\searrow$
$$\frac{4}{9} \leftarrow \text{Fraction bar}$$
Denominator $\nearrow$

Lowest Terms
A fraction is in lowest terms if the numerator and denominator have no factors in common.

Example: The fraction $\frac{3}{5}$ is in lowest terms because 3 and 5 have no factors in common.

Simplifying Fractions

$$\frac{a \cdot c}{b \cdot c} = \frac{a}{b}$$

Example: $\frac{20}{35} = \frac{4 \cdot 5}{7 \cdot 5} = \frac{4}{7}$

Multiplicative Inverse, or Reciprocal
The reciprocal of a nonzero number a is $\frac{1}{a}$.

Examples: The reciprocal of -5 is $-\frac{1}{5}$, and the reciprocal of $\frac{2x}{y}$ is $\frac{y}{2x}$, provided $x \neq 0$ and $y \neq 0$.

Multiplication and Division

$$\frac{a}{b} \cdot \frac{c}{d} = \frac{ac}{bd} \quad \text{and} \quad \frac{a}{b} \div \frac{c}{d} = \frac{a}{b} \cdot \frac{d}{c}$$
b and d are nonzero. b, c, and d are nonzero.

Examples: $\frac{3}{4} \cdot \frac{7}{5} = \frac{21}{20}$ and $\frac{3}{4} \div \frac{7}{5} = \frac{3}{4} \cdot \frac{5}{7} = \frac{3 \cdot 5}{4 \cdot 7} = \frac{15}{28}$

Addition and Subtraction with Like Denominators

$$\frac{a}{b} + \frac{c}{b} = \frac{a+c}{b} \quad \text{and} \quad \frac{a}{b} - \frac{c}{b} = \frac{a-c}{b}$$

Examples: $\frac{3}{5} + \frac{1}{5} = \frac{3+1}{5} = \frac{4}{5}$ and $\frac{3}{5} - \frac{1}{5} = \frac{3-1}{5} = \frac{2}{5}$

Addition and Subtraction with Unlike Denominators
Write the expressions with the LCD. Then add or subtract the numerators, keeping the denominator unchanged.

Examples: $\frac{2}{9} + \frac{1}{6} = \frac{2}{9} \cdot \frac{2}{2} + \frac{1}{6} \cdot \frac{3}{3} = \frac{4}{18} + \frac{3}{18} = \frac{7}{18}$ LCD is 18.

$\frac{2}{9} - \frac{1}{6} = \frac{2}{9} \cdot \frac{2}{2} - \frac{1}{6} \cdot \frac{3}{3} = \frac{4}{18} - \frac{3}{18} = \frac{1}{18}$

SECTION 1.3 ■ EXPONENTS AND ORDER OF OPERATIONS

Exponential Expression

$$\text{Base} \rightarrow 5^3 \leftarrow \text{Exponent}$$

Example: $3^4 = 3 \cdot 3 \cdot 3 \cdot 3 = 81$

Order of Operations

Use the following order of operations. First perform all calculations within parentheses and absolute values, or above and below the fraction bar.

1. Evaluate all exponential expressions.
2. Do all multiplication and division from *left to right*.
3. Do all addition and subtraction from *left to right*.

NOTE: Negative signs are evaluated after exponents, so $-2^4 = -16$.

Examples:

$$100 - 5^2 \cdot 2 = 100 - 25 \cdot 2 \qquad \text{and} \qquad \frac{4+2}{5-3} \cdot 4 = \frac{6}{2} \cdot 4$$

$$= 100 - 50 \qquad\qquad\qquad\qquad\qquad = 3 \cdot 4$$

$$= 50 \qquad\qquad\qquad\qquad\qquad\qquad = 12$$

SECTION 1.4 ■ REAL NUMBERS AND THE NUMBER LINE

Opposite or Additive Inverse The opposite of the number a is $-a$.

Examples: The opposite of 5 is -5, and the opposite of -8 is $-(-8) = 8$.

Sets of Numbers

Integers $\ldots, -3, -2, -1, 0, 1, 2, 3, \ldots$

Rational Numbers $\frac{p}{q}$, where p and $q \neq 0$ are integers; rational numbers can be written as decimal numbers that either repeat or terminate.

     Examples: $-\frac{3}{4}, 5, -7.6, \frac{6}{3}$, and $\frac{1}{3}$

Real Numbers   Numbers that can be written as decimal numbers

     Examples: $-\frac{3}{4}, 5, -7.6, \frac{6}{3}, \pi, \sqrt{3},$ and $-\sqrt{7}$

Irrational Numbers   Real numbers that are not rational

     Examples: $\pi, \sqrt{3},$ and $-\sqrt{7}$

Average To calculate the average of a set of numbers, find the sum of the numbers and then divide the sum by how many numbers there are in the set.

Example: The average of 4, 5, 20, and 11 is

$$\frac{4 + 5 + 20 + 11}{4} = \frac{40}{4} = 10.$$

We divide by 4 because we are finding the average of 4 numbers.

The Number Line

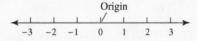

Origin

The origin corresponds to the number 0.

Absolute Value If a is positive or 0, then $|a| = a$, and if a is negative, then $|a| = -a$. The absolute value of a number is *never* negative.

Examples: $|5| = 5, \quad |-5| = 5, \quad$ and $\quad |0| = 0$

Inequality If a is located to the left of b on the number line, then $a < b$. If a is located to the right of b on the number line, then $a > b$.

Examples: $-3 < 6$ and $-1 > -2$

SECTION 1.5 ■ ADDITION AND SUBTRACTION OF REAL NUMBERS

Addition of Opposites

$$a + (-a) = 0$$

Examples: $3 + (-3) = 0$ and $-\frac{5}{7} + \frac{5}{7} = 0$

Addition of Real Numbers
To add two real numbers with *like* signs, do the following.

1. Find the sum of the absolute values of the numbers.
2. Keep the common sign of the two numbers as the sign of the sum.

To add two real numbers with *unlike* signs, do the following.

1. Find the absolute values of the numbers.
2. Subtract the smaller absolute value from the larger absolute value.
3. Keep the sign of the number with the larger absolute value as the sign of the sum.

Examples: $-4 + 5 = 1$, $3 + (-7) = -4$, $-4 + (-2) = -6$,   and $8 + 2 = 10$

Subtraction of Real Numbers For any real numbers a and b, $a - b = a + (-b)$.

Examples: $5 - 9 = 5 + (-9) = -4$ and $-4 - (-3) = -4 + 3 = -1$

SECTION 1.6 ■ MULTIPLICATION AND DIVISION OF REAL NUMBERS

Important Terms

Factors — Numbers multiplied in a multiplication problem

Example: 5 and 4 are factors of 20 because $5 \cdot 4 = 20$.

Product — The answer to a multiplication problem

Example: The product of 5 and 4 is 20.

Dividend, Divisor, and Quotient — If $\frac{a}{b} = c$, then a is the dividend, b is the divisor, and c is the quotient.

Example: In the division problems $30 \div 5 = 6$ and $\frac{30}{5} = 6$, 30 is the dividend, 5 is the divisor, and 6 is the quotient.

Dividing Real Numbers For real numbers a and b with $b \neq 0$,

$$\frac{a}{b} = a \cdot \frac{1}{b}.$$

Examples: $\dfrac{8}{\frac{1}{2}} = \dfrac{8}{1} \cdot \dfrac{2}{1} = 16$, $14 \div \dfrac{2}{3} = \dfrac{14}{1} \cdot \dfrac{3}{2} = \dfrac{42}{2} = 21$,   and $5 \div 0$ is undefined.

Signs of Products or Quotients The product or quotient of two numbers with like signs is positive. The product or quotient of two numbers with unlike signs is negative.

Examples: $-4 \cdot 6 = -24$, $-2 \cdot (-5) = 10$, $\frac{-18}{6} = -3$,   and $-4 \div (-2) = 2$

Writing Fractions as Decimals To write the fraction $\frac{a}{b}$ as a decimal, divide b into a.

Example: $\frac{4}{9} = 0.\overline{4}$ because division of 4 by 9 gives the repeating decimal $0.4444\dots$.

Writing Decimals as Fractions Write the decimal as a fraction with a denominator equal to a power of 10 and then simplify this fraction.

Example: $0.45 = \frac{45}{100} = \frac{9 \cdot 5}{20 \cdot 5} = \frac{9}{20}$

SECTION 1.7 ■ PROPERTIES OF REAL NUMBERS

Important Properties

Commutative

$a + b = b + a$ and $a \cdot b = b \cdot a$

Examples: $3 + 4 = 4 + 3$ and $-6 \cdot 3 = 3 \cdot (-6)$

Associative

$(a + b) + c = a + (b + c)$ and $(a \cdot b) \cdot c = a \cdot (b \cdot c)$

Examples: $(2 + 3) + 4 = 2 + (3 + 4)$
$(2 \cdot 3) \cdot 4 = 2 \cdot (3 \cdot 4)$

Distributive

$a(b + c) = ab + ac$ and $a(b - c) = ab - ac$

Examples: $3(x + 5) = 3 \cdot x + 3 \cdot 5$
$4(5 - 2) = 4 \cdot 5 - 4 \cdot 2$

Identity

$a + 0 = 0 + a = a$ Additive identity is 0.
$a \cdot 1 = 1 \cdot a = a$ Multiplicative identity is 1.

Examples: $5 + 0 = 0 + 5 = 5$ and $1 \cdot (-4) = -4 \cdot 1 = -4$

Inverse

$a + (-a) = 0$ and $-a + a = 0$
$a \cdot \frac{1}{a} = 1$ and $\frac{1}{a} \cdot a = 1$

Examples: $5 + (-5) = 0$ and $\frac{1}{2} \cdot 2 = 1$

NOTE: The commutative and associative properties apply to addition and multiplication but *not* to subtraction and division.

SECTION 1.8 ■ SIMPLIFYING AND WRITING ALGEBRAIC EXPRESSIONS

Important Terms

Term

A term is a number, a variable, or a product of numbers and variables raised to natural number powers.

Examples: 5, $-10x$, $3xy$, and x^2

Coefficient

The number portion of a term

Examples: The coefficients for the terms $3xy$, $-x^2$, and -7 are 3, -1, and -7, respectively.

Like Terms

Terms containing the same variables raised to the same powers; their coefficients may be different.

Examples: The following pairs are like terms:

$5x$ and $-x$; $6x^2$ and $-2x^2$; $3y$ and $-\frac{1}{2}y$.

Combining Like Terms To add or subtract like terms, apply a distributive property.

Examples: $4x + 5x = (4 + 5)x = 9x$ and $5y - 7y = (5 - 7)y = -2y$

CHAPTER 1   Review Exercises

SECTION 1.1

Exercises 1–6: Classify the number as prime, composite, or neither. If the number is composite, write it as a product of prime numbers.

1. 29

2. 27

3. 108

4. 91

5. 0

6. 1

Exercises 7–10: Evaluate the expression for the given values of x and y.

7. $2x - 5$ $\qquad x = 4$

8. $7 - \dfrac{10}{x}$ $\qquad x = 5$

9. $9x - 2y$ $\qquad x = 2, \quad y = 3$

10. $\dfrac{2x}{x - y}$ $\qquad x = 6, \quad y = 4$

Exercises 11–14: Find the value of y for the given values of x and z.

11. $y = x - 5$ $\qquad x = 12$

12. $y = xz + 1$ $\qquad x = 2, \quad z = 3$

13. $y = 4(x - z)$ $\qquad x = 7, \quad z = 5$

14. $y = \dfrac{x + z}{4}$ $\qquad x = 14, \quad z = 10$

Exercises 15–18: Translate the phrase into an algebraic expression. State precisely what each variable represents when appropriate.

15. Three squared increased by five

16. Two cubed divided by the quantity three plus one

17. The product of three and a number

18. The difference between a number and four

SECTION 1.2

Exercises 19 and 20: Find the greatest common factor.

19. 15, 35

20. 12, 30, 42

21. Use the basic principle of fractions to simplify each expression.

(a) $\frac{5 \cdot 7}{8 \cdot 7}$ $\qquad\qquad$ (b) $\frac{3a}{4a}$

22. Simplify each fraction to lowest terms.

(a) $\frac{9}{12}$ $\qquad\qquad$ (b) $\frac{36}{60}$

Exercises 23–30: Multiply and then simplify the result to lowest terms when appropriate.

23. $\frac{3}{4} \cdot \frac{5}{6}$ $\qquad\qquad$ **24.** $\frac{1}{2} \cdot \frac{4}{9}$

25. $\frac{2}{3} \cdot \frac{9}{10}$ $\qquad\qquad$ **26.** $\frac{12}{11} \cdot \frac{22}{23}$

27. $4 \cdot \frac{5}{8}$ $\qquad\qquad$ **28.** $\frac{2}{3} \cdot 9$

29. $\frac{x}{3} \cdot \frac{6}{x}$ $\qquad\qquad$ **30.** $\frac{2}{3} \cdot \frac{9x}{4y}$

31. Find the fractional part: one-fifth of three-sevenths.

32. Find the reciprocal of each number.

(a) 8 $\quad$ (b) 1 $\quad$ (c) $\frac{5}{19}$ $\quad$ (d) $\frac{3}{2}$

Exercises 33–38: Divide and then simplify to lowest terms when appropriate.

33. $\frac{3}{2} \div \frac{1}{6}$ $\qquad\qquad$ **34.** $\frac{9}{10} \div \frac{7}{5}$

35. $8 \div \frac{2}{3}$ $\qquad\qquad$ **36.** $\frac{3}{4} \div 6$

37. $\frac{x}{y} \div \frac{3}{y}$ $\qquad\qquad$ **38.** $\frac{4x}{3y} \div \frac{9x}{5}$

Exercises 39 and 40: Find the least common denominator for the fractions.

39. $\frac{1}{8}, \frac{5}{12}$ $\qquad\qquad$ **40.** $\frac{3}{14}, \frac{1}{21}$

Exercises 41–46: Add or subtract and then simplify to lowest terms when appropriate.

41. $\frac{2}{15} + \frac{3}{15}$ $\qquad\qquad$ **42.** $\frac{5}{4} - \frac{3}{4}$

43. $\frac{11}{12} - \frac{1}{8}$ $\qquad\qquad$ **44.** $\frac{6}{11} - \frac{3}{22}$

45. $\frac{2}{3} - \frac{1}{2} + \frac{1}{4}$ $\qquad\qquad$ **46.** $\frac{1}{6} + \frac{2}{3} - \frac{1}{9}$

SECTION 1.3

Exercises 47–52: Write the expression as an exponential expression.

47. $5 \cdot 5 \cdot 5 \cdot 5 \cdot 5 \cdot 5$ $\qquad$ **48.** $\frac{7}{6} \cdot \frac{7}{6} \cdot \frac{7}{6}$

49. $x \cdot x \cdot x \cdot x \cdot x$ $\qquad\qquad$ **50.** $3 \cdot 3 \cdot 3 \cdot 3$

51. $(x + 1) \cdot (x + 1)$

52. $(a - 5) \cdot (a - 5) \cdot (a - 5)$

53. Use multiplication to rewrite each expression, and then evaluate the result.

(a) 4^3 $\qquad$ (b) 7^2 $\qquad$ (c) 8^1

54. Find a natural number n such that $2^n = 32$.

Exercises 55–66: Evaluate the expression by hand.

55. $7 + 3 \cdot 6$

56. $15 - 5 - 3$

57. $24 \div 4 \div 2$

58. $30 - 15 \div 3$

59. $18 \div 6 - 2$

60. $\frac{18}{4 + 5}$

61. $9 - 3^2$

62. $2^3 - 8$

63. $2^4 - 8 + \frac{4}{2}$

64. $3^2 - 4(5 - 3)$

65. $7 - \frac{4 + 6}{2 + 3}$

66. $3^3 - 2^3$

SECTION 1.4

Exercises 67 and 68: Find the opposite of each expression.

67. (a) -8 **(b)** $-(-(-3))$

68. (a) $-\left(\frac{-3}{7}\right)$ **(b)** $\frac{-2}{-5}$

Exercises 69 and 70: Find the decimal equivalent for the rational number.

69. (a) $\frac{4}{5}$ **(b)** $\frac{3}{20}$

70. (a) $\frac{5}{9}$ **(b)** $\frac{7}{11}$

Exercises 71–76: Classify the number as one or more of the following: natural number, whole number, integer, rational number, or irrational number.

71. 0

72. $-\frac{5}{6}$

73. -7

74. $\sqrt{17}$

75. π

76. 3.4

77. Plot each number on the same number line.
     (a) 0 **(b)** -2 **(c)** $\frac{5}{4}$

78. Evaluate each expression.
     (a) $|-5|$ **(b)** $|-\pi|$ **(c)** $|4 - 4|$

79. Insert the symbol $>$ or $<$ to make each statement true.
     (a) -5 ___ 4 **(b)** $-\frac{1}{2}$ ___ $-\frac{5}{2}$
     (c) -3 ___ $|-9|$ **(d)** $|-8|$ ___ $|-1|$

80. List the numbers $\sqrt{3}, -3, 3, -\frac{2}{3},$ and $\pi - 1$ from least to greatest.

SECTIONS 1.5 AND 1.6

Exercises 81 and 82: (Refer to Example 3 in Section 1.5.) Find the sum visually.

81. $-5 + 9$

82. $4 + (-7)$

Exercises 83 and 84: Use a number line to find the sum.

83. $-1 + 2$

84. $-2 + (-3)$

Exercises 85–96: Evaluate the expression.

85. $5 + (-4)$

86. $-9 - (-7)$

87. $11 \cdot (-4)$

88. $-8 \cdot (-5)$

89. $11 \div (-4)$

90. $-4 \div \frac{4}{7}$

91. $-\frac{5}{9} - \left(-\frac{1}{3}\right)$

92. $-\frac{1}{2} + \left(-\frac{3}{4}\right)$

93. $-\frac{1}{3} \cdot \left(-\frac{6}{7}\right)$

94. $\frac{\frac{4}{5}}{-7}$

95. $-\frac{3}{2} \div \left(-\frac{3}{8}\right)$

96. $\frac{3}{8} \div (-0.5)$

Exercises 97 and 98: Write an arithmetic expression for the given phrase and then simplify.

97. Three plus negative five

98. Subtract negative four from two

Exercises 99 and 100: Write the fraction or mixed number as a decimal.

99. $\frac{7}{9}$

100. $2\frac{1}{5}$

Exercises 101 and 102: Write the decimal number as a fraction in lowest terms.

101. 0.6

102. 0.375

SECTION 1.7

Exercises 103 and 104. Use a commutative property to rewrite the expression. Do not simplify.

103. $3 + 16$

104. $14 \cdot (-x)$

Exercises 105 and 106: Use an associative property to rewrite the expression by changing the parentheses. Do not simplify.

105. $-4 + (1 + 3)$

106. $(x \cdot y) \cdot 5$

Exercises 107 and 108: Use a distributive property to rewrite the expression. Then simplify the expression.

107. $5(x + 12)$

108. $-(a - 3)$

Exercises 109–112: State the property or properties that are illustrated.

109. $y + 0 = y$

110. $b \cdot 1 = b$

111. $\frac{1}{4} \cdot 4 = 1$

112. $-3a + 3a = 0$

Exercises 113–122: State the property that the equation illustrates.

113. $z \cdot 3 = 3z$

114. $6 + (7 + 5x) = (6 + 7) + 5x$

115. $2(5x - 2) = 10x - 4$

116. $5 + x + 3 = 5 + 3 + x$

117. $1 \cdot a = a$ **118.** $3 \cdot (5x) = (3 \cdot 5)x$

119. $12 - (x + 7) = 12 - x - 7$

120. $a + 0 = a$ **121.** $-5x + 5x = 0$

122. $-5 \cdot \left(-\frac{1}{5}\right) = 1$

Exercises 123–128: Use properties of real numbers to evaluate the expression mentally.

123. $7 + 9 + 12 + 8 + 1 + 3$

124. $500 - 199$

125. $25 \cdot 99$ **126.** $4581 + 1999$

127. 54.98×10 **128.** $4356 \div 100$

SECTION 1.8

Exercises 129–132: Determine whether the expression is a term. If the expression is a term, identify its coefficient.

129. $55x$ **130.** $-xy$

131. $9xy + 2z$ **132.** $x - 7$

Exercises 133–144: Simplify the expression.

133. $-10x + 4x$ **134.** $19z - 4z$

135. $3x^2 + x^2$ **136.** $7 + 2x - 6 + x$

137. $-\frac{1}{2} + \frac{3}{2}z - z + \frac{5}{2}$

138. $5(x - 3) - (4x + 3)$

139. $4x^2 - 3 + 5x^2 - 3$ **140.** $3x^2 + 4x^2 - 7x^2$

141. $\dfrac{35a}{7a}$ **142.** $\dfrac{0.5c}{0.5}$

143. $\dfrac{15y + 10}{5}$ **144.** $\dfrac{24x - 60}{12}$

APPLICATIONS

145. *Painting a Wall* Two people are painting a large wall. The first person paints 3 square feet per minute while the second person paints 4 square feet per minute.
  (a) Write a simplified expression that gives the total number of square feet the two people can paint in x minutes.
  (b) Find the number of square feet painted in 1 hour.
  (c) How many minutes would it take for them to paint a wall 8 feet tall and 21 feet wide?

146. *Area of a Triangle* Find the area of the triangle shown.

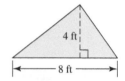

147. *Gallons to Pints* There are 8 pints in 1 gallon. Let $G = 1, 2, 3, \ldots, 6$, and make a table of values that converts G gallons to P pints. Write a formula that converts G gallons to P pints.

148. *Text Messages* The table lists the cost C of sending x text messages after the number of text messages included in a monthly plan is reached. Write an equation that relates C and x.

Texts (x)	1	2	3	4
Cost (C)	$0.05	$0.10	$0.15	$0.20

149. *Aging in the United States* In 2050, about $\frac{1}{5}$ of the population will be age 65 or over and about $\frac{1}{20}$ of the population will be age 85 or over. Estimate the fraction of the population that will be between the ages of 65 and 85 in 2050. (*Source:* U.S. Census Bureau.)

150. *Rule of 72* (Refer to Exercise 79 in Section 1.3.) If an investment of $25,000 earns 9% annual interest, approximate the value of the investment after 24 years.

151. *Carpentry* A board measures $5\frac{3}{4}$ feet and needs to be cut in five equal pieces. Find the length of each piece.

152. *Distance* Over four days, an athlete jogs $3\frac{1}{8}$ miles, $4\frac{3}{8}$ miles, $6\frac{1}{4}$ miles, and $1\frac{5}{8}$ miles. How far does the athlete jog in all?

153. *Checking Account* The initial balance in a checking account is $1652. Find the final balance resulting from the following sequence of withdrawals and deposits: −$78, −$91, $256, and −$638.

154. *Temperature Range* The highest temperature ever recorded in Amarillo, Texas, was 108° F and the lowest was −16° F. Find the difference between these two temperatures. (*Source:* The Weather Almanac.)

155. *Top-Grossing Movies Titanic* (1997) is the sixth top-grossing movie of all time. Find the total admissions for *Titanic* if they were $\frac{16}{25}$ of the total admissions for the top-grossing movie of all time, *Gone With the Wind* (1939), which had total admissions of 202 million. (*Source:* Box Office Mojo.)

CHAPTER 1   Extended and Discovery Exercises

1. *Arithmetic Operations* Insert one of the symbols $+$, $-$, $\cdot$, or $\div$ in each blank to obtain the given answer. Do not use any parentheses.

$$2 \_ 2 \_ 2 \_ 2 = 0$$

$$3 \_ 3 \_ 3 \_ 3 = 10$$

$$4 \_ 4 \_ 4 \_ 4 = 1$$

$$6 \_ 6 \_ 6 \_ 6 = 36$$

$$7 \_ 7 \_ 7 \_ 7 = 63$$

2. *Magic Squares* The following square is called a "magic square" because it contains each of the numbers from 1 to 9 and the numbers in each row, column, and diagonal sum to 15.

8	3	4
1	5	9
6	7	2

Complete the following magic square having 4 rows and 4 columns by arranging the numbers 1 through 16 so that each row, column, and diagonal sums to 34. The four corners will also sum to 34.

	2		13
5			
		6	
4			1

2

Linear Equations and Inequalities

2.1 Introduction to
    Equations
2.2 Linear Equations
2.4 Formulas
2.5 Linear Inequalities

Education is not the filling of a pail, but the lighting of a fire.
— WILLIAM BUTLER YEATS

Mathematics is a unique subject that is essential for describing, or modeling, events in the real world. For example, ultraviolet light from the sun is responsible for both tanning and burning exposed skin. Mathematics lets us use numbers to describe the intensity of ultraviolet light. The table shows the maximum ultraviolet intensity measured in milliwatts per square meter for various latitudes and dates.

Latitude	Mar. 21	June 21	Sept. 21	Dec. 21
0°	325	254	325	272
10°	311	275	280	220
20°	249	292	256	143
30°	179	248	182	80
40°	99	199	127	34
50°	57	143	75	13

If a student from Chicago, located at a latitude of 42°, spends spring break in Hawaii with a latitude of 20°, the sun's ultraviolet rays in Hawaii will be approximately $\frac{249}{99} \approx 2.5$ times as intense as they are in Chicago. Equations can be used to describe, or model, the intensity of the sun at various latitudes. In this chapter we will focus on *linear equations* and the related concept of *linear inequalities*.

Source: J. Williams, *The USA Today Weather Almanac.*

89

2.1 Introduction to Equations

Basic Concepts • Equations and Solutions • The Addition Property of Equality •
The Multiplication Property of Equality

A LOOK INTO MATH ▶

The Global Positioning System (GPS) consists of 24 satellites that travel around Earth in nearly circular orbits. GPS can be used to determine locations and velocities of cars, airplanes, and hikers with an amazing degree of accuracy. New cars often come equipped with GPS, and their drivers can determine their cars' locations to within a few feet. To create GPS, thousands of equations were solved, and mathematics was essential in finding their solutions. In this section we discuss many of the basic concepts needed to solve equations. (*Source:* J. Van Sickle, *GPS for Land Surveyors.*)

Basic Concepts

NEW VOCABULARY

☐ Solution
☐ Solution set
☐ Equivalent equations

▶ REAL-WORLD CONNECTION Suppose that during a storm it rains 2 inches before noon and 1 inch per hour thereafter until 5 P.M. Table 2.1 lists the total rainfall R after various elapsed times x, where $x = 0$ corresponds to noon.

TABLE 2.1 **Rainfall x Hours Past Noon**

Elapsed Time: x (hours)	0	1	2	3	4	5
Total Rainfall: R (inches)	2	3	4	5	6	7

The data suggest that the total rainfall R in inches is 2 more than the elapsed time x. A formula that *models*, or *describes*, the rainfall x hours past noon is given by

$$R = x + 2.$$

For example, 3 hours past noon, or at 3 P.M.,

$$R = 3 + 2 = 5$$

inches of rain have fallen. Even though $x = 4.5$ does not appear in the table, we can calculate the amount of rainfall at 4:30 P.M. with the formula as

$$R = 4.5 + 2 = 6.5 \text{ inches.}$$

The advantage that a formula has over a table of values is that a formula can be used to calculate the rainfall at *any* time x, not just at the times listed in the table.

Equations and Solutions

In the rainfall example above, how can we determine when 6 inches of rain have fallen? From Table 2.1 the *solution* is 4, or 4 P.M. To find this solution without the table, we can *solve* the equation

$$x + 2 = 6.$$

READING CHECK

• What is a solution to an equation?

An equation can be either true or false. For example, the equation $1 + 2 = 3$ is true, whereas the equation $1 + 2 = 4$ is false. When an equation contains a variable, the equation may be true for some values of the variable and false for other values of the variable. Each value of the variable that makes the equation true is called a **solution** to the equation, and the *set of all solutions* is called the **solution set**. *Solving an equation* means finding all of its solutions. Because $4 + 2 = 6$, the solution to the equation

$$x + 2 = 6$$

is 4, and the solution set is {4}. Note that *braces* {} are used to denote a set. Table 2.2 shows examples of equations and their solution sets. Note that some equations, such as the third one in the table, can have more than one solution.

TABLE 2.2 **Equations and Solution Sets**

Equation	Solution Set	True Equation(s)
$3 - x = 1$	{2}	$3 - 2 = 1$
$10 - 4y = 6$	{1}	$10 - 4(1) = 6$
$x^2 = 4$	{-2, 2}	$(-2)^2 = 4$ and $2^2 = 4$

Many times we cannot solve an equation simply by looking at it. In these situations we must use a step-by-step procedure. During each step an equation is transformed into a different but equivalent equation. **Equivalent equations** are equations that have the same solution set. For example, the equations

$$x + 2 = 5 \quad \text{and} \quad x = 3$$

are equivalent equations because the solution set for both equations is {3}.

MAKING CONNECTIONS

Equations and Expressions

Although the words "equation" and "expression" occur frequently in mathematics, they are *not* interchangeable. An equation *always* contains an equals sign but an expression *never* contains an equals sign. We often want to *solve* an equation, whereas an expression can sometimes be *simplified*. Furthermore, the equals sign in an equation separates two expressions. For example, $3x - 5 = x + 1$ is an equation where $3x - 5$ and $x + 1$ are each expressions.

When solving equations, it is often helpful to transform a more complicated equation into an equivalent equation that has an obvious solution, such as $x = 3$. The *addition property of equality* and the *multiplication property of equality* can be used to transform an equation into an equivalent equation that is easier to solve.

The Addition Property of Equality

When solving an equation, we have to apply the same operation to each side of the equation. For example, one way to solve the equation

$$x + 2 = 5$$

is to add -2 to each side. This step results in isolating the x on one side of the equation.

$x + 2 = 5$	Given equation
$x + 2 + (-2) = 5 + (-2)$	Add -2 to each side.
$x + 0 = 3$	Addition of real numbers
$x = 3$	Additive identity

These four equations (on the bottom of the previous page) are equivalent, but the solution is easiest to see in the last equation. When -2 is added to each side of the given equation, the addition property of equality is used.

ADDITION PROPERTY OF EQUALITY

If a, b, and c are real numbers, then

$$a = b \quad \text{is equivalent to} \quad a + c = b + c.$$

That is, adding the same number to each side of an equation results in an equivalent equation.

NOTE: Because any subtraction problem can be changed to an addition problem, *the addition property of equality also works for subtraction.* That is, if the same number is subtracted from each side of an equation, the result is an equivalent equation.

EXAMPLE 1 Using the addition property of equality

Solve each equation.
(a) $x + 10 = 7$ (b) $t - 4 = 3$ (c) $\frac{1}{2} = -\frac{3}{4} + y$

Solution
(a) When solving an equation, we try to isolate the variable on one side of the equation. If we add -10 to (or **subtract 10** from) each side of the equation, we find the value of x.

$x + 10 = 7$	Given equation
$x + 10 - 10 = 7 - 10$	Subtract 10 from each side.
$x + 0 = -3$	Addition of real numbers
$x = -3$	Additive identity

The solution is -3.
(b) To isolate the variable t, **add 4** to each side.

$t - 4 = 3$	Given equation
$t - 4 + 4 = 3 + 4$	Add 4 to each side.
$t + 0 = 7$	Addition of real numbers
$t = 7$	Additive identity

The solution is 7.
(c) To isolate the variable y, **add $\frac{3}{4}$** to each side.

$\frac{1}{2} = -\frac{3}{4} + y$	Given equation
$\frac{1}{2} + \frac{3}{4} = -\frac{3}{4} + \frac{3}{4} + y$	Add $\frac{3}{4}$ to each side.
$\frac{5}{4} = 0 + y$	Addition of real numbers
$\frac{5}{4} = y$	Additive identity

The solution is $\frac{5}{4}$.

Now Try Exercises 17, 19, 23

Equations and Scales

Think of an equation as an old-fashioned scale, where two pans must balance, as shown in the figure. If the two identical golden weights balance the pans, then adding identical red weights to each pan results in the pans remaining balanced. Similarly, removing (subtracting) identical weights from each side will also keep the pans balanced.

CHECKING A SOLUTION To check a solution, substitute it in the *given* equation to find out if a true statement results. To check the solution for Example 1(c), substitute $\frac{5}{4}$ for y in the given equation. Note that a question mark is placed over the equals sign when a solution is being checked.

CRITICAL THINKING

When you are checking a solution, why do you substitute your answer in the *given* equation?

$$\frac{1}{2} = -\frac{3}{4} + y \qquad \text{Given equation}$$

$$\frac{1}{2} \stackrel{?}{=} -\frac{3}{4} + \frac{5}{4} \qquad \text{Replace } y \text{ with } \tfrac{5}{4}.$$

$$\frac{1}{2} \stackrel{?}{=} \frac{2}{4} \qquad \text{Add fractions.}$$

$$\frac{1}{2} = \frac{1}{2} \checkmark \qquad \text{The answer checks.}$$

The answer of $\frac{5}{4}$ checks because the resulting equation is true.

EXAMPLE 2   Solving an equation and checking a solution

Solve the equation $-5 + y = 3$ and then check the solution.

Solution

Isolate y by **adding 5** to each side.

$$-5 + y = 3 \qquad \text{Given equation}$$

$$-5 + 5 + y = 3 + 5 \quad \text{Add 5 to each side.}$$

$$0 + y = 8 \qquad \text{Addition of real numbers}$$

$$y = 8 \qquad \text{Additive identity}$$

The solution is 8. To check this solution, substitute **8** for y in the given equation.

$$-5 + y = 3 \qquad \text{Given equation}$$

$$-5 + 8 \stackrel{?}{=} 3 \qquad \text{Replace } y \text{ with 8.}$$

$$3 = 3 \checkmark \qquad \text{Add; the answer checks.}$$

Now Try Exercise 21

The Multiplication Property of Equality

We can illustrate the multiplication property of equality by considering a formula that converts yards to feet. Because there are 3 feet in 1 yard, the formula $F = 3Y$ computes F, the number of feet in Y yards. For example, if $Y = 5$ yards, then $F = 3 \cdot 5 = 15$ feet.

Now consider the reverse, converting 27 feet to yards. The answer to this conversion corresponds to the solution to the equation

$$27 = 3Y.$$

To find the solution, **multiply** each side of the equation by the reciprocal of 3, or $\frac{1}{3}$.

$$27 = 3Y \qquad \text{Given equation}$$

$$\frac{1}{3} \cdot 27 = \frac{1}{3} \cdot 3 \cdot Y \qquad \text{Multiply each side by } \tfrac{1}{3}.$$

$$9 = 1 \cdot Y \qquad \text{Multiplication of real numbers}$$

$$9 = Y \qquad \text{Multiplicative identity}$$

Thus 27 feet are equivalent to 9 yards.

MULTIPLICATION PROPERTY OF EQUALITY

If a, b, and c are real numbers with $c \neq 0$, then

$$a = b \quad \text{is equivalent to} \quad ac = bc.$$

That is, multiplying each side of an equation by the same nonzero number results in an equivalent equation.

NOTE: Because any division problem can be changed to a multiplication problem, *the multiplication property of equality also works for division.* That is, if each side of an equation is divided by the same nonzero number, the result is an equivalent equation.

READING CHECK

• Why do we use the multiplication property of equality?

EXAMPLE 3 **Using the multiplication property of equality**

Solve each equation.
(a) $\frac{1}{3}x = 4$ **(b)** $-4y = 8$ **(c)** $5 = \frac{3}{4}z$

Solution
(a) We start by **multiplying** each side of the equation by 3, the reciprocal of $\frac{1}{3}$.

$$\frac{1}{3}x = 4 \qquad \text{Given equation}$$

$$3 \cdot \frac{1}{3}x = 3 \cdot 4 \qquad \text{Multiply each side by 3.}$$

$$1 \cdot x = 12 \qquad \text{Multiplication of real numbers}$$

$$x = 12 \qquad \text{Multiplicative identity}$$

The solution is 12.

(b) The coefficient of the y-term is -4, so we can either multiply each side of the equation by $-\frac{1}{4}$ or **divide** each side by -4. This step will make the coefficient of y equal to 1.

$$-4y = 8 \qquad \text{Given equation}$$

$$\frac{-4y}{-4} = \frac{8}{-4} \qquad \text{Divide each side by } -4.$$

$$y = -2 \qquad \text{Simplify fractions.}$$

The solution is -2.

(c) To change the coefficient of z from $\frac{3}{4}$ to 1, **multiply** each side of the equation by $\frac{4}{3}$, the reciprocal of $\frac{3}{4}$.

$$5 = \frac{3}{4}z \qquad \text{Given equation}$$

$$\frac{4}{3} \cdot 5 = \frac{4}{3} \cdot \frac{3}{4}z \qquad \text{Multiply each side by } \frac{4}{3}.$$

$$\frac{20}{3} = 1 \cdot z \qquad \text{Multiplication of real numbers}$$

$$\frac{20}{3} = z \qquad \text{Multiplicative identity}$$

The solution is $\frac{20}{3}$.

Now Try Exercises 37, 43, 45

EXAMPLE 4   **Solving an equation and checking a solution**

Solve the equation $\frac{3}{4} = -\frac{3}{7}t$ and then check the solution.

Solution
Multiply each side of the equation by $-\frac{7}{3}$, the reciprocal of $-\frac{3}{7}$.

$$\frac{3}{4} = -\frac{3}{7}t \qquad \text{Given equation}$$

$$-\frac{7}{3} \cdot \frac{3}{4} = -\frac{7}{3} \cdot \left(-\frac{3}{7}\right)t \qquad \text{Multiply each side by } -\frac{7}{3}.$$

$$-\frac{7}{4} = 1 \cdot t \qquad \text{Multiplication of real numbers}$$

$$-\frac{7}{4} = t \qquad \text{Multiplicative identity}$$

The solution is $-\frac{7}{4}$. To check this answer, substitute $-\frac{7}{4}$ for t in the given equation.

$$\frac{3}{4} = -\frac{3}{7}t \qquad \text{Given equation}$$

$$\frac{3}{4} \stackrel{?}{=} -\frac{3}{7} \cdot \left(-\frac{7}{4}\right) \qquad \text{Replace } t \text{ with } -\frac{7}{4}.$$

$$\frac{3}{4} = \frac{3}{4} \checkmark \qquad \text{Multiply; the answer checks.}$$

Now Try Exercise 47

▶ **REAL-WORLD CONNECTION** Twitter is a microblogging Web site that is used to post short messages called "tweets" on the Internet. In its early years, Twitter's popularity increased dramatically and new accounts were added at an amazing rate. People from around the world began posting millions of tweets every day. (*Source:* Twitter.)

EXAMPLE 5   **Analyzing Twitter account data**

In the early months of 2010, Twitter added 0.3 million new accounts every day.
(a) Write a formula that gives the number of new Twitter accounts T added in x days.
(b) At this rate, how many days would be needed to add 18 million new accounts?

Solution
(a) In 1 day $0.3 \cdot 1 = 0.3$ million new accounts were added, in 2 days $0.3 \cdot 2 = 0.6$ million new accounts were added, and in x days $0.3 \cdot x = 0.3x$ new accounts were added. So the formula is $T = 0.3x$, where x is in days and T is in millions.
(b) To find the number of days needed for Twitter to add 18 million new accounts, replace the variable T in the formula with 18 and solve the resulting equation.

$$T = 0.3x \quad \text{Formula from part (a)}$$

$$18 = 0.3x \quad \text{Replace } T \text{ with 18.}$$

$$\frac{18}{0.3} = \frac{0.3x}{0.3} \quad \text{Divide each side by 0.3.}$$

$$60 = x \quad \text{Simplify.}$$

At this rate, it takes 60 days to add 18 million accounts.

▌ Now Try Exercise 59

2.1   Putting It All Together

CONCEPT	COMMENTS	EXAMPLES
Equation	An equation is a mathematical statement that two expressions are equal. An equation can be either true or false.	The equation $2 + 3 = 5$ is true. The equation $1 + 3 = 7$ is false.
Solution	A value for a variable that makes an equation a true statement	The solution to $x + 5 = 20$ is 15, and the solutions to $x^2 = 9$ are -3 and 3.
Solution Set	The set of all solutions to an equation	The solution set to $x + 5 = 20$ is $\{15\}$, and the solution set to $x^2 = 9$ is $\{-3, 3\}$.
Equivalent Equations	Two equations are equivalent if they have the same solution set.	The equations $$2x = 14 \quad \text{and} \quad x = 7$$ are equivalent because the solution set to both equations is $\{7\}$.

CONCEPT	COMMENTS	EXAMPLES
Addition Property of Equality	The equations $$a = b \quad \text{and} \quad a + c = b + c$$ are equivalent. This property is used to solve equations.	To solve $x - 3 = 8$, add 3 to each side of the equation. $$x - 3 + 3 = 8 + 3$$ $$x = 11$$ The solution is 11.
Multiplication Property of Equality	When $c \neq 0$, the equations $$a = b \quad \text{and} \quad a \cdot c = b \cdot c$$ are equivalent. This property is used to solve equations.	To solve $\frac{1}{5}x = 10$, multiply each side of the equation by 5. $$5 \cdot \frac{1}{5}x = 5 \cdot 10$$ $$x = 50$$ The solution is 50.
Checking a Solution	Substitute the solution for the variable in the given equation and then simplify each side to see if a true statement results.	To show that 8 is a solution to $$x + 12 = 20,$$ substitute 8 for x. $$8 + 12 \overset{?}{=} 20$$ $$20 = 20 \quad \text{True}$$

2.1 Exercises

MyMathLab Math XL PRACTICE   WATCH   DOWNLOAD   READ   REVIEW

CONCEPTS AND VOCABULARY

1. Each value of a variable that makes an equation true is called a(n) _____.

2. The equation $1 + 3 = 4$ is (true/false).

3. The equation $2 + 3 = 6$ is (true/false).

4. The _____ is the set of all solutions to an equation.

5. To solve an equation, find all _____.

6. Equations with the same solution set are called _____ equations.

7. If $a = b$, then $a + c = $ _____.

8. Because any subtraction problem can be changed to an addition problem, the addition property of equality also works for _____.

9. If $a = b$ and $c \neq 0$, then $ac = $ _____.

10. Because any division problem can be changed to a multiplication problem, the multiplication property of equality also works for _____.

11. To solve an equation, transform the equation into a(n) _____ equation that is easier to solve.

12. To check a solution, substitute it for the variable in the _____ equation.

THE ADDITION PROPERTY OF EQUALITY

13. To solve $x - 22 = 4$, add _____ to each side.

14. To solve $\frac{5}{6} = \frac{1}{6} + x$, add _____ to each side.

15. To solve $x + 3 = 13$, subtract _____ from each side.

16. To solve $\frac{3}{4} = \frac{1}{4} + x$, subtract _____ from each side.

Exercises 17–30: Solve the equation. Check your answer.

17. $x + 5 = 0$ **18.** $x + 3 = 7$

19. $a - 12 = -3$ **20.** $a - 19 = -11$

21. $9 = y - 8$ **22.** $97 = -23 + y$

23. $\frac{1}{5} = z - \frac{3}{2}$ **24.** $\frac{3}{4} + z = -\frac{1}{2}$

25. $t - 0.8 = 4.3$ **26.** $y - 1.23 = -0.02$

27. $4 + x = 1$ **28.** $16 + x = -2$

29. $1 = \frac{1}{3} + y$ **30.** $\frac{7}{2} = -2 + y$

31. Thinking Generally To solve $x - a = b$ for x, add _____ to each side.

32. Thinking Generally To solve $x + a = b$ for x, subtract _____ from each side.

THE MULTIPLICATION PROPERTY OF EQUALITY

33. To solve $5x = 4$, multiply each side by _____.

34. To solve $\frac{4}{3}y = 8$, multiply each side by _____.

35. To solve $6x = 11$, divide each side by _____.

36. To solve $0.2x = 4$, divide each side by _____.

Exercises 37–52: Solve the equation. Check your answer.

37. $5x = 15$ **38.** $-2x = 8$

39. $-7x = 0$ **40.** $25x = 0$

41. $-35 = -5a$ **42.** $-32 = -4a$

43. $-18 = 3a$ **44.** $-70 = 10a$

45. $\frac{1}{2}x = \frac{3}{2}$ **46.** $\frac{3}{4}x = \frac{5}{8}$

47. $\frac{1}{2} = \frac{2}{5}z$ **48.** $-\frac{3}{4} = -\frac{1}{8}z$

49. $0.5t = 3.5$ **50.** $2.2t = -9.9$

51. $-1.7 = 0.2x$ **52.** $6.4 = 1.6x$

53. Thinking Generally To solve $\frac{1}{a} \cdot x = b$ for x, multiply each side by _____.

54. Thinking Generally To solve $ax = b$ for x, where $a \neq 0$, divide each side by _____.

APPLICATIONS

55. *Rainfall* On a stormy day it rains 3 inches before noon and $\frac{1}{2}$ inch per hour thereafter until 6 P.M.
 (a) Make a table that shows the total rainfall R in inches, x hours past noon, ending at 6 P.M.
 (b) Write a formula that calculates R.

 (c) Use your formula to calculate the total rainfall at 3 P.M. Does the answer agree with the value in your table from part (a)?
 (d) How much rain has fallen by 2:15 P.M.?

56. *Cold Weather* A furnace is turned on at midnight when the temperature inside a cabin is 0° F. The cabin warms at a rate of 10° F per hour until 7 A.M.
 (a) Make a table that shows the cabin temperature T in degrees Fahrenheit, x hours past midnight, ending at 7 A.M.
 (b) Write a formula that calculates T.
 (c) Use your formula to calculate the temperature at 5 A.M. Does the answer agree with the value in your table from part (a)?
 (d) Find the cabin temperature at 2:45 A.M.

57. *Football Field* A football field is 300 feet long.
 (a) Write a formula that gives the length L in feet of x football fields.
 (b) Use your formula to write an equation whose solution gives the number of football fields in 870 feet.
 (c) Solve your equation from part (b).

58. *Acreage* An acre equals 43,560 square feet.
 (a) Write a formula that converts A acres to S square feet.
 (b) Use your formula to write an equation whose solution gives the number of acres in 871,200 square feet.
 (c) Solve your equation from part (b).

59. *Twitter Accounts* (Refer to Example 5.) In the early months of 2010, Twitter added 0.3 million new accounts every day. At this rate, how many days would be needed to add 15 million new Twitter accounts? (*Source:* Twitter.)

60. *Web Site Visits* If a Web site was increasing its number of visitors by 14,000 every day, how many days would it take for the site to gain a total of 98,000 new visitors?

61. Online Exploration The city of Winnipeg is located in the province of Manitoba in Canada.
 (a) Use the Internet to find the latitude of Winnipeg to the nearest degree.
 (b) Use the table on page 89 to determine how many times as intense the sun's ultraviolet rays are at the equator (latitude 0°) on March 21 compared to the sun's intensity in Winnipeg. Round your answer to 1 decimal place.

62. Online Exploration Columbus is a city located in the center of Ohio. It is the state's capital city.
 (a) Use the Internet to find the latitude of Columbus to the nearest degree.

(b) Use the table on page 89 to determine how many times as intense the sun's ultraviolet rays are in Limon, Costa Rica, (latitude 10°N) on June 21 compared to the sun's intensity in Columbus. Round your answer to 1 decimal place.

63. *Cost of a Car* When the cost of a car is multiplied by 0.07 the result is $1750. Find the cost of the car.

64. *Raise in Salary* If an employee's salary is multiplied by 1.06, which corresponds to a 6% raise, the result is $58,300. Find the employee's current salary.

WRITING ABOUT MATHEMATICS

65. A student solves an equation as follows.

$$x + 30 = 64$$
$$x \overset{?}{=} 64 + 30$$
$$x \overset{?}{=} 94$$

Identify the student's mistake. What is the solution?

66. What is a good first step for solving the equation $\frac{a}{b}x = 1$, where a and b are natural numbers? What is the solution? Explain your answers.

2.2   Linear Equations

Basic Concepts • Solving Linear Equations • Applying the Distributive Property • Clearing Fractions and Decimals • Equations with No Solutions or Infinitely Many Solutions

A LOOK INTO MATH ▶

Billions of dollars are spent each year to solve equations that lead to the creation of better products. If our society could not solve equations, we would not have HDTV, high-speed Internet, satellites, fiber optics, CAT scans, smart phones, or accurate weather forecasts. In this section we discuss *linear equations* and some of their applications. Linear equations can always be solved by hand.

NEW VOCABULARY

☐ Linear equation
☐ Identity
☐ Contradiction

Basic Concepts

Suppose that a bicyclist is 5 miles from home, riding *away* from home at 10 miles per hour, as shown in Figure 2.1. The distance between the bicyclist and home for various elapsed times is shown in Table 2.3.

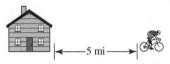

Figure 2.1 Distance from Home

TABLE 2.3 Distance from Home

Elapsed Time (hours)	0	1	2	3
Distance (miles)	5	15	25	35

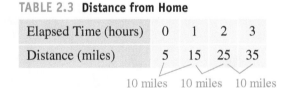

The bicyclist is moving at a constant speed, so the distance increases by 10 miles every hour. The distance D from home after x hours can be calculated by the formula

$$D = 10x + 5.$$

For example, after 2 hours the distance is

$$D = 10(2) + 5 = 25 \text{ miles.}$$

Table 2.3 verifies that the bicyclist is 25 miles from home after 2 hours. However, the table is less helpful if we want to find the elapsed time when the bicyclist is 18 miles from home. To answer this question, we could begin by substituting 18 for D in the formula to obtain the equation

$$18 = 10x + 5.$$

The equation $18 = 10x + 5$ can be written in a different form by applying the addition property of equality. Subtracting 18 from each side gives an equivalent equation.

$$18 - 18 = 10x + 5 - 18 \qquad \text{Subtract 18 from each side.}$$
$$0 = 10x - 13 \qquad \text{Simplify.}$$
$$10x - 13 = 0 \qquad \text{Rewrite the equation.}$$

Even though these steps did not result in a solution to the equation $18 = 10x + 5$, applying the addition property of equality allowed us to rewrite the equation as $10x - 13 = 0$, which is an example of a *linear equation*. (See Example 3(a) for a solution to the equation $10x - 13 = 0$.) Linear equations can model applications in which things move or change at a constant rate.

LINEAR EQUATION IN ONE VARIABLE

A **linear equation** in one variable is an equation that can be written in the form

$$ax + b = 0,$$

where a and b are constants with $a \neq 0$.

If an equation is linear, writing it in the form $ax + b = 0$ should not require any properties or processes other than the following.

- using the distributive property to clear any parentheses
- combining like terms
- applying the addition property of equality

For example, the equation $18 = 10x + 5$ is linear because applying the addition property of equality results in $10x - 13 = 0$, as shown above.

Table 2.4 gives examples of linear equations and values for a and b.

TABLE 2.4 **Linear Equations**

Equation	In $ax + b = 0$ Form	a	b
$x = 1$	$x - 1 = 0$	1	-1
$-5x + 4 = 3$	$-5x + 1 = 0$	-5	1
$2.5x = 0$	$2.5x + 0 = 0$	2.5	0

READING CHECK

- Name three things that tell you that an equation is not a linear equation.

NOTE: An equation *cannot* be written in the form $ax + b = 0$ if after clearing parentheses and combining like terms, any of the following statements are true.

1. The variable has an exponent other than 1.
2. The variable appears in a denominator of a fraction.
3. The variable appears under the symbol $\sqrt{}$ or within an absolute value.

EXAMPLE 1   **Determining whether an equation is linear**

Determine whether the equation is linear. If the equation is linear, give values for a and b that result when the equation is written in the form $ax + b = 0$.

(a) $4x + 5 = 0$ **(b)** $5 = -\frac{3}{4}x$ **(c)** $4x^2 + 6 = 0$ **(d)** $\frac{3}{x} + 5 = 0$

Solution

(a) The equation is linear because it is in the form $ax + b = 0$ with $a = 4$ and $b = 5$.

(b) The equation can be rewritten as follows.

$$5 = -\frac{3}{4}x \qquad \text{Given equation}$$

$$\frac{3}{4}x + 5 = \frac{3}{4}x + \left(-\frac{3}{4}x\right) \qquad \text{Add } \tfrac{3}{4}x \text{ to each side.}$$

$$\frac{3}{4}x + 5 = 0 \qquad \text{Additive inverse}$$

The given equation is linear because it can be written in the form $ax + b = 0$ with $a = \frac{3}{4}$ and $b = 5$.

NOTE: If 5 had been subtracted from each side, the result would be $0 = -\frac{3}{4}x - 5$, which is an equivalent linear equation with $a = -\frac{3}{4}$ and $b = -5$.

(c) The equation is *not* linear because it cannot be written in the form $ax + b = 0$. The variable has exponent 2.

(d) The equation is *not* linear because it cannot be written in the form $ax + b = 0$. The variable appears in the denominator of a fraction.

Now Try Exercises 9, 11, 13, 15

Solving Linear Equations

Every linear equation has *exactly one* solution. Showing that this is true is left as an exercise (see Exercise 59). Solving a linear equation means finding the value of the variable that makes the equation true.

SOLVING LINEAR EQUATIONS NUMERICALLY One way to solve a linear equation is to make a table of values. A table provides an organized way of checking possible values of the variable to see if there is a value that makes the equation true. For example, if we want to solve the equation

$$2x - 5 = -7,$$

we substitute various values for x in the left side of the equation. If one of these values results in -7, then the value makes the equation true and is the solution. In the next example a table of values is used to solve this equation.

EXAMPLE 2 **Using a table to solve an equation**

Complete Table 2.5 for the given values of x. Then solve the equation $2x - 5 = -7$.

TABLE 2.5

x	-3	-2	-1	0	1	2	3
$2x - 5$	-11						

Solution

To complete the table, substitute $x = -2, -1, 0, 1, 2$, and 3 into the expression $2x - 5$. For example, if $x = -2$, then $2x - 5 = 2(-2) - 5 = -9$. The other values shown in Table 2.6 on the next page can be found similarly.

TECHNOLOGY NOTE

Graphing Calculators and Tables

Many graphing calculators have the capability to make tables. Table 2.6 is shown in the accompanying figure.

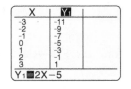

CALCULATOR HELP

To make a table on a calculator, see Appendix A (pages AP-2 and AP-3).

STUDY TIP

We will be solving equations throughout the remainder of the text. Spend a little extra time practicing these steps so that they are familiar and easy to recall when needed later.

TABLE 2.6

x	-3	-2	-1	0	1	2	3
$2x - 5$	-11	-9	-7	-5	-3	-1	1

From the table, $2x - 5$ equals -7 when $x = -1$. So the solution to $2x - 5 = -7$ is -1.

Now Try Exercise 25

SOLVING LINEAR EQUATIONS SYMBOLICALLY Although tables can be used to solve some linear equations, the process of creating a table that contains the solution can take a significant amount of time. For example, the solution to the equation $9x - 4 = 0$ is $\frac{4}{9}$. However, creating a table that reveals this solution would be quite challenging.

The following strategy, which involves the addition and multiplication properties of equality, is a method for solving linear equations symbolically.

SOLVING A LINEAR EQUATION SYMBOLICALLY

STEP 1: Use the distributive property to clear any parentheses on each side of the equation. Combine any like terms on each side.

STEP 2: Use the addition property of equality to get all of the terms containing the variable on one side of the equation and all other terms on the other side of the equation. Combine any like terms on each side.

STEP 3: Use the multiplication property of equality to isolate the variable by multiplying each side of the equation by the reciprocal of the number in front of the variable (or divide each side by that number).

STEP 4: Check the solution by substituting it in the given equation.

When a linear equation does not contain parentheses, we can start with the second step in the strategy shown above. This is the case for the equations in the next example.

EXAMPLE 3   **Solving linear equations**

Solve each linear equation. Check the answer for part (b).
(a) $10x - 13 = 0$ **(b)** $\frac{1}{2}x + 3 = 6$ **(c)** $5x + 7 = 2x + 3$

Solution
(a) First, isolate the x-term on the left side of the equation by adding 13 to each side.

$$10x - 13 = 0 \qquad \text{Given equation}$$
$$10x - 13 + 13 = 0 + 13 \qquad \text{Add 13 to each side. (Step 2)}$$
$$10x = 13 \qquad \text{Add the real numbers.}$$

To obtain a coefficient of 1 on the x-term, divide each side by 10.

$$\frac{10x}{10} = \frac{13}{10} \qquad \text{Divide each side by 10. (Step 3)}$$

$$x = \frac{13}{10} \qquad \text{Simplify.}$$

The solution is $\frac{13}{10}$.

(b) Start by subtracting 3 from each side.

$$\frac{1}{2}x + 3 = 6 \qquad \text{Given equation}$$

$$\frac{1}{2}x + 3 - 3 = 6 - 3 \qquad \text{Subtract 3 from each side. (Step 2)}$$

$$\frac{1}{2}x = 3 \qquad \text{Subtract the real numbers.}$$

$$2 \cdot \frac{1}{2}x = 2 \cdot 3 \qquad \text{Multiply each side by 2. (Step 3)}$$

$$x = 6 \qquad \text{Multiply the real numbers.}$$

The solution is 6. To check it, substitute **6** for x in the equation, $\frac{1}{2}x + 3 = 6$.

$$\frac{1}{2} \cdot 6 + 3 \stackrel{?}{=} 6 \qquad \text{Replace } x \text{ with 6. (Step 4)}$$

$$3 + 3 \stackrel{?}{=} 6 \qquad \text{Multiply.}$$

$$6 = 6 \checkmark \qquad \text{Add; the answer checks.}$$

(c) Since this equation has two x-terms, we need to get all x-terms on one side of the equation and all real numbers on the other side. To do this, begin by subtracting $2x$ from each side.

$$5x + 7 = 2x + 3 \qquad \text{Given equation}$$
$$5x - 2x + 7 = 2x - 2x + 3 \qquad \text{Subtract } 2x \text{ from each side. (Step 2)}$$
$$3x + 7 = 3 \qquad \text{Combine like terms.}$$
$$3x + 7 - 7 = 3 - 7 \qquad \text{Subtract 7 from each side. (Step 2)}$$
$$3x = -4 \qquad \text{Simplify.}$$
$$\frac{3x}{3} = \frac{-4}{3} \qquad \text{Divide each side by 3. (Step 3)}$$
$$x = -\frac{4}{3} \qquad \text{Simplify the fractions.}$$

The solution is $-\frac{4}{3}$.

Now Try Exercises 31, 33, 37

▶ **REAL-WORLD CONNECTION** In recent years, the number of worldwide Internet users has increased at a constant rate. Recall that linear equations are often used to model situations that exhibit a constant rate of change. In the next example we solve a linear equation that models Internet use.

EXAMPLE 4 **Estimating numbers of worldwide Internet users**

The number of Internet users I in millions during year x can be approximated by the formula

$$I = 241x - 482,440,$$

where $x \geq 2007$. Estimate the year when there were 2210 million (2.21 billion) Internet users. (*Source:* Internet World Stats.)

Solution

Let $I = 2210$ in the formula $I = 241x - 482{,}440$ and solve for x.

$$2210 = 241x - 482{,}440 \qquad \text{Equation to be solved}$$

$$484{,}650 = 241x \qquad \text{Add 482,440 to each side.}$$

$$\frac{484{,}650}{241} = \frac{241x}{241} \qquad \text{Divide each side by 241.}$$

$$\frac{484{,}650}{241} = x \qquad \text{Simplify.}$$

$$x \approx 2011 \qquad \text{Approximate.}$$

During 2011 the number of Internet users reached 2210 million.

Now Try Exercise 73

READING CHECK

• In the strategy for solving linear equations symbolically, which step involves the use of the distributive property?

Applying the Distributive Property

Sometimes the distributive property is helpful in solving linear equations. The next example demonstrates how to apply the distributive property in such situations. Use of the distributive property appeared in Step 1 of the strategy for solving linear equations discussed earlier.

EXAMPLE 5 Applying the distributive property

Solve each linear equation. Check the answer for part (a).
(a) $4(x - 3) + x = 0$ **(b)** $2(3z - 4) + 1 = 3(z + 1)$

Solution

(a) Begin by applying the distributive property.

$$4(x - 3) + x = 0 \qquad \text{Given equation}$$

$$4x - 12 + x = 0 \qquad \text{Distributive property (Step 1)}$$

$$5x - 12 = 0 \qquad \text{Combine like terms.}$$

$$5x - 12 + 12 = 0 + 12 \qquad \text{Add 12 to each side. (Step 2)}$$

$$5x = 12 \qquad \text{Add the real numbers.}$$

$$\frac{5x}{5} = \frac{12}{5} \qquad \text{Divide each side by 5. (Step 3)}$$

$$x = \frac{12}{5} \qquad \text{Simplify.}$$

To see if $\frac{12}{5}$ is the solution, substitute $\frac{12}{5}$ for x in the equation $4(x - 3) + x = 0$.

$$4\left(\frac{12}{5} - 3\right) + \frac{12}{5} \stackrel{?}{=} 0 \qquad \text{Replace } x \text{ with } \frac{12}{5}. \text{ (Step 4)}$$

$$4\left(\frac{12}{5} - \frac{15}{5}\right) + \frac{12}{5} \stackrel{?}{=} 0 \qquad \text{Common denominator}$$

$$4\left(-\frac{3}{5}\right) + \frac{12}{5} \stackrel{?}{=} 0 \qquad \text{Subtract within parentheses.}$$

$$-\frac{12}{5} + \frac{12}{5} \stackrel{?}{=} 0 \qquad \text{Multiply.}$$

$$0 = 0 \checkmark \qquad \text{Add; the answer checks.}$$

(b) Begin by applying the distributive property to each side of the equation. Then get all z-terms on the left side and terms containing only real numbers on the right side.

$$2(3z - 4) + 1 = 3(z + 1) \quad \text{Given equation}$$
$$6z - 8 + 1 = 3z + 3 \quad \text{Distributive property (Step 1)}$$
$$6z - 7 = 3z + 3 \quad \text{Add the real numbers.}$$
$$3z - 7 = 3 \quad \text{Subtract } 3z \text{ from each side. (Step 2)}$$
$$3z = 10 \quad \text{Add 7 to each side. (Step 2)}$$
$$\frac{3z}{3} = \frac{10}{3} \quad \text{Divide each side by 3. (Step 3)}$$
$$z = \frac{10}{3} \quad \text{Simplify.}$$

The solution is $\frac{10}{3}$.

Now Try Exercises 43, 45

- Why do some people prefer to clear fractions or decimals from an equation?

Clearing Fractions and Decimals

Some people prefer to do calculations without fractions or decimals. For this reason, clearing an equation of fractions or decimals before solving it can be helpful. To clear fractions or decimals, multiply each side of the equation by the least common denominator (LCD).

EXAMPLE 6   **Clearing fractions from linear equations**

Solve each linear equation.
(a) $\frac{1}{7}x - \frac{5}{7} = \frac{3}{7}$ **(b)** $\frac{2}{3}x - \frac{1}{6} = x$

Solution
(a) Multiply each side of the equation by the LCD 7 to clear (remove) fractions.

$$\frac{1}{7}x - \frac{5}{7} = \frac{3}{7} \quad \text{Given equation}$$
$$7\left(\frac{1}{7}x - \frac{5}{7}\right) = 7 \cdot \frac{3}{7} \quad \text{Multiply each side by 7.}$$
$$\frac{7}{1} \cdot \frac{1}{7}x - \frac{7}{1} \cdot \frac{5}{7} = \frac{7}{1} \cdot \frac{3}{7} \quad \text{Distributive property}$$
$$x - 5 = 3 \quad \text{Simplify.}$$
$$x = 8 \quad \text{Add 5 to each side.}$$

The solution is 8.
(b) The LCD for 3 and 6 is 6. Multiply each side of the equation by 6.

$$\frac{2}{3}x - \frac{1}{6} = x \quad \text{Given equation}$$
$$6\left(\frac{2}{3}x - \frac{1}{6}\right) = 6 \cdot x \quad \text{Multiply each side by 6.}$$
$$\frac{6}{1} \cdot \frac{2}{3}x - \frac{6}{1} \cdot \frac{1}{6} = 6 \cdot x \quad \text{Distributive property}$$
$$4x - 1 = 6x \quad \text{Simplify.}$$
$$-1 = 2x \quad \text{Subtract } 4x \text{ from each side.}$$
$$-\frac{1}{2} = x \quad \text{Divide each side by 2.}$$

The solution is $-\frac{1}{2}$.

Now Try Exercises 53, 55

EXAMPLE 7 **Clearing decimals from a linear equation**

Solve each linear equation.
(a) $0.2x - 0.7 = 0.4$ **(b)** $0.01x - 0.42 = -0.2x$

Solution
(a) The least common denominator for 0.2, 0.7, and 0.4 $\left(\text{or } \frac{2}{10}, \frac{7}{10}, \text{ and } \frac{4}{10}\right)$ is 10. Multiply each side by 10. When multiplying by 10, move the decimal point 1 place to the right.

$0.2x - 0.7 = 0.4$	Given equation
$10(0.2x - 0.7) = 10(0.4)$	Multiply each side by 10.
$10(0.2x) - 10(0.7) = 10(0.4)$	Distributive property
$2x - 7 = 4$	Simplify.
$2x = 11$	Add 7 to each side.
$x = \dfrac{11}{2}$	Divide each side by 2.

The solution is $\frac{11}{2}$, or 5.5.

(b) The least common denominator for 0.01, 0.42, and 0.2 $\left(\text{or } \frac{1}{100}, \frac{42}{100}, \text{ and } \frac{2}{10}\right)$ is 100. Multiply each side by 100. To do this move the decimal point 2 places to the right.

$0.01x - 0.42 = -0.2x$	Given equation
$100(0.01x - 0.42) = 100(-0.2x)$	Multiply each side by 100.
$100(0.01x) - 100(0.42) = 100(-0.2x)$	Distributive property
$x - 42 = -20x$	Simplify.
$x - 42 + 20x + 42 = -20x + 20x + 42$	Add 20x and 42.
$21x = 42$	Combine like terms.
$x = 2$	Divide each side by 21.

The solution is 2.

▌ Now Try Exercises 49, 51

Equations with No Solutions or Infinitely Many Solutions

Some equations that appear to be linear are not because when they are written in the form $ax + b = 0$ the value of a is 0 and no x-term appears. This type of equation can have no solutions or infinitely many solutions. An example of an equation that has no solutions is

$$x = x + 1$$

because a number x cannot equal itself plus 1. If we attempt to solve this equation by subtracting x from each side, we obtain the equation $0 = 1$, which has no x-term and is *always false*. An equation that is always false has no solutions.

An example of an equation with infinitely many solutions is

$$5x = 2x + 3x,$$

because the equation simplifies to

$$5x = 5x,$$

which is true for any real number x. If $5x$ is subtracted from each side the result is $0 = 0$, which has no x-term and is *always true*. When an equation containing a variable is always true, it has infinitely many solutions.

NOTE: An equation that is always true is called an **identity**, and an equation that is always false is called a **contradiction**.

EXAMPLE 8 Determining numbers of solutions

Determine whether the equation has no solutions, one solution, or infinitely many solutions.

(a) $3x = 2(x + 1) + x$ **(b)** $2x - (x + 1) = x - 1$ **(c)** $5x = 2(x - 4)$

Solution

(a) Start by applying the distributive property.

$$3x = 2(x + 1) + x \qquad \text{Given equation}$$
$$3x = 2x + 2 + x \qquad \text{Distributive property}$$
$$3x = 3x + 2 \qquad \text{Combine like terms.}$$
$$0 = 2 \qquad \text{Subtract } 3x \text{ from each side.}$$

The equation $0 = 2$ is always false, so the given equation is a contradiction with no solutions.

(b) Start by applying the distributive property.

$$2x - (x + 1) = x - 1 \qquad \text{Given equation}$$
$$2x - x - 1 = x - 1 \qquad \text{Distributive property}$$
$$x - 1 = x - 1 \qquad \text{Combine like terms.}$$
$$x = x \qquad \text{Add 1 to each side.}$$
$$0 = 0 \qquad \text{Subtract } x \text{ from each side.}$$

The equation $0 = 0$ is always true, so the given equation is an identity that has infinitely many solutions. Note that the solution set contains all real numbers.

(c) Start by applying the distributive property.

$$5x = 2(x - 4) \qquad \text{Given equation}$$
$$5x = 2x - 8 \qquad \text{Distributive property}$$
$$3x = -8 \qquad \text{Subtract } 2x \text{ from each side.}$$
$$x = -\frac{8}{3} \qquad \text{Divide each side by 3.}$$

Thus there is one solution.

Now Try Exercises 61, 63, 67

CRITICAL THINKING

What must be true about b and d for the equation

$$bx - 2 = dx + 7$$

to have no solutions? What must be true about b and d for this equation to have exactly one solution?

READING CHECK

- How can you tell when an equation will have no solutions, one solution, or infinitely many solutions?

MAKING CONNECTIONS

Number of Solutions

When solving the general form $ax + b = 0$, where a and b can be *any* real numbers, the resulting equivalent equation will indicate whether the given equation has no solutions, one solution, or infinitely many solutions.

No Solutions: The result is an equation such as $4 = 0$ or $3 = 2$, which is *always false* for any value of the variable.

One Solution: The result is an equation such as $x = 1$ or $x = -12$, which is true for *only one* value of the variable.

Infinitely Many Solutions: The result is an equation such as $0 = 0$ or $-3 = -3$, which is *always true* for any value of the variable.

2.2   Putting It All Together

CONCEPT	COMMENTS	EXAMPLES
Linear Equation	Can be written as $$ax + b = 0,$$ where $a \neq 0$; has one solution	The equation $5x - 8 = 0$ is linear, with $a = 5$ and $b = -8$. The equation $2x^2 + 4 = 0$ is not linear.
Solving Linear Equations Numerically	To solve a linear equation numerically, complete a table for various values of the variable and then select the solution from the table, if possible.	The solution to $2x - 4 = -2$ is 1. <table><tr><td>x</td><td>-1</td><td>0</td><td>1</td></tr><tr><td>$2x - 4$</td><td>-6</td><td>-4</td><td>-2</td></tr></table>
Solving Linear Equations Symbolically	Use the addition and multiplication properties of equality to isolate the variable. See the four-step approach to solving a linear equation on page 102.	$5x - 8 = 0$ Given equation $5x = 8$ Add 8 to each side. $x = \dfrac{8}{5}$ Divide each side by 5.
Equations with No Solutions	Some equations that appear to be linear have no solutions. Solving will result in an equivalent equation that is always false.	The equation $$x = x + 5$$ has no solutions because a number cannot equal itself plus 5.
Equations with Infinitely Many Solutions	Some equations that appear to be linear have infinitely many solutions. Solving will result in an equivalent equation that is always true.	The equation $$2x = x + x$$ has infinitely many solutions because the equation is true for all values of x.

2.2   Exercises

MyMathLab   Math XL PRACTICE   WATCH   DOWNLOAD   READ   REVIEW

CONCEPTS AND VOCABULARY

1. Linear equations can model applications in which things move or change at a(n) _____ rate.

2. A linear equation can be written in the form _____ with $a \neq 0$.

3. How many solutions does a linear equation in one variable have?

4. When a table of values is used to solve a linear equation, the equation is being solved _____.

5. What two properties of equality are frequently used to solve linear equations?

6. To clear fractions or decimals from an equation, multiply each side by the _____.

7. If solving an equation results in $0 = 4$, how many solutions does it have?

8. If solving an equation results in $0 = 0$, how many solutions does it have?

IDENTIFYING LINEAR EQUATIONS

Exercises 9–22: (Refer to Example 1.) Is the equation linear? If it is linear, give values for a and b that result when the equation is written in the form ax + b = 0.

9. $3x - 7 = 0$ 10. $-2x + 1 = 4$

11. $\frac{1}{2}x = 0$ **12.** $-\frac{3}{4}x = 0$

13. $4x^2 - 6 = 11$ **14.** $-2x^2 + x = 4$

15. $\frac{6}{x} - 4 = 2$ **16.** $2\sqrt{x} - 1 = 0$

17. $1.1x + 0.9 = 1.8$ **18.** $-5.7x - 3.4 = -6.8$

19. $2(x - 3) = 0$ **20.** $\frac{1}{2}(x + 4) = 0$

21. $|3x| + 2 = 1$ **22.** $3x = 4x^3$

SOLVING LINEAR EQUATIONS

Exercises 23–28: Complete the table for the given values of x. Then use the table to solve the given equation numerically.

23. $x - 3 = -1$

x	-1	0	1	2	3
$x - 3$	-4				

24. $-2x = 0$

x	-2	-1	0	1	2
$-2x$	4				

25. $-3x + 7 = 1$

x	0	1	2	3	4
$-3x + 7$	7				

26. $5x - 2 = 3$

x	-1	0	1	2	3
$5x - 2$	-7				

27. $4 - 2x = 6$

x	-2	-1	0	1	2
$4 - 2x$	8				

28. $9 - (x + 3) = 4$

x	-2	-1	0	1	2
$9 - (x + 3)$	8				

Exercises 29–58: Solve the given equation and check the solution.

29. $11x = 3$ **30.** $-5x = 15$

31. $x - 18 = 5$ **32.** $8 = 5 + 3x$

33. $\frac{1}{2}x - 1 = 13$ **34.** $\frac{1}{4}x + 3 = 9$

35. $-6 = 5x + 5$ **36.** $31 = -7x - 4$

37. $3z + 2 = z - 5$ **38.** $z - 5 = 5z - 3$

39. $12y - 6 = 33 - y$ **40.** $-13y + 2 = 22 - 3y$

41. $4(x - 1) = 5$ **42.** $-2(2x + 7) = 1$

43. $1 - (3x + 1) = 5 - x$

44. $6 + 2(x - 7) = 10 - 3(x - 3)$

45. $(5t - 6) = 2(t + 1) + 2$

46. $-2(t - 7) - (t + 5) = 5$

47. $3(4z - 1) - 2(z + 2) = 2(z + 1)$

48. $-(z + 4) + (3z + 1) = -2(z + 1)$

49. $7.3x - 1.7 = 5.6$ **50.** $5.5x + 3x = 51$

51. $-9.5x - 0.05 = 10.5x + 1.05$

52. $0.04x + 0.03 = 0.02x - 0.1$

53. $\frac{1}{2}x - \frac{3}{2} = \frac{5}{2}$ **54.** $-\frac{1}{4}x + \frac{5}{4} = \frac{3}{4}$

55. $-\frac{3}{8}x + \frac{1}{4} = \frac{1}{8}$ **56.** $\frac{1}{3}x + \frac{1}{4} = \frac{1}{6} - x$

57. $4y - 2(y + 1) = 0$

58. $(15y + 20) - 5y = 5 - 10y$

59. **Thinking Generally** A linear equation has exactly one solution. Find the solution to the equation $ax + b = 0$, where $a \neq 0$, by solving for x.

60. **Thinking Generally** Solve the linear equation given by $\frac{1}{a}x - b = 0$ for x.

EQUATIONS WITH NO SOLUTIONS OR INFINITELY MANY SOLUTIONS

Exercises 61–70: Determine whether the equation has no solutions, one solution, or infinitely many solutions.

61. $5x = 5x + 1$ **62.** $2(x - 3) = 2x - 6$

63. $8x = 0$ **64.** $9x = x + 1$

65. $4x = 5(x + 3) - x$ **66.** $5x = 15 - 2(x + 7)$

67. $5(2x + 7) - (10x + 5) = 30$

68. $4(x + 2) - 2(2x + 3) = 10$

69. $x - (3x + 2) = 15 - 2x$

70. $2x - (x + 5) = x - 5$

APPLICATIONS

71. *Distance Traveled* A bicyclist is 4 miles from home, riding away from home at 8 miles per hour.
   (a) Make a table that shows the bicyclist's distance D from home after 0, 1, 2, 3, and 4 hours.
   (b) Write a formula that calculates D after x hours.
   (c) Use your formula to determine D when $x = 3$ hours. Does your answer agree with the value found in your table?
   (d) Find x when $D = 22$ miles. Interpret the result.

72. *Distance Traveled* An athlete is 16 miles from home, running *toward* home at 6 miles per hour.
   (a) Write a formula that calculates the distance D that the athlete is from home after x hours.
   (b) Determine D when $x = 1.5$ hours.
   (c) Find x when $D = 5.5$ miles. Interpret the result.

73. *Internet Users* (Refer to Example 4.) The number of Internet users I in millions during year x, where $x \geq 2007$, can be approximated by the formula

$$I = 241x - 482,440.$$

Approximate the year in which there were 1730 million (1.73 billion) Internet users.

74. *HIV Infections* The cumulative number of HIV infections N in thousands for the United States in year x can be approximated by the formula

$$N = 42x - 83,197,$$

where $x \geq 2000$. Approximate the year when this number reached 970 thousand. (*Source:* Centers for Disease Control and Prevention.)

75. *State and Federal Inmates* The number N of state and federal inmates in millions during year x, where $x \geq 2002$, can be approximated by the formula $N = 0.03x - 58.62$. Determine the year in which there were 1.5 million inmates. (*Source:* Bureau of Justice.)

76. *Government Costs* From 1960 to 2000 the cost C (in billions of 1992 dollars) to regulate social and economic programs could be approximated by the formula $C = 0.35x - 684$ during year x. Estimate the year in which the cost reached $6.6 billion. (*Source:* Center for the Study of American Business.)

77. *Hospitals* The number of hospitals H with more than 100 beds during year x is estimated by the formula $H = -33x + 69,105$, where x is any year from 2002 to 2008. In which year were there 2841 hospitals of this type? (*Source:* AHA Hospital Statistics.)

78. *Home Size* The average size F in square feet of new U.S. homes built during year x is estimated by the formula $F = 34x - 65,734$, where x is any year from 2002 to 2008. In which year was the average home size 2504 square feet? (*Source:* U.S. Census Bureau.)

WRITING ABOUT MATHEMATICS

79. A student says that the equation $4x - 1 = 1 - x$ is not a linear equation because it is not in the form $ax + b = 0$. Is the student correct? Explain.

80. A student solves a linear equation as follows.

$$4(x + 3) = 5 - (x + 3)$$
$$4x + 3 \overset{?}{=} 5 - x + 3$$
$$4x + 3 \overset{?}{=} 8 - x$$
$$5x \overset{?}{=} 5$$
$$x \overset{?}{=} 1$$

Identify and explain the errors that the student made. What is the correct answer?

SECTIONS 2.1 and 2.2 — Checking Basic Concepts

1. Determine whether the equation is linear.
   (a) $4x^3 - 2 = 0$ (b) $2(x + 1) = 4$

2. Complete the table for each value of x. Then use the table to solve $4x - 3 = 13$.

x	3	3.5	4	4.5	5
$4x - 3$	9				17

3. Solve each equation and check your answer.
   (a) $x - 12 = 6$
   (b) $\frac{3}{4}z = \frac{1}{8}$
   (c) $0.6t + 0.4 = 2$
   (d) $5 - 2(x - 2) = 3(4 - x)$

4. Determine whether each equation has no solutions, one solution, or infinitely many solutions.
   (a) $x - 5 = 6x$
   (b) $-2(x - 5) = 10 - 2x$
   (c) $-(x - 1) = -x - 1$

5. *Distance Traveled* A driver is 300 miles from home and is traveling toward home on a freeway at a constant speed of 75 miles per hour.
   (a) Write a formula to calculate the distance D that the driver is from home after x hours.
   (b) Write an equation whose solution gives the hours needed for the driver to reach home.
   (c) Solve the equation from part (b).

2.4   Formulas

Formulas from Geometry • Solving for a Variable • Other Formulas

A LOOK INTO MATH ▶

Have you ever wondered how your grade point average (GPA) is calculated? A formula is used that involves the number of credits earned at each possible grade. Once a formula has been derived, it can be used over and over by any number of people. For this reason, formulas provide a convenient and easy way to solve certain types of recurring problems. In this section we discuss several types of formulas.

STUDY TIP

If you are studying with classmates, make sure that they do not "do the work for you." A classmate with the best intentions may give too many verbal hints while helping you work through a problem. Remember that members of your study group will not be giving hints during an exam.

NEW VOCABULARY

☐ Degree
☐ Circumference

Formulas from Geometry

Formulas from geometry are frequently used in various fields, including surveying and construction. In this subsection we discuss several important formulas from geometry.

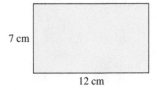

7 cm

12 cm

Figure 2.6 Rectangle

RECTANGLES If a rectangle has length l and width w, then its perimeter P and its area A are given by the formulas

$$P = 2l + 2w \quad \text{and} \quad A = lw.$$

For example, the rectangle in Figure 2.6 has length **12** centimeters and width **7** centimeters. Its perimeter is

$$P = 2(12) + 2(7) = 24 + 14 = 38 \text{ centimeters,}$$

and its area is

$$A = 12 \cdot 7 = 84 \text{ square centimeters.}$$

NOTE: All measurements used in a geometry formula must have the same units.

TRIANGLES If a triangle has base b and height h, as shown in Figure 2.7(a), then its area A is given by the formula

$$A = \frac{1}{2}bh.$$

For example, to find the area of a triangle with base **4** feet and height **18** inches as illustrated in Figure 2.7(b), we begin by making sure that all measurements have the same units. By converting 18 inches to **1.5** feet, the area of the triangle is

$$A = \frac{1}{2}bh = \frac{1}{2}(4)(1.5) = 3 \text{ square feet.}$$

If the base had been converted to **48** inches, the area is

$$A = \frac{1}{2}bh = \frac{1}{2}(48)(18) = 432 \text{ square inches.}$$

READING CHECK

- What do l and w stand for in formulas for rectangles?

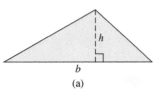

h

b

(a)

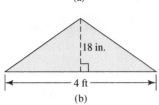

18 in.

4 ft

(b)

Figure 2.7 Triangles

READING CHECK

- What do b and h stand for in the triangle area formula?

EXAMPLE 1   **Calculating area of a region**

A residential lot is shown in Figure 2.8. It comprises a rectangular region and an adjacent triangular region.
(a) Find the area of this lot.
(b) An acre contains 43,560 square feet. How many acres are there in this lot?

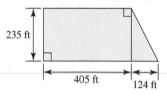

235 ft

405 ft   124 ft

Figure 2.8

Solution
(a) The rectangular portion of the lot has length **405** feet and width **235** feet. Its area A_R is

$$A_R = lw = 405 \cdot 235 = 95{,}175 \text{ square feet.}$$

The triangular region has base **124** feet and height **235** feet. Its area A_T is

$$A_T = \frac{1}{2}bh = \frac{1}{2} \cdot 124 \cdot 235 = 14{,}570 \text{ square feet.}$$

The total area A of the lot equals the sum of A_R and A_T.

$$A = 95{,}175 + 14{,}570 = 109{,}745 \text{ square feet}$$

(b) Each acre equals 43,560 square feet, so divide 109,745 by 43,560 to calculate the number of acres.

$$\frac{109{,}745}{43{,}560} \approx 2.5 \text{ acres}$$

Now Try Exercise 27

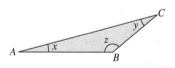

Figure 2.9

ANGLES Angles are often measured in degrees. A **degree** (°) is $\frac{1}{360}$ of a revolution, so there are 360° in one complete revolution. In any triangle, the sum of the measures of the angles equals 180°. In Figure 2.9, triangle ABC has angles with measures x, y, and z. Therefore

$$x + y + z = 180°.$$

EXAMPLE 2   **Finding angles in a triangle**

In a triangle the two smaller angles are equal in measure and are each half the measure of the largest angle. Find the measure of each angle.

Solution
Let x represent the measure of each of the two smaller angles, as illustrated in Figure 2.10. Then the measure of the largest angle is $2x$, and the sum of the measures of the three angles is given by

$$x + x + 2x = 180°.$$

This equation can be solved as follows.

$$x + x + 2x = 180° \quad \text{Equation to be solved}$$
$$4x = 180° \quad \text{Combine like terms.}$$
$$\frac{4x}{4} = \frac{180°}{4} \quad \text{Divide each side by 4.}$$
$$x = 45° \quad \text{Divide the real numbers.}$$

The measure of the largest angle is $2x = 2 \cdot 45° = 90°$. Thus the measures of the three angles are 45°, 45°, and 90°.

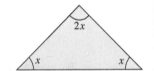

Figure 2.10

▌ Now Try Exercise 33

Figure 2.11 Circle

CIRCLES The *radius* of a circle is the distance from its center to the perimeter of the circle. The perimeter of a circle is called its **circumference** C and is given by $C = 2\pi r$, where r is the radius of the circle. The area A of a circle is given by $A = \pi r^2$. See Figure 2.11. The distance across a circle, through its center, is called the *diameter*. Note that a circle's radius is half of its diameter. (Recall that $\pi \approx 3.14$.)

EXAMPLE 3   **Finding the circumference and area of a circle**

A circle has a diameter of 25 inches. Find its circumference and area.

Solution
The radius is half the diameter, or 12.5 inches.

$$\textit{Circumference: } C = 2\pi r = 2\pi(12.5) = 25\pi \approx 78.5 \text{ inches.}$$
$$\textit{Area: } A = \pi r^2 = \pi(12.5)^2 = 156.25\pi \approx 491 \text{ square inches.}$$

▌ Now Try Exercise 37

READING CHECK

• What is the approximate value of π when rounded to the nearest hundredth?

CALCULATOR HELP

To evaluate π on a calculator, see Appendix A (page AP-1).

CRITICAL THINKING

Write formulas for the circumference and area of a circle having diameter d.

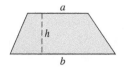

Figure 2.12 Trapezoid

TRAPEZOIDS A trapezoid such as the one shown in Figure 2.12 has bases a and b, and height h. The area A of a trapezoid is given by the formula

$$A = \frac{1}{2}(a + b)h.$$

> EXAMPLE 4

Finding the area of a trapezoid

Find the area of the trapezoid shown in Figure 2.13.

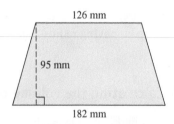

Figure 2.13

Solution

The bases of the trapezoid in Figure 2.13 are **126** millimeters and **182** millimeters, and its height is **95** millimeters. Substituting these values in the area formula gives an area of

$$A = \frac{1}{2}(a + b)h = \frac{1}{2}(126 + 182) \cdot 95 = \frac{1}{2}(308) \cdot 95 = 14{,}630 \text{ square millimeters.}$$

Now Try Exercise 19

BOXES The box in Figure 2.14 has length l, width w, and height h. Its volume V is given by

$$V = lwh.$$

The surface of the box comprises six rectangular regions: top and bottom, front and back, and left and right sides. The total surface area S of the box is given by

$$S = lw + \quad lw \quad + wh + wh + \quad lh \quad + \quad lh.$$
$$\text{(top + bottom + front + back + left side + right side)}$$

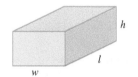

Figure 2.14 Rectangular Box

When we combine like terms, this expression simplifies to

$$S = 2lw + 2wh + 2lh.$$

> EXAMPLE 5

Finding the volume and surface area of a box

Find the volume and surface area of the box shown in Figure 2.15.

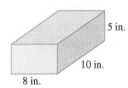

Figure 2.15

Solution

Figure 2.15 shows that the box has length $l = 10$ inches, width $w = 8$ inches, and height $h = 5$ inches. The volume of the box is

$$V = lwh = 10 \cdot 8 \cdot 5 = 400 \text{ cubic inches.}$$

Since $l = 10$, $w = 8$, and $h = 5$, the surface area of the box is

$$S = 2lw + 2wh + 2lh$$
$$= 2(10)(8) + 2(8)(5) + 2(10)(5)$$
$$= 160 + 80 + 100$$
$$= 340 \text{ square inches.}$$

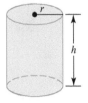

Figure 2.16 Cylinder

Now Try Exercise **41**

CYLINDERS A soup can is usually made in the shape of a cylinder. The volume of a cylinder having radius r and height h is $V = \pi r^2 h$. See Figure 2.16.

EXAMPLE 6   **Calculating the volume of a soda can**

A cylindrical soda can has a radius of $1\frac{1}{4}$ inches and a height of $4\frac{3}{8}$ inches.
(a) Find the volume of the can.
(b) If 1 cubic inch equals 0.554 fluid ounce, find the number of fluid ounces in the can.

Solution
(a) Changing mixed numbers to improper fractions gives the radius as $r = \frac{5}{4}$ inches and the height as $h = \frac{35}{8}$ inches.

$$V = \pi r^2 h \qquad\qquad \text{Volume of the soda can}$$

$$= \pi \left(\frac{5}{4}\right)^2 \left(\frac{35}{8}\right) \qquad \text{Substitute.}$$

$$= \pi \left(\frac{875}{128}\right) \qquad\qquad \text{Multiply the fractions.}$$

$$\approx 21.48 \text{ cubic inches} \quad \text{Approximate.}$$

(b) To calculate the number of fluid ounces in 21.48 cubic inches, multiply by 0.554.

$$21.48(0.554) \approx 11.9 \text{ fluid ounces}$$

Note that a typical aluminum soda can holds 12 fluid ounces.

Now Try Exercise **49**

Solving for a Variable

A formula establishes a relationship between two or more variables (or quantities). Sometimes a formula must be rewritten to solve for the needed variable. For example, if the area A and the width w of a rectangular region are given, then its length l can be found by solving the formula $A = lw$ for l.

$$A = lw \qquad\qquad \text{Area formula}$$

$$\frac{A}{w} = \frac{lw}{w} \qquad\qquad \text{Divide each side by } w.$$

$$\frac{A}{w} = l \qquad\qquad \text{Simplify the fraction.}$$

$$l = \frac{A}{w} \qquad\qquad \text{Rewrite the equation.}$$

If the area A of a rectangle is 400 square inches and its width w is 16 inches, then the rectangle's length l is

$$l = \frac{A}{w} = \frac{400}{16} = 25 \text{ inches.}$$

Once the area formula has been solved for l, the resulting formula can be used to find the length of *any* rectangle whose area and width are known.

EXAMPLE 7 **Finding the base of a trapezoid**

The area of a trapezoid is given by

$$A = \frac{1}{2}(a + b)h,$$

where a and b are the bases of the trapezoid and h is the height.
(a) Solve the formula for b.
(b) A trapezoid has area $A = 36$ square inches, height $h = 4$ inches, and base $a = 8$ inches. Find b.

Solution
(a) To clear the equation of the fraction, multiply each side by 2.

$$A = \frac{1}{2}(a + b)h \qquad \text{Area formula}$$

$$2A = (a + b)h \qquad \text{Multiply each side by 2.}$$

$$\frac{2A}{h} = a + b \qquad \text{Divide each side by } h.$$

$$\frac{2A}{h} - a = b \qquad \text{Subtract } a \text{ from each side.}$$

$$b = \frac{2A}{h} - a \qquad \text{Rewrite the formula.}$$

(b) Let $A = 36$, $h = 4$, and $a = 8$ in $b = \frac{2A}{h} - a$. Then

$$b = \frac{2(36)}{4} - 8 = 18 - 8 = 10 \text{ inches.}$$

Now Try Exercise 59

EXAMPLE 8 **Solving for a variable**

Solve each equation for the indicated variable.
(a) $c = \frac{a + b}{2}$ for b **(b)** $ab - bc = ac$ for c

Solution
(a) To clear the equation of the fraction, multiply each side by 2.

$$c = \frac{a + b}{2} \qquad \text{Given formula}$$

$$2c = a + b \qquad \text{Multiply each side by 2.}$$

$$2c - a = b \qquad \text{Subtract } a.$$

The formula solved for b is $b = 2c - a$.

(b) In $ab - bc = ac$, the variable c appears in two terms. We will combine the terms containing c by using the distributive property. Begin by moving the term on the left side containing c to the right side of the equation.

$$ab - bc = ac \qquad \text{Given formula}$$

$$ab - bc + bc = ac + bc \qquad \text{Add } bc \text{ to each side.}$$

$$ab = (a + b)c \qquad \text{Combine terms; distributive property.}$$

$$\frac{ab}{a + b} = \frac{(a + b)c}{(a + b)} \qquad \text{Divide each side by } (a + b).$$

$$\frac{ab}{a + b} = c \qquad \text{Simplify the fraction.}$$

The formula solved for c is $c = \frac{ab}{a + b}$.

Now Try Exercises 63, 67

CRITICAL THINKING

Are the formulas $c = \frac{1}{a - b}$ and $c = \frac{-1}{b - a}$ equivalent? Why?

Other Formulas

To calculate a student's GPA, the number of credits earned with a grade of A, B, C, D, and F must be known. If a, b, c, d, and f represent these credit counts respectively, then

$$\text{GPA} = \frac{4a + 3b + 2c + d}{a + b + c + d + f}.$$

This formula is based on the assumption that a 4.0 GPA is an A, a 3.0 GPA is a B, and so on.

EXAMPLE 9 **Calculating a student's GPA**

A student has earned 16 credits of A, 32 credits of B, 12 credits of C, 2 credits of D, and 5 credits of F. Calculate the student's GPA to the nearest hundredth.

Solution
Let $a = 16$, $b = 32$, $c = 12$, $d = 2$, and $\tilde{} = 5$. Then

$$\text{GPA} = \frac{4 \cdot 16 + 3 \cdot 32 + 2 \cdot 12 + 2}{16 + 32 + 12 + 2 + 5} = \frac{186}{67} \approx 2.78.$$

The student's GPA is 2.78.

Now Try Exercise 71

EXAMPLE 10 **Converting temperature scales**

In the United States, temperature is measured with either the Fahrenheit or the Celsius temperature scale. To convert Fahrenheit degrees F to Celsius degrees C, the formula $C = \frac{5}{9}(F - 32)$ can be used.
(a) Solve the formula for F to find a formula that converts Celsius degrees to Fahrenheit degrees.
(b) If the outside temperature is $20°C$, find the equivalent Fahrenheit temperature.

Solution

(a) The reciprocal of $\frac{5}{9}$ is $\frac{9}{5}$, so multiply each side by $\frac{9}{5}$.

$$C = \frac{5}{9}(F - 32) \qquad \text{Given equation}$$

$$\frac{9}{5}C = \frac{9}{5} \cdot \frac{5}{9}(F - 32) \qquad \text{Multiply each side by } \frac{9}{5}.$$

$$\frac{9}{5}C = F - 32 \qquad \text{Multiplicative inverses}$$

$$\frac{9}{5}C + 32 = F \qquad \text{Add 32 to each side.}$$

The required formula is $F = \frac{9}{5}C + 32$.

(b) If $C = 20°C$, then $F = \frac{9}{5}(20) + 32 = 36 + 32 = 68°F$.

▌ Now Try Exercise 75

2.4   Putting It All Together

In this section we discussed formulas and how to solve for a variable. The following table summarizes some of these formulas.

CONCEPT	FORMULA	EXAMPLES
Area and Perimeter of a Rectangle	$A = lw$ and $P = 2l + 2w$, where l is the length and w is the width.	If $l = 10$ feet and $w = 5$ feet, then $A = 10 \cdot 5 = 50$ square feet and $P = 2(10) + 2(5) = 30$ feet.
Area of a Triangle	$A = \frac{1}{2}bh$, where b is the base and h is the height.	If $b = 5$ inches and $h = 6$ inches, then the area is $A = \frac{1}{2}(5)(6) = 15$ square inches.
Angle Measure in a Triangle	$x + y + z = 180°$, where x, y, and z are the angle measures.	If $x = 40°$ and $y = 60°$, then $z = 80°$ because $40° + 60° + 80° = 180°$

continued on next page

continued from previous page

CONCEPT	FORMULA	EXAMPLES
Circumference and Area of a Circle	If a circle has radius r, then its circumference is $$C = 2\pi r$$ and its area is $$A = \pi r^2.$$	If $r = 6$ inches, $C = 2\pi(6) = 12\pi \approx 37.7$ inches and $A = \pi(6)^2 = 36\pi \approx 113.1$ square inches.
Area of a Trapezoid	$$A = \tfrac{1}{2}(a + b)h,$$ where a and b are the bases and h is the height.	If $a = 4$, $b = 6$, and $h = 3$, then the area is $$A = \frac{1}{2}(4 + 6)(3) = 15 \text{ square units.}$$
Volume and Surface Area of a Box	If a box has length l, width w, and height h, then its volume is $$V = lwh$$ and its surface area is $$S = 2lw + 2wh + 2lh.$$	If a box has dimensions $l = 4$ feet, $w = 3$ feet, and $h = 2$ feet, then $$V = 4(3)(2) = 24 \text{ cubic feet}$$ and $$S = 2(4)(3) + 2(3)(2) + 2(4)(2)$$ $$= 52 \text{ square feet.}$$
Volume of a Cylinder	$$V = \pi r^2 h,$$ where r is the radius and h is the height.	If $r = 5$ inches and $h = 20$ inches, then the volume is $$V = \pi(5^2)(20) = 500\pi \text{ cubic inches.}$$
Calculating Grade Point Average (GPA)	GPA is calculated by $$\frac{4a + 3b + 2c + d}{a + b + c + d + f},$$ where a, b, c, d, and f represent the number of credits earned with grades of A, B, C, D, and F, respectively.	10 credits of A, 8 credits of B, 6 credits of C, 12 credits of D, and 8 credits of F results in a GPA of $$\frac{4(10) + 3(8) + 2(6) + 12}{10 + 8 + 6 + 12 + 8} = 2.0.$$

CONCEPT	FORMULA	EXAMPLES
Converting Between Fahrenheit and Celsius Degrees	$C = \dfrac{5}{9}(F - 32)$ $F = \dfrac{9}{5}C + 32$	$212°F$ is equivalent to $C = \dfrac{5}{9}(212 - 32) = 100°C.$ $100°C$ is equivalent to $F = \dfrac{9}{5}(100) + 32 = 212°F.$

2.4 Exercises

MyMathLab | Math XL PRACTICE | WATCH | DOWNLOAD | READ | REVIEW

CONCEPTS AND VOCABULARY

1. A(n) _____ can be used to calculate one quantity by using known values of other quantities.

2. The area A of a rectangle with length l and width w is $A =$ _____.

3. The area A of a triangle with base b and height h is $A =$ _____.

4. One degree equals _____ of a revolution.

5. There are _____ degrees in one revolution.

6. The sum of the measures of the angles in a triangle equals _____ degrees.

7. The volume V of a box with length l, width w, and height h is $V =$ _____.

8. The surface area S of a box with length l, width w, and height h is $S =$ _____.

9. The circumference C of a circle with radius r is $C =$ _____.

10. The area A of a circle with radius r is $A =$ _____.

11. The volume V of a cylinder with radius r and height h is $V =$ _____.

12. The area A of a trapezoid with height h and bases a and b is $A =$ _____.

FORMULAS FROM GEOMETRY

Exercises 13–20: Find the area of the region shown.

13.
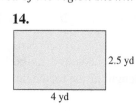
6 ft, 3 ft

14.
2.5 yd, 4 yd

15.

3 in.
6 in.

16.

1 mi
3 mi

17.

4 cm

18.

6 km

19.
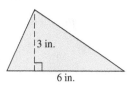
6 mm
2 mm
5 mm

20.
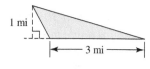
3 ft
2 ft
4 ft

21. Find the area of a rectangle having a 7-inch width and a 13-inch length.

22. Find the area of a triangle having a 9-centimeter base and a 72-centimeter height.

23. Find the area of a rectangle having a 5-foot width and a 7-yard length.

24. Find the area of a triangle having a 12-millimeter base and a 6-millimeter height.

25. Find the circumference of a circle having an 8-inch diameter.

26. Find the area of a circle having a 9-foot radius.

27. *Area of a Lot* Find the area of the lot shown, which consists of a square and a triangle.

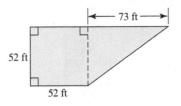

28. *Area of a Lot* Find the area of the lot shown, which consists of a rectangle and two triangles.

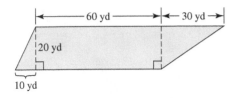

Exercises 29 and 30: Angle Measure Find the measure of the third angle in the triangle.

29.

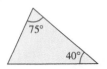

30.

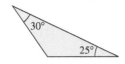

31. A triangle contains two angles having measures of 23° and 76°. Find the measure of the third angle.

32. The measures of the angles in an *equilateral triangle* are equal. Find their measure.

33. The measures of the angles in a triangle are x, $2x$, and $2x$. Find the value of x.

34. The measures of the angles in a triangle are $3x$, $4x$, and $11x$. Find the value of x.

35. In a triangle the two smaller angles are equal in measure and are each one third of the measure of the larger angle. Find the measure of each angle.

36. In a triangle the two larger angles differ by 10°. The smaller angle is 50° less than the largest angle. Find the measure of each angle.

37. The diameter of a circle is 12 inches. Find its circumference and area.

38. The radius of a circle is $\frac{5}{4}$ feet. Find its circumference and area.

39. The circumference of a circle is 2π inches. Find its radius and area.

40. The circumference of a circle is 13π feet. Find its radius and area.

Exercises 41–44: A box with a top has length l, width w, and height h. Find the volume and surface area of the box.

41. $l = 22$ inches, $w = 12$ inches, $h = 10$ inches

42. $l = 5$ feet, $w = 3$ feet, $h = 6$ feet

43. $l = \frac{2}{3}$ yard, $w = \frac{2}{3}$ foot, $h = \frac{3}{2}$ feet

44. $l = 1.2$ meters, $w = 0.8$ meter, $h = 0.6$ meter

Exercises 45–48: Use the formula $V = \pi r^2 h$ to find the volume of a cylindrical container for the given r and h. Leave your answer in terms of π.

45. $r = 2$ inches, $h = 5$ inches

46. $r = \frac{1}{2}$ inch, $h = \frac{3}{2}$ inches

47. $r = 5$ inches, $h = 2$ feet

48. $r = 2.5$ feet, $h = 1.5$ yards

49. *Volume of a Can* (Refer to Example 6.)
 (a) Find the volume of a can with a radius of $\frac{3}{4}$ inch and a height of $2\frac{1}{2}$ inches.
 (b) Find the number of fluid ounces in the can if one cubic inch equals 0.554 fluid ounces.

50. *Volume of a Barrel* (Refer to Example 6.) A cylindrical barrel has a diameter of $1\frac{3}{4}$ feet and a height of 3 feet. Find the volume of the barrel.

SOLVING FOR A VARIABLE

Exercises 51–68: Solve the formula for the given variable.

51. $9x + 3y = 6$ for y **52.** $-2x - 2y = 10$ for y

53. $4x + 3y = 12$ for y **54.** $5x - 2y = 22$ for y

55. $A = lw$ for w **56.** $A = \frac{1}{2}bh$ for b

57. $V = \pi r^2 h$ for h **58.** $V = \frac{1}{3}\pi r^2 h$ for h

59. $A = \frac{1}{2}(a + b)h$ for a **60.** $C = 2\pi r$ for r

61. $V = lwh$ for w **62.** $P = 2l + 2w$ for w

63. $s = \dfrac{a + b + c}{2}$ for b **64.** $t = \dfrac{x - y}{3}$ for x

65. $\dfrac{a}{b} - \dfrac{c}{b} = 1$ for b **66.** $\dfrac{x}{y} + \dfrac{z}{y} = 5$ for z

67. $ab = cd + ad$ for a

68. $S = 2lw + 2lh + 2wh$ for w

69. *Perimeter of a Rectangle* If the width of a rectangle is 5 inches and its perimeter is 40 inches, find the length of the rectangle.

70. *Perimeter of a Triangle* Two sides of a triangle have lengths of 5 feet and 7 feet. If the triangle's perimeter is 21 feet, what is the length of the third side?

OTHER FORMULAS AND APPLICATIONS

Exercises 71–74: (Refer to Example 9.) Let the variable a represent the number of credits with a grade of A, b the number of credits with a grade of B, and so on. Calculate the corresponding grade point average (GPA). Round your answer to the nearest hundredth.

71. $a = 30, b = 45, c = 12, d = 4, \tilde{} = 4$

72. $a = 70, b = 35, c = 5, d = 0, \tilde{} = 0$

73. $a = 0, b = 60, c = 80, d = 10, \tilde{} = 6$

74. $a = 3, b = 5, c = 8, d = 0, \tilde{} = 22$

Exercises 75–78: (Refer to Example 10.) Convert the Celsius temperature to an equivalent Fahrenheit temperature.

75. $25°C$ **76.** $100°C$ **77.** $-40°C$ **78.** $0°C$

Exercises 79–82: (Refer to Example 10.) Convert the Fahrenheit temperature to an equivalent Celsius temperature.

79. $23°F$ **80.** $98.6°F$ **81.** $-4°F$ **82.** $-31°F$

83. *Gas Mileage* The formula $M = \frac{D}{G}$ can be used to calculate a car's gas mileage M after it has traveled D miles on G gallons of gasoline. Suppose that a truck driver leaves a gas station with a full tank of gas and the odometer showing 87,625 miles. At the next gas stop, it takes 38 gallons to fill the tank and the odometer reads 88,043 miles. Find the gas mileage for the truck.

84. *Gas Mileage* (Refer to Exercise 83.) A car that gets 34 miles per gallon is driven 578 miles. How many gallons of gasoline are used on this trip?

85. *Lightning* If there is an x-second delay between seeing a flash of lightning and hearing the thunder, then the lightning is $D = \frac{x}{5}$ miles away. Suppose that the time delay between a flash of lightning and the sound of thunder is 12 seconds. How far away is the lightning?

86. *Lightning* (Refer to Exercise 85.) Doppler radar shows an electrical storm 2.5 miles away. If you see the lightning from this storm, how long will it be before you hear the thunder?

WRITING ABOUT MATHEMATICS

87. A student solves the formula $A = \frac{1}{2}bh$ for h and obtains the formula $h = \frac{1}{2}bA$. Explain the error that the student is making. What is the correct answer?

88. Give an example of a formula that you have used and explain how you used it.

SECTION 2.4   Checking Basic Concepts

1. Translate the sentence into an equation containing the variable x. Then solve the resulting equation.
   (a) The product of 3 and a number is 36.
   (b) A number subtracted from 35 is 43.

2. When three consecutive integers are added, the sum is -93. Find the three integers.

3. Convert 9.5% to a decimal.

4. Convert $\frac{5}{4}$ to a percentage.

5. *Violent Crime* In 2009, New York City experienced 46,357 violent crimes. This figure represented a 38.8% decrease from the number in 2000. Find the number of violent crimes in 2000. (*Source: New York State Crime Update.*)

6. *Driving a Car* How many hours does it take the driver of a car to travel 390 miles at 60 miles per hour?

7. *College Loans* A student takes out two loans, one at 6% and the other at 7%. The 6% loan is $2000 more than the 7% loan, and the total interest for one year is $510. Find the amount of each loan.

8. *Gas Mileage* A car that gets 28 miles per gallon is driven 504 miles. How many gallons of gasoline are used on this trip?

9. *Height of a Triangle* The area of a triangle having a base of 6 inches is 36 square inches. Find the height of the triangle.

10. *Area and Circumference* Find the area and circumference of the circle shown.

11. *Angles* Find the value of x in the triangle shown.

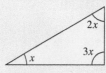

12. *Solving a Formula* Solve $A = \pi r^2 + \pi r l$ for l.

2.5   Linear Inequalities

Solutions and Number Line Graphs ▪ The Addition Property of Inequalities ▪ The Multiplication Property of Inequalities ▪ Applications

A LOOK INTO MATH ▶ At an amusement park, a particular ride might be restricted to people at least 48 inches tall. A child who is x inches tall may go on the ride if $x \geq 48$ but may not go on the ride if $x < 48$. A height of 48 inches represents the *boundary* between being allowed on the ride and being denied access to the ride.

Solving linear inequalities is closely related to solving linear equations because equality is the boundary between *greater than* and *less than*. In this section we discuss techniques used to solve linear inequalities.

Solutions and Number Line Graphs

A **linear inequality** results whenever the equals sign in a linear equation is replaced with any one of the symbols $<$, $\leq$, $>$, or $\geq$. Examples of linear equations include

$$x = 5, \quad 2x + 1 = 0, \quad 1 - x = 6, \quad \text{and} \quad 5x + 1 = 3 - 2x.$$

Therefore examples of linear inequalities include

$$x > 5, \quad 2x + 1 < 0, \quad 1 - x \geq 6, \quad \text{and} \quad 5x + 1 \leq 3 - 2x.$$

Table 2.9 shows how each of the inequality symbols is read.

NEW VOCABULARY

☐ Linear inequality
☐ Solution
☐ Solution set
☐ Interval notation
☐ Set-builder notation

TABLE 2.9 Inequality Symbols

Symbol	How the Symbol Is Read
$>$	greater than
$<$	less than
$\geq$	greater than or equal to
$\leq$	less than or equal to

A **solution** to an inequality is a value of the variable that makes the statement true. The set of all solutions is called the **solution set**. Two inequalities are *equivalent* if they have the same solution set. Inequalities often have infinitely many solutions. For example, the solution set for the inequality $x > 5$ includes all real numbers greater than 5.

A number line can be used to graph the solution set for an inequality. The graph of all real numbers satisfying $x < 2$ is shown in Figure 2.17(a), and the graph of all real numbers satisfying $x \leq 2$ is shown in Figure 2.17(b). A parenthesis ")" is used to show that 2 is not included in Figure 2.17(a), and a bracket "]" is used to show that 2 is included in Figure 2.17(b).

READING CHECK

• How many solutions do inequalities have?

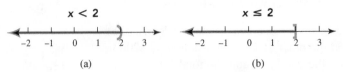

(a)   (b)

Figure 2.17

EXAMPLE 1   **Graphing inequalities on a number line**

Use a number line to graph the solution set to each inequality.
(a) $x > 0$ **(b)** $x \geq 0$ **(c)** $x \leq -1$ **(d)** $x < 3$

Solution
(a) First locate $x = 0$ (or the origin) on a number line. Numbers greater than 0 are located to the right of the origin, so shade the number line to the right of the origin. Because the inequality is $x > 0$, the number 0 is not included, so place a parenthesis "(" at 0, as shown in Figure 2.18(a).
(b) Figure 2.18(b) is similar to the graph in part (a) except that a bracket "[" is placed at the origin because the inequality symbol is $\geq$ and 0 is included in the solution set.
(c) First locate $x = -1$ on the number line. Numbers less than -1 are located to the left of -1. Because -1 is included, a bracket "]" is placed at -1, as shown in Figure 2.18(c).
(d) Real numbers less than 3 are graphed in Figure 2.18(d).

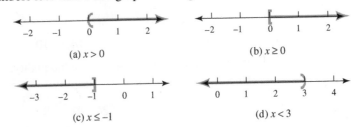

Figure 2.18

Now Try Exercises 11, 13, 15, 17

INTERVAL NOTATION (OPTIONAL) The solution sets graphed in Figure 2.18 can also be represented in a convenient notation called **interval notation**. Rather than draw the entire number line, we can use brackets or parentheses to indicate the interval of values that represent the solution set. For example, the solution set shown in Figure 2.18(a) can be represented by the interval $(0, \infty)$, and the solution set shown in Figure 2.18(b) can be represented by the interval $[0, \infty)$. The symbol ∞ refers to infinity and is used to indicate that the values increase without bound. Similarly, $-\infty$ can be used when the values decrease without bound. The solution sets shown in Figure 2.18(c) and (d) can be represented by $(-\infty, -1]$ and $(-\infty, 3)$, respectively.

EXAMPLE 2   **Writing solution sets in interval notation**

Write the solution set to each inequality in interval notation.
(a) $x > 4$ **(b)** $y \leq -3$ **(c)** $z \geq -1$

Solution
(a) Real numbers greater than 4 are represented by the interval $(4, \infty)$.
(b) Real numbers less than or equal to -3 are represented by the interval $(-\infty, -3]$.
(c) The solution set is represented by the interval $[-1, \infty)$.

Now Try Exercises 25, 27, 29

CHECKING SOLUTIONS We can check possible solutions to an inequality in the same way that we checked possible solutions to an equation. For example, to check whether 5 is a solution to the equation $2x + 3 = 13$, we substitute 5 for x in the equation.

$$2(5) + 3 \stackrel{?}{=} 13 \quad \text{Replace } x \text{ with 5.}$$
$$13 = 13 \quad \text{A true statement}$$

Thus 5 is a solution to this equation. Similarly, to check whether 7 is a solution to the inequality $2x + 3 > 13$, we substitute 7 for x in the inequality.

$$2(7) + 3 \overset{?}{>} 13 \qquad \text{Replace } x \text{ with 7.}$$

$$17 > 13 \checkmark \qquad \text{A true statement}$$

Thus 7 is a solution to the inequality.

EXAMPLE 3 **Checking possible solutions**

Determine whether the given value of x is a solution to the inequality.
(a) $3x - 4 < 10, \quad x = 6$ **(b)** $4 - 2x \le 8, \quad x = -2$

Solution
(a) Substitute 6 for x and simplify.

$$3(6) - 4 \overset{?}{<} 10 \qquad \text{Replace } x \text{ with 6.}$$

$$14 < 10 \; ✗ \qquad \text{A false statement}$$

Thus 6 is *not* a solution to the inequality.
(b) Substitute -2 for x and simplify.

$$4 - 2(-2) \overset{?}{\le} 8 \qquad \text{Replace } x \text{ with } -2.$$

$$8 \le 8 \checkmark \qquad \text{A true statement}$$

Thus -2 is a solution to the inequality.

▮ Now Try Exercises 33, 35

Just as solving a linear equation means finding the value of the variable that makes the equation true, solving a linear inequality means finding the *values* of the variable that make the inequality true.

Making a table is an organized way of checking possible values of the variable to see if there are values that make an inequality true. In the next example, we use a table to find solutions to an equation and related inequalities.

EXAMPLE 4 **Finding solutions to equations and inequalities**

In Table 2.10 the expression $2x - 6$ has been evaluated for several values of x. Use the table to determine any solutions to each equation or inequality.
(a) $2x - 6 = 0$ **(b)** $2x - 6 > 0$ **(c)** $2x - 6 \ge 0$ **(d)** $2x - 6 < 0$

TABLE 2.10

x	0	1	2	3	4	5	6
$2x - 6$	-6	-4	-2	0	2	4	6

Solution
(a) From Table 2.10, $2x - 6$ equals 0 when $x = 3$.
(b) The values of x in the table that make the expression $2x - 6$ greater than 0 are 4, 5, and 6. These values are all greater than 3, which is the solution found in part (a). It follows that $2x - 6 > 0$ when $x > 3$.
(c) The values of x in the table that make the expression $2x - 6$ greater than or equal to 0 are 3, 4, 5, and 6. It follows that $2x - 6 \ge 0$ when $x \ge 3$.
(d) The expression $2x - 6$ is less than 0 when $x < 3$.

▮ Now Try Exercise 39

The Addition Property of Inequalities

▶ **REAL-WORLD CONNECTION** Suppose that the speed limit on a country road is 55 miles per hour, and this is 25 miles per hour faster than the speed limit in town. If x represents lawful speeds in town, then x satisfies the inequality

$$x + 25 \leq 55.$$

To solve this inequality we **add** -25 to (or subtract 25 from) each side of the inequality.

$$x + 25 + (-25) \leq 55 + (-25) \qquad \text{Add } -25 \text{ to each side.}$$
$$x \leq 30 \qquad \text{Add the real numbers.}$$

Thus drivers are obeying the speed limit in town when they travel at 30 miles per hour or less. To solve this inequality the addition property of inequalities was used.

ADDITION PROPERTY OF INEQUALITIES

Let a, b, and c be expressions that represent real numbers. The inequalities

$$a < b \quad \text{and} \quad a + c < b + c$$

are equivalent. That is, the same number may be added to (or subtracted from) each side of an inequality. Similar properties exist for $>$, $\leq$, and $\geq$.

To solve some inequalities, we apply the addition property of inequalities to obtain a simpler, equivalent inequality.

EXAMPLE 5 ▶ **Applying the addition property of inequalities**

Solve each inequality. Then graph the solution set.
(a) $x - 1 > 4$ **(b)** $3 + 2x \leq 5 + x$

Solution
(a) Begin by adding 1 to each side of the inequality.

$$x - 1 > 4 \qquad \text{Given inequality}$$
$$x - 1 + 1 > 4 + 1 \qquad \text{Add 1 to each side.}$$
$$x > 5 \qquad \text{Add the real numbers.}$$

The solution set is given by $x > 5$ and is graphed as follows.

$$\xleftarrow{\qquad} \overset{\;}{\underset{-2\quad 0\quad 2\quad 4\quad 6\quad 8}{\longmapsto}} \xrightarrow{\qquad}$$

(b) Begin by subtracting x from (or adding $-x$ to) each side of the inequality.

$$3 + 2x \leq 5 + x \qquad \text{Given inequality}$$
$$3 + 2x - x \leq 5 + x - x \qquad \text{Subtract } x \text{ from each side.}$$
$$3 + x \leq 5 \qquad \text{Combine like terms.}$$
$$3 + x - 3 \leq 5 - 3 \qquad \text{Subtract 3 from each side.}$$
$$x \leq 2 \qquad \text{Subtract the real numbers.}$$

The solution set is given by $x \leq 2$ and is graphed as follows.

■ Now Try Exercise 47

The addition property of inequalities can be illustrated by an old-fashioned pan balance. In the figure on the left, the weight on the right pan is heavier than the weight on the left because the right pan rests lower than the left pan. If we add an equal amount of weight (blue in the figure) to both pans, or if we subtract an equal amount of weight from both pans, the pan on the right still weighs more than the pan on the left by the same amount that it previously did.

EXAMPLE 6 **Applying the addition property of inequalities**

Solve $5 + \frac{1}{2}x \leq 3 - \frac{1}{2}x$. Then graph the solution set.

Solution
Begin by subtracting 5 from each side of the inequality.

$$5 + \frac{1}{2}x \leq 3 - \frac{1}{2}x \qquad \text{Given inequality}$$

$$5 + \frac{1}{2}x - 5 \leq 3 - \frac{1}{2}x - 5 \qquad \text{Subtract 5 from each side.}$$

$$\frac{1}{2}x \leq -\frac{1}{2}x - 2 \qquad \text{Subtract real numbers.}$$

$$\frac{1}{2}x + \frac{1}{2}x \leq -\frac{1}{2}x + \frac{1}{2}x - 2 \qquad \text{Add } \tfrac{1}{2}x \text{ to each side.}$$

$$x \leq -2 \qquad \text{Combine like terms.}$$

The solution set is given by $x \leq -2$ and is graphed as follows.

Now Try Exercise 53

The Multiplication Property of Inequalities

The multiplication property of inequalities differs from the multiplication property of *equality*. When we multiply each side of an inequality by the same nonzero number, we may need to reverse the inequality symbol to make sure that the resulting inequality remains true. Table 2.11 shows various results that occur when each side of a true inequality is multiplied by the same nonzero number.

TABLE 2.11 Determining When the Inequality Symbol Should Be Reversed

True Statement	Multiply Each Side By	Resulting Inequality	Is the Result True or False?	Reverse the Inequality Symbol
$-3 < 5$	4	$-12 \overset{?}{<} 20$	True	Not needed
$7 > -1$	-2	$-14 \overset{?}{>} 2$	False	$-14 < 2$
$-2 > -5$	3	$-6 \overset{?}{>} -15$	True	Not needed
$4 < 9$	-11	$-44 \overset{?}{<} -99$	False	$-44 > -99$

Table 2.11 indicates that the inequality symbol must be reversed when each side of the given inequality is *multiplied by a negative number*. This result is summarized below.

MULTIPLICATION PROPERTY OF INEQUALITIES

Let a, b, and c be expressions that represent real numbers with $c \neq 0$.

1. If $c > 0$, then the inequalities $a < b$ and $ac < bc$ are equivalent. That is, each side of an inequality may be multiplied (or divided) by the same positive number.
2. If $c < 0$, then the inequalities $a < b$ and $ac > bc$ are equivalent. That is, each side of an inequality may be multiplied (or divided) by the same negative number, provided the inequality symbol is reversed.

Note that similar properties exist for $\leq$ and $\geq$.

NOTE: Remember to reverse the inequality symbol when either multiplying or *dividing* by a negative number.

READING CHECK

- When solving an inequality, when does it become necessary to reverse the inequality symbol?

EXAMPLE 7 | **Applying the multiplication property of inequalities**

Solve each inequality. Then graph the solution set.
(a) $3x < 18$ **(b)** $-7 \leq -\frac{1}{2}x$

Solution
(a) To solve for x, divide each side by 3.

$$3x < 18 \quad \text{Given inequality}$$

$$\frac{3x}{3} < \frac{18}{3} \quad \text{Divide each side by 3.}$$

$$x < 6 \quad \text{Simplify fractions.}$$

The solution set is given by $x < 6$ and is graphed as follows.

(b) To isolate x in $-7 \leq -\frac{1}{2}x$, multiply each side by -2 and reverse the inequality symbol.

$$-7 \leq -\frac{1}{2}x \qquad \text{Given inequality}$$

$$-2(-7) \geq -2\left(-\frac{1}{2}\right)x \quad \text{Multiply by } -2; \text{ reverse the inequality.}$$

$$14 \geq 1 \cdot x \qquad \text{Multiply the real numbers.}$$

$$x \leq 14 \qquad \text{Rewrite the inequality.}$$

The solution set is given by $x \leq 14$ and is graphed as follows.

Now Try Exercises 55, 57

SET-BUILDER NOTATION Because $x \leq 14$ is an inequality with infinitely many solutions and is not itself a set of solutions, a notation called **set-builder notation** has been devised for writing the solutions to an inequality as a set. For example, the solution set consisting of "all real numbers x such that x is less than or equal to 14" can be written as $\{x \mid x \leq 14\}$. The vertical line segment "$\mid$" is read "such that."

In the next example, the solution sets are expressed in set-builder notation. However, this notation is not widely used throughout this text.

EXAMPLE 8   **Applying both properties of inequalities**

Solve each inequality. Write the solution set in set-builder notation.
(a) $4x - 7 \geq -6$ **(b)** $-8 + 4x \leq 5x + 3$ **(c)** $0.4(2x - 5) < 1.1x + 2$

Solution
(a) Start by adding 7 to each side.

$$4x - 7 \geq -6 \qquad \text{Given inequality}$$

$$4x - 7 + 7 \geq -6 + 7 \quad \text{Add 7 to each side.}$$

$$4x \geq 1 \qquad \text{Add real numbers.}$$

$$\frac{4x}{4} \geq \frac{1}{4} \qquad \text{Divide each side by 4.}$$

$$x \geq \frac{1}{4} \qquad \text{Simplify.}$$

In set-builder notation, the solution set is $\left\{x \mid x \geq \frac{1}{4}\right\}$.
(b) Begin by adding 8 to each side.

$$-8 + 4x \leq 5x + 3 \qquad \text{Given inequality}$$

$$-8 + 4x + 8 \leq 5x + 3 + 8 \quad \text{Add 8 to each side.}$$

$$4x \leq 5x + 11 \qquad \text{Add real numbers.}$$

$$4x - 5x \leq 5x + 11 - 5x \quad \text{Subtract } 5x \text{ from each side.}$$

$$-x \leq 11 \qquad \text{Combine like terms.}$$

$$-1 \cdot (-x) \geq -1 \cdot 11 \quad \text{Multiply by } -1; \text{ reverse the inequality.}$$

$$x \geq -11 \qquad \text{Simplify.}$$

The solution set is $\{x \mid x \geq -11\}$.

(c) Begin by applying the distributive property.

$$0.4(2x - 5) < 1.1x + 2 \quad \text{Given inequality}$$

$$0.8x - 2 < 1.1x + 2 \quad \text{Distributive property}$$

$$0.8x < 1.1x + 4 \quad \text{Add 2 to each side.}$$

$$-0.3x < 4 \quad \text{Subtract } 1.1x \text{ from each side.}$$

$$x > -\frac{4}{0.3} \quad \text{Divide by } -0.3; \text{ reverse the inequality.}$$

Since $-\frac{4}{0.3} = -\frac{40}{3}$, the solution set is $\left\{ x \mid x > -\frac{40}{3} \right\}$.

Now Try Exercises 67, 77, 85

CRITICAL THINKING

Solve
$-5 - 3x > -2x + 7$ without having to reverse the inequality symbol.

Applications

To solve applications involving inequalities, we often have to translate words or phrases to mathematical statements. Table 2.12 lists words and phrases that are associated with each inequality symbol.

READING CHECK

• Give two phrases associated with each inequality symbol.

TABLE 2.12 **Words and Phrases Associated with Inequality Symbols**

Symbol	Associated Words and Phrases
$>$	greater than, more than, exceeds, above, over
$<$	less than, fewer than, below, under
$\geq$	greater than or equal to, at least, is not less than
$\leq$	less than or equal to, at most, does not exceed

EXAMPLE 9   **Translating words to inequalities**

Translate each phrase to an inequality. Let the variable be x.
(a) A number that is more than 30
(b) An age that is at least 18
(c) A grade point average that is at most 3.25

Solution
(a) The inequality $x > 30$ represents a number x that is more than 30.
(b) The inequality $x \geq 18$ represents an age x that is at least 18.
(c) The inequality $x \leq 3.25$ represents a grade point average x that is at most 3.25.

Now Try Exercises 95, 101

▶ **REAL-WORLD CONNECTION** In the atmosphere the air temperature generally becomes colder as the altitude increases. One mile above Earth's surface the temperature is about 19°F colder than the ground-level temperature. As the air cools, there is an increased chance of clouds forming. In the next example we estimate the altitudes where clouds may form. (*Source:* A. Miller and R. Anthes, *Meteorology.*)

EXAMPLE 10   **Finding the altitude of clouds**

If the ground temperature is 79°F, then the temperature T above Earth's surface is given by the formula $T = 79 - 19x$, where x is the altitude in miles. Suppose that clouds form only where the temperature is 3°F or colder. Determine the heights at which clouds may form.

Solution

Clouds may form at altitudes at which $T \leq 3$ degrees. Since $T = 79 - 19x$, we can substitute the expression $79 - 19x$ for T to obtain the inequality $79 - 19x \leq 3$.

$$79 - 19x \leq 3 \qquad \text{Inequality to be solved}$$
$$-19x \leq -76 \qquad \text{Subtract 79 from each side.}$$
$$\frac{-19x}{-19} \geq \frac{-76}{-19} \qquad \text{Divide by } -19; \text{ reverse the inequality.}$$
$$x \geq 4 \qquad \text{Simplify the fractions.}$$

Clouds may form at 4 miles or higher.

▌ Now Try Exercise 115

EXAMPLE 11 **Calculating revenue, cost, and profit**

For a computer company, the cost to produce one laptop computer (variable cost) is $1320 plus a one-time cost (fixed cost) of $200,000 for research and development. The revenue received from selling one laptop computer is $1850.
(a) Write a formula that gives the cost C of producing x laptop computers.
(b) Write a formula that gives the revenue R from selling x laptop computers.
(c) Profit equals revenue minus cost. Write a formula that calculates the profit P from selling x laptop computers.
(d) How many computers need to be sold to yield a positive profit?

Solution

(a) The cost of producing the first laptop is

$$1320 \times 1 + 200{,}000 = \$201{,}320.$$

The cost of producing two laptops is

$$1320 \times 2 + 200{,}000 = \$202{,}640.$$

And, in general, the cost of producing x laptops is

$$1320 \times x + 200{,}000 = 1320x + 200{,}000.$$

Thus $C = 1320x + 200{,}000$.
(b) Because the company receives $1850 for each laptop, the revenue for x laptops is given by $R = 1850x$.
(c) Profit equals revenue minus cost, so

$$P = R - C$$
$$= 1850x - (1320x + 200{,}000)$$
$$= 530x - 200{,}000.$$

Thus $P = 530x - 200{,}000$.
(d) To determine how many laptops need to be sold to yield a positive profit, we must solve the inequality $P > 0$.

$$530x - 200{,}000 > 0 \qquad \text{Inequality to be solved}$$
$$530x > 200{,}000 \qquad \text{Add 200,000 to each side.}$$
$$x > \frac{200{,}000}{530} \qquad \text{Divide each side by 530.}$$

Because $\frac{200{,}000}{530} \approx 377.4$, the company must sell at least 378 laptops. Note that the company cannot sell a fraction of a laptop.

▌ Now Try Exercise 111

2.5 Putting It All Together

CONCEPT	COMMENTS	EXAMPLES
Linear Inequality	If the equals sign in a linear equation is replaced with $<$, $>$, $\leq$, or $\geq$, a linear inequality results.	*Linear Equation* *Linear Inequality* $4x - 1 = 0$ $4x - 1 > 0$ $2 - x = 3x$ $2 - x \leq 3x$ $4(x + 3) = 1 - x$ $4(x + 3) < 1 - x$ $-6x + 3 = 5$ $-6x + 3 \geq 5$
Solution to an Inequality	A value for the variable that makes the inequality a true statement	6 is a solution to $2x > 5$ because $2(6) > 5$ is a true statement.
Set-Builder Notation	A notation that can be used to identify the solution set to an inequality	The solution set for $x - 2 < 5$ can be written as $\{x \mid x < 7\}$ and is read "the set of real numbers x such that x is less than 7."
Solution Set to an Inequality	The set of all solutions to an inequality	The solution set to $x + 1 > 5$ is given by $x > 4$ and can be written in set-builder notation as $\{x \mid x > 4\}$.
Number Line Graphs	The solutions to an inequality can be graphed on a number line.	$x < 2$ is graphed as follows. $x \geq -1$ is graphed as follows.
Addition Property of Inequalities	$a < b$ is equivalent to $a + c < b + c$, where a, b, and c represent real number expressions.	$x - 5 \geq 6$ Given inequality $x \geq 11$ Add 5. $3x > 5 + 2x$ Given inequality $x > 5$ Subtract $2x$.
Multiplication Property of Inequalities	$a < b$ is equivalent to $ac < bc$ when $c > 0$, and is equivalent to $ac > bc$ when $c < 0$.	$\dfrac{1}{2}x \geq 6$ Given inequality $x \geq 12$ Multiply by 2. $-3x > 5$ Given inequality $x < -\dfrac{5}{3}$ Divide by -3; reverse the inequality symbol.

2.5   Exercises

MyMathLab   Math XL   PRACTICE   WATCH   DOWNLOAD   READ   REVIEW

CONCEPTS AND VOCABULARY

1. A linear inequality results whenever the equals sign in a linear equation is replaced by any one of the symbols _____, _____, _____, or _____.

2. Equality is the boundary between _____ and _____.

3. A(n) _____ is a value of the variable that makes an inequality statement true.

4. Two linear inequalities are _____ if they have the same solution set.

5. (True or False?) When a linear equation is solved, the solution set contains one solution.

6. (True or False?) When a linear inequality is solved, the solution set contains infinitely many solutions.

7. The solution set to a linear inequality can be graphed by using a(n) _____.

8. The addition property of inequalities states that if $a > b$, then $a + c$ _____ $b + c$.

9. The multiplication property of inequalities states that if $a < b$ and $c > 0$, then ac _____ bc.

10. The multiplication property of inequalities states that if $a < b$ and $c < 0$, then ac _____ bc.

SOLUTIONS AND NUMBER LINE GRAPHS

Exercises 11–18: Use a number line to graph the solution set to the inequality.

11. $x < 0$

12. $x > -2$

13. $x > 1$

14. $x < -\frac{5}{2}$

15. $x \le 1.5$

16. $x \ge -3$

17. $z \ge -2$

18. $z \le -\pi$

Exercises 19–24: Express the set of real numbers graphed on the number line as an inequality.

19.

20.

21.

22.

23.

24.

Exercises 25–30

Exercises 25–30: Write the solution set to the inequality in interval notation.

25. $x \ge 6$

26. $x < 3$

27. $y > -2$

28. $y \ge 1$

29. $z \le 7$

30. $z < -5$

Exercises 31–38: Determine whether the given value of the variable is a solution to the inequality.

31. $x + 5 > 5$ $x = 4$

32. $-3x \le -8$ $x = -2$

33. $5x \ge 25$ $x = 3$

34. $4y - 3 \le 5$ $y = -3$

35. $3y + 5 \ge -8$ $y = -3$

36. $-(z + 7) > 3(6 - z)$ $z = 2$

37. $5(z + 1) < 3z - 7$ $z = -4$

38. $\frac{3}{2}t - \frac{1}{2} \ge 1 - t$ $t = \frac{3}{5}$

TABLES AND LINEAR INEQUALITIES

Exercises 39–42: Use the table to solve the inequality.

39. $3x + 6 > 0$

x	−4	−3	−2	−1	0
$3x + 6$	−6	−3	0	3	6

40. $6 - 3x \le 0$

x	1	2	3	4	5
$6 - 3x$	3	0	−3	−6	−9

41. $-2x + 7 > 5$

x	−1	0	1	2	3
$-2x + 7$	9	7	5	3	1

42. $5(x - 3) \le 4$

x	3.2	3.4	3.6	3.8	4
$5(x - 3)$	1	2	3	4	5

Exercises 43–46: Complete the table. Then use the table to solve the inequality.

43. $-2x + 6 \le 0$

x	1	2	3	4	5
$-2x + 6$	4				-4

44. $3x - 1 < 8$

x	0	1	2	3	4
$3x - 1$	-1				

45. $5 - x > x + 7$

x	-3	-2	-1	0	1
$5 - x$	8				4
$x + 7$	4				8

46. $2(3 - x) \ge -3(x - 2)$

x	-2	-1	0	1	2
$2(3 - x)$					
$-3(x - 2)$					

SOLVING LINEAR INEQUALITIES

Exercises 47–54: Use the addition property of inequalities to solve the inequality. Graph the solution set.

47. $x - 3 > 0$ **48.** $x + 6 < 3$

49. $3 - y \le 5$ **50.** $8 - y \ge 10$

51. $12 < 4 + z$ **52.** $2z \le z + 17$

53. $5 - 2t \ge 10 - t$ **54.** $-2t > -3t + 1$

Exercises 55–62: Use the multiplication property of inequalities to solve the inequality. Graph the solution set.

55. $2x < 10$ **56.** $3x > 9$

57. $-\frac{1}{2}t \ge 1$ **58.** $-5t \le -6$

59. $\frac{3}{4} > -5y$ **60.** $10 \ge -\frac{1}{7}y$

61. $-\frac{2}{3} \le \frac{1}{7}z$ **62.** $-\frac{3}{10}z < 11$

Exercises 63–68: Solve the linear inequality and write the solution in set-builder notation.

63. $x + 6 > 7$ **64.** $x + 4 < 1$

65. $-3x \le 21$ **66.** $4x \ge -20$

67. $2x - 3 < 9$ **68.** $-5x + 4 < 44$

Exercises 69–94: Solve the linear inequality.

69. $3x + 1 < 22$ **70.** $4 + 5x \le 9$

71. $5 - \frac{3}{4}x \ge 6$ **72.** $10 - \frac{2}{5}x > 0$

73. $45 > 6 - 2x$ **74.** $69 \ge 3 - 11x$

75. $5x - 2 \le 3x + 1$ **76.** $12x + 1 < 25 - 3x$

77. $-x + 24 < x + 23$ **78.** $6 - 4x \le x + 1$

79. $-(x + 1) \ge 3(x - 2)$

80. $5(x + 2) > -2(x - 3)$

81. $3(2x + 1) > -(5 - 3x)$

82. $4x \ge -3(7 - 2x) + 1$

83. $1.6x + 0.4 \le 0.4x$

84. $-5.1x + 1.1 < 0.1 - 0.1x$

85. $0.8x - 0.5 < x + 1 - 0.5x$

86. $0.1(x + 1) - 0.1 \le 0.2x - 0.5$

87. $-\frac{1}{2}\left(\frac{2}{3}x + 4\right) \ge x$

88. $-5x > \frac{4}{5}\left(\frac{10}{3}x + 10\right)$

89. $\frac{3}{7}x + \frac{2}{7} > -\frac{1}{7}x - \frac{5}{14}$

90. $\frac{5}{6} - \frac{1}{3}x \ge -\frac{1}{3}\left(\frac{5}{6}x - 1\right)$

91. $\frac{x}{3} + \frac{5x}{6} \le \frac{2}{3}$ **92.** $\frac{3x}{4} - \frac{x}{2} < 1$

93. $\frac{6x}{7} < \frac{1}{3}x + 1$ **94.** $\frac{5x}{8} - \frac{3x}{4} \le 8$

TRANSLATING PHRASES TO INEQUALITIES

Exercises 95–102: Translate each phrase to an inequality. Let x be the variable.

95. A speed that is greater than 60 miles per hour

96. A speed that is at most 60 miles per hour

97. An age that is at least 21 years old

98. An age that is less than 21 years old

99. A salary that is more than $40,000

100. A salary that is less than or equal to $40,000

101. A speed that does not exceed 70 miles per hour

102. A speed that is not less than 70 miles per hour

APPLICATIONS

103. *Geometry* Find all values for x so that the perimeter of the rectangle is less than 50 feet.

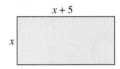

104. *Geometry* A triangle with height 12 inches is to have area less than 120 square inches. What must be true about the base of the triangle?

105. *Grade Average* A student scores 74 out of 100 on a test. If the maximum score on the next test is also 100 points, what score does the student need to maintain at least an average of 80?

106. *Grade Average* A student scores 65 and 82 on two different 100-point tests. If the maximum score on the next test is also 100 points, what score does the student need to maintain at least an average of 70?

107. *Parking Rates* Parking in a student lot costs $2 for the first half hour and $1.25 for each hour thereafter. A partial hour is charged the same as a full hour. What is the longest time that a student can park in this lot for $8?

108. *Parking Rates* Parking in a student lot costs $2.50 for the first hour and $1 for each hour thereafter. A nearby lot costs $1.25 for each hour. In both lots a partial hour is charged as a full hour. In which lot can a student park the longest for $5? For $11?

109. *Car Rental* A rental car costs $25 per day plus $0.20 per mile. If someone has $200 to spend and needs to drive the car 90 miles each day, for how many days can that person rent the car? Assume that the car cannot be rented for part of a day.

110. *Car Rental* One car rental agency charges $20 per day plus $0.25 per mile. A different agency charges $37 per day with unlimited mileage. For what mileages is the second rental agency a better deal?

111. *Revenue and Cost* (Refer to Example 11.) The cost to produce one compact disc is $1.50 plus a one-time fixed cost of $2000. The revenue received from selling one compact disc is $12.
(a) Write a formula that gives the cost C of producing x compact discs. Be sure to include the fixed cost.
(b) Write a formula that gives the revenue R from selling x compact discs.
(c) Profit equals revenue minus cost. Write a formula that calculates the profit P from selling x compact discs.

(d) How many compact discs need to be sold to yield a positive profit?

112. *Revenue and Cost* The cost to produce one laptop computer is $890 plus a one-time fixed cost of $100,000 for research and development. The revenue received from selling one laptop computer is $1520.
(a) Write a formula that gives the cost C of producing x laptop computers.
(b) Write a formula that gives the revenue R from selling x laptop computers.
(c) Profit equals revenue minus cost. Write a formula that calculates the profit P from selling x laptop computers.
(d) How many computers need to be sold to yield a positive profit?

113. *Distance and Time* Two athletes are jogging in the same direction along an exercise path. After x minutes the first athlete's distance in miles from a parking lot is given by $\frac{1}{6}x$ and the second athlete's distance is given by $\frac{1}{8}x + 2$.
(a) When are the athletes the same distance from the parking lot?
(b) When is the first athlete farther from the parking lot than the second?

114. *Altitude and Dew Point* If the dew point on the ground is $65°\text{F}$, then the dew point x miles high is given by $D = 65 - 5.8x$. Determine the altitudes at which the dew point is greater than $36°\text{F}$. (*Source:* A. Miller.)

115. *Altitude and Temperature* (Refer to Example 10.) If the temperature on the ground is $90°\text{F}$, then the air temperature x miles high is given by $T = 90 - 19x$. Determine the altitudes at which the air temperature is less than $4.5°\text{F}$. (*Source:* A. Miller.)

116. *Size and Weight of a Fish* If the length of a bass is between 20 and 25 inches, its weight W in pounds can be estimated by the formula $W = 0.96x - 14.4$, where x is the length of the fish. (*Source:* Minnesota Department of Natural Resources.)
(a) What length of bass is likely to weigh 7.2 pounds?
(b) What lengths of bass are likely to weigh less than 7.2 pounds?

WRITING ABOUT MATHEMATICS

117. Explain each of the terms and give an example.
(a) Linear equation   (b) Linear inequality

118. Suppose that a student says that a linear equation and a linear inequality can be solved the same way. How would you respond?

Checking Basic Concepts

1. Use a number line to graph the solution set to the inequality $x + 1 \geq -1$.

2. Express the set of real numbers graphed on the number line by using an inequality.

3. Determine whether -3 is a solution to the inequality $4x - 5 \leq -15$.

4. Complete the table. Then use the table to solve the inequality $5 - 2x \leq 7$.

x	-2	-1	0	1	2
$5 - 2x$					1

5. Solve each inequality.
   (a) $x + 5 > 8$
   (b) $-\frac{5}{7}x \leq 25$
   (c) $3x \geq -2(1 - 2x) + 3$

6. Translate the phrase "a price that is not more than $12" to an inequality using the variable x.

7. *Geometry* The length of a rectangle is 5 inches longer than twice its width. If the perimeter of the rectangle is more than 88 inches, find all possible widths for the rectangle.

CHAPTER 2   Summary

SECTION 2.1 ■ INTRODUCTION TO EQUATIONS

Equations An equation is a mathematical statement that two expressions are equal. Every equation contains an equals sign. An equation can be either true or false.

Important Terms

Solution	A value for a variable that makes the equation true
Solution Set	The set of all solutions
Equivalent Equations	Equations that have the same solution set
Checking a Solution	Substituting the solution in the given equation to verify that the solution makes the equation true

Example: 3 is the solution to $4x - 2 = 10$ because $4(3) - 2 = 10$ is a true statement.

Properties of Equality

Addition Property $a = b$ is equivalent to $a + c = b + c$.

Example: $x - 3 = 0$ and $x - 3 + 3 = 0 + 3$ are equivalent equations.

Multiplication Property $a = b$ is equivalent to $ac = bc$, provided $c \neq 0$.

Example: $2x = 5$ and $2x \cdot \frac{1}{2} = 5 \cdot \frac{1}{2}$ are equivalent equations.

SECTION 2.2 ■ LINEAR EQUATIONS

Linear Equation Can be written in the form $ax + b = 0$, where $a \neq 0$

Examples: $3x - 5 = 0$ is linear, whereas $5x^2 + 2x = 0$ is *not* linear.

Solving Linear Equations Numerically To solve a linear equation numerically, complete a table for various values of the variable and then select the solution from the table.

Example: The solution to $3x - 4 = -1$ is 1.

x	-1	0	1
$3x - 4$	-7	-4	-1

Solving Linear Equations Symbolically The following steps can be used as a guide for solving linear equations symbolically.

STEP 1: Use the distributive property to clear any parentheses on each side of the equation. Combine any like terms on each side.

STEP 2: Use the addition property of equality to get all of the terms containing the variable on one side of the equation and all other terms on the other side of the equation. Combine any like terms on each side.

STEP 3: Use the multiplication property of equality to isolate the variable by multiplying each side of the equation by the reciprocal of the number in front of the variable (or divide each side by that number).

STEP 4: Check the solution by substituting it in the given equation.

Distributive Properties $a(b + c) = ab + ac$ or $a(b - c) = ab - ac$

Examples: $5(2x + 3) = 10x + 15$ and $5(2x - 3) = 10x - 15$

Clearing Fractions and Decimals When fractions or decimals appear in an equation, multiplying each side by the least common denominator can be helpful.

Examples: Multiply each side of $\frac{1}{3}x - \frac{1}{6} = \frac{2}{3}$ by 6 to obtain $2x - 1 = 4$.

Multiply each side of $0.04x + 0.1 = 0.07$ by 100 to obtain $4x + 10 = 7$.

Number of Solutions Equations that can be written in the form $ax + b = 0$, where a and b are *any* real number, can have no solutions, one solution, or infinitely many solutions.

Examples: $x + 3 = x$ is equivalent to $3 = 0$. (No solutions)

$2y + 1 = 9$ is equivalent to $y = 4$. (One solution)

$z + z = 2z$ is equivalent to $0 = 0$. (Infinitely many solutions)

SECTION 2.4 ■ FORMULAS

Formula A formula is an equation that can be used to calculate a quantity by using known values of other quantities.

Formulas from Geometry

Area of a Rectangle	$A = lw$, where l is the length and w is the width.
Perimeter of a Rectangle	$P = 2l + 2w$, where l is the length and w is the width.
Area of a Triangle	$A = \frac{1}{2}bh$, where b is the base and h is the height.
Degree Measure	There are 360° in one complete revolution.
Angle Measure	The sum of the measures of the angles in a triangle equals 180°.
Circumference	$C = 2\pi r$, where r is the radius.

Area of a Circle	$A = \pi r^2$, where r is the radius.
Area of a Trapezoid	$A = \frac{1}{2}(a + b)h$, where h is the height and a and b are the bases of the trapezoid.
Volume of a Box	$V = lwh$, where l is the length, w is the width, and h is the height.
Surface Area of a Box	$S = 2lw + 2wh + 2lh$, where l is the length, w is the width, and h is the height.
Volume of a Cylinder	$V = \pi r^2 h$, where r is the radius and h is the height.

Other Formulas

Grade Point Average (GPA) $\text{GPA} = \frac{4a + 3b + 2c + d}{a + b + c + d + \cdots}$, where a represents the number of A credits earned, b the number of B credits earned, and so on.

Temperature Scales $F = \frac{9}{5}C + 32$ and $C = \frac{5}{9}(F - 32)$, where F is the Fahrenheit temperature and C is the Celsius temperature.

See Putting It All Together in Section 2.4 for examples.

SECTION 2.5 ■ LINEAR INEQUALITIES

Linear Inequality When the equals sign in a linear equation is replaced with any one of the symbols $<$, $\leq$, $>$, or $\geq$, a linear inequality results.

Examples: $x > 0$, $6 - \frac{2}{3}x \leq 7$,   and $4(x - 1) < 3x - 1$

Solution to an Inequality Any value for the variable that makes the inequality a true statement

Example: 3 is a solution to $2x < 9$ because $2(3) < 9$ is a true statement.

Number Line Graphs A number line can be used to graph the solution set to a linear inequality.

Example: The graph of $x \leq 1$ is shown in the figure.

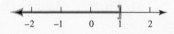

Properties of Inequality

Addition Property $a < b$ is equivalent to $a + c < b + c$.

Example: $x - 3 < 0$ and $x - 3 + 3 < 0 + 3$ are equivalent inequalities.

Multiplication Property   When $c > 0$, $a < b$ is equivalent to $ac < bc$.
When $c < 0$, $a < b$ is equivalent to $ac > bc$.

Examples: $2x < 6$ is equivalent to $2x\left(\frac{1}{2}\right) < 6\left(\frac{1}{2}\right)$ or $x < 3$.

$-2x < 6$ is equivalent to $-2x\left(-\frac{1}{2}\right) > 6\left(-\frac{1}{2}\right)$ or $x > -3$.

CHAPTER 2 Review Exercises

SECTION 2.1

Exercises 1–8: Solve the equation. Check your solution.

1. $x + 9 = 3$

2. $x - 4 = -2$

3. $x - \frac{3}{4} = \frac{3}{2}$

4. $x + 0.5 = 0$

5. $4x = 12$

6. $3x = -7$

7. $-0.5x = 1.25$

8. $-\frac{1}{3}x = \frac{7}{6}$

SECTION 2.2

Exercises 9 and 10: Decide whether the equation is linear. If the equation is linear, give values for a and b so that it can be written in the form $ax + b = 0$.

9. $-4x + 3 = 2$

10. $\frac{3}{8}x^2 - x = \frac{1}{4}$

Exercises 11–20: Solve the equation. Check the solution.

11. $4x - 5 = 3$

12. $7 - \frac{1}{2}x = -4$

13. $5(x - 3) = 12$

14. $3 + x = 2x - 4$

15. $2(x - 1) = 4(x + 3)$

16. $1 - (x - 3) = 6 + 2x$

17. $3.4x - 4 = 5 - 0.6x$

18. $-\frac{1}{3}(3 - 6x) = -(x + 2) + 1$

19. $\frac{2}{3}x - \frac{1}{6} = \frac{5}{12}$

20. $2y - 3(2 - y) = 5 + y$

Exercises 21–24: Determine whether the equation has no solutions, one solution, or infinitely many solutions.

21. $4(3x - 2) = 2(6x + 5)$

22. $5(3x - 1) = 15x - 5$

23. $8x = 5x + 3x$

24. $9x - 2 = 8x - 2$

Exercises 25 and 26: Complete the table. Then use the table to solve the given equation.

25. $-2x + 3 = 0$

x	0.5	1.0	1.5	2.0	2.5
$-2x + 3$	2				

26. $-(x + 1) + 3 = 2$

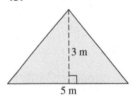

x	-2	-1	0	1	2
$-(x + 1) + 3$					

SECTION 2.4

Exercises 45 and 46: Find the area of the region shown.

45.

46.

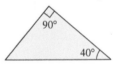

47. Find the area of a rectangle having a 24-inch width and a 3-foot length.

48. Find the perimeter of a rectangle having a 13-inch length and a 7-inch width.

49. Find the circumference of a circle having an 18-foot diameter.

50. Find the area of a circle having a 5-inch radius.

51. Find the measure of the third angle in the triangle.

52. The angles in a triangle have measures x, $3x$, and $4x$. Find the value of x.

53. If a cylinder has radius 5 inches and height 25 inches, find its volume. (*Hint:* $V = \pi r^2 h$.)

54. Find the area of a trapezoid with height 5 feet and bases 3 feet and 18 inches. (*Hint:* $A = \frac{1}{2}(a + b)h$.)

Exercises 55 and 56: Find the area of the figure shown.

55.

56.

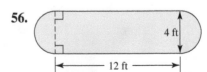

Exercises 57–62: Solve the given formula for the specified variable.

57. $3x = 5 + y$ for y

58. $16 = 2x + 2y$ for y

59. $z = 2xy$ for y

60. $S = \dfrac{a + b + c}{3}$ for b

61. $T = \dfrac{a}{3} + \dfrac{b}{4}$ for b

62. $cd = ab + bc$ for c

Exercises 63 and 64: Let the variable a represent the number of credits with a grade of A, b the number of credits with a grade of B, and so on. Calculate the grade point average (GPA). Round your answer to the nearest hundredth.

63. $a = 20, b = 25, c = 12, d = 4, \tilde{} = 4$

64. $a = 64, b = 32, c = 20, d = 10, \tilde{} = 3$

65. Convert 15°C to an equivalent Fahrenheit temperature.

66. Convert 113°F to an equivalent Celsius temperature.

SECTION 2.5

Exercises 67–70: Use a number line to graph the solution set to the inequality.

67. $x < 2$

68. $x > -1$

69. $y \geq -\dfrac{3}{2}$

70. $y \leq 2.5$

Exercises 71 and 72: Express the set of real numbers graphed on the number line with an inequality.

71.

72.

Exercises 73 and 74: Determine whether the given value of x is a solution to the inequality.

73. $1 - (x + 3) \geq x$ $x = -2$

74. $4(x + 1) < -(5 - x)$ $x = -1$

Exercises 75 and 76: Complete the table and then use the table to solve the inequality.

75. $5 - x > 3$

x	0	1	2	3	4
$5 - x$	5				

76. $2x - 5 \leq 0$

x	1	1.5	2	2.5	3
$2x - 5$	-3				

Exercises 77–82: Solve the inequality.

77. $x - 3 > 0$

78. $-2x \leq 10$

79. $5 - 2x \geq 7$

80. $3(x - 1) < 20$

81. $5x \leq 3 - (4x + 2)$

82. $3x - 2(4 - x) \geq x + 1$

Exercises 83–86: Translate the phrase to an inequality. Let x be the variable.

83. A speed that is less than 50 miles per hour

84. A salary that is at most $45,000

85. An age that is at least 16 years old

86. A year before 1995

APPLICATIONS

87. *Rainfall* On a stormy day 2 inches of rain fall before noon and $\frac{3}{4}$ inch per hour fall thereafter until 5 P.M.
  (a) Make a table that shows the total rainfall at each hour starting at noon and ending at 5 P.M.
  (b) Write a formula that calculates the rainfall R in inches, x hours past noon.
  (c) Use your formula to calculate the total rainfall at 5 P.M. Does your answer agree with the value in your table from part (a)?
  (d) How much rain had fallen at 3:45 P.M.?

88. *Cost of a Laptop* A 5% sales tax on a laptop computer amounted to $106.25. Find the cost of the laptop.

89. *Distance Traveled* At noon a bicyclist is 50 miles from home, riding toward home at 10 miles per hour.
  (a) Make a table that shows the bicyclist's distance D from home after 1, 2, 3, 4, and 5 hours.
  (b) Write a formula that calculates the distance D from home after x hours.
  (c) Use your formula to determine D when $x = 3$ hours. Does your answer agree with the value shown in your table?
  (d) For what times was the bicyclist at least 20 miles from home? Assume that $0 \leq x \leq 5$.

90. *Master's Degree* In 2001, about 468,500 people received a master's degree, and in 2008, about 625,000 did. Find the percent change in the number of master's degrees received between 2001 and 2008.

91. *Car Speeds* One car passes another car on a freeway. The faster car is traveling 12 miles per hour faster than the slower car. Determine how long it will be before the faster car is 2 miles ahead of the slower car.

92. *Dimensions of a Rectangle* The width of a rectangle is 10 inches less than its length. If the perimeter is 112 inches, find the dimensions of the rectangle.

93. *Saline Solution* A saline solution contains 3% salt. How much water should be added to 100 milliliters of this solution to dilute it to a 2% solution?

94. *Investment Money* A student invests two sums of money, $500 and $800, at different interest rates, receiving a total of $55 in interest after one year. The $500 investment receives an interest rate 2% lower than the interest rate for the $800 investment. Find the interest rate for each investment.

95. *Geometry* A triangle with height 8 inches is to have an area that is not more than 100 square inches. What lengths are possible for the base of the triangle?

96. *Grade Average* A student scores 75 and 91 on two different tests of 100 points. If the maximum score on the next test is also 100 points, what score does the student need to maintain an average of at least 80?

97. *Parking Rates* Parking in a lot costs $2.25 for the first hour and $1.25 for each hour thereafter. A partial hour is charged the same as a full hour. What is the longest time that someone can park for $9?

98. *Profit* The cost to produce one DVD player is $85 plus a one-time fixed cost of $150,000. The revenue received from selling one DVD player is $225.
   (a) Write a formula that gives the cost C of producing x DVD players.
   (b) Write a formula that gives the revenue R from selling x DVD players.
   (c) Profit equals revenue minus cost. Write a formula that calculates the profit P from selling x DVD players.
   (d) What numbers of DVD players sold will result in a loss? (*Hint:* A loss corresponds to a negative profit.)

CHAPTER 2   Extended and Discovery Exercises

Exercises 1–4: *Average Speed* If someone travels a distance d in time t, then the person's average speed is $\frac{d}{t}$. Use this fact to solve the problem.

1. A driver travels at 50 mph for the first hour and then travels at 70 mph for the second hour. What is the average speed of the car?

2. A bicyclist rides 1 mile uphill at 5 mph and then rides 1 mile downhill at 10 mph. Find the average speed of the bicyclist. Does your answer agree with what you expected?

3. At a 3-mile cross-country race an athlete runs 2 miles at 8 mph and 1 mile at 10 mph. What is the athlete's average speed?

4. A pilot flies an airplane between two cities and travels half the distance at 200 mph and the other half at 100 mph. Find the average speed of the airplane.

5. *A Puzzle About Coins* Suppose that seven coins look exactly alike but that one coin weighs less than any of the other six coins. If you have only a balance with two pans, devise a plan to find the lighter coin. What is the minimum number of weighings necessary? Explain your answer.

6. *Global Warming* If the global climate were to warm significantly as a result of the greenhouse effect or other climatic change, the Arctic ice cap would start to melt. This ice cap contains the equivalent of some 680,000 cubic miles of water. More than 200 million people live on land that is less than 3 feet above sea level. In the United States several large cities have low average elevations. Three examples are Boston (14 feet), New Orleans (4 feet), and San Diego (13 feet). In this exercise you are to estimate the rise in sea level if the Arctic ice cap were to melt and to determine whether this event would have a significant impact on people living in coastal areas.

   (a) The surface area of a sphere is given by the formula $4\pi r^2$, where r is its radius. Although the shape of Earth is not exactly spherical, it has an average radius of 3960 miles. Estimate the surface area of Earth.

   (b) Oceans cover approximately 71% of the total surface area of Earth. How many square miles of Earth's surface are covered by oceans?

   (c) Approximate the potential rise in sea level by dividing the total volume of the water from the ice cap by the surface area of the oceans. Convert your answer from miles to feet.

   (d) Discuss the implications of your calculation. How would cities such as Boston, New Orleans, and San Diego be affected?

   (e) The Antarctic ice cap contains some 6,300,000 cubic miles of water. Estimate how much the sea level would rise if this ice cap melted. (*Source:* Department of the Interior, Geological Survey.)

3 Graphing Equations

3.1 Introduction to Graphing

3.2 Linear Equations in Two Variables

3.3 More Graphing of Lines

3.4 Slope and Rates of Change

3.5 Slope–Intercept Form

3.6 Point–Slope Form

3.7 Introduction to Modeling

We all have ability. The difference is how we use it.

—STEVIE WONDER

During the first decade of the 21st century, the U.S. economy experienced both incredible growth and substantial decline. One way that economists monitor changes in the economy is by tracking median home prices. The *line graph* in the accompanying figure shows median home prices displayed in two-year intervals. Graphs such as this one provide an excellent way to visualize data trends. In this chapter, we discuss line graphs and other types of graphs that can be used to represent mathematical information visually.

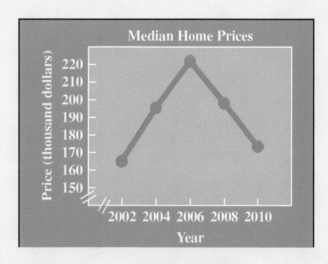

Source: National Association of Realtors.

3.1   Introduction to Graphing

Tables and Graphs • The Rectangular Coordinate System • Scatterplots and Line Graphs

A LOOK INTO MATH ▶

As Internet connection speeds have improved, the amount of visual information displayed on Web pages has increased dramatically. A page of computer graphics contains much more information than a page of printed text. In math, we visualize data by plotting points to make *scatterplots* and *line graphs*. In this section, we discuss the rectangular coordinate system and practice basic point-plotting skills.

Tables and Graphs

NEW VOCABULARY

☐ Rectangular coordinate
   system (xy-plane)
☐ x-axis
☐ y-axis
☐ Origin
☐ Quadrants
☐ Ordered pair
☐ Scatterplot
☐ x-coordinate
☐ y-coordinate
☐ Line graph

When data are displayed in a table, it is often difficult to recognize any trends. In order to visualize information provided by a set of data, it can be helpful to create a graph.

▶ **REAL-WORLD CONNECTION** Table 3.1 lists the per capita (per person) income for the United States for selected years. These income amounts have *not* been adjusted for inflation. When a table contains only four data values, as in Table 3.1, we can easily see that income increased from 2002 to 2008. However, if a table contained 1000 data values, determining trends in the data would be extremely difficult. In mathematical problems, there are frequently infinitely many data points!

Rather than always using tables to display data, presenting data on a graph is often more useful. For example, the data in Table 3.1 are graphed in Figure 3.1. This line graph is more visual than the table and shows the trend at a glance. Line graphs will be discussed further later in this section.

STUDY TIP

Have you been completing all of the assigned homework on time? Regular and timely practice is one of the keys to having a successful experience in any math class. Don't miss the important opportunity to learn math through doing math.

TABLE 3.1 U.S. Per Capita Income

Year	Amount
2002	$31,444
2004	$33,857
2006	$37,679
2008	$40,649

Source: Bureau of Economic Analysis.

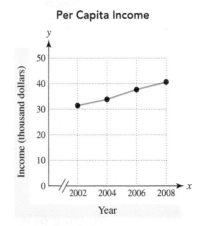

Per Capita Income

Figure 3.1

NOTE: In Figure 3.1 the double hash marks // on the *x*-axis indicate a break in the *x*-axis data values. The years before 2002 have been skipped.

The Rectangular Coordinate System

One common way to graph data is to use the **rectangular coordinate system**, or *xy*-**plane**. In the *xy*-plane the horizontal axis is the *x*-**axis**, and the vertical axis is the *y*-**axis**. The axes can be thought of as intersecting number lines. The point of intersection is called the **origin** and is associated with zero on each axis. Negative values are located left of the origin on the x-axis and below the origin on the y-axis. Similarly, positive values are located right of the origin on the x-axis and above the origin on the y-axis. The axes divide the xy-plane into four regions called **quadrants**, which are numbered I, II, III, and IV counterclockwise, as shown in Figure 3.2.

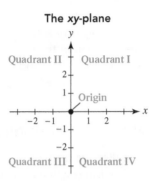

The xy-plane

Figure 3.2

Before we can plot data, we must understand the concept of an **ordered pair** (x, y). In Table 3.1 we can let x-values correspond to the year and y-values correspond to the per capita income. Then the fact that the per capita income in 2002 was $31,444 can be summarized by the ordered pair (2002, 31444). Similarly, the ordered pair (2006, 37679) indicates that the per capita income was $37,679 in 2006.

Order is important in an ordered pair. The ordered pairs given by (1950, 2025) and (2025, 1950) are different. The first ordered pair indicates that the per capita income in 1950 was $2025, whereas the second ordered pair indicates that the per capita income in 2025 will be $1950.

To plot an ordered pair such as $(-2, 3)$ in the xy-plane, begin at the origin and move left to locate $x = -2$ on the x-axis. Then move upward until a height of $y = 3$ is reached. Thus the point $(-2, 3)$ is located 2 units left of the origin and 3 units above the origin. In Figure 3.3, the point $(-2, 3)$ is plotted in quadrant II.

Plotting a Point

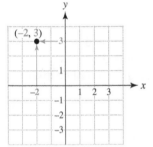

Figure 3.3

NOTE: A point that lies on an axis is not located in a quadrant.

READING CHECK

• Is the order of the numbers in an ordered pair important? Explain.

EXAMPLE 1   **Plotting points**

Plot the following ordered pairs on the same xy-plane. State the quadrant in which each point is located, if possible.
(a) $(3, 2)$ **(b)** $(-2, -3)$ **(c)** $(-3, 0)$

Solution
(a) The point $(3, 2)$ is located in quadrant I, 3 units to the right of the origin and 2 units above the origin. See Figure 3.4.
(b) The point $(-2, -3)$ is located 2 units to the left of the origin and 3 units below the origin. Figure 3.4 shows the point $(-2, -3)$ in quadrant III.
(c) The point $(-3, 0)$ is not in any quadrant because it is located 3 units left of the origin on the x-axis, as shown in Figure 3.4.

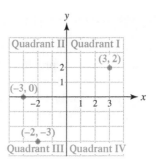

Figure 3.4

■ Now Try Exercise 13

EXAMPLE 2   **Reading a graph containing YouTube data**

Figure 3.5 shows the average number of hours of video posted to YouTube every *minute* during selected months. Use the graph to estimate the number of hours of video posted to YouTube every minute in June 2009 and December 2010. (*Source:* YouTube.)

**Hours of Video Posted to YouTube
Every Minute**

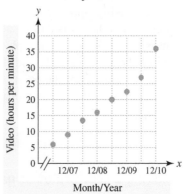

Figure 3.5

Solution

To find the number of hours of video posted to YouTube every minute in June 2009, start by locating Jun. '09 (halfway between Dec. '08 and Dec. '09) on the *x*-axis and then move vertically upward to the data point. From the data point, move horizontally to the *y*-axis. Figure 3.6(a) shows that about 20 hours of video was posted every minute in June 2009. Similarly, about 36 hours of video was posted every minute in December 2010, as shown in Figure 3.6(b).

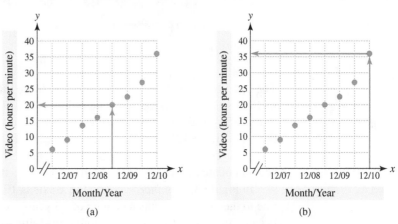

(a)   (b)

Figure 3.6

■ Now Try Exercise 41

Scatterplots and Line Graphs

If distinct points are plotted in the *xy*-plane, then the resulting graph is called a **scatterplot**. Figure 3.5 on the previous page is an example of a scatterplot that displays information about YouTube videos. A different scatterplot is shown in Figure 3.7, in which the points (1, 3), (2, 2), (3, 1), (4, 4), and (5, 1) are plotted.

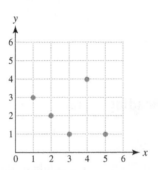

Figure 3.7 A Scatterplot

READING CHECK

• Which value in an ordered pair is the *x*-coordinate, and which is the *y*-coordinate?

Choosing appropriate scales for the axes is important when plotting points and making graphs. This can be accomplished by looking at the *coordinates* of the ordered pairs to be plotted. When plotting in the *xy*-plane, the first value in an ordered pair is called the ***x*-coordinate** and the second value is called the ***y*-coordinate**. In Figure 3.7, the *x*-coordinates of the points are 1, 2, 3, 4, and 5 and the *y*-coordinates are 1, 2, 3, and 4. Because no coordinate is more than 6 units from the origin, the scale shown in Figure 3.7 is appropriate.

EXAMPLE 3 **Making a scatterplot of gasoline prices**

Table 3.2 lists the average price of a gallon of gasoline for selected years. Make a scatterplot of the data. These prices have *not* been adjusted for inflation.

TABLE 3.2 **Average Price of Gasoline**

Year	1960	1970	1980	1990	2000	2010
Cost (per gal)	31¢	36¢	119¢	115¢	156¢	273¢

Source: Department of Energy.

Solution
The data point (1960, 31) can be used to indicate that the average cost of a gallon of gasoline in 1960 was 31¢. Plot the six data points (1960, 31), (1970, 36), (1980, 119), (1990, 115), (2000, 156), and (2010, 273) in the *xy*-plane. The *x*-values vary from 1960 to 2010, so label the *x*-axis from 1960 to 2020 every 10 years. The *y*-values vary from 31 to 273, so label the *y*-axis from 0 to 350 every 50¢. Note that the *x*- and *y*-scales must be large enough to accommodate every data point. Figure 3.8 shows the scatterplot.

In Figure 3.8 the *increment* on the *x*-axis is 10 because each step from one vertical grid line to the next represents a change of 10 years. Similarly, the increment on the *y*-axis is 50 because each step from one horizontal grid line to the next represents a 50-cent change in price. This example demonstrates that the scale and increment on one axis are not always the same as those on the other axis.

Price of Gasoline

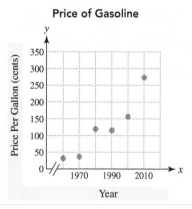

Figure 3.8

■ Now Try Exercise 25

Sometimes it is helpful to connect consecutive data points in a scatterplot with line segments. This type of graph visually emphasizes changes in the data and is called a **line graph**. When making a line graph, be sure to plot all of the given data points *before* connecting the points with line segments. The points should be connected consecutively from left to right on the scatterplot, even if the data are given "out of order" in a table.

NOTE: In Section 3.2 we will discuss the graph of a linear equation. It is important to note that a line graph is **not** the same as the graph of a linear equation. A line graph is a *finite* number of data points connected with line segments, while a graph of a linear equation is a single straight line that represents an *infinite* number of data points.

EXAMPLE 4 **Making a line graph**

Use the data in Table 3.3 to make a line graph.

TABLE 3.3

x	−2	−1	0	1	2
y	1	2	−2	−1	1

Solution
The data in Table 3.3 are represented by the five ordered pairs $(-2, 1)$, $(-1, 2)$, $(0, -2)$, $(1, -1)$, and $(2, 1)$. Plot these points and then connect consecutive points with line segments, as shown in Figure 3.9.

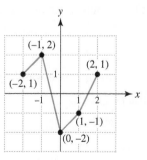

Figure 3.9 A Line Graph

■ Now Try Exercise 35

Scatterplots and Line Graphs
Graphing calculators are capable of creating line graphs and scatterplots. The line graph in Figure 3.9 is shown (below) to the left, and the corresponding scatterplot is shown to the right.

CALCULATOR HELP

To make a scatterplot or a line graph, see Appendix A (pages AP-3 and AP-4).

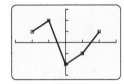

EXAMPLE 5   **Analyzing a line graph**

The line graph in Figure 3.10 shows the per capita energy consumption in the United States from 1960 to 2010. Units are in millions of Btu, where 1 Btu equals the amount of energy necessary to heat 1 pound of water $1°F$. (*Source:* Department of Energy.)

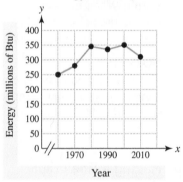

U.S. Energy Consumption

Figure 3.10

(a) Did energy consumption ever decrease during this time period? Explain.
(b) Estimate the energy consumption in 1960 and in 2000.
(c) Estimate the percent change in energy consumption from 1960 to 2000.

Solution
(a) Yes, energy consumption decreased slightly between 1980 and 1990, and again between 2000 and 2010.
(b) From the graph, per capita energy consumption in 1960 was about 250 million Btu. In 2000 it was about 350 million Btu.

  NOTE: When different people read a graph, values they obtain may vary slightly.

(c) The percent change from 1960 to 2000 was

$$\frac{350 - 250}{250} \cdot 100 = 40,$$

so the increase was 40%.

Now Try Exercise 49

READING CHECK

• What is the main difference between a scatterplot and a line graph?

CRITICAL THINKING

When analyzing data, do you prefer a table of values, a scatterplot, or a line graph? Explain your answer.

3.1 Putting It All Together

CONCEPT	EXPLANATION	EXAMPLES
Ordered Pair	Has the form (x, y), where the order of x and y is important	$(1, 2)$, $(-2, 3)$, $(2, 1)$ and $(-4, -2)$ are distinct ordered pairs.
Rectangular Coordinate System, or xy-plane	Consists of a horizontal x-axis and a vertical y-axis that intersect at the origin Has four quadrants, which are numbered counterclockwise as I, II, III, and IV	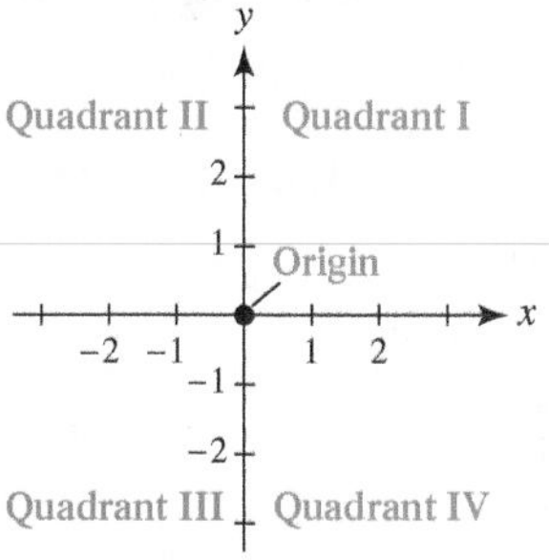
Scatterplot	Individual points that are plotted in the xy-plane	The points $(1, 1)$, $(2, 3)$, $(3, 2)$, $(4, 5)$, and $(5, 4)$ are plotted in the graph. 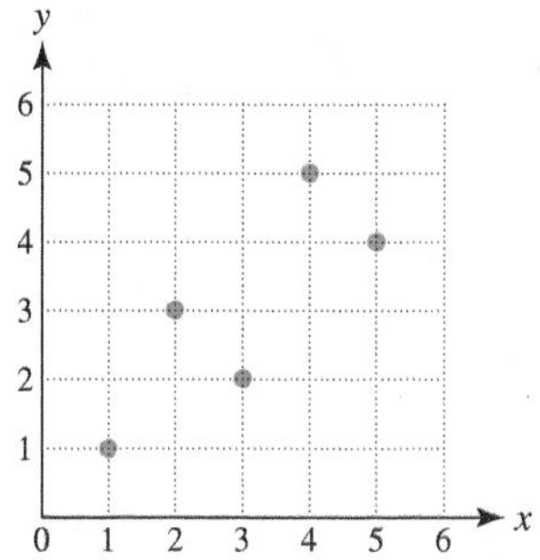
Line Graph	Similar to a scatterplot except that line segments are drawn between consecutive data points	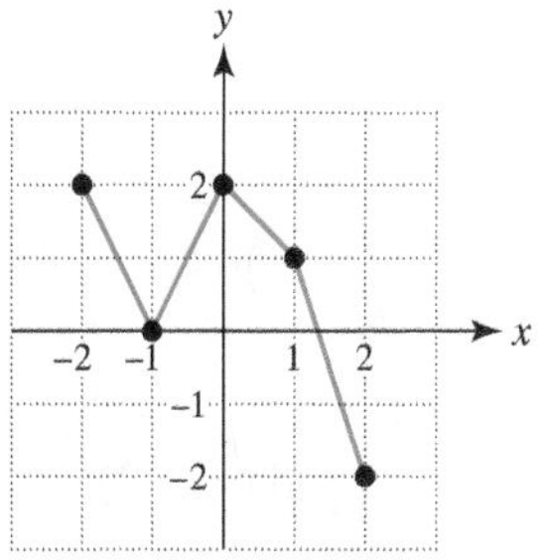

3.1 Exercises

MyMathLab | Math XL PRACTICE | WATCH | DOWNLOAD | READ | REVIEW

CONCEPTS AND VOCABULARY

1. Another name for the rectangular coordinate system is the _____.

2. The point where the x-axis and y-axis intersect is called the _____.

3. In the xy-plane, the origin corresponds to the ordered pair _____.

4. How many quadrants are there in the xy-plane?

5. (True or False?) Every point in the xy-plane is located in one of the quadrants.

6. In the *xy*-plane, the first value in an ordered pair is called the _____ -coordinate and the second value is called the _____ -coordinate.

7. If distinct points are plotted in the *xy*-plane, the resulting graph is called a(n) _____.

8. If the consecutive points in a scatterplot are connected with line segments, the resulting graph is called a(n) _____ graph.

RECTANGULAR COORDINATE SYSTEM

Exercises 9–12: Identify the coordinates of each point in the graph.

9.
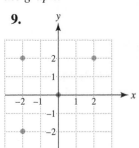

10.
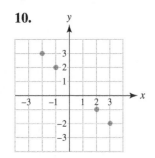

11.
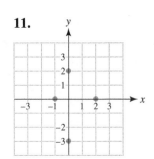

12.
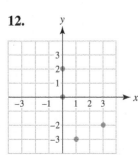

Exercises 13–16: Plot the given ordered pairs in the same xy-plane. If possible, state the quadrant in which each of the points is located.

13. $(1, 3)$, $(0, -3)$, and $(-2, 2)$

14. $(4, 0)$, $(-3, -4)$, and $(2, -3)$

15. $(0, 6)$, $(8, -4)$, and $(-6, -6)$

16. $(-4, 8)$, $(6, 8)$, and $(-8, 0)$

Exercises 17–22: If possible, identify the quadrant in which each point is located.

17. (a) $(1, 4)$ **(b)** $(-1, -4)$

18. (a) $(-2, -3)$ **(b)** $(2, -3)$

19. (a) $(7, 0)$ **(b)** $(0.1, 7)$

20. (a) $(100, -3)$ **(b)** $(-100, 3)$

21. (a) $\left(-\frac{1}{2}, \frac{3}{4}\right)$ **(b)** $\left(\frac{3}{4}, -\frac{1}{2}\right)$

22. (a) $(1.2, 0)$ **(b)** $(0, -1.2)$

23. Thinking Generally Which of the four quadrants contain points whose *x*- and *y*-coordinates have the same sign?

24. Thinking Generally Which of the four quadrants contain points whose *x*- and *y*-coordinates have different signs?

SCATTERPLOTS AND LINE GRAPHS

Exercises 25–34: Make a scatterplot by plotting the given points. Be sure to label each axis.

25. $(0, 0)$, $(1, 2)$, $(-3, 2)$, $(-1, -2)$

26. $(0, -3)$, $(-2, 1)$, $(2, 2)$, $(-4, -4)$

27. $(-1, 0)$, $(4, -3)$, $(0, -1)$, $(3, 4)$

28. $(1, 1)$, $(-2, 2)$, $(-3, -3)$, $(4, -4)$

29. $(2, 4)$, $(-4, 4)$, $(0, -4)$, $(-6, 2)$

30. $(4, 8)$, $(8, 4)$, $(-8, -4)$, $(-4, 0)$

31. $(5, 0)$, $(5, -5)$, $(-10, -20)$, $(10, -10)$

32. $(10, 30)$, $(-20, 10)$, $(40, 0)$, $(-30, -10)$

33. $(0, 0.1)$, $(0.2, -0.3)$, $(-0.1, 0.4)$

34. $(1.5, 2.5)$, $(-1, -1.5)$, $(-2.5, 0)$

Exercises 35–40: Use the table to make a line graph.

35.

x	-2	-1	0	1	2
y	2	1	0	-1	-2

36.

x	-4	-2	0	2	4
y	4	-2	3	-1	2

37.

x	-10	-5	0	5	10
y	20	-10	10	0	-20

38.

x	1	2	3	4	5
y	2	3	1	5	4

39.

x	-5	5	-10	10	0
y	10	20	30	20	40

40.

x	3	−2	2	1	−3
y	4	3	3	−2	−3

Exercises 41 and 42: Identify the coordinates of each point in the graph. Then explain what the coordinates of the first point indicate.

41. Cigarette consumption in the United States (*Source:* U.S. Department of Health and Human Services.)

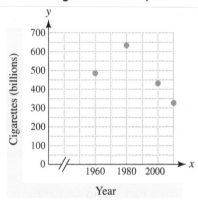

U.S. Cigarette Consumption

42. Number of unhealthy air quality days in Pittsburgh (*Source:* Environmental Protection Agency.)

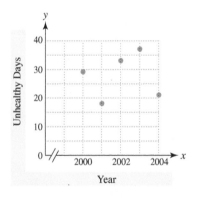

GRAPHING REAL DATA

Exercises 43–48: Graphing Real Data The table contains real data.
   (a) Make a line graph of the data. Be sure to label the axes.
   (b) Comment on any trends in the data.

43. Percent *P* of total music sales that were digital downloads during year *t*

t	2006	2007	2008	2009	2010
P	10%	20%	30%	40%	50%

Source: The NPD Group.

44. Federal income tax receipts *I* in billions during year *t*

t	1970	1980	1990	2000	2010
I	90	244	467	1003	2165

Source: Office of Management and Budget.

45. Welfare beneficiaries *B* in millions during year *t*

t	1970	1980	1990	2000	2010
B	7	11	12	6	4

Source: Administration for Children and Families.

46. U.S. cotton production *C* in millions of bales during year *t*

t	2003	2004	2005	2006	2007
C	18	23	24	22	19

Source: U.S. Department of Agriculture.

47. Projected U.S. Internet users *y* in millions during year *x*

x	2010	2011	2012	2013	2014
y	221	229	237	244	251

Source: eMarketer.

48. Number of farms in Iowa *F* in thousands during year *x*

x	2001	2003	2005	2007
F	92	90	89	92

Source: U.S. Department of Agriculture.

49. The line graph shows the U.S. infant mortality rate for selected years.

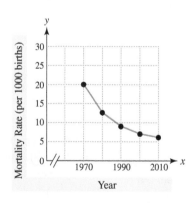

   (a) Comment on any trends in the data.
   (b) Estimate the infant mortality rate in 1990.
   (c) Estimate the percent change in the infant mortality rate from 1970 to 2010.

50. The line graph shows the population of the midwestern states, in millions, for selected years.

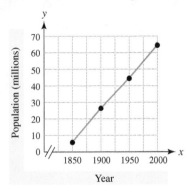

Year

(a) Comment on any trends in the data.
(b) Estimate this population in 1900.
(c) Estimate the percent change in population from 1850 to 2000.

WRITING ABOUT MATHEMATICS

51. Explain how to identify the quadrant that a point lies in if it has coordinates (x, y).

52. Explain the difference between a scatterplot and a line graph. Give an example of each.

3.2   Linear Equations in Two Variables

Basic Concepts • Tables of Solutions • Graphing Linear Equations in Two Variables

A LOOK INTO MATH ▶

Figure 3.11 shows a scatterplot of average college tuition and fees at public colleges and universities (in 2010 dollars), together with a line that models the data. If we could find an equation for this line, then we could use it to estimate tuition and fees for years without data points, such as 2015. In this section we discuss linear equations, whose graphs are lines. Linear equations and lines are often used to approximate data. (*Source:* The College Board.)

Tuition and Fees at Public Colleges

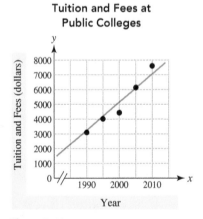

Year

Figure 3.11

NEW VOCABULARY

☐ Standard form (of a linear equation in two variables)
☐ Linear equation in two variables

STUDY TIP

If you have tried to solve a homework problem but need help, ask a question in class. Other students will likely have the same question.

NOTE: The graph shown in Figure 3.11 is *not* a line graph that has consecutive points connected with line segments. Rather, it is a scatterplot together with a single straight line that closely models the data.

Basic Concepts

Equations can have any number of variables. In Chapter 2 we solved equations having one variable. The following are examples of equations with two variables.

$$y = 2x, \quad 3x + 2y = 4, \quad z = t^2, \quad \text{and} \quad a - b = 1$$

Equations with two variables

A solution to an equation with one variable is one number that makes the statement true. For example, the solution to $x - 1 = 3$ is 4 because $4 - 1 = 3$ is a true statement. A solution to an equation with two variables consists of two numbers, one for each variable, which can be expressed as an ordered pair. For example, one solution to the equation $y = 5x$ is given by $x = 1$ and $y = 5$ because $5 = 5(1)$ is a true statement. This solution can be expressed as the ordered pair $(1, 5)$. Table 3.4 lists several ordered pairs and shows whether each ordered pair is a solution to the equation $y = 5x$.

TABLE 3.4 **Checking Ordered-Pair Solutions to $y = 5x$**

Ordered Pair	Check	Is it a solution?
$(1, 5)$	$5 \overset{?}{=} 5(1)$	Yes, because $5 = 5$
$(2, 12)$	$12 \overset{?}{=} 5(2)$	No, because $12 \neq 10$
$(-2, -10)$	$-10 \overset{?}{=} 5(-2)$	Yes, because $-10 = -10$
$(4, 20)$	$20 \overset{?}{=} 5(4)$	Yes, because $20 = 20$

READING CHECK

• How are solutions to an equation in two variables expressed?

EXAMPLE 1   **Testing solutions to equations**

Determine whether the given ordered pair is a solution to the given equation.

(a) $y = x + 3, (1, 4)$ (b) $2x - y = 5, \left(\frac{1}{2}, -4\right)$ (c) $-4x + 5y = 20, (-5, 1)$

Solution

(a) Let $x = 1$ and $y = 4$ in the given equation.

$$y = x + 3 \qquad \text{Given equation}$$
$$4 \overset{?}{=} 1 + 3 \qquad \text{Substitute.}$$
$$4 = 4 \checkmark \qquad \text{The solution checks.}$$

The ordered pair $(1, 4)$ is a solution.

(b) Let $x = \frac{1}{2}$ and $y = -4$ in the given equation.

$$2x - y = 5 \qquad \text{Given equation}$$
$$2\left(\frac{1}{2}\right) - (-4) \overset{?}{=} 5 \qquad \text{Substitute.}$$
$$1 + 4 \overset{?}{=} 5 \qquad \text{Simplify the left side.}$$
$$5 = 5 \checkmark \qquad \text{The solution checks.}$$

The ordered pair $\left(\frac{1}{2}, -4\right)$ is a solution.

(c) Let $x = -5$ and $y = 1$ in the given equation.

$$-4x + 5y = 20 \qquad \text{Given equation}$$
$$-4(-5) + 5(1) \overset{?}{=} 20 \qquad \text{Substitute.}$$
$$20 + 5 \overset{?}{=} 20 \qquad \text{Simplify the left side.}$$
$$25 \neq 20 \ \text{✗} \qquad \text{The solution does } not \text{ check.}$$

The ordered pair $(-5, 1)$ is *not* a solution.

Now Try Exercises 11, 15, 17

Tables of Solutions

A table can be used to list solutions to an equation. For example, Table 3.5 lists solutions to $x + y = 5$, where the sum of each xy-pair equals 5.

TABLE 3.5 $x + y = 5$

x	−2	−1	0	1	2
y	7	6	5	4	3

READING CHECK

• When is it helpful to have a table that lists a few solutions to an equation?

Most equations in two variables have infinitely many solutions, so it is impossible to list all solutions in a table. However, when you are graphing an equation, having a table that lists a few solutions to the equation is often helpful. The next two examples demonstrate how to complete a table for a given equation.

EXAMPLE 2 **Completing a table of solutions**

Complete the table for the equation $y = 2x - 3$.

x	−4	−2	0	2
y				

Solution

Start by determining the corresponding y-value for each x-value in the table. For example, when $x = -2$, the equation $y = 2x - 3$ implies that $y = 2(-2) - 3 = -4 - 3 = -7$. Filling in the y-values results in Table 3.6.

TABLE 3.6 $y = 2x - 3$

x	−4	−2	0	2
y	−11	−7	−3	1

Now Try Exercise 21

EXAMPLE 3 **Making a table of solutions**

Use $y = 0, 5, 10$, and 15 to make a table of solutions to $5x + 2y = 10$.

Solution

Begin by listing the required y-values in the table. Next determine the corresponding x-values for each y-value by using the equation $5x + 2y = 10$.

When $y = 0$,	When $y = 5$,	When $y = 10$,	When $y = 15$,
$5x + 2(0) = 10$	$5x + 2(5) = 10$	$5x + 2(10) = 10$	$5x + 2(15) = 10$
$5x + 0 = 10$	$5x + 10 = 10$	$5x + 20 = 10$	$5x + 30 = 10$
$5x = 10$	$5x = 0$	$5x = -10$	$5x = -20$
$x = 2$	$x = 0$	$x = -2$	$x = -4$

TABLE 3.7 $5x + 2y = 10$

x	2	0	−2	−4
y	0	5	10	15

Filling in the x-values results in Table 3.7.

Now Try Exercise 23

▶ **REAL-WORLD CONNECTION** Formulas can sometimes be difficult for people to understand. As a result, newspapers, magazines, and books often list numbers in a table rather than presenting a formula for the reader to use. The next example illustrates a situation in which a table might be preferable to a formula.

EXAMPLE 4   **Calculating appropriate lengths of crutches**

People with leg injuries often need crutches. An appropriate crutch length L in inches for an injured person who is t inches tall is estimated by $L = 0.72t + 2$. (*Source: Journal of the American Physical Therapy Association.*)

(a) Complete the table. Round values to the nearest inch.

t	60	65	70	75	80
L					

(b) Use the table to determine the appropriate crutch length for a person 5 feet 10 inches tall.

Solution

(a) In the formula $L = 0.72t + 2$, if $t = 60$, then $L = 0.72(60) + 2 = 43.2 + 2 = 45.2$, or about 45 inches. If $t = 65$, then $L = 0.72(65) + 2 = 46.8 + 2 = 48.8 \approx 49$. Other values in Table 3.8 are found similarly.

TABLE 3.8   **Crutch Lengths**

t	60	65	70	75	80
L	45	49	52	56	60

(b) A person who is 5 feet 10 inches tall is $5 \cdot 12 + 10 = 70$ inches tall. Table 3.8 shows that a person 70 inches tall needs crutches that are about 52 inches long.

▌ Now Try Exercise 71

Graphing Linear Equations in Two Variables

Many times graphs are used in mathematics to make concepts easier to visualize and understand. Graphs can be either curved or straight; however, graphs of linear equations in two variables are always straight lines.

EXAMPLE 5   **Graphing a linear equation in two variables**

Make a table of values for the equation $y = 2x$, and then use the table to graph this equation.

Solution

Start by selecting a few convenient values for x, such as $x = -1, 0, 1$, and 2. Then complete the table by doubling each x-value to obtain the corresponding y-value.

NOTE: Tables can be either horizontal or vertical. Table 3.9 is given in a vertical format.

TABLE 3.9   **$y = 2x$**

x	y
-1	-2
0	0
1	2
2	4

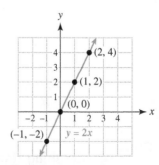

Figure 3.12

To graph the equation $y = 2x$, start by plotting the points $(-1, -2)$, $(0, 0)$, $(1, 2)$, and $(2, 4)$ given in Table 3.9, as shown in Figure 3.12.

Note that all four points in Figure 3.12 on the previous page appear to lie on the same (straight) line. Because there are infinitely many points that satisfy the equation, we can draw a line through these points.

NOTE: Because the graph of a linear equation in two variables is a straight line, you may want to use a ruler or other straight edge when graphing this kind of equation.

▌ Now Try Exercise 39

> **MAKING CONNECTIONS**
>
> Line graphs and graphs of linear equations
>
> Do not confuse a line graph with the graph of a linear equation. A *line graph* results when consecutive points from a table of values are connected with line segments. However, the *graph of a linear equation* is a single, straight line that passes through points from a table of values and continues indefinitely in two directions.

READING CHECK

• Is a line graph the same as a graph of a linear equation?

Not every equation with two variables has a graph that is a straight line. Those equations whose graphs are straight lines are called *linear* equations in two variables. Every linear equation in two variables can be written in the following **standard form**.

> **LINEAR EQUATION IN TWO VARIABLES**
>
> A **linear equation in two variables** can be written as
> $$Ax + By = C,$$
> where A, B, and C are fixed numbers (constants) and A and B are not both equal to 0. The graph of a linear equation in two variables is a line.

NOTE: In mathematics a line is always *straight*.

In Example 5, the equation $y = 2x$ is a linear equation because it can be written in standard form by adding $-2x$ to each side.

$$y = 2x \qquad \text{Given equation}$$
$$-2x + y = -2x + 2x \qquad \text{Add } -2x \text{ to each side.}$$
$$-2x + y = 0 \qquad \text{Simplify.}$$

The equation $-2x + y = 0$ is a linear equation in two variables because it is in the form $Ax + By = C$ with $A = -2$, $B = 1$, and $C = 0$.

EXAMPLE 6 **Graphing linear equations**

Graph each linear equation.
(a) $y = \frac{1}{2}x - 1$ (b) $x + y = 4$

Solution

(a) Because $y = \frac{1}{2}x - 1$ can be written in standard form as $-\frac{1}{2}x + y = -1$, it is a linear equation in two variables and its graph is a line. Two points determine a line. However, it is a good idea to plot three points to be sure that the line is graphed correctly. Start by choosing three values for x and then calculate the corresponding y-values, as shown in Table 3.10. In Figure 3.13, the points $(-2, -2)$, $(0, -1)$, and $(2, 0)$ are plotted and the line passing through these points is drawn.

TABLE 3.10 $y = \frac{1}{2}x - 1$

x	y
-2	-2
0	-1
2	0

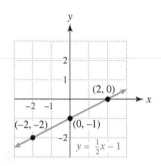

Figure 3.13

(b) The equation $x + y = 4$ is a linear equation in two variables, so its graph is a line. If an ordered pair (x, y) is a solution to the given equation, then the sum of x and y is 4. Table 3.11 shows three examples. In Figure 3.14, the points $(0, 4)$, $(2, 2)$, and $(4, 0)$ are plotted with the line passing through each one.

TABLE 3.11 $x + y = 4$

x	y
0	4
2	2
4	0

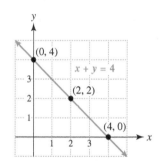

Figure 3.14

Now Try Exercises 43, 57

TECHNOLOGY NOTE

CALCULATOR HELP

To graph an equation, see Appendix A (page AP-5).

Graphing Equations

Graphing calculators can be used to graph equations. Before graphing the equation $x + y = 4$, solve the equation for y to obtain $y = 4 - x$. A calculator graph of Figure 3.14 is shown, except that the three points have not been plotted.

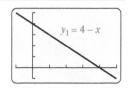

When a linear equation in two variables is given in standard form, it is sometimes difficult to create a table of solutions. Solving an equation for y often makes it easier to select x-values for the table that will make the y-values simpler to calculate. This is demonstrated in the next example.

EXAMPLE 7   **Solving for *y* and then graphing**

Graph the linear equation $4x - 3y = 12$ by solving for *y* first.

Solution
First solve the given equation for *y*.

$$4x - 3y = 12 \qquad \text{Given equation}$$

$$-3y = -4x + 12 \qquad \text{Subtract } 4x \text{ from each side.}$$

$$\frac{-3y}{-3} = \frac{-4x + 12}{-3} \qquad \text{Divide each side by } -3.$$

$$\frac{-3y}{-3} = \frac{-4x}{-3} + \frac{12}{-3} \qquad \text{Property of fractions, } \frac{a+b}{c} = \frac{a}{c} + \frac{b}{c}$$

$$y = \frac{4}{3}x - 4 \qquad \text{Simplify fractions.}$$

Note that dividing each side of an equation by -3 is equivalent to dividing each term in the equation by -3.

Select multiples of 3 (the denominator of $\frac{4}{3}$) as *x*-values for the table of solutions. For example, if $x = 6$ is chosen, $y = \frac{4}{3}(6) - 4 = \frac{24}{3} - 4 = 8 - 4 = 4$. Table 3.12 lists the solutions $(0, -4)$, $(3, 0)$, and $(6, 4)$, which are plotted in Figure 3.15 with the line passing through each one.

TABLE 3.12 $y = \frac{4}{3}x - 4$

x	*y*
0	−4
3	0
6	4

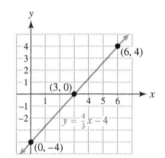

Figure 3.15

Now Try Exercise 59

MAKING CONNECTIONS

Graphs and Solution Sets

A graph visually depicts the set of solutions to an equation. Each point on the graph represents one solution to the equation.

NOTE: In a linear equation, each *x*-value determines a unique *y*-value. Because there are infinitely many *x*-values, there are infinitely many points located on the graph of a linear equation. Thus the graph of a linear equation is a *continuous* line with no breaks.

3.2 Putting It All Together

CONCEPT	EXPLANATION	EXAMPLES
Equation in Two Variables	An equation that has two variables	$y = 4x + 5, 4x - 5y = 20$, and $u - v = 100$
Solution to an Equation in Two Variables	An ordered pair (x, y) whose x- and y-values satisfy the equation Equations in two variables often have infinitely many solutions.	$(1, 3)$ is a solution to $3x + y = 6$ because $3(1) + 3 = 6$ is a true statement. The equation $y = 2x$ has infinitely many solutions, such as $(1, 2), (2, 4), (3, 6)$, and so on.
Table of Solutions	A table can be used to list solutions to an equation in two variables.	The following table lists solutions to the equation $y = 3x - 1$. <table><tr><td>x</td><td>−1</td><td>0</td><td>1</td><td>2</td></tr><tr><td>y</td><td>−4</td><td>−1</td><td>2</td><td>5</td></tr></table>
Linear Equation in Two Variables	Can be written as $$Ax + By = C,$$ where A, B, and C are fixed numbers and A and B are not both equal to 0	$3x + 4y = 5$ $y = 4 - 3x$ (or $3x + y = 4$) $x = 2y + 1$ (or $x - 2y = 1$) The graph of each equation is a line.

3.2 Exercises

MyMathLab   MathXL PRACTICE   WATCH   DOWNLOAD   READ   REVIEW

CONCEPTS AND VOCABULARY

1. (True or False?) The equation $4x + 6y = 24$ is an equation in two variables.

2. (True or False?) The equation $4x - 3x = 10$ is a linear equation in two variables.

3. A solution to an equation with two variables consists of two numbers expressed as a(n) _____.

4. A(n) _____ equation in two variables can be written in the form $Ax + By = C$.

5. (True or False?) A table of solutions lists all of the solutions to an equation in two variables.

6. (True or False?) A linear equation in two variables has infinitely many solutions.

7. An equation's _____ visually depicts its solution set.

8. The graph of a linear equation in two variables is a(n) _____.

9. (True or False?) Every equation in two variables has a graph that is a straight line.

10. (True or False?) A line graph and the graph of a linear equation in two variables are the same thing.

SOLUTIONS TO EQUATIONS

Exercises 11–20: Determine whether the ordered pair is a solution to the given equation.

11. $y = x + 1$, $(5, 6)$ 12. $y = 4 - x$, $(6, 2)$

13. $y = 4x + 7$, $(2, 13)$ 14. $y = -3x + 2$, $(-2, 8)$

15. $4x - y = -13$, $(-2, 3)$

16. $3y + 2x = 0$, $(-2, 3)$

17. $y - 6x = -1$, $\left(\frac{1}{2}, 2\right)$

18. $\frac{1}{2}x + \frac{3}{2}y = 0$, $\left(-\frac{3}{2}, \frac{1}{2}\right)$

19. $0.31x - 0.42y = -9$, $(100, 100)$

20. $0.5x - 0.6y = 4$, $(20, 10)$

TABLES OF SOLUTIONS

Exercises 21–28: Complete the table for the given equation.

21. $y = 4x$

x	-2	-1	0	1	2
y	-8				

22. $y = \frac{1}{2}x - 1$

x	0	1	2	3	4
y	-1				

23. $3y + 2x = 6$

x					
y	-2	0	2	4	8

24. $3x - 5y = 30$

x					
y	-9	-6	-3	0	3

25. $y = x + 4$

x	y
-8	-4
	0
	4
	8
	12

26. $2x - y = 1$

x	y
-1	-3
	-1
	0
	1
	3

27. $2x - 6y = 12$

x	y
-6	
0	
6	
12	
18	

28. $4x + 3y = 12$

x	y
	9
	6
	3
	0
	-3

Exercises 29–32: Use the given values of the variable to make a horizontal table of solutions for the equation.

29. $y = 3x$ $\qquad$ $x = -3, 0, 3, 6$

30. $y = 1 - 2x$ $\qquad$ $x = 0, 1, 2, 3$

31. $x + y = 6$ $\qquad$ $y = -2, 0, 2, 4$

32. $2x - 3y = 9$ $\qquad$ $y = -3, 0, 1, 2$

Exercises 33–36: Use the given values of the variable to make a vertical table of solutions for the equation.

33. $y = \dfrac{x + 4}{2}$ $\qquad$ $x = -8, -4, 0, 4$

34. $y = \dfrac{x}{3} - 1$ $\qquad$ $x = 0, 2, 4, 6$

35. $y - 4x = 0$ $\qquad$ $y = -2, -1, 0, 1$

36. $-4x = 6y - 4$ $\qquad$ $y = -1, 0, 1, 2$

37. Thinking Generally If a student wishes to avoid fractional y-values when making a table of solutions for $y = \frac{3}{5}x - 7$, what must be true about any selected integer x-values?

38. Thinking Generally If a student wishes to avoid fractional y-values when making a table of solutions for $y = \frac{a}{b}x$, where a and b are natural numbers, what must be true about any selected integer x-values?

GRAPHING EQUATIONS

Exercises 39–44: Make a table of solutions for the equation, and then use the table to graph the equation.

39. $y = -2x$ $\qquad$ **40.** $y = 2x - 1$

41. $x = 3 - y$ $\qquad$ **42.** $x = y + 1$

43. $x + 2y = 4$ $\qquad$ **44.** $2x - y = 1$

Exercises 45–58: Graph the equation.

45. $y = x$ $\qquad$ **46.** $y = \frac{1}{2}x$

47. $y = \frac{1}{3}x$ $\qquad$ **48.** $y = -2x$

49. $y = x + 3$ $\qquad$ **50.** $y = x - 2$

51. $y = 2x + 1$ $\qquad$ **52.** $y = \frac{1}{2}x - 1$

53. $y = 4 - 2x$ $\qquad$ **54.** $y = 2 - 3x$

55. $y = 7 + x$ $\qquad$ **56.** $y = 2 + 2x$

57. $y = -\frac{1}{2}x + \frac{1}{2}$ $\qquad$ **58.** $y = -\frac{3}{4}x + 2$

Exercises 59–70: Graph the linear equation by solving for y first.

59. $2x + 3y = 6$ **60.** $3x + 2y = 6$

61. $x + 4y = 4$ **62.** $4x + y = -4$

63. $-x + 2y = 8$ **64.** $-2x + 6y = 12$

65. $y - 2x = 7$ **66.** $3y - x = 2$

67. $5x - 4y = 20$ **68.** $4x - 5y = -20$

69. $3x + 5y = -9$ **70.** $5x - 3y = 10$

APPLICATIONS

71. *U.S. Population* For the years 2010 to 2050, the projected percentage P of the U.S. population that will be over the age of 65 during year t is estimated by $P = 0.178t - 344.6$. (*Source:* U.S. Census Bureau.)
(a) Complete the table. Round each resulting value to the nearest tenth.

t	2010	2020	2030	2040	2050
P					

(b) Use the table to find the year when the percentage of the population over the age of 65 is expected to reach 16.7%.

72. *U.S. Population* For the years 2010 to 2050, the projected percentage P of the U.S. population that will be 18 to 24 years old during year t is estimated by $P = -0.025t + 60.35$. (*Source:* U.S. Census Bureau.)
(a) Complete the table. Round each resulting value to the nearest tenth.

t	2010	2020	2030	2040	2050
P					

(b) Use the table to find the year when the percentage of the population that is 18 to 24 years old is expected to be 9.4%.

73. *Solid Waste in the Past* In 1960 the amount A of garbage in pounds produced after t days by the average American is given by $A = 2.7t$. (*Source:* Environmental Protection Agency.)
(a) Graph the equation for $t \geq 0$.
(b) How many days did it take for the average American in 1960 to produce 100 pounds of garbage?

74. *Solid Waste Today* Today the amount A of garbage in pounds produced after t days by the average American is given by $A = 4.5t$. (*Source:* Environmental Protection Agency.)
(a) Graph the equation for $t \geq 0$.
(b) How many days does it take for the average American to produce 100 pounds of garbage today?

75. *Digital Music Sales* From 2006 to 2010 the percent P of total music sales from digital downloads is modeled by $P = 10t - 20{,}050$, where t is the year. (*Source:* Recording Industry Association of America.)
(a) Evaluate P for $t = 2006$ and for $t = 2010$.
(b) Use your results from part (a) to graph the equation from 2006 to 2010.
(c) In what year was $P = 30\%$?

76. *U.S. HIV Infections* The cumulative number of HIV infections I in thousands during year t is modeled by the equation $I = 42t - 83{,}197$ where $t \geq 2000$. (*Source:* Department of Health and Human Services.)
(a) Evaluate I for $t = 2000$ and for $t = 2005$.
(b) Use your results from part (a) to graph the equation from 2000 to 2005.
(c) In what year was $I = 971$?

WRITING ABOUT MATHEMATICS

77. The number of welfare beneficiaries B in millions during year t is shown in the table. Discuss whether a linear equation might work to approximate these data from 1970 to 2010.

t	1970	1980	1990	2000	2010
B	7	11	12	6	4

Source: Administration for Children and Families.

78. The Asian-American population P in millions during year t is shown in the table. Discuss whether a linear equation might model these data from 2002 to 2010.

t	2002	2004	2006	2008	2010
P	12.0	12.8	13.6	14.4	15.2

Source: U.S. Census Bureau.

Checking Basic Concepts

1. Identify the coordinates of the four points in the graph. State the quadrant, if any, in which each point lies.

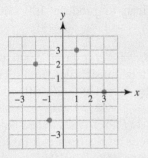

2. Make a scatterplot of the five points $(-2, -2)$, $(-1, -3)$, $(0, 0)$, $(1, 2)$, and $(2, 3)$.

3. *U.S. Population* The table gives the percentage P of the U.S. population that was over the age of 85 during year t. Make a line graph of the data in the table, and then comment on any trends. (*Source:* U.S. Census Bureau.)

t	1970	1980	1990	2000	2010
P	0.7	1.0	1.2	1.5	2.1

4. Determine whether $(-2, -3)$ is a solution to the equation $-2x - y = 7$.

5. Complete the table for the equation $y = -2x + 1$.

x	-2	-1	0	1	2
y	5				

6. Graph the equation.
   (a) $y = \frac{1}{2}x$ **(b)** $4x + 6y = 12$

7. *Total Federal Receipts* The total amount of money A in trillions of dollars collected by the federal government in year t from 1990 to 2010 can be approximated by $A = 0.085t - 168.68$. (*Source:* Internal Revenue Service.)
   (a) Find A when $t = 1990$ and $t = 2010$. Interpret each result.
   (b) Use your results from part (a) to graph the equation from 1990 to 2010. Be sure to label the axes.
   (c) In what year were the total receipts equal to $1.83 trillion?

3.3   More Graphing of Lines

Finding Intercepts ▪ Horizontal Lines ▪ Vertical Lines

A LOOK INTO MATH ▶ When things move or change at a *constant* rate, linear equations can often be used to describe or model the situation. For example, when a car moves at a constant speed, a graph of a linear equation can be used to visualize its driver's distance from a particular location. In real-world situations such as this, the x- and y-*intercepts* of the graph often provide important information. We begin this section by discussing intercepts and their significance in applications.

Finding Intercepts

NEW VOCABULARY

☐ x-intercept
☐ y-intercept

▶ **REAL-WORLD CONNECTION** Suppose that someone leaves a family gathering at a state park and drives home at a constant speed of 50 miles per hour. The graph in Figure 3.16 shows the distance of the driver from home at various times. The graph intersects the y-axis at 200 miles, which is called the y-*intercept*. In this situation the y-intercept represents the initial distance (when $x = 0$) between the driver and home. The graph also intersects the *x*-axis at 4 hours, which is called the *x-intercept*. This intercept represents the elapsed time when the distance of the driver from home is 0 miles (when $y = 0$.) In other words, the driver arrived at home after 4 hours of driving.

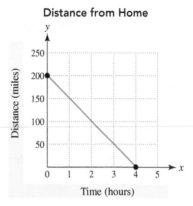

Distance from Home

Figure 3.16

STUDY TIP

Before you go to your instructor's office or a tutor center for help, be sure that you have tried a problem several times in different ways. Organize your questions so that you can be specific about the part of the problem that is giving you difficulty.

FINDING *x*- AND *y*-INTERCEPTS

The *x*-coordinate of a point where a graph intersects the *x*-axis is an **x-intercept**. To find an *x*-intercept, let $y = 0$ in the equation and solve for *x*.

The *y*-coordinate of a point where a graph intersects the *y*-axis is a **y-intercept**. To find a *y*-intercept, let $x = 0$ in the equation and solve for *y*.

READING CHECK

• Where are the intercepts located on a graph?

NOTE: Each intercept is defined as a single number, rather than an ordered pair. The *x*-coordinate of the point where a graph intersects the *x*-axis and the *y*-coordinate of the point where a graph intersects the *y*-axis often have special meaning in applications.

The graph of the linear equation $3x + 2y = 6$ is shown in Figure 3.17. The *x*-intercept is **2** and the *y*-intercept is **3**. These two intercepts can be found without a graph. To find the *x*-intercept, let $y = 0$ in the equation and solve for *x*.

$$3x + 2(0) = 6 \quad \text{Let } y = 0.$$
$$3x = 6 \quad \text{Simplify.}$$
$$x = 2 \quad \text{Divide each side by 3.}$$

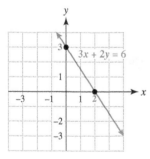

Figure 3.17

To find the *y*-intercept, let $x = 0$ in the equation and solve for *y*.

$$3(0) + 2y = 6 \quad \text{Let } x = 0.$$
$$2y = 6 \quad \text{Simplify.}$$
$$y = 3 \quad \text{Divide each side by 2.}$$

Note that the *x*-intercept **2** corresponds to the point $(2, 0)$ on the graph and the *y*-intercept **3** corresponds to the point $(0, 3)$ on the graph.

CRITICAL THINKING

If a line has no *x*-intercept, what can you say about the line?
If a line has no *y*-intercept, what can you say about the line?

EXAMPLE 1 | **Using intercepts to graph a line**

Use intercepts to graph $2x - 6y = 12$.

Solution
The x-intercept is found by letting $y = 0$.

$$2x - 6(0) = 12 \qquad \text{Let } y = 0.$$
$$x = 6 \qquad \text{Solve for } x.$$

The y-intercept is found by letting $x = 0$.

$$2(0) - 6y = 12 \qquad \text{Let } x = 0.$$
$$y = -2 \qquad \text{Solve for } y.$$

Therefore the graph passes through the points $(6, 0)$ and $(0, -2)$, as shown in Figure 3.18.

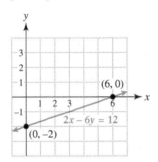

Figure 3.18

Now Try Exercise 21

In the next example a table of solutions is used to determine the x- and y-intercepts.

EXAMPLE 2 | **Using a table to find intercepts**

Complete the table for the equation $x - y = -1$. Then determine the x-intercept and y-intercept for the graph of the equation $x - y = -1$.

x	-2	-1	0	1	2
y					

Solution
Substitute -2 for x in $x - y = -1$ to find the corresponding y-value.

$$-2 - y = -1 \qquad \text{Let } x = -2.$$
$$-y = 1 \qquad \text{Add 2 to each side.}$$
$$y = -1 \qquad \text{Multiply each side by } -1.$$

The other y-values can be found similarly. See Table 3.13.
The x-intercept corresponds to a point on the graph whose y-coordinate is 0. Table 3.13 shows that the y-coordinate is 0 when $x = -1$. So the x-intercept is -1. Similarly, the y-intercept corresponds to a point on the graph whose x-coordinate is 0. Table 3.13 shows that the x-coordinate is 0 when $y = 1$. So the y-intercept is 1.

READING CHECK

• How can the intercepts of a graph be found using a table of values?

TABLE 3.13 $x - y = -1$

x	-2	-1	0	1	2
y	-1	0	1	2	3

Now Try Exercise 17

EXAMPLE 3   **Modeling the velocity of a toy rocket**

A toy rocket is shot vertically into the air. Its velocity v in feet per second after t seconds is given by $v = 160 - 32t$. Assume that $t \geq 0$ and $t \leq 5$.

(a) Graph the equation by finding the intercepts. Let t correspond to the horizontal axis (x-axis) and v correspond to the vertical axis (y-axis).

(b) Interpret each intercept.

Solution

(a) To find the t-intercept, let $v = 0$.

$$0 = 160 - 32t \qquad \text{Let } v = 0.$$
$$32t = 160 \qquad \text{Add } 32t \text{ to each side.}$$
$$t = 5 \qquad \text{Divide each side by 32.}$$

To find the v-intercept, let $t = 0$.

$$v = 160 - 32(0) \qquad \text{Let } t = 0.$$
$$v = 160 \qquad \text{Simplify.}$$

Therefore the graph passes through $(5, 0)$ and $(0, 160)$, as shown in Figure 3.19.

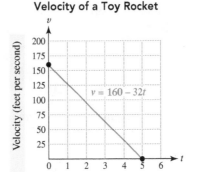

Velocity of a Toy Rocket

$v = 160 - 32t$

Figure 3.19

(b) The t-intercept indicates that the rocket had a velocity of 0 feet per second after **5** seconds. The v-intercept indicates that the rocket's initial velocity was **160** feet per second.

▮ Now Try Exercise 77

Horizontal Lines

▶ **REAL-WORLD CONNECTION** Suppose that someone drives a car on a freeway at a constant speed of 70 miles per hour. Table 3.14 shows the speed y after x hours.

TABLE 3.14 **Speed of a Car**

x	1	2	3	4	5
y	70	70	70	70	70

We can make a scatterplot of the data by plotting the five points $(1, 70)$, $(2, 70)$, $(3, 70)$, $(4, 70)$, and $(5, 70)$, as shown in Figure 3.20(a) on the next page. The speed is always

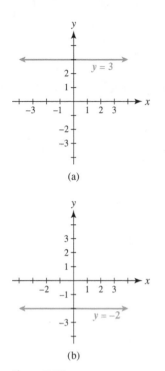

(a)

(b)

Figure 3.21

70 miles per hour and the graph of the car's speed is a horizontal line, as shown in Figure 3.20(b). The equation of this line is $y = 70$ with y-intercept 70. There are no x-intercepts.

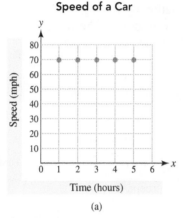

(a)

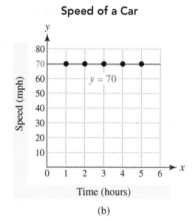

(b)

Figure 3.20

In general, the equation of a horizontal line is $y = b$, where b is a constant that corresponds to the y-intercept. Examples of horizontal lines are shown in Figure 3.21. Note that every point on the graph of $y = 3$ in Figure 3.21(a) has a y-coordinate of 3, and that every point on the graph of $y = -2$ in Figure 3.21(b) has a y-coordinate of -2.

READING CHECK

• Which variable, x or y, is *not* present in the equation for a horizontal line?

HORIZONTAL LINE

The equation of a horizontal line with y-intercept b is $y = b$.

NOTE: The equation $y = b$ is a linear equation in the form $Ax + By = C$ with $A = 0$, $B = 1$, and $C = b$. (In general B and b do not represent the same number.)

EXAMPLE 4 **Graphing a horizontal line**

Graph the equation $y = -1$ and identify its y-intercept.

Solution
The graph of $y = -1$ is a horizontal line passing through the point $(0, -1)$, as shown in Figure 3.22. Its y-intercept is -1.

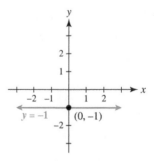

Figure 3.22

Now Try Exercise 45(a)

TABLE 3.15 **Text Messages**

x (months)	y (texts)
1	1631
1	12
1	2314
1	359

Vertical Lines

▶ **REAL-WORLD CONNECTION** A father looks at the number of text messages sent in one month by each of the four people on his wireless family plan. Table 3.15 shows the results of his research, where x represents the number of months and y represents the number of text messages.

We can make a scatterplot of the data by plotting the points $(1, 1631)$, $(1, 12)$, $(1, 2314)$, and $(1, 359)$, as shown in Figure 3.23(a). In each case the time is always 1 month and each point lies on the graph of a vertical line, as shown in Figure 3.23(b). This vertical line has the equation $x = 1$ because each point on the line has an x-coordinate of 1 and there are no restrictions on the y-coordinate. This line has x-intercept 1 but no y-intercept.

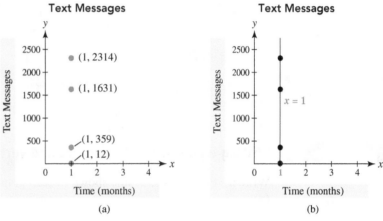

Figure 3.23

In general, the graph of a vertical line is $x = k$, where k is a constant that corresponds to the x-intercept. Examples of vertical lines are shown in Figure 3.24. Note that every point on the graph of $x = 3$ in Figure 3.24(a) has an x-coordinate of 3 and that every point on the graph of $x = -2$ shown in Figure 3.24(b) has an x-coordinate of -2.

CALCULATOR HELP

To graph a vertical line, see Appendix A (page AP-5).

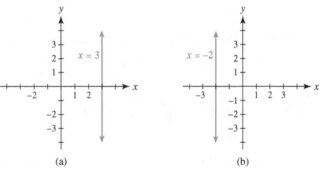

Figure 3.24

READING CHECK

• Which variable, x or y, is not present in the equation for a vertical line?

VERTICAL LINE

The equation of a vertical line with x-intercept k is $x = k$.

NOTE: The equation $x = k$ is a linear equation in the form $Ax + By = C$ with $A = 1$, $B = 0$, and $C = k$.

EXAMPLE 5   **Graphing a vertical line**

Graph the equation $x = -3$, and identify its x-intercept.

Solution
The graph of $x = -3$ is a vertical line passing through the point $(-3, 0)$, as shown in Figure 3.25. Its x-intercept is -3.

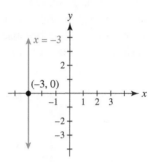

Figure 3.25

Now Try Exercise 45(b)

EXAMPLE 6   **Writing equations of horizontal and vertical lines**

Write the equation of the line shown in each graph.

(a)

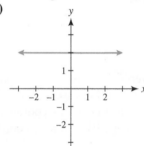

(b)

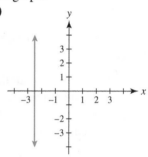

Solution
(a) The graph is a horizontal line with y-intercept 2. Its equation is $y = 2$.
(b) The graph is a vertical line with x-intercept -2.5. Its equation is $x = -2.5$.

Now Try Exercises 51, 53

EXAMPLE 7   **Writing equations of horizontal and vertical lines**

Find an equation for a line satisfying the given conditions.
(a) Vertical, passing through $(2, -3)$
(b) Horizontal, passing through $(3, 1)$
(c) Perpendicular to $x = 3$, passing through $(-1, 2)$

Solution
(a) A vertical line passing through $(2, -3)$ has x-intercept 2, as shown in Figure 3.26(a). The equation of a vertical line with x-intercept 2 is $x = 2$.
(b) A horizontal line passing through $(3, 1)$ has y-intercept 1, as shown in Figure 3.26(b). The equation of a horizontal line with y-intercept 1 is $y = 1$.
(c) Because the line $x = 3$ is vertical, a line that is perpendicular to this line is horizontal, as shown in Figure 3.26(c). The equation of a horizontal line passing through the point $(-1, 2)$ is $y = 2$.

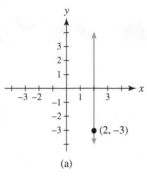 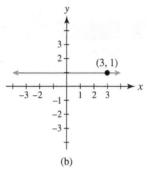 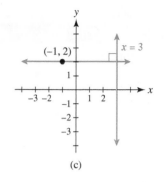

(a) (b) (c)

Figure 3.26 Horizontal and Vertical Lines

Now Try Exercises 65, 67, 69

MAKING CONNECTIONS

Lines and Linear Equations

The equation of any line can be written in the standard form $Ax + By = C$.

1. If $A = 0$ and $B \neq 0$, the line is horizontal.
2. If $A \neq 0$ and $B = 0$, the line is vertical.
3. If $A \neq 0$ and $B \neq 0$, the line is neither horizontal nor vertical.

3.3 Putting It All Together

CONCEPT	EXPLANATION	EXAMPLES
x- and y-Intercepts	The x-coordinate of a point at which a graph intersects the x-axis is called an x-intercept. The y-coordinate of a point at which a graph intersects the y-axis is called a y-intercept.	**x-intercept −3 and y-intercept 2**
Finding Intercepts	To find x-intercepts, let $y = 0$ in the equation and solve for x. To find y-intercepts, let $x = 0$ in the equation and solve for y.	Let $4x - 5y = 20$. x-intercept: $4x - 5(0) = 20$ $x = 5$ y-intercept: $4(0) - 5y = 20$ $y = -4$ The x-intercept is 5, and the y-intercept is -4.

continued on next page

continued from previous page

CONCEPT	EXPLANATION	EXAMPLES
Horizontal Line	A horizontal line has equation $y = b$, where b is a constant. It also has y-intercept b and no x-intercept when $b \neq 0$.	**y-intercept b**
Vertical Line	A vertical line has equation $x = k$, where k is a constant. It also has x-intercept k and no y-intercept when $k \neq 0$.	**x-intercept k**

3.3   Exercises

MyMathLab   Math XL PRACTICE   WATCH   DOWNLOAD   READ   REVIEW

CONCEPTS AND VOCABULARY

1. The x-coordinate of a point where a graph intersects the x-axis is a(n) _____.

2. To find an x-intercept, let $y =$ _____ and solve for x.

3. The y-coordinate of a point at which a graph intersects the y-axis is a(n) _____.

4. To find a y-intercept, let $x =$ _____ and solve for y.

5. The graph of the linear equation $Ax + By = C$ with $A = 0$ and $B = 1$ is a(n) _____ line.

6. A horizontal line with y-intercept b has equation _____.

7. The graph of the linear equation $Ax + By = C$ with $A = 1$ and $B = 0$ is a(n) _____ line.

8. A vertical line with x-intercept k has equation _____.

FINDING INTERCEPTS

Exercises 9–16: Identify any x-intercepts and y-intercepts in the graph.

9.
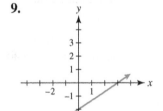

10.
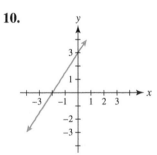

11.
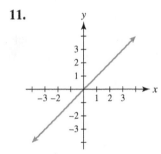

12.
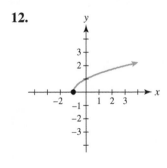

13.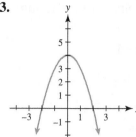

14.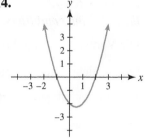

15.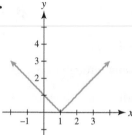

16.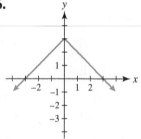

27. $3x + 7y = 21$ **28.** $-3x + 8y = 24$

29. $40y - 30x = -120$ **30.** $10y - 20x = 40$

31. $\frac{1}{2}x - y = 2$ **32.** $x - \frac{1}{2}y = 4$

33. $-\dfrac{x}{4} + \dfrac{y}{3} = 1$ **34.** $\dfrac{x}{3} - \dfrac{y}{4} = 1$

35. $\dfrac{x}{3} + \dfrac{y}{2} = 1$ **36.** $\dfrac{x}{5} - \dfrac{y}{4} = 1$

37. $0.6y - 1.5x = 3$ **38.** $0.5y - 0.4x = 2$

39. Thinking Generally Find any intercepts for the graph of $Ax + By = C$.

40. Thinking Generally Find any intercepts for the graph of $\frac{x}{A} + \frac{y}{B} = 1$.

HORIZONTAL AND VERTICAL LINES

Exercises 41–44: Write an equation for the line that passes through the points shown in the table.

41.

x	-2	-1	0	1	2
y	1	1	1	1	1

42.

x	0	1	2	3	4
y	-10	-10	-10	-10	-10

43.

x	-6	-6	-6	-6	-6
y	5	4	3	2	1

44.

x	20	20	20	20	20
y	-2	-1	0	1	2

Exercises 17–20: Complete the table. Then determine the x-intercept and the y-intercept for the graph of the equation.

17. $y = x + 2$

x	-2	-1	0	1	2
y					

18. $y = 2x - 4$

x	-2	-1	0	1	2
y					

19. $-x + y = -2$

x	-4	-2	0	2	4
y					

20. $x + y = 1$

x	-2	-1	0	1	2
y					

Exercises 21–38: Find any intercepts for the graph of the equation and then graph the linear equation.

21. $-2x + 3y = -6$ **22.** $4x + 3y = 12$

23. $x - 3y = 6$ **24.** $5x + y = -5$

25. $6x - y = -6$ **26.** $5x + 7y = -35$

Exercises 45–50: Graph each equation.

45. (a) $y = 2$ **(b)** $x = 2$

46. (a) $y = -4$ **(b)** $x = -4$

47. (a) $y = 0$ **(b)** $x = 0$

48. (a) $y = -\frac{1}{2}$ **(b)** $x = -\frac{1}{2}$

49. (a) $y = \frac{3}{2}$ **(b)** $x = \frac{3}{2}$

50. (a) $y = -1.5$ **(b)** $x = -1.5$

Exercises 51–58: Write an equation for the line shown in the graph.

51.
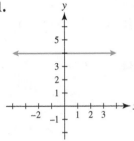

52.
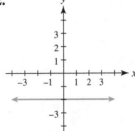

53.
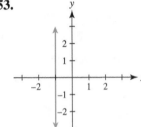

54.
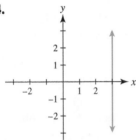

55.
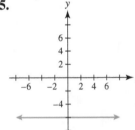

56.
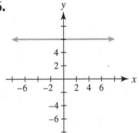

57.
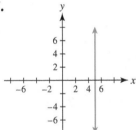

58.
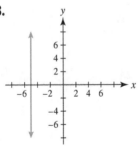

Exercises 59–64: Write the equations of a horizontal line and a vertical line that pass through the given point. (Hint: Make a sketch.)

59. $(1, 2)$

60. $(-3, 4)$

61. $(20, -45)$

62. $(-5, 12)$

63. $(0, 5)$

64. $(-3, 0)$

Exercises 65–72: Find an equation for a line satisfying the following conditions.

65. Vertical, passing through $(-1, 6)$

66. Vertical, passing through $(2, -7)$

67. Horizontal, passing through $\left(\frac{3}{4}, -\frac{5}{6}\right)$

68. Horizontal, passing through $(5.1, 6.2)$

69. Perpendicular to $y = \frac{1}{2}$, passing through $(4, -9)$

70. Perpendicular to $x = 2$, passing through $(3, 4)$

71. Parallel to $x = 4$, passing through $\left(-\frac{2}{3}, \frac{1}{2}\right)$

72. Parallel to $y = -2.1$, passing through $(7.6, 3.5)$

73. Thinking Generally Write the equation of the *x*-axis. (*Hint:* The *x*-axis is a horizontal line.)

74. Thinking Generally Write the equation of the *y*-axis. (*Hint:* The *y*-axis is a vertical line.)

APPLICATIONS

Exercises 75 and 76: Distance The distance of a driver from home is illustrated in the graph.

(a) *Find the intercepts.*
(b) *Interpret each intercept.*

75.
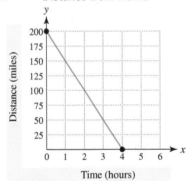

76.
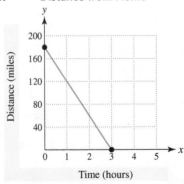

Exercises 77 and 78: Modeling a Toy Rocket (Refer to Example 3.) The velocity v of a toy rocket in feet per second after t seconds of flight is given. Assume that t ≥ 0 and t does not take on values greater than the t-intercept.

(a) *Find the intercepts and then graph the equation.*
(b) *Interpret each intercept.*

77. $v = 128 - 32t$ **78.** $v = 96 - 32t$

Exercises 79 and 80: Water in a Pool The amount of water in a swimming pool is depicted in the graph.

(a) *Find the intercepts.*
(b) *Interpret each intercept.*

79.

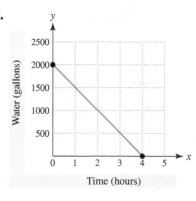

80.

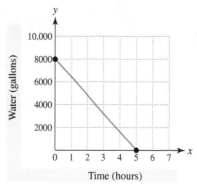

WRITING ABOUT MATHEMATICS

81. Given an equation, explain how to find an x-intercept and a y-intercept.

82. The form $\frac{x}{a} + \frac{y}{b} = 1$ is called the **intercept form** of a linear equation. Explain how you can use this equation to find the intercepts. (*Hint:* Graph $\frac{x}{2} + \frac{y}{3} = 1$ and find its intercepts.)

Group Activity   Working with Real Data

Directions: Form a group of 2 to 4 people. Select someone to record the group's responses for this activity. All members of the group should work cooperatively to answer the questions. If your instructor asks for the results, each member of the group should be prepared to respond.

1. *Radio Stations* The approximate number of radio stations on the air for selected years from 1960 to 2010 is shown in the table.

x (year)	1960	1970	1980
y (stations)	4100	6800	8600

x (year)	1990	2000	2010
y (stations)	10,800	12,600	14,500

Source: M. Street Corporation.

Make a line graph of the data. Be sure to label both axes.

2. *Estimation* Discuss ways to estimate the number of radio stations on the air in 1975. Compare your estimates with the actual value of 7700 stations. Repeat this estimate for 1985 and compare it to the actual value of 10,400. Discuss your results.

3. *Modeling Equation* Substitute each x-value from the table into the equation $y = 220x - 427,100$ and determine the corresponding y-value. Do these y-values give reasonable approximations to the y-values in the table? Explain your answer.

4. *Making Estimates* Use $y = 220x - 427,100$ to estimate the number of radio stations on the air in 1975 and 1985. Compare the results to your answer in Exercise 2.

3.4   Slope and Rates of Change

Finding Slopes of Lines • Slope as a Rate of Change

Take a moment to look at the graphs in Figure 3.27, where the horizontal axis represents time.

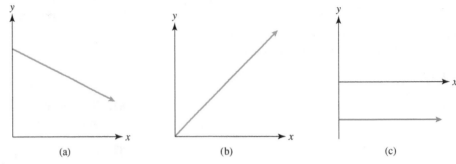

Figure 3.27

NEW VOCABULARY

☐ Rise
☐ Run
☐ Slope
☐ Positive slope
☐ Negative slope
☐ Zero slope
☐ Undefined slope
☐ Rate of change

Which graph might represent the distance traveled by you if you are walking?

Which graph might represent the temperature in your freezer?

Which graph might represent the amount of gasoline in a moving car's tank?

To be able to answer these questions, you probably used the concept of slope. In mathematics, slope is a real number that measures the "tilt" or "angle" of a line. In this section we discuss slope and how it is used in applications.

Finding Slopes of Lines

▶ **REAL-WORLD CONNECTION** The graph shown in Figure 3.28 illustrates the cost of parking for x hours. The graph tilts upward from left to right, which indicates that the cost increases as the number of hours increases. Note that, for each hour of parking, the cost increases by $2.

Cost of Parking

Figure 3.28

Slope m of a Line

$$m = \frac{\text{rise}}{\text{run}} = \frac{y_2 - y_1}{x_2 - x_1}$$

(x_2, y_2)

(x_1, y_1) Rise

Run

Figure 3.29

The graph *rises* 2 units vertically for every horizontal unit of *run*, and the ratio $\frac{\text{rise}}{\text{run}}$ equals the *slope* of the line. The slope m of this line is 2, which indicates that the cost of parking is $2 per hour. In applications, slope indicates a *rate of change*.

A more general case of the slope of a line is shown in Figure 3.29, where a line passes through the points (x_1, y_1) and (x_2, y_2). The **rise**, or *change in y*, is $y_2 - y_1$, and the **run**, or *change in x*, is $x_2 - x_1$. Slope m is given by $m = \frac{y_2 - y_1}{x_2 - x_1}$.

NOTE: The symbol x_1 has a *subscript* of 1 and is read "*x* sub one" or "*x* one". Thus x_1 and x_2 are used to denote two different *x*-values. Similar comments apply to y_1 and y_2.

READING CHECK

• By looking at the *x*-coordinates of two points on a line, how can you tell if the line has undefined slope?

SLOPE

The **slope** m of the line passing through the points (x_1, y_1) and (x_2, y_2) is

$$m = \frac{\text{rise}}{\text{run}} = \frac{y_2 - y_1}{x_2 - x_1},$$

where $x_1 \neq x_2$. That is, slope equals rise over run.

NOTE: If $x_1 = x_2$, the line is vertical and the slope is undefined.

EXAMPLE 1 **Calculating the slope of a line**

Use the two points labeled in Figure 3.30 to find the slope of the line. What are the rise and run between these two points? Interpret the slope in terms of rise and run.

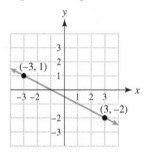

Figure 3.30

Solution
The line passes through the points $(-3, 1)$ and $(3, -2)$, so let $(x_1, y_1) = (-3, 1)$ and $(x_2, y_2) = (3, -2)$. The slope is

$$m = \frac{y_2 - y_1}{x_2 - x_1} = \frac{-2 - 1}{3 - (-3)} = \frac{-3}{6} = -\frac{1}{2}.$$

Starting at the point $(-3, 1)$, count 3 units downward and then 6 units to the right to return to the graph at the point $(3, -2)$. Thus the "rise" is -3 units and the run is 6 units. See Figure 3.31(a). The ratio $\frac{\text{rise}}{\text{run}}$ is $\frac{-3}{6}$, or $-\frac{1}{2}$.

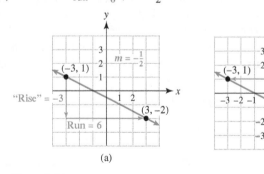

(a)   (b)

Figure 3.31

Figure 3.31(b) shows an alternate way of finding this slope. Starting at the point $(3, -2)$, count 3 units upward and then 6 units to the left to return to the graph at the point $(-3, 1)$. Here, the rise is 3 units and the run is -6 units so that the ratio $\frac{\text{rise}}{\text{run}}$ is $\frac{3}{-6}$, or $-\frac{1}{2}$. In either case, the slope is $-\frac{1}{2}$, which can be written as $\frac{-1}{2}$ indicating that the graph falls 1 unit for every 2 units of run (to the right).

Now Try Exercise 27

NOTE: In Example 1 the same slope would result if we let $(x_1, y_1) = (3, -2)$ and $(x_2, y_2) = (-3, 1)$. In this case the calculation would be

$$m = \frac{y_2 - y_1}{x_2 - x_1} = \frac{1 - (-2)}{-3 - 3} = \frac{3}{-6} = -\frac{1}{2}.$$

A graph is not needed to find slope. Any two points on a line can be used to find the line's slope, as demonstrated in the next example.

EXAMPLE 2   **Calculating the slope of a line**

Calculate the slope of the line passing through each pair of points. Graph the line.
(a) $(-2, 3), (2, 1)$ **(b)** $(-1, 3), (2, 3)$ **(c)** $(-3, 3), (-3, -2)$

Solution
(a) $m = \frac{y_2 - y_1}{x_2 - x_1} = \frac{1 - 3}{2 - (-2)} = \frac{-2}{4} = -\frac{1}{2}$. This slope indicates that the line falls 1 unit for every 2 units of horizontal run, as shown in Figure 3.32(a).
(b) $m = \frac{y_2 - y_1}{x_2 - x_1} = \frac{3 - 3}{2 - (-1)} = \frac{0}{3} = 0$. The line is horizontal, as shown in Figure 3.32(b).
(c) Because $x_1 = x_2 = -3$, the slope formula does not apply. If we try to use it, we obtain $m = \frac{y_2 - y_1}{x_2 - x_1} = \frac{-2 - 3}{-3 - (-3)} = \frac{-5}{0}$, which is an undefined expression. The line has undefined slope and is vertical, as shown in Figure 3.32(c).

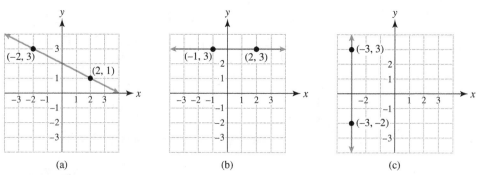

(a)   (b)   (c)

Figure 3.32

Now Try Exercises 41, 43, 45

READING CHECK

• When a line is neither vertical nor horizontal, how can you tell if it has a positive or a negative slope?

If a line has **positive slope**, it *rises from left to right*, as shown in Figure 3.33(a). If a line has **negative slope**, it *falls from left to right*, as shown in Figure 3.33(b). A line with **zero slope** (slope 0) is horizontal, which is shown in Figure 3.33(c). Any two points on a vertical line have the same x-coordinate, so the run always equals 0. Thus a vertical line has **undefined slope**, which is shown in Figure 3.33(d).

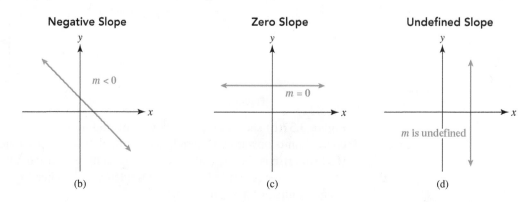

Positive Slope   Negative Slope   Zero Slope   Undefined Slope

(a)   (b)   (c)   (d)

Figure 3.33

SLOPE OF A LINE

1. A line that rises *from left to right* has positive slope.
2. A line that falls *from left to right* has negative slope.
3. A horizontal line has zero slope.
4. A vertical line has undefined slope.

EXAMPLE 3 **Finding slope from a graph**

Find the slope of each line.

(a)

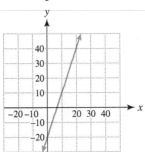

(b)

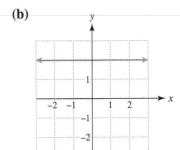

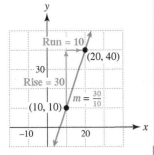

Figure 3.34

Solution

(a) The graph rises 30 units for every 10 units of run. For example, the graph passes through $(10, 10)$ and $(20, 40)$, so the line rises $40 - 10 = 30$ units with $20 - 10 = 10$ units of run, as shown in Figure 3.34. Therefore the slope is

$$m = \frac{\text{rise}}{\text{run}} = \frac{30}{10} = 3.$$

(b) The line is horizontal, so the slope is 0.

Now Try Exercises 19, 29

A point and a slope also determine a line, as illustrated in the next example.

EXAMPLE 4 **Sketching a line with a given slope**

Sketch a line passing through the point $(1, 4)$ and having slope $-\frac{2}{3}$.

Solution

Start by plotting the point $(1, 4)$. A slope of $-\frac{2}{3}$ can be written as $\frac{-2}{3}$, which indicates that the *y*-values *decrease* 2 units each time the *x*-values increase by 3 units. That is, the line *falls* 2 units for every 3-unit increase in the run. Because the line passes through $(1, 4)$, a 2-unit decrease in y and a 3-unit increase in x results in the line passing through the point $(1 + 3, 4 - 2)$ or $(4, 2)$. See Figure 3.35.

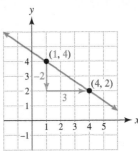

Figure 3.35 Slope $m = -\frac{2}{3}$

Now Try Exercise 59

EXAMPLE 5

Sketching a line with a given *y*-intercept

Sketch a line with slope -2 and *y*-intercept 3.

Solution

For the *y*-intercept of 3, plot the point (0, 3). The slope of -2 can be written as $\frac{-2}{1}$, so the *y*-values decrease 2 units for each unit increase in *x*. Increasing the *x*-value in the point (0, 3) by 1 and decreasing the *y*-value by 2 results in the point $(0 + 1, 3 - 2)$ or (1, 1). Plot (0, 3) and (1, 1) and then sketch the line, as shown in Figure 3.36.

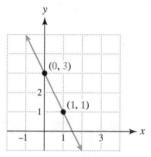

Figure 3.36 Slope: -2; *y*-intercept: 3

Now Try Exercise 55

If we know the slope of a line and a point on the line, we can complete a table of values that gives the coordinates of other points on the line, as demonstrated in the next example.

EXAMPLE 6

Completing a table of values

A line has slope 2 and passes through the first point listed in the table. Complete the table so that each point lies on the line.

x	-2	-1	0	1
y	1			

Solution

Slope 2 indicates that $\frac{\text{rise}}{\text{run}} = 2$. Because consecutive *x*-values in the table increase by 1 unit, the run from one point in the table to the next is 1 unit. Substituting 1 for the **run** in the slope equation results in $\frac{\text{rise}}{1} = 2$. Thus the **rise** is **2** and consecutive *y*-values shown in Table 3.16 increase by 2 units.

TABLE 3.16

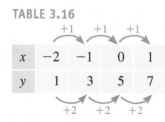

Now Try Exercise 63

Slope as a Rate of Change

▶ **REAL-WORLD CONNECTION** When lines are used to model physical quantities in applications, their slopes provide important information. Slope measures the **rate of change** in a quantity. We illustrate this concept in the next four examples.

EXAMPLE 7 ► **Interpreting slope**

The distance y in miles that an athlete training for a marathon is from home after x hours is shown in Figure 3.37.
(a) Find the y-intercept. What does it represent?
(b) The graph passes through the point $(1, 10)$. Discuss the meaning of this point.
(c) Find the slope of this line. Interpret the slope as a rate of change.

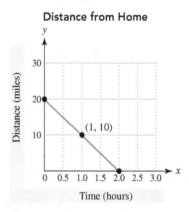

Distance from Home

Figure 3.37

Solution
(a) On the graph the y-intercept is 20, so the athlete is initially 20 miles from home.
(b) The point $(1, 10)$ means that after 1 hour the athlete is 10 miles from home.
(c) The line passes through the points $(0, 20)$ and $(1, 10)$. Its slope is

$$m = \frac{10 - 20}{1 - 0} = -10.$$

Slope -10 means that the athlete is running *toward* home at 10 miles per hour. A *negative* slope indicates that the distance between the runner and home is decreasing.

Now Try Exercise 87

NOTE: The units for a rate of change are determined by putting the y-axis units over the x-axis units. In Example 7, the units for the rate of change are $\frac{\text{miles}}{\text{hour}}$, or miles per hour.

EXAMPLE 8 ► **Interpreting slope**

When a company manufactures 2000 MP3 players, its profit is \$10,000, and when it manufactures 4500 MP3 players, its profit is \$35,000.
(a) Find the slope of the line passing through $(2000, 10000)$ and $(4500, 35000)$.
(b) Interpret the slope as a rate of change.

Solution
(a) $m = \frac{35,000 - 10,000}{4500 - 2000} = \frac{25,000}{2500} = 10$

(b) Profit increases, *on average*, by \$10 for each additional MP3 player made.

Now Try Exercise 91

EXAMPLE 9   **Analyzing tetanus cases**

Table 3.17 lists numbers of reported cases of tetanus in the United States for selected years.

TABLE 3.17

Year	1960	1970	1980	1990	2000	2010
Cases of Tetanus	368	148	95	64	45	18

Source: Department of Health and Human Services.

(a) Make a line graph of the data.
(b) Find the slope of each line segment.
(c) Interpret each slope as a rate of change.

Solution

(a) A line graph connecting the points (1960, 368), (1970, 148), (1980, 95), (1990, 64), (2000, 45), and (2010, 18) is shown in Figure 3.38.

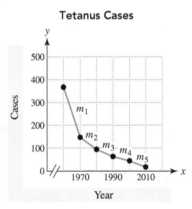

Figure 3.38

(b) The slope of each line segment may be calculated as follows.

$$m_1 = \frac{148 - 368}{1970 - 1960} = -22.0, \qquad m_2 = \frac{95 - 148}{1980 - 1970} = -5.3,$$

$$m_3 = \frac{64 - 95}{1990 - 1980} = -3.1, \qquad m_4 = \frac{45 - 64}{2000 - 1990} = -1.9$$

$$m_5 = \frac{18 - 45}{2010 - 2000} = -2.7$$

(c) Slope $m_1 = -22.0$ indicates that, *on average*, the number of tetanus cases *decreased* by 22.0 cases per year between 1960 and 1970. The other four slopes can be interpreted similarly.

NOTE: The number of tetanus cases did not decrease by *exactly* 22.0 cases each year between 1960 and 1970. However, the yearly *average* decrease was 22.0 cases.

▌ Now Try Exercise 89

READING CHECK

• When a line models a real-world situation, how are the units of the slope found?

EXAMPLE 10   Sketching a model

During a storm, rain falls at the constant rates of 2 inches per hour from 1 A.M. to 3 A.M., 1 inch per hour from 3 A.M. to 4 A.M., and $\frac{1}{2}$ inch per hour from 4 A.M. to 6 A.M.
(a) Sketch a graph that shows the total accumulation of rainfall from 1 A.M. to 6 A.M.
(b) What does the slope of each line segment represent?

Solution

(a) At 1 A.M. the accumulated rainfall is 0, so place a point at $(1, 0)$. Rain falls at a constant rate of 2 inches per hour for the next 2 hours, so at 3 A.M. the total rainfall is 4 inches. Place a point at $(3, 4)$. Because the rainfall is constant, sketch a line segment from $(1, 0)$ to $(3, 4)$, as shown in Figure 3.39. Similarly, during the next hour 1 inch of rain falls, so draw a line segment from $(3, 4)$ to $(4, 5)$. Finally, 1 inch of rain falls from 4 A.M. to 6 A.M., so draw a line segment from $(4, 5)$ to $(6, 6)$.

Total Rainfall

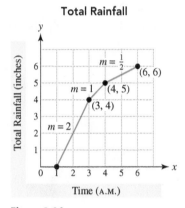

Figure 3.39

(b) The slope of each line segment represents the rate at which rain is falling. For example, the first segment has slope 2 because rain falls at a rate of 2 inches per hour during that period of time.

▌ Now Try Exercise 81

3.4   Putting It All Together

CONCEPT	COMMENTS	EXAMPLE
Rise, Run, and Slope	Rise is a vertical change in a line, and run is a horizontal change in a line. The ratio $\frac{\text{rise}}{\text{run}}$ is the slope m when run is nonzero. **1.** A line that rises from left to right has positive slope. **2.** A line that falls from left to right has negative slope. **3.** A horizontal line has zero slope. **4.** A vertical line has undefined slope.	$m = \frac{\text{rise}}{\text{run}} = \frac{1}{2}$ Run = 2 Rise = 1

continued on next page

continued on previous page

CONCEPT	COMMENTS	EXAMPLE
Calculating Slope	For any two points (x_1, y_1) and (x_2, y_2), slope m is $$m = \frac{y_2 - y_1}{x_2 - x_1},$$ where $x_1 \neq x_2$.	The slope of the line passing through $(-2, 3)$ and $(1, 5)$ is $$m = \frac{5 - 3}{1 - (-2)} = \frac{2}{3}.$$ The line rises vertically 2 units for every 3 horizontal units of run.
Slope as a Rate of Change	Slope measures the "tilt" or "angle" of a line. In applications, slope measures the rate of change in a quantity.	Slope $m = -66\frac{2}{3}$ indicates that water is *leaving* the pool at the rate of $66\frac{2}{3}$ gallons per hour. **Water in a Pool**

3.4   Exercises

MyMathLab Math XL PRACTICE WATCH DOWNLOAD READ REVIEW

CONCEPTS AND VOCABULARY

1. (True or False?) The change in the horizontal distance along a line is called run.

2. (True or False?) The change in the vertical distance along a line is called rise.

3. Slope m of a line equals _____ over _____.

4. Slope 0 indicates that a line is _____.

5. Undefined slope indicates that a line is _____.

6. If a line passes through (x_1, y_1) and (x_2, y_2) where $x_1 \neq x_2$, then $m = $ _____.

7. A line that rises from left to right has _____ slope.

8. A line that falls from left to right has _____ slope.

9. When a line models a physical quantity in an application, its slope measures the _____ of change in the quantity.

10. If a line that models the distance between a hiker and camp has a negative slope, is the hiker moving away from or toward camp?

Exercises 11–18: *State whether the slope of the line is positive, negative, zero, or undefined.*

11.

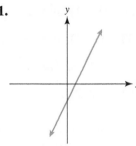

12.

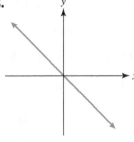

13.

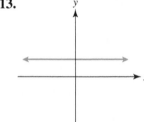

14.

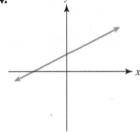

15.

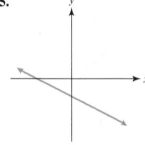

16.

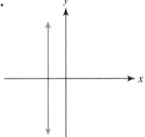

17.

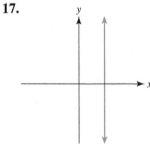

18.

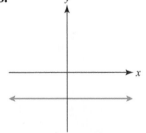

FINDING SLOPES OF LINES

Exercises 19–30: *If possible, find the slope of the line. Interpret the slope in terms of rise and run.*

19.

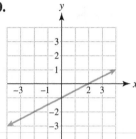

20.

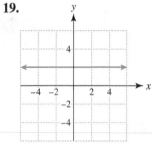

21.

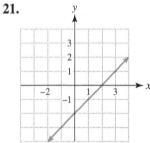

22.

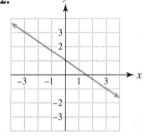

23.

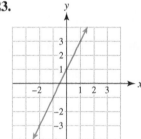

24.

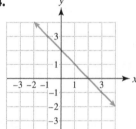

25.

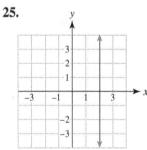

26.

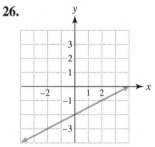

27.

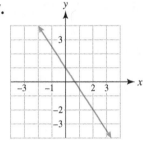

28.

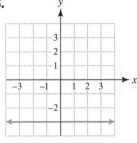

29.

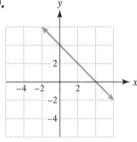

30.

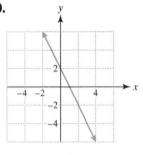

Exercises 31–38: If possible, find the slope of the line passing through the two points. Graph the line.

31. $(1, 2), (2, 4)$

32. $(-4, 7), (7, -4)$

33. $(2, 1), (2, 4)$

34. $(-1, 3), (-1, -1)$

35. $(1, 3), (-2, 5)$

36. $(0, -4), (-4, 6)$

37. $(2, -1), (-2, -1)$

38. $(-2, 3), (1, 3)$

Exercises 39–54: If possible, find the slope of the line passing through the two points.

39. $(4, -2), (-3, -9)$

40. $(15, -3), (20, 9)$

41. $(-3, 4), (4, -2)$

42. $(1, -3), (3, -5)$

43. $(-3, 5), (2, 5)$

44. $(-3, 3), (-5, 3)$

45. $(-1, 6), (-1, -4)$

46. $\left(\frac{1}{2}, -\frac{2}{7}\right), \left(\frac{1}{2}, \frac{13}{17}\right)$

47. $(1980, 5), (2000, 18)$

48. $(1989, 10), (1999, 16)$

49. $(1950, 6.1), (2000, 10.6)$

50. $(1900, 10), (1950, 35)$

51. $\left(\frac{1}{3}, -\frac{2}{7}\right), \left(-\frac{2}{3}, \frac{3}{7}\right)$

52. $(-1.3, 5.6), (-2.6, -2.5)$

53. $(12, -34), (14, 64)$

54. $(-25, 105), (60, 55)$

Exercises 55–62: (Refer to Example 4.) Sketch a line passing through the point and having slope m.

55. $(0, 2), m = -1$

56. $(0, -1), m = 2$

57. $(1, 1), m = 3$

58. $(1, -1), m = -2$

59. $(-2, 3), m = -\frac{1}{2}$

60. $(-1, -2), m = \frac{3}{4}$

61. $(-3, 1), m = \frac{1}{2}$

62. $(-2, 2), m = -3$

Exercises 63–68: (Refer to Example 6.) A line has the given slope m and passes through the first point listed in the table. Complete the table so that each point in the table lies on the line.

63. $m = 2$

x	0	1	2	3
y	−4			

64. $m = -\frac{1}{2}$

x	0	1	2	3
y	2			

65. $m = -3$

x	1	2	3	4
y	4			

66. $m = -1$

x	−1	0	1	2
y	10			

67. $m = \frac{3}{2}$

x	−4	−2	0	2
y	0			

68. $m = 3$

x	−2	0	2	4
y	−4			

SLOPE AS A RATE OF CHANGE

Exercises 69–72: Modeling Choose the graph (a.–d.) in the next column that models the situation best.

69. Cost of buying x gum balls at a price of 25¢ each

70. Total number of movies in VHS format (videotape) purchased during the past 5 years

71. Average cost of a new car over the past 30 years

72. Height of the Empire State Building after x people have entered it

a.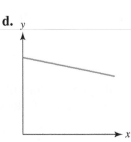

b.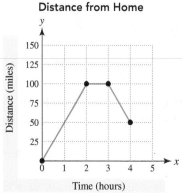

c.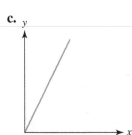

d.

Exercises 73 and 74: Modeling The line graph represents the gallons of water in a small swimming pool after x hours. Assume that there is a pump that can either add water to or remove water from the pool.

(a) *Estimate the slope of each line segment.*
(b) *Interpret each slope as a rate of change.*
(c) *Describe what happened to the amount of water in the pool.*

73. Water in a Pool

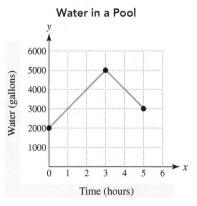

74. Water in a Pool

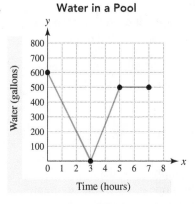

Exercises 75 and 76: Modeling An individual is driving a car along a straight road. The graph shows the distance that the driver is from home after x hours.

(a) *Find the slope of each line segment in the graph.*
(b) *Interpret each slope as a rate of change.*
(c) *Describe both the motion of the car and its distance from home.*

75. Distance from Home

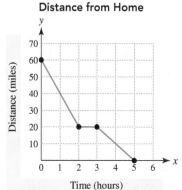

76. Distance from Home

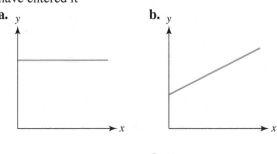

77. Thinking Generally If a line is used to model physical data where the x-axis is labeled "Time (minutes)" and the y-axis is labeled "Volume (cubic meters)," what are the units for the rate of change represented by the slope of the line?

78. Thinking Generally If a line is used to model physical data where the x-axis is labeled "Cookies" and the y-axis is labeled "Chocolate Chips," what are the units for the rate of change represented by the slope of the line?

Exercises 79–82: Sketching a Model Sketch a graph that models the given situation.

79. The distance that a boat is from a harbor if the boat is initially 6 miles from the harbor and arrives at the harbor after sailing at a constant speed for 3 hours

80. The distance that a person is from home if the person starts at home, walks away from home at 4 miles per hour for 90 minutes, and then walks back home at 3 miles per hour

81. The distance that an athlete is from home if the athlete jogs for 1 hour to a park that is 7 miles away, stays for 30 minutes, and then jogs home at the same pace

82. The amount of oil in a 55-gallon drum that is initially full, then is drained at a rate of 5 gallons per minute for 4 minutes, is left for 6 minutes, and then is emptied at a rate of 7 gallons per minute

83. Online Exploration Search the "Fast Facts" pages on the U.S. Census Bureau's Web site to complete the following.
  (a) Rounding to the nearest million, what was the U.S. population in 1900?
  (b) Rounding to the nearest million, what was the U.S. population in 2000?
  (c) Using the concept of slope, find the average rate of change in the U.S. population over this time.

84. Online Exploration Search the "Fast Facts" pages on the U.S. Census Bureau's Web site to complete the following.
  (a) Find the population of New York City in 1900. Round to the nearest hundred-thousand.
  (b) Find the population of New York City in 2000. Round to the nearest hundred-thousand.
  (c) Using the concept of slope, find the average rate of change in the New York City population over this time.

APPLICATIONS

85. *Twitter Followers* One year after a celebrity first began posting comments on Twitter, she had 25,600 followers. Four years after this celebrity first began posting comments, she had 148,000 followers.
  (a) Find the slope of the line that passes through the points (1, 25600) and (4, 148000).
  (b) Interpret the slope as a rate of change.

86. *Profit from Tablet Computers* When a company manufactures 500 tablet computers, its profit is $100,000, and when it manufactures 1500 tablet computers, its profit is $400,000.
  (a) Find the slope of the line passing through the points (500, 100000) and (1500, 400000).
  (b) Interpret the slope as a rate of change.

87. *Revenue* The graph shows revenue received from selling x flash drives.

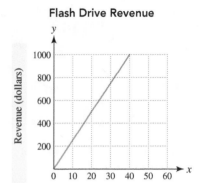

Flash Drive Revenue

  (a) Find the slope of the line shown.
  (b) Interpret the slope as a rate of change.

88. *Electricity* The graph shows how voltage is related to amperage in an electrical circuit. The slope corresponds to the resistance in ohms. Find the resistance in this electrical circuit.

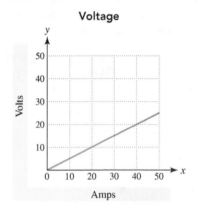

Voltage

89. *Walking for Charities* The table lists the amount of money M in dollars raised for walking various distances x in miles for a charity.

x	0	5	10	15
M	0	100	250	450

  (a) Make a line graph of the data.
  (b) Calculate the slope of each line segment.
  (c) Interpret each slope as a rate of change.

90. *Insect Population* The table lists the number N of black flies in thousands per acre after x weeks.

x	0	2	4	6
N	3	4	10	18

  (a) Make a line graph of the data.
  (b) Calculate the slope of each line segment.
  (c) Interpret each slope as a rate of change.

91. *Median Household Income* In 2000, median family income was about $42,000, and in 2008 it was about $50,000. (*Source:* Department of the Treasury.)
  (a) Find the slope of the line passing through the points (2000, 42000) and (2008, 50000).
  (b) Interpret the slope as a rate of change.
  (c) If this trend continues, estimate the median family income in 2014.

92. *Minimum Wage* In 1995, the minimum wage was $4.25 per hour, and by 2010 it had increased to $7.25 per hour. (*Source:* Department of Labor.)
  (a) Find the slope of the line passing through the points (1995, 4.25) and (2010, 7.25).
  (b) Interpret the slope as a rate of change.
  (c) If this trend continues, estimate the minimum wage in 2015.

93. *Rate of Change* Suppose that $y = -2x + 10$ is graphed in the first quadrant of the xy-plane where the x-axis is labeled "Time (minutes)" and the y-axis is labeled "Distance (feet)." If this graph represents the distance y that an ant is from a stone after x minutes, answer each of the following.
  (a) Is the ant moving toward or away from the stone?
  (b) Initially, how far from the stone is the ant?
  (c) At what rate is the ant moving?
  (d) What is the value of x (time) when the ant reaches the stone?

94. *Rate of Change* Suppose that we graph $y = 15x + 8$ in the first quadrant of the xy-plane where the x-axis is labeled "Time (minutes)" and the y-axis is labeled "Distance (feet)." If this graph represents the distance y that a frog is from a tree after x minutes, answer each of the following.
  (a) Is the frog moving toward or away from the tree?
  (b) Initially, how far from the tree is the frog?
  (c) At what rate is the frog moving?
  (d) What is the value of x when the frog is 53 feet from the tree?

WRITING ABOUT MATHEMATICS

95. If you are given two points and the slope formula $m = \frac{y_2 - y_1}{x_2 - x_1}$, does it matter which point is (x_1, y_1) and which point is (x_2, y_2)? Explain.

96. Suppose that a line approximates the distance y in miles that a person drives in x hours. What does the slope of the line represent? Give an example.

97. Describe the information that the slope m gives about a line. Be as complete as possible.

98. Could one line have two slopes? Explain.

SECTIONS 3.3 and 3.4 — Checking Basic Concepts

1. Identify the x- and y-intercepts in the graph.

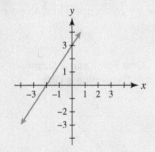

2. Complete the table for the equation $2x - y = 2$. Then determine the x- and y-intercepts.

x	−2	−1	0	1	2
y	−6				

3. Find any intercepts for the graphs of the equations and then graph each linear equation.
  (a) $x - 2y = 6$ **(b)** $y = 2$ **(c)** $x = -1$

4. Write the equations of a horizontal line and a vertical line that pass through the point $(-2, 4)$.

5. If possible, find the slope of the line passing through each pair of points.
  (a) $(-2, 3), (2, 6)$ **(b)** $(-5, 3), (0, 3)$
  (c) $(1, 5), (1, 8)$

6. Find the slope of the line shown.

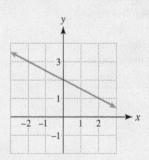

continued on next page

continued from previous page

7. Sketch a line passing through the point $(-3, 1)$ and having slope 2.

8. *Modeling* The line graph to the right shows the depth of water in a small pond before and after a rain storm.
   (a) Estimate the slope of each line segment.
   (b) Interpret each slope as a rate of change.
   (c) Describe what happened to the amount of water in the pond.

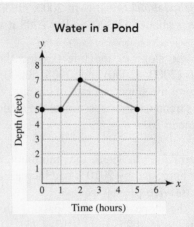

Water in a Pond

3.5   Slope–Intercept Form

Basic Concepts • Finding Slope–Intercept Form • Parallel and Perpendicular Lines

A LOOK INTO MATH ▶ When a line models a real-world situation, slope represents a rate of change and the y-intercept often represents an initial value. For example, if there are initially **30** gallons of water in a small wading pool, and the pool is being filled by a garden hose at a constant rate of **2** gallons per minute, a line representing this situation has a slope of **2** and a y-intercept of **30**. In this section we discuss how to find the equation of a nonvertical line, given its slope and y-intercept.

Basic Concepts

For any two points in the xy-plane, we can draw a unique line passing through them, as illustrated in Figure 3.40(a). Another way we can determine a unique line is to know the y-intercept and the slope. For example, if a line has y-intercept 2 and slope $m = 1$, then the resulting line is shown in Figure 3.40(b).

NEW VOCABULARY

☐ Slope–intercept form
☐ Negative reciprocals

STUDY TIP

A new concept is often easier to learn when we can find a relationship between the concept and our personal experience. Try to list five real-life situations that have an initial value and a constant rate of change.

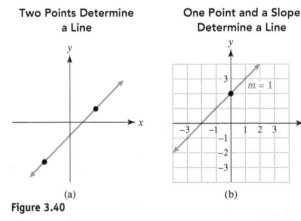

Two Points Determine a Line

One Point and a Slope Determine a Line

(a)

(b)

Figure 3.40

READING CHECK

• How many points does it take to determine a line?

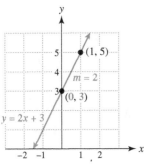

Figure 3.41 Slope 2, y-intercept 3

Finding Slope–Intercept Form

The graph of $y = 2x + 3$ passes through $(0, 3)$ and $(1, 5)$, as shown in Figure 3.41. The slope of this line is

$$m = \frac{5 - 3}{1 - 0} = 2.$$

If $x = 0$ in $y = 2x + 3$, then $y = 2(0) + 3 = 3$. Thus the graph of $y = 2x + 3$ has slope 2 and y-intercept 3. In general, the graph of $y = mx + b$ has slope m and y-intercept b. The form $y = mx + b$ is called the *slope–intercept form*.

SLOPE–INTERCEPT FORM

The line with slope m and y-intercept b is given by

$$y = mx + b,$$

the **slope–intercept form** of a line.

Table 3.18 shows several equations in the form $y = mx + b$ and lists the corresponding slope and y-intercept for the graph associated with each.

READING CHECK

- In $y = mx + b$, which value is the slope and which is the y-intercept?

TABLE 3.18 $y = mx + b$ **Form**

Equation	Slope	y-intercept
$y = 4x - 3$	4	-3
$y = 12$	0	12
$y = -x - \frac{5}{8}$	-1	$-\frac{5}{8}$
$y = -\frac{2}{3}x$	$-\frac{2}{3}$	0

EXAMPLE 1 **Using a graph to write the slope–intercept form**

For each graph write the slope–intercept form of the line.

(a)

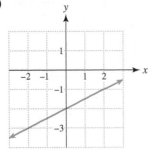

(b)

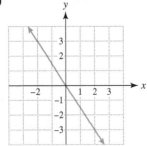

Solution

(a) The graph intersects the y-axis at -2, so the y-intercept is -2. Because the graph rises 1 unit for each 2-unit increase in x, the slope is $\frac{1}{2}$. The slope–intercept form of the line is $y = \frac{1}{2}x - 2$.

(b) The graph intersects the y-axis at 0, so the y-intercept is 0. Because the graph falls 3 units for each 2-unit increase in x, the slope is $-\frac{3}{2}$. The slope–intercept form of the line is $y = -\frac{3}{2}x + 0$, or $y = -\frac{3}{2}x$.

Now Try Exercises 15, 19

EXAMPLE 2 **Sketching a line**

Sketch a line with slope $-\frac{1}{2}$ and y-intercept 1. Write its slope–intercept form.

Solution
For the y-intercept of 1 plot the point $(0, 1)$. Slope $-\frac{1}{2}$ indicates that the graph falls 1 unit for each 2-unit increase in x. Thus the line passes through the point $(0 + 2, 1 - 1)$, or $(2, 0)$, as shown in Figure 3.42. The slope–intercept form of this line is $y = -\frac{1}{2}x + 1$.

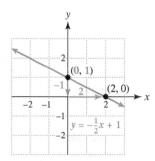

Figure 3.42

▌ Now Try Exercise 23

When a linear equation is not given in slope–intercept form, the coefficient of the x-term may not represent the slope and the constant term may not represent the y-intercept. For example, the graph of $2x + 3y = 12$ does *not* have slope 2 and it does *not* have y-intercept 12. To find the correct slope and y-intercept, the equation can first be written in slope–intercept form. This is demonstrated in the next example.

EXAMPLE 3 **Writing an equation in slope–intercept form**

Write each equation in slope–intercept form. Then give the slope and y-intercept of the line.
(a) $2x + 3y = 12$ **(b)** $x = 2y + 4$

Solution
(a) To write the equation in slope–intercept form, solve for y.

$$2x + 3y = 12 \qquad \text{Given equation}$$
$$3y = -2x + 12 \qquad \text{Subtract } 2x \text{ from each side.}$$
$$y = -\frac{2}{3}x + 4 \qquad \text{Divide each side by 3.}$$

The slope of the line is $-\frac{2}{3}$, and the y-intercept is 4.

(b) This equation is *not* in slope–intercept form because it is solved for x, not y.

$$x = 2y + 4 \qquad \text{Given equation}$$
$$x - 4 = 2y \qquad \text{Subtract 4 from each side.}$$
$$\frac{1}{2}x - 2 = y \qquad \text{Divide each side by 2.}$$
$$y = \frac{1}{2}x - 2 \qquad \text{Rewrite the equation.}$$

The slope of the line is $\frac{1}{2}$, and the y-intercept is -2.

▌ Now Try Exercises 39, 41

EXAMPLE 4 **Writing an equation in slope–intercept form and graphing it**

Write the equation $2x + y = 3$ in slope–intercept form and then graph it.

Solution
First write the given equation in slope–intercept form.

$$2x + y = 3 \qquad \text{Given equation}$$
$$y = -2x + 3 \qquad \text{Subtract } 2x \text{ from each side.}$$

The slope–intercept form is $y = -2x + 3$, with slope -2 and y-intercept 3. To graph this equation, plot the y-intercept as the point $(0, 3)$. The line falls **2** units for each **1**-unit increase in x, so plot the point $(0 + 1, 3 - 2) = (1, 1)$. Sketch a line passing through $(0, 3)$ and $(1, 1)$, as shown in Figure 3.43.

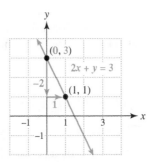

Figure 3.43

■ Now Try Exercise 51

MAKING CONNECTIONS

Different Ways to Graph the Same Line

In Example 4 the line $2x + y = 3$ was graphed by finding its slope–intercept form. A second way to graph this line is to find the x- and y-intercepts of the line. If $y = 0$, then $x = \frac{3}{2}$ makes this equation true, and if $x = 0$, then $y = 3$ makes this equation true. Thus the x-intercept is $\frac{3}{2}$, and the y-intercept is 3. Note that the line in Figure 3.43 passes through the points $\left(\frac{3}{2}, 0\right)$ and $(0, 3)$, which could be used to graph the line.

EXAMPLE 5 **Modeling cell phone costs**

Roaming with a cell phone costs \$5 for the initial connection and \$0.50 per minute.
(a) If someone talks for 23 minutes while roaming, what is the charge?
(b) Write the slope–intercept form that gives the cost of talking for x minutes.
(c) If the charge is \$8.50, how long did the person talk?

Solution
(a) The charge for 23 minutes at \$0.50 per minute plus \$5 would be

$$0.50 \cdot 23 + 5 = \$16.50.$$

(b) The rate of increase is \$0.50 per minute with an initial cost of \$5. Let $y = 0.5x + 5$, where the slope or rate of change is **0.5** and the y-intercept is **5**.

(c) To determine how long a person can talk for $8.50, we solve the following equation.

$$0.5x + 5 = 8.5 \quad \text{Equation to solve}$$
$$0.5x = 3.5 \quad \text{Subtract 5 from each side.}$$
$$x = \frac{3.5}{0.5} \quad \text{Divide each side by 0.5.}$$
$$x = 7 \quad \text{Simplify.}$$

The person talked for 7 minutes. Note that this solution is based on the assumption that the phone company did not round up a fraction of a minute.

▌ **Now Try Exercise 73**

Parallel and Perpendicular Lines

Parallel Lines

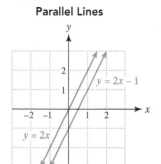

Figure 3.44

Slope is an important concept for determining whether two lines are parallel. If two lines have the same slope, they are parallel. For example, the lines $y = 2x$ and $y = 2x - 1$ are parallel because they both have slope 2, as shown in Figure 3.44.

> **PARALLEL LINES**
>
> Two lines with the same slope are parallel.
>
> Two nonvertical parallel lines have the same slope.

NOTE: Two vertical lines are parallel and the slope of each is undefined.

EXAMPLE 6 **Finding parallel lines**

Find the slope–intercept form of a line parallel to $y = -2x + 3$ and passing through the point $(-2, 3)$. Sketch each line in the same xy-plane.

Solution
Because the line $y = -2x + 3$ has slope -2, any parallel line also has slope -2 with slope–intercept form $y = -2x + b$ for some value of b. The value of b can be found by substituting the point $(-2, 3)$ in the slope–intercept form.

$$y = -2x + b \quad \text{Slope–intercept form}$$
$$3 = -2(-2) + b \quad \text{Let } x = -2 \text{ and } y = 3.$$
$$3 = 4 + b \quad \text{Multiply.}$$
$$-1 = b \quad \text{Subtract 4 from each side.}$$

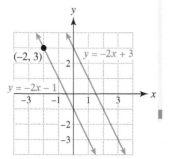

Figure 3.45

The y-intercept is -1, and so the slope–intercept form is $y = -2x - 1$. The graphs of the equations $y = -2x + 3$ and $y = -2x - 1$ are shown in Figure 3.45. Note that they are parallel lines, both with slope -2 but with different y-intercepts, 3 and -1.

▌ **Now Try Exercise 63**

The lines shown in Figure 3.46 are perpendicular because they intersect at a 90° angle. Rather than measure the angle between two intersecting lines, we can determine whether two lines are perpendicular from their slopes. The slopes of perpendicular lines satisfy the properties given in the box below Figure 3.46.

Perpendicular Lines

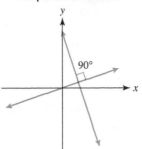

Figure 3.46

PERPENDICULAR LINES

If two perpendicular lines have nonzero slopes m_1 and m_2, then $m_1 \cdot m_2 = -1$.

If two lines have slopes m_1 and m_2 such that $m_1 \cdot m_2 = -1$, then they are perpendicular lines.

NOTE: A vertical line and a horizontal line are perpendicular.

Table 3.19 shows examples of slopes m_1 and m_2 that result in perpendicular lines. Note that $m_1 \cdot m_2 = -1$ and that $m_2 = -\frac{1}{m_1}$. That is, the product of the two slopes is -1, and the two slopes are **negative reciprocals** of each other. Note that in each case $m_1 \cdot m_2 = -1$.

TABLE 3.19 Slopes of Perpendicular Lines

m_1	1	$-\frac{1}{2}$	-4	$\frac{2}{3}$	$\frac{3}{4}$
m_2	-1	2	$\frac{1}{4}$	$-\frac{3}{2}$	$-\frac{4}{3}$

READING CHECK

• What does it mean for one number to be a negative reciprocal of another?

We can use these concepts to find equations of perpendicular lines, as illustrated in the next two examples.

EXAMPLE 7 **Finding equations of perpendicular lines**

For each of the given lines, find the slope–intercept form of a line passing through the origin that is perpendicular to the given line.

(a) $y = 3x$ (b) $y = -\frac{2}{5}x + 5$ (c) $-3x + 4y = 24$

Solution

(a) If a line passes through the origin, then its y-intercept is 0 with slope–intercept form $y = mx$. The given line $y = 3x$ has slope $m_1 = 3$, so a line perpendicular to it has a slope that is the negative reciprocal of 3.

$$m_2 = -\frac{1}{m_1} = -\frac{1}{3}$$

The required slope–intercept form is $y = -\frac{1}{3}x$.

(b) The given line $y = -\frac{2}{5}x + 5$ has slope $m_1 = -\frac{2}{5}$, so a line perpendicular to it has slope $m_2 = \frac{5}{2}$ because $-\frac{2}{5} \cdot \frac{5}{2} = -1$. The required slope–intercept form is $y = \frac{5}{2}x$.

(c) To find the slope of the given line, write $-3x + 4y = 24$ in slope–intercept form.

$$-3x + 4y = 24 \qquad \text{Given equation}$$
$$4y = 3x + 24 \qquad \text{Add } 3x \text{ to each side.}$$
$$y = \frac{3}{4}x + 6 \qquad \text{Divide each side by 4.}$$

The slope of the given line is $m_1 = \frac{3}{4}$, so a line perpendicular to it has slope $m_2 = -\frac{4}{3}$. The required slope–intercept form is $y = -\frac{4}{3}x$.

❚ **Now Try Exercise 67**

EXAMPLE 8   **Finding a perpendicular line equation**

Find the slope–intercept form of the line perpendicular to $y = -\frac{1}{2}x + 1$ and passing through the point $(1, -1)$. Sketch each line in the same xy-plane.

Solution
The line $y = -\frac{1}{2}x + 1$ has slope $m_1 = -\frac{1}{2}$. Any line perpendicular to it has slope $m_2 = 2$ (because $-\frac{1}{2} \cdot 2 = -1$) with slope–intercept form $y = 2x + b$ for some value of b. The value of b can be found by substituting the point $(1, -1)$ in the slope–intercept form.

$$y = 2x + b \qquad \text{Slope–intercept form}$$
$$-1 = 2(1) + b \qquad \text{Let } x = 1 \text{ and } y = -1.$$
$$-1 = 2 + b \qquad \text{Multiply.}$$
$$-3 = b \qquad \text{Subtract 2 from each side.}$$

The slope–intercept form is $y = 2x - 3$. The graphs of $y = -\frac{1}{2}x + 1$ and $y = 2x - 3$ are shown in Figure 3.47. Note that the point $(1, -1)$ lies on the graph of $y = 2x - 3$.

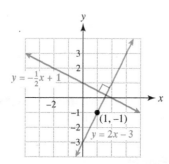

Figure 3.47

❚ **Now Try Exercise 69**

3.5	**Putting It All Together**

CONCEPT	COMMENTS	EXAMPLE
Slope–Intercept Form $y = mx + b$	A unique equation for a line, determined by the slope m and the y-intercept b	An equation of the line with slope $m = 3$ and y-intercept $b = -5$ is $y = 3x - 5$.

CONCEPT	COMMENTS	EXAMPLE
Parallel Lines	$y = m_1x + b_1$ and $y = m_2x + b_2$, where $m_1 = m_2$ Nonvertical parallel lines have the same slope. Two vertical lines are parallel.	The lines $y = 2x - 1$ and $y = 2x + 2$ are parallel because they both have slope 2. 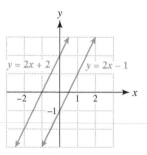
Perpendicular Lines	$y = m_1x + b_1$ and $y = m_2x + b_2$, where $m_1m_2 = -1$ Perpendicular lines which are neither vertical nor horizontal have slopes whose product equals -1. A vertical line and a horizontal line are perpendicular.	The lines $y = 3x - 1$ and $y = -\frac{1}{3}x + 2$ are perpendicular because $$m_1m_2 = 3\left(-\frac{1}{3}\right) = -1.$$ 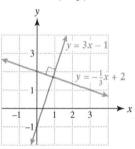

3.5 Exercises

MyMathLab   Math XL PRACTICE   WATCH   DOWNLOAD   READ   REVIEW

CONCEPTS AND VOCABULARY

1. The slope–intercept form of a line is _____.

2. In the slope–intercept form of a line, m represents the _____ of the line.

3. In the slope–intercept form of a line, b represents the _____ of the line.

4. If $b = 0$ in the slope–intercept form of a line, then its graph passes through the _____.

5. Two lines with the same slope are _____.

6. Two nonvertical parallel lines have the same _____.

7. If m_1 and m_2 are the slopes of two lines where $m_1 \cdot m_2 = -1$, the lines are _____.

8. If two perpendicular lines have nonzero slopes, the slopes are negative _____.

Exercises 9–14: Match the description with its graph (a.–f.) at the top of the next page.

9. A line with positive slope and negative y-intercept

10. A line with positive slope and positive y-intercept

11. A line with negative slope and y-intercept 0

12. A line with negative slope and nonzero y-intercept

13. A line with no x-intercept

14. A line with no y-intercept

a.

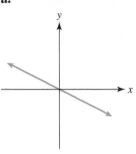

b.

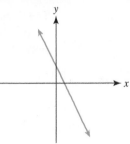

c.

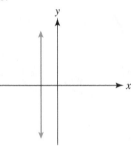

d.

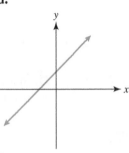

e.

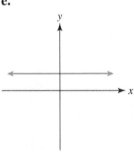

f.

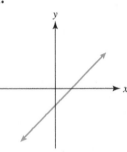

SLOPE–INTERCEPT FORM

Exercises 15–22: Write the slope–intercept form for the line shown in the graph.

15.

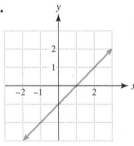

16.

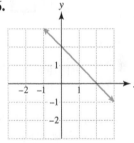

17.

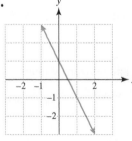

18.

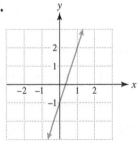

19.

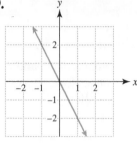

20.

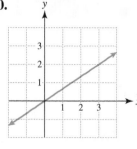

21.

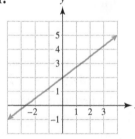

22.

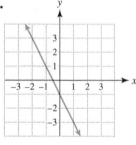

Exercises 23–32: Sketch a line with the given slope m and y-intercept b. Write its slope–intercept form.

23. $m = 1, b = 2$

24. $m = -1, b = 3$

25. $m = 2, b = -1$

26. $m = -3, b = 2$

27. $m = -\frac{1}{2}, b = -2$

28. $m = -\frac{2}{3}, b = 0$

29. $m = \frac{1}{3}, b = 0$

30. $m = 3, b = -3$

31. $m = 0, b = 3$

32. $m = 0, b = -3$

Exercises 33–44: Do the following.

   (**a**) *Write the equation in slope–intercept form.*
   (**b**) *Give the slope and y-intercept of the line.*

33. $x + y = 4$

34. $x - y = 6$

35. $2x + y = 4$

36. $-4x + y = 8$

37. $x - 2y = -4$

38. $x + 3y = -9$

39. $2x - 3y = 6$

40. $4x + 5y = 20$

41. $x = 4y - 6$

42. $x = -3y + 2$

43. $\frac{1}{2}x + \frac{3}{2}y = 1$

44. $-\frac{3}{4}x + \frac{1}{2}y = \frac{1}{2}$

Exercises 45–56: Graph the equation.

45. $y = -3x + 2$

46. $y = \frac{1}{2}x - 1$

47. $y = \frac{1}{3}x$

48. $y = -2x$

49. $y = 2$

50. $y = -3$

51. $x + y = 3$

52. $-\frac{2}{3}x + y = -2$

53. $x + 2y = 2$ **54.** $-2x - y = -2$

55. $x = 2 - y$ **56.** $x = -\frac{1}{3}y + \frac{2}{3}$

Exercises 57–60: The table shows points that all lie on the same line. Find the slope–intercept form for the line.

57.

x	0	1	2
y	2	4	6

58.

x	-1	0	1
y	4	8	12

59.

x	-2	0	2
y	-4	-2	0

60.

x	0	2	4
y	6	3	0

PARALLEL AND PERPENDICULAR LINES

Exercises 61–70: Find the slope–intercept form of the line satisfying the given conditions.

61. Slope $\frac{4}{7}$, y-intercept 3

62. Slope $-\frac{1}{2}$, y-intercept -7

63. Parallel to $y = 3x + 1$, passing through $(0, 0)$

64. Parallel to $y = -2x$, passing through $(0, 1)$

65. Parallel to $2x + 4y = 5$, passing through $(1, 2)$

66. Parallel to $-x - 3y = 9$, passing through $(-3, 1)$

67. Perpendicular to $y = -\frac{1}{2}x - 3$, passing through $(0, 0)$

68. Perpendicular to $y = \frac{3}{4}x - \frac{1}{2}$, passing through $(3, -2)$

69. Perpendicular to $x = -\frac{1}{3}y$, passing through $(-1, 0)$

70. Perpendicular to $6x - 3y = 18$, passing through $(4, -3)$

APPLICATIONS

71. *Rental Cars* Driving a rental car x miles costs $y = 0.25x + 25$ dollars.
   (a) How much would it cost to rent the car but not drive it?
   (b) How much does it cost to drive the car 1 *additional* mile?
   (c) What is the y-intercept of $y = 0.25x + 25$? What does it represent?
   (d) What is the slope of $y = 0.25x + 25$? What does it represent?

72. *Calculating Rainfall* The total rainfall y in inches that fell x hours past noon is given by $y = \frac{1}{2}x + 3$.
   (a) How much rainfall was there at noon?
   (b) At what rate was rain falling in the afternoon?

(c) What is the y-intercept of $y = \frac{1}{2}x + 3$? What does it represent?
(d) What is the slope of $y = \frac{1}{2}x + 3$? What does it represent?

73. *Cell Phone Plan* A cell phone plan costs $3.95 per month plus $0.07 per minute. (Assume that a partial minute is not rounded up.)
   (a) During July, a person talks a total of 50 minutes. What is the charge?
   (b) Write an equation in slope–intercept form that gives the monthly cost C of talking on this plan for x minutes.
   (c) If the charge for one month amounts to $8.64, how much time did the person spend talking on the phone?

74. *Electrical Rates* Electrical service costs $8 per month plus $0.10 per kilowatt-hour of electricity used. (Assume that a partial kilowatt-hour is not rounded up.)
   (a) If the resident of an apartment uses 650 kilowatt-hours in 1 month, what is the charge?
   (b) Write an equation in slope–intercept form that gives the cost C of using x kilowatt-hours in 1 month.
   (c) If the monthly electrical bill for the apartment's resident is $43, how many kilowatt-hours were used?

75. *Cost of Driving* The cost of driving a car includes both fixed costs and mileage costs. Assume that it costs $164.30 per month for insurance and car payments and $0.35 per mile for gasoline, oil, and routine maintenance.
   (a) Find values for m and b so that $y = mx + b$ models the monthly cost of driving the car x miles.
   (b) What does the value of b represent?

76. *Antarctic Ozone Layer* The ozone layer occurs in Earth's atmosphere between altitudes of 12 and 18 miles and is an important filter of ultraviolet light from the sun. The thickness of the ozone layer is frequently measured in Dobson units. An average value is 300 Dobson units. In 2007, the reported minimum in the antarctic *ozone hole* was about 83 Dobson units. (Source: NASA.)
   (a) The equation $T = 0.01D$ describes the thickness T in millimeters of an ozone layer that is D Dobson units. How many millimeters thick was the ozone layer over the antarctic in 2007?
   (b) What is the average thickness of the ozone layer in millimeters?

WRITING ABOUT MATHEMATICS

77. Explain how the values of m and b can be used to graph the equation $y = mx + b$.

78. Explain how to find the value of b in the equation $y = 2x + b$ if the point $(3, 4)$ lies on the line.

Group Activity | Working with Real Data

Directions: Form a group of 2 to 4 people. Select someone to record the group's responses for this activity. All members of the group should work cooperatively to answer the questions. If your instructor asks for the results, each member of the group should be prepared to respond.

Exercises 1–5: In this set of exercises you are to use your knowledge of equations of lines to model the average annual cost of tuition and fees (in 2010 dollars).

1. *Cost of Tuition* In 2005, the average cost of tuition and fees at *private* four-year colleges was $23,410, and in 2010 it was $27,290. Sketch a line that passes through the points (2005, 23410) and (2010, 27290). (*Source:* The College Board.)

2. *Rate of Change in Tuition* Calculate the slope of the line in your graph. Interpret this slope as a rate of change.

3. *Modeling Tuition* Find the slope–intercept form of the line in your sketch. What is the *y*-intercept and does it have meaning in this situation?

4. *Predicting Tuition* Use your equation to estimate tuition and fees in 2008 and compare it to the known value of $24,950. Estimate tuition and fees in 2015.

5. *Public Tuition* In 2005, the average cost of tuition and fees at *public* four-year colleges was $6130, and in 2010 it was $7610. Repeat Exercises 1–4 for these data. Note that the known value for 2008 is $6530. (*Source:* The College Board.)

3.6 | Point–Slope Form

Derivation of Point–Slope Form • Finding Point–Slope Form • Applications

A LOOK INTO MATH ▶

In 1995, there were 690 female officers in the Marine Corps, and by 2010 this number had increased to about 1110. This growth is illustrated in Figure 3.48, where the line passes through the points (1995, 690) and (2010, 1110). Because two points determine a unique line, we can find the equation of this line and use it to *estimate* the number of female officers in other years (see Example 6). In this section we discuss how to find this equation by using the *point–slope form*, rather than the slope–intercept form of the equation of a line. (*Source:* Department of Defense.)

NEW VOCABULARY

☐ Equation of a line
☐ Point–slope form

STUDY TIP

Spend some extra time learning words in the language of mathematics. A strong mathematical vocabulary is one of the keys to success in any math course.

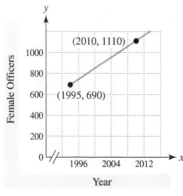

Female Officers in the Marine Corps

Figure 3.48

Derivation of Point–Slope Form

If we know the slope and y-intercept of a line, we can write its slope–intercept form, $y = mx + b$, which is an example of an **equation of a line**. The point–slope form is a different type of equation of a line.

Suppose that a (nonvertical) line with slope m passes through the point (x_1, y_1). If (x, y) is a different point on this line, then $m = \frac{y - y_1}{x - x_1}$. See Figure 3.49. Using this slope formula, we can find the point–slope form.

Slope of a Line

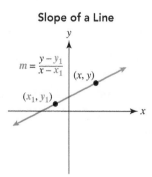

Figure 3.49

$$m = \frac{y - y_1}{x - x_1} \qquad \text{Slope formula}$$

$$m \cdot (x - x_1) = \frac{y - y_1}{x - x_1} \cdot (x - x_1) \quad \text{Multiply each side by } (x - x_1).$$

$$m(x - x_1) = y - y_1 \qquad \text{Simplify.}$$

$$y - y_1 = m(x - x_1) \qquad \text{Rewrite the equation.}$$

The equation $y - y_1 = m(x - x_1)$ is traditionally called the *point–slope form*. By adding y_1 to each side of this equation we get $y = m(x - x_1) + y_1$, which is an equivalent form that is helpful when graphing. Both equations are in *point–slope form*.

POINT–SLOPE FORM

The line with slope m passing through the point (x_1, y_1) is given by

$$y - y_1 = m(x - x_1)$$

$$\text{or, equivalently,} \qquad y = m(x - x_1) + y_1,$$

the **point–slope form** of a line.

Finding Point–Slope Form

In the next example we find a point–slope form for a line. Note that *any* point that lies on the line can be used in its point–slope form.

EXAMPLE 1 **Finding a point–slope form**

Use the labeled point in each figure to write a point–slope form for the line and then simplify it to the slope–intercept form.

(a)

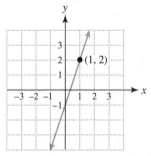

(b)

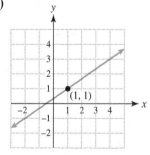

Solution

(a) The graph rises 3 units for each unit of horizontal run, so the slope is $\frac{3}{1}$, or 3. Let $m = 3$ and $(x_1, y_1) = (1, 2)$ in the point–slope form.

$$y - y_1 = m(x - x_1) \quad \text{Point–slope form}$$

$$y - 2 = 3(x - 1) \quad \text{Let } m = 3, x_1 = 1, \text{ and } y_1 = 2.$$

A point–slope form for the line is $y - 2 = 3(x - 1)$.

To simplify to the slope–intercept form, apply the distributive property to the equation $y - 2 = 3(x - 1)$.

$$y - 2 = 3x - 3 \qquad \text{Distributive property}$$

$$y = 3x - 1 \qquad \text{Add 2 to each side.}$$

The slope–intercept form is $y = 3x - 1$.

(b) The graph rises 2 units for each 3 units of horizontal run, so the slope is $\frac{2}{3}$. Let $m = \frac{2}{3}$ and $(x_1, y_1) = (1, 1)$ in the point–slope form.

$$y - y_1 = m(x - x_1) \qquad \text{Point–slope form}$$

$$y - 1 = \frac{2}{3}(x - 1) \qquad \text{Let } m = \frac{2}{3}, x_1 = 1, \text{ and } y_1 = 1.$$

A point–slope form for the line is $y - 1 = \frac{2}{3}(x - 1)$.

To simplify to the slope–intercept form, apply the distributive property to the equation $y - 1 = \frac{2}{3}(x - 1)$.

$$y - 1 = \frac{2}{3}x - \frac{2}{3} \qquad \text{Distributive property}$$

$$y = \frac{2}{3}x + \frac{1}{3} \qquad \text{Add 1, or } \frac{3}{3}, \text{ to each side.}$$

The slope–intercept form is $y = \frac{2}{3}x + \frac{1}{3}$.

| Now Try Exercises 13, 15

EXAMPLE 2 | **Finding a point–slope form**

Find a point–slope form for a line passing through the point $(-2, 3)$ with slope $-\frac{1}{2}$. Does the point $(2, 1)$ lie on this line?

Solution

Let $m = -\frac{1}{2}$ and $(x_1, y_1) = (-2, 3)$ in the point–slope form.

$$y - y_1 = m(x - x_1) \qquad \text{Point–slope form}$$

$$y - 3 = -\frac{1}{2}(x - (-2)) \qquad x_1 = -2, y_1 = 3, \text{ and } m = -\frac{1}{2}$$

$$y - 3 = -\frac{1}{2}(x + 2) \qquad \text{Simplify.}$$

To determine whether $(2, 1)$ lies on the line, substitute $x = 2$ and $y = 1$ in the equation.

$$1 - 3 \stackrel{?}{=} -\frac{1}{2}(2 + 2) \qquad \text{Let } x = 2 \text{ and } y = 1.$$

$$-2 \stackrel{?}{=} -\frac{1}{2}(4) \qquad \text{Simplify.}$$

$$-2 = -2 \; \checkmark \qquad \text{A true statement}$$

The point $(2, 1)$ lies on the line because it satisfies the point–slope form.

| Now Try Exercises 9, 19

In the next example we use the point–slope form to find the equation of a line passing through two points.

EXAMPLE 3   Finding an equation of a line passing through two points

Use the point–slope form to find an equation of the line passing through the points $(1, -4)$ and $(-2, 5)$.

Solution
Before we can apply the point–slope form, we must find the slope.

$$m = \frac{y_2 - y_1}{x_2 - x_1} \qquad \text{Slope formula}$$

$$= \frac{5 - (-4)}{-2 - 1} \qquad x_1 = 1, y_1 = -4, x_2 = -2, \text{ and } y_2 = 5$$

$$= -3 \qquad \text{Simplify.}$$

We can let either the point $(1, -4)$ or the point $(-2, 5)$ be (x_1, y_1) in the point–slope form. If $(x_1, y_1) = (1, -4)$, then the equation of the line becomes the following.

$$y - y_1 = m(x - x_1) \qquad \text{Point–slope form}$$

$$y - (-4) = -3(x - 1) \qquad x_1 = 1, y_1 = -4, \text{ and } m = -3$$

$$y + 4 = -3(x - 1) \qquad \text{Simplify.}$$

If we let $(x_1, y_1) = (-2, 5)$, the point–slope form becomes

$$y - 5 = -3(x + 2).$$

Now Try Exercise 25

NOTE: Although the two point–slope forms in Example 3 might appear to be different, they actually are equivalent because they simplify to the same slope–intercept form.

$y + 4 = -3(x - 1)$	$y - 5 = -3(x + 2)$	Point–slope forms
$y = -3(x - 1) - 4$	$y = -3(x + 2) + 5$	Addition property
$y = -3x + 3 - 4$	$y = -3x - 6 + 5$	Distributive property
$y = -3x - 1$	$y = -3x - 1$	Same slope–intercept form

MAKING CONNECTIONS

Slope–Intercept and Point–Slope Forms

The slope–intercept form, $y = mx + b$, is unique because any nonvertical line has one slope m and one y-intercept b. The point–slope form, $y - y_1 = m(x - x_1)$, is *not* unique because (x_1, y_1) can be any point that lies on the line. However, any point–slope form can be simplified to a unique slope–intercept form.

READING CHECK

• Is the point–slope form of the equation of a line unique?

EXAMPLE 4   Finding equations of lines

Find the slope–intercept form for the line that satisfies the conditions.
(a) Slope $\frac{1}{2}$, passing through $(-2, 4)$
(b) x-intercept -3, y-intercept 2
(c) Perpendicular to $y = -\frac{2}{3}x$, passing through $\left(\frac{2}{3}, 3\right)$

Solution

(a) Substitute $m = \frac{1}{2}$, $x_1 = -2$, and $y_1 = 4$ in the point–slope form.

$$y - y_1 = m(x - x_1) \qquad \text{Point–slope form}$$

$$y - 4 = \frac{1}{2}(x + 2) \qquad \text{Substitute and simplify.}$$

$$y - 4 = \frac{1}{2}x + 1 \qquad \text{Distributive property}$$

$$y = \frac{1}{2}x + 5 \qquad \text{Add 4 to each side.}$$

(b) The line passes through the points $(-3, 0)$ and $(0, 2)$. The slope of the line is

$$m = \frac{2 - 0}{0 - (-3)} = \frac{2}{3}.$$

Because the line has slope $\frac{2}{3}$ and y-intercept 2, the slope–intercept form is

$$y = \frac{2}{3}x + 2.$$

(c) The slope of $y = -\frac{2}{3}x$ is $m_1 = -\frac{2}{3}$, so the slope of a line perpendicular to it is the negative reciprocal of $-\frac{2}{3}$, or $\frac{3}{2}$. Let $m = \frac{3}{2}$, $x_1 = \frac{2}{3}$, and $y_1 = 3$ in the point–slope form.

$$y - y_1 = m(x - x_1) \qquad \text{Point–slope form}$$

$$y - 3 = \frac{3}{2}\left(x - \frac{2}{3}\right) \qquad \text{Substitute.}$$

$$y - 3 = \frac{3}{2}x - 1 \qquad \text{Distributive property}$$

$$y = \frac{3}{2}x + 2 \qquad \text{Add 3 to each side.}$$

▌ Now Try Exercises 43, 47, 51

In the next example the point–slope form is used to find the slope–intercept form of a line that passes through several points given in a table.

EXAMPLE 5   **Using a table to find slope–intercept form**

The points in the table lie on a line. Find the slope–intercept form of the line.

x	2	4	6	8
y	2	1	0	-1

Solution

The y-values in the table decrease one unit for every two-unit increase in the x-values, so the line has a "rise" of -1 when the run is 2. The slope is $m = \frac{\text{rise}}{\text{run}} = \frac{-1}{2} = -\frac{1}{2}$. *Any* point from the table can be used to obtain a point–slope form of the line, which can then be simplified to slope–intercept form. Letting $(x_1, y_1) = (2, 2)$ and $m = -\frac{1}{2}$ in the point–slope form yields the following result.

$$y - y_1 = m(x - x_1) \qquad \text{Point–slope form}$$

$$y - 2 = -\frac{1}{2}(x - 2) \qquad \text{Substitute.}$$

$$y - 2 = -\frac{1}{2}x + 1 \qquad \text{Distributive property}$$

$$y = -\frac{1}{2}x + 3 \qquad \text{Add 2 to each side.}$$

This result can be checked by substituting each x-value from the table in the equation. For example, when $x = 4$, the corresponding y-value is $y = -\frac{1}{2}(4) + 3 = -2 + 3 = 1$. This agrees with the table.

▌Now Try Exercise 53

MAKING CONNECTIONS

Finding Slope–Intercept Form Without Using Point–Slope Form

The equation in Example 5 can be obtained without using the point–slope form. The value of b can be found by letting $(x, y) = (2, 2)$ and $m = -\frac{1}{2}$ in the slope–intercept form.

$$y = mx + b \qquad \text{Slope–intercept form}$$

$$2 = -\frac{1}{2}(2) + b \quad \text{Substitute.}$$

$$2 = -1 + b \qquad \text{Multiply.}$$

$$3 = b \qquad \text{Add 1 to each side.}$$

Because $m = -\frac{1}{2}$ and $b = 3$, the slope–intercept form is $y = -\frac{1}{2}x + 3$.

Applications

In the next example we find the equation of the line that models the Marine Corps data presented in A Look into Math at the beginning of this section.

EXAMPLE 6 **Modeling numbers of female officers**

In 1995, there were 690 female officers in the Marine Corps, and by 2010 this number had increased to about 1110. Refer to Figure 3.48 at the beginning of this section.
(a) Use the point (1995, 690) to find a point–slope form of the line shown in Figure 3.48.
(b) Interpret the slope as a rate of change.
(c) Use Figure 3.48 to estimate the number of female officers in 2006. Then use your equation from part (a) to approximate this number. How do your answers compare?

Solution
(a) The slope of the line passing through (1995, 690) and (2010, 1110) is

$$m = \frac{1110 - 690}{2010 - 1995} = 28.$$

If we let $x_1 = 1995$ and $y_1 = 690$, then the point–slope form becomes

$$y - 690 = 28(x - 1995) \quad \text{or} \quad y = 28(x - 1995) + 690.$$

(b) Slope $m = 28$ indicates that the number of female officers increased, *on average,* by about 28 officers per year.
(c) From Figure 3.48, it appears that the number of female officers in 2006 was about 1000. To estimate this value let $x = 2006$ in the equation found in part (a).

$$y = 28(2006 - 1995) + 690 = 998$$

Although the graphical estimate and calculated answers are not exactly equal, they are approximately equal. Estimations made from a graph usually are not exact.

▌Now Try Exercise 65

In the next example we review several concepts related to lines.

EXAMPLE 7   **Modeling water in a pool**

A small swimming pool is being emptied by a pump that removes water at a constant rate. After 1 hour the pool contains 5000 gallons, and after 3 hours it contains 3000 gallons.
(a) How fast is the pump removing water?
(b) Find the slope–intercept form of a line that models the amount of water in the pool. Interpret the slope.
(c) Find the y-intercept and the x-intercept. Interpret each.
(d) Sketch a graph of the amount of water in the pool during the first 6 hours.
(e) The point $(2, 4000)$ lies on the graph. Explain its meaning.

Solution
(a) The pump removes $5000 - 3000 = 2000$ gallons of water in 2 hours, or 1000 gallons per hour.
(b) The line passes through the points $(1, 5000)$ and $(3, 3000)$, so the slope is

$$m = \frac{3000 - 5000}{3 - 1} = -1000.$$

One way to find the slope–intercept form is to use the point–slope form.

$$y - y_1 = m(x - x_1) \qquad \text{Point–slope form}$$
$$y - 5000 = -1000(x - 1) \qquad m = -1000, x_1 = 1, \text{ and } y_1 = 5000$$
$$y - 5000 = -1000x + 1000 \qquad \text{Distributive property}$$
$$y = -1000x + 6000 \qquad \text{Add 5000 to each side.}$$

Slope -1000 means that the pump is *removing* 1000 gallons of water per hour.
(c) The y-intercept is 6000 and indicates that the pool initially contained 6000 gallons of water. To find the x-intercept let $y = 0$ in the slope–intercept form.

$$0 = -1000x + 6000 \qquad \text{Let } y = 0.$$
$$1000x = 6000 \qquad \text{Add } 1000x \text{ to each side.}$$
$$x = \frac{6000}{1000} \qquad \text{Divide by 1000.}$$
$$x = 6 \qquad \text{Simplify.}$$

An x-intercept of 6 indicates that the pool is empty after 6 hours.
(d) The x-intercept is 6, and the y-intercept is 6000. Sketch a line from $(6, 0)$ to $(0, 6000)$, as shown in Figure 3.50.

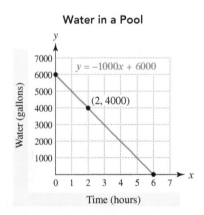

Water in a Pool

Figure 3.50

CRITICAL THINKING

Suppose that a line models the amount of water in a swimming pool. What does a positive slope indicate? What does a negative slope indicate?

(e) The point $(2, 4000)$ indicates that after 2 hours the pool contains 4000 gallons of water.

Now Try Exercise 59

3.6 Putting It All Together

CONCEPT	COMMENTS	EXAMPLE
Point–Slope Form $$y - y_1 = m(x - x_1) \quad \text{or}$$ $$y = m(x - x_1) + y_1$$	Used to find an equation of a line, given two points or one point and the slope. Can always be simplified to slope–intercept form. Does *not* provide a unique equation for a line because *any* point on the line can be used	For two points $(1, 2)$ and $(3, 5)$, first compute $m = \frac{5-2}{3-1} = \frac{3}{2}$. An equation of this line is $$y - 2 = \frac{3}{2}(x - 1).$$ 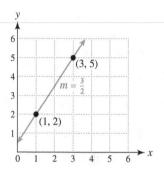

3.6 Exercises

MyMathLab   Math XL PRACTICE   WATCH   DOWNLOAD   READ   REVIEW

CONCEPTS AND VOCABULARY

1. (True or False?) One line is determined by two distinct points.

2. (True or False?) One line is determined by a point and a slope.

3. Give the slope–intercept form of a line.

4. Give the point–slope form of a line.

5. If the point–slope form is written for a line passing through $(1, 3)$, then $x_1 = $ _____ and $y_1 = $ _____.

6. To write a point–slope equation in slope–intercept form, use the _____ property to clear the parentheses.

7. Is the slope–intercept form of a line unique? Explain.

8. Is the point–slope form of a line unique? Explain.

POINT–SLOPE FORM

Exercises 9–12: Determine whether the given point lies on the line.

9. $(3, -11)$ $y + 1 = -2(x + 3)$

10. $(1, 4)$ $y - 3 = -(x - 1)$

11. $(0, 4)$ $y = \frac{1}{2}(x + 4) + 2$

12. $(2, -5)$ $y = -\frac{1}{3}(x - 5) - 6$

Exercises 13–18: Use the labeled point to write a point–slope form for the line.

13.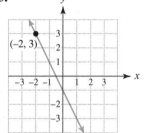

14.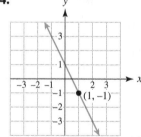

15.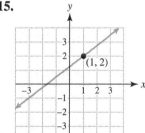

16.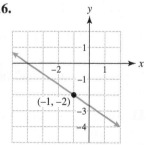

17.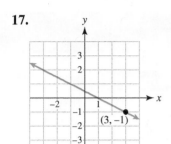

18.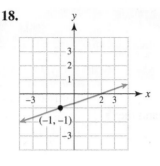

Exercises 19–30: Find a point–slope form for the line that satisfies the stated conditions. When two points are given, use the first point in the point–slope form.

19. Slope 4, passing through $(-3, 1)$

20. Slope -3, passing through $(1, -2)$

21. Slope $\frac{1}{2}$, passing through $(-5, -3)$

22. Slope $-\frac{2}{3}$, passing through $(-3, 6)$

23. Slope 1.5, passing through $(2010, 30)$

24. Slope -10, passing through $(2014, 100)$

25. Passing through $(2, 4)$ and $(-1, -3)$

26. Passing through $(3, -1)$ and $(1, -4)$

27. Passing through $(5, 0)$ and $(0, -3)$

28. Passing through $(-2, 0)$ and $(0, -1)$

29. Passing through $(2003, 15)$ and $(2013, 65)$

30. Passing through $(2009, 5)$ and $(2014, 30)$

Exercises 31–42: Write the point–slope form in slope–intercept form.

31. $y - 4 = 3(x - 2)$ **32.** $y - 3 = -2(x + 1)$

33. $y + 2 = \frac{1}{3}(x + 6)$ **34.** $y - 1 = \frac{2}{5}(x + 10)$

35. $y - \frac{3}{4} = \frac{2}{3}(x - 1)$ **36.** $y + \frac{2}{3} = -\frac{1}{6}(x - 2)$

37. $y = -2(x - 2) + 5$ **38.** $y = 4(x + 3) - 7$

39. $y = \frac{3}{5}(x - 5) + 1$ **40.** $y = -\frac{1}{2}(x + 4) - 6$

41. $y = -16(x + 1.5) + 5$

42. $y = -15(x - 1) + 100$

Exercises 43–52: Find the slope–intercept form for the line satisfying the conditions.

43. Slope -2, passing through $(4, -3)$

44. Slope $\frac{1}{5}$, passing through $(-2, 5)$

45. Passing through $(3, -2)$ and $(2, -1)$

46. Passing through $(8, 3)$ and $(-7, 3)$

47. x-intercept 3, y-intercept $\frac{1}{3}$

48. x-intercept 2, y-intercept -3

49. Parallel to $y = 2x - 1$, passing through $(2, -3)$

50. Parallel to $y = -\frac{3}{2}x$, passing through $(0, 20)$

51. Perpendicular to $y = -\frac{1}{2}x + 3$, passing through the point $(6, -3)$

52. Perpendicular to $y = \frac{3}{5}(x + 1) + 3$, passing through the point $(1, -2)$

Exercises 53–56: The points in the table lie on a line. Find the slope–intercept form of the line.

53.

x	1	2	3	4
y	-3	-5	-7	-9

54.

x	2	3	4	5
y	5	8	11	14

55.

x	-1	1	3	5
y	-3	-2	-1	0

56.

x	-1	5	11	17
y	1	-3	-7	-11

57. Thinking Generally Find the y-intercept of the line given by $y - y_1 = m(x - x_1)$.

58. Thinking Generally Find the x-intercept of the line given by $y - y_1 = m(x - x_1)$.

GRAPHICAL INTERPRETATION

59. *Change in Temperature* The outside temperature was 40°F at 1 A.M. and 15°F at 6 A.M. Assume that the temperature changed at a constant rate.
  (a) At what rate did the temperature change?
  (b) Find the slope–intercept form of a line that models the temperature T at x A.M. Interpret the slope as a rate of change.
  (c) Assuming that your equation is valid for times after 6 A.M., find and interpret the x-intercept.
  (d) Sketch a graph that shows the temperature from 1 A.M. to 9 A.M.
  (e) The point $(4, 25)$ lies on the graph. Explain its meaning.

60. *Cost of Fuel* The cost of buying 5 gallons of fuel oil is $12 and the cost of buying 15 gallons of fuel oil is $36.
  (a) What is the cost of a gallon of fuel oil?
  (b) Find the slope–intercept form of a line that models the cost of buying x gallons of fuel oil. Interpret the slope as a rate of change.
  (c) Find and interpret the x-intercept.
  (d) Sketch a graph that shows the cost of buying 20 gallons or less of fuel oil.
  (e) The point $(11, 26.40)$ lies on the graph. Explain its meaning.

61. *Water and Flow* The graph shows the amount of water y in a 500-gallon tank after x minutes have elapsed.
  (a) Is water entering or leaving the tank? How much water is in the tank after 4 minutes?
  (b) Find the y-intercept. Explain its meaning.
  (c) Find the slope–intercept form of the line. Interpret the slope as a rate of change.
  (d) After how many minutes will the tank be full?

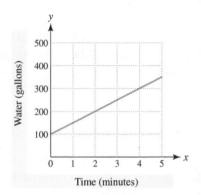

62. *Water and Flow* A hose is used to fill a 100-gallon barrel. If the hose delivers 5 gallons of water per minute, sketch a graph of the amount A of water in the barrel during the first 20 minutes.

63. *Distance and Speed* A person is driving a car along a straight road. The graph at the top of the next column shows the distance y in miles that the driver is from home after x hours.
  (a) Is the person traveling toward or away from home?
  (b) The graph passes through $(1, 250)$ and $(4, 100)$. Discuss the meaning of these points.
  (c) How fast is the driver traveling?
  (d) Find the slope–intercept form of the line. Interpret the slope as a rate of change.

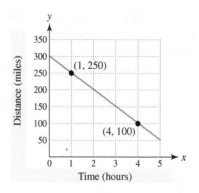

64. *Distance and Speed* A person rides a bicycle at 10 miles per hour, first away from home for 1 hour and then toward home for 1 hour. Sketch a graph that shows the distance d between the bicyclist and home after x hours.

APPLICATIONS

65. *Home Size* The graph models the average size in square feet of new U.S. homes built from 2002 to 2008. (*Source:* U.S. Census Bureau.)
  (a) The line passes through the points $(2002, 2334)$ and $(2008, 2538)$. Explain the meaning of the first point.
  (b) Use the first point to write a point–slope form for the equation of this line.
  (c) Use the graph to estimate the average size of a new home in 2007. Then use your equation from part (b) to estimate the average size of a new home in 2007.
  (d) Interpret the slope as a rate of change.

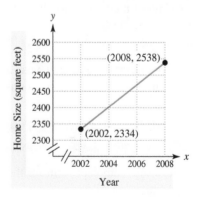

66. *Wyoming Tuition* The graph on the next page models average tuition at Wyoming public 2-year colleges after 2000, where 1 corresponds to 2001, 2 corresponds to 2002, and so on. (*Source:* SSTI *Weekly Digest.*)
  (a) The line passes through the points $(3, 1557)$ and $(8, 1912)$. What is the meaning of the first of these two points?
  (b) Use the first point to write a point–slope form for the equation of this line.

(c) Use the graph to estimate average tuition in 2005. Then use your equation from part (b) to estimate tuition in 2005.

(d) Interpret the slope as a rate of change.

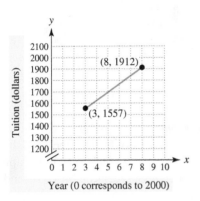

Year (0 corresponds to 2000)

67. *International Adoption* In 2006, there were 731 children adopted into the United States from Ethiopia, and this number was increasing by 515 children per year. (*Source:* U.S. Department of State.)

(a) Determine a point–slope equation of a line that approximates the number of children who were adopted into the United States from Ethiopia during year x, where $x \geq 2006$.

(b) Estimate the number of children adopted into the United States from Ethiopia in 2008.

68. *Median Family Income* In 2000, median income for U.S. families was $41,950, and this number was increasing at a rate of $1250 per year. (*Source:* Department of the Treasury.)

(a) Determine a point–slope equation of a line that approximates median family income during year x, where $x \geq 2000$.

(b) Estimate median family income in 2010.

69. *Cigarette Consumption* For any year x from 1975 to 2015, the number of cigarettes y consumed in the United States is modeled by $y = -10.33x + 21{,}087$, where y is in billions. Interpret the slope as a rate of change. (*Source:* The Tobacco Outlook Report.)

70. *Alcohol Consumption* If x represents a year from 2000 to 2008, then the *average* number of gallons y of pure alcohol consumed annually in the United States by each person age 14 years and older is modeled by $y = 0.015x - 27.825$. Interpret the slope as a rate of change. (*Source:* National Institutes of Health.)

71. *HIV Infection Rates* In 2009, there were an estimated 33 million HIV infections worldwide, with an annual infection rate of 2.7 million. (*Source:* UNAIDS)

(a) Find the slope–intercept form of a line that approximates the cumulative number of HIV infections in millions during year x, where $x \geq 2009$.

(b) Estimate the number of HIV infections in 2012.

72. *Hospitals* In 2002, there were 3039 U.S. hospitals with more than 100 beds, and this number was decreasing at a rate of 33 hospitals per year. (*Source:* AHA Hospital Statistics.)

(a) Determine a slope–intercept equation of a line that approximates the number of U.S. hospitals with more than 100 beds during year x, where $x \geq 2002$.

(b) Estimate the number of hospitals with more than 100 beds in 2009.

WRITING ABOUT MATHEMATICS

73. Explain how to find the equation of a line passing through two points with coordinates (x_1, y_1) and (x_2, y_2). Give an example.

74. Explain how slope is related to rate of change. Give an example.

Checking Basic Concepts

1. Write the slope–intercept form for the line shown in the graph.

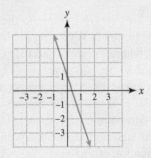

2. Write $4x - 5y = 20$ in slope–intercept form. Give the slope and y-intercept.

3. Graph $y = \frac{1}{2}x - 3$.

4. Write the slope–intercept form of a line that satisfies the given conditions.

(a) Slope 3, passing through $(0, -2)$

(b) Perpendicular to $y = \frac{2}{3}x$, passing through the point $(-2, 3)$

(c) Passing through $(1, -4)$ and $(-2, 3)$

5. Write a point–slope form for a line with slope -2, passing through $(-1, 3)$.

6. Write the equation $y + 3 = -2(x - 2)$ in slope–intercept form.

7. Find the slope–intercept form of the line passing through the points in the table.

x	-3	-1	1	3
y	-3	1	5	9

8. *Distance and Speed* A bicyclist is riding at a constant speed and is 36 miles from home at 1 P.M. Two hours later the bicyclist is 12 miles from home.

(a) Find the slope–intercept form of a line passing through $(1, 36)$ and $(3, 12)$.
(b) How fast is the bicyclist traveling?
(c) When will the bicyclist arrive home?
(d) How far was the bicyclist from home at noon?

9. *Snowfall* The total amount of snowfall S in inches t hours past noon is given by $S = 2t + 5$.
(a) How many inches of snow fell by noon?
(b) At what rate did snow fall in the afternoon?
(c) What is the S-intercept for the graph of this equation? What does it represent?
(d) What is the slope for the graph of this equation? What does it represent?

3.7 Introduction to Modeling

Basic Concepts ▫ Modeling Linear Data

For centuries people have tried to understand the world around them by creating models. For example, a weather forecast is based on a model. Mathematics is used to create these weather models, which often contain thousands of equations.

A model is an *abstraction* of something that people observed. Not only should a good model describe *known* data, but it should also be able to predict *future* data. In this section we discuss linear models, which are used to describe data that have a constant rate of change.

Basic Concepts

STUDY TIP

There is often more than one way to accurately model data. Don't be afraid to try different methods. Part of the modeling process is trying to justify the reasoning behind a particular modeling choice.

READING CHECK

• What are some uses for a mathematical model?

▶ **REAL-WORLD CONNECTION** Figure 3.51(a) shows a scatterplot of the number of inmates in the federal prison system from 2003 to 2009. The four points in the graph appear to be "nearly" collinear. That is, they appear almost to lie on the same line. Using mathematical modeling, we can find an equation for such a line. Once we have found it, we can use it to make estimates about the federal inmate population. An example of such a line is shown in Figure 3.51(b). (See Exercise 49 at the end of this section.)

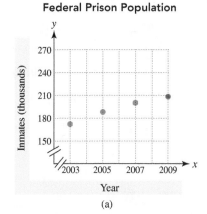

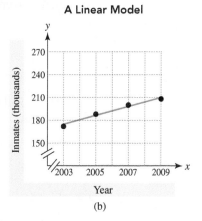

Figure 3.51

Generally, mathematical models are not *exact* representations of data. Data that might appear to be linear may not be. Although the line in Figure 3.51(b) on the previous page appears to touch every point, it does not pass through all four points exactly. Figure 3.52(a) shows data modeled *exactly* by a line, whereas Figure 3.52(b) shows data modeled *approximately* by a line. In applications a model is more likely to be approximate than exact.

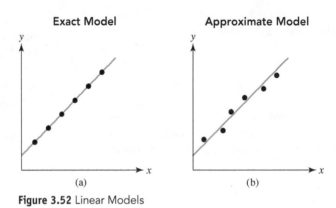

Exact Model   **Approximate Model**

(a)   (b)

Figure 3.52 Linear Models

READING CHECK

• Does a mathematical model always touch every point in a scatterplot?

EXAMPLE 1   **Determining whether a model is exact**

A person can vote in the United States at age 18 or over. Table 3.20 shows the voting-age population P in millions for selected years x. Does the equation $P = 2.75x - 5291.5$ model the data exactly? Explain.

TABLE 3.20 **Voting-Age Population**

x	2006	2008	2010
P	225	230	236

Source: U.S. Census Bureau.

Solution

To determine whether the equation models the data exactly, let $x = 2006$, 2008, and 2010 in the given equation.

$$x = 2006: \quad P = 2.75(2006) - 5291.5 = 225$$
$$x = 2008: \quad P = 2.75(2008) - 5291.5 = 230.5$$
$$x = 2010: \quad P = 2.75(2010) - 5291.5 = 236$$

The model is *not exact* because it does not predict a voting-age population of 230 million in 2008.

Now Try Exercise 13

Modeling Linear Data

A line can model linear data. In the next example we use a line to model gas mileage.

EXAMPLE 2 **Determining gas mileage**

TABLE 3.21

x	2	4	6	8
y	30	60	90	120

Table 3.21 shows the number of miles y traveled by an SUV on x gallons of gasoline.
(a) Plot the data in the xy-plane. Be sure to label each axis.
(b) Sketch a line that models the data. (You may want to use a ruler.)
(c) Find the equation of the line and interpret the slope of the line.
(d) How far could this SUV travel on 11 gallons of gasoline?

Solution
(a) Plot the points (2, 30), (4, 60), (6, 90), and (8, 120), as shown in Figure 3.53(a).

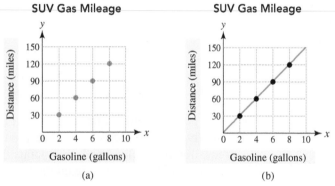

Figure 3.53

(b) Sketch a line similar to the one shown in Figure 3.53(b). This particular line passes through each data point.
(c) First find the slope m of the line by choosing two points that the line passes through, such as (2, 30) and (8, 120).

$$m = \frac{120 - 30}{8 - 2} = \frac{90}{6} = 15$$

Now find the equation of the line passing through (**2**, **30**) with slope **15**.

$$y - y_1 = m(x - x_1) \quad \text{Point–slope form}$$
$$y - 30 = 15(x - 2) \quad x_1 = 2, y_1 = 30, \text{ and } m = 15$$
$$y - 30 = 15x - 30 \quad \text{Distributive property}$$
$$y = 15x \quad \text{Add 30 to each side.}$$

The data are modeled by the equation $y = 15x$. Slope 15 indicates that the mileage of this SUV is 15 miles per gallon.
(d) On 11 gallons of gasoline the SUV could go $y = 15(11) = 165$ miles.

▌ Now Try Exercise 51

EXAMPLE 3 **Modeling linear data**

Table 3.22 contains ordered pairs that can be modeled *approximately* by a line.
(a) Plot the data. Could a line pass through all five points?
(b) Sketch a line that models the data and then determine its equation.

TABLE 3.22

x	1	2	3	4	5
y	3	5	6	10	11

Solution

(a) Plot the ordered pairs (1, 3), (2, 5), (3, 6), (4, 10), and (5, 11), as shown in Figure 3.54(a). The points are not collinear, so it is impossible to sketch a line that passes through *all* five points.

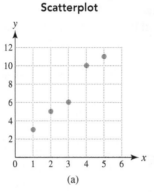

Scatterplot   Approximate Model

(a)   (b)

Figure 3.54

(b) One possibility for a line is shown in Figure 3.54(b). This line passes through three of the five points, and is above one point and below another point. To determine the equation of this line, pick two points that the line passes through. For example, the points (1, 3) and (5, 11) lie on the line. The slope of this line is

$$m = \frac{11 - 3}{5 - 1} = \frac{8}{4} = 2.$$

The equation of the line passing through (1, 3) with slope 2 can be found as follows.

$$y - y_1 = m(x - x_1) \quad \text{Point–slope form}$$
$$y - 3 = 2(x - 1) \quad x_1 = 1, y_1 = 3, \text{ and } m = 2$$
$$y - 3 = 2x - 2 \quad \text{Distributive property}$$
$$y = 2x + 1 \quad \text{Add 3 to each side.}$$

The equation of this line is $y = 2x + 1$.

▌ Now Try Exercise 33

NOTE: The equation found in Example 3 represents one possible linear model. Other linear models are possible.

▶ **REAL-WORLD CONNECTION** When a quantity increases at a constant rate, it can be modeled with the linear equation $y = mx + b$. This concept is illustrated in the next example.

EXAMPLE 4 ▌ **Modeling worldwide HIV/AIDS cases in children**

At the beginning of 2009, a total of 2.5 million children (under age 15) were living with HIV/AIDS. The rate of new infections was 0.4 million per year.

(a) Write a linear equation $C = mx + b$ that models the total number of children C in millions that were living with HIV/AIDS, x years after January 1, 2009.

(b) Estimate C at the beginning of 2012.

Solution

(a) In the equation $C = mx + b$, the rate of change in HIV infections corresponds to the slope m, and the initial number of cases at the beginning of 2009 corresponds to b. Therefore the equation $C = 0.4x + 2.5$ models the data.

(b) The beginning of 2012 is 3 years after January 1, 2009, so let $x = 3$.

$$C = 0.4(3) + 2.5 = 3.7 \text{ million}$$

NOTE: A total of 2.5 million children were living with HIV/AIDS at the beginning of 2009, with an infection rate of 0.4 million per year. After 3 years an additional $0.4(3) = 1.2$ million children would be infected, raising the total number to $2.5 + 1.2 = 3.7$ million.

▌ Now Try Exercise 47

EXAMPLE 5   ## Modeling with linear equations

Find a linear equation in the form $y = mx + b$ that models the quantity y after x days.
(a) A quantity y is initially 500 and increases at a rate of 6 per day.
(b) A quantity y is initially 1800 and decreases at a rate of 25 per day.
(c) A quantity y is initially 10,000 and remains constant.

Solution
(a) In the equation $y = mx + b$, the y-intercept b represents the initial amount and the slope m represents the rate of change. Therefore $y = 6x + 500$.
(b) The quantity y is decreasing at the rate of 25 per day with an initial amount of 1800, so $y = -25x + 1800$.
(c) The quantity is constant, so $m = 0$. The equation is $y = 10,000$.

▌ Now Try Exercises 25, 27, 29

MODELING WITH A LINEAR EQUATION

To model a quantity y that has a constant rate of change, use the equation

$$y = mx + b,$$

where $m =$ (constant rate of change) and $b =$ (initial amount).

3.7   Putting It All Together

CONCEPT	COMMENTS	EXAMPLE
Linear Model	Used to model a quantity that has a constant rate of change	If a total of 2 inches of rain falls before noon, and if rain falls at the rate of $\frac{1}{2}$ inch per hour, then $y = \frac{1}{2}x + 2$ models the total rainfall x hours past noon.
Modeling Linear Data with a Line	**1.** Plot the data. **2.** Sketch a line that passes either through or nearly through the points. **3.** Pick two points on the line and find the equation of the line.	To model $(0, 4)$, $(1, 3)$, and $(2, 2)$, plot the points and sketch a line as shown in the accompanying figure. Many times one line cannot pass through all the points. The equation of the line is $y = -x + 4$.

3.7 Exercises

CONCEPTS AND VOCABULARY

1. Linear data are modeled by a(n) _____ equation.

2. If a line passes through all the data points, it is a(n) _____ model.

3. If a line passes near but not through each data point, it is a(n) _____ model.

4. Linear models are used to describe data that have a(n) _____ rate of change.

5. If a quantity is modeled by the equation $y = mx + b$, then m represents the _____.

6. If a quantity is modeled by the equation $y = mx + b$, then b represents the _____.

Exercises 7–12: Modeling Match the situation to the graph (a.–f.) that models it best.

7. College tuition from 2000 to 2012

8. Yearly average temperature in degrees Celsius at the North Pole

9. Profit from selling boxes of candy if it costs $200 to make the candy

10. Height of Mount Hood in Oregon

11. Total amount of water delivered by a garden hose if it flows at a constant rate

12. Sales of music on CDs from 2000 to 2010

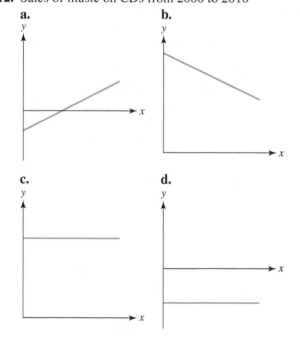

e. **f.**

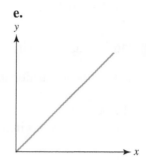

MODELING LINEAR DATA

Exercises 13–18: State whether the ordered pairs in the table are modeled exactly by the linear equation.

13. $y = 2x + 2$

x	0	1	2
y	2	4	6

14. $y = -2x + 5$

x	0	1	2
y	5	3	0

15. $y = -4x$

x	-1	0	1
y	4	0	-8

16. $y = 5 - x$

x	-2	1	4
y	7	4	1

17. $y = 1.4x - 4$

x	0	5	10
y	-4	3	9

18. $y = -\frac{4}{3}x - \frac{13}{3}$

x	-7	-4	-1
y	5	1	-3

Exercises 19–24: State whether the linear model in the graph is exact or approximate. Then find the equation of the line.

19.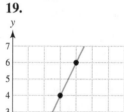

20.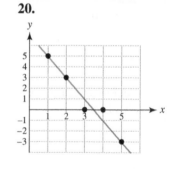

21.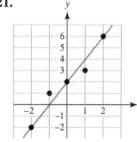

22.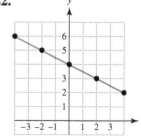

23.

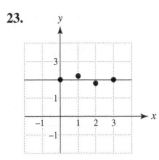

24.

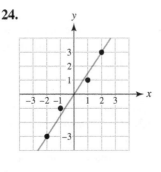

36.

x	−4	−2	0	2	4
y	1	2	3	4	5

37.

x	−6	−3	0	3	6
y	−3	−2	−0.5	0	0.5

38.

x	−3	−2	−1	0	1
y	1	2	3	4	5

Exercises 25–30: Find an equation $y = mx + b$ that models the quantity y after x units of time.

25. A quantity y is initially 40 and increases at a rate of 5 per minute.

26. A quantity y is initially −60 and increases at a rate of 1.7 per minute.

27. A quantity y is initially −5 and decreases at a rate of 20 per day.

28. A quantity y is initially 5000 and decreases at a rate of 35 per day.

29. A quantity y is initially 8 and remains constant.

30. A quantity y is initially −45 and remains constant.

Exercises 31–38: Modeling Data   For the ordered pairs in the table, do the following.

(a) *Plot the data. Could a line pass through all five points?*
(b) *Sketch a line that models the data.*
(c) *Determine an equation of the line. For data that are not exactly linear, answers may vary.*

31.

x	0	1	2	3	4
y	4	2	0	−2	−4

32.

x	0	1	2	2	3
y	7	6	5	4	3

33.

x	−2	−1	0	1	2
y	4	1	0	−1	−4

34.

x	−2	−1	0	1	2
y	7	5	1	−3	−5

35.

x	−6	−4	−2	0	2
y	1	0	−1	−2	−3

APPLICATIONS

Exercises 39–46: Write an equation that models the described quantity. Specify what each variable represents.

39. A barrel contains 200 gallons of water and is being filled at a rate of 5 gallons per minute.

40. A barrel contains 40 gallons of gasoline and is being drained at a rate of 3 gallons per minute.

41. An athlete has run 5 miles and is jogging at 6 miles per hour.

42. A new car has 141 miles on its odometer and is traveling at 70 miles per hour.

43. A worker has already earned $200 and is being paid $8 per hour.

44. A gambler has lost $500 and is losing money at a rate of $150 per hour.

45. A carpenter has already shingled 5 garage roofs and is shingling roofs at a rate of 1 per day.

46. A hard drive has been spinning for 2 minutes and is spinning at 7200 revolutions per minute.

47. *Kilimanjaro Glacier* Mount Kilimanjaro is located in Tanzania, Africa, and has an elevation of 19,340 feet. In 1912, the glacier on this peak covered 5 acres. By 2002 this glacier had melted to only 1 acre. (*Source:* NBC News.)
(a) Assume that this glacier melted at a constant rate each year. Find this *yearly* rate.
(b) Use your answer in part (a) to write a linear equation that gives the acreage A of this glacier t years past 1912.

48. *World Population* In 1987, the world's population reached 5 billion people, and by 2012 the world's population reached 7 billion people.

(*Source:* U.S. Census Bureau.)

(a) Find the average yearly increase in the world's population from 1987 to 2012.

(b) Write a linear equation that estimates the world's population P in billions x years after 1987.

49. *Prison Population* The points in Figure 3.51 are (2003, 172), (2005, 188), (2007, 200), and (2009, 208), where the y-coordinates are in thousands.

(a) Use the first and last data points to determine a line that models the data. Write the equation in slope–intercept form.

(b) Use the line to estimate the population in 2013.

50. *Niagara Falls* The average flow of water over Niagara Falls is 212,000 cubic feet of water per second.

(a) Write an equation that gives the number of cubic feet of water F that flow over the falls in x seconds.

(b) How many cubic feet of water flow over Niagara Falls in 1 minute?

51. *Gas Mileage* The table shows the number of miles y traveled by a car on x gallons of gasoline.

x (gallons)	3	6	9	12
y (miles)	60	120	180	240

(a) Plot the data in the xy-plane. Label each axis.

(b) Sketch a line that models these data. (You may want to use a ruler.)

(c) Calculate the slope of the line. Interpret the slope.

(d) Find an equation of the line.

(e) How far could this car travel on 7 gallons of gasoline?

52. *Air Temperature* Generally, the air temperature becomes colder as the altitude above the ground increases. The table lists typical air temperatures x miles high when the ground temperature is $80°$ F.

x (miles)	0	1	2	3
y (°F)	80	61	42	23

(a) Plot the data in the xy-plane. Label each axis.

(b) Sketch a line that models these data. (You may want to use a ruler.)

(c) Calculate the slope of the line. Interpret the slope.

(d) Find the slope–intercept form of the line.

(e) Estimate the air temperature 5 miles high.

WRITING ABOUT MATHEMATICS

53. In Example 2 the gas mileage of an SUV is modeled with a linear equation. Explain why it is reasonable to use a linear equation to model this situation.

54. Explain the steps for finding the equation of a line that models data points in a table.

SECTION 3.7   **Checking Basic Concepts**

1. State whether the ordered pairs shown in the table are modeled exactly by $y = -5x + 10$.

x	-2	-1	0	1
y	20	15	10	5

2. State whether the linear model in the graph is exact or approximate. Find the equation of the line.

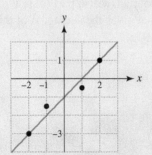

3. Find an equation, $y = mx + b$, that models the quantity y after x units of time.

(a) A quantity y is initially 50 pounds and increases at a rate of 10 pounds per day.

(b) A quantity y is initially $200°$ F and decreases at a rate of $2°$ F per minute.

4. The table contains ordered pairs.

(a) Plot the data.

(b) Sketch a line that models the data.

(c) Determine the equation of the line.

x	-2	0	2	4
y	2	1	0	-1

5. *Global Warming* Since 1945 the average annual recorded temperature on the Antarctic Peninsula has increased by $0.075°$ F per year.

(a) Write an equation that models the average temperature *increase* T, x years after 1945.

(b) Use your equation to calculate the temperature increase between 1945 and 2013.

CHAPTER 3   Summary

SECTION 3.1 ■ INTRODUCTION TO GRAPHING

The Rectangular Coordinate System (xy-plane)

Points   Plotted as (x, y) ordered pairs

Four Quadrants   The x- and y-axes divide the xy-plane into quadrants I, II, III, and IV.

NOTE: A point on an axis, such as $(1, 0)$, does not lie in a quadrant.

xy-plane	Scatterplot	Line Graph
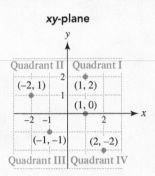	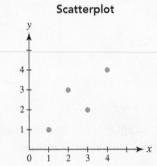	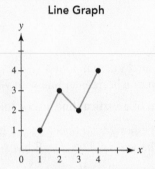

SECTION 3.2 ■ LINEAR EQUATIONS IN TWO VARIABLES

Equations in Two Variables   An equation with two variables and possibly some constants

Examples: $y = 3x + 7$ and $x + y = 100$

Solution to an Equation in Two Variables   The solution to an equation in two variables is an ordered pair that makes the equation a true statement.

Example: $(1, 2)$ is a solution to $2x + y = 4$ because $2(1) + 2 = 4$ is true.

Graphing a Linear Equation in Two Variables

Linear Equation $y = mx + b$ or $Ax + By = C$

Graphing   Plot at least three points and sketch a line passing through each one.

Example: $y = 2x - 1$

x	y
0	−1
1	1
2	3

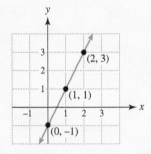

SECTION 3.3 ■ MORE GRAPHING OF LINES

Intercepts

x-Intercept   The x-coordinate of a point at which a graph intersects the x-axis; to find an x-intercept, let $y = 0$ in the equation and solve for x.

y-Intercept   The y-coordinate of a point at which a graph intersects the y-axis; to find a y-intercept, let $x = 0$ in the equation and solve for y.

Example: $x + 3y = 3$

x-intercept: Solve $x + 3(0) = 3$ to find the *x*-intercept of 3.

y-intercept: Solve $0 + 3y = 3$ to find the *y*-intercept of 1.

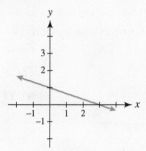

x-intercept: 3, *y*-intercept: 1

Horizontal and Vertical Lines

The equation of a horizontal line with *y*-intercept *b* is $y = b$.

The equation of a vertical line with *x*-intercept *k* is $x = k$.

Example: The horizontal line $y = -1$ has *y*-intercept -1 and no *x*-intercepts.

The vertical line $x = 2$ has *x*-intercept 2 and no *y*-intercepts.

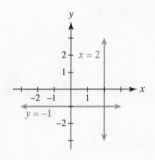

SECTION 3.4 ■ SLOPE AND RATES OF CHANGE

Slope The ratio $\frac{\text{rise}}{\text{run}}$, or $\frac{\text{change in } y}{\text{change in } x}$, is the slope *m* of a line when run (change in *x*) is nonzero. A positive slope indicates that a line rises from left to right, and a negative slope indicates that a line falls from left to right.

Example: Slope $\frac{2}{3}$ indicates that a line rises 2 units for every 3 units of horizontal run.

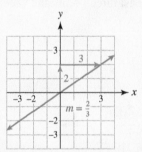

Calculating Slope   A line passing through (x_1, y_1) and (x_2, y_2) has slope

$$m = \frac{y_2 - y_1}{x_2 - x_1}, \text{ where } x_1 \neq x_2.$$

Example: The line through $(-2, 2)$ and $(3, 4)$ has slope

$$m = \frac{4 - 2}{3 - (-2)} = \frac{2}{5}.$$

Horizontal Line   Has zero slope

Vertical Line   Has undefined slope

Slope as a Rate of Change Slope measures the "tilt" or "angle" of a line. In applications, slope measures the rate of change in a quantity.

Example: The line shown in the graph has slope -2 and depicts an initial outside temperature of $6°F$. Slope -2 indicates that the temperature is *decreasing* at a rate of $2°F$ per hour.

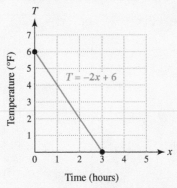

Slope–Intercept Form

For the line given by $y = mx + b$, the slope is m and the y-intercept is b.

Example: $y = -\frac{1}{2}x + 2$ has slope $-\frac{1}{2}$ and y-intercept 2, as shown in the graph.

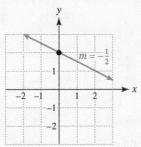

Parallel Lines Lines with the same slope are parallel; nonvertical parallel lines have the same slope. Two vertical lines are parallel.

Example: The equations $y = -2x + 1$ and $y = -2x$ determine two parallel lines because $m_1 = m_2 = -2$. See the graph shown below.

Perpendicular Lines

If two perpendicular lines have nonzero slopes m_1 and m_2, then $m_1 \cdot m_2 = -1$.

If two lines have nonzero slopes satisfying $m_1 \cdot m_2 = -1$, then they are perpendicular.

A vertical line and a horizontal line are perpendicular.

Example: The equations $y = -\frac{1}{2}x$ and $y = 2x - 2$ determine perpendicular lines because $m_1 \cdot m_2 = -\frac{1}{2} \cdot 2 = -1$. See the graph shown below.

Parallel Lines   **Perpendicular Lines**

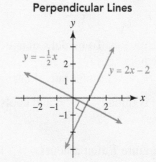

SECTION 3.6 ■ **POINT–SLOPE FORM**

Point–Slope Form   An equation of the line passing through (x_1, y_1) with slope m is

$$y - y_1 = m(x - x_1) \quad \text{or} \quad y = m(x - x_1) + y_1.$$

Example: If $m = -2$ and $(x_1, y_1) = (-2, 3)$, then the point–slope form is either

$$y - 3 = -2(x + 2) \quad \text{or} \quad y = -2(x + 2) + 3.$$

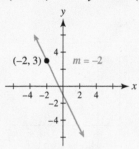

Example: To find an equation of a line passing through $(-2, 5)$ and $(4, 2)$, first find the slope.

$$m = \frac{2 - 5}{4 - (-2)} = \frac{-3}{6} = -\frac{1}{2}$$

Either $(-2, 5)$ or $(4, 2)$ may be used in the point–slope form. The point $(4, 2)$ results in the equation

$$y - 2 = -\frac{1}{2}(x - 4) \quad \text{or} \quad y = -\frac{1}{2}(x - 4) + 2.$$

SECTION 3.7 ■ **INTRODUCTION TO MODELING**

Mathematical Modeling   Mathematics can be used to describe or approximate the behavior of real-world phenomena.

Exact Model   The equation describes the data precisely without error.

Example: The equation $y = 3x$ models the data in the table exactly.

x	0	1	2	3
y	0	3	6	9

Approximate Model   The modeling equation describes the data approximately. An approximate model occurs most often in applications.

Example: The line in the graph models the data approximately.

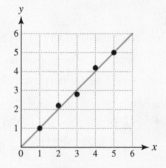

Modeling with a Linear Equation   To model a quantity y that has a constant rate of change, use the equation $y = mx + b$, where

$$m = \text{(constant rate of change)} \quad \text{and} \quad b = \text{(initial amount)}.$$

Example: If the temperature is initially $100°F$ and cools at $5°F$ per hour, then

$$T = -5x + 100$$

models the temperature T after x hours.

CHAPTER 3   Review Exercises

SECTION 3.1

1. Identify the coordinates of each point in the graph. Identify the quadrant, if any, in which each point lies.

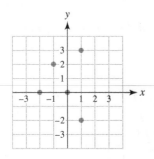

2. Make a scatterplot by plotting the following four points: $(-2, 3), (-1, -1), (0, 3)$, and $(2, -1)$.

Exercises 3 and 4: If possible, identify the quadrant in which each point is located.

3. (a) $(-4, 3)$ **(b)** $\left(\frac{1}{3}, -\frac{1}{2}\right)$

4. (a) $(0, 3.2)$ **(b)** $(-5, -1.7)$

Exercises 5 and 6: Use the table of xy-values to make a line graph.

5.

x	-2	-1	0	1	2
y	-3	2	-1	-2	3

6.

x	-10	-5	0	5	10
y	5	-10	10	-5	0

SECTION 3.2

Exercises 7–10: Determine whether the ordered pair is a solution for the given equation.

7. $y = x - 3$ $(6, 3)$

8. $y = 5 - 2x$ $(-2, 1)$

9. $3x - y = 3$ $(-1, 6)$

10. $\frac{1}{2}x + 2y = -8$ $(-4, -3)$

Exercises 11 and 12: Complete the table for the given equation.

11. $y = -3x$

x	-2	-1	0	1	2
y					

12. $2x + y = 5$

x					
y	-3	-1	0	1	3

Exercises 13–16: Use the given values of the variable to make a horizontal table of solutions for the equation.

13. $y = 3x + 2$ $x = -2, 0, 2, 4$

14. $y = 7 - x$ $x = 1, 2, 3, 4$

15. $y - 2x = 0$ $y = -1, 0, 1, 2$

16. $2y + x = 1$ $y = 1, 2, 3, 4$

Exercises 17–24: Graph the equation.

17. $y = 2x$ **18.** $y = x + 1$

19. $y = \frac{1}{2}x - 1$ **20.** $y = -3x + 2$

21. $x + y = 2$ **22.** $3x - 2y = 6$

23. $-4x + y = 8$ **24.** $2x + 3y = 12$

SECTION 3.3

Exercises 25 and 26: Identify the x- and y-intercepts.

25. 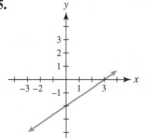   **26.**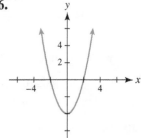

Exercises 27 and 28: Complete the table. Then determine the x- and y-intercepts for the graph of the equation.

27. $y = 2 - x$

x	-2	-1	0	1	2
y					

28. $x - 2y = 4$

x	-4	-2	0	2	4
y					

Exercises 29–32: Find any intercepts for the graph of the equation and then graph the linear equation.

29. $2x - 3y = 6$ **30.** $5x - y = 5$

31. $0.1x - 0.2y = 0.4$ **32.** $\dfrac{x}{2} + \dfrac{y}{3} = 1$

Exercises 33 and 34: Write an equation for the line that passes through the points shown in the table.

33.

x	−2	−1	0	1	2
y	1	1	1	1	1

34.

x	3	3	3	3	3
y	−2	−1	0	1	2

35. Graph each equation.
   (a) $y = 1$ **(b)** $x = -3$

36. Write an equation for each line shown in the graph.

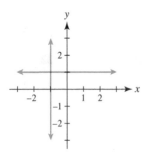

37. Write the equations of a horizontal line and a vertical line that pass through the point $(-2, 3)$.

38. Write the equation of a line that is perpendicular to $y = -\frac{1}{2}$ and passes through $(4, 1)$.

39. Write the equation of a line that is parallel to $y = 3$ and passes through $(-6, -5)$.

40. *Distance* The distance a driver is from home is illustrated in the graph.
   (a) Find the intercepts.
   (b) Interpret each intercept.

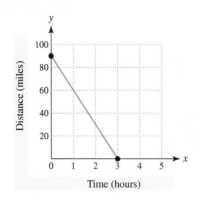

Exercises 41–44: Find the slope, if possible, of the line passing through the two points.

41. $(2, 3), (4, 7)$ **42.** $(-3, 1), (2, -1)$

43. $(2, 1), (5, 1)$ **44.** $(-5, 6), (-5, 10)$

Exercises 45 and 46: Find the slope of the line shown in the graph.

45.

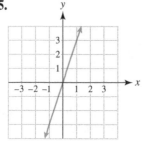

46.

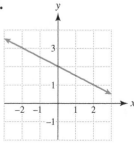

Exercises 47–50: Do the following.

   (a) Graph the linear equation.
   (b) What are the slope and y-intercept of the line?

47. $y = -2x$ **48.** $y = x - 1$

49. $x + 2y = 4$ **50.** $2x - 3y = -6$

Exercises 51–54: Sketch a line passing through the given point and having slope m.

51. $(0, -3), m = 2$ **52.** $(0, 1), m = -\frac{1}{2}$

53. $(-1, 1), m = -\frac{2}{3}$ **54.** $(2, 2), m = 1$

55. A line with slope $\frac{1}{2}$ passes through the first point shown in the table. Complete the table so that each point in the table lies on the line.

x	0	1	2	3
y	1			

56. If a line models the cost of buying x coffee drinks at \$3.49 each, does the line have positive or negative slope?

SECTION 3.5

Exercises 57 and 58: Write the slope–intercept form for the line shown in the graph.

57. 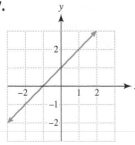 **58.**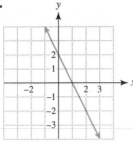

Exercises 59 and 60: Sketch a line with slope m and y-intercept b. Write its slope–intercept form.

59. $m = 2, b = -2$ **60.** $m = -\frac{3}{4}, b = 3$

Exercises 61–64: Do the following.

    (a) Write the equation in slope–intercept form.
    (b) Give the slope and y-intercept of the line.

61. $x + y = 3$ **62.** $-3x + 2y = -6$

63. $20x - 10y = 200$ **64.** $5x - 6y = 30$

Exercises 65–72: Graph the equation.

65. $y = \frac{1}{2}x + 1$ **66.** $y = 3x - 2$

67. $y = -\frac{1}{3}x$ **68.** $y = 3x$

69. $y = 2$ **70.** $y = -1$

71. $y = 4 - x$ **72.** $y = 2 - \frac{2}{3}x$

Exercises 73 and 74: All the points shown in the table lie on the same line. Find the slope–intercept form for the line.

73.

x	0	1	2
y	-5	0	5

74.

x	-1	0	1
y	2	0	-2

Exercises 75–78: Find the slope–intercept form for the line satisfying the given conditions.

75. Slope $-\frac{5}{6}$, y-intercept 2

76. Parallel to $y = -2x + 1$, passing through $(1, -5)$

77. Perpendicular to $y = -\frac{3}{2}x$, passing through $(3, 0)$

78. Perpendicular to $y = 5x - 3$, passing through the point $(0, -2)$

SECTION 3.6

Exercises 79 and 80: Determine whether the given point lies on the line.

79. $(-3, 1)$ $y - 1 = 2(x + 3)$

80. $(3, -8)$ $y = -3(x - 1) + 2$

Exercises 81–88: Find a point–slope form for the line that satisfies the conditions given. When two points are given, use the first point in the point–slope form.

81. Slope 5, passing through $(1, 2)$

82. Slope 20, passing through $(3, -5)$

83. Passing through $(-2, 1)$ and $(1, -1)$

84. Passing through $(20, -30)$ and $(40, 30)$

85. x-intercept 3, y-intercept -4

86. x-intercept $\frac{1}{2}$, y-intercept -1

87. Parallel to $y = 2x$, passing through $(5, 7)$

88. Perpendicular to $y - 4 = \frac{3}{2}(x + 1)$, passing through $(-1, 0)$

Exercises 89–92: Write the given point–slope form in slope–intercept form.

89. $y - 2 = 3(x + 1)$ **90.** $y - 9 = \frac{1}{3}(x - 6)$

91. $y = 2(x + 3) + 5$ **92.** $y = -\frac{1}{4}(x - 8) + 1$

SECTION 3.7

93. State whether the ordered pairs shown in the table are modeled exactly by $y = -x + 4$.

x	0	1	2	2
y	4	3	2	1

94. State whether the linear model shown in the graph is exact or approximate. Then find the equation of the line.

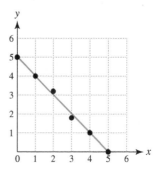

Exercises 95–98: Find an equation y = mx + b that models y after x units of time.

95. y is initially 40 pounds and decreases at a rate of 2 pounds per minute.

96. y is initially 200 gallons and increases at 20 gallons per hour.

97. y is initially 50 and remains constant.

98. y is initially 20 feet *below* sea level and rises at 5 feet per second.

Exercises 99 and 100: For the ordered pairs in the table, do the following.

    (a) Plot the data. Could a line pass through all five points?

    (b) Sketch a line that models the data.

    (c) Determine an equation of the line. For data that are not exactly linear, answers may vary.

99.

x	0	1	2	3	4
y	10	6	2	−2	−6

100.

x	−4	−2	0	2	4
y	1	2.1	3	3.9	5

APPLICATIONS

101. *Graphing Real Data* The table contains real data on divorces D in millions during year t.
    (a) Make a line graph of the data. Label the axes.
    (b) Comment on any trends in the data.

t	1970	1980	1990	2000	2010
D	0.7	1.2	1.2	1.2	1.0

Source: National Center for Health Statistics.

102. *Water Usage* The average American uses 100 gallons of water each day.
    (a) Write an equation that gives the gallons G of water that a person uses in t days.
    (b) Graph the equation for $t \geq 0$.
    (c) How many days does it take for the average American to use 5000 gallons of water?

103. *Modeling a Toy Rocket* The velocity v of a toy rocket in feet per second after t seconds of flight is given by $v = 160 - 32t$, where $t \geq 0$.
    (a) Graph the equation.
    (b) Interpret each intercept.

104. *Modeling* The accompanying line graph represents the insect population on 1 acre of land after x weeks. During this time a farmer sprayed pesticides on the land.
    (a) Estimate the slope of each line segment.
    (b) Interpret each slope as a rate of change.
    (c) Describe what happened to the insect population.

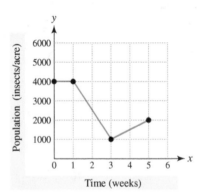

105. *Sketching a Graph* An athlete jogs 4 miles away from home at a constant rate of 8 miles per hour and then turns around and jogs back home at the same speed. Sketch a graph that shows the distance that the athlete is from home. Be sure to label each axis.

106. *Nursing Homes* In 1985, there were 19,100 nursing homes, and in 2010, there were 16,100. (*Source: National Center for Health Statistics.*)
  (a) Calculate the slope of the line passing through (1985, 19100) and (2010, 16100).
  (b) Interpret the slope as a rate of change.

107. *Rental Cars* The cost C in dollars for driving a rental car x miles is $C = 0.2x + 35$.
  (a) How much would it cost to rent the car but not drive it?
  (b) How much does it cost to drive the car one *additional* mile?
  (c) Determine the C-intercept for the graph of $C = 0.2x + 35$. What does it represent?
  (d) What is the slope of the graph of $C = 0.2x + 35$? What does it represent?

108. *Distance and Speed* A person is driving a car along a straight road. The graph at the top of the next page shows the distance y in miles that the driver is from home after x hours.
  (a) Is the person traveling toward or away from home? Why?
  (b) The graph passes through (1, 200) and (3, 100). Discuss the meaning of these points.
  (c) Find the slope–intercept form of the line. Interpret the slope as a rate of change.
  (d) Use the graph to estimate the distance from home after 2 hours. Then check your answer by using your equation from part (c).

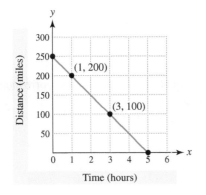

109. *Arctic Glaciers* The arctic ice cap has been breaking up. As a result there has been an increase in the number of icebergs floating in the Arctic Ocean. The table gives an iceberg count I for various years t. (*Source: NBC News.*)

t	1970	1980	2000
I	400	600	1000

  (a) Make a scatterplot of the data.
  (b) Find the slope–intercept form of a line that models the number of icebergs I in year t. Interpret the slope of this line.
  (c) Is the line you found in part (b) an exact model for the data in the table?
  (d) If this trend continued, what was the iceberg count in 2005?

110. *Gas Mileage* The table shows the number of miles y traveled by a car on x gallons of gasoline.

x	2	4	8	10
y	40	79	161	200

  (a) Plot the data in the xy-plane. Be sure to label each axis.
  (b) Sketch a line that models these data. (You may want to use a ruler.)
  (c) Calculate the slope of the line. Interpret the slope of this line.
  (d) Find the equation of the line. Is your line an *exact* model?
  (e) How far could this car travel on 9 gallons of gasoline?

CHAPTER 3   Extended and Discovery Exercises

Exercises 1 and 2: The table of real data can be modeled by a line. However, the line may not be an exact model, so answers may vary.

1. *Women in Politics* The table lists percentages P of women in state legislatures during year x.

x	1993	1995	1997	1999
P	20.5	20.6	21.6	22.4

x	2001	2003	2005	2007
P	22.4	22.4	22.7	23.5

Source: National Women's Political Caucus.

   (a) Make a scatterplot of the data.
   (b) Find a point–slope form of a line that models these data.
   (c) Use your equation to estimate the percentage of women in state legislatures in 2010.

2. *U.S. Population* The population P of the United States in millions during year x is shown in the table.

x	1970	1980	1990	2000	2010
P	203	227	249	281	309

Source: U.S. Census Bureau.

   (a) Make a scatterplot of the data.
   (b) Find a point–slope form of a line that models these data.
   (c) Use your equation to estimate what the U.S. population was in 2005.

CREATING GEOMETRIC SHAPES

Exercises 3–6: Many geometric shapes can be created with intersecting lines. For example, a triangle is formed when three lines intersect at three distinct points called vertices. Find equations of lines that satisfy the characteristics described. Sketching a graph may be helpful.

3. *Triangle* A triangle has vertices $(0, 0)$, $(2, 3)$, and $(3, 6)$.
   (a) Find slope–intercept forms for three lines that pass through each pair of points.
   (b) Graph the three lines. Is a triangle formed by the line segments connecting the three points?

4. *Parallelogram* A parallelogram has four sides, with opposite sides parallel. Three sides of a parallelogram are given by the equations $y = 2x + 2$, $y = 2x - 1$, and $y = -x - 2$.
   (a) If the fourth side of the parallelogram passes through the point $(-2, 3)$, find its equation.
   (b) Graph all four lines. Is a parallelogram formed?

5. *Rectangle* The two vertices $(0, 0)$ and $(4, 2)$ determine one side of a rectangle. The side parallel to this side passes through the point $(0, 3)$.
   (a) Find slope–intercept forms for the four lines that determine the sides of the rectangle.
   (b) Graph all four lines. Is a rectangle formed? (*Hint:* If you use a graphing calculator be sure to set a square window.)

6. *Square* Three vertices of a square are $(1, 2)$, $(4, 2)$, and $(4, 5)$.
   (a) Find the fourth vertex.
   (b) Find equations of lines that correspond to the four sides of the square.
   (c) Graph all four lines. Is a square formed?

4

Systems of Linear Equations in Two Variables

4.1 Solving Systems of Linear Equations Graphically and Numerically

4.2 Solving Systems of Linear Equations by Substitution

4.3 Solving Systems of Linear Equations by Elimination

We can do anything we want to do if we stick to it long enough.

—HELEN KELLER

Source: National Center for Health Statistics.

$\mathbf{A}$mericans have been moving toward a more mobile lifestyle. In recent years, the percentage of U.S. households relying solely on mobile phone service has increased, while the percentage of households relying solely on landline phone service has decreased. The following figure shows that linear equations can be used to model the percentage P of households relying on each type of phone service during year x. What does the point of intersection represent?

This graph illustrates a *system of linear equations*. If we use the graph to estimate both the year and the percentage at the intersection point, we are *solving* the system of linear equations graphically. In this chapter we discuss graphical, numerical, and symbolic methods for solving systems of linear equations.

4.1 Solving Systems of Linear Equations Graphically and Numerically

Basic Concepts • Solutions to Systems of Equations

A LOOK INTO MATH ▶

In business, linear equations are sometimes used to model supply and demand for a product. For example, if the price of a gourmet coffee drink is too high, the demand for the drink will decrease because consumers are interested in saving money. Similarly, if the price of the coffee drink is too low, supply will decrease because suppliers are interested in making money. To find an appropriate price for the coffee drink, a system of linear equations can be solved. In this section, we will solve systems of linear equations graphically and numerically.

Basic Concepts

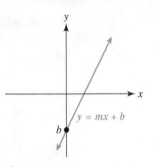

Figure 4.1

In Chapter 3 we showed that the graph of $y = mx + b$ is a line with slope m and y-intercept b, as illustrated in Figure 4.1. Each point on this line represents a solution to the equation $y = mx + b$. Because there are infinitely many points on a line, there are infinitely many solutions to this equation. However, many applications require that we find one particular solution to a linear equation. One way to find such a solution is to graph a second line in the same xy-plane and determine the point of intersection (if one exists).

▶ REAL-WORLD CONNECTION Consider the following application of a line. If renting a moving truck for one day costs $25 plus $0.50 per mile driven, then the equation $C = 0.5x + 25$ represents the cost C in dollars of driving the rental truck x miles. The graph of this line is shown in Figure 4.2(a) for $x \geq 0$.

NEW VOCABULARY

☐ Intersection-of-graphs method
☐ System of linear equations in two variables
☐ Solution to a system
☐ Inconsistent system
☐ Consistent system with independent equations
☐ Consistent system with dependent equations

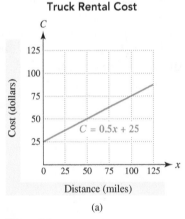

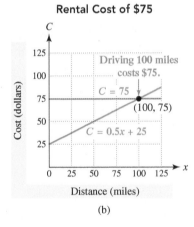

(a)   (b)

Figure 4.2

Suppose that we want to determine the number of miles that the truck is driven when the rental cost is $75. One way to solve this problem *graphically* is to graph both $C = 0.5x + 25$ and $C = 75$ in the same coordinate plane, as shown in Figure 4.2(b). The lines intersect at the point $(100, 75)$, which is a solution to $C = 0.5x + 25$ and to $C = 75$. That is, if the rental cost is $75, then the mileage must be 100 miles. This graphical technique for solving two equations is sometimes called the **intersection-of-graphs method**. To find a solution with this method, we locate a point where two graphs intersect.

EXAMPLE 1   ## Solving an equation graphically

The equation $P = 10x$ calculates an employee's pay for working x hours at $10 per hour. Use the intersection-of-graphs method to find the number of hours that the employee worked if the amount paid is $40.

Solution

Begin by graphing the equations $P = 10x$ and $P = 40$, as illustrated in Figure 4.3.

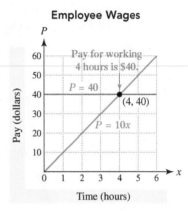

Employee Wages

Figure 4.3

READING CHECK

• How is the intersection-of-graphs method used to find a solution to two equations?

The graphs intersect at the point $(4, 40)$. Since the x-coordinate represents the number of hours worked and the P-coordinate represents pay, the point $(4, 40)$ indicates that the employee must work 4 hours to earn $40.

▌ Now Try Exercise 67(a), (b)

Equations can be solved in more than one way. In Example 1 we determined graphically that $P = 10x$ is equal to 40 when $x = 4$. We could also solve this problem by making a table of values, as illustrated by Table 4.1. Note that, when $x = 4$, $P = \$40$. A table of values provides a *numerical solution*.

TABLE 4.1 **Wages Earned at $10 per Hour**

x (hours)	0	1	2	3	4	5	6
P (pay)	$0	$10	$20	$30	$40	$50	$60

NOTE: Although graphical and numerical methods are different, both methods should give the same solution. However, slight variations may occur because reading a graph precisely may be difficult, or a needed value may not appear in a table.

TECHNOLOGY NOTE

Intersection of Graphs and Table of Values
A graphing calculator can be used to find the intersection of the two graphs shown in Figure 4.3. It can also be used to create Table 4.1. The accompanying figures illustrate how a calculator can be used to determine that $y_1 = 10x$ equals $y_2 = 40$ when $x = 4$.

CALCULATOR HELP

To find a point of intersection, see Appendix A (page AP-6).

To make a table, see Appendix A (pages AP-2 and AP-3).

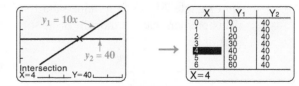

EXAMPLE 2 | **Solving an equation graphically**

Use a graph to find the x-value when $y = 3$.
(a) $y = 2x - 1$ **(b)** $-3x + 2y = 12$

Solution

(a) Begin by graphing the equations $y = 2x - 1$ and $y = 3$. The graph of $y = 2x - 1$ is a line with slope 2 and y-intercept -1. The graph of $y = 3$ is a horizontal line with y-intercept 3. In Figure 4.4(a) the graphs intersect at the point $(2, 3)$. Therefore an x-value of 2 corresponds to a y-value of 3.

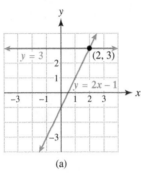
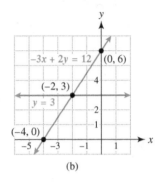

(a)   (b)

Figure 4.4

(b) One way to graph $-3x + 2y = 12$ is to write this equation in slope–intercept form.

$$-3x + 2y = 12 \qquad \text{Given equation}$$

$$2y = 3x + 12 \qquad \text{Add } 3x \text{ to each side.}$$

$$y = \frac{3}{2}x + 6 \qquad \text{Divide each side by 2.}$$

The line has slope $\frac{3}{2}$ and y-intercept 6. Its graph and the graph of $y = 3$ are shown in Figure 4.4(b). The graphs intersect at $(-2, 3)$. Therefore an x-value of -2 corresponds to a y-value of 3.

▌ Now Try Exercises 15, 17

MAKING CONNECTIONS

Different Ways to Graph the Same Line

In Example 2(b) the line $-3x + 2y = 12$ was graphed by finding its slope–intercept form. A second way to graph this line is to find the x- and y-intercepts of the line. If $y = 0$, then $x = -4$ makes this equation true, and if $x = 0$, then $y = 6$ makes this equation true. Thus the x-intercept is -4, and the y-intercept is 6. Note that the (slanted) line in Figure 4.4(b) passes through the points $(-4, 0)$ and $(0, 6)$, which could be used to graph the line.

Solutions to Systems of Equations

In Example 2(b) we determined the x-value when $y = 3$ in the equation $-3x + 2y = 12$. This problem can be thought of as solving the following *system of two equations in two variables.*

$$-3x + 2y = 12$$
$$y = 3$$

READING CHECK

• How do we express the solution to a system of equations in two variables?

The solution is the ordered pair $(-2, 3)$, which indicates that when $x = -2$ and $y = 3$, each equation is a true statement.

$$-3(-2) + 2(3) = 12 \checkmark \quad \text{A true statement}$$
$$3 = 3 \checkmark \quad \text{A true statement}$$

Suppose that the sum of two numbers is 10 and that their difference is 4. If we let x and y represent the two numbers, then the equations

$$x + y = 10 \quad \text{Sum is 10.}$$
$$x - y = 4 \quad \text{Difference is 4.}$$

describe this situation. Each equation is a linear equation in two variables, so we call these equations a **system of linear equations in two variables**. Its graph typically consists of two lines. A **solution to a system** of two equations is an ordered pair (x, y) that makes *both* equations true. If a single solution exists, the ordered pair gives the coordinates of a point where the two lines intersect.

NOTE: For two distinct lines, there can be no more than one intersection point. If such an intersection point exists, the ordered pair corresponding to it represents the only solution to the system of linear equations. In this case, we say the ordered pair is *the* solution to the system of equations.

TYPES OF EQUATIONS AND NUMBER OF SOLUTIONS When a system of two linear equations in two variables is graphed, exactly one of the following situations will result.

1. The two lines are parallel, as shown in Figure 4.5(a).
2. The two lines intersect exactly once, as shown in Figure 4.5(b).
3. The two lines are identical (they coincide), as shown in Figure 4.5(c).

READING CHECK

• How many solutions are possible for a system of linear equations in two variables?

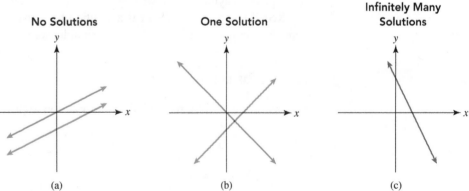

Figure 4.5

In the first situation, there are no solutions, and it is an **inconsistent system**. In the second situation, there is exactly one solution, and it is a **consistent system** with **independent equations**. In the third situation, there are infinitely many solutions, and it is a **consistent system** with **dependent equations**. This information is summarized in Table 4.2.

TABLE 4.2 **Types of Systems of Equations**

Type of Graph	Number of Solutions	Type of System	Type of Equations
Parallel Lines	0	Inconsistent	—
Intersecting Lines	1	Consistent	Independent
Identical Lines	Infinitely many	Consistent	Dependent

EXAMPLE 3   **Identifying types of equations**

Graphs of two equations are shown. State the number of solutions to each system of equations. Then state whether the system is consistent or inconsistent. If it is consistent, state whether the equations are dependent or independent.

(a) 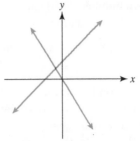   **(b)** 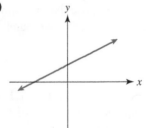   **(c)**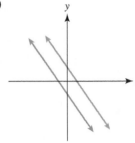

Solution
(a) The lines intersect at one point, so there is one solution. The system is consistent, and the equations are independent.
(b) There is only one line, which indicates that the graphs are identical, or coincide, so there are infinitely many solutions. The system is consistent and the equations are dependent.
(c) The lines are parallel, so there are no solutions. The system is inconsistent.

▌ Now Try Exercises 19, 21, 23

SYSTEMS WITH EXACTLY ONE SOLUTION For the remainder of this section, we focus on systems of linear equations in two variables that have exactly one solution. We will solve the systems by graphing and by making a table of values. Methods for solving two equations symbolically will be discussed later in the chapter.

Recall that an ordered pair is a solution to a system of two equations if its coordinates make *both* equations true. In the next example, we test possible solutions.

EXAMPLE 4   **Testing for solutions**

Determine whether $(4, 6)$ or $(7, 3)$ is the solution to the system of equations

$$x + y = 10$$
$$x - y = \ \ 4.$$

Solution
To determine whether $(4, 6)$ is the solution, substitute $x = 4$ and $y = 6$ in each equation. It must make *both* equations true.

$x + y = 10$	$x - y = 4$	Given equations
$4 + 6 \overset{?}{=} 10$	$4 - 6 \overset{?}{=} 4$	Let $x = 4, y = 6.$
$10 = 10$ (True) ✓	$-2 = 4$ (False) ✗	Second equation is false.

Because $(4, 6)$ does not satisfy *both* equations, it is not the solution for the system of equations. Next let $x = 7$ and $y = 3$ to determine whether $(7, 3)$ is the solution.

$x + y = 10$	$x - y = 4$	Given equations
$7 + 3 \overset{?}{=} 10$	$7 - 3 \overset{?}{=} 4$	Let $x = 7, y = 3.$
$10 = 10$ (True) ✓	$4 = 4$ (True) ✓	Both are true.

Because $(7, 3)$ makes *both* equations true, it is the solution to the system of equations.

▌ Now Try Exercise 25

In the next example we find the solution to a system of linear equations graphically and numerically.

EXAMPLE 5   Solving a system graphically and numerically

Solve the system of linear equations

$$x + 2y = 4$$
$$2x - y = 3$$

with a graph and with a table of values.

Solution

Graphically Begin by writing each equation in slope–intercept form.

$x + 2y = 4$	First equation	$2x - y = 3$	Second equation
$2y = -x + 4$	Subtract x.	$-y = -2x + 3$	Subtract $2x$.
$y = -\dfrac{1}{2}x + 2$	Divide by 2.	$y = 2x - 3$	Multiply by -1.

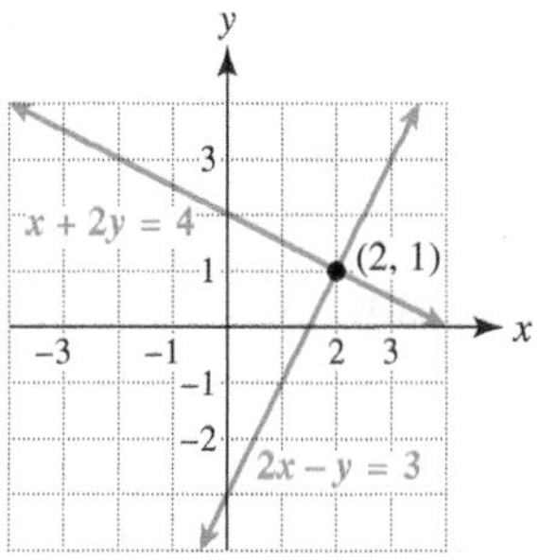

The graphs of $y = -\frac{1}{2}x + 2$ and $y = 2x - 3$ are shown in Figure 4.6. The graphs intersect at the point $(2, 1)$, thus $(2, 1)$ is the solution.

Numerically Table 4.3 shows the equations $y = -\frac{1}{2}x + 2$ and $y = 2x - 3$ evaluated for various values of x. Note that when $x = 2$, both equations have a y-value of 1. Thus $(2, 1)$ is the solution.

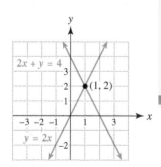

Figure 4.6

TABLE 4.3 **A Numerical Solution**

x	-1	0	1	2	3
$y = -\frac{1}{2}x + 2$	2.5	2	1.5	1	0.5
$y = 2x - 3$	-5	-3	-1	1	3

Find an x-value where the y-values are equal.

Now Try Exercise 45

EXAMPLE 6   Solving a system graphically

Solve the system of equations graphically.

$$y = 2x$$
$$2x + y = 4$$

Solution

The equation $y = 2x$ can be written in slope–intercept form as $y = 2x + 0$. Its graph is a line passing through the origin with slope 2, as shown in Figure 4.7. The equation $2x + y = 4$ can be written in slope–intercept form as $y = -2x + 4$. Its graph is a line passing through the point $(0, 4)$ with slope -2. This line is also graphed in Figure 4.7. Because the intersection point is $(1, 2)$, the solution to the system of equations is the ordered pair $(1, 2)$.

Now Try Exercise 59

Figure 4.7

A FOUR-STEP PROCESS FOR SOLVING APPLICATIONS In the next example, we use a four-step process to solve an application involving a system of linear equations, with Step 3 split into two parts to emphasize the importance of using the solution to the system of equations to determine the solution to the given problem.

EXAMPLE 7 | **Traveling to watch sports**

In 2010, about 50 million Americans traveled to watch either football or basketball. About 10 million more people traveled to watch football than basketball. How many Americans traveled to watch each sport? (*Source: Sports Travel Magazine.*)

Solution

STEP 1: *Identify each variable.*

x: millions of Americans who traveled to watch football
y: millions of Americans who traveled to watch basketball

STEP 2: *Write a system of equations.* The total number of Americans who watched either sport is 50 million, so we know that $x + y = 50$. Because 10 million more people watched football than basketball, we also know that $x - y = 10$. Thus a system of equations representing this situation is

$$x + y = 50$$
$$x - y = 10.$$

STEP 3A: *Solve the system of equations.* To solve this system graphically, write each equation in slope–intercept form.

$$y = -x + 50$$
$$y = x - 10$$

Their graphs intersect at the point (30, 20), as shown in Figure 4.8.

Traveling Sports Fans

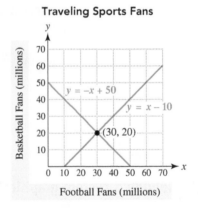

Figure 4.8

STEP 3B: *Determine the solution to the problem.* The point (30, 20) corresponds to $x = 30$ and $y = 20$. Thus about 30 million Americans traveled to watch football and 20 million Americans traveled to watch basketball.

STEP 4: *Check your solution.* Note that $30 + 20 = 50$ million Americans traveled to watch either football or basketball and that $30 - 20 = 10$ million more Americans watched football than basketball.

▌ Now Try Exercise 69

TECHNOLOGY NOTE

CALCULATOR HELP

To find a point of intersection, see Appendix A (page AP-6).

Checking Solutions

The solution to the system in Example 7 can be checked with a graphing calculator, as shown in the accompanying figure where the graphs of $y_1 = -x + 50$ and $y_2 = x - 10$ intersect at the point (30, 20). However, a graphing calculator cannot read Example 7 and write down the system of equations. A human mind is needed for these tasks.

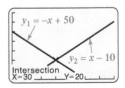

4.1	**Putting It All Together**

CONCEPT	EXPLANATION	EXAMPLE
System of Linear Equations in Two Variables	Can be written as $$Ax + By = C$$ $$Dx + Ey = F$$	$$x + y = 8$$ $$x - y = 2$$
Solution to a System of Equations	An ordered pair (x, y) that satisfies *both* equations	The solution to the preceding system is $(5, 3)$ because, when $x = 5$ and $y = 3$ are substituted, both equations are true. $$5 + 3 \stackrel{?}{=} 8 \;\checkmark \quad \text{True}$$ $$5 - 3 \stackrel{?}{=} 2 \;\checkmark \quad \text{True}$$
Inconsistent System	A system of linear equations in two variables that has no solutions is an inconsistent system. Graphing the system results in parallel lines.	**No Solutions**
Consistent System with Independent Equations	A system of linear equations in two variables that has 1 solution is a consistent system. Graphing the system results in intersecting lines.	**One Solution**
Consistent System with Dependent Equations	A system of linear equations in two variables that has infinitely many solutions is a consistent system. Graphing the system results in identical lines, or lines that coincide.	**Infinitely Many Solutions**

continued on next page

continued from previous page

CONCEPT	EXPLANATION	EXAMPLE
Graphical Solution to a System of Equations	Graph each equation. A point of intersection represents a solution.	The graphs of $y = -x + 8$ and $y = x - 2$ intersect at $(5, 3)$.
Numerical Solution to a System of Equations	Make a table for each equation. A solution occurs when one x-value gives the same y-values in both equations.	Make a table for $y = -x + 8$ and $y = x - 2$. When $x = 5$, $y = 3$ in both equations, so $(5, 3)$ is the solution.

x	4	5	6
$y = -x + 8$	4	3	2
$y = x - 2$	2	3	4

4.1 Exercises

MyMathLab | Math XL PRACTICE | WATCH | DOWNLOAD | READ | REVIEW

CONCEPTS AND VOCABULARY

1. A solution to a system of two equations in two variables is a(n) _____ pair.

2. A graphical technique for solving a system of two equations in two variables is the _____ method.

3. A system of linear equations can have _____, _____, or _____ solutions.

4. If a system of linear equations has at least one solution, then it is a(n) (consistent/inconsistent) system.

5. If a system of linear equations has no solutions, then it is a(n) (consistent/inconsistent) system.

6. If a system of linear equations has exactly one solution, then the equations are (dependent/independent).

7. If a system of linear equations has infinitely many solutions, then the equations are (dependent/independent).

8. To find a numerical solution to a system, start by creating a(n) _____ of values for the equations.

9. If a graphical method and a numerical method (table of values) are used to solve the same system of equations, then the two solutions should be (the same/different).

10. One way to graph a line is to write its equation in slope–intercept form. A second method is to find the x- and y-_____.

SOLVING SYSTEMS OF EQUATIONS

Exercises 11–18: Determine graphically the x-value when $y = 2$ in the given equation.

11. $y = 2x$

12. $y = \frac{1}{3}x$

13. $y = 4 - x$

14. $y = -2 - x$

15. $y = -\frac{1}{2}x + 1$

16. $y = 3x - 1$

17. $2x + y = 6$

18. $-3x + 4y = 11$

Exercises 19–24: The graphs of two equations are shown. State the number of solutions to each system of equations. Then state whether the system is consistent or inconsistent. If it is consistent, state whether the equations are dependent or independent.

19.
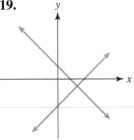

20.
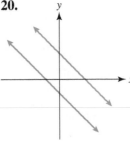

21.
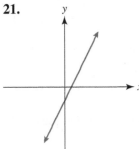

22.
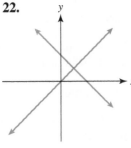

23.
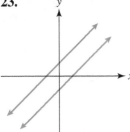

24.
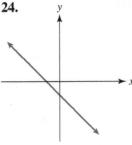

Exercises 25–30: Determine which ordered pair is a solution to the system of equations.

25. $(0, 0), (1, 1)$
$$x + y = 2$$
$$x - y = 0$$

26. $(-1, 2), (1, -2)$
$$2x + y = 0$$
$$x - 2y = -5$$

27. $(-1, -1), (2, -3)$
$$2x + 3y = -5$$
$$4x - 5y = 23$$

28. $(2, -1), (-2, -2)$
$$-x + 4y = -6$$
$$6x - 7y = 19$$

29. $(2, 0), (-1, -3)$
$$-5x + 5y = -10$$
$$4x + 9y = 8$$

30. $\left(\frac{1}{2}, \frac{3}{2}\right), \left(\frac{3}{4}, \frac{5}{4}\right)$
$$x + y = 2$$
$$3x - y = 0$$

Exercises 31–36: The graphs of two equations are shown. Use the intersection-of-graphs method to identify the solution to both equations. Then check your answer.

31.
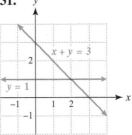

32.
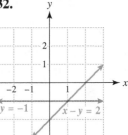

33.
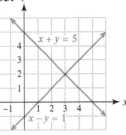

34.
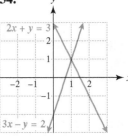

35.
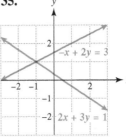

36.
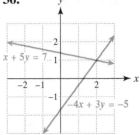

Exercises 37–40: A table for two equations is given. Identify the solution to both equations.

37.

x	1	2	3	4
$y = 2x$	2	4	6	8
$y = 4$	4	4	4	4

38.

x	2	3	4	5
$y = 6 - x$	4	3	2	1
$y = x - 2$	0	1	2	3

39.

x	1	2	3	4
$y = 4 - x$	3	2	1	0
$y = x - 2$	-1	0	1	2

40.

x	1	2	3	4
$y = 6 - 3x$	3	0	-3	-6
$y = 2 - x$	1	0	-1	-2

Exercises 41 and 42: Complete the table for each equation. Then identify the solution to both equations.

41.

x	0	1	2	3
$y = x + 2$				
$y = 4 - x$				

42.

x	-5	-4	-3	-2
$y = 2x + 1$				
$y = x - 1$				

Exercises 43–48: Use the specified method to solve the system of equations.

    (a) Graphically
    (b) Numerically (table of values)

43. $y = 2x + 3$
    $y = 1$

44. $y = 2 - x$
    $y = 0$

45. $y = 4 - x$
    $y = x - 2$

46. $y = 2x$
    $y = -\frac{1}{2}x$

47. $y = 3x$
    $y = x + 2$

48. $y = 2x - 3$
    $y = -x + 3$

Exercises 49–60: Solve the system of equations graphically.

49. $x + y = -3$
    $x - y = 1$

50. $x - y = 3$
    $2x + y = 3$

51. $2x - y = 3$
    $3x + y = 2$

52. $x + 2y = 6$
    $-x + 3y = 4$

53. $-4x + 2y = 0$
    $x - y = -1$

54. $4x - y = 2$
    $y = 2x$

55. $2x - y = 4$
    $x + 2y = 7$

56. $x - y = 2$
    $\frac{1}{2}x + y = 4$

57. $x = -y + 4$
    $x = 3y$

58. $x = 2y$
    $y = -\frac{1}{2}x$

59. $x + y = 3$
    $x = \frac{1}{2}y$

60. $2x - 4y = 8$
    $\frac{1}{2}x + y = -4$

Exercises 61–66: Number Problems For each problem, complete each of the following.

    (a) Write a system of equations for the problem.
    (b) Find the unknown numbers by solving the system of equations graphically.

61. The sum of two numbers is 4 and their difference is 0.

62. The sum of two numbers is -5 and their difference is 1.

63. The sum of twice a number and another number is 7. Their difference is 2.

64. Three times a number subtracted from another number results in 1. Their sum is 5.

65. One number is triple another number. Their difference is 4.

66. Half of a number added to another number equals 5. Their difference is 1.

APPLICATIONS

67. *Renting a Truck* A rental truck costs $50 plus $0.50 per mile.
    (a) Write an equation that gives the cost C of driving the truck x miles.
    (b) Use the intersection-of-graphs method to determine the number of miles that the truck is driven if the rental cost is $80.
    (c) Solve part (b) numerically with a table of values.

68. *Renting a Car* A rental car costs $25 plus $0.25 per mile.
    (a) Write an equation that gives the cost C of driving the car x miles.
    (b) Use the intersection-of-graphs method to determine the number of miles that the car is driven if the rental cost is $100.
    (c) Solve part (b) numerically with a table of values.

69. *Recorded Music* In 2009, rock and R&B music accounted for 42% of all music sales. Rock music sales were double the R&B music sales. (*Source:* Recording Industry Association of America.)
    (a) Let x be the percentage of sales due to rock music and let y be the percentage of music sales due to R&B music. Write a system of two equations that describes the given information.
    (b) Solve your system graphically.

70. *Sales of iPods* During the first and second quarters of 2010, about 32 million iPods were sold. The first quarter sales exceeded the second quarter sales by 10 million iPods. (*Source:* Apple.)

(a) Let x be the iPod sales in millions during the first quarter of 2010 and y be the iPod sales in millions during the second quarter of 2010. Write a system of two equations that describes the given information.

(b) Solve your system graphically.

71. *Dimensions of a Rectangle* A rectangle is 4 inches longer than it is wide. Its perimeter is 28 inches.

(a) Write a system of two equations in two variables that describes this information. Be sure to specify what each variable means.

(b) Solve your system graphically. Interpret your results.

72. *Dimensions of a Triangle* An isosceles triangle has a perimeter of 17 inches with its two shorter sides equal in length. The longest side measures 2 inches more than either of the shorter sides.

(a) Write a system of two equations in two variables that describes this information. Be sure to specify what each variable means.

(b) Solve your system graphically. Explain what your results mean.

WRITING ABOUT MATHEMATICS

73. Use the intersection-of-graphs method to help explain why you typically expect a linear system in two variables to have one solution.

74. Could a system of two linear equations in two variables have exactly two solutions? Explain your reasoning.

75. Give one disadvantage of using a table to solve a system of equations. Explain your answer.

76. Do the equations $y = 2x + 1$ and $y = 2x - 1$ have a common solution? Explain your answer.

4.2 Solving Systems of Linear Equations by Substitution

The Method of Substitution • Recognizing Other Types of Systems • Applications

A LOOK INTO MATH ▶

Suppose that a boy and a girl sent a total of 760 text messages in one month. With only this information, it is impossible to know how many messages were sent by each person. The boy may have sent 432 messages while the girl sent 328. However, 11 and 749 also total 760, as do many other possibilities. If we are told that the boy sent three times as many messages as the girl, a system of linear equations can be written and solved to find the answer. Refer to Example 4. In this section, we discuss a symbolic method for solving systems of linear equations.

The Method of Substitution

NEW VOCABULARY

☐ Method of substitution

In Section 4.1 we solved systems of linear equations by using graphs and tables. A disadvantage of a graph is that reading the graph precisely can be difficult. A disadvantage of using a table is that locating the solution can be difficult when it is either a fraction or a large number. In this subsection we introduce the *method of substitution*, in which we solve systems of equations symbolically. The advantage of this method is that the *exact* solution can always be found (provided it exists).

READING CHECK

• What is an advantage of using the method of substitution rather than using a graph or table to solve a system of linear equations?

STUDY TIP

Questions on exams do not always come in the order that they are presented in the text. When studying for an exam, choose review exercises randomly so that the topics are studied in the same random way that they may appear on an exam.

▶ **REAL-WORLD CONNECTION** Suppose that you and a friend earned $120 together. If x represents how much your friend earned and y represents how much you earned, then the equation $x + y = 120$ describes this situation. Now, if we also know that you earned twice as much as your friend, then we can include a second equation, $y = 2x$. The amount that each of you earned can now be determined by *substituting* $2x$ for y in the first equation.

$$x + y = 120 \qquad \text{First equation}$$
$$x + 2x = 120 \qquad \text{Substitute } 2x \text{ for } y.$$
$$3x = 120 \qquad \text{Combine like terms.}$$
$$x = 40 \qquad \text{Divide each side by 3.}$$

So your friend earned $40, and you earned twice as much, or $80.

This technique of substituting an expression for a variable and solving the resulting equation is called the **method of substitution**.

EXAMPLE 1   **Using the method of substitution**

Solve each system of equations.
(a) $2x + y = 10$ (b) $-2x + 3y = -8$
    $\quad\ \ y = 3x$ $\quad\quad x = 3y + 1$

Solution
(a) From the second equation, substitute $3x$ for y in the first equation.

$$2x + y = 10 \qquad \text{First equation}$$
$$2x + 3x = 10 \qquad \text{Substitute } 3x \text{ for } y.$$
$$5x = 10 \qquad \text{Combine like terms.}$$
$$x = 2 \qquad \text{Divide each side by 5.}$$

The solution to this system is an *ordered pair*, so we must also find y. Because $y = 3x$ and $x = 2$, it follows that $y = 3(2) = 6$. The solution is $(2, 6)$. (Check it.)

(b) The second equation, $x = 3y + 1$, is solved for x. Substitute $(3y + 1)$ for x in the first equation. Be sure to include parentheses around the expression $3y + 1$ since this entire expression is to be multiplied by -2.

$$-2x + 3y = -8 \qquad \text{First equation}$$
$$-2(3y + 1) + 3y = -8 \qquad \text{Substitute } (3y + 1) \text{ for } x.$$

Be sure to include parentheses

$$-6y - 2 + 3y = -8 \qquad \text{Distributive property}$$
$$-3y - 2 = -8 \qquad \text{Combine like terms.}$$
$$-3y = -6 \qquad \text{Add 2 to each side.}$$
$$y = 2 \qquad \text{Divide each side by } -3.$$

To find x, substitute 2 for y in $x = 3y + 1$ to obtain $x = 3(2) + 1 = 7$. The solution is $(7, 2)$. (Check it.)

Now Try Exercises 5, 11

NOTE: When an expression contains two or more terms, it is usually best to place parentheses around it when substituting it for a single variable in an equation. In Example 1(b), the distributive property would not have been applied correctly without the parentheses.

READING CHECK

• When substituting an expression with two or more terms for a single variable, why is it important to use parentheses?

Sometimes it is necessary to solve for a variable before substitution can be used, as demonstrated in the next example.

> EXAMPLE 2   **Using the method of substitution**

Solve each system of equations.

(a) $x + y = 8$ (b) $3a - 2b = 2$
     $2x - 3y = 6$ $a + 4b = 3$

Solution

(a) Neither equation is solved for a variable, but we can easily solve the first equation for y.

$$x + y = 8 \qquad \text{First equation}$$
$$y = 8 - x \qquad \text{Subtract } x \text{ from each side.}$$

Now we can substitute $(8 - x)$ for y in the second equation.

$$2x - 3y = 6 \qquad \text{Second equation}$$
$$2x - 3(8 - x) = 6 \qquad \text{Substitute } (8 - x) \text{ for } y.$$
$$2x - 24 + 3x = 6 \qquad \text{Distributive property}$$
$$5x = 30 \qquad \text{Combine like terms; add 24.}$$
$$x = 6 \qquad \text{Divide each side by 5.}$$

Because $y = 8 - x$ and $x = 6$, we know that $y = 8 - 6 = 2$. The solution is $(6, 2)$.

(b) Although we could solve either equation for either variable, solving the second equation for a is easiest because the coefficient of a is 1 and we can avoid fractions.

$$a + 4b = 3 \qquad \text{Second equation}$$
$$a = 3 - 4b \qquad \text{Subtract } 4b \text{ from each side.}$$

Now substitute $(3 - 4b)$ for a in the first equation.

$$3a - 2b = 2 \qquad \text{First equation}$$
$$3(3 - 4b) - 2b = 2 \qquad \text{Substitute } (3 - 4b) \text{ for } a.$$
$$9 - 12b - 2b = 2 \qquad \text{Distributive property}$$
$$-14b = -7 \qquad \text{Combine like terms; subtract 9.}$$
$$b = \frac{1}{2} \qquad \text{Divide each side by } -14.$$

To find a, substitute $b = \frac{1}{2}$ in $a = 3 - 4b$ to obtain $a = 1$. The solution is $\left(1, \frac{1}{2}\right)$.

▌ Now Try Exercises 17, 23

NOTE: When a system of equations contains variables other than x and y, we will list them alphabetically in an ordered pair.

Recognizing Other Types of Systems

A system of linear equations typically has exactly one solution. However, in the next example we see how the method of substitution can be used on systems that have no solutions or infinitely many solutions.

EXAMPLE 3 **Solving other types of systems**

If possible, use substitution to solve the system of equations. Then use graphing to help explain the result.

(a) $3x + y = 4$ **(b)** $x + y = 2$
   $6x + 2y = 2$ $2x + 2y = 4$

Solution

(a) Solve the first equation for y to obtain $y = 4 - 3x$. Next substitute $(4 - 3x)$ for y in the second equation.

$$6x + 2y = 2 \qquad \text{Second equation}$$
$$6x + 2(4 - 3x) = 2 \qquad \text{Substitute } (4 - 3x) \text{ for } y.$$
$$6x + 8 - 6x = 2 \qquad \text{Distributive property}$$
$$8 = 2 \text{ (False)} \qquad \text{Combine like terms.}$$

The equation $8 = 2$ is *always false*, which indicates that there are *no solutions*. One way to graph each equation is to write the equations in slope–intercept form.

$3x + y = 4$	First equation	$6x + 2y = 2$	Second equation
$y = -3x + 4$	Subtract $3x$.	$y = -3x + 1$	Subtract $6x$; divide by 2.

The graphs of these equations are parallel lines with slope -3, as shown in Figure 4.9(a). Because the lines *do not intersect*, there are *no solutions* to the system of equations.

(b) Solve the first equation for y to obtain $y = 2 - x$. Now substitute $(2 - x)$ for y in the second equation.

$$2x + 2y = 4 \qquad \text{Second equation}$$
$$2x + 2(2 - x) = 4 \qquad \text{Substitute } (2 - x) \text{ for } y.$$
$$2x + 4 - 2x = 4 \qquad \text{Distributive property}$$
$$4 = 4 \text{ (True)} \qquad \text{Combine like terms.}$$

The equation $4 = 4$ is *always true*, which means that there are *infinitely many solutions*. One way to graph these equations is to write them in slope–intercept form.

$x + y = 2$	First equation	$2x + 2y = 4$	Second equation
$y = -x + 2$	Subtract x.	$y = -x + 2$	Subtract $2x$; divide by 2.

Because the equations have the same slope–intercept form, their graphs are identical, resulting in a single line, as shown in Figure 4.9(b). *Every point* on this line *represents a solution* to the system of equations, so there are infinitely many solutions.

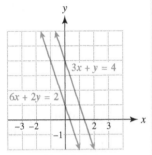

(a) No Solutions

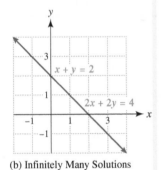

(b) Infinitely Many Solutions

Figure 4.9

▌ Now Try Exercises 33, 35

Applications

In the next example, we use the method of substitution to solve a system of equations that represents the information presented in A Look Into Math at the beginning of this section.

EXAMPLE 4 **Finding numbers of text messages**

A boy and a girl sent a total of 760 text messages in one month. If the boy sent three times as many messages as the girl, how many text messages did each person send?

Solution

If x represents the number of text messages sent by the girl and y represents the number of text messages sent by the boy, then the equation $x + y = 760$ can be written because the total number of messages is 760. Also, the equation $y = 3x$ can be included because the boy sent three times as many messages as the girl. The system is

$$x + y = 760$$
$$y = 3x.$$

Substitute $3x$ for y in the first equation.

$x + y = 760$	First equation
$x + 3x = 760$	Substitute $3x$ for y.
$4x = 760$	Combine like terms.
$x = 190$	Divide each side by 4.

The girl sent 190 text messages and the boy sent 3 times as many, or $3(190) = 570$. This answer checks because $190 + 570 = 760$ and 570 is three times 190.

▌ Now Try Exercise 67

The next two examples illustrate how the method of substitution can be used to solve applications. In these examples we apply the same four-step process that was used to solve application problems in Section 4.1.

EXAMPLE 5   **Determining pizza sales**

In 2009, combined sales of frozen and ready-to-eat pizza reached $36.9 billion. Ready-to-eat pizza sales were 7.2 times frozen pizza sales. Find the amount of sales for each type of pizza. (*Source: Business Trend Analyst.*)

Solution
STEP 1: *Identify each variable.* Clearly identify what each variable represents.

x: sales of ready-to-eat pizza, in billions of dollars
y: sales of frozen pizza, in billions of dollars

STEP 2: *Write a system of equations.*

$x + y = 36.9$	Sales total $36.9 billion.
$x = 7.2y$	Ready-to-eat pizza sales x are 7.2 times frozen pizza sales y.

STEP 3A: *Solve the system of linear equations.* Substitute $7.2y$ for x in the first equation.

$x + y = 36.9$	First equation
$7.2y + y = 36.9$	Substitute $7.2y$ for x.
$8.2y = 36.9$	Combine like terms.
$y = \dfrac{36.9}{8.2}$	Divide each side by 8.2.
$y = 4.5$	Simplify.

Because $x = 7.2y$, it follows that $x = 7.2(4.5) = 32.4$.

STEP 3B: *Determine the solution to the problem.* The solution $y = 4.5$ and $x = 32.4$ indicates that frozen pizza sales were $4.5 billion and ready-to-eat pizza sales were $32.4 billion in 2009.

STEP 4: *Check the solution.* The sum of these sales was $32.4 + 4.5 = \$36.9$ billion, and ready-to-eat pizza sales were $\frac{32.4}{4.5} = 7.2$ times frozen pizza sales. The answer checks.

▌ Now Try Exercise 57

EXAMPLE 6   **Determining airplane speed and wind speed**

An airplane flies 2400 miles into (or against) the wind in 8 hours. The return trip takes 6 hours. Find the speed of the airplane with no wind and the speed of the wind.

Solution

STEP 1:   *Identify each variable.*

x: the speed of the airplane without wind
y: the speed of the wind

STEP 2:   *Write a system of equations.* The speed of the airplane against the wind is $\frac{2400}{8} = 300$ miles per hour, because it traveled 2400 miles in 8 hours. The wind slowed the plane, so $x - y = 300$. Similarly, the airplane flew $\frac{2400}{6} = 400$ miles per hour with the wind because it traveled 2400 miles in 6 hours. The wind made the plane fly faster, so $x + y = 400$.

$$x - y = 300 \quad \text{Speed against the wind}$$
$$x + y = 400 \quad \text{Speed with the wind}$$

STEP 3A: *Solve the system of linear equations.* Solve the first equation for x to obtain $x = y + 300$. Substitute $(y + 300)$ for x in the second equation.

$$x + y = 400 \quad \text{Second equation}$$
$$(y + 300) + y = 400 \quad \text{Substitute } (y + 300) \text{ for } x.$$
$$2y = 100 \quad \text{Combine like terms; subtract 300.}$$
$$y = 50 \quad \text{Divide each side by 2.}$$

CRITICAL THINKING

A boat travels 10 miles per hour upstream and 16 miles per hour downstream. How fast is the current?

Because $x = y + 300$, it follows that $x = 50 + 300 = 350$.

STEP 3B: *Determine the solution to the problem.* The solution $x = 350$ and $y = 50$ indicates that the airplane can fly 350 miles per hour with no wind, and the wind speed is 50 miles per hour.

STEP 4:   *Check the solution.* The plane flies $350 - 50 = 300$ miles per hour into the wind, taking $\frac{2400}{300} = 8$ hours. The plane flies $350 + 50 = 400$ miles per hour with the wind, taking $\frac{2400}{400} = 6$ hours. The answers check.

▮ Now Try Exercise 63

4.2   Putting It All Together

CONCEPT	EXPLANATION	EXAMPLE
Method of Substitution	Can be used to solve a system of equations Gives the exact solution, provided one exists **STEP 1:** Solve one equation for one variable. **STEP 2:** Substitute the result in the other equation and solve. **STEP 3:** Use the solution for the first variable to find the other variable. **STEP 4:** Check the solution.	$x + y = 5$ Sum is 5. $x - y = 1$ Difference is 1. **STEP 1:** Solve for x in the second equation. $x = y + 1$ **STEP 2:** Substitute $(y + 1)$ in the first equation for x. $(y + 1) + y = 5$ $2y = 4$ $y = 2$ **STEP 3:** $x = 2 + 1 = 3$ **STEP 4:** $3 + 2 = 5 \checkmark$ $3 - 2 = 1 \checkmark$ (3, 2) checks.

4.2 Exercises

CONCEPTS AND VOCABULARY

1. One advantage of solving a linear system using the method of substitution rather than graphical or numerical methods is that the _____ solution can always be found (provided it exists).

2. When substituting an expression that contains two or more terms for a single variable in an equation, it is usually best to place _____ around it.

3. Suppose that the method of substitution results in the equation $1 = 1$. What does this indicate about the number of solutions to the system of equations?

4. Suppose that the method of substitution results in the equation $0 = 1$. What does this indicate about the number of solutions to the system of equations?

SOLVING SYSTEMS OF EQUATIONS

Exercises 5–32: Use the method of substitution to solve the system of linear equations.

5. $x + y = 9$
   $y = 2x$

6. $x + y = -12$
   $y = -3x$

7. $x + 2y = 4$
   $x = 2y$

8. $-x + 3y = -12$
   $x = 5y$

9. $2x + y = -2$
   $y = x + 1$

10. $-3x + y = -10$
    $y = x - 2$

11. $x + 3y = 3$
    $x = y + 3$

12. $x - 2y = -5$
    $x = 4 - y$

13. $3x + 2y = \frac{3}{2}$
    $y = 2x - 1$

14. $-3x + 5y = 4$
    $y = 2 - 3x$

15. $2x - 3y = -12$
    $x = 2 - \frac{1}{2}y$

16. $\frac{3}{4}x + \frac{1}{4}y = -\frac{7}{4}$
    $x = 1 - 2y$

17. $2x - 3y = -4$
    $3x - y = 1$

18. $\frac{1}{2}x - y = -1$
    $2x - \frac{1}{2}y = \frac{13}{2}$

19. $x - 5y = 26$
    $2x + 6y = -12$

20. $4x - 3y = -4$
    $x + 7y = -63$

21. $\frac{1}{2}y - z = 5$
    $y - 3z = 13$

22. $3y - 7z = -2$
    $5y - z = 2$

23. $10r - 20t = 20$
    $r + 60t = -29$

24. $-r + 10t = 22$
    $-10r + 5t = 30$

25. $3x + 2y = 9$
    $2x - 3y = -7$

26. $5x - 2y = -5$
    $2x - 5y = 19$

27. $2a - 3b = 6$
    $-5a + 4b = -8$

28. $-5a + 7b = -1$
    $3a + 2b = 13$

29. $-\frac{1}{2}x + 3y = 5$
    $2x - \frac{1}{2}y = 3$

30. $3x - \frac{1}{2}y = 2$
    $-\frac{1}{2}x + 5y = \frac{19}{2}$

31. $3a + 5b = 16$
    $-8a + 2b = 34$

32. $5a - 10b = 20$
    $10a + 5b = 15$

Exercises 33–50: Use the method of substitution to solve the system of linear equations. These systems may have no solutions, one solution, or infinitely many solutions.

33. $x + y = 9$
    $x + y = 7$

34. $x - y = 8$
    $x - y = 4$

35. $x - y = 4$
    $2x - 2y = 8$

36. $2x + y = 5$
    $4x + 2y = 10$

37. $x + y = 4$
    $x - y = 2$

38. $x - y = 3$
    $2x - y = 7$

39. $x - y = 7$
    $-x + y = -7$

40. $2u - v = 6$
    $-4u + 2v = -12$

41. $u - 2v = 5$
    $2u - 4v = -2$

42. $3r + 3t = 9$
    $2r + 2t = 4$

43. $2r + 3t = 1$
    $r - 3t = -5$

44. $5x - y = -1$
    $2x - 7y = 7$

45. $y = 5x$
    $y = -3x$

46. $a = b + 1$
    $a = b - 1$

47. $5a = 4 - b$
    $5a = 3 - b$

48. $3y = x$
    $3y = 2x$

49. $2x + 4y = 0$
    $3x + 6y = 5$

50. $-5x + 10y = 3$
    $\frac{1}{2}x - y = 1$

51. **Thinking Generally** If the method of substitution results in an equation that is always true, what can be said about the graphs of the two equations?

52. **Thinking Generally** If the method of substitution results in an equation that is always false, what can be said about the graphs of the two equations?

APPLICATIONS

53. *Rectangle* A rectangular garden is 10 feet longer than it is wide. Its perimeter is 72 feet.
   (a) Let W be the width of the garden and L be the length. Write a system of linear equations whose solution gives the width and length of the garden.
   (b) Use the method of substitution to solve the system. Check your answer.

54. *Isosceles Triangle* The measures of the two smaller angles in a triangle are equal and their sum equals the largest angle.
   (a) Let x be the measure of each of the two smaller angles and y be the measure of the largest angle. Write a system of linear equations whose solution gives the measures of these angles.
   (b) Use the method of substitution to solve the system. Check your answer.

55. *Complementary Angles* The smaller of two complementary angles is half the measure of the larger angle.
   (a) Let x be the measure of the smaller angle and y be the measure of the larger angle. Write a system of linear equations whose solution gives the measures of these angles.
   (b) Use the method of substitution to solve your system.
   (c) Use graphing to solve the system.

56. *Supplementary Angles* The smaller of two supplementary angles is one-fourth the measure of the larger angle.
   (a) Let x be the measure of the smaller angle and y be the measure of the larger angle. Write a system of linear equations whose solution gives the measures of these angles.
   (b) Use the method of substitution to solve the system.

57. *Average Room Prices* In 2009, the average room price for a hotel chain in Seattle was $21 less than in 2008. The 2009 room price was 86% of the 2008 room price. (*Source:* Hotel Price Index.)
   (a) Let x be the average room price in 2008 and y be this price in 2009. Write a system of linear equations whose solution gives the average room prices for each year.
   (b) Use the method of substitution to solve the system.

58. *Ticket Prices* Two hundred tickets were sold for a baseball game, which amounted to $840. Student tickets cost $3, and adult tickets cost $5.
   (a) Let x be the number of student tickets sold and y be the number of adult tickets sold. Write a system of linear equations whose solution gives the number of each type of ticket sold.
   (b) Use the method of substitution to solve the system of equations.

59. *NBA Basketball Court* An official NBA basketball court is 44 feet longer than it is wide. If its perimeter is 288 feet, find its dimensions.

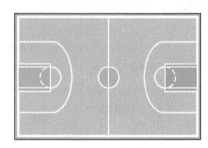

60. *Football Field* A U.S. football field is 139.5 feet longer than it is wide. If its perimeter is 921 feet, find its dimensions.

61. *Number Problem* The sum of two numbers is 70. The larger number is two more than three times the smaller number. Find the two numbers.

62. *Number Problem* The difference of two numbers is 12. The larger number is one less than twice the smaller number. Find the two numbers.

63. *Speed Problem* A tugboat goes 120 miles upstream in 15 hours. The return trip downstream takes 10 hours. Find the speed of the tugboat without a current and the speed of the current.

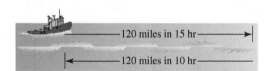

64. *Speed Problem* An airplane flies 1200 miles into the wind in 3 hours. The return trip takes 2 hours. Find the speed of the airplane without a wind and the speed of the wind.

65. *Mixture Problem* A chemist has 20% and 50% solutions of acid available. How many liters of each solution should be mixed to obtain 10 liters of a 40% acid solution?

66. *Mixture Problem* A mechanic needs a radiator to have a 40% antifreeze solution. The radiator currently is filled with 4 gallons of a 25% antifreeze solution. How much of the antifreeze mixture should be drained from the car if the mechanic replaces it with pure antifreeze?

67. *Great Lakes* Together, Lake Superior and Lake Michigan cover 54 thousand square miles. Lake Superior is approximately 10 thousand square miles larger than Lake Michigan. Find the size of each lake. (*Source:* National Oceanic and Atmospheric Administration.)

68. *Longest Rivers* The two longest rivers in the world are the Nile and the Amazon. Together, they are 8145 miles, with the Amazon being 145 miles shorter than the Nile. Find the length of each river. (*Source:* National Oceanic and Atmospheric Administration.)

WRITING ABOUT MATHEMATICS

69. State one advantage that the method of substitution has over the intersection-of-graphs method. Explain your answer.

70. When applying the method of substitution, how do you know that there are no solutions?

71. When applying the method of substitution, how do you know that there are infinitely many solutions?

72. When applying the intersection-of-graphs method, how do you know that there are no solutions?

SECTIONS 4.1 and 4.2 | **Checking Basic Concepts**

1. Determine graphically the x-value in each equation when $y = 2$.
   (a) $y = 1 - \frac{1}{2}x$ **(b)** $2x - 3y = 6$

2. Determine whether $(-1, 0)$ or $(4, 2)$ is a solution to the system

$$2x - 5y = -2$$
$$3x + 2y = 16.$$

3. Solve the system of equations graphically. Check your answer.

$$x - y = 1$$
$$2x + y = 5$$

4. If possible, use the method of substitution to solve each system of equations.

   (a) $x + y = -1$
         $y = 2 - x$
   (b) $4x - y = 5$
         $-x + y = -2$
   (c) $x + 2y = 3$
         $-x - 2y = -3$

5. *Room Prices* A hotel rents single and double rooms for $150 and $200, respectively. The hotel receives $55,000 for renting 300 rooms.
   (a) Let x be the number of single rooms rented and let y be the number of double rooms rented. Write a system of linear equations whose solution gives the values of x and y.
   (b) Use the method of substitution to solve the system. Check your answer.

4.3 Solving Systems of Linear Equations by Elimination

The Elimination Method ▪ Recognizing Other Types of Systems ▪ Applications

A LOOK INTO MATH ▶ Anyone who has used Internet map services such as MapQuest or Google maps knows that there are often several ways to get from one location to another. Sometimes the route with the shortest physical distance is desirable. At other times, we want a route on faster roads with the least amount of driving time. In this section, we introduce a second symbolic method for solving systems of linear equations. With two symbolic "routes" to the same solution, you can choose the method that may work best for a particular system. This second method, called the *elimination method*, is very efficient for solving some types of systems of linear equations.

NEW VOCABULARY

☐ Elimination method

STUDY TIP

Much of mathematics builds on previous knowledge. We learned about the addition property of equality in Chapter 2. In this section, we see how we can use this property to solve a system of linear equations.

The Elimination Method

The **elimination method** is based on the addition property of equality. If

$$a = b \quad \text{and} \quad c = d,$$

then

$$a + c = b + d.$$

For example, if the sum of two numbers is 20 and their difference is 4, then the system of equations

$$x + y = 20$$
$$x - y = 4$$

describes these two numbers. By the addition property of equality, the sum of the left sides of these equations equals the sum of their right sides.

$$(x + y) + (x - y) = 20 + 4 \quad \text{Add left sides of these equations.}$$
$$\text{Add right sides of these equations.}$$
$$2x = 24 \quad \text{Combine terms.}$$

Note that the y-variable is eliminated when the left sides are added. The resulting equation, $2x = 24$, simplifies to $x = 12$. Thus the value of x in the solution to the system of equations is 12. The value of y can be found by substituting 12 for x in either of the given equations. Substituting 12 for x in the first equation, $x + y = 20$, results in $12 + y = 20$ or $y = 8$. The solution to the system of equations is $x = 12$, $y = 8$, which can be written as the ordered pair (12, 8).

To organize the elimination method better, we can carry out the addition vertically.

$$x + y = 20$$
$$\underline{x - y = 4}$$
$$2x + 0y = 24 \qquad \text{Add left sides and add right sides.}$$
$$2x = 24 \qquad \text{Simplify.}$$
$$x = 12 \qquad \text{Divide each side by 2.}$$

READING CHECK

• What is eliminated from both of the equations when the elimination method is used to solve a system of linear equations?

Once the value of one variable is known, in this case $x = 12$, don't forget to find the value of the other variable by substituting this known value in either of the *given* equations. By substituting 12 for x in the second equation, we obtain $12 - y = 4$ or $y = 8$. The solution is the ordered pair (12, 8).

EXAMPLE 1 **Applying the elimination method**

Solve each system of equations. Check each solution.
(a) $2x + y = 1$ **(b)** $-2a + b = -3$
     $3x - y = 9$ $2a + 3b = 7$

Solution
(a) Adding these two equations eliminates the y-variable.

$$2x + y = 1 \qquad \text{First equation}$$
$$\underline{3x - y = 9} \qquad \text{Second equation}$$
$$5x = 10, \quad \text{or} \quad x = 2 \qquad \text{Add and solve for } x.$$

To find y, substitute **2** for x in either of the *given* equations. We will use $2x + y = 1$.

$$2(2) + y = 1 \qquad \text{Let } x = 2 \text{ in first equation.}$$
$$y = -3 \qquad \text{Subtract 4 from each side.}$$

The solution is the *ordered pair* $(2, -3)$, which can be checked by substituting 2 for x and -3 for y in each of the given equations.

$$
\begin{array}{llll}
2x + y = 1 & 3x - y = 9 & \text{Given equations} \\
2(2) + (-3) \stackrel{?}{=} 1 & 3(2) - (-3) \stackrel{?}{=} 9 & \text{Let } x = 2 \text{ and } y = -3. \\
4 - 3 \stackrel{?}{=} 1 & 6 + 3 \stackrel{?}{=} 9 & \text{Simplify.} \\
1 = 1 \checkmark & 9 = 9 \checkmark & \text{The solution checks.}
\end{array}
$$

(b) Adding these two equations eliminates the a-variable.

$$
\begin{array}{ll}
-2a + b = -3 & \text{First equation} \\
\underline{2a + 3b = 7} & \text{Second equation} \\
4b = 4, \quad \text{or} \quad b = 1 & \text{Add and solve for } b.
\end{array}
$$

To find a, substitute 1 for b in either of the *given* equations. We will use $2a + 3b = 7$.

$$
\begin{array}{ll}
2a + 3(1) = 7 & \text{Let } b = 1 \text{ in second equation.} \\
2a = 4 & \text{Subtract 3 from each side.} \\
a = 2 & \text{Divide each side by 2.}
\end{array}
$$

The solution is the *ordered pair* $(2, 1)$, which can be checked by substituting 2 for a and 1 for b in each of the given equations.

$$
\begin{array}{llll}
-2a + b = -3 & 2a + 3b = 7 & \text{Given equations} \\
-2(2) + 1 \stackrel{?}{=} -3 & 2(2) + 3(1) \stackrel{?}{=} 7 & \text{Let } a = 2 \text{ and } b = 1. \\
-4 + 1 \stackrel{?}{=} -3 & 4 + 3 \stackrel{?}{=} 7 & \text{Simplify.} \\
-3 = -3 \checkmark & 7 = 7 \checkmark & \text{The solution checks.}
\end{array}
$$

▎**Now Try Exercises 15, 17**

Adding two equations does not always eliminate a variable. For example, adding the following equations eliminates neither variable.

$$
\begin{array}{ll}
3x - 2y = 11 & \text{First equation} \\
\underline{4x + y = 11} & \text{Second equation} \\
7x - y = 22 & \text{Add the equations.}
\end{array}
$$

READING CHECK

• In using the elimination method, when is it necessary to apply the multiplication property of equality?

However, by the multiplication property of equality, we can multiply the second equation by 2. Then adding the equations eliminates the y-variable.

$$
\begin{array}{ll}
3x - 2y = 11 & \text{First equation} \\
\underline{8x + 2y = 22} & \text{Multiply the second equation by 2.} \\
11x = 33, \quad \text{or} \quad x = 3 & \text{Add and solve for } x.
\end{array}
$$

EXAMPLE 2   **Multiplying before applying elimination**

Solve each system of equations.
(a) $5x - y = -11$ **(b)** $3x + 2y = 1$
$\quad\ \ 2x + 3y = -1$ $\qquad 2x - 3y = 5$

Solution
(a) We multiply the first equation by 3 and then add to eliminate the y-variable.

$$
\begin{array}{ll}
15x - 3y = -33 & \text{Multiply the first equation by 3.} \\
\underline{2x + 3y = -1} & \text{Second equation} \\
17x = -34, \quad \text{or} \quad x = -2 & \text{Add and solve for } x.
\end{array}
$$

We can find y by substituting -2 for x in the second equation, $2x + 3y = -1$.

$$2(-2) + 3y = -1 \qquad \text{Let } x = -2 \text{ in second equation.}$$
$$3y = 3 \qquad \text{Add 4 to each side.}$$
$$y = 1 \qquad \text{Divide each side by 3.}$$

The solution is $(-2, 1)$.

(b) We must apply the multiplication property to both equations. If we multiply the first equation, $3x + 2y = 1$, by 3, and the second equation, $2x - 3y = 5$, by 2, then the coefficients of the y-variables will be opposites. Adding eliminates the y-variable.

$$9x + 6y = 3 \qquad \text{Multiply the first equation by 3.}$$
$$\underline{4x - 6y = 10} \qquad \text{Multiply the second equation by 2.}$$
$$13x = 13, \quad \text{or} \quad x = 1 \qquad \text{Add and solve for } x.$$

To find y, substitute 1 for x in the first *given* equation, $3x + 2y = 1$.

$$3(1) + 2y = 1 \qquad \text{Let } x = 1 \text{ in first equation.}$$
$$2y = -2 \qquad \text{Subtract 3 from each side.}$$
$$y = -1 \qquad \text{Divide each side by 2.}$$

The solution is $(1, -1)$.

▌ **Now Try Exercises 29, 33**

In practice, it is possible to eliminate *either* variable from a system of linear equations. It is often best to choose the variable that requires the least amount of computation to complete the elimination. In the next example, we solve a system of equations twice—first by using the multiplication property of equality to eliminate the x-variable and then by using it to eliminate the y-variable.

EXAMPLE 3 **Multiplying before applying elimination**

Solve the system of equations two times, first by eliminating x and then by eliminating y.

$$2y = -6 - 5x$$
$$2x = -5y + 6$$

Solution
It is best to write each equation in the standard form: $Ax + By = C$.

$$5x + 2y = -6 \qquad \text{First equation in standard form}$$
$$2x + 5y = 6 \qquad \text{Second equation in standard form}$$

Eliminate x If we multiply the first equation in standard form by -2 and the second equation in standard form by 5, then we can eliminate the x-variable by adding.

$$-10x - 4y = 12 \qquad \text{Multiply the first equation by } -2.$$
$$\underline{10x + 25y = 30} \qquad \text{Multiply the second equation by 5.}$$
$$21y = 42, \quad \text{or} \quad y = 2 \qquad \text{Add and solve for } y.$$

To find x, substitute 2 for y in the first *given* equation, $2y = -6 - 5x$.

$$2(2) = -6 - 5x \qquad \text{Let } y = 2 \text{ in first equation.}$$
$$10 = -5x \qquad \text{Add 6 to each side.}$$
$$-2 = x \qquad \text{Divide each side by } -5.$$

The solution is $(-2, 2)$.

Eliminate y If we multiply the first equation in standard form by -5 and the second equation in standard form by 2, then we can eliminate the y-variable by adding.

$$
\begin{array}{ll}
-25x - 10y = 30 & \text{Multiply the first equation by } -5. \\
\underline{4x + 10y = 12} & \text{Multiply the second equation by } 2. \\
-21x \quad\quad = 42, \quad \text{or} \quad x = -2 & \text{Add and solve for } x.
\end{array}
$$

To find y, substitute -2 for x in the second given equation, $2x = -5y + 6$.

$$
\begin{array}{ll}
2(-2) = -5y + 6 & \text{Let } x = -2 \text{ in second equation.} \\
-10 = -5y & \text{Subtract 6 from each side.} \\
2 = y & \text{Divide each side by } -5.
\end{array}
$$

The solution is $(-2, 2)$.

▌ Now Try Exercise 31

In the next example we use three different methods to solve a system of equations.

> **EXAMPLE 4** **Solving a system with different methods**

Solve the system of equations symbolically, graphically, and numerically.

$$
\begin{array}{r}
x + \ y = 2 \\
x - 3y = 6
\end{array}
$$

Solution

Symbolic Solution Both the method of substitution and the elimination method are symbolic methods. The elimination method is used here. We can solve the system by multiplying the second equation by -1 and adding to eliminate the x-variable.

$$
\begin{array}{ll}
x + \ y = \ \ 2 & \text{First equation} \\
\underline{-x + 3y = -6} & \text{Multiply the second equation by } -1. \\
4y = -4, \quad \text{or} \quad y = -1 & \text{Add and solve for } y.
\end{array}
$$

We can find x by substituting -1 for y in the first equation, $x + y = 2$.

$$
\begin{array}{ll}
x + (-1) = 2 & \text{Let } y = -1 \text{ in first equation.} \\
x = 3 & \text{Add 1 to each side.}
\end{array}
$$

The solution is $(3, -1)$.

Graphical Solution For a graphical solution, we solve each equation for y to obtain the slope–intercept form.

$$
\begin{array}{ll}
x + y = 2 & \text{First equation} \\
y = -x + 2 & \text{Subtract } x.
\end{array}
\qquad
\begin{array}{ll}
x - 3y = 6 & \text{Second equation} \\
-3y = -x + 6 & \text{Subtract } x. \\
y = \dfrac{1}{3}x - 2 & \text{Divide by } -3.
\end{array}
$$

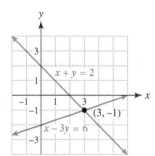

Figure 4.10

The graphs of $y = -x + 2$ and $y = \frac{1}{3}x - 2$ are shown in Figure 4.10. They intersect at $(3, -1)$. (These graphs could also be obtained by finding the x- and y-intercepts for each equation.)

Numerical Solution A numerical solution consists of a table of values, as shown in Table 4.4. Note that when $x = 3$, both y-values equal -1. Therefore the solution is $(3, -1)$.

TABLE 4.4

x	0	1	2	3	4
$y = -x + 2$	2	1	0	-1	-2
$y = \frac{1}{3}x - 2$	-2	$-\frac{5}{3}$	$-\frac{4}{3}$	-1	$-\frac{2}{3}$

▮ Now Try Exercise 41

Recognizing Other Types of Systems

In Section 4.1 we discussed how a system of linear equations can have no solutions, one solution, or infinitely many solutions. Elimination can also be used on systems that have no solutions or infinitely many solutions.

EXAMPLE 5   **Solving other types of systems**

Solve each system of equations by using the elimination method. Then graph the system.

(a) $x - 2y = 4$ (b) $3x + 3y = 6$
      $-2x + 4y = -8$ $x + y = 1$

Solution

(a) We multiply the first equation by 2 and then add, which eliminates both variables.

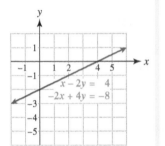

Figure 4.11

$$
\begin{array}{ll}
2x - 4y = 8 & \text{Multiply the first equation by 2.} \\
-2x + 4y = -8 & \text{Second equation} \\
\hline
0 = 0 \quad \textbf{(True)} & \text{Add.}
\end{array}
$$

The equation $0 = 0$ is *always true*, which indicates that the system has *infinitely many solutions*. A graph of the two equations is shown in Figure 4.11. The two lines are identical so there actually is only one line, and *every point on this line represents a solution.* For example, $(0, -2)$ and $(4, 0)$ lie on the line and are both solutions.

(b) We multiply the second equation by -3 and add, eliminating both variables.

$$
\begin{array}{ll}
3x + 3y = 6 & \text{First equation} \\
-3x - 3y = -3 & \text{Multiply the second equation by } -3. \\
\hline
0 = 3 \quad \text{(False)} & \text{Add.}
\end{array}
$$

The equation $0 = 3$ is *always false*, which indicates that the system has *no solutions*. A graph of the two equations is shown in Figure 4.12. Note that the two lines are parallel and thus do not intersect.

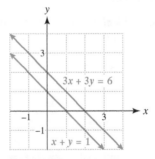

Figure 4.12

▮ Now Try Exercises 51, 55

MAKING CONNECTIONS

Numerical and Graphical Solutions

The left-hand figure below shows a numerical solution for Example 5(a), where each equation is solved for y to obtain

$$y_1 = (4 - x)/(-2) \quad \text{and} \quad y_2 = (-8 + 2x)/4.$$

Note that $y_1 = y_2$ for each value of x, indicating that the graphs of y_1 and y_2 are the same line. Similarly, the right-hand figure shows a numerical solution for Example 5(b), where

$$y_1 = (6 - 3x)/3 \quad \text{and} \quad y_2 = 1 - x.$$

Note that $y_1 \neq y_2$ and the difference $y_1 - y_2$ is 1 for every value of x, indicating that the graphs of y_1 and y_2 are parallel lines that do not intersect.

X	Y₁	Y₂
0	-2	-2
1	-1.5	-1.5
2	-1	-1
3	-.5	-.5
4	0	0
5	.5	.5
6	1	1

Y₁ ■ (4−X)/(−2)

X	Y₁	Y₂
-1	3	2
0	2	1
1	1	0
2	0	-1
3	-1	-2
4	-2	-3
5	-3	-4

Y₁ ■ (6−3X)/3

Applications

▶ **REAL-WORLD CONNECTION** In the next two examples we use elimination to solve applications relating to new cancer cases and to burning calories during exercise.

EXAMPLE 6

Determining new cancer cases

In 2010, there were 1,530,000 new cancer cases. Men accounted for 50,000 more new cases than women. How many new cases of cancer were there for each gender? (*Source:* American Cancer Society.)

Solution

STEP 1: *Identify each variable.*

x: new cancer cases for men in 2010
y: new cancer cases for women in 2010

STEP 2: *Write a system of equations.*

$$x + y = 1{,}530{,}000 \quad \text{New cases totaled 1,530,000.}$$
$$x - y = 50{,}000 \quad \text{Men had 50,000 more cases than women.}$$

STEP 3A: *Solve the system of linear equations.* Add the two equations to eliminate the y-variable.

$$
\begin{aligned}
x + y &= 1{,}530{,}000 \\
\underline{x - y} &= \underline{50{,}000} \\
2x &= 1{,}580{,}000, \quad \text{or} \quad x = 790{,}000
\end{aligned}
$$

Substituting 790,000 for x in the first equation results in $790{,}000 + y = 1{,}530{,}000$ or $y = 740{,}000$. The solution is $x = 790{,}000$ and $y = 740{,}000$.

STEP 3B: *Determine the solution to the problem.* There were 790,000 new cases of cancer for men and 740,000 new cases for women in 2010.

STEP 4: *Check the solution.* The total number of cases was

$$790{,}000 + 740{,}000 = 1{,}530{,}000.$$

The number of new cases for men exceeded the number of new cases for women by

$$790{,}000 - 740{,}000 = 50{,}000.$$

The answer checks.

▌ Now Try Exercise 57

EXAMPLE 7   **Burning calories during exercise**

During strenuous exercise, an athlete can burn 10 calories per minute on a rowing machine and 11.5 calories per minute on a stair climber. If an athlete uses both machines and burns 433 calories in a 40-minute workout, how many minutes does the athlete spend on each machine? (*Source: Runner's World.*)

Solution

STEP 1: *Identify each variable.*

x: number of minutes on a rowing machine
y: number of minutes on a stair climber

STEP 2: *Write a system of equations.* The total workout takes 40 minutes, so $x + y = 40$. The athlete burns $10x$ calories on the rowing machine and $11.5y$ calories on the stair climber. Because the total number of calories equals 433, it follows that $10x + 11.5y = 433$.

$$x + \quad y = \quad 40 \qquad \text{Workout is 40 minutes.}$$
$$10x + 11.5y = 433 \qquad \text{Total calories is 433.}$$

STEP 3A: *Solve the system of linear equations.* Multiply the first equation by -10 and add the two equations.

$$-10x - \quad 10y = -400 \qquad \text{Multiply by } -10.$$
$$\underline{10x + 11.5y = \quad 433} \qquad \text{Second equation}$$
$$1.5y = \quad 33, \quad \text{or} \quad y = \frac{33}{1.5} = 22 \quad \text{Add and solve for } y.$$

Because $x + y = 40$ and $y = 22$, it follows that $x = 18$.

STEP 3B: *Determine the solution to the problem.* The athlete spends 18 minutes on the rowing machine and 22 minutes on the stair climber.

STEP 4: *Check your answer.* Because $18 + 22 = 40$, the athlete works out for 40 minutes. Also, the athlete burns $10(18) + 11.5(22) = 433$ calories. The answer checks.

Now Try Exercise 59

4.3   Putting It All Together

CONCEPT	EXPLANATION	EXAMPLE
Elimination Method	Is based on the addition property of equality If $a = b$ and $c = d$, then $$a + c = b + d.$$ May be used to solve systems of equations	$x + y = \quad 5$ $\underline{x - y = -1}$ $2x \quad = \quad 4, \quad \text{or} \quad x = 2 \quad \text{Add.}$ Because $x + y = 5$ and $x = 2$, it follows that $y = 3$. The solution is $(2, 3)$.
Other Types of Systems	Elimination can be used to recognize systems having **1.** no solutions **2.** infinitely many solutions.	**1.** $\quad -x - y = -4$ $\quad \underline{x + y = \quad 2}$ $\quad 0 = -2 \quad \text{Add.}$ Because $0 = -2$ is always false, there are no solutions.

CONCEPT	EXPLANATION	EXAMPLE
Other Types of Systems (continued)		**2.** $\begin{aligned} x + y &= 4 \\ 2x + 2y &= 8 \end{aligned}$ Multiply the first equation by -2. $\begin{aligned} -2x - 2y &= -8 \\ \underline{2x + 2y} &= \underline{8} \\ 0 &= 0 \quad \text{Add.} \end{aligned}$ Because $0 = 0$ is always true, there are infinitely many solutions.

4.3 Exercises

MyMathLab | Math XL PRACTICE | WATCH | DOWNLOAD | READ | REVIEW

CONCEPTS AND VOCABULARY

1. Name two symbolic methods for solving a system of linear equations.

2. The elimination method is based on the _____ property of equality.

3. The addition property of equality states that if $a = b$ and $c = d$, then $a + c$ _____ $b + d$.

4. The multiplication property of equality states that if $a = b$, then ca _____ cb.

5. Suppose that the elimination method results in the equation $0 = 0$. What does this indicate about the number of solutions to the system of equations?

6. Suppose that the elimination method results in the equation $0 = 1$. What does this indicate about the number of solutions to the system of equations?

USING ELIMINATION

Exercises 7–14: If possible, use the given graph to solve the system of equations. Then use the elimination method to verify your answer.

7. $\begin{aligned} x - y &= 0 \\ x + y &= 2 \end{aligned}$

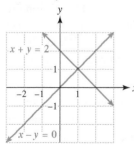

8. $\begin{aligned} x + y &= 6 \\ 2x - y &= 3 \end{aligned}$

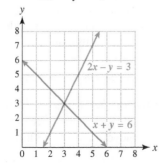

9. $\begin{aligned} 2x + 3y &= -1 \\ 2x - 3y &= -7 \end{aligned}$

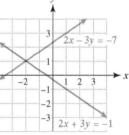

10. $\begin{aligned} -2x + y &= -3 \\ 4x - 3y &= 7 \end{aligned}$

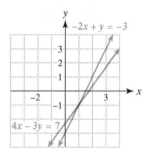

11. $\begin{aligned} x + y &= 3 \\ x + y &= -1 \end{aligned}$

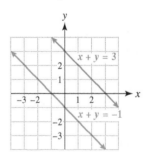

12. $\begin{aligned} 2x - y &= 4 \\ -2x + y &= -4 \end{aligned}$

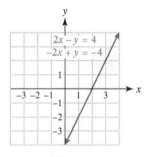

13. $\begin{aligned} 2x + 2y &= 6 \\ x + y &= 3 \end{aligned}$

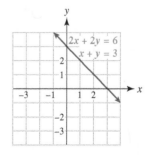

14. $\begin{aligned} -x + 3y &= 4 \\ x - 3y &= 3 \end{aligned}$

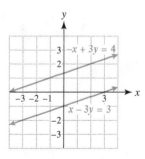

Exercises 15–36: Use the elimination method to solve the system of equations.

15. $x + y = 7$
$x - y = 5$

16. $x - y = 8$
$x + y = 4$

17. $-x + y = 5$
$x + y = 3$

18. $x - y = 10$
$-x - y = 20$

19. $2x + y = 8$
$3x - y = 2$

20. $-x + 2y = 3$
$x + 6y = 5$

21. $-2x + y = -3$
$2x - 4y = 0$

22. $2x + 6y = -5$
$7x - 6y = -4$

23. $\frac{1}{2}x - y = 3$
$\frac{3}{2}x + y = 5$

24. $x - \frac{1}{4}y = 4$
$-4x + \frac{1}{4}y = -9$

25. $a + 6b = 2$
$a + 3b = -1$

26. $3r - t = 7$
$2r - t = 2$

27. $5a - 6b = -2$
$5a + 5b = 9$

28. $-r + 2t = 0$
$3r + 2t = 8$

29. $3u + 2v = -16$
$2u + v = -9$

30. $5u - v = 0$
$3u + 3v = -18$

31. $5x - 7y = 5$
$-2x + 2y = -2$

32. $2x + 7y = 6$
$4x - 3y = -22$

33. $5x - 3y = 4$
$3x + 2y = 10$

34. $-3x - 8y = 1$
$2x + 5y = 0$

35. $-5x - 10y = -22$
$10x + 15y = 35$

36. $-15x + 4y = -20$
$5x + 7y = 90$

Exercises 37–40: A table of values is given for two linear equations. Use the table to solve this system.

37.

x	0	1	2	3	4
$y = -x + 5$	5	4	3	2	1
$y = 2x - 4$	-4	-2	0	2	4

38.

x	-3	-2	-1	0	1
$y = x + 1$	-2	-1	0	1	2
$y = -x - 3$	0	-1	-2	-3	-4

39.

x	-2	-1	0	1	2
$y = 3x + 1$	-5	-2	1	4	7
$y = -x + 1$	3	2	1	0	-1

40.

x	-2	-1	0	1	2
$y = 2x$	-4	-2	0	2	4
$y = -x$	2	1	0	-1	-2

USING MORE THAN ONE METHOD

Exercises 41–46: Solve the system of equations

(a) *symbolically,*
(b) *graphically, and*
(c) *numerically.*

41. $2x + y = 5$
$x - y = 1$

42. $-x + y = 2$
$3x + y = -2$

43. $2x + y = 5$
$x + y = 1$

44. $-x + y = 2$
$3x - y = -2$

45. $6x + 3y = 6$
$-2x + 2y = -2$

46. $-x + 2y = 5$
$2x + 2y = 8$

ELIMINATION AND OTHER TYPES OF SYSTEMS

Exercises 47–56: Use elimination to determine whether the system of equations has no solutions, one solution, or infinitely many solutions. Then graph the system.

47. $2x - 2y = 4$
$-x + y = -2$

48. $-2x + y = 4$
$4x - 2y = -8$

49. $x - y = 0$
$x + y = 0$

50. $x - y = 2$
$x + y = 2$

51. $x - y = 4$
$x - y = 1$

52. $-2x + 3y = 5$
$4x - 6y = 10$

53. $x - 3y = 2$
$-x + 3y = 4$

54. $6x + 9y = 18$
$4x + 6y = 12$

55. $4x - 8y = 24$
$6x - 12y = 36$

56. $x - y = 5$
$2x - y = 4$

APPLICATIONS

57. *Skin Cancer* In 2010, there were 68,000 new cases of skin cancer in the United States. Men represented 10,000 more cases than women. How many new cases of skin cancer were there for men and for women? (*Source:* American Cancer Society.)

58. *Millionaires* In 2009, there were 84,000 millionaires in Kentucky and Rhode Island. If there were 42,000 more millionaires in Kentucky than in Rhode Island, find the number of millionaires in each state that year. (*Source:* Internal Revenue Service.)

59. *Burning Calories* During strenuous exercise an athlete can burn 9 calories per minute on a stationary bicycle and 11.5 calories per minute on a stair climber.

In a 30-minute workout an athlete burns 300 calories. How many minutes does the athlete spend on each type of exercise equipment? (*Source: Runner's World.*)

60. *Distance Running* An athlete runs at 9 mph and then at 12 mph, covering 10 miles in 1 hour. How long does the athlete run at each speed?

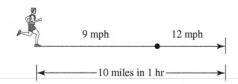

61. *River Current* A riverboat takes 8 hours to travel 64 miles downstream and 16 hours for the return trip. What is the speed of the current and the speed of the riverboat in still water?

62. *Airplane Speed* An airplane travels 3000 miles with the wind in 5 hours and takes 6 hours for the return trip into the wind. What is the speed of the wind and the speed of the airplane without any wind?

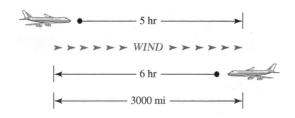

63. *Investments* A total of $5000 is invested at 3% and 5% annual interest. After 1 year the total interest equals $210. How much money is invested at each interest rate?

64. *Mixing Antifreeze* A car radiator holds 2 gallons of fluid and initially is empty. If a mixture of water and antifreeze contains 70% antifreeze and another mixture contains 15% antifreeze, how much of each should be combined to fill the radiator with a 50% antifreeze mixture?

65. *Number Problem* The sum of two integers is −17, and their difference is −69. Find the two integers.

66. *Supplementary Angles* The measures of two supplementary angles differ by 74°. Find the two angles.

67. *Picture Dimensions* The figure at the top of the next column shows a red graph that gives possible dimensions for a rectangular picture frame with perimeter 120 inches. The blue graph shows possible dimensions for a rectangular frame whose length L is twice its width W.

Picture Dimensions

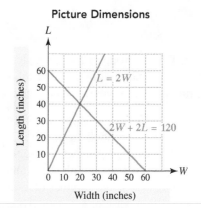

Width (inches)

(a) Use the figure to determine the dimensions of a frame with a perimeter of 120 inches and a length that is twice the width.

(b) Solve this problem symbolically.

68. *Sales of DVDs and CDs* A company sells DVDs d and CDs c. The figure shows a red graph of $d + c = 2000$. The blue graph shows a revenue of $15,000 received from selling d DVDs at $12 each and c CDs at $6 each.

Digital Media

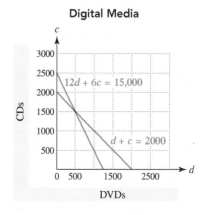

DVDs

(a) If the total number of DVDs and CDs sold is 2000, determine how many of each were sold to obtain a revenue of $15,000.

(b) Solve this problem symbolically.

WRITING ABOUT MATHEMATICS

69. Suppose that a system of linear equations is solved symbolically, numerically, and graphically. How do the solutions from each method compare? Explain your answer.

70. When you are solving a system of linear equations by elimination, how can you recognize that the system has no solutions?

Group Activity   Working with Real Data

Directions: Form a group of 2 to 4 people. Select someone to record the group's responses for this activity. All members of the group should work cooperatively to answer the questions. If your instructor asks for your results, each member of the group should be prepared to respond.

Exercises 1–4: *Facebook Apps* In early 2011, the two most popular Facebook Apps were CityVille and FarmVille. The average number of users for the two apps was 74.5 million per month. The number of users of CityVille exceeded the number of users of Farm-Ville by 45 million per month. (*Source:* allfacebook.com)

1. Set up a system of equations whose solution gives the monthly number of users in millions for each app. Identify what each variable represents.

2. Use substitution to solve this system. Interpret the result.

3. Use elimination to solve this system.

4. Solve this system graphically. Do all your answers agree?

CHAPTER 4   Summary

SECTION 4.1 ■ SOLVING SYSTEMS OF LINEAR EQUATIONS GRAPHICALLY AND NUMERICALLY

System of Linear Equations

Solution	An ordered pair (x, y) that satisfies *both* equations
Solution Set	The set of all solutions
Graphical Solution	Graph each equation. A point of intersection is a solution. (Sometimes determining the exact answer when estimating from a graph may be difficult.)
Numerical Solution	Solve each equation for y and make a table for each equation. A solution occurs when two y-values are equal for a given x-value.

Example: The ordered pair $(3, 1)$ is the solution to the following system.

$$x + y = 4 \qquad 3 + 1 = 4 \text{ is a true statement.}$$
$$x - y = 2 \qquad 3 - 1 = 2 \text{ is a true statement.}$$

A Graphical Solution
The point of intersection, $(3, 1)$, is the solution to the system of equations.

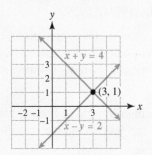

A Numerical Solution
The ordered pair $(3, 1)$ is the solution. When $x = 3$, both y-values equal 1.

x	1	2	3	3
$y = 4 - x$	3	2	1	0
$y = x - 2$	−1	0	1	2

Types of Systems of Linear Equations   A system of linear equations can have no solutions, one solution, or infinitely many solutions.

No Solutions	One Solution	Infinitely Many Solutions
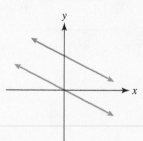	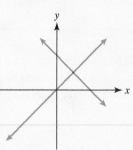	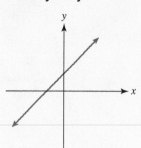
Inconsistent System	Consistent System Independent Equations	Consistent System Dependent Equations

SECTION 4.2 ■ SOLVING SYSTEMS OF LINEAR EQUATIONS BY SUBSTITUTION

Method of Substitution   This method can be used to solve a system of equations symbolically and always gives the exact solution, provided one exists.

Example: $-2x + y = -3$
$x + y = 3$

STEP 1: Solve one of the equations for a convenient variable.

$$x + y = 3 \quad \text{becomes} \quad y = 3 - x.$$

STEP 2: Substitute this result in the other equation and then solve.

$$-2x + (3 - x) = -3 \quad \text{Substitute } (3 - x) \text{ for } y.$$
$$-3x = -6 \quad \text{Combine like terms; subtract 3.}$$
$$x = 2 \quad \text{Divide each side by } -3.$$

STEP 3: Find the value of the other variable. Because $y = 3 - x$ and $x = 2$, it follows that $y = 3 - 2 = 1$.

STEP 4: Check to determine that $(2, 1)$ is the solution.

$$-2(2) + (1) \stackrel{?}{=} -3 \checkmark \quad \text{A true statement}$$
$$2 + 1 \stackrel{?}{=} 3 \checkmark \quad \text{A true statement}$$

The solution $(2, 1)$ checks.

Recognizing Types of Systems

No solutions	The final equation is always false, such as $0 = 1$.
One solution	The final equation has one solution, such as $x = 1$.
Infinitely many solutions	The final equation is always true, such as $0 = 0$.

SECTION 4.3 ■ SOLVING SYSTEMS OF LINEAR EQUATIONS BY ELIMINATION

Method of Elimination   This method can be used to solve a system of linear equations symbolically and always gives the exact solution, provided one exists.

Example: $x + 3y = 1$
$\underline{-x + y = 3}$
$4y = 4, \quad \text{or} \quad y = 1 \quad \text{Add and solve for } y.$

Substitute $y = 1$ in either of the given equations: $x + 3(1) = 1$ implies that $x = -2$, so $(-2, 1)$ is the solution.

NOTE: To eliminate a variable, it may be necessary to multiply one or both equations by a constant before adding.

Recognizing Types of Systems

No solutions	The final equation is always false, such as $0 = 1$.
One solution	The final equation has one solution, such as $x = 1$.
Infinitely many solutions	The final equation is always true, such as $0 = 0$.

CHAPTER 4   Review Exercises

SECTION 4.1

Exercises 1 and 2: Determine graphically the x-value for the equation when $y = 3$.

1. $y = 2x - 3$

2. $y = \frac{3}{2}x$

Exercises 3–6: The graphs of two equations are shown.

(a) *State the number of solutions to the system of equations.*

(b) *Is the system consistent or inconsistent? If the system is consistent, state whether the equations are dependent or independent.*

3.
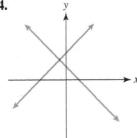

4.
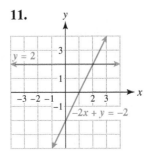

5.
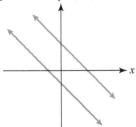

6.
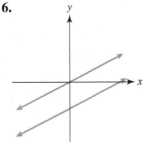

Exercises 7–10: Determine which ordered pair is a solution to the system of equations.

7. $(0, 1), (1, 2)$
$$x + 2y = 5$$
$$x - y = -1$$

8. $(5, 2), (4, 0)$
$$2x - y = 8$$
$$x + 3y = 11$$

9. $(2, 2), (4, 3)$
$$\tfrac{1}{2}x = y - 1$$
$$2x = 3y - 1$$

10. $(2, -4), (-1, 2)$
$$5x - 2y = 18$$
$$y = -2x$$

Exercises 11 and 12: The graphs for two equations are shown. Use the intersection-of-graphs method to identify the solution to both equations. Then check your result.

11.
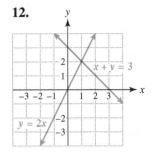

12.

Exercises 13 and 14: A table for two equations is given. Identify the solution to both equations.

13.

x	1	2	3	4
$y = 3x$	3	6	9	12
$y = 6$	6	6	6	6

14.

x	-1	0	1	2
$y = 2x - 1$	-3	-1	1	3
$y = 2 - x$	3	2	1	0

Exercises 15–20: Solve the system of linear equations graphically.

15. $\begin{aligned} y &= -3 \\ x + y &= 1 \end{aligned}$

16. $\begin{aligned} x &= 1 \\ x - y &= -1 \end{aligned}$

17. $\begin{aligned} 2x + y &= 3 \\ -x + y &= 0 \end{aligned}$

18. $\begin{aligned} y &= 2x \\ 2x + y &= 4 \end{aligned}$

19. $\begin{aligned} x + 2y &= 3 \\ 2x + y &= 3 \end{aligned}$

20. $\begin{aligned} -3x - y &= 7 \\ 2x + 3y &= -7 \end{aligned}$

SECTION 4.2

Exercises 21–28: Use the method of substitution to solve the system of linear equations. These systems may have no solutions, one solution, or infinitely many solutions.

21. $\begin{aligned} x + y &= 8 \\ y &= 3x \end{aligned}$

22. $\begin{aligned} x - 2y &= 22 \\ y &= -5x \end{aligned}$

23. $\begin{aligned} x + 3y &= 1 \\ -2x + 2y &= 6 \end{aligned}$

24. $\begin{aligned} 3x - 2y &= -4 \\ 2x - y &= -4 \end{aligned}$

25. $\begin{aligned} x + y &= 2 \\ y &= -x \end{aligned}$

26. $\begin{aligned} x + y &= -2 \\ x + y &= 3 \end{aligned}$

27. $\begin{aligned} -x + 2y &= 2 \\ x - 2y &= -2 \end{aligned}$

28. $\begin{aligned} -x - y &= -2 \\ 2x - y &= 1 \end{aligned}$

SECTION 4.3

Exercises 29 and 30: Use the graph to solve the system of equations. Then use the elimination method to verify your answer.

29. $\begin{aligned} x + y &= 3 \\ x - y &= 1 \end{aligned}$

30. $\begin{aligned} 2x + 3y &= 4 \\ x - 2y &= -5 \end{aligned}$

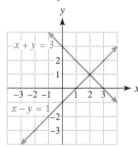

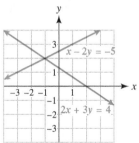

Exercises 31–38: Use the elimination method to solve the system of equations.

31. $\begin{aligned} x + y &= 10 \\ x - y &= 12 \end{aligned}$

32. $\begin{aligned} 2x - y &= 2 \\ 3x + y &= 3 \end{aligned}$

33. $\begin{aligned} -2x + 2y &= -1 \\ x - 3y &= -3 \end{aligned}$

34. $\begin{aligned} 2x - 5y &= 0 \\ 2x + 4y &= 9 \end{aligned}$

35. $\begin{aligned} 2a + b &= 3 \\ -3a - 2b &= -1 \end{aligned}$

36. $\begin{aligned} a - 3b &= 2 \\ 3a + b &= 26 \end{aligned}$

37. $\begin{aligned} 5r + 3t &= -1 \\ -2r - 5t &= -11 \end{aligned}$

38. $\begin{aligned} 5r + 2t &= 5 \\ 3r - 7t &= 3 \end{aligned}$

*Exercises 39 and 40: Solve the system of equations (**a**) symbolically, (**b**) graphically, and (**c**) numerically.*

39. $\begin{aligned} 3x + y &= 6 \\ x - y &= -2 \end{aligned}$

40. $\begin{aligned} 2x + y &= 3 \\ -x + 2y &= -4 \end{aligned}$

Exercises 41–44: Use elimination to determine whether the system of equations has no solutions, one solution, or infinitely many solutions.

41. $\begin{aligned} x - y &= 5 \\ -x + y &= -5 \end{aligned}$

42. $\begin{aligned} 3x - 3y &= 0 \\ -x + y &= 0 \end{aligned}$

43. $\begin{aligned} -2x + y &= 3 \\ 2x - y &= 3 \end{aligned}$

44. $\begin{aligned} -2x + y &= 2 \\ 3x - y &= 3 \end{aligned}$

APPLICATIONS

67. *Traffic Fatalities* The number of traffic fatalities increased by 12 times from 1912 to 2008. There were 34,100 more deaths in 2008 than in 1912. Find the number of traffic fatalities in each of the two years. Note that the number of vehicles on the road increased from 1 million to 255 million between 1912 and 2008. (*Source:* Department of Health and Human Services.)

68. *Lymphoma* In 2010, 74,000 new cases of lymphoma were reported. There were 6000 more new cases for men than for women. How many new cases of lymphoma were there for men and for women? (*Source:* American Cancer Society.)

69. *Renting a Car* A rental car costs $40 plus $0.20 per mile that it is driven.
   (a) Write an equation that gives the cost C of driving the car x miles.
   (b) Use the intersection-of-graphs method to determine the number of miles that the car is driven if the rental cost is $90.
   (c) Solve part (b) numerically with a table of values.

70. *Supplementary Angles* The smaller of two supplementary angles is 30° less than the measure of the larger angle. Find each angle.

71. *Triangle* In an isosceles triangle, the measures of the two smaller angles are equal and their sum is 40° more than the larger angle.
   (a) Let x be the measure of each of the two smaller angles and y be the measure of the larger angle. Write a system of linear equations whose solution gives the measures of these angles.
   (b) Use the method of substitution to solve the system.
   (c) Use the method of elimination to solve the system.

72. *Garden Dimensions* A rectangular garden has 88 feet of fencing around it. The garden is 4 feet longer than it is wide. Find the dimensions of the garden.

73. *Room Prices* Ten rooms are rented at rates of $80 and $120 per night. The total collected for the 10 rooms is $920.
   (a) Write a system of linear equations whose solution gives the number of each type of room rented. Be sure to state what each variable represents.
   (b) Solve the system of equations.

74. *Mixture Problem* One type of candy sells for $2 per pound, and another type sells for $3 per pound. An order for 18 pounds of candy costs $47. How much of each type of candy was bought?

75. *Burning Calories* An athlete burns 9 calories per minute on a stationary bicycle and 11 calories per minute on a stair climber. In a 60-minute workout the athlete burns 590 calories. How many minutes does the athlete spend on each type of exercise equipment?
(*Source: Runner's World.*)

76. *River Current* A riverboat travels 140 miles downstream in 10 hours, and the return trip takes 14 hours. What is the speed of the current?

77. *Garage Dimensions* The blue graph shown in the figure gives possible dimensions for a rectangular garage with perimeter 80 feet. The red graph shows possible dimensions for a garage that has width W two-thirds of its length L.

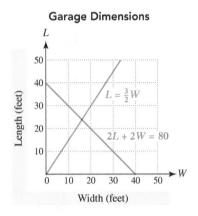

Garage Dimensions

   (a) Use the graph to estimate the dimensions of a garage with perimeter 80 feet and width two-thirds its length.
   (b) Solve this problem symbolically.

78. *Wheels and Trailers* A business manufactures at least two wheels for each trailer it makes. The total number of trailers and wheels manufactured cannot exceed 30 per week. Shade the region that represents numbers of wheels W and trailers T that can be produced each week within these restrictions. Label the horizontal axis W and the vertical axis T.

79. *Target Heart Rate* A target heart rate T that is 70% of a person's maximum heart rate is approximated by $T = 150 - 0.7A$, where A is a person's age.
   (a) What is T for a person 20 years old? 60 years old?
   (b) Sketch a graph of $T \geq 150 - 0.7A$. Assume that A is between 20 and 60.
   (c) Interpret this graph.

CHAPTER 4   Extended and Discovery Exercises

Exercises 1–4: Plant Growth The following figure illustrates the relationships among forests, grasslands, and deserts, suggested by annual temperature T in degrees Fahrenheit and precipitation P in inches.

Climate and Vegetation

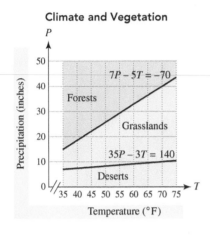

1. The equation of the line that separates grasslands and forests is

$$7P - 5T = -70.$$

   Write an inequality that describes temperatures and amounts of precipitation that correspond to forested regions. (Include the line.)

2. The equation of the line that separates grasslands and deserts is

$$35P - 3T = 140.$$

   Write an inequality that describes temperatures and amounts of precipitation that correspond to desert regions. (Include the line.)

3. Using the information from Exercises 1 and 2, write a system of inequalities that describes temperatures and amounts of precipitation that correspond to grassland regions.

4. Cheyenne, Wyoming, has an average annual temperature of about 50°F and an average annual precipitation of about 14 inches. Use the graph to predict the type of plant growth you might expect near Cheyenne. Then check to determine whether $T = 50$ and $P = 14$ satisfy the proper inequalities.

Exercises 5–8: Numerical Solutions If a solution to a linear equation does not appear in a table of values, can you still find it? Use only the table to solve the equation. Then explain how you got your answer.

5. $2x + 1 = 0$

x	-2	-1	0	1	2
$y = 2x + 1$	-3	-1	1	3	5

6. $4x + 3 = 5$

x	-2	-1	0	1	2
$y = 4x + 3$	-5	-1	3	7	11

7. $\frac{1}{2}x + 3 = 3.75$

x	-2	-1	0	1	2
$y = \frac{1}{2}x + 3$	2	2.5	3	3.5	4

8. $3x - 1 = 0$

x	-2	-1	0	1	2
$y = 3x - 1$	-7	-4	-1	2	5

5 Polynomials and Exponents

5.1 Rules for Exponents
5.2 Addition and Subtraction of Polynomials
5.3 Multiplication of Polynomials
5.5 Integer Exponents and the Quotient Rule
5.6 Division of Polynomials

If you want to do something, do it!

—PLAUTUS

D igital images were first sent between New York and London by cable in the early 1920s. Unfortunately, the transmission time was 3 hours and the quality was poor. Digital photography was developed further by NASA in the 1960s because ordinary pictures were subject to interference when transmitted through space. Today, digital pictures remain crystal clear even if they travel millions of miles. The following digital picture shows the planet Mars.

Whether they are taken with a webcam, with a smartphone, or by the Mars rover, digital images comprise tiny units called pixels, which are represented by numbers. As a result, mathematics plays an important role in digital images. In this chapter we illustrate some of the ways mathematics is used to describe digital pictures. We also discuss how mathematics is used to model things such as heart rate, computer sales, motion of the planets, and interest on money.

Source: NASA.

5.1 Rules for Exponents

Review of Bases and Exponents • Zero Exponents • The Product Rule • Power Rules

A LOOK INTO MATH ▶

Electronic devices such as tablet computers and smartphones store information as *bits*. A bit is either a 0 or a 1, and a string of 8 bits is called a *byte*. In the 1970s, IBM developed punch cards made out of paper that could hold up to 120 bits of information. Today, many computer hard drives can hold more than 1 terabyte of information; that's more than 8,000,000,000,000 bits! In mathematics, we often use *exponents* to express such large numbers. In this section, we discuss the rules for exponents.

Review of Bases and Exponents

The expression 5^3 is an exponential expression with *base 5* and *exponent 3*. Its value is

$$5 \cdot 5 \cdot 5 = 125.$$

In general, b^n is an exponential expression with base b and exponent n. If n is a natural number, it indicates the number of times the base b is to be multiplied with itself.

$$\text{Exponent} \longrightarrow \quad b^n = \underbrace{b \cdot b \cdot b \cdot \cdots \cdot b}_{n \text{ times}}$$
$$\text{Base} \longrightarrow$$

When evaluating expressions, evaluate exponents *before* performing addition, subtraction, multiplication, division, or negation.

STUDY TIP

Exponents occur throughout mathematics. Because exponents are so important, this section is essential for your success in mathematics. It takes practice, so set aside some extra time.

EVALUATING EXPRESSIONS

When evaluating expressions, use the following order of operations.

1. Evaluate exponents.
2. Perform negation.
3. Do multiplication and division from left to right.
4. Do addition and subtraction from left to right.

EXAMPLE 1 **Evaluating exponential expressions**

Evaluate each expression.

(a) $1 + \dfrac{2^4}{4}$ **(b)** $3\left(\dfrac{1}{3}\right)^2$ **(c)** -2^4 **(d)** $(-2)^4$

Solution
(a) Evaluate the exponent first.

$$1 + \frac{2^4}{4} = 1 + \frac{\overbrace{2 \cdot 2 \cdot 2 \cdot 2}^{4 \text{ factors}}}{4} = 1 + \frac{16}{4} = 1 + 4 = 5$$

(b) $3\left(\dfrac{1}{3}\right)^2 = 3\left(\overbrace{\dfrac{1}{3} \cdot \dfrac{1}{3}}^{2 \text{ factors}}\right) = 3 \cdot \dfrac{1}{9} = \dfrac{3}{9} = \dfrac{1}{3}$

(c) Because exponents are evaluated before negation is performed,

$$-2^4 = -\overbrace{(2 \cdot 2 \cdot 2 \cdot 2)}^{\text{4 factors}} = -16.$$

(d) $(-2)^4 = \overbrace{(-2)(-2)(-2)(-2)}^{\text{4 factors}} = 16$

Now Try Exercises 9, 11, 15, 17

NOTE: Parts (c) and (d) of Example 1 appear to be very similar. However, the negation sign is inside the parentheses in part (d), which means that the base for the exponential expression is -2. In part (c), no parentheses are used, indicating that the base of the exponential expression is 2.

READING CHECK

- Explain how to tell the difference between a negative number raised to a power and the opposite of a positive number raised to a power.

TECHNOLOGY NOTE

Evaluating Exponents
Exponents can often be evaluated on calculators by using the ^ key. The four expressions from Example 1 are evaluated with a calculator and the results are shown in the following two figures. When evaluating the last two expressions on your calculator, remember to use the negation key rather than the subtraction key.

CALCULATOR HELP

To evaluate exponents, see Appendix A (page AP-1).

```
1+2^4/4
              5
3(1/3)²▶Frac
            1/3
```

```
-2^4
            -16
(-2)^4
             16
```

Zero Exponents

So far we have discussed natural number exponents. What if an exponent is 0? What does 2^0 equal? To answer these questions, consider Table 5.1, which shows values for decreasing powers of 2. Note that each time the power of 2 decreases by 1, the resulting value is divided by 2. For this pattern to continue, we need to define 2^0 to be 1 because dividing 2 by 2 results in 1.

This discussion suggests that $2^0 = 1$, and is generalized as follows.

TABLE 5.1 Powers of 2

Power of 2	Value
2^3	8
2^2	4
2^1	2
2^0	?

ZERO EXPONENT

For any nonzero real number b,

$$b^0 = 1.$$

The expression 0^0 is undefined.

EXAMPLE 2 **Evaluating zero exponents**

Evaluate each expression. Assume that all variables represent nonzero numbers.

(a) 7^0 **(b)** $3\left(\dfrac{4}{9}\right)^0$ **(c)** $\left(\dfrac{x^2 y^5}{3z}\right)^0$

Solution

(a) $7^0 = 1$

(b) $3\left(\dfrac{4}{9}\right)^0 = 3(1) = 3$. (Note that the exponent 0 does not apply to 3.)

(c) All variables are nonzero, so the expression inside the parentheses is also nonzero.
Thus $\left(\dfrac{x^2 y^5}{3z}\right)^0 = 1$.

▍ Now Try Exercises **13, 41, 67**

The Product Rule

We can use a special rule to calculate products of exponential expressions *provided their bases are the same.* For example,

$$4^3 \cdot 4^2 = \underbrace{(4 \cdot 4 \cdot 4) \cdot (4 \cdot 4)}_{\text{5 factors}} = 4^5.$$

The expression $4^3 \cdot 4^2$ has $3 + 2 = 5$ factors of 4, so the result is $4^{3+2} = 4^5$. To multiply exponential expressions with the *same base*, add exponents and keep the base.

READING CHECK

• State the product rule in your own words.

THE PRODUCT RULE

For any real number a and natural numbers m and n,

$$a^m \cdot a^n = a^{m+n}.$$

NOTE: The product $2^4 \cdot 3^5$ cannot be simplified by using the product rule because the exponential expressions have different bases: 2 and 3.

EXAMPLE 3 **Using the product rule**

Multiply and simplify.

(a) $2^3 \cdot 2^2$ **(b)** $x^4 x^5$ **(c)** $2x^2 \cdot 5x^6$ **(d)** $x^3(2x + 3x^2)$

Solution

(a) $2^3 \cdot 2^2 = 2^{3+2} = 2^5 = 32$

(b) $x^4 x^5 = x^{4+5} = x^9$

(c) Begin by applying the commutative property of multiplication to write the product in a more convenient order.

$$2x^2 \cdot 5x^6 = 2 \cdot 5 \cdot x^2 \cdot x^6 = 10x^{2+6} = 10x^8$$

(d) To simplify this expression, first apply the distributive property.

$$x^3(2x + 3x^2) = x^3 \cdot 2x + x^3 \cdot 3x^2 = 2x^4 + 3x^5$$

$\overset{3+1}{\frown} \qquad \overset{3+2}{\frown}$

└─ Exponent is 1.

▍ Now Try Exercises **21, 23, 27, 71**

NOTE: If an exponent does not appear in an expression, it is assumed to be 1. For example, x can be written as x^1 and $(x + y)$ can be written as $(x + y)^1$.

EXAMPLE 4   **Applying the product rule**

Multiply and simplify.
(a) $x \cdot x^3$ (b) $(a + b)(a + b)^4$

Solution
(a) Begin by writing x as x^1. Then $x^1 \cdot x^3 = x^{1+3} = x^4$.
(b) First write $(a + b)$ as $(a + b)^1$. Then

$$(a + b)^1 \cdot (a + b)^4 = (a + b)^{1+4} = (a + b)^5.$$

Now Try Exercises 19, 63

Power Rules

How should $(4^3)^2$ be evaluated? To answer this question, consider how the product rule can be used in evaluating

$$(4^3)^2 = \underbrace{4^3 \cdot 4^3}_{\text{Product rule}} = 4^{\overset{3+3=3\cdot2}{3+3}} = 4^6.$$

Similarly,

$$(a^5)^3 = \underbrace{a^5 \cdot a^5 \cdot a^5}_{\text{Product rule}} = a^{\overset{5+5+5=5\cdot3}{5+5+5}} = a^{15}.$$

This discussion suggests that to raise a power to a power, we multiply the exponents.

> **RAISING A POWER TO A POWER**
>
> For any real number a and natural numbers m and n,
>
> $$(a^m)^n = a^{mn}.$$

EXAMPLE 5   **Raising a power to a power**

Simplify each expression.
(a) $(3^2)^4$ (b) $(a^3)^2$

Solution
(a) $(3^2)^4 = 3^{2\cdot4} = 3^8$ (b) $(a^3)^2 = a^{3\cdot2} = a^6$

Now Try Exercises 31, 33

To decide how to simplify the expression $(2x)^3$, consider

$$(2x)^3 = \underbrace{2x \cdot 2x \cdot 2x}_{\text{3 factors}} = \underbrace{(2 \cdot 2 \cdot 2)}_{\text{3 factors}} \cdot \underbrace{(x \cdot x \cdot x)}_{\text{3 factors}} = 2^3 x^3.$$

To raise a product to a power, we raise each factor to the power.

READING CHECK

• State the rule for raising a product to a power in your own words.

RAISING A PRODUCT TO A POWER

For any real numbers a and b and natural number n,

$$(ab)^n = a^n b^n.$$

EXAMPLE 6   **Raising a product to a power**

Simplify each expression.
(a) $(3z)^2$ **(b)** $(-2x^2)^3$ **(c)** $4(x^2y^3)^5$ **(d)** $(-2^2a^5)^3$

Solution
(a) $(3z)^2 = 3^2 z^2 = 9z^2$
(b) $(-2x^2)^3 = (-2)^3(x^2)^3 = -8x^6$
(c) $4(x^2y^3)^5 = 4(x^2)^5(y^3)^5 = 4x^{10}y^{15}$
(d) $(-2^2a^5)^3 = (-4a^5)^3 = (-4)^3(a^5)^3 = -64a^{15}$

Now Try Exercises 37, 39, 43, 45

The following equation illustrates another power rule.

$$\left(\frac{2}{3}\right)^4 = \underbrace{\frac{2}{3} \cdot \frac{2}{3} \cdot \frac{2}{3} \cdot \frac{2}{3}}_{4 \text{ factors}} = \frac{2 \cdot 2 \cdot 2 \cdot 2}{3 \cdot 3 \cdot 3 \cdot 3} = \frac{2^4}{3^4}$$

To raise a quotient to a power, raise both the numerator and the denominator to the power.

RAISING A QUOTIENT TO A POWER

For any real numbers a and b and natural number n,

$$\left(\frac{a}{b}\right)^n = \frac{a^n}{b^n}. \quad b \neq 0$$

EXAMPLE 7   **Raising a quotient to a power**

Simplify each expression.

(a) $\left(\dfrac{2}{3}\right)^3$ **(b)** $\left(\dfrac{a}{b}\right)^9$ **(c)** $\left(\dfrac{a+b}{5}\right)^2$

Solution

(a) $\left(\dfrac{2}{3}\right)^3 = \dfrac{2^3}{3^3} = \dfrac{8}{27}$ **(b)** $\left(\dfrac{a}{b}\right)^9 = \dfrac{a^9}{b^9}$

(c) Because the numerator is an expression with more than one term, we must place parentheses around it before raising it to the power 2.

$$\left(\frac{a+b}{5}\right)^2 = \frac{(a+b)^2}{5^2} = \frac{(a+b)^2}{25}$$

Now Try Exercises 51, 53, 55

Raising a Sum or Difference to a Power

Although there are power rules for products and quotients, there are not similar rules for sums and differences. In general, $(a + b)^n \neq a^n + b^n$ and $(a - b)^n \neq a^n - b^n$. For example, $(3 + 4)^2 = 7^2 = 49$ but $3^2 + 4^2 = 9 + 16 = 25$. Similarly, $(4 - 1)^3 = 3^3 = 27$ but $4^3 - 1^3 = 64 - 1 = 63$.

The five rules for exponents discussed in this section are summarized as follows.

RULES FOR EXPONENTS

The following rules hold for real numbers a and b, and natural numbers m and n.

Description	Rule	Example
Zero Exponent	$b^0 = 1$, for $b \neq 0$	$(-13)^0 = 1$
The Product Rule	$a^m \cdot a^n = a^{m+n}$	$5^4 \cdot 5^3 = 5^{4+3} = 5^7$
Power to a Power	$(a^m)^n = a^{m \cdot n}$	$(y^2)^5 = y^{2 \cdot 5} = y^{10}$
Product to a Power	$(ab)^n = a^n b^n$	$(pq)^7 = p^7 q^7$
Quotient to a Power	$\left(\dfrac{a}{b}\right)^n = \dfrac{a^n}{b^n}$, for $b \neq 0$	$\left(\dfrac{x}{y}\right)^3 = \dfrac{x^3}{y^3}$, for $y \neq 0$

Simplification of some expressions may require the application of more than one rule of exponents. This is demonstrated in the next example.

EXAMPLE 8   **Combining rules for exponents**

Simplify each expression.

(a) $(2a)^2(3a)^3$ **(b)** $\left(\dfrac{a^2 b^3}{c}\right)^4$ **(c)** $(2x^3 y)^2(-4x^2 y^3)^3$

Solution

(a) $(2a)^2(3a)^3 = 2^2 a^2 \cdot 3^3 a^3$ Raising a product to a power

$\qquad\qquad\qquad = 4 \cdot 27 \cdot a^2 \cdot a^3$ Evaluate powers; commutative property

$\qquad\qquad\qquad = 108a^5$ Product rule

(b) $\left(\dfrac{a^2 b^3}{c}\right)^4 = \dfrac{(a^2)^4 (b^3)^4}{c^4}$ Raising a quotient to a power; raising a product to a power

$\qquad\qquad\quad = \dfrac{a^8 b^{12}}{c^4}$ Raising a power to a power

(c) $(2x^3 y)^2(-4x^2 y^3)^3 = 2^2 (x^3)^2 y^2 (-4)^3 (x^2)^3 (y^3)^3$ Raising a product to a power

$\qquad\qquad\qquad\qquad = 4x^6 y^2 (-64) x^6 y^9$ Raising a power to a power

$\qquad\qquad\qquad\qquad = 4(-64) x^6 x^6 y^2 y^9$ Commutative property

$\qquad\qquad\qquad\qquad = -256 x^{12} y^{11}$ Product rule

Now Try Exercises 47, 49, 61

▶ **REAL-WORLD CONNECTION** Exponents occur frequently in calculations involving yearly percent increases, such as the increase in property value illustrated in the next example.

EXAMPLE 9 **Calculating growth in property value**

If a parcel of property increases in value by about 11% each year for 20 years, then its value will double three times.
(a) Write an exponential expression that represents "doubling three times."
(b) If the property is initially worth $25,000, how much will it be worth after it doubles 3 times?

Solution
(a) Doubling three times is represented by 2^3.
(b) $2^3(25,000) = 8(25,000) = \$200,000$

■ Now Try Exercise 85

5.1 Putting It All Together

CONCEPT	EXPLANATION	EXAMPLES
Bases and Exponents	In the expression b^n, b is the base and n is the exponent. If n is a natural number, then $$b^n = \underbrace{b \cdot b \cdot \cdots \cdot b.}_{n \text{ times}}$$	2^3 has base 2 and exponent 3. $9^1 = 9$, $3^2 = 3 \cdot 3 = 9$, $4^3 = 4 \cdot 4 \cdot 4 = 64$, and $-6^2 = -(6 \cdot 6) = -36$
Zero Exponents	For any nonzero number b, $b^0 = 1$.	$5^0 = 1$, $x^0 = 1$, and $(xy^3)^0 = 1$
The Product Rule	For any real number a and natural numbers m and n, $$a^m \cdot a^n = a^{m+n}.$$	$2^4 \cdot 2^3 = 2^{4+3} = 2^7$, $x \cdot x^2 \cdot x^6 = x^{1+2+6} = x^9$, and $(x + 1) \cdot (x + 1)^2 = (x + 1)^3$
Raising a Power to a Power	For any real number a and natural numbers m and n, $$(a^m)^n = a^{mn}.$$	$(2^4)^2 = 2^{4 \cdot 2} = 2^8$, $(x^2)^5 = x^{2 \cdot 5} = x^{10}$, and $(a^4)^3 = a^{4 \cdot 3} = a^{12}$
Raising a Product to a Power	For any real numbers a and b and natural number n, $$(ab)^n = a^n b^n.$$	$(3x)^3 = 3^3 x^3 = 27x^3$, $(x^2 y)^4 = (x^2)^4 y^4 = x^8 y^4$, and $(-xy)^6 = (-x)^6 y^6 = x^6 y^6$
Raising a Quotient to a Power	For any real numbers a and b and natural number n, $$\left(\frac{a}{b}\right)^n = \frac{a^n}{b^n}, \quad b \neq 0$$	$\left(\frac{x}{y}\right)^5 = \frac{x^5}{y^5}$ and $\left(\frac{a^2 b}{d^3}\right)^4 = \frac{(a^2)^4 b^4}{(d^3)^4} = \frac{a^8 b^4}{d^{12}}$

5.1 Exercises

CONCEPTS AND VOCABULARY

1. In the expression b^n, b is the _____ and n is the _____.

2. The expression $b^0 =$ _____ for any nonzero number b.

3. $a^m \cdot a^n =$ _____

4. $(a^m)^n =$ _____

5. $(ab)^n =$ _____

6. $\left(\dfrac{a}{b}\right)^n =$ _____

PROPERTIES OF EXPONENTS

Exercises 7–18: Evaluate the expression.

7. 8^2

8. 4^3

9. $(-2)^3$

10. $(-3)^4$

11. -2^3

12. -3^4

13. 6^0

14. $(-0.5)^0$

15. $3 + \dfrac{4^2}{2}$

16. $6 - \left(\dfrac{-4}{2}\right)^2$

17. $4\left(\dfrac{1}{2}\right)^3$

18. $16\left(\dfrac{1}{4}\right)^2$

Exercises 19–74: Simplify the expression. Assume that all variables represent nonzero numbers.

19. $3 \cdot 3^2$

20. $5^3 \cdot 5^3$

21. $4^2 \cdot 4^6$

22. $10^4 \cdot 10^3$

23. $x^3 x^6$

24. $a^5 a^2$

25. $x^2 x^2 x^2$

26. $y^7 y^3 y^0$

27. $4x^2 \cdot 5x^5$

28. $-2y^6 \cdot 5y^2$

29. $3(-xy^3)(x^2 y)$

30. $(a^2 b^3)(-ab^2)$

31. $(2^3)^2$

32. $(10^3)^4$

33. $(n^3)^4$

34. $(z^7)^3$

35. $x(x^3)^2$

36. $(z^3)^2(5z^5)$

37. $(-7b)^2$

38. $(-4z)^3$

39. $(ab)^3$

40. $(xy)^8$

41. $(2x^2)^0$

42. $(3a^2)^4$

43. $(-4b^2)^3$

44. $(-3r^4 t^3)^2$

45. $(x^2 y^3)^7$

46. $(rt^2)^5$

47. $(y^3)^2(x^4 y)^3$

48. $(ab^3)^2(ab)^3$

49. $(a^2 b)^2(a^2 b^2)^3$

50. $(x^3 y)(x^2 y^4)^2$

51. $\left(\dfrac{1}{3}\right)^3$

52. $\left(\dfrac{5}{2}\right)^2$

53. $\left(\dfrac{a}{b}\right)^5$

54. $\left(\dfrac{x}{2}\right)^4$

55. $\left(\dfrac{x-y}{3}\right)^3$

56. $\left(\dfrac{4}{x+y}\right)^2$

57. $\left(\dfrac{5}{a+b}\right)^2$

58. $\left(\dfrac{a-b}{2}\right)^3$

59. $\left(\dfrac{2x}{5}\right)^3$

60. $\left(\dfrac{3y}{2}\right)^4$

61. $\left(\dfrac{3x^2}{5y^4}\right)^3$

62. $\left(\dfrac{a^2 b^3}{3}\right)^5$

63. $(x+y)(x+y)^3$

64. $(a-b)^2(a-b)$

65. $(a+b)^2(a+b)^3$

66. $(x-y)^5(x-y)^4$

67. $6(x^4 y^6)^0$

68. $\left(\dfrac{xy}{z^2}\right)^0$

69. $a(a^2 + 2b^2)$

70. $x^3(3x - 5y^4)$

71. $3a^3(4a^2 + 2b)$

72. $2x^2(5 - 4y^3)$

73. $(r+t)(rt)$

74. $(x-y)(x^2 y^3)$

75. Thinking Generally Students sometimes mistakenly apply the "rule" $a^m \cdot b^n \stackrel{?}{=} (ab)^{m+n}$. In general, this equation is *not true*. Find values for a, b, m, and n with $a \neq b$ and $m \neq n$ that will make this equation true.

76. Thinking Generally Students sometimes mistakenly apply the "rule" $(a+b)^n \stackrel{?}{=} a^n + b^n$. In general, this equation is *not true*. Find values for a, b, and n with $a \neq b$ that will make this equation true.

APPLICATIONS

Exercises 77–80: Write a simplified expression for the area of the given figure.

77.

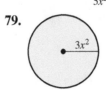

$2x^2$

$5x^2$

78.

$2ab$

$2ab$

79.

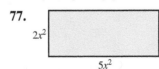

$3x^2$

80.

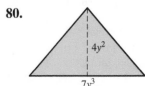

$4y^2$

$7y^3$

Exercises 81 and 82: Write a simplified expression for the volume of the given figure.

81.

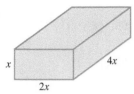

82.

83. *Compound Interest* If P dollars are deposited in an account that pays 5% annual interest, then the amount of money in the account after 3 years is $P(1 + 0.05)^3$. Find the amount when $P = \$1000$.

84. *Compound Interest* If P dollars are deposited in an account that pays 9% annual interest, then the amount of money in the account after 4 years is $P(1 + 0.09)^4$. Find the amount when $P = \$500$.

85. *Investment Growth* If an investment increases in value by about 10% each year for 22 years, then its value will triple two times.

(a) Write an exponential expression that represents "tripling two times."

(b) If the investment has an initial value of $8000, how much will it be worth if it triples two times?

86. *Stock Value* If a stock decreases in value by about 23% each year for 9 years, then its value will be halved three times.

(a) Write an exponential expression that represents "halved three times."

(b) If the stock is initially worth $88 per share, how much will it be worth if it is halved three times?

WRITING ABOUT MATHEMATICS

87. Are the expressions $(4x)^2$ and $4x^2$ equal in value? Explain your answer.

88. Are the expressions $3^3 \cdot 2^3$ and 6^6 equal in value? Explain your answer.

5.2 Addition and Subtraction of Polynomials

Monomials and Polynomials • Addition of Polynomials • Subtraction of Polynomials • Evaluating Polynomial Expressions

A LOOK INTO MATH ▶

If you have ever exercised strenuously and then taken your pulse immediately afterward, you may have discovered that your pulse slowed quickly at first and then gradually leveled off. A typical scatterplot of this phenomenon is shown in Figure 5.1(a). These data points cannot be modeled accurately with a line, so a new expression, called a *polynomial*, is needed to model them. A graph of a polynomial that models these data is shown in Figure 5.1(b) and discussed in Exercise 71. (*Source:* V. Thomas, *Science and Sport.*)

NEW VOCABULARY

☐ Monomial
☐ Degree of a monomial
☐ Coefficient of a monomial
☐ Polynomial
☐ Polynomial in one variable
☐ Binomial
☐ Trinomial
☐ Degree of a polynomial
☐ Like terms

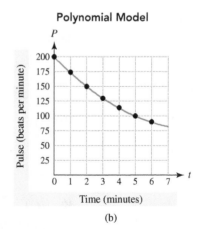

Figure 5.1 Heart Rate After Exercising

Monomials and Polynomials

A **monomial** is a number, a variable, or a product of numbers and variables raised to natural number powers. Examples of monomials include

$$-3, \quad xy^2, \quad 5a^2, \quad -z^3, \quad \text{and} \quad -\frac{1}{2}xy^3.$$

A monomial may contain more than one variable, but monomials do not contain division by variables. For example, the expression $\frac{3}{z}$ is not a monomial. If an expression contains addition or subtraction signs, it is *not* a monomial.

READING CHECK

• How do you determine the degree of a monomial?

The **degree of a monomial** is the sum of the exponents of the variables. If the monomial has only one variable, its degree is the exponent of that variable. Remember, when a variable does not have a written exponent, the exponent is implied to be 1. A nonzero number has degree 0, and the number 0 has *undefined* degree. The number in a monomial is called the **coefficient of the monomial**. Table 5.2 contains the degree and coefficient of several monomials.

TABLE 5.2 Properties of Monomials

Monomial	-5	$6a^3b$	$-xy$	$7y^3$
Degree	0	4	2	3
Coefficient	-5	6	-1	7

A **polynomial** is a monomial or the sum of two or more monomials. Each monomial is called a *term* of the polynomial. Addition or subtraction signs separate terms. The expression $2x^2 - 3x + 5$ is a **polynomial in one variable** with three terms. Examples of polynomials in one variable include

$$-2x, \quad 3x + 1, \quad 4y^2 - y + 7, \quad \text{and} \quad x^5 - 3x^3 + x - 7.$$

These polynomials have 1, 2, 3, and 4 terms, respectively. A polynomial with *two terms* is called a **binomial**, and a polynomial with *three terms* is called a **trinomial**.

A polynomial can have more than one variable, as in

$$x^2y^2, \quad 2xy^2 + 5x^2y - 1, \quad \text{and} \quad a^2 + 2ab + b^2.$$

READING CHECK

• How do you determine the degree of a polynomial?

Note that all variables in a polynomial are raised to natural number powers. The **degree of a polynomial** is the degree of the term (or monomial) with greatest degree.

EXAMPLE 1   Identifying properties of polynomials

Determine whether the expression is a polynomial. If it is, state how many terms and variables the polynomial contains and give its degree.

(a) $7x^2 - 3x + 1$ **(b)** $5x^3 - 3x^2y^3 + xy^2 - 2y^3$ **(c)** $4x^2 + \dfrac{5}{x + 1}$

Solution

(a) The expression $7x^2 - 3x + 1$ is a polynomial with three terms and one variable. The first term $7x^2$ has degree 2 because the exponent on the variable is 2. The second term $-3x$ has degree 1 because the exponent on the variable is implied to be 1. The third term 1 has degree 0 because it is a nonzero number. The term with greatest degree is $7x^2$, so the polynomial has degree 2.

(b) The expression $5x^3 - 3x^2y^3 + xy^2 - 2y^3$ is a polynomial with four terms and two variables, x and y. The first term has degree 3 because the exponent on the variable is 3. The second term has degree 5 because the *sum* of the exponents on the variables x and y is 5. Likewise, the third term has degree 3 and the fourth term has degree 3. The term with greatest degree is $-3x^2y^3$, so the polynomial has degree $2 + 3 = 5$.

(c) The expression $4x^2 + \dfrac{5}{x + 1}$ is not a polynomial because it contains division by the polynomial $x + 1$.

▎ **Now Try Exercises 21, 23, 27**

Addition of Polynomials

Suppose that we have 2 identical rectangles with length l and width w, as illustrated in Figure 5.2. Then the area of one rectangle is lw and the total area is

$$lw + lw.$$

This area is equivalent to 2 times lw, which can be expressed as $2lw$, or

$$lw + lw = 2lw.$$

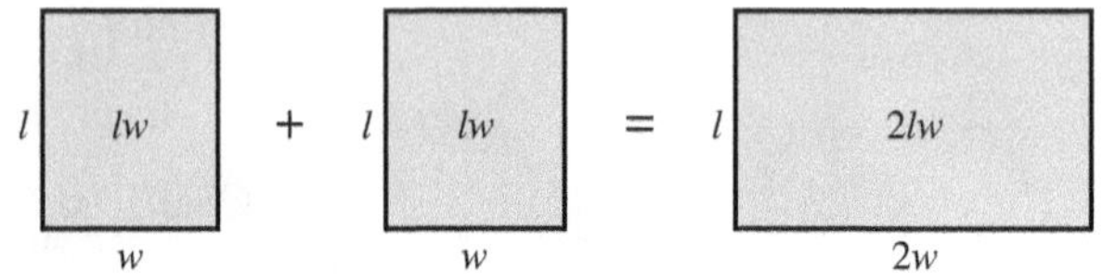

![Three rectangles: one labeled lw with sides l and w, plus another lw, equals a rectangle labeled 2lw with sides l and 2w.]

Figure 5.2 Adding $lw + lw$

If two monomials contain the same variables raised to the same powers, we call them **like terms**. We can add or subtract (combine) *like* terms but cannot combine *unlike* terms. The terms lw and $2lw$ are like terms and can be combined geometrically, as shown in Figure 5.3. If we joined one of the small rectangles with area lw and a larger rectangle with area $2lw$, then the total area is $3lw$.

![Three rectangles: one labeled lw with sides l and w, plus one labeled 2lw with sides l and 2w, equals a rectangle labeled 3lw with sides l and 3w.]

Figure 5.3 Adding $lw + 2lw$

The *distributive property* justifies combining like terms.

$$1lw + 2lw = (1 + 2)lw = 3lw$$

The rectangles shown in Figure 5.4 have areas of ab and xy. Together, their area is the sum, $ab + xy$. However, because these monomials are unlike terms, they cannot be combined into one term.

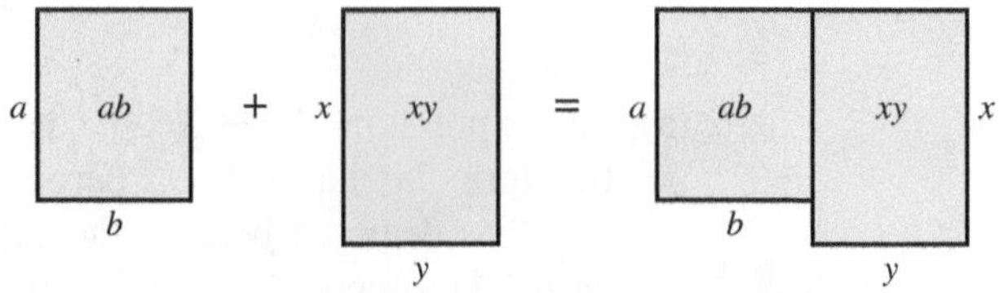

Figure 5.4 Unlike terms: $ab + xy$

EXAMPLE 2   **Adding like terms**

State whether each pair of expressions contains like terms or unlike terms. If they are like terms, add them.

(a) $5x^2, -x^2$ **(b)** $7a^2b, 10ab^2$ **(c)** $4rt^2, \frac{1}{2}rt^2$

Solution

(a) The terms $5x^2$ and $-x^2$ have the same variable raised to the same power, so they are like terms. To add like terms, add their coefficients. Note that the coefficient of $-x^2$ is -1.

$$5x^2 + (-x^2) = (5 + (-1))x^2 \quad \text{Distributive property}$$
$$= 4x^2 \quad \text{Add.}$$

(b) The terms $7a^2b$ and $10ab^2$ have the same variables, but these variables are not raised to the same powers. They are unlike terms and cannot be added.

(c) The terms $4rt^2$ and $\frac{1}{2}rt^2$ have the same variables raised to the same powers, so they are like terms. We add them as follows.

$$4rt^2 + \frac{1}{2}rt^2 = \left(4 + \frac{1}{2}\right)rt^2 \quad \text{Distributive property}$$
$$= \frac{9}{2}rt^2 \quad \text{Add.}$$

▌ Now Try Exercises 29, 31, 33

To add two polynomials, combine like terms, as illustrated in the next example.

EXAMPLE 3   **Adding polynomials**

Add by combining like terms.
(a) $(3x + 4) + (-4x + 2)$
(b) $(y^2 - 2y + 1) + (3y^2 + y + 11)$

Solution

(a) $(3x + 4) + (-4x + 2) = 3x + (-4x) + 4 + 2$
$$= (3 - 4)x + (4 + 2)$$
$$= -x + 6$$

(b) $(y^2 - 2y + 1) + (3y^2 + y + 11) = y^2 + 3y^2 - 2y + y + 1 + 11$
$$= (1 + 3)y^2 + (-2 + 1)y + (1 + 11)$$
$$= 4y^2 - y + 12$$

▌ Now Try Exercises 37, 39

Recall that the commutative and associative properties of addition allow us to rearrange a sum in any order. For example, if we write each subtraction in $2x - 5 - 4x + 10$ as addition of the opposite, we have

$$2x - 5 - 4x + 10 = 2x + (-5) + (-4x) + 10,$$

and the terms can be rearranged as

$$2x + (-4x) + (-5) + 10 = 2x - 4x - 5 + 10.$$

If we pay attention to the sign in front of each term in a polynomial, the like terms can be combined without rearranging the terms, as demonstrated in the next example.

EXAMPLE 4 **Adding polynomials**

Add $(x^3 - 3x^2 + 7x - 4) + (4x^3 - 5x + 9)$ by combining like terms.

Solution
Remove parentheses and identify like terms with their signs as shown.

$$x^3 - 3x^2 + 7x - 4 + 4x^3 - 5x + 9$$

When like terms (of the same color) are added, the resulting sum is

$$5x^3 - 3x^2 + 2x + 5.$$

▍ Now Try Exercise 41

Polynomials can also be added vertically, as demonstrated in the next example.

EXAMPLE 5 **Adding polynomials vertically**

Simplify $(3x^2 - 3x + 5) + (-x^2 + x - 6)$.

Solution
Write the polynomials in a vertical format and then add each column of like terms.

$$\begin{array}{r} 3x^2 - 3x + 5 \\ -x^2 + x - 6 \\ \hline 2x^2 - 2x - 1 \end{array} \quad \text{Add like terms in each column.}$$

Regardless of the method used, the same answer should be obtained. However, adding vertically requires that *like terms be placed in the same column.*

▍ Now Try Exercise 47

Subtraction of Polynomials

To subtract one integer from another, add the first integer and the *additive inverse* or *opposite* of the second integer. For example, $3 - 5$ is evaluated as follows.

$$3 - 5 = 3 + (-5) \quad \text{Add the opposite.}$$
$$= -2 \quad \text{Simplify.}$$

Similarly, to subtract one polynomial from another, add the first polynomial and the *opposite* of the second polynomial. To find the opposite of a polynomial, simply negate each term. Table 5.3 lists some polynomials and their opposites.

READING CHECK

• How do you subtract one polynomial from another?

CRITICAL THINKING

What is the result when a polynomial and its opposite are added?

TABLE 5.3 **Opposites of Polynomials**

Polynomial	Opposite
$2x - 4$	$-2x + 4$
$-x^2 - 2x + 9$	$x^2 + 2x - 9$
$6x^3 - 12$	$-6x^3 + 12$
$-3x^4 - 2x^2 - 8x + 3$	$3x^4 + 2x^2 + 8x - 3$

EXAMPLE 6 **Subtracting polynomials**

Simplify each expression.
(a) $(3x - 4) - (5x + 1)$
(b) $(5x^2 + 2x - 3) - (6x^2 - 7x + 9)$
(c) $(6x^3 + x^2) - (-3x^3 - 9)$

Solution
(a) To subtract $(5x + 1)$ from $(3x - 4)$, we add the opposite of $(5x + 1)$, or $(-5x - 1)$.

$$(3x - 4) - (5x + 1) = (3x - 4) + (-5x - 1)$$
$$= (3 - 5)x + (-4 - 1)$$
$$= -2x - 5$$

(b) The opposite of $(6x^2 - 7x + 9)$ is $(-6x^2 + 7x - 9)$.

$$(5x^2 + 2x - 3) - (6x^2 - 7x + 9) = (5x^2 + 2x - 3) + (-6x^2 + 7x - 9)$$
$$= (5 - 6)x^2 + (2 + 7)x + (-3 - 9)$$
$$= -x^2 + 9x - 12$$

(c) The opposite of $(-3x^3 - 9)$ is $(3x^3 + 9)$.

$$(6x^3 + x^2) - (-3x^3 - 9) = (6x^3 + x^2) + (3x^3 + 9)$$
$$= (6 + 3)x^3 + x^2 + 9$$
$$= 9x^3 + x^2 + 9$$

Now Try Exercises 57, 59, 61

NOTE: Some students prefer to subtract one polynomial from another by noting that a subtraction sign in front of parentheses changes the signs of all of the terms within the parentheses. For example, part (a) of the previous example could be worked as follows.

$$(3x - 4) - (5x + 1) = 3x - 4 - 5x - 1$$
$$= (3 - 5)x + (-4 - 1)$$
$$= -2x - 5$$

EXAMPLE 7 **Subtracting polynomials vertically**

Simplify $(5x^2 - 2x + 7) - (-3x^2 + 3)$.

Solution
To subtract one polynomial from another vertically, simply add the first polynomial and the opposite of the second polynomial. No x-term occurs in the second polynomial, so insert $0x$.

$$
\begin{array}{l}
5x^2 - 2x + 7 \\
\underline{3x^2 + 0x - 3} \quad \text{The opposite of } -3x^2 + 3 \text{ is } 3x^2 - 3 \text{ or } 3x^2 + 0x - 3. \\
8x^2 - 2x + 4 \quad \text{Add like terms in each column.}
\end{array}
$$

Now Try Exercise 69

Evaluating Polynomial Expressions

Frequently, monomials and polynomials represent formulas that may be evaluated. We illustrate such applications in the next two examples.

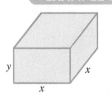

Figure 5.5

EXAMPLE 8 ## Writing and evaluating a monomial

Write the monomial that represents the volume of the box having a square bottom, as shown in Figure 5.5. Find the volume of the box if $x = 3$ feet and $y = 2$ feet.

Solution

The volume of a box is found by multiplying the length, width, and height together. Because the length and width are both x and the height is y, the monomial xxy represents the volume of the box. This can be written x^2y. To calculate the volume, let $x = 3$ and $y = 2$ in the monomial x^2y.

$$x^2y = 3^2 \cdot 2 = 9 \cdot 2 = 18 \text{ cubic feet}$$

▌ Now Try Exercise 73

EXAMPLE 9 ## Modeling sales of personal computers

Worldwide sales of personal computers have increased dramatically in recent years, as illustrated in Figure 5.6. The polynomial

$$0.7868x^2 + 16.72x + 122.58$$

approximates the number of computers sold in millions, where $x = 0$ corresponds to 2000, $x = 1$ to 2001, and so on. Estimate the number of personal computers sold in 2008 by using both the graph and the polynomial. (*Source:* International Data Corporation.)

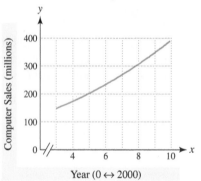

Figure 5.6

Solution

From the graph shown in Figure 5.7, it appears that personal computer sales were slightly more than 300 million, or about 310 million, in 2008.

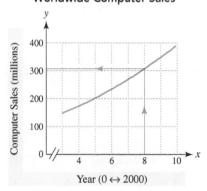

Figure 5.7

The year 2008 corresponds to $x = 8$ in the given polynomial, so substitute 8 for x and evaluate the resulting expression.

$$0.7868x^2 + 16.72x + 122.58 = 0.7868(8)^2 + 16.72(8) + 122.58$$
$$\approx 307 \text{ million}$$

The graph and the polynomial give similar results.

▮ Now Try Exercise 71

5.2   Putting It All Together

CONCEPT	EXPLANATION	EXAMPLES
Monomial	A number, variable, or product of numbers and variables raised to natural number powers The degree is the sum of the exponents. The coefficient is the number in a monomial.	$4x^2y$ Degree: 3; coefficient: 4 $-6x^2$ Degree: 2; coefficient: -6 $-a^4$ Degree: 4; coefficient: -1 x Degree: 1; coefficient: 1 -8 Degree: 0; coefficient: -8
Polynomial	A monomial or the sum of two or more monomials	$4x^2 + 8xy^2 + 3y^2$ Trinomial $-9x^4 + 100$ Binomial $-3x^2y^3$ Monomial
Like Terms	Monomials containing the same variables raised to the same powers	$10x$ and $-2x$, $4x^2$ and $3x^2$ $5ab^2$ and $-ab^2$, $5z$ and $\frac{1}{2}z$
Addition of Polynomials	To add polynomials, combine like terms.	$(x^2 + 3x + 1) + (2x^2 - 2x + 7)$ $= (1 + 2)x^2 + (3 - 2)x + (1 + 7)$ $= 3x^2 + x + 8$ $3xy + 5xy = (3 + 5)xy = 8xy$
Opposite of a Polynomial	To obtain the opposite of a polynomial, negate each term.	*Polynomial* *Opposite* $-2x^2 + x - 6$ $2x^2 - x + 6$ $a^2 - b^2$ $-a^2 + b^2$ $-3x - 18$ $3x + 18$
Subtraction of Polynomials	To subtract one polynomial from another, add the first polynomial and the opposite of the second polynomial.	$(x^2 + 3x) - (2x^2 - 5x)$ $= (x^2 + 3x) + (-2x^2 + 5x)$ $= (1 - 2)x^2 + (3 + 5)x$ $= -x^2 + 8x$
Evaluating a Polynomial	To evaluate a polynomial in x, substitute a value for x in the expression and simplify.	To evaluate the polynomial $3x^2 - 2x + 1$ for $x = 2$, substitute 2 for x and simplify. $3(2)^2 - 2(2) + 1 = 9$

5.2 Exercises

CONCEPTS AND VOCABULARY

1. A(n) _____ is a number, a variable, or a product of numbers and variables raised to a natural number power.

2. A(n) _____ is a monomial or a sum of monomials.

3. The _____ of a monomial is the sum of the exponents of the variables.

4. The _____ of a polynomial is the degree of the term with the greatest degree.

5. A polynomial with two terms is called a(n) _____.

6. A polynomial with three terms is called a(n) _____.

7. Two monomials with the same variables raised to the same powers are _____ terms.

8. To add two polynomials, combine _____ terms.

9. To subtract two polynomials, add the first polynomial to the _____ of the second polynomial.

10. Polynomials can be added horizontally or _____.

PROPERTIES OF POLYNOMIALS

Exercises 11–18: Identify the degree and coefficient of the monomial.

11. $3x^2$

12. y

13. $-ab$

14. $-2xy$

15. $-5rt$

16. $8x^2y^5$

17. 6

18. $-\frac{1}{2}$

Exercises 19–28: Determine whether the expression is a polynomial. If it is, state how many terms and variables the polynomial contains. Then state its degree.

19. $-x$

20. $7z$

21. $4x^2 - 5x + 9$

22. $x^3 - 9$

23. $x + \dfrac{1}{x}$

24. $\dfrac{5}{xy + 1}$

25. $3x^{-2}y^{-3}$

26. $5^2a^3b^4$

27. -2^3a^4bc

28. $-7y^{-1}z^{-3}$

Exercises 29–36: State whether the given pair of expressions are like terms. If they are like terms, add them.

29. $5x, -4x$

30. $x^2, 8x^2$

31. $x^3, -6x^3$

32. $4xy, -9xy$

33. $9x, -xy$

34. $5x^2y, -3xy^2$

35. ab, ba

36. $rt^2, -2t^2r$

ADDITION OF POLYNOMIALS

Exercises 37–46: Add the polynomials.

37. $(3x + 5) + (-4x + 4)$

38. $(-x + 5) + (2x - 5)$

39. $(3x^2 + 4x + 1) + (x^2 + 4x)$

40. $(-x^2 - x) + (2x^2 + 3x - 1)$

41. $(y^3 + 3y^2 - 5) + (3y^3 + 4y - 4)$

42. $(4z^4 + z^2 - 10) + (-z^4 + 4z - 5)$

43. $(-xy + 5) + (5xy - 4)$

44. $(2a^2 + b^2) + (3a^2 - 5b^2)$

45. $(a^3b^2 + a^2b^3) + (a^2b^3 - a^3b^2)$

46. $(a^2 + ab + b^2) + (a^2 - ab + b^2)$

Exercises 47–50: Add the polynomials vertically.

47. $4x^2 - 2x + 1$
$\underline{5x^2 + 3x - 7}$

48. $8x^2 + 3x + 5$
$\underline{-x^2 - 3x - 9}$

49. $-x^2 + x$
$\underline{2x^2 - 8x - 1}$

50. $a^3 - 3a^2b + 3ab^2 - b^3$
$\underline{a^3 + 3a^2b + 3ab^2 + b^3}$

SUBTRACTION OF POLYNOMIALS

Exercises 51–56: Write the opposite of the polynomial.

51. $5x^2$

52. $17x + 12$

53. $3a^2 - a + 4$

54. $-b^3 + 3b$

55. $-2t^2 - 3t + 4$

56. $7t^2 + t - 10$

Exercises 57–66: Subtract the polynomials.

57. $(3x + 1) - (-x + 3)$

58. $(-2x + 5) - (x + 7)$

59. $(-x^2 + 6x) - (2x^2 + x - 2)$

60. $(2y^2 + 3y - 2) - (y^2 - y)$

61. $(z^3 - 2z^2 - z) - (4z^2 + 5z + 1)$

62. $(3z^4 - z) - (-z^4 + 4z^2 - 5)$

63. $(4xy + x^2y^2) - (xy - x^2y^2)$

64. $(a^2 + b^2) - (-a^2 + b^2)$

65. $(ab^2) - (ab^2 + a^3b)$

66. $(x^2 + 3xy + 4y^2) - (x^2 - xy + 4y^2)$

Exercises 67–70: Subtract the polynomials vertically.

67. $(x^2 + 2x - 3) - (2x^2 + 7x + 1)$

68. $(5x^2 - 9x - 1) - (x^2 - x + 3)$

69. $(3x^3 - 2x) - (5x^3 + 4x + 2)$

70. $(a^2 + 3ab + 2b^2) - (a^2 - 3ab + 2b^2)$

APPLICATIONS

71. *Exercise and Heart Rate* The polynomial given by $1.6t^2 - 28t + 200$ calculates the heart rate shown in Figure 5.1(b) in A Look Into Math for this section, where t represents the elapsed time in minutes since exercise stopped.
  (a) What is the heart rate when the athlete first stops exercising?
  (b) What is the heart rate after 5 minutes?
  (c) Describe what happens to the heart rate after exercise stops.

72. *Cellular Phone Subscribers* In the early years of cellular phone technology—from 1986 through 1991—the number of subscribers in millions could be modeled by the polynomial $0.163x^2 - 0.146x + 0.205$, where $x = 1$ corresponds to 1986, $x = 2$ to 1987, and so on. The graph illustrates this growth.

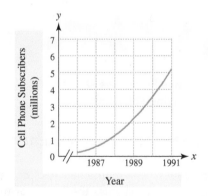

  (a) Use the graph to estimate the number of cellular phone subscribers in 1990.

  (b) Use the polynomial to estimate the number of cellular phone subscribers in 1990.
  (c) Do your answers from parts (a) and (b) agree?

73. *Areas of Squares* Write a monomial that equals the sum of the areas of the squares. Then calculate this sum for $z = 10$ inches.

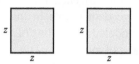

74. *Areas of Rectangles* Find a monomial that equals the sum of the areas of the three rectangles. Find this sum for $a = 5$ yards and $b = 3$ yards.

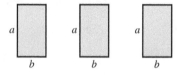

75. *Area of a Figure* Find a polynomial that equals the area of the figure. Calculate its area for $x = 6$ feet.

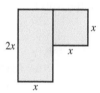

76. *Area of a Rectangle* Write a polynomial that gives the area of the rectangle. Calculate its area for $x = 3$ feet.

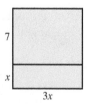

77. *Areas of Circles* Write a polynomial that gives the sum of the areas of two circles, one with radius x and the other with radius y. Find this sum for $x = 2$ feet and $y = 3$ feet. Leave your answer in terms of π.

78. *Squares and Circles* Write a polynomial that gives the sum of the areas of a square having sides of length x and a circle having diameter x. Approximate this sum to the nearest hundredth of a square foot for $x = 6$ feet.

79. *World Population* The table lists actual and projected world population P in billions for selected years t.

t	1974	1987	1999	2012
P	4	5	6	7

Source: U.S. Census Bureau.

(a) Find the slope of each line segment connecting consecutive data points in the table. Can these data be modeled with a line? Explain.

(b) Does the polynomial $0.077t - 148$ give good estimates for the world population in year t? Explain how you decided.

80. *Price of a Stamp* The table lists the price P of a first-class postage stamp for selected years t.

t	1963	1975	1987	2002	2007	2011
P	5¢	13¢	25¢	37¢	41¢	44¢

Source: U.S. Postal Service.

(a) Does the polynomial $0.835t - 1635$ model the data in the table exactly?

(b) Does it give approximations that are within 1.5¢ of the actual values?

WRITING ABOUT MATHEMATICS

81. Explain what the terms monomial, binomial, trinomial, and polynomial mean. Give an example of each.

82. Explain how to determine the degree of a polynomial having one variable. Give an example.

83. Explain how to obtain the opposite of a polynomial. Give an example.

84. Explain how to subtract two polynomials. Give an example.

SECTIONS 5.1 and 5.2   Checking Basic Concepts

1. Evaluate each expression.
   (a) -5^2 **(b)** $3^2 - 2^3$

2. Simplify each expression.
   (a) $10^3 \cdot 10^5$ **(b)** $(3x^2)(-4x^5)$
   (c) $(a^3b)^2$ **(d)** $\left(\dfrac{x}{z^3}\right)^4$

3. Simplify each expression.
   (a) $(4y^3)^0$ **(b)** $(x^3)^2(3x^4)^2$
   (c) $2a^2(5a^3 - 7)$

4. State the number of terms and variables in the polynomial $5x^3y - 2x^2y + 5$. What is its degree?

5. A box has a rectangular bottom twice as long as it is wide.
   (a) If the bottom has width w and the box has height h, write a monomial that gives the volume of the box.
   (b) Find the volume of the box for $w = 12$ inches and $h = 10$ inches.

6. Simplify each expression.
   (a) $(2a^2 + 3a - 1) + (a^2 - 3a + 7)$
   (b) $(4z^3 + 5z) - (2z^3 - 2z + 8)$
   (c) $(x^2 + 2xy + y^2) - (x^2 - 2xy + y^2)$

5.3   Multiplication of Polynomials

Multiplying Monomials ● Review of the Distributive Properties ●
Multiplying Monomials and Polynomials ● Multiplying Polynomials

A LOOK INTO MATH ▶   The study of polynomials dates back to Babylonian civilization in about 1800–1600 B.C. Many eighteenth-century mathematicians devoted their entire careers to the study of polynomials. Today, polynomials still play an important role in mathematics, often being used to approximate unknown quantities. In this section we discuss the basics of multiplying polynomials. (*Source: Historical Topics for the Mathematics Classroom, Thirty-first Yearbook, NCTM.*)

Multiplying Monomials

A monomial is a number, a variable, or a product of numbers and variables raised to natural number powers. To multiply monomials, we often use the product rule for exponents.

EXAMPLE 1 **Multiplying monomials**

Multiply.
(a) $-5x^2 \cdot 4x^3$ **(b)** $(7xy^4)(x^3y^2)$

Solution
(a) $-5x^2 \cdot 4x^3 = (-5)(4)x^2x^3$ Commutative property

$= -20x^{2+3}$ The product rule

$= -20x^5$ Simplify.

(b) $(7xy^4)(x^3y^2) = 7xx^3y^4y^2$ Commutative property

$= 7x^{1+3}y^{4+2}$ The product rule

$= 7x^4y^6$ Simplify.

Now Try Exercises 9, 13

READING CHECK

• Which rule for exponents is commonly used to multiply monomials?

Review of the Distributive Properties

Distributive Property
$3(x + 2) = 3x + 6$

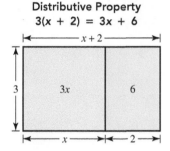

Figure 5.8 Area: $3x + 6$

Distributive properties are used frequently for multiplying monomials and polynomials. For all real numbers a, b, and c,

$$a(b + c) = ab + ac \quad \text{and} \quad a(b - c) = ab - ac.$$

The first distributive property above can be visualized geometrically. For example,

$$3(x + 2) = 3x + 6$$

is illustrated in Figure 5.8. The dimensions of the large rectangle are 3 by $x + 2$, and its area is $3(x + 2)$. The areas of the two small rectangles, $3x$ and 6, equal the area of the large rectangle. Therefore $3(x + 2) = 3x + 6$.

In the next example we use the distributive properties to multiply expressions.

EXAMPLE 2 **Using distributive properties**

Multiply.
(a) $2(3x + 4)$ **(b)** $(3x^2 + 4)5$ **(c)** $-x(3x - 6)$

Solution

(a) $2(3x + 4) = 2 \cdot 3x + 2 \cdot 4 = 6x + 8$

(b) $(3x^2 + 4)5 = 3x^2 \cdot 5 + 4 \cdot 5 = 15x^2 + 20$

(c) $-x(3x - 6) = -x \cdot 3x + x \cdot 6 = -3x^2 + 6x$

Now Try Exercises 15, 19, 21

READING CHECK

• What properties are commonly used to multiply a monomial and a polynomial?

Multiplying Monomials and Polynomials

A monomial consists of one term, whereas a polynomial consists of one or more terms separated by $+$ or $-$ signs. To multiply a monomial by a polynomial, we apply the distributive properties and the product rule.

EXAMPLE 3 **Multiplying monomials and polynomials**

Multiply.
(a) $9x(2x^2 - 3)$ (b) $(5x - 8)x^2$
(c) $-7(2x^2 - 4x + 6)$ (d) $4x^3(x^4 + 9x^2 - 8)$

Solution

(a) $\quad 9x(2x^2 - 3) = 9x \cdot 2x^2 - 9x \cdot 3$ Distributive property
$\qquad\qquad\qquad = 18x^3 - 27x$ The product rule

(b) $\quad (5x - 8)x^2 = 5x \cdot x^2 - 8 \cdot x^2$ Distributive property
$\qquad\qquad\qquad = 5x^3 - 8x^2$ The product rule

(c) $-7(2x^2 - 4x + 6) = -7 \cdot 2x^2 + 7 \cdot 4x - 7 \cdot 6$ Distributive property
$\qquad\qquad\qquad = -14x^2 + 28x - 42$ Simplify.

(d) $4x^3(x^4 + 9x^2 - 8) = 4x^3 \cdot x^4 + 4x^3 \cdot 9x^2 - 4x^3 \cdot 8$ Distributive property
$\qquad\qquad\qquad = 4x^7 + 36x^5 - 32x^3$ The product rule

▌ Now Try Exercises 23, 25, 27, 29

We can also multiply monomials and polynomials that contain more than one variable.

EXAMPLE 4 **Multiplying monomials and polynomials**

Multiply.
(a) $2xy(7x^2y^3 - 1)$ (b) $-ab(a^2 - b^2)$

Solution

(a) $2xy(7x^2y^3 - 1) = 2xy \cdot 7x^2y^3 - 2xy \cdot 1$ Distributive property
$\qquad\qquad\qquad = 14xx^2yy^3 - 2xy$ Commutative property
$\qquad\qquad\qquad = 14x^3y^4 - 2xy$ The product rule

(b) $\quad -ab(a^2 - b^2) = -ab \cdot a^2 + ab \cdot b^2$ Distributive property
$\qquad\qquad\qquad = -aa^2b + abb^2$ Commutative property
$\qquad\qquad\qquad = -a^3b + ab^3$ The product rule

▌ Now Try Exercises 31, 35

Multiplying Polynomials

Monomials, binomials, and trinomials are examples of polynomials. Recall that a monomial has one term, a binomial has two terms, and a trinomial has three terms. In the next example we multiply two binomials, using both geometric and symbolic techniques.

EXAMPLE 5 **Multiplying binomials**

Multiply $(x + 4)(x + 2)$
(a) geometrically and **(b)** symbolically.

Solution
(a) To multiply $(x + 4)(x + 2)$ geometrically, draw a rectangle $x + 4$ long and $x + 2$ wide, as shown in Figure 5.9(a). The area of this rectangle equals length times width, or $(x + 4)(x + 2)$. The large rectangle can be divided into four smaller rectangles, which have areas of x^2, $4x$, $2x$, and 8, as shown in Figure 5.9(b). Thus

$$(x + 4)(x + 2) = x^2 + 4x + 2x + 8$$
$$= x^2 + 6x + 8.$$

(b) To multiply $(x + 4)(x + 2)$ symbolically, apply the distributive property two times.

$$(x + 4)(x + 2) = (x + 4)(x) + (x + 4)(2)$$
$$= x \cdot x + 4 \cdot x + x \cdot 2 + 4 \cdot 2$$
$$= x^2 + 4x + 2x + 8$$
$$= x^2 + 6x + 8$$

Now Try Exercise 39

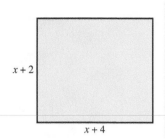

$x + 2$

$x + 4$
(a) Area $= (x + 4)(x + 2)$

| 2 | 2x | 8 |
| x | x^2 | 4x |

x 4
(b) Area $= x^2 + 4x + 2x + 8$

Figure 5.9

The distributive properties used in part (b) of the previous example show that if we want to multiply $(x + 4)$ by $(x + 2)$, we should multiply every term in $x + 4$ by every term in $x + 2$.

$$(x + 4)(x + 2) = x^2 + 2x + 4x + 8$$
$$= x^2 + 6x + 8$$

NOTE: This process of multiplying *binomials* is sometimes called *FOIL*. This acronym may be used to remind us to multiply the first terms (F), outside terms (O), inside terms (I), and last terms (L). The *FOIL* process is a shortcut for the process used in Example 5(b).

Multiply the *First terms* to obtain x^2. $(x + 4)(x + 2)$

Multiply the *Outside terms* to obtain $2x$. $(x + 4)(x + 2)$

Multiply the *Inside terms* to obtain $4x$. $(x + 4)(x + 2)$

Multiply the *Last terms* to obtain 8. $(x + 4)(x + 2)$

READING CHECK

• What kind of polynomials can be multiplied using the *FOIL* method?

The following statement summarizes how to multiply two polynomials in general.

MULTIPLYING POLYNOMIALS

The product of two polynomials may be found by multiplying every term in the first polynomial by every term in the second polynomial and then combining like terms.

EXAMPLE 6   **Multiplying binomials**

Multiply. Draw arrows to show how each term is found.
(a) $(3x + 2)(x + 1)$ **(b)** $(1 - x)(1 + 2x)$ **(c)** $(4x - 3)(x^2 - 2x)$

Solution

(a) $(3x + 2)(x + 1) = 3x \cdot x + 3x \cdot 1 + 2 \cdot x + 2 \cdot 1$
$$= 3x^2 + 3x + 2x + 2$$
$$= 3x^2 + 5x + 2$$

(b) $(1 - x)(1 + 2x) = 1 \cdot 1 + 1 \cdot 2x - x \cdot 1 - x \cdot 2x$
$$= 1 + 2x - x - 2x^2$$
$$= 1 + x - 2x^2$$

(c) $(4x - 3)(x^2 - 2x) = 4x \cdot x^2 - 4x \cdot 2x - 3 \cdot x^2 + 3 \cdot 2x$
$$= 4x^3 - 8x^2 - 3x^2 + 6x$$
$$= 4x^3 - 11x^2 + 6x$$

Now Try Exercises 51, 53, 59

The *FOIL* process may be helpful for remembering how to multiply two *binomials*, but it cannot be used for every product of polynomials. In the next example, the general process for multiplying polynomials is used to find products of binomials and trinomials.

EXAMPLE 7   **Multiplying polynomials**

Multiply.
(a) $(2x + 3)(x^2 + x - 1)$ **(b)** $(a - b)(a^2 + ab + b^2)$
(c) $(x^4 + 2x^2 - 5)(x^2 + 1)$

Solution
(a) Multiply every term in $(2x + 3)$ by every term in $(x^2 + x - 1)$.

$(2x + 3)(x^2 + x - 1) = 2x \cdot x^2 + 2x \cdot x - 2x \cdot 1 + 3 \cdot x^2 + 3 \cdot x - 3 \cdot 1$
$$= 2x^3 + 2x^2 - 2x + 3x^2 + 3x - 3$$
$$= 2x^3 + 5x^2 + x - 3$$

(b) $(a - b)(a^2 + ab + b^2) = a \cdot a^2 + a \cdot ab + a \cdot b^2 - b \cdot a^2 - b \cdot ab - b \cdot b^2$
$$= a^3 + a^2b + ab^2 - a^2b - ab^2 - b^3$$
$$= a^3 - b^3$$

(c) $(x^4 + 2x^2 - 5)(x^2 + 1) = x^4 \cdot x^2 + x^4 \cdot 1 + 2x^2 \cdot x^2 + 2x^2 \cdot 1 - 5 \cdot x^2 - 5 \cdot 1$
$$= x^6 + x^4 + 2x^4 + 2x^2 - 5x^2 - 5$$
$$= x^6 + 3x^4 - 3x^2 - 5$$

Now Try Exercises 63, 67, 69

STUDY TIP

Even if you know exactly how to do a math problem correctly, a simple computational error will often cause you to get an incorrect answer. Be sure to take your time on simple calculations.

Polynomials can be multiplied vertically in a manner similar to multiplication of real numbers. For example, multiplication of 123 times 12 is performed as follows.

$$
\begin{array}{r}
1\ 2\ 3 \\
\times\ 1\ 2 \\
\hline
2\ 4\ 6 \\
1\ 2\ 3 \\
\hline
1\ 4\ 7\ 6
\end{array}
$$

A similar method can be used to multiply polynomials vertically.

EXAMPLE 8 | **Multiplying polynomials vertically**

Multiply $2x^2 - 4x + 1$ and $x + 3$ vertically.

Solution

Write the polynomials vertically. Then multiply every term in the first polynomial by each term in the second polynomial. Arrange the results so that *like terms are in the same column*.

$$
\begin{array}{r}
2x^2 - 4x + 1 \\
x + 3 \\
\hline
6x^2 - 12x + 3 \quad \text{Multiply top polynomial by 3.}\\
2x^3 - 4x^2 + x \quad \text{Multiply top polynomial by } x.\\
\hline
2x^3 + 2x^2 - 11x + 3 \quad \text{Add each column.}
\end{array}
$$

Now Try Exercise 71

MAKING CONNECTIONS

Vertical and Horizontal Formats

Whether you decide to add, subtract, or multiply polynomials vertically or horizontally, remember that the same answer is obtained either way.

EXAMPLE 9 | **Finding the volume of a box**

A box has a width 3 inches less than its height and a length 4 inches more than its height.
(a) If h represents the height of the box, write a polynomial that represents the volume of the box.
(b) Use this polynomial to calculate the volume of the box if $h = 10$ inches.

Solution
(a) If h is the height, then $h - 3$ is the width and $h + 4$ is the length, as illustrated in Figure 5.10. Its volume equals the product of these three expressions.

$$h(h - 3)(h + 4) = (h^2 - 3h)(h + 4)$$
$$= h^2 \cdot h + h^2 \cdot 4 - 3h \cdot h - 3h \cdot 4$$
$$= h^3 + 4h^2 - 3h^2 - 12h$$
$$= h^3 + h^2 - 12h$$

(b) If $h = 10$, then the volume is

$$10^3 + 10^2 - 12(10) = 1000 + 100 - 120 = 980 \text{ cubic inches.}$$

Now Try Exercise 79

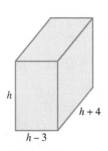

h

$h + 4$

$h - 3$

Figure 5.10

5.3   Putting It All Together

CONCEPT	EXPLANATION	EXAMPLES
Distributive Properties	For all real numbers a, b, and c, $a(b + c) = ab + ac$ and $a(b - c) = ab - ac.$	$5(x + 3) = 5x + 15$, $3(x - 6) = 3x - 18$, and $-2x(3 - 5x^3) = -6x + 10x^4$
Multiplying Polynomials	The product of two polynomials may be found by multiplying every term in the first polynomial by every term in the second polynomial and then combining like terms.	$3x(5x^2 + 2x - 7)$ $\quad = 3x \cdot 5x^2 + 3x \cdot 2x - 3x \cdot 7$ $\quad = 15x^3 + 6x^2 - 21x$ $(x + 2)(7x - 3)$ $\quad = x \cdot 7x - x \cdot 3 + 2 \cdot 7x - 2 \cdot 3$ $\quad = 7x^2 - 3x + 14x - 6$ $\quad = 7x^2 + 11x - 6$

5.3   Exercises

MyMathLab   Math XL PRACTICE   WATCH   DOWNLOAD   READ   REVIEW

CONCEPTS AND VOCABULARY

1. The equation $x^2 \cdot x^3 = x^5$ illustrates what rule of exponents?

2. The equation $3(x - 2) = 3x - 6$ illustrates what property?

3. The product of two polynomials may be found by multiplying every _____ in the first polynomial by every _____ in the second polynomial and then combining like terms.

4. Polynomials can be multiplied horizontally or _____.

MULTIPLICATION OF MONOMIALS

Exercises 5–14: Multiply.

5. $x^2 \cdot x^5$

6. $-a \cdot a^5$

7. $-3a \cdot 4a$

8. $7x \cdot 5x$

9. $4x^3 \cdot 5x^2$

10. $6b^6 \cdot 3b^5$

11. $xy^2 \cdot 4xy$

12. $3ab \cdot ab^2$

13. $(-3xy^2)(4x^2y)$

14. $(-r^2t^2)(-r^3t)$

MULTIPLICATION OF MONOMIALS AND POLYNOMIALS

Exercises 15–36: Multiply and simplify the expression.

15. $3(x + 4)$

16. $-7(4x - 1)$

17. $-5(9x + 1)$

18. $10(1 - 6x)$

19. $(4 - z)z$

20. $3z(1 - 5z)$

21. $-y(5 + 3y)$

22. $(2y - 8)2y$

23. $3x(5x^2 - 4)$

24. $-6x(2x^3 + 1)$

25. $(6x - 6)x^2$

26. $(1 - 2x^2)3x^2$

27. $-8(4t^2 + t + 1)$

28. $7(3t^2 - 2t - 5)$

29. $n^2(-5n^2 + n - 2)$

30. $6n^3(2 - 4n + n^2)$

31. $xy(x + y)$

32. $ab(2a - 3b)$

33. $x^2(x^2y - xy^2)$

34. $2y^2(xy - 5)$

35. $-ab(a^3 - 2b^3)$

36. $5rt(r^2 + 2rt + t^2)$

MULTIPLICATION OF POLYNOMIALS

Exercises 37–42: (Refer to Example 5.) Multiply the given expression (a) geometrically and (b) symbolically.

37. $x(x + 3)$

38. $2x(x + 5)$

39. $(x + 2)(x + 2)$

40. $(x + 1)(x + 3)$

41. $(x + 3)(x + 6)$

42. $(x + 5)(x + 2)$

Exercises 43–70: Multiply and simplify the expression.

43. $(x + 3)(x + 5)$

44. $(x - 4)(x - 7)$

45. $(x - 8)(x - 9)$

46. $(x + 10)(x + 10)$

47. $(3z - 2)(2z - 5)$

48. $(z + 6)(2z - 1)$

49. $(8b - 1)(8b + 1)$

50. $(3t + 2)(3t - 2)$

51. $(10y + 7)(y - 1)$

52. $(y + 6)(2y + 7)$

53. $(5 - 3a)(1 - 2a)$

54. $(4 - a)(5 + 3a)$

55. $(1 - 3x)(1 + 3x)$

56. $(10 - x)(5 - 2x)$

57. $(x - 1)(x^2 + 1)$

58. $(x + 2)(x^2 - x)$

59. $(x^2 + 4)(4x - 3)$

60. $(3x^2 - 1)(3x^2 + 1)$

61. $(2n + 1)(n^2 + 3)$

62. $(2 - n^2)(1 + n^2)$

63. $(m + 1)(m^2 + 3m + 1)$

64. $(m - 2)(m^2 - m + 5)$

65. $(3x - 2)(2x^2 - x + 4)$

66. $(5x + 4)(x^2 - 3x + 2)$

67. $(x + 1)(x^2 - x + 1)$

68. $(x - 2)(x^2 + 4x + 4)$

69. $(4b^2 + 3b + 7)(b^2 + 3)$

70. $(-3a^2 - 2a + 1)(3a^2 - 3)$

Exercises 71–76: Multiply the polynomials vertically.

71. $(x + 2)(x^2 - 3x + 1)$

72. $(2y - 3)(3y^2 - 2y - 2)$

73. $(a - 2)(a^2 + 2a + 4)$

74. $(b - 3)(b^2 + 3b + 9)$

75. $(3x^2 - x + 1)(2x^2 + 1)$

76. $(2x^2 - 3x - 5)(2x^2 + 3)$

77. Thinking Generally If a polynomial with m terms and a polynomial with n terms are multiplied, how many terms are there in the product before like terms are combined?

78. Thinking Generally When a polynomial with m terms is multiplied by a second polynomial, the product contains k terms before like terms are combined. How many terms does the second polynomial contain?

APPLICATIONS

79. *Volume of a Box* (Refer to Example 9.) A box has a width 4 inches less than its height and a length 2 inches more than its height.
  (a) If h is the height of the box, write a polynomial that represents the volume of the box.
  (b) Use this polynomial to calculate the volume for $h = 25$ inches.

80. *Surface Area of a Box* Use the drawing of the box to write a polynomial that represents each of the following.

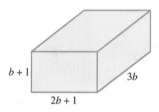

  (a) The area of its bottom
  (b) The area of its front
  (c) The area of its right side
  (d) The total area of its six sides

81. *Perimeter of a Pen* A rectangular pen for a pet has a perimeter of 100 feet. If one side of the pen has length x, then its area is given by $x(50 - x)$.
  (a) Multiply this expression.
  (b) Evaluate the expression obtained in part (a) for $x = 25$.

82. *Rectangular Garden* A rectangular garden has a perimeter of 500 feet.
  (a) If one side of the garden has length x, then write a polynomial expression that gives its area. Multiply this expression completely.
  (b) Evaluate the expression for $x = 50$ and interpret your answer.

83. *Surface Area of a Cube* Write a polynomial that represents the total area of the six sides of the cube having edges with length $x + 1$.

84. *Surface Area of a Sphere* The surface area of a sphere with radius r is $4\pi r^2$. Write a polynomial that gives the surface area of a sphere with radius $x + 2$. Leave your answer in terms of π.

85. *Toy Rocket* A toy rocket is shot straight up into the air. Its height h in feet above the ground after t seconds is represented by the expression $t(64 - 16t)$.
  (a) Multiply this expression.
  (b) Evaluate the expression obtained in part (a) and the given expression for $t = 2$.
  (c) Are your answers in part (b) the same? Should they be the same?

86. *Toy Rocket on the Moon* (Refer to the preceding exercise.) If the same toy rocket were flown on the moon, then its height h in feet after t seconds would be $t\left(64 - \frac{5}{2}t\right)$.
  (a) Multiply this expression.
  (b) Evaluate the expression obtained in part (a) and the given expression for $t = 2$. Did the rocket go higher on the moon?

WRITING ABOUT MATHEMATICS

87. Explain how the acronym FOIL relates to multiplying two binomials, such as $x + 3$ and $2x + 1$.

88. Does the FOIL method work for multiplying a binomial and a trinomial? Explain.

89. Explain in words how to multiply any two polynomials. Give an example.

90. Give two properties of real numbers that are used for multiplying $3x(5x^2 - 3x + 2)$. Explain your answer.

Group Activity   Working with Real Data

Directions: Form a group of 2 to 4 people. Select someone to record the group's responses for this activity. All members of the group should work cooperatively to answer the questions. If your instructor asks for your results, each member of the group should be prepared to respond.

Biology Some types of worms have a remarkable ability to live without moisture. The following table from one study shows the number of worms W surviving after x days without moisture.

x (days)	0	20	40	80	120	160
W (worms)	50	48	45	36	20	3

Source: D. Brown and P. Rothery, *Models in Biology.*

  (a) Use the equation $W = -0.0014x^2 - 0.076x + 50$ to find W for each x-value in the table.
  (b) Discuss how well this equation approximates the data.
  (c) Use this equation to estimate the number of worms on day 60 and on day 180. Which answer is most accurate? Explain.

5.5 Integer Exponents and the Quotient Rule

Negative Integers as Exponents • The Quotient Rule • Other Rules for Exponents •
Scientific Notation

A LOOK INTO MATH ▶

In 2009, astronomers discovered a large planet that orbits a distant star. The planet, named WASP-17b, is about 5,880,000,000,000,000 miles from Earth. Also in 2009, the H1N1 virus was identified in a worldwide influenza pandemic. A typical flu virus measures about 0.00000468 inch across. In this section, we will discuss how integer exponents can be used to write such numbers in *scientific notation*. (*Source: Scientific American.*)

NEW VOCABULARY

☐ Scientific notation

Negative Integers as Exponents

So far we have defined exponents that are whole numbers. For example,

$$5^0 = 1 \quad \text{and} \quad 2^3 = 2 \cdot 2 \cdot 2 = 8.$$

What if an exponent is a negative integer? To answer this question, consider Table 5.4, which shows values for decreasing powers of 2. Note that each time the exponent on 2 decreases by 1, the resulting value is divided by 2.

TABLE 5.4 Powers of 2

Power of 2	Value
2^1	2
2^0	1
2^{-1}	$\frac{1}{2} = \frac{1}{2^1}$
2^{-2}	$\frac{1}{4} = \frac{1}{2^2}$

Decrease exponent by 1 — Divide by 2
Decrease exponent by 1 — Divide by 2
Decrease exponent by 1 — Divide by 2

Table 5.4 shows that $2^{-1} = \frac{1}{2^1}$ and $2^{-2} = \frac{1}{2^2}$. In other words, if the exponent on 2 is negative, then the expression is equal to the reciprocal of the corresponding expression with a positive exponent on 2. This discussion suggests the following definition for negative integer exponents.

READING CHECK

• How is a negative integer power on a base related to the corresponding positive integer power on that base?

NEGATIVE INTEGER EXPONENTS

Let a be a nonzero real number and n be a positive integer. Then

$$a^{-n} = \frac{1}{a^n}.$$

That is, a^{-n} is the reciprocal of a^n.

STUDY TIP

Mathematics often builds on concepts that have already been studied. Try to get in the regular habit of reviewing topics from earlier parts of the text.

EXAMPLE 1   Evaluating negative exponents

Simplify each expression.

(a) 2^{-3} **(b)** 7^{-1} **(c)** x^{-2} **(d)** $(x + y)^{-8}$

Solution

(a) Because $a^{-n} = \dfrac{1}{a^n}$, $\quad 2^{-3} = \dfrac{1}{2^3} = \dfrac{1}{2 \cdot 2 \cdot 2} = \dfrac{1}{8}$.

(b) $7^{-1} = \dfrac{1}{7^1} = \dfrac{1}{7}$

(c) $x^{-2} = \dfrac{1}{x^2}$

(d) $(x + y)^{-8} = \dfrac{1}{(x + y)^8}$

▮ Now Try Exercises 7, 19, 25(b)

TECHNOLOGY NOTE

Negative Exponents

Calculators can be used to evaluate negative exponents. The figure shows how a graphing calculator evaluates the expressions in parts (a) and (b) of Example 1.

CALCULATOR HELP

To use the fraction feature (Frac), see Appendix A (pages AP-1 and AP-2).

```
2^(-3)▶Frac
              1/8
7^(-1)▶Frac
              1/7
```

The rules for exponents discussed in this chapter so far also apply to expressions having negative exponents. For example, we can apply the product rule, $a^m \cdot a^n = a^{m+n}$, as follows.

$$2^{-3} \cdot 2^2 \overset{\text{Add}}{=} 2^{-3+2} = 2^{-1} = \dfrac{1}{2}$$

We can check this result by evaluating the expression without using the product rule.

$$2^{-3} \cdot 2^2 = \dfrac{1}{2^3} \cdot 2^2 = \dfrac{1}{8} \cdot 4 = \dfrac{4}{8} = \dfrac{1}{2}$$

EXAMPLE 2   Using the product rule with negative exponents

Evaluate each expression.

(a) $5^2 \cdot 5^{-4}$ **(b)** $3^{-2} \cdot 3^{-1}$

Solution

(a) $5^2 \cdot 5^{-4} \overset{\text{Add}}{=} 5^{2+(-4)} = 5^{-2} = \dfrac{1}{5^2} = \dfrac{1}{25}$

(b) $3^{-2} \cdot 3^{-1} = 3^{-2+(-1)} = 3^{-3} = \dfrac{1}{3^3} = \dfrac{1}{27}$

▮ Now Try Exercise 9

EXAMPLE 3 **Using the rules of exponents**

Simplify the expression. Write the answer using positive exponents.
(a) $x^2 \cdot x^{-5}$ **(b)** $(y^3)^{-4}$ **(c)** $(rt)^{-5}$ **(d)** $(ab)^{-3}(a^{-2}b)^3$

Solution
(a) Using the product rule, $a^m \cdot a^n = a^{m+n}$, gives

$$x^2 \cdot x^{-5} = x^{2+(-5)} = x^{-3} = \frac{1}{x^3}.$$

(b) Using the power rule, $(a^m)^n = a^{mn}$, gives

$$(y^3)^{-4} = y^{3(-4)} = y^{-12} = \frac{1}{y^{12}}.$$

(c) Using the power rule, $(ab)^n = a^n b^n$, gives

$$(rt)^{-5} = r^{-5}t^{-5} = \frac{1}{r^5} \cdot \frac{1}{t^5} = \frac{1}{r^5 t^5}.$$

This expression could also be simplified as follows.

$$(rt)^{-5} = \frac{1}{(rt)^5} = \frac{1}{r^5 t^5}$$

(d) $(ab)^{-3}(a^{-2}b)^3 = a^{-3}b^{-3}a^{-6}b^3$
$$= a^{-3+(-6)}b^{-3+3}$$
$$= a^{-9}b^0$$
$$= \frac{1}{a^9} \cdot 1$$
$$= \frac{1}{a^9}$$

Now Try Exercises 21, 27, 29(a)

The Quotient Rule

Consider the division problem

$$\frac{3^4}{3^2} = \frac{3 \cdot 3 \cdot 3 \cdot 3}{3 \cdot 3} = \frac{3}{3} \cdot \frac{3}{3} \cdot 3 \cdot 3 = 1 \cdot 1 \cdot 3^2 = 3^2.$$

Because there are two more 3s in the numerator than in the denominator, the result is

$$3^{4-2} = 3^2.$$

That is, to divide exponential expressions having the *same base*, subtract the exponent of the denominator from the exponent of the numerator and keep the same base. This rule is called the *quotient rule*, which we express in symbols as follows.

THE QUOTIENT RULE

For any nonzero number a and integers m and n,

$$\frac{a^m}{a^n} = a^{m-n}.$$

EXAMPLE 4   **Using the quotient rule**

Simplify each expression. Write the answer using positive exponents.

(a) $\dfrac{4^3}{4^5}$ (b) $\dfrac{6a^7}{3a^4}$ (c) $\dfrac{xy^7}{x^2y^5}$

Solution

(a) $\dfrac{4^3}{4^5} = 4^{3-5} = 4^{-2} = \dfrac{1}{4^2} = \dfrac{1}{16}$ $\overset{\text{Subtract}}{\downarrow}$

(b) $\dfrac{6a^7}{3a^4} = \dfrac{6}{3} \cdot \dfrac{a^7}{a^4} = 2a^{7-4} = 2a^3$

(c) $\dfrac{xy^7}{x^2y^5} = \dfrac{x^1}{x^2} \cdot \dfrac{y^7}{y^5} = x^{1-2}y^{7-5} = x^{-1}y^2 = \dfrac{y^2}{x}$

Now Try Exercises 13(b), 31(b), 33(a)

MAKING CONNECTIONS

The Quotient Rule and Simplifying Quotients

Some quotients can be simplified mentally. Because

$$\frac{x^5}{x^3} = \frac{x \cdot x \cdot x \cdot x \cdot x}{x \cdot x \cdot x},$$

the quotient $\frac{x^5}{x^3}$ has five factors of x in the numerator and three factors of x in the denominator. There are two more factors of x in the numerator than in the denominator, $5 - 3 = 2$, so this expression simplifies to x^2. Similarly,

$$\frac{x^3}{x^5} = \frac{x \cdot x \cdot x}{x \cdot x \cdot x \cdot x \cdot x}$$

has two more factors of x in the denominator than in the numerator. This quotient $\frac{x^3}{x^5}$ simplifies to $\frac{1}{x^2}$. Use this technique to simplify the expressions

$$\frac{z^7}{z^4}, \quad \frac{a^5}{a^8}, \quad \text{and} \quad \frac{x^6y^2}{x^3y^7}.$$

Other Rules for Exponents

Other rules can be used to simplify expressions with negative exponents.

QUOTIENTS AND NEGATIVE EXPONENTS

The following three rules hold for any nonzero real numbers a and b and positive integers m and n.

1. $\dfrac{1}{a^{-n}} = a^n$ 2. $\dfrac{a^{-n}}{b^{-m}} = \dfrac{b^m}{a^n}$ 3. $\left(\dfrac{a}{b}\right)^{-n} = \left(\dfrac{b}{a}\right)^n$

We demonstrate the validity of these rules as follows.

1. $\dfrac{1}{a^{-n}} = \dfrac{1}{\dfrac{1}{a^n}} = 1 \cdot \dfrac{a^n}{1} = a^n$

2. $\dfrac{a^{-n}}{b^{-m}} = \dfrac{\dfrac{1}{a^n}}{\dfrac{1}{b^m}} = \dfrac{1}{a^n} \cdot \dfrac{b^m}{1} = \dfrac{b^m}{a^n}$

3. $\left(\dfrac{a}{b}\right)^{-n} = \dfrac{a^{-n}}{b^{-n}} = \dfrac{\dfrac{1}{a^n}}{\dfrac{1}{b^n}} = \dfrac{1}{a^n} \cdot \dfrac{b^n}{1} = \dfrac{b^n}{a^n} = \left(\dfrac{b}{a}\right)^n$

EXAMPLE 5   **Working with quotients and negative exponents**

Simplify each expression. Write the answer using positive exponents.

(a) $\dfrac{1}{2^{-5}}$ **(b)** $\dfrac{3^{-3}}{4^{-2}}$ **(c)** $\dfrac{5x^{-4}y^2}{10x^2y^{-4}}$ **(d)** $\left(\dfrac{2}{z^2}\right)^{-4}$

Solution

(a) $\dfrac{1}{2^{-5}} = 2^5 = 2 \cdot 2 \cdot 2 \cdot 2 \cdot 2 = 32$ **(b)** $\dfrac{3^{-3}}{4^{-2}} = \dfrac{4^2}{3^3} = \dfrac{16}{27}$

(c) $\dfrac{5x^{-4}y^2}{10x^2y^{-4}} = \dfrac{y^2y^4}{2x^2x^4} = \dfrac{y^6}{2x^6}$ **(d)** $\left(\dfrac{2}{z^2}\right)^{-4} = \left(\dfrac{z^2}{2}\right)^4 = \dfrac{z^8}{2^4} = \dfrac{z^8}{16}$

Now Try Exercises 15(b), 17, 37, 47

The rules for natural number exponents that are summarized in Section 5.1 on page 273 also hold for integer exponents. Additional rules for integer exponents are summarized as follows.

RULES FOR INTEGER EXPONENTS

The following rules hold for nonzero real numbers a and b, and positive integers m and n.

Description	Rule	Example
Negative Exponents (1)	$a^{-n} = \dfrac{1}{a^n}$	$9^{-2} = \dfrac{1}{9^2} = \dfrac{1}{81}$
The Quotient Rule	$\dfrac{a^m}{a^n} = a^{m-n}$	$\dfrac{2^3}{2^{-2}} = 2^{3-(-2)} = 2^5$
Negative Exponents (2)	$\dfrac{1}{a^{-n}} = a^n$	$\dfrac{1}{7^{-5}} = 7^5$
Negative Exponents (3)	$\dfrac{a^{-n}}{b^{-m}} = \dfrac{b^m}{a^n}$	$\dfrac{4^{-3}}{2^{-5}} = \dfrac{2^5}{4^3}$
Negative Exponents (4)	$\left(\dfrac{a}{b}\right)^{-n} = \left(\dfrac{b}{a}\right)^n$	$\left(\dfrac{1}{5}\right)^{-2} = \left(\dfrac{5}{1}\right)^2 = 25$

Scientific Notation

Powers of 10 are important because they are used in science to express numbers that are either very small or very large in absolute value. Table 5.5 lists some powers of 10. Note that if the power of 10 decreases by 1, the result decreases by a factor of $\frac{1}{10}$, or equivalently, the decimal point is moved one place to the left. Table 5.6 shows the names of some important powers of 10.

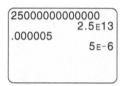
TABLE 5.5 **Powers of 10**

Power of 10	Value
10^3	1000
10^2	100
10^1	10
10^0	1
10^{-1}	$\frac{1}{10} = 0.1$
10^{-2}	$\frac{1}{100} = 0.01$
10^{-3}	$\frac{1}{1000} = 0.001$

TABLE 5.6 **Important Powers of 10**

Power of 10	Name
10^{12}	Trillion
10^9	Billion
10^6	Million
10^3	Thousand
10^{-1}	Tenth
10^{-2}	Hundredth
10^{-3}	Thousandth
10^{-6}	Millionth

Recall that numbers written in decimal notation are sometimes said to be in *standard form*. Decimal numbers that are either very large or very small in absolute value can be expressed in *scientific notation*.

REAL-WORLD CONNECTION As mentioned in A Look Into Math for this section, the distance to the planet WASP-17b is about 5,880,000,000,000,000 miles. This distance can be written in scientific notation as 5.88×10^{15} because

$$5,880,000,000,000,000 = 5.88 \times 10^{15}.$$

15 decimal places

The 10^{15} indicates that the decimal point in 5.88 should be moved 15 places to the right.

A typical virus is about 0.00000468 inch in diameter, which can be written in scientific notation as 4.68×10^{-6} because

$$0.00000468 = 4.68 \times 10^{-6}.$$

6 decimal places

The 10^{-6} indicates that the decimal point in 4.68 should be moved 6 places to the left.

The following definition provides a more complete explanation of scientific notation.

SCIENTIFIC NOTATION

A real number a is in **scientific notation** when a is written in the form $b \times 10^n$, where $1 \le |b| < 10$ and n is an integer.

EXAMPLE 6   **Converting scientific notation to standard form**

Write each number in standard form.
(a) 5.23×10^4 **(b)** 8.1×10^{-3} **(c)** 6×10^{-2}

Solution
(a) The positive exponent 4 indicates that the decimal point in 5.23 is to be moved 4 places to the **right**.

$$5.23 \times 10^4 = 5.\underset{1\ 2\ 3\ 4}{2\ 3\ 0\ 0.} = 52,300$$

(b) The negative exponent -3 indicates that the decimal point in 8.1 is to be moved 3 places to the **left**.

$$8.1 \times 10^{-3} = 0.\underset{1\ 2\ 3}{0\ 0\ 8.}1 = 0.0081$$

(c) $6 \times 10^{-2} = 0.\underset{1\ 2}{0\ 6.} = 0.06$

Now Try Exercises 61, 63

The following steps can be used for writing a positive number a in scientific notation.

WRITING A POSITIVE NUMBER IN SCIENTIFIC NOTATION

For a positive, rational number a expressed as a decimal, if $1 \le a < 10$, then $a = a \times 10^0$. Otherwise, use the following process to write a in scientific notation.

1. Move the decimal point in a until it becomes a number b such that $1 \le b < 10$.
2. Let the positive integer n be the number of places the decimal point was moved.
3. Write a in scientific notation as follows.
   • If $a \ge 10$, then $a = b \times 10^n$.
   • If $a < 1$, then $a = b \times 10^{-n}$.

NOTE: The scientific notation for a negative number a is the opposite of the scientific notation of $|a|$. For example, $450 = 4.5 \times 10^2$ and $-450 = -4.5 \times 10^2$.

EXAMPLE 7   **Writing a number in scientific notation**

Write each number in scientific notation.
(a) 308,000,000   (U.S. population in 2010)
(b) 0.001   (Approximate time in seconds for sound to travel one foot)

Solution
(a) Move the assumed decimal point in 308,000,000 eight places to obtain 3.08.

$$3.\underset{1\ 2\ 3\ 4\ 5\ 6\ 7\ 8}{0\ 8\ 0\ 0\ 0\ 0\ 0\ 0.}$$

Since $308,000,000 \ge 10$, the scientific notation is 3.08×10^8.

(b) Move the decimal point in 0.001 three places to obtain 1.

$$0.\underset{1\,2\,3}{\underbrace{0\,0\,1}}.$$

Since $0.001 < 1$, the scientific notation is 1×10^{-3}.

■ Now Try Exercises 75, 79

Numbers in scientific notation can be multiplied by applying properties of real numbers and properties of exponents.

$$
\begin{aligned}
(6 \times 10^4) \cdot (3 \times 10^3) &= (6 \cdot 3) \times (10^4 \cdot 10^3) && \text{Properties of real numbers} \\
&= 18 \times 10^7 && \text{Product rule} \\
&= 1.8 \times 10^8 && \text{Scientific notation}
\end{aligned}
$$

CALCULATOR HELP

To display numbers in scientific notation, see Appendix A (page AP-2).

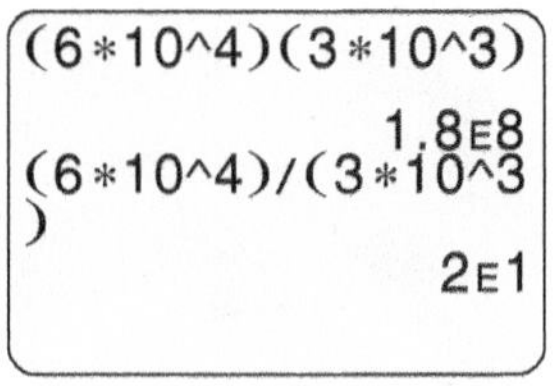

```
(6*10^4)(3*10^3)
            1.8E8
(6*10^4)/(3*10^3
)
              2E1
```

Figure 5.16

Division can also be performed with scientific notation.

$$
\begin{aligned}
\frac{6 \times 10^4}{3 \times 10^3} &= \frac{6}{3} \times \frac{10^4}{10^3} && \text{Property of fractions} \\
&= 2 \times 10^1 && \text{Quotient rule}
\end{aligned}
$$

These results are supported in Figure 5.16, where the calculator is in scientific mode.

In the next example we show how to use scientific notation in an application.

EXAMPLE 8   **Analyzing the cost of Internet advertising**

In 2009, a total of 2.38×10^{10} was spent on Internet advertising in the United States. At that time the population of the United States was 3.05×10^8. Determine how much was spent per person on Internet advertising. (*Source: New York Times.*)

CRITICAL THINKING

Estimate the number of seconds that you have been alive. Write your answer in scientific notation.

Solution

To determine the amount spent per person, divide 2.38×10^{10} by 3.05×10^8.

$$\frac{2.38 \times 10^{10}}{3.05 \times 10^8} = \frac{2.38}{3.05} \times 10^{10-8} \approx 0.78 \times 10^2 = 78$$

In 2009, about $78 per person was spent on Internet advertising.

■ Now Try Exercise 97

5.5   Putting It All Together

For the rules for integer exponents in this table, assume that a and b are nonzero real numbers and that m and n are integers.

CONCEPT	EXPLANATION	EXAMPLES
Negative Integer Exponents	$a^{-n} = \dfrac{1}{a^n}$	$2^{-4} = \dfrac{1}{2^4} = \dfrac{1}{16}, \quad a^{-8} = \dfrac{1}{a^8}, \quad$ and $(xy)^{-2} = \dfrac{1}{(xy)^2} = \dfrac{1}{x^2 y^2}$

continued on next page

continued from previous page

CONCEPT	EXPLANATION	EXAMPLES
Quotient Rule	$\dfrac{a^m}{a^n} = a^{m-n}$	$\dfrac{7^2}{7^4} = 7^{2-4} = 7^{-2} = \dfrac{1}{7^2} = \dfrac{1}{49}$ and $\dfrac{x^6}{x^3} = x^{6-3} = x^3$
Quotients and Negative Integer Exponents	1. $\dfrac{1}{a^{-n}} = a^n$ 2. $\dfrac{a^{-n}}{b^{-m}} = \dfrac{b^m}{a^n}$ 3. $\left(\dfrac{a}{b}\right)^{-n} = \left(\dfrac{b}{a}\right)^n$	1. $\dfrac{1}{5^{-2}} = 5^2 = 25$ 2. $\dfrac{x^{-4}}{y^{-2}} = \dfrac{y^2}{x^4}$ 3. $\left(\dfrac{2}{3}\right)^{-3} = \left(\dfrac{3}{2}\right)^3 = \dfrac{3^3}{2^3} = \dfrac{27}{8}$
Scientific Notation	Write a as $b \times 10^n$, where $1 \le |b| < 10$ and n is an integer.	$23{,}500 = 2.35 \times 10^4$, $0.0056 = 5.6 \times 10^{-3}$, and $1000 = 1 \times 10^3$

5.5 Exercises

CONCEPTS AND VOCABULARY

Exercises 1–5: Complete the given rule for integer exponents m and n, where a and b are nonzero real numbers.

1. $a^{-n} = $ _____

2. $\dfrac{1}{a^{-n}} = $ _____

3. $\dfrac{a^m}{a^n} = $ _____

4. $\dfrac{a^{-n}}{b^{-m}} = $ _____

5. $\left(\dfrac{a}{b}\right)^{-n} = $ _____

6. To write a positive number a in scientific notation as $b \times 10^n$, the number b must satisfy _____.

NEGATIVE EXPONENTS

Exercises 7–18: Simplify the expression.

7. (a) 4^{-1} (b) $\left(\dfrac{1}{3}\right)^{-2}$

8. (a) 6^{-2} (b) 2.5^{-1}

9. (a) $2^3 \cdot 2^{-2}$ (b) $10^{-1} \cdot 10^{-2}$

10. (a) $3^{-4} \cdot 3^2$ (b) $10^4 \cdot 10^{-2}$

11. (a) $3^{-2} \cdot 3^{-1} \cdot 3^{-1}$ (b) $(2^3)^{-1}$

12. (a) $2^{-3} \cdot 2^5 \cdot 2^{-4}$ (b) $(3^{-2})^{-2}$

13. (a) $(3^2 4^3)^{-1}$ (b) $\dfrac{4^5}{4^2}$

14. (a) $(2^{-2} 3^2)^{-2}$ (b) $\dfrac{5^5}{5^3}$

15. (a) $\dfrac{1^9}{1^7}$ (b) $\dfrac{1}{4^{-3}}$

16. (a) $\dfrac{-6^4}{6}$ (b) $\dfrac{1}{6^{-2}}$

17. (a) $\dfrac{5^{-2}}{5^{-4}}$ (b) $\left(\dfrac{2}{7}\right)^{-2}$

18. (a) $\dfrac{7^{-3}}{7^{-1}}$ (b) $\left(\dfrac{3}{4}\right)^{-3}$

Exercises 19–50: Simplify the expression. Write the answer using positive exponents.

19. (a) x^{-1} (b) a^{-4}

20. (a) y^{-2} (b) z^{-7}

21. (a) $x^{-2} \cdot x^{-1} \cdot x$ (b) $a^{-5} \cdot a^{-2} \cdot a^{-1}$

22. (a) $y^{-3} \cdot y^4 \cdot y^{-5}$ (b) $b^5 \cdot b^{-3} \cdot b^{-6}$

23. (a) $x^2 y^{-3} x^{-5} y^6$ (b) $(xy)^{-3}$

24. (a) $a^{-2} b^{-6} b^3 a^{-1}$ (b) $(ab)^{-1}$

25. (a) $(2t)^{-4}$ (b) $(x+1)^{-7}$

26. (a) $(8c)^{-2}$ (b) $(a+b)^{-9}$

27. (a) $(a^{-2})^{-4}$ (b) $(rt^3)^{-2}$

28. (a) $(4x^3)^{-3}$ (b) $(xy^{-3})^{-2}$

29. (a) $(ab)^2 (a^2)^{-3}$ (b) $\dfrac{x^4}{x^2}$

30. (a) $(x^3)^{-2}(xy)^4 y^{-5}$ (b) $\dfrac{y^9}{y^5}$

31. (a) $\dfrac{a^{10}}{a^{-3}}$ (b) $\dfrac{4z}{2z^4}$

32. (a) $\dfrac{b^5}{b^{-2}}$ (b) $\dfrac{12x^2}{24x^7}$

33. (a) $\dfrac{-4xy^5}{6x^3y^2}$ (b) $\dfrac{x^{-4}}{x^{-1}}$

34. (a) $\dfrac{12a^6 b^2}{8ab^3}$ (b) $\dfrac{y^{-2}}{y^{-7}}$

35. (a) $\dfrac{10b^{-4}}{5b^{-5}}$ (b) $\left(\dfrac{a}{b}\right)^3$

36. (a) $\dfrac{8a^{-2}}{2a^{-3}}$ (b) $\left(\dfrac{2x}{y}\right)^5$

37. (a) $\dfrac{6x^2 y^{-4}}{18x^{-5} y^4}$ (b) $\dfrac{16a^{-3} b^{-5}}{4a^{-8} b}$

38. (a) $\dfrac{m^2 n^4}{3m^{-5} n^4}$ (b) $\dfrac{7x^{-3} y^{-5}}{x^{-3} y^{-2}}$

39. (a) $\dfrac{1}{y^{-5}}$ (b) $\dfrac{4}{2t^{-3}}$

40. (a) $\dfrac{1}{z^{-6}}$ (b) $\dfrac{5}{10b^{-5}}$

41. (a) $\dfrac{3a^4}{(2a^{-2})^3}$ (b) $\dfrac{(2b^5)^{-3}}{4b^{-6}}$

42. (a) $\dfrac{(2x^4)^{-2}}{5x^{-2}}$ (b) $\dfrac{2y^5}{(3y^{-4})^{-2}}$

43. (a) $\dfrac{1}{(xy)^{-2}}$ (b) $\dfrac{1}{(a^2 b)^{-3}}$

44. (a) $\dfrac{1}{(ab)^{-1}}$ (b) $\dfrac{1}{(rt^4)^{-2}}$

45. (a) $\dfrac{(3m^4 n)^{-2}}{(2mn^{-2})^3}$ (b) $\dfrac{(-4x^4 y)^2}{(xy^{-5})^{-3}}$

46. (a) $\dfrac{(x^4 y^2)^2}{(-2x^2 y^{-2})^3}$ (b) $\dfrac{(m^2 n^{-6})^{-2}}{(4m^2 n^{-4})^{-3}}$

47. (a) $\left(\dfrac{a}{b}\right)^{-2}$ (b) $\left(\dfrac{u}{4v}\right)^{-1}$

48. (a) $\left(\dfrac{2x}{y}\right)^{-3}$ (b) $\left(\dfrac{5u}{3v}\right)^{-2}$

49. (a) $\left(\dfrac{3a^4 b}{2ab^{-2}}\right)^{-2}$ (b) $\left(\dfrac{4m^4 n}{5m^{-3} n^2}\right)^2$

50. (a) $\left(\dfrac{2x^4 y^2}{3x^3 y^{-3}}\right)^3$ (b) $\left(\dfrac{a^{-5} b^2}{2ab^{-2}}\right)^{-2}$

51. Thinking Generally For positive integers m and n show that $\dfrac{a^n}{a^m} = \dfrac{1}{a^{m-n}}$.

52. Thinking Generally For positive integers m and n show that $\dfrac{a^{-n}}{a^{-m}} = a^{m-n}$.

SCIENTIFIC NOTATION

Exercises 53–58: (Refer to Table 5.6.) Write the value of the power of 10 in words.

53. 10^3 **54.** 10^6

55. 10^9 **56.** 10^{-1}

57. 10^{-2} **58.** 10^{-6}

Exercises 59–70: Write the expression in standard form.

59. 2×10^3 **60.** 5×10^2

61. 4.5×10^4 **62.** 7.1×10^6

63. 8×10^{-3} **64.** 9×10^{-1}

65. 4.56×10^{-4} **66.** 9.4×10^{-2}

67. 3.9×10^7 **68.** 5.27×10^6

69. -5×10^5 **70.** -9.5×10^3

Exercises 71–82: Write the number in scientific notation.

71. 2000

72. 11,000

73. 567

74. 9300

75. 12,000,000

76. 600,000

77. 0.004

78. 0.0008

79. 0.000895

80. 0.0123

81. −0.05

82. −0.934

Exercises 83–90: Evaluate the expression. Write the answer in standard form.

83. $(5 \times 10^3)(3 \times 10^2)$

84. $(2.1 \times 10^2)(2 \times 10^4)$

85. $(-3 \times 10^{-3})(5 \times 10^2)$

86. $(4 \times 10^2)(1 \times 10^3)(5 \times 10^{-4})$

87. $\dfrac{4 \times 10^5}{2 \times 10^2}$

88. $\dfrac{9 \times 10^2}{3 \times 10^6}$

89. $\dfrac{8 \times 10^{-6}}{4 \times 10^{-3}}$

90. $\dfrac{6.3 \times 10^2}{2 \times 10^{-3}}$

APPLICATIONS

91. *Light-year* The distance that light travels in 1 year is called a *light-year*. Light travels at 1.86×10^5 miles per second, and there are about 3.15×10^7 seconds in 1 year.
(a) Estimate the number of miles in 1 light-year.
(b) Except for the sun, Alpha Centauri is the nearest star, and its distance is 4.27 light-years from Earth. Estimate its distance in miles. Write your answer in scientific notation.

92. *Milky Way* It takes 2×10^8 years for the sun to make one orbit around the Milky Way galaxy. Write this number in standard form.

93. *Speed of the Sun* (Refer to the two previous exercises.) Assume that the sun's orbit in the Milky Way galaxy is circular with a diameter of 10^5 light-years. Estimate how many miles the sun travels in 1 year.

94. *Distance to the Moon* The moon is about 240,000 miles from Earth.
(a) Write this number in scientific notation.
(b) If a rocket traveled at 4×10^4 miles per hour, how long would it take for it to reach the moon?

95. Online Exploration In 1997, the creators of the Internet search engine BackRub renamed it Google. This new name is a play on the word *googol*, which is a very large number. Look up a googol and write it in scientific notation.

96. Online Exploration An astronomical unit (AU) is based on the distance from Earth to the sun. Look up the distance in kilometers from Earth to the sun.
(a) Write an astronomical unit in standard form to the nearest million kilometers.
(b) Convert your rounded answer from part (a) to scientific notation.

97. *Gross Domestic Product* The gross domestic product (GDP) is the total national output of goods and services valued at market prices *within* the United States. The GDP of the United States in 2005 was $12,460,000,000,000. (*Source:* Bureau of Economic Analysis.)
(a) Write this number in scientific notation.
(b) In 2005, the U.S. population was 2.98×10^8. On average, how many dollars of goods and services were produced by each individual?

98. *Average Family Net Worth* A family refers to a group of two or more people related by birth, marriage, or adoption who reside together. In 2000, the average family net worth was $280,000, and there were about 7.2×10^7 families. Calculate the total family net worth in the United States in 2000. (*Source:* U.S. Census Bureau.)

WRITING ABOUT MATHEMATICS

99. Explain what a negative exponent is and how it is different from a positive exponent. Give an example.

100. Explain why scientific notation is helpful for writing some numbers.

Group Activity   Working with Real Data

Directions: Form a group of 2 to 4 people. Select a person to record the group's responses for this activity. All members of the group should work cooperatively to answer the questions. If your instructor asks for your results, each member of the group should be prepared to respond.

Water in a Lake East Battle Lake in Minnesota covers an area of about 1950 acres, or 8.5×10^7 square feet, and its average depth is about 3.2×10^1 feet.

(a) Estimate the cubic feet of water in the lake. (*Hint:* volume = area × average depth.)

(b) One cubic foot of water equals about 7.5 gallons. How many gallons of water are in this lake?

(c) The population of the United States is about 3.1×10^8, and the average American uses about 1.5×10^2 gallons of water per day. Could this lake supply the American population with water for 1 day?

5.6   Division of Polynomials

Division by a Monomial • Division by a Polynomial

Girolamo Cardano (1501–1576)

A LOOK INTO MATH ▶ The study of polynomials has occupied the minds of mathematicians for centuries. During the sixteenth century, Girolamo Cardano and other Italian mathematicians discovered how to solve higher degree polynomial equations. In this section we demonstrate how to divide polynomials. Division is often needed to factor polynomials and to solve polynomial equations. (*Source:* H. Eves, *An Introduction to the History of Mathematics.*)

Division by a Monomial

To add two fractions with like denominators, we use the property

$$\frac{a}{d} + \frac{b}{d} = \frac{a+b}{d}.$$

For example, $\frac{1}{7} + \frac{3}{7} = \frac{1+3}{7} = \frac{4}{7}$.

To divide a polynomial by a monomial, we use the same property, only in reverse. That is,

$$\frac{a+b}{d} = \frac{a}{d} + \frac{b}{d}.$$

Note that each term in the numerator is divided by the monomial in the denominator. The next example shows how to divide a polynomial by a monomial.

EXAMPLE 1   **Dividing a polynomial by a monomial**

Divide.

(a) $\dfrac{a^5 + a^3}{a^2}$ **(b)** $\dfrac{5x^4 + 10x}{10x}$ **(c)** $\dfrac{3y^2 + 2y - 12}{6y}$

Solution

(a) $\dfrac{a^5 + a^3}{a^2} = \dfrac{a^5}{a^2} + \dfrac{a^3}{a^2} = a^{5-2} + a^{3-2} = a^3 + a$

(b) $\dfrac{5x^4 + 10x}{10x} = \dfrac{5x^4}{10x} + \dfrac{10x}{10x} = \dfrac{x^3}{2} + 1$

(c) $\dfrac{3y^2 + 2y - 12}{6y} = \dfrac{3y^2}{6y} + \dfrac{2y}{6y} - \dfrac{12}{6y} = \dfrac{y}{2} + \dfrac{1}{3} - \dfrac{2}{y}$

▌ Now Try Exercises 17, 19, 21

MAKING CONNECTIONS

Division and Simplification

A common mistake made when dividing expressions is to "cancel" incorrectly. Note in Example 1(b) that

$$\dfrac{5x^4 + 10x}{10x} \neq 5x^4 + \dfrac{10x}{10x}.$$

The monomial must be divided into *every* term in the numerator.

When dividing two natural numbers, we can check our work by multiplying. For example, $\frac{10}{5} = 2$, and we can check this result by finding the product $5 \cdot 2 = 10$. Similarly, to check

$$\dfrac{a^5 + a^3}{a^2} = a^3 + a$$

in Example 1(a) we can multiply a^2 and $a^3 + a$.

$$a^2(a^3 + a) = a^2 \cdot a^3 + a^2 \cdot a \qquad \text{Distributive property}$$
$$= a^5 + a^3 \ \checkmark \qquad \text{It checks.}$$

EXAMPLE 2 **Dividing and checking**

Divide the expression $\dfrac{8x^3 - 4x^2 + 6x}{2x^2}$ and then check the result.

Solution
Be sure to divide $2x^2$ into *every* term in the numerator.

$$\dfrac{8x^3 - 4x^2 + 6x}{2x^2} = \dfrac{8x^3}{2x^2} - \dfrac{4x^2}{2x^2} + \dfrac{6x}{2x^2} = 4x - 2 + \dfrac{3}{x}$$

Check:

$$2x^2\left(4x - 2 + \dfrac{3}{x}\right) = 2x^2 \cdot 4x - 2x^2 \cdot 2 + 2x^2 \cdot \dfrac{3}{x}$$
$$= 8x^3 - 4x^2 + 6x \ \checkmark$$

▌ Now Try Exercise 23

EXAMPLE 3 **Finding the length of a rectangle**

The rectangle in Figure 5.17 has an area $A = x^2 + 2x$ and width x. Write an expression for its length l in terms of x.

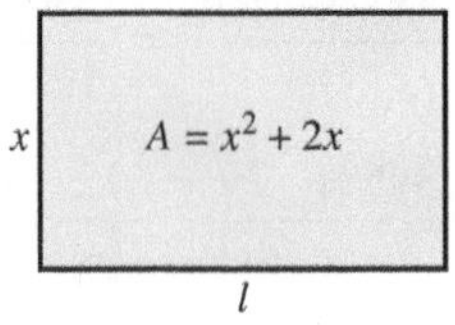

Figure 5.17

STUDY TIP

Do you have enough time to study your notes and complete your assignments? One way to manage your time is to make a list of your time commitments and determine the amount of time that each activity requires. Remember to include time for eating, sleeping, and relaxing!

Solution

The area A of a rectangle equals length l times width w, or $A = lw$. Solving for l gives

$$l = \frac{A}{w}.$$

Thus to find the length of the given rectangle, divide the area by the width.

$$l = \frac{x^2 + 2x}{x} = \frac{x^2}{x} + \frac{2x}{x} = x + 2$$

The length of the rectangle is $x + 2$. The answer checks because $x(x + 2) = x^2 + 2x$.

Now Try Exercise 49

Division by a Polynomial

To understand division by a polynomial better, we first need to review some terminology related to long division of natural numbers. To compute $271 \div 4$, we complete long division as follows.

$$
\begin{array}{r}
\text{Quotient} \longrightarrow 67 \text{ R } 3 \longleftarrow \text{Remainder} \\
\text{Divisor} \longrightarrow 4\overline{)271} \quad \longleftarrow \text{Dividend} \\
\underline{24} \\
31 \\
\underline{28} \\
3
\end{array}
$$

To check this result, we find the product of the quotient and divisor and then add the remainder. Because $67 \cdot 4 + 3 = 271$, the answer checks. The quotient and remainder can also be expressed as $67\frac{3}{4}$. Division of polynomials is similar to long division of natural numbers.

EXAMPLE 4 **Dividing polynomials**

Divide $\frac{6x^2 + 13x + 3}{3x + 2}$ and check.

Solution

Begin by dividing the first term of $3x + 2$ into the first term of $6x^2 + 13x + 3$. That is, divide $3x$ into $6x^2$ to obtain $2x$. Then find the product of $2x$ and $3x + 2$, or $6x^2 + 4x$, place it below $6x^2 + 13x$, and subtract. Bring down the 3.

$$
\begin{array}{r}
2x \\
3x + 2\overline{)6x^2 + 13x + 3} \\
\underline{6x^2 + 4x} \\
9x + 3
\end{array}
\qquad
\begin{array}{l}
\frac{6x^2}{3x} = 2x \\[4pt]
2x(3x + 2) = 6x^2 + 4x \\
\text{Subtract: } 13x - 4x = 9x. \text{ Bring down the 3.}
\end{array}
$$

In the next step, divide $3x$ into the first term of $9x + 3$ to obtain 3. Then find the product of 3 and $3x + 2$, or $9x + 6$, place it below $9x + 3$, and subtract.

$$
\begin{array}{r}
2x + 3 \\
3x + 2\overline{)6x^2 + 13x + 3} \\
6x^2 + 4x \\
\hline
9x + 3 \\
9x + 6 \\
\hline
-3
\end{array}
\qquad
\begin{array}{l}
\dfrac{9x}{3x} = 3 \\[2mm]
\\
3(3x + 2) = 9x + 6 \\
\text{Subtract: } 3 - 6 = -3.
\end{array}
$$

The quotient is $2x + 3$ with remainder -3. This result can also be written as

$$2x + 3 + \frac{-3}{3x + 2}, \qquad \text{Quotient} + \frac{\text{Remainder}}{\text{Divisor}}$$

in the same manner that 67 R 3 was written as $67\frac{3}{4}$.

Check polynomial division by adding the remainder to the product of the divisor and the quotient. That is,

(Divisor)(Quotient) + Remainder = Dividend.

For this example, the equation becomes

$$
(3x + 2)(2x + 3) + (-3) = 3x \cdot 2x + 3x \cdot 3 + 2 \cdot 2x + 2 \cdot 3 - 3
$$
$$
= 6x^2 + 9x + 4x + 6 - 3
$$
$$
= 6x^2 + 13x + 3. \ \checkmark \quad \text{It checks.}
$$

▮ Now Try Exercise 27

READING CHECK

• How can you check a polynomial division problem?

EXAMPLE 5 ▶ **Dividing polynomials having a missing term**

Simplify $(3x^3 + 2x - 4) \div (x - 2)$.

Solution
Because the dividend does not have an x^2-term, insert $0x^2$ as a "place holder." Then begin by dividing x into $3x^3$ to obtain $3x^2$.

$$
\begin{array}{r}
3x^2 \\
x - 2\overline{)3x^3 + 0x^2 + 2x - 4} \\
3x^3 - 6x^2 \\
\hline
6x^2 + 2x
\end{array}
\qquad
\begin{array}{l}
\dfrac{3x^3}{x} = 3x^2 \\[2mm]
3x^2(x - 2) = 3x^3 - 6x^2 \\
\text{Subtract } 0x^2 - (-6x^2) = 6x^2. \text{ Bring down } 2x.
\end{array}
$$

In the next step, divide x into $6x^2$.

$$
\begin{array}{r}
3x^2 + 6x \\
x - 2\overline{)3x^3 + 0x^2 + 2x - 4} \\
3x^3 - 6x^2 \\
\hline
6x^2 + 2x \\
6x^2 - 12x \\
\hline
14x - 4
\end{array}
\qquad
\begin{array}{l}
\dfrac{6x^2}{x} = 6x \\[4mm]
\\
6x(x - 2) = 6x^2 - 12x \\
\text{Subtract: } 2x - (-12x) = 14x. \text{ Bring down } -4.
\end{array}
$$

Now divide x into $14x$.

$$\begin{array}{r} 3x^2 + 6x + 14 \\ x - 2\overline{)3x^3 + 0x^2 + 2x - 4} \\ \underline{3x^3 - 6x^2} \\ 6x^2 + 2x \\ \underline{6x^2 - 12x} \\ 14x - 4 \\ \underline{14x - 28} \\ 24 \end{array}$$

$$\frac{14x}{x} = 14$$

$14(x - 2) = 14x - 28$

Subtract: $-4 - (-28) = 24.$

The quotient is $3x^2 + 6x + 14$ with remainder 24. This result can also be written as

$$3x^2 + 6x + 14 + \frac{24}{x - 2}.$$

▌ Now Try Exercise 37

EXAMPLE 6   **Dividing when the divisor is not linear**

Divide $x^3 - 3x^2 + 3x + 2$ by $x^2 + 1$.

Solution
Begin by writing $x^2 + 1$ as $x^2 + 0x + 1$.

$$\begin{array}{r} x - 3 \\ x^2 + 0x + 1\overline{)x^3 - 3x^2 + 3x + 2} \\ \underline{x^3 + 0x^2 + x} \\ -3x^2 + 2x + 2 \\ \underline{-3x^2 + 0x - 3} \\ 2x + 5 \end{array}$$

The quotient is $x - 3$ with remainder $2x + 5$. This result can also be written as

$$x - 3 + \frac{2x + 5}{x^2 + 1}.$$

▌ Now Try Exercise 41

5.6   Putting It All Together

CONCEPT	EXPLANATION	EXAMPLES
Division by a Monomial	Use the property $$\frac{a + b}{d} = \frac{a}{d} + \frac{b}{d}.$$ Be sure to divide the denominator into every term in the numerator.	$\dfrac{2x^3 + 4x}{2x^2} = \dfrac{2x^3}{2x^2} + \dfrac{4x}{2x^2} = x + \dfrac{2}{x}$ and $\dfrac{a^2 - 2a}{4a} = \dfrac{a^2}{4a} - \dfrac{2a}{4a} = \dfrac{a}{4} - \dfrac{1}{2}$

continued on next page

continued from previous page

CONCEPT	EXPLANATION	EXAMPLES
Division by a Polynomial	Is done similarly to the way long division of natural numbers is performed If either the divisor or the dividend is missing a term, be sure to insert as a "place holder" the missing term with coefficient 0.	Divide $x^2 + 3x + 3$ by $x + 1$. $$\begin{array}{r} x + 2 \\ x + 1\overline{)x^2 + 3x + 3} \\ \underline{x^2 + x} \\ 2x + 3 \\ \underline{2x + 2} \\ 1 \end{array}$$ The quotient is $x + 2$ with remainder 1, which can be expressed as $$x + 2 + \frac{1}{x + 1}.$$
Checking a Result	Dividend = (Divisor)(Quotient) + Remainder	When $x^2 + 3x + 3$ is divided by $x + 1$, the quotient is $x + 2$ with remainder 1. Thus $$(x + 1)(x + 2) + 1 = x^2 + 3x + 3,$$ and the answer checks.

5.6 Exercises

CONCEPTS AND VOCABULARY

1. $\frac{a + b}{d} =$ _____

2. $\frac{a + b - c}{d} =$ _____

3. When dividing a polynomial by a monomial, the monomial must be divided into every _____ of the polynomial.

4. (True or False?) The expressions $\frac{5x^2 + 2x}{2x}$ and $5x^2 + 1$ are equal.

5. (True or False?) The expressions $\frac{5x^2 + 2x}{2x}$ and $\frac{5x^2}{2x}$ are equal.

6. Because $\frac{37}{9} = 4$ with remainder 1, it follows that $37 =$ _____ $\cdot$ _____ $+$ _____.

7. Because $2x^3 - x + 5$ divided by $x + 1$ equals $2x^2 - 2x + 1$ with remainder 4, it follows that $2x^3 - x + 5 =$ _____ $\cdot$ _____ $+$ _____.

8. When dividing $2x^3 + 3x - 1$ by $x - 1$, insert _____ into the dividend as a "place holder" for the missing x^2-term.

DIVISION BY A MONOMIAL

Exercises 9–16: Divide and check.

9. $\frac{6x^2}{3x}$

10. $\frac{-5x^2}{10x^4}$

11. $\frac{z^4 + z^3}{z}$

12. $\frac{t^3 - t}{t}$

13. $\frac{a^5 - 6a^3}{2a^3}$

14. $\frac{b^4 - 4b}{4b^2}$

15. $\frac{y + 6y^2}{3y^3}$

16. $\frac{8z^2 - z}{4z^2}$

Exercises 17–26: Divide.

17. $\frac{4x - 7x^4}{x^2}$

18. $\frac{1 + 6x^4}{3x^3}$

19. $\frac{6y^2 + 3y}{3y^3}$

20. $\frac{5z^2 - 10z^3}{5z^4}$

21. $\frac{9x^4 - 3x + 6}{3x}$

22. $\frac{y^3 - 4y + 6}{y}$

23. $\frac{12y^4 - 3y^2 + 6y}{3y^2}$

24. $\frac{2x^2 - 6x + 9}{12x}$

25. $\frac{15m^4 - 10m^3 + 20m^2}{5m^2}$

26. $\frac{n^8 - 8n^6 + 4n^4}{2n^5}$

Exercises 27–34: Divide and check.

27. $\dfrac{2x^2 - 3x + 1}{x - 2}$

28. $\dfrac{4x^2 - x + 3}{x + 2}$

29. $\dfrac{x^2 + 2x + 1}{x + 1}$

30. $\dfrac{4x^2 - 4x + 1}{2x - 1}$

31. $\dfrac{x^3 - x^2 + x - 2}{x - 1}$

32. $\dfrac{2x^3 + 3x^2 + 3x - 1}{2x + 1}$

33. $\dfrac{x^3 + x^2 - 7x + 2}{x - 2}$

34. $\dfrac{x^3 + x^2 - 2x + 12}{x + 3}$

Exercises 35–46: Divide.

35. $\dfrac{4x^3 - 3x^2 + 7x + 3}{4x + 1}$

36. $\dfrac{10x^3 - x^2 - 17x - 7}{5x + 2}$

37. $\dfrac{x^3 - x + 2}{x - 2}$

38. $\dfrac{6x^3 + 8x^2 + 4}{3x + 4}$

39. $(3x^3 + 2) \div (x - 1)$

40. $(-3x^3 + 8x^2 + x) \div (3x + 4)$

41. $(x^3 + 3x^2 + 1) \div (x^2 + 1)$

42. $(x^4 - x^3 + x^2 - x + 1) \div (x^2 - 1)$

43. $\dfrac{x^3 + 1}{x^2 - x + 1}$

44. $\dfrac{4x^3 + 3x + 2}{2x^2 - x + 1}$

45. $\dfrac{x^3 + 8}{x + 2}$

46. $\dfrac{x^4 - 16}{x - 2}$

47. **Thinking Generally** If the quotient in a polynomial division problem is an integer, what must be true about the degrees of the dividend and divisor?

48. **Thinking Generally** If the quotient in a polynomial division problem is a polynomial of degree 1, what must be true about the degrees of the dividend and divisor?

APPLICATIONS

Exercises 49 and 50: Area of a Rectangle The area of a rectangle and its width are given. Find an expression for the length l.

49.

50.

51. *Volume of a Box* The volume V of a box is $2x^3 + 4x^2$, and the area of its bottom is $2x^2$. Find the height of the box in terms of x. Make a possible sketch of the box, and label the length of each side.

52. *Area of a Triangle* A triangle has height h and area $A = 2h^2 - 4h$. Find its base b in terms of h. Make a possible sketch of the triangle, and label the height and base. (*Hint:* $A = \frac{1}{2}bh$.)

WRITING ABOUT MATHEMATICS

53. Suppose that one polynomial is divided into another polynomial and the remainder is 0. What does the product of the divisor and quotient equal? Explain.

54. A student simplifies the expression $\frac{4x^3 - 1}{4x^2}$ to $x - 1$. Explain the student's error.

SECTIONS 5.5 and 5.6 **Checking Basic Concepts**

1. Simplify each expression. Write the result with positive exponents.

   (a) 9^{-2} (b) $\dfrac{3x^{-3}}{6x^4}$ (c) $(4ab^{-4})^{-2}$

2. Simplify each expression. Write the result with positive exponents.

   (a) $\dfrac{1}{z^{-5}}$ (b) $\dfrac{x^{-3}}{y^{-6}}$ (c) $\left(\dfrac{3}{x^2}\right)^{-3}$

3. Write each number in scientific notation.
   (a) 45,000   (b) 0.000234   (c) 0.01

4. Write each expression in standard form.
   (a) 4.71×10^4 (b) 6×10^{-3}

5. Simplify $\dfrac{25a^4 - 15a^3}{5a^3}$.

6. Divide $3x^2 - x - 4$ by $x - 1$. State the quotient and remainder.

7. Divide $x^4 + 2x^3 - 2x^2 - 5x - 2$ by $x^2 - 3$. State the quotient and remainder.

8. *Distance to the Sun* The distance to the sun is approximately 93 million miles.
   (a) Write this distance in scientific notation.
   (b) Light travels at 1.86×10^5 miles per second. How long does it take for the sun's light to reach Earth?

CHAPTER 5   Summary

Bases and Exponents The expression b^n has base b and exponent n and equals the expression $\underbrace{b \cdot b \cdot b \cdot \cdots \cdot b}_{n \text{ times}}$, when n is a natural number.

Example: 2^3 has base 2 and exponent 3 and equals $2 \cdot 2 \cdot 2 = 8$.

Evaluating Expressions When evaluating expressions, evaluate exponents *before* performing addition, subtraction, multiplication, division, or negation. In general, operations within parentheses should be evaluated *before* using the order of operations.

1. Evaluate exponents.
2. Perform negation.
3. Do multiplication and division from left to right.
4. Do addition and subtraction from left to right.

Example: $-3^2 + 3 \cdot 4 = -9 + 3 \cdot 4 = -9 + 12 = 3$

Zero Exponents For any nonzero number b, $b^0 = 1$. Note that 0^0 is undefined.

Examples: $5^0 = 1$ and $\left(\dfrac{x}{y}\right)^0 = 1$, where x and y are nonzero.

Product Rule For any real number a and natural numbers m and n,

$$a^m \cdot a^n = a^{m+n}.$$

Examples: $3^4 \cdot 3^2 = 3^6$ and $x^3 x^2 x^4 = x^9$

Power Rules For any real numbers a and b and natural numbers m and n,

$$(a^m)^n = a^{mn}, \quad (ab)^n = a^n b^n, \quad \text{and} \quad \left(\frac{a}{b}\right)^n = \frac{a^n}{b^n}, \quad b \neq 0.$$

Examples: $(x^2)^3 = x^6$, $(3x)^4 = 3^4 x^4 = 81x^4$, and $\left(\dfrac{2}{y}\right)^3 = \dfrac{2^3}{y^3} = \dfrac{8}{y^3}$

Terms Related to Polynomials

Monomial	A number, variable, or product of numbers and variables raised to natural number powers
Degree of a Monomial	Sum of the exponents of the variables
Coefficient of a Monomial	The number in a monomial
	Example: The monomial $-3x^2 y^3$ has degree 5 and coefficient -3.
Polynomial	A monomial or the sum of two or more monomials
Term of a Polynomial	Each monomial is a term of the polynomial.
Binomial	A polynomial with two terms
Trinomial	A polynomial with three terms
Degree of a Polynomial	The degree of the term with highest degree

Opposite of a Polynomial   The opposite is found by negating each term.

Example: $2x^3 - 4x + 5$ is a trinomial with degree 3. Its opposite is $-2x^3 + 4x - 5$.

Like Terms   Two monomials with the same variables raised to the same powers

Examples: $3xy^2$ and $-xy^2$ are like terms.

$5x^3$ and $3x^3$ are like terms.

$5x^2$ and $5x$ are *unlike* terms.

Addition of Polynomials Combine like terms, using the distributive property.

Example: $(2x^2 - 4x) + (-x^2 - x) = (2 - 1)x^2 + (-4 - 1)x$
$$= x^2 - 5x$$

Subtraction of Polynomials Add the first polynomial to the opposite of the second polynomial.

Example: $(4x^4 - 5x) - (7x^4 + 6x) = (4x^4 - 5x) + (-7x^4 - 6x)$
$$= (4 - 7)x^4 + (-5 - 6)x$$
$$= -3x^4 - 11x$$

SECTION 5.3 ■ MULTIPLICATION OF POLYNOMIALS

Multiplication of Monomials Use the commutative property and the product rule.

Examples: $-2x^3 \cdot 3x^2 = -2 \cdot 3 \cdot x^3 \cdot x^2 = -6x^5$

$(2xy^2)(3x^2y^3) = 2 \cdot 3 \cdot x \cdot x^2 \cdot y^2 \cdot y^3 = 6x^3y^5$
$$\uparrow$$
$$\text{Assumed exponent of 1}$$

Distributive Properties

$$a(b + c) = ab + ac \quad \text{and} \quad a(b - c) = ab - ac$$

Examples: $4x(3x + 6) = 4x \cdot 3x + 4x \cdot 6 = 12x^2 + 24x$

$ab(a^2 - b^2) = ab \cdot a^2 - ab \cdot b^2 = a^3b - ab^3$

Multiplication of Monomials and Polynomials Apply the distributive properties. Be sure to multiply every term in the polynomial by the monomial.

Example: $-2x^2(4x^2 - 5x - 3) = -8x^4 + 10x^3 + 6x^2$

Multiplication of Polynomials The product of two polynomials may be found by multiplying every term in the first polynomial by every term in the second polynomial. Be sure to combine like terms.

Examples: $(x + 3)(2x - 5) = 2x^2 - 5x + 6x - 15$
$$= 2x^2 + x - 15$$

$(2x + 1)(x^2 - 5x + 2) = 2x^3 - 10x^2 + 4x + x^2 - 5x + 2$
$$= 2x^3 - 9x^2 - x + 2$$

Negative Integers as Exponents For any nonzero real number a and positive integer n,

$$a^{-n} = \frac{1}{a^n},$$

Examples: $5^{-2} = \dfrac{1}{5^2}$ and $x^{-4} = \dfrac{1}{x^4}$

The Quotient Rule For any nonzero real number a and integers m and n,

$$\frac{a^m}{a^n} = a^{m-n}.$$

Examples: $\dfrac{6^4}{6^2} = 6^{4-2} = 6^2 = 36$ and $\dfrac{xy^3}{x^4y^2} = x^{1-4}y^{3-2} = x^{-3}y^1 = \dfrac{y}{x^3}$

Other Rules For any nonzero real numbers a and b and positive integers m and n,

$$\frac{1}{a^{-n}} = a^n, \quad \frac{a^{-n}}{b^{-m}} = \frac{b^m}{a^n}, \quad \text{and} \quad \left(\frac{a}{b}\right)^{-n} = \left(\frac{b}{a}\right)^n.$$

Examples: $\dfrac{1}{4^{-3}} = 4^3$, $\dfrac{x^{-3}}{y^{-2}} = \dfrac{y^2}{x^3}$,   and $\left(\dfrac{4}{5}\right)^{-2} = \left(\dfrac{5}{4}\right)^2$

Scientific Notation A real number a written as $b \times 10^n$, where $1 \le |b| < 10$ and n is an integer

Examples: $2.34 \times 10^3 = 2340$ Move the decimal point 3 places to the right.
$2.34 \times 10^{-3} = 0.00234$ Move the decimal point 3 places to the left.

Division of a Polynomial by a Monomial Divide the monomial into *every* term of the polynomial.

Example: $\dfrac{5x^3 - 10x^2 + 15x}{5x} = \dfrac{5x^3}{5x} - \dfrac{10x^2}{5x} + \dfrac{15x}{5x} = x^2 - 2x + 3$

Division of a Polynomial by a Polynomial Division of polynomials is performed similarly to long division of natural numbers.

Example: Divide $2x^3 + 4x^2 - 3x + 1$ by $x + 1$.

$$
\begin{array}{r}
2x^2 + 2x - 5 \\
x + 1 \overline{)\, 2x^3 + 4x^2 - 3x + 1} \\
\underline{2x^3 + 2x^2} \\
2x^2 - 3x \\
\underline{2x^2 + 2x} \\
-5x + 1 \\
\underline{-5x - 5} \\
6
\end{array}
$$

The quotient is $2x^2 + 2x - 5$ with remainder 6, which can be written as

$$2x^2 + 2x - 5 + \frac{6}{x + 1}.$$

CHAPTER 5   Review Exercises

SECTION 5.1

Exercises 1–6: Evaluate the expression.

1. 5^3

2. -3^4

3. $4(-2)^0$

4. $3 + 3^2 - 3^0$

5. $\dfrac{-5^2}{5}$

6. $\left(\dfrac{-5}{5}\right)^2$

Exercises 7–24: Simplify the expression.

7. $6^2 \cdot 6^3$

8. $10^5 \cdot 10^7$

9. $z^4 \cdot z^5$

10. $y^2 \cdot y \cdot y^3$

11. $5x^2 \cdot 6x^7$

12. $(ab^3)(a^3b)$

13. $(2^5)^2$

14. $(m^4)^5$

15. $(ab)^3$

16. $(x^2y^3)^4$

17. $(xy)^3(x^2y^4)^2$

18. $(a^2b^9)^0$

19. $(r - t)^4(r - t)^5$

20. $(a + b)^2(a + b)^4$

21. $\left(\dfrac{3}{x - y}\right)^2$

22. $\left(\dfrac{x + y}{2}\right)^3$

23. $2x^2(3x - 5)$

24. $3x(4x + x^3)$

SECTION 5.2

Exercises 25 and 26: Identify the degree and coefficient of the monomial.

25. $6x^7$

26. $-x^2y^3$

Exercises 27–30: Determine whether the expression is a polynomial. If it is, state how many terms and variables the polynomial contains. Then state its degree.

27. $8y$

28. $8x^3 - 3x^2 + x - 5$

29. $a^2 + 2ab + b^2$

30. $\dfrac{1}{xy}$

31. Add the polynomials vertically.
$$3x^2 + 4x + 8$$
$$\underline{2x^2 - 5x - 5}$$

32. Write the opposite of $6x^2 - 3x - 7$.

Exercises 33–40: Simplify.

33. $(4x - 3) + (-x + 7)$

34. $(3x^2 - 1) - (5x^2 + 12)$

35. $(x^2 + 5x + 6) - (3x^2 - 4x + 1)$

36. $(x^2 + 3x - 5) + (2x^2 - 5x - 1)$

37. $(a^3 + 4a^2) + (a^3 - 5a^2 + 7a)$

38. $(4x^3 - 2x + 6) - (4x^3 - 6)$

39. $(xy + y^2) + (4y^2 - 4xy)$

40. $(7x^2 + 2xy + y^2) - (7x^2 - 2xy + y^2)$

SECTION 5.3

Exercises 41–54: Multiply and simplify.

41. $-x^2 \cdot x^3$

42. $-(r^2t^3)(rt)$

43. $-3(2t - 5)$

44. $2y(1 - 6y)$

45. $6x^3(3x^2 + 5x)$

46. $-x(x^2 - 2x + 9)$

47. $-ab(a^2 - 2ab + b^2)$

48. $(a - 2)(a + 5)$

49. $(8x - 3)(x + 2)$

50. $(2x - 1)(1 - x)$

51. $(y^2 + 1)(2y + 1)$

52. $(y^2 - 1)(2y^2 + 1)$

53. $(z + 1)(z^2 - z + 1)$

54. $(4z - 3)(z^2 - 3z + 1)$

Exercises 55 and 56: Multiply the expression
(a) geometrically and
(b) symbolically.

55. $z(z + 1)$

56. $2x(x + 2)$

SECTION 5.5

Exercises 75–82: Simplify the expression.

75. 9^{-1} **76.** 3^{-2}

77. $4^3 \cdot 4^{-2}$ **78.** $10^{-6} \cdot 10^3$

79. $\dfrac{1}{6^{-2}}$ **80.** $\dfrac{5^7}{5^9}$

81. $(3^{-1} 2^2)^{-2}$ **82.** $(2^{-4} 5^3)^0$

Exercises 83–98: Simplify the expression. Write the answer using positive exponents.

83. z^{-2} **84.** y^{-4}

85. $a^{-4} \cdot a^2$ **86.** $x^2 \cdot x^{-5} \cdot x$

87. $(2t)^{-2}$ **88.** $(ab^2)^{-3}$

89. $(xy)^{-2}(x^{-2}y)^{-1}$ **90.** $\dfrac{x^6}{x^2}$

91. $\dfrac{4x}{2x^4}$ **92.** $\dfrac{20x^5y^3}{30xy^6}$

93. $\left(\dfrac{a}{b}\right)^5$ **94.** $\dfrac{4}{t^{-4}}$

95. $\dfrac{(3m^3n)^{-2}}{(2m^2n^{-3})^3}$ **96.** $\left(\dfrac{x^{-4}y^2}{3xy^{-3}}\right)^{-2}$

97. $\left(\dfrac{x}{y}\right)^{-2}$ **98.** $\left(\dfrac{3u}{2v}\right)^{-1}$

Exercises 99–102: Write the expression in standard form.

99. 6×10^2 **100.** 5.24×10^4

101. 3.7×10^{-3} **102.** 6.234×10^{-2}

Exercises 103–106: Write the number in scientific notation.

103. 10,000   **104.** 56,100,000

105. 0.000054   **106.** 0.001

Exercises 107 and 108: Evaluate the expression. Write the result in standard form.

107. $(4 \times 10^2)(6 \times 10^4)$ **108.** $\dfrac{8 \times 10^3}{4 \times 10^4}$

SECTION 5.6

Exercises 109–116: Divide and check.

109. $\dfrac{5x^2 + 3x}{3x}$ **110.** $\dfrac{6b^4 - 4b^2 + 2}{2b^2}$

111. $\dfrac{3x^2 - x + 2}{x - 1}$ **112.** $\dfrac{9x^2 - 6x - 2}{3x + 2}$

113. $\dfrac{4x^3 - 11x^2 - 7x - 1}{4x + 1}$

114. $\dfrac{2x^3 - x^2 - 1}{2x - 1}$ **115.** $\dfrac{x^3 - x^2 - x + 1}{x^2 + 1}$

116. $\dfrac{x^4 + 3x^3 + 8x^2 + 7x + 5}{x^2 + x + 1}$

APPLICATIONS

117. *Heart Rate* An athlete starts running and continues for 10 seconds. The polynomial $\frac{1}{2}t^2 + 60$ calculates the heart rate of the athlete in beats per minute t seconds after beginning the run, where $t \le 10$.
   (a) What is the athlete's heart rate when the athlete first starts to run?
   (b) What is the athlete's heart rate after 10 seconds?
   (c) What happens to the athlete's heart rate while the athlete is running?

118. *Areas of Rectangles* Find a monomial equal to the sum of the areas of the rectangles. Calculate this sum for $x = 3$ feet and $y = 4$ feet.

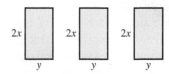

119. *Area of a Rectangle* Write a polynomial that gives the area of the rectangle. Calculate its area for $z = 6$ inches.

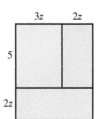

120. *Area of a Square* Find the area of the square whose sides have length x^2y.

121. *Compound Interest* If P dollars are deposited in an account that pays 6% annual interest, then the amount of money after 3 years is given by $P(1 + 0.06)^3$. Find this amount when $P = \$700$.

122. *Volume of a Sphere* The expression for the volume of a sphere with radius r is $\frac{4}{3}\pi r^3$. Find a polynomial that gives the volume of a sphere with radius $x + 2$. Leave your answer in terms of π.

123. *Height Reached by a Baseball* A baseball is hit straight up. Its height h in feet above the ground after t seconds is given by $t(96 - 16t)$.
(a) Multiply this expression.
(b) Evaluate both the expression in part (a) and the given expression for $t = 2$. Interpret the result.

124. *Rectangular Building* A rectangular building has a perimeter of 1200 feet.
(a) If one side of the building has length L, write a polynomial expression that gives its area. (Be sure to multiply your expression.)
(b) Evaluate the expression in part (a) for $L = 50$ and interpret the answer.

125. *Geometry* Complete each part and verify that your answers are equal.
(a) Find the area of the large square by multiplying its length and width.
(b) Find the sum of the areas of the smaller rectangles inside the large square.

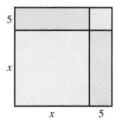

126. *Digital Picture* A digital picture, including its border, is $x + 4$ pixels by $x + 4$ pixels, and the actual picture inside the border is $x - 4$ pixels by $x - 4$ pixels.

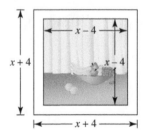

(a) Find a polynomial that gives the number of pixels in the border.
(b) Let $x = 100$ and evaluate the polynomial.

127. *Federal Debt* In 1990, the federal debt held by the public was \$2.19 trillion, and the population of the United States was 249 million. Use scientific notation to approximate the national debt per person. (*Source:* U.S. Department of the Treasury.)

128. *Alcohol Consumption* In 2007, about 239 million people in the United States were age 14 or older. They consumed, on average, 2.31 gallons of alcohol per person. Use scientific notation to estimate the total number of gallons of alcohol consumed by this age group. (*Source:* Department of Health and Human Services.)

CHAPTER 5   Extended and Discovery Exercises

Exercises 1–6: Arithmetic and Scientific Notation The product $(4 \times 10^3) \times (2 \times 10^2)$ can be evaluated as

$$(4 \times 2) \times (10^3 \times 10^2) = 8 \times 10^5,$$

and the quotient $(4 \times 10^3) \div (2 \times 10^2)$ can be evaluated as

$$\frac{4 \times 10^3}{2 \times 10^2} = \frac{4}{2} \times \frac{10^3}{10^2} = 2 \times 10^1.$$

How would you evaluate $(4 \times 10^3) + (2 \times 10^2)$? How would you evaluate $(4 \times 10^3) - (2 \times 10^2)$? Make a conjecture as to how numbers in scientific notation should be added and subtracted. Try your method on these problems and then check your answers with a calculator set in scientific mode. Does your method work?

1. $(4 \times 10^3) + (3 \times 10^3)$

2. $(5 \times 10^{-2}) - (2 \times 10^{-2})$

3. $(1.2 \times 10^4) - (3 \times 10^3)$

4. $(2 \times 10^2) + (6 \times 10^1)$

5. $(2 \times 10^{-1}) + (4 \times 10^{-2})$

6. $(2 \times 10^{-3}) - (5 \times 10^{-2})$

Exercises 7 and 8: Constructing a Box A box is constructed from a rectangular piece of metal by cutting squares from the corners and folding up the sides. The square, cutout corners are x inches by x inches.

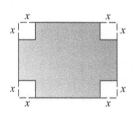 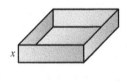

7. Suppose that the dimensions of the metal piece are 20 inches by 30 inches.
   (a) Write a polynomial that gives the volume of the box.
   (b) Find the volume of the box for $x = 4$ inches.

8. Suppose that the metal piece is square with sides of length 25 inches.
   (a) Write a polynomial expression that gives the outside surface area of the box. (Assume that the box does not have a top.)
   (b) Find this area for $x = 3$ inches.

Exercises 9–12: Calculators and Polynomials A graphing calculator can be used to help determine whether two polynomial expressions in one variable are equal. For example, suppose that a student believes that $(x + 2)^2$ and $x^2 + 4$ are equal. Then the first two calculator tables shown demonstrate that the two expressions are not equal except for $x = 0$.

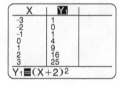

The next two calculator tables support the fact that $(x + 1)^2$ and $x^2 + 2x + 1$ are equal for all x.

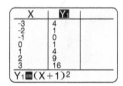

Use a graphing calculator to determine whether the first expression is equal to the second expression. If the expressions are not equal, multiply the first expression and simplify it.

9. $3x(4 - 5x)$, $12x - 5x$

10. $(x - 1)^2$, $x^2 - 1$

11. $(x - 1)(x^2 + x + 1)$, $x^3 - 1$

12. $(x - 2)^3$, $x^3 - 8$

8

Introduction to Functions

8.1 Functions and Their
   Representations
8.2 Linear Functions
8.3 Compound Inequalities
8.4 Other Functions and
   Their Properties

> **"Our competitive advantage is our *math skills*, which is probably not something you would expect of a media company."**
>
> —MAX LEVCHIN,
> CEO OF SLIDE
>
> (Slide is the number one company for writing Facebook applications.)

Every day millions of people create trillions of bytes of information. The only way we can make sense out of these data and determine what is occurring within society is to use mathematics. One of the most important mathematical concepts used to discover trends and patterns is that of a *function*. A function typically receives an input (or question), performs a computation, and gives the output (or answer).

Functions have been used in science and engineering for centuries to answer questions related to things like eclipses, communication, and transportation. However, today functions are also being used to describe human behavior and to design social networks. (See Section 8.1, Exercise 75.) In fact, you may have noticed that new features available on Twitter and Facebook are sometimes referred to as applications or *functions*. People are creating thousands of new functions every day. *Math skills are essential* for writing successful applications and functions.

8.1 Functions and Their Representations

Basic Concepts • Representations of a Function • Definition of a Function • Identifying a Function • Graphing Calculators (Optional)

A LOOK INTO MATH ▶

NEW VOCABULARY

☐ Function
☐ Function notation
☐ Input/Output
☐ Name of the function
☐ Dependent variable
☐ Independent variable
☐ Verbal representation
☐ Numerical representation
☐ Symbolic representation
☐ Graphical representation
☐ Diagrams/Diagrammatic representation
☐ Relation
☐ Domain/Range
☐ Nonlinear functions
☐ Vertical line test

In earlier chapters we showed how to use numbers to describe data. For example, instead of simply saying that there are *a lot* of people on Twitter, we might say that there are about 50 million tweets per day. A number helps explain what "a lot" means. We also showed that data can be summarized with formulas and graphs. Formulas and graphs are sometimes used to represent *functions*, which are essential in mathematics. In this section we introduce functions and their representations.

Basic Concepts

▶ **REAL-WORLD CONNECTION** Functions are used to calculate many important quantities. For example, suppose that a person works for $7 per hour. Then we could use a function *named* f to calculate the amount of money the person earned after working x hours simply by multiplying the *input* x by 7. The result y is called the *output*. This concept is shown visually in the following diagram.

$$\text{Input } x \longrightarrow \text{Function } f \longrightarrow \text{Output } y = f(x)$$

Uses input x to
compute a value of y

For each valid input x, a function computes *exactly one* output y, which may be represented by the ordered pair (x, y). If the input is 5 hours, f outputs $7 \cdot 5 = \$35$; if the input is 8 hours, f outputs $7 \cdot 8 = \$56$. These results can be represented by the ordered pairs $(5, 35)$ and $(8, 56)$. Sometimes an input may not be valid. For example, if $x = -3$, there is no reasonable output because a person cannot work -3 hours.

We say that y *is a function of* x because the output y is determined by and *depends* on the input x. As a result, y is called the *dependent variable* and x is the *independent variable*. To emphasize that y is a function of x, we use the notation $y = f(x)$. The symbol $f(x)$ does not represent multiplication of a variable f and a variable x. The notation $y = f(x)$ is called *function notation*, is read "y equals f of x," and means that function f with input x produces output y. For example, if $x = 3$ hours, $y = f(3) = \$21$.

FUNCTION NOTATION

The notation $y = f(x)$ is called **function notation**. The **input** is x, the **output** is y, and the **name of the function** is f.

$$\overset{\text{Name}}{\underset{\text{Output} \quad \text{Input}}{y = f(x)}}$$

The variable y is called the **dependent variable** and the variable x is called the **independent variable**. The expression $f(4) = 28$ is read "f of 4 equals 28" and indicates that f outputs 28 when the input is 4. A function computes *exactly one* output for each valid input. The letters f, g, and h are often used to denote names of functions.

NOTE: Functions can be given *meaningful* names and variables. For example, function f could have been defined by $P(h) = 7h$, where function P calculates the pay after working h hours for $7 per hour.

▶ **REAL-WORLD CONNECTION** Functions can be used to compute a variety of quantities. For example, suppose that a boy has a sister who is exactly 5 years older than he is. If the age of the boy is x, then a function g can calculate the age of his sister by adding 5 to x. Thus $g(4) = 4 + 5 = 9$, $g(10) = 10 + 5 = 15$, and in general $g(x) = x + 5$. That is, function g adds 5 to input x to obtain the output $y = g(x)$.

Functions can be represented by an input–output machine, as illustrated in Figure 8.1. This machine represents function g and receives input $x = 4$, adds 5 to this value, and then outputs $g(4) = 4 + 5 = 9$.

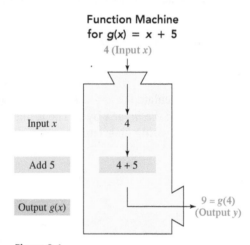

Function Machine
for g(x) = x + 5

Figure 8.1

Representations of a Function

▶ **REAL-WORLD CONNECTION** A function f forms a relation between inputs x and outputs y that can be represented verbally, numerically, symbolically, and graphically. Functions can also be represented with diagrams. We begin by considering a function f that converts yards to feet.

VERBAL REPRESENTATION (WORDS) To convert x yards to y feet we multiply x by 3. Therefore, if function f computes the number of feet in x yards, a **verbal representation** of f is "Multiply the input x in yards by 3 to obtain the output y in feet."

NUMERICAL REPRESENTATION (TABLE OF VALUES) A function f that converts yards to feet is shown in Table 8.1, where $y = f(x)$.

A *table of values* is called a **numerical representation** of a function. Many times it is impossible to list all valid inputs x in a table. On the one hand, if a table does not contain every x-input, it is a *partial* numerical representation. On the other hand, a *complete* numerical representation includes *all* valid inputs. Table 8.1 is a partial numerical representation of f because many valid inputs, such as $x = 10$ or $x = 5.3$, are not shown in it. Note that for each valid input x there is exactly one output y. *For a function, inputs are not listed more than once in a table.*

SYMBOLIC REPRESENTATION (FORMULA) A *formula* provides a **symbolic representation** of a function. The computation performed by f to convert x yards to y feet is expressed by $y = 3x$. A formula for f is $f(x) = 3x$, where $y = f(x)$. We say that function f is *defined by* or *given by* $f(x) = 3x$. Thus $f(2) = 3 \cdot 2 = 6$.

GRAPHICAL REPRESENTATION (GRAPH) A **graphical representation**, or **graph**, visually associates an x-input with a y-output. The ordered pairs

$$(1, 3), (2, 6), (3, 9), (4, 12), (5, 15), (6, 18), \text{ and } (7, 21)$$

TABLE 8.1

x (yards)	y (feet)
1	3
2	6
3	9
4	12
5	15
6	18
7	21

from Table 8.1 are plotted in Figure 8.2(a). This scatterplot suggests a line for the graph f. For each real number x there is exactly one real number y determined by $y = 3x$. If we restrict inputs to $x \geq 0$ and plot all ordered pairs $(x, 3x)$, then a line with no breaks will appear, as shown in Figure 8.2(b).

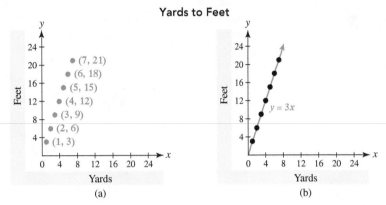

Figure 8.2

Because $f(1) = 3$, it follows that the point $(1, 3)$ lies on the graph of f, as shown in Figure 8.3. Graphs can sometimes be used to define a function f. For example, because the point $(1, 3)$ lies on the graph of f in Figure 8.3, we can conclude that $f(1) = 3$. That is, each point on the graph of f defines an input–output pair for f.

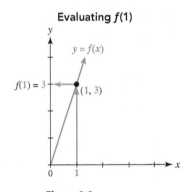

Figure 8.3

MAKING CONNECTIONS

Functions, Points, and Graphs

If $f(a) = b$, then the point (a, b) lies on the graph of f. Conversely, if the point (a, b) lies on the graph of f, then $f(a) = b$. See Figure 8.4(a). Thus each point on the graph of f can be written in the form $(a, f(a))$. See Figure 8.4(b).

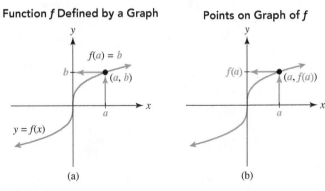

Figure 8.4

Yards to Feet

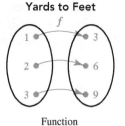

Function

Figure 8.5

DIAGRAMMATIC REPRESENTATION (DIAGRAM) Functions may be represented by **diagrams**. Figure 8.5 is a diagram of a function where an arrow is used to identify the output y associated with input x. For example, an arrow is drawn from input **2** to output **6**, which is written in function notation as $f(2) = 6$. That is, **2** yards are equivalent to **6** feet.

Figure 8.6(a) shows a (different) function f even though $f(1) = 4$ and $f(2) = 4$. Although two inputs for f have the same output, each valid input has exactly one output. In contrast, Figure 8.6(b) is *not* a function because input 2 results in two different outputs, 5 and 6.

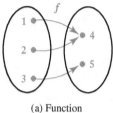 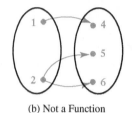

(a) Function   (b) Not a Function

Figure 8.6

MAKING CONNECTIONS

Four Representations of a Function

Symbolic Representation $f(x) = x + 1$

Numerical Representation

x	y
-2	-1
-1	0
0	1
1	2
2	3

Graphical Representation

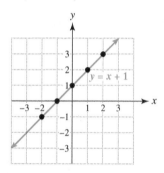

Verbal Representation f adds 1 to an input x to produce an output y.

EXAMPLE 1 **Evaluating symbolic representations (formulas)**

Evaluate each function f at the given value of x.
(a) $f(x) = 3x - 7$ $x = -2$

(b) $f(x) = \dfrac{x}{x + 2}$ $x = 0.5$

(c) $f(x) = \sqrt{x - 1}$ $x = 10$

Solution
(a) $f(-2) = 3(-2) - 7 = -6 - 7 = -13$

(b) $f(0.5) = \dfrac{0.5}{0.5 + 2} = \dfrac{0.5}{2.5} = 0.2$

(c) $f(10) = \sqrt{10 - 1} = \sqrt{9} = 3$

Now Try Exercises 21, 23, 31

▶ **REAL-WORLD CONNECTION** In the next example we calculate sales tax by evaluating different representations of a function.

EXAMPLE 2 **Calculating sales tax**

Let a function f compute a sales tax of 7% on a purchase of x dollars. Use the given representation to evaluate $f(2)$.

(a) *Verbal Representation* Multiply a purchase of x dollars by 0.07 to obtain a sales tax of y dollars.
(b) *Numerical Representation (partial)* Shown in Table 8.2
(c) *Symbolic Representation* $f(x) = 0.07x$
(d) *Graphical Representation* Shown in Figure 8.7
(e) *Diagrammatic Representation* Shown in Figure 8.8

TABLE 8.2

x	$f(x)$
$1.00	$0.07
$2.00	$0.14
$3.00	$0.21
$4.00	$0.28

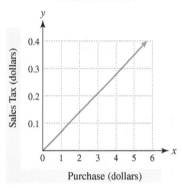

Sales Tax of 7%

Figure 8.7

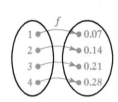

Figure 8.8

Solution
(a) *Verbal* Multiply the input 2 by 0.07 to obtain 0.14. The sales tax on a $2.00 purchase is $0.14.
(b) *Numerical* From Table 8.2, $f(2) = \$0.14$.
(c) *Symbolic* Because $f(x) = 0.07x$, $f(2) = 0.07(2) = 0.14$, or $0.14.
(d) *Graphical* To evaluate $f(2)$ with a graph, first find 2 on the x-axis in Figure 8.9. Then move vertically upward until you reach the graph of f. The point on the graph may be estimated as $(2, 0.14)$, meaning that $f(2) = 0.14$. Note that it may not be possible to find the exact answer from a graph. For example, one might estimate $f(2)$ to be 0.13 or 0.15 instead of 0.14.

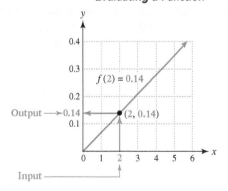

Evaluating a Function

Figure 8.9

(e) *Diagrammatic* In Figure 8.8, follow the arrow from 2 to 0.14. Thus $f(2) = 0.14$.

▌ Now Try Exercises 25, 33, 53, 59, 61

▶ **REAL-WORLD CONNECTION** There are many examples of functions. To give more meaning to a function, sometimes we change both its name and its input variable. For instance, if we know the radius r of a circle, we can calculate its circumference by using $C(r) = 2\pi r$. The next example illustrates how functions are used in physical therapy.

EXAMPLE 3   Computing crutch length

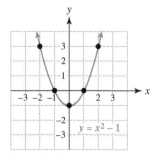

People who sustain leg injuries often require crutches. A proper crutch length can be estimated without using trial and error. The function L, given by $L(t) = 0.72t + 2$, outputs an appropriate crutch length L in inches for a person t inches tall. (*Source: Journal of the American Physical Therapy Association.*)

(a) Find $L(60)$ and interpret the result.
(b) If one person is 70 inches tall and another person is 71 inches tall, what should be the difference in their crutch lengths?

Solution
(a) $L(60) = 0.72(60) + 2 = 45.2$. Thus a person 60 inches tall needs crutches that are about 45.2 inches long.
(b) From the formula $L(t) = 0.72t + 2$, we can see that each 1-inch increase in t results in a 0.72-inch increase in $L(t)$. For example,

$$L(71) - L(70) = 53.12 - 52.4 = 0.72.$$

■ Now Try Exercise 75

In the next example we find a formula and then sketch a graph of a function.

EXAMPLE 4   Finding representations of a function

Let function f square the input x and then subtract 1 to obtain the output y.
(a) Write a formula, or symbolic representation, for f.
(b) Make a table of values, or numerical representation, for f. Use $x = -2, -1, 0, 1, 2$.
(c) Sketch a graph, or graphical representation, of f.

Solution
(a) **Symbolic Representation** If we square x and then subtract 1, we obtain $x^2 - 1$. Thus a formula for f is $f(x) = x^2 - 1$.
(b) **Numerical Representation** Make a table of values for $f(x)$, as shown in Table 8.3. For example,

$$f(-2) = (-2)^2 - 1 = 4 - 1 = 3.$$

(c) **Graphical Representation** To obtain a graph of $f(x) = x^2 - 1$, plot the points from Table 8.3 and then connect them with a smooth curve, as shown in Figure 8.10. Note that we need to plot enough points so that we can determine the overall shape of the graph.

READING CHECK

Give a verbal, numerical, symbolic, and graphical representation of a function that calculates the number of days in a given number of weeks. Choose meaningful variables.

TABLE 8.3

x	$f(x)$
-2	3
-1	0
0	-1
1	0
2	3

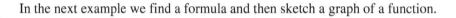

Figure 8.10

■ Now Try Exercise 63

Definition of a Function

A function is a fundamental concept in mathematics. Its definition should allow for all representations of a function. *A function receives an input x and produces exactly one output y,* which can be expressed as an ordered pair:

$$(x, y).$$

Input   Output

A **relation** is a set of ordered pairs, and a function is a special type of relation.

FUNCTION

A **function** f is a set of ordered pairs (x, y) where each x-value corresponds to exactly one y-value.

The **domain** of f is the set of all x-values, and the **range** of f is the set of all y-values. For example, a function f that converts 1, 2, 3, and 4 yards to feet could be expressed as

$$f = \{(1, 3), (2, 6), (3, 9), (4, 12)\}.$$

The domain of f is $D = \{1, 2, 3, 4\}$, and the range of f is $R = \{3, 6, 9, 12\}$.

MAKING CONNECTIONS

Relations and Functions

A relation can be thought of as a set of input–output pairs. A function is a special type of relation whereby each input results in exactly one output.

▶ **REAL-WORLD CONNECTION** In the next example, we see how education can improve a person's chances for earning a higher income.

EXAMPLE 5 **Computing average income**

A function f computes the average individual income in dollars in relation to educational attainment. This function is defined by $f(N) = 21{,}484$, $f(H) = 31{,}286$, $f(B) = 57{,}181$, and $f(M) = 70{,}181$, where N denotes no diploma, H a high school diploma, B a bachelor's degree, and M a master's degree. (*Source:* 2010 Statistical Abstract.)
(a) Write f as a set of ordered pairs.
(b) Give the domain and range of f.
(c) Discuss the relationship between education and income.

Solution
(a) $f = \{(N, 21484), (H, 31286), (B, 57181), (M, 70181)\}$
(b) The domain of function f is given by $D = \{N, H, B, M\}$, and the range of function f is given by $R = \{21484, 31286, 57181, 70181\}$.
(c) Education pays—the greater the educational attainment, the greater are annual earnings.

Now Try Exercise 101

EXAMPLE 6 | **Finding the domain and range graphically**

Use the graphs of f shown in Figures 8.11 and 8.12 to find each function's domain and range.

(a)

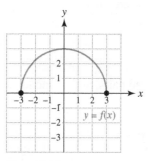

Figure 8.11

(b)

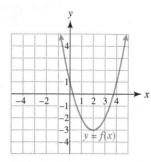

Figure 8.12

READING CHECK

Use the graph in
Figure 8.12 to evaluate $f(3)$.

Solution

(a) The domain is the set of all x-values that correspond to points on the graph of f. Figure 8.13 shows that the domain D includes all x-values satisfying $-3 \leq x \leq 3$. (Recall that the symbol $\leq$ is read "*less than or equal to*.") Because the graph is a semi-circle with no breaks, the domain includes all real numbers between and including -3 and 3. The range R is the set of y-values that correspond to points on the graph of f. Thus R includes all y-values satisfying $0 \leq y \leq 3$.

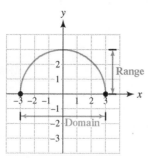

Figure 8.13

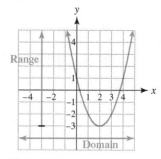

Figure 8.14

(b) The arrows on the ends of the graph in Figure 8.12 indicate that the graph extends indefinitely left and right, as well as upward. Thus D includes **all real numbers**. See Figure 8.14. The smallest y-value on the graph is $y = -3$, which occurs when $x = 2$. Thus the range R is $y \geq -3$. (Recall that the symbol $\geq$ is read "*greater than or equal to*.")

Now Try Exercises 77, 81

CRITICAL THINKING

Suppose that a car travels at 50 miles per hour to a city that is 250 miles away. Sketch a graph of a function f that gives the distance y traveled after x hours. Identify the domain and range of f.

The domain of a function is the set of all valid inputs. To determine the domain of a function from a formula, we must find x-values for which the formula is defined. To do this, we must determine if we can substitute any real number in the formula for $f(x)$. If we can, then the domain of f is *all real numbers*. However, there are situations in which we must limit the domain of f. For example, the domain must often be limited when there is either division or a square root in the formula for f. When division occurs, we must be careful to avoid values of the variable that result in division by 0, which is undefined. When a square root occurs, we must be careful to avoid values of the variable that result in the square root of a negative number, which is not a real number. This concept is demonstrated in the next example.

EXAMPLE 7   **Finding the domain of a function**

Use $f(x)$ to find the domain of f.

(a) $f(x) = 5x$ **(b)** $f(x) = \dfrac{1}{x - 2}$ **(c)** $f(x) = \sqrt{x}$

Solution
(a) Because we can always multiply a real number x by 5, $f(x) = 5x$ is defined for all real numbers. Thus the domain of f includes all real numbers.
(b) Because we cannot divide by 0, input $x = 2$ is not valid for $f(x) = \frac{1}{x-2}$. The expression for $f(x)$ is defined for all other values of x. Thus the domain of f includes all real numbers except 2, or $x \neq 2$.
(c) Because square roots of negative numbers are not real numbers, the inputs for $f(x) = \sqrt{x}$ cannot be negative. Thus the domain of f includes all nonnegative numbers, or $x \geq 0$.

Now Try Exercises 87, 91, 95

Symbolic, numerical, and graphical representations of three common functions are shown in Figure 8.15. Note that their graphs are not lines. For this reason they are called **nonlinear functions**. Use the graphs to find the domain and range of each function.

Absolute value: $f(x) = |x|$

x	-2	-1	0	1	2
$|x|$	2	1	0	1	2

Square: $f(x) = x^2$

x	-2	-1	0	1	2
x^2	4	1	0	1	4

Square root: $f(x) = \sqrt{x}$

x	0	1	4	9
$\sqrt{x}$	0	1	2	3

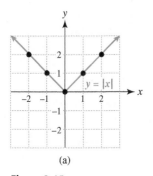

(a)

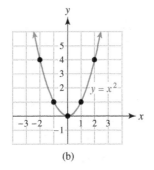

(b)

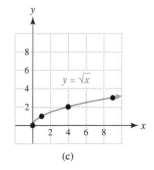

(c)

Figure 8.15

Identifying a Function

Recall that for a function each valid input x produces exactly one output y. In the next three examples we demonstrate techniques for identifying a function.

EXAMPLE 8   **Determining whether a set of ordered pairs is a function**

The set S of ordered pairs (x, y) represents the number of mergers and acquisitions y in 2010 for selected technology companies x.

$$S = \{(\text{IBM}, 12), (\text{HP}, 7), (\text{Oracle}, 5), (\text{Apple}, 5), (\text{Microsoft}, 0)\}$$

Determine if S is a function. (*Source:* cbinsights.)

Solution

The input x is the name of the technology company, and the output y is the number of mergers and acquisitions associated with that company. The set S *is* a function because each company x is associated with exactly one number y. Note that even though there were 5 mergers and acquisitions corresponding to both Oracle and Apple, S is nonetheless a function.

▮ Now Try Exercise 123

EXAMPLE 9 | **Determining whether a table of values represents a function**

TABLE 8.4

x	y
1	−4
2	8
3	2
1	5
4	−6

Determine whether Table 8.4 represents a function.

Solution

The table does not represent a function because input $x = 1$ produces two outputs: −4 and 5. That is, the following two ordered pairs both belong to this relation.

Same input x

$(1, -4)$ $(1, 5)$ ← Not a function

Different outputs y

▮ Now Try Exercise 125

VERTICAL LINE TEST To determine whether a graph represents a function, we must be convinced that it is impossible for an input x to have two or more outputs y. If two distinct points have the *same* x-coordinate on a graph, then the graph cannot represent a function. For example, the ordered pairs $(-1, 1)$ and $(-1, -1)$ could not lie on the graph of a function because input -1 results in *two* outputs: 1 and −1. When the points $(-1, 1)$ and $(-1, -1)$ are plotted, they lie on the same vertical line, as shown in Figure 8.16(a). A graph passing through these points intersects the vertical line twice, as illustrated in Figure 8.16(b).

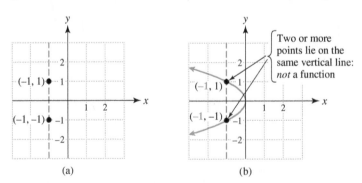

(a)   (b)

Figure 8.16

To determine whether a graph represents a function, visualize vertical lines moving across the xy-plane. If each vertical line intersects the graph *at most once*, then it is a graph of a function. This test is called the **vertical line test**. Note that the graph in Figure 8.16(b) fails the vertical line test and therefore does not represent a function.

READING CHECK

What is the vertical line test used for?

VERTICAL LINE TEST

If every vertical line intersects a graph at no more than one point, then the graph represents a function.

EXAMPLE 10   **Determining whether a graph represents a function**

Determine whether the graphs shown in Figure 8.17 represent functions.

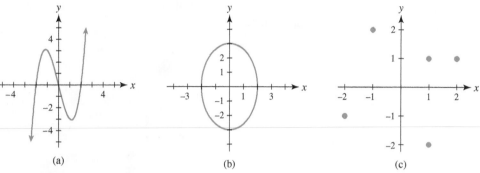

(a)   (b)   (c)

Figure 8.17

Solution

(a) Visualize vertical lines moving across the *xy*-plane from left to right. Any (red) vertical line will intersect the graph at most once, as depicted in Figure 8.18(a). Therefore the graph *does* represent a function.

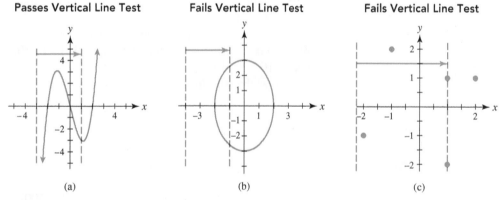

Passes Vertical Line Test   Fails Vertical Line Test   Fails Vertical Line Test

(a)   (b)   (c)

Figure 8.18

(b) Visualize vertical lines moving across the *xy*-plane from left to right. The graph *does not* represent a function because there exist (red) vertical lines that can intersect the graph twice. One such line is shown in Figure 8.18(b).

(c) Visualize vertical lines moving across the *xy*-plane from left to right. The graph is a scatterplot and *does not* represent a function because there exists one (red) vertical line that intersects two points: $(1, 1)$ and $(1, -2)$ with the same *x*-coordinate, as shown in Figure 8.18(c).

▌ Now Try Exercises 111, 113, 119

Graphing Calculators (Optional)

Graphing calculators provide several features beyond those found on scientific calculators. Graphing calculators have additional keys that can be used to create tables, scatterplots, and graphs.

▶ **REAL-WORLD CONNECTION** The **viewing rectangle**, or **window**, on a graphing calculator is similar to the viewfinder in a camera. A camera cannot take a picture of an entire scene.

The camera must be centered on some object and can photograph only a portion of the available scenery. A camera can capture different views of the same scene by zooming in and out, as can graphing calculators. The xy-plane is infinite, but the calculator screen can show only a finite, rectangular region of the xy-plane. The viewing rectangle must be specified by setting minimum and maximum values for both the x- and y-axes before a graph can be drawn.

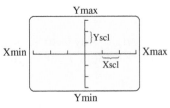

Figure 8.19

We use the following terminology regarding the size of a viewing rectangle. **Xmin** is the minimum x-value along the x-axis, and **Xmax** is the maximum x-value. Similarly, **Ymin** is the minimum y-value along the y-axis, and **Ymax** is the maximum y-value. Most graphs show an x-scale and a y-scale with tick marks on the respective axes. Sometimes the distance between consecutive tick marks is 1 unit, but at other times it might be 5 or 10 units. The distance represented by consecutive tick marks on the x-axis is called **Xscl**, and the distance represented by consecutive tick marks on the y-axis is called **Yscl** (see Figure 8.19).

This information about the viewing rectangle can be written as [Xmin, Xmax, Xscl] by [Ymin, Ymax, Yscl]. For example, $[-10, 10, 1]$ by $[-10, 10, 1]$ means that Xmin $= -10$, Xmax $= 10$, Xscl $= 1$, Ymin $= -10$, Ymax $= 10$, and Yscl $= 1$. This setting is referred to as the **standard viewing rectangle**. The window in Figure 8.19 is $[-3, 3, 1]$ by $[-3, 3, 1]$.

EXAMPLE 11 **Setting the viewing rectangle**

Show the viewing rectangle $[-2, 3, 0.5]$ by $[-100, 200, 50]$ on your calculator.

Solution
The window setting and viewing rectangle are displayed in Figure 8.20. Note that in Figure 8.20(b) there are 6 tick marks on the positive x-axis because its length is 3 units and the distance between consecutive tick marks is 0.5 unit.

CALCULATOR HELP

To set a viewing rectangle, see Appendix A (page AP-3).

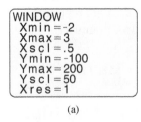

(a)

$[-2, 3, 0.5]$ by $[-100, 200, 50]$

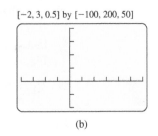

(b)

Figure 8.20

Now Try Exercise 133

SCATTERPLOTS Many graphing calculators have the capability to create scatterplots and line graphs. The next example illustrates how to make a scatterplot with a graphing calculator.

EXAMPLE 12   **Making a scatterplot with a graphing calculator**

Plot the points $(-2, -2)$, $(-1, 3)$, $(1, 2)$, and $(2, -3)$ in $[-4, 4, 1]$ by $[-4, 4, 1]$.

Solution

We entered the points $(-2, -2)$, $(-1, 3)$, $(1, 2)$, and $(2, -3)$ shown in Figure 8.21(a), using the STAT EDIT feature. The variable L1 represents the list of x-values, and the variable L2 represents the list of y-values. In Figure 8.21(b) we set the graphing calculator to make a scatterplot with the STATPLOT feature, and in Figure 8.21(c) the points have been plotted. If you have a different model of calculator you may need to consult your owner's manual.

CALCULATOR HELP

To make a scatterplot, see Appendix A (pages AP-3 and AP-4).

$[-4, 4, 1]$ by $[-4, 4, 1]$

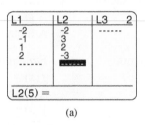
(a)

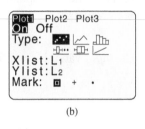
(b)

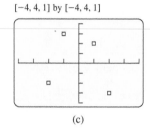
(c)

Figure 8.21

▌ Now Try Exercise 137

GRAPHS AND TABLES We can use graphing calculators to create graphs and tables, usually more efficiently and reliably than with pencil-and-paper techniques. However, a graphing calculator uses the same techniques that we might use to sketch a graph. For example, one way to sketch a graph of $y = 2x - 1$ is first to make a table of values, as shown in Table 8.5.

We can plot these points in the xy-plane, as shown in Figure 8.22. Next we might connect the points, as shown in Figure 8.23.

TABLE 8.5

x	y
-1	-3
0	-1
1	1
2	3

Plotting Points

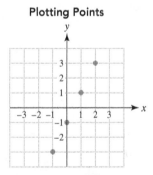

Figure 8.22

Graphing a Line

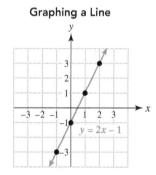

Figure 8.23

In a similar manner, a graphing calculator plots numerous points and connects them to make a graph. To create a similar graph with a graphing calculator, we enter the formula $Y_1 = 2X - 1$, set an appropriate viewing rectangle, and graph as shown in Figures 8.24 and 8.25. A table of values can also be generated as illustrated in Figure 8.26.

CALCULATOR HELP

To make a graph, see Appendix A (page AP-5). To make a table, see Appendix A (pages AP-2 and AP-3).

$[-10, 10, 1]$ by $[-10, 10, 1]$

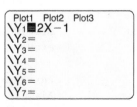
Figure 8.24

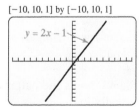
Figure 8.25

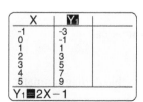
Figure 8.26

8.1   Putting It All Together

A function calculates exactly one output for each valid input and produces input–output ordered pairs in the form (x, y). A function typically computes something such as area, speed, or sales tax.

CONCEPT	EXPLANATION	EXAMPLES
Function	A set of ordered pairs (x, y), where each x-value corresponds to exactly one y-value	$f = \{(1, 3), (2, 3), (3, 1)\}$ $f(x) = 2x$ A graph of $y = x + 2$ A table of values for $y = 4x$
Independent Variable	The *input* variable for a function	*Function* *Independent Variable* $f(x) = 2x$ x $A(r) = \pi r^2$ r $V(s) = s^3$ s
Dependent Variable	The *output* variable of a function There is exactly one output for each valid input.	*Function* *Dependent Variable* $y = f(x)$ y $T = F(r)$ T $V = g(r)$ V
Domain and Range of a Function	The domain D is the set of all valid inputs. The range R is the set of all outputs.	For $S = \{(-1, 0), (3, 4), (5, 0)\}$, $D = \{-1, 3, 5\}$ and $R = \{0, 4\}$. For $f(x) = \frac{1}{x}$ the domain includes all real numbers except 0, or $x \neq 0$.
Vertical Line Test	If every vertical line intersects a graph at no more than one point, the graph represents a function.	This graph does *not* pass this test and thus does not represent a function. Two points lie on the same vertical line: *not* a function

A function can be represented verbally, symbolically, numerically, and graphically.

REPRESENTATION	EXPLANATION	COMMENTS
Verbal	Precise word description of what is computed	May be oral or written Must be stated *precisely*
Symbolic	Mathematical formula	Efficient and concise way of representing a function (e.g., $f(x) = 2x - 3$)
Numerical	List of specific inputs and their outputs	May be in the form of a table or an explicit set of ordered pairs
Graphical, diagrammatic	Shows inputs and outputs visually	No words, formulas, or tables Many types of graphs and diagrams are possible.

8.1   Exercises

CONCEPTS AND VOCABULARY

1. The notation $y = f(x)$ is called _____ notation.

2. The notation $y = f(x)$ is read _____.

3. The notation $f(x) = x^2 + 1$ is a(n) _____ representation of a function.

4. A table of values is a(n) _____ representation of a function.

5. The set of valid inputs for a function is the _____.

6. The set of outputs for a function is the _____.

7. A function computes _____ output for each valid input.

8. (True or False?) The vertical line test is used to identify graphs of relations.

9. (True or False?) Four ways to represent functions are verbal, numerical, symbolic, and graphical.

10. If $f(3) = 4$, the point _____ is on the graph of f. If $(3, 6)$ is on the graph of f, then $f($_____$) = $ _____.

11. **Thinking Generally** If $f(a) = b$, the point _____ is on the graph of f.

12. **Thinking Generally** If (c, d) is on the graph of g, then $g(c) = $ _____.

13. **Thinking Generally** If a is in the domain of f, then $f(a)$ represents how many outputs?

14. **Thinking Generally** If $f(x) = x$ for every x in the domain of f, then the domain and range of f are _____.

Exercises 15–20: Determine whether the phrase describes a function.

15. Calculating the square of a number

16. Calculating the low temperature for a day

17. Listing the students who passed a given math exam

18. Listing the children of parent x

19. Finding sales tax on a purchase

20. Naming the people in your class

REPRESENTING AND EVALUATING FUNCTIONS

Exercises 21–32: Evaluate $f(x)$ at the given values of x.

21. $f(x) = 4x - 2$ $x = -1, 0$

22. $f(x) = 5 - 3x$ $x = -4, 2$

23. $f(x) = \sqrt{x}$ $x = 0, \frac{9}{4}$

24. $f(x) = \sqrt[3]{x}$ $x = -1, 27$

25. $f(x) = x^2$ $x = -5, \frac{3}{2}$

26. $f(x) = x^3$ $x = -2, 0.1$

27. $f(x) = 3$ $x = -8, \frac{7}{3}$

28. $f(x) = 100$ $x = -\pi, \frac{1}{3}$

29. $f(x) = 5 - x^3$ $x = -2, 3$

30. $f(x) = x^2 + 5$ $x = -\frac{1}{2}, 6$

31. $f(x) = \dfrac{2}{x + 1}$ $x = -5, 4$

32. $f(x) = \dfrac{x}{x - 4}$ $x = -3, 1$

Exercises 33–38: Do the following.

   (a) *Write a formula for the function described.*
   (b) *Evaluate the function for input 10 and interpret the result.*

33. Function I computes the number of inches in x yards.

34. Function A computes the area of a circle with radius r.

35. Function M computes the number of miles in x feet.

36. Function C computes the circumference of a circle with radius r.

37. Function A computes the square feet in x acres. (*Hint:* There are 43,560 square feet in one acre.)

38. Function K computes the number of kilograms in x pounds. (*Hint:* There are about 2.2 pounds in one kilogram.)

Exercises 39–42: Write each function f as a set of ordered pairs. Give the domain and range of f.

39. $f(1) = 3, f(2) = -4, f(3) = 0$

40. $f(-1) = 4, f(0) = 6, f(1) = 4$

41. $f(a) = b, f(c) = d, f(e) = a, f(d) = b$

42. $f(a) = 7, f(b) = 7, f(c) = 7, f(d) = 7$

Exercises 43–52: Sketch a graph of f.

43. $f(x) = -x + 3$ 44. $f(x) = -2x + 1$

45. $f(x) = 2x$ 46. $f(x) = \frac{1}{2}x - 2$

47. $f(x) = 4 - x$ **48.** $f(x) = 6 - 3x$

49. $f(x) = x^2$ **50.** $f(x) = \sqrt{x}$

51. $f(x) = \sqrt{x + 1}$ **52.** $f(x) = \frac{1}{2}x^2 - 1$

Exercises 53–58: Use the graph of f to evaluate the given expressions.

53. $f(0)$ and $f(2)$ **54.** $f(-2)$ and $f(2)$

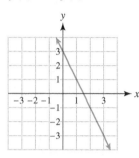   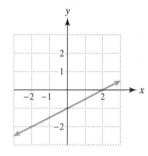

55. $f(-2)$ and $f(1)$ **56.** $f(-1)$ and $f(0)$

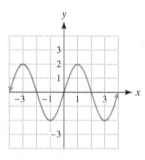   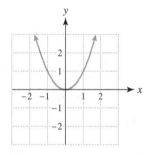

57. $f(1)$ and $f(2)$ **58.** $f(-1)$ and $f(4)$

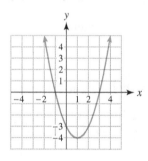   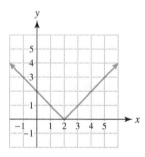

Exercises 59 and 60: Use the table to evaluate the given expressions.

59. $f(0)$ and $f(2)$

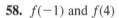

x	0	1	2	3	4
$f(x)$	5.5	4.3	3.7	2.5	1.9

60. $f(-10)$ and $f(5)$

x	-10	-5	0	5	10
$f(x)$	23	96	-45	-33	23

Exercises 61 and 62: Use the diagram to evaluate f(1990). Interpret your answer.

61. The function f computes average fuel efficiency of new U.S. passenger cars in miles per gallon during year x. (*Source:* Department of Transportation.)

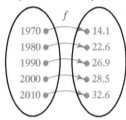

62. The function f computes average cost of tuition at public colleges and universities during academic year x. (*Source:* The College Board.)

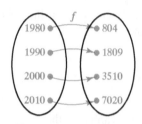

Exercises 63–66: Express the verbal representation for the function f numerically, symbolically, and graphically. Let $x = -3, -2, -1, \ldots, 3$ for the numerical representation (table), and let $-3 \le x \le 3$ for the graph.

63. Add 5 to the input x to obtain the output y.

64. Square the input x to obtain the output y.

65. Multiply the input x by 5 and then subtract 2 to obtain the output y.

66. Divide the input x by 2 and then add 3 to obtain the output y.

Exercises 67–72: Give a verbal representation for $f(x)$.

67. $f(x) = x - \frac{1}{2}$ **68.** $f(x) = \frac{3}{4}x$

69. $f(x) = \frac{x}{3}$ **70.** $f(x) = x^2 + 1$

71. $f(x) = \sqrt{x - 1}$ **72.** $f(x) = 1 - 3x$

73. *Cost of Driving* In 2010, the average cost of driving a new car in the United States was about 50 cents per mile. Symbolically, graphically, and numerically represent a function f that computes the cost in dollars of driving x miles. For the numerical representation (table) let $x = 10, 20, 30, \ldots, 70$. (*Source:* Associated Press.)

74. *Federal Income Taxes* In 2010, the lowest U.S. income tax rate was 10 percent. Symbolically, graphically, and numerically represent a function f that computes the tax on a taxable income of x dollars. For the numerical representation (table) let $x = 1000, 2000, 3000, \ldots, 7000$, and for the graphical representation let $0 \le x \le 10{,}000$. (*Source:* Internal Revenue Service.)

75. *Global Web Searches* The number of World Wide Web searches S in billions during year x can be approximated by $S(x) = 225x - 450{,}650$ from 2009 to 2012. Evaluate $S(2011)$ and interpret the result. (*Source:* RBC Capital Markets Corp.)

76. *Cost of Smartphones* The average cost difference D in dollars between smartphones and all other types of phones during year x can be approximated by $D(x) = -23.5x + 47{,}275$ from 2005 to 2009. Evaluate $D(2009)$ and interpret the result. (*Source:* Business Insider.)

IDENTIFYING DOMAINS AND RANGES

Exercises 77–84: Use the graph of f to identify its domain and range.

77.

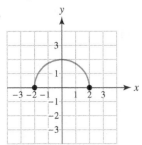

78.

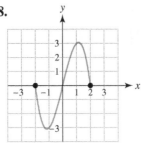

79.

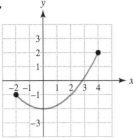

80.

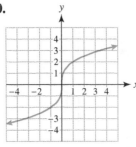

81.

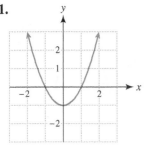

82.

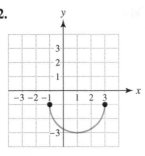

83.

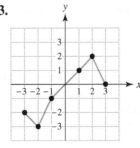

84.

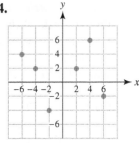

Exercises 85 and 86: Use the diagram to find the domain and range of f.

85.

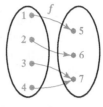

86.

Exercises 87–100: Find the domain.

87. $f(x) = 10x$

88. $f(x) = 5 - x$

89. $f(x) = x^2 - 3$

90. $f(x) = \frac{1}{2}x^2$

91. $f(x) = \dfrac{3}{x - 5}$

92. $f(x) = \dfrac{x}{x + 1}$

93. $f(x) = \dfrac{2x}{x^2 + 1}$

94. $f(x) = \dfrac{6}{1 - x}$

95. $f(x) = \sqrt{x - 1}$

96. $f(x) = |x|$

97. $f(x) = |x - 5|$

98. $f(x) = \sqrt{2 - x}$

99. $f(x) = \dfrac{1}{x}$

100. $f(x) = 1 - 3x^2$

101. *Humpback Whales* The number of humpback whales W sighted in Maui's annual whale census for year x is given by $W(2005) = 649$, $W(2006) = 1265$, $W(2007) = 959$, $W(2008) = 1726$, and $W(2009) = 1010$. (*Source:* Pacific Whale Foundation.)
(a) Evaluate $W(2008)$ and interpret the result.
(b) Identify the domain and range of W.
(c) Describe the pattern in the data.

102. *Digital Music Downloads* The percentage of digital music D that was purchased through downloads during year x is given by $D(2004) = 0.9$, $D(2005) = 5.7$, $D(2006) = 6.7$, $D(2007) = 11.2$, and $D(2008) = 12.8$. (*Source:* The Recording Industry Association of America.)

(a) Evaluate $D(2006)$ and interpret the result.

(b) Identify the domain and range of D.

(c) Describe the pattern in the data.

103. *Cost of Tuition* Suppose that a student can take from 1 to 20 credits at a college and that each credit costs \$200. If function C calculates the cost of taking x credits, determine the domain and range of C.

104. *Falling Ball* Suppose that a ball is dropped from a window that is 64 feet above the ground and that the ball strikes the ground after 2 seconds. If function H calculates the height of the ball after t seconds, determine a domain and range for H, while the ball is falling.

IDENTIFYING A FUNCTION

Exercises 105–108: Determine whether the diagram could represent a function.

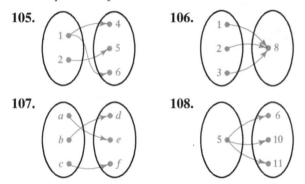

105. **106.**

107. **108.**

109. *Average Precipitation* The table lists the monthly average precipitation P in Las Vegas, Nevada, where $x = 1$ corresponds to January and $x = 12$ corresponds to December.

x (month)	1	2	3	4	5	6
P (inches)	0.5	0.4	0.4	0.2	0.2	0.1

x (month)	7	8	9	10	11	12
P (inches)	0.4	0.5	0.3	0.2	0.4	0.3

Source: J. Williams.

(a) Determine the value of P during May.

(b) Is P a function of x? Explain.

(c) If $P = 0.4$, find x.

110. *Wind Speeds* The table at the top of the next column lists the monthly average wind speed W in Louisville, Kentucky, where $x = 1$ corresponds to January and $x = 12$ corresponds to December.

x (month)	1	2	3	4	5	6
W (mph)	10.4	12.7	10.4	10.4	8.1	8.1

x (month)	7	8	9	10	11	12
W (mph)	6.9	6.9	6.9	8.1	9.2	9.2

Source: J. Williams.

(a) Determine the month with the highest average wind speed.

(b) Is W a function of x? Explain.

(c) If $W = 6.9$, find x.

Exercises 111–122: Determine whether the graph represents a function. If it does, identify the domain and range.

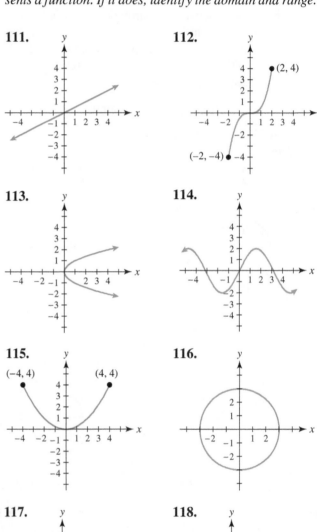

111. **112.**

113. **114.**

115. **116.**

117. **118.**

119.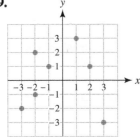

120.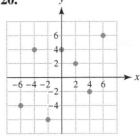

121.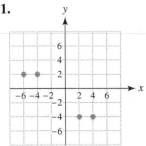

122.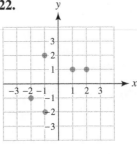

Exercises 123–126: Determine whether S is a function.

123. $S = \{(1, 2), (4, 5), (7, 8), (5, 4), (2, 2)\}$

124. $S = \{(4, 7), (-2, 1), (3, 8), (4, 9)\}$

125. S is given by the table.

x	5	10	5
y	2	1	0

126. S is given by the table.

x	-3	-2	-1
y	10	10	10

GRAPHICAL INTERPRETATION

Exercises 127 and 128: The graph represents the distance that a person is from home while walking on a straight path. The x-axis represents time and the y-axis represents distance. Interpret the graph.

127.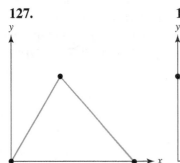

128.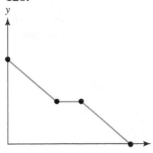

129. *Texting* The average 18- to 24-year-old person texts about 1500 messages per month. Sketch a graph that shows the total number of text messages sent over a period of 4 months. Assume that the same number of texts is sent each day. (*Source:* The Nielsen Company.)

130. *Computer Viruses* In 2000 there were about 50 thousand computer viruses. In 2010 there were about 1.6 million computer viruses. Sketch a graph of this increase from 2000 to 2010. Answers may vary. (*Source:* Symantec.)

GRAPHING CALCULATORS

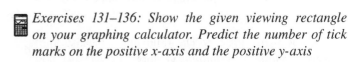 *Exercises 131–136: Show the given viewing rectangle on your graphing calculator. Predict the number of tick marks on the positive x-axis and the positive y-axis*

131. Standard viewing rectangle

132. $[-12, 12, 2]$ by $[-8, 8, 2]$

133. $[0, 100, 10]$ by $[-50, 50, 10]$

134. $[-30, 30, 5]$ by $[-20, 20, 5]$

135. $[1980, 1995, 1]$ by $[12000, 16000, 1000]$

136. $[1900, 1990, 10]$ by $[1700, 2800, 100]$

Exercises 137–142: Use your calculator to make a scatterplot of the relation after determining an appropriate viewing rectangle.

137. $\{(4, 3), (-2, 1), (-3, -3), (5, -2)\}$

138. $\{(5, 5), (2, 0), (-2, 7), (2, -8), (-1, -5)\}$

139. $\{(20, 40), (-25, -15), (-20, 25), (15, -25)\}$

140. $\{(-13, 12), (3, 10), (-15, -4), (12, -9)\}$

141. $\{(100, -100), (50, 200), (-150, -140), (-30, 80)\}$

142. $\{(-125, 75), (45, 65), (-53, -67), (150, -80)\}$

Exercises 143–146: Make a table and graph of $y = f(x)$. Let $x = -3, -2, -1, \ldots, 3$ for your table and use the standard window for your graph.

143. $f(x) = \sqrt{x + 3}$

144. $f(x) = x^3 - \frac{1}{2}x^2$

145. $f(x) = \dfrac{5 - x}{5 + x}$

146. $f(x) = |2 - x| + \sqrt[3]{x}$

WRITING ABOUT MATHEMATICS

147. Give an example of a function. Identify the domain and range of your function.

148. Explain in your own words what a function is. How is a function different from other relations?

149. Explain how to evaluate a function by using a graph. Give an example.

150. Give one difficulty that may occur when you use a table of values to evaluate a function.

Group Activity · Working with Real Data

Directions: Form a group of 2 to 4 people. Select someone to record the group's responses for this activity. All members should work cooperatively to answer the questions. If your instructor asks for the results, each member of the group should be prepared to respond.

U.S. Craigslist Visitors The following table lists the average number of *unique* visitors to Craigslist for selected years.

Year	2006	2007	2008
Visitors	180,000	288,000	420,000

Year	2009	2010
Visitors	516,000	624,000

Source: Citi Investment Research and Analysis.

(a) Make a scatterplot of the data. Let *x* represent the number of years after 2006. Discuss any trend in numbers of visitors to Craigslist.

(b) Estimate the slope of a line that could be used to model the data.

(c) Find an equation of a line $y = mx + b$ that models the data.

(d) Interpret the slope as a rate of change.

(e) Use your results to estimate the number of *unique* visitors to Craigslist in 2012.

8.2 Linear Functions

Basic Concepts • Representations of Linear Functions • Modeling Data with Linear Functions • The Midpoint Formula (Optional)

A LOOK INTO MATH ▶ Functions are frequently used to model, or describe, the real world. For example, people are becoming more energy conscious. As a result, there is an increase in the number of *green* buildings that are being constructed. Table 8.6 lists estimated U.S. sales of green building material. Because sales increase by $5 billion each year, a *linear function* can be used to model these data. (See Example 7.) In this section we discuss this important type of function.

NEW VOCABULARY

☐ Linear function
☐ Rate of change
☐ Constant function
☐ Midpoint

TABLE 8.6 **Green Material Sales ($ billions)**

Year	2010	2011	2012	2013
Sales	65	70	75	80

Source: Freedonia Group, Green Building Material.

Basic Concepts

▶ **REAL-WORLD CONNECTION** Suppose that the air conditioner is turned on when the temperature inside a house is 80°F. The resulting temperatures are listed in Table 8.7 for various elapsed times. Note that for each 1-hour increase in elapsed time, the temperature decreases by 2°F.

1-hour increase

TABLE 8.7 House Temperature

Elapsed Time (hours)	0	1	2	3	4	5
Temperature (°F)	80	78	76	74	72	70

2°F decrease

We want to determine a function f that models, or calculates, the house temperature after x hours. To do this, we will find numerical, graphical, verbal, and symbolic representations of f.

NUMERICAL REPRESENTATION (TABLE OF VALUES) We can think of Table 8.7 as a numerical representation (table of values) for the function f. A similar numerical representation that uses x and $f(x)$ is shown in Table 8.8.

TABLE 8.8 Numerical Representation of $f(x)$

x	0	1	2	3	4	5
$f(x)$	80	78	76	74	72	70

GRAPHICAL REPRESENTATION (GRAPH) To graph $y = f(x)$, we begin by plotting the points in Table 8.8, as shown in Figure 8.27. This scatterplot suggests that a line models these data, as shown in Figure 8.28. We call f a *linear function* because its graph is a *line*.

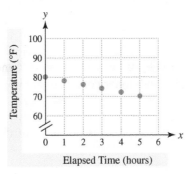

House Temperature

Figure 8.27 A Scatterplot

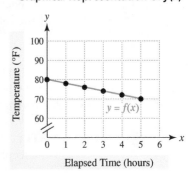

Graphical Representation of $f(x)$

Figure 8.28 A Linear Function

Another graph of $y = f(x)$ with a different y-scale is shown in Figure 8.29 on the next page. Because the y-values always decrease by the same amount for each 1-hour increase on the x-axis, we say that function f has a *constant rate of change*. In this example, the constant rate of change is −2°F per hour.

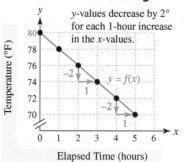

Figure 8.29

VERBAL REPRESENTATION (WORDS) Over a 5-hour period, the air conditioner lowers the initial temperature of 80°F by 2°F for each elapsed hour x. Thus a description of how to calculate the temperature is:

> "Multiply x by -2°F and then add 80°F."   Verbal representation of $f(x)$

SYMBOLIC REPRESENTATION (FORMULA) Our verbal representation of $f(x)$ makes it straightforward for us to write a formula.

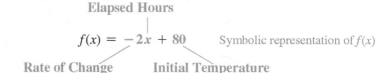

$$f(x) = -2x + 80 \qquad \text{Symbolic representation of } f(x)$$

For example,

$$f(2.5) = -2(2.5) + 80 = 75$$

means that the temperature is 75°F after the air conditioner has run for 2.5 hours. In this instance, it might be appropriate to *limit the domain* of f to x-values between 0 and 5, inclusive.

LINEAR FUNCTION

A function f defined by $f(x) = mx + b$, where m and b are constants, is a **linear function**.

For $f(x) = -2x + 80$, we have $m = -2$ and $b = 80$. The constant m represents the rate at which the air conditioner cools the building, and the constant b represents the initial temperature.

NOTE: The value of m represents the slope of the graph of $f(x) = mx + b$, and b is the y-intercept.

▶ **REAL-WORLD CONNECTION** In general, a linear function defined by $f(x) = mx + b$ changes by m units for each unit increase in x. This **rate of change** is an increase if $m > 0$ and a decrease if $m < 0$. For example, if new carpet costs \$20 per square yard, then the linear function defined by $C(x) = 20x$ gives the cost of buying x square yards of carpet. The value of $m = 20$ gives the cost (rate of change) for each additional square yard of carpet. For function C, the value of b is 0 because it costs \$0 to buy 0 square yards of carpet.

READING CHECK

Explain what a linear function is and what its graph looks like.

NOTE: If f is a linear function, then $f(0) = m(0) + b = b$. Thus b can be found by evaluating $f(x)$ at $x = 0$.

EXAMPLE 1 **Identifying linear functions**

Determine whether f is a linear function. If f is a linear function, find values for m and b so that $f(x) = mx + b$.

(a) $f(x) = 4 - 3x$ (b) $f(x) = 8$ (c) $f(x) = 2x^2 + 8$

Solution

(a) Let $m = -3$ and $b = 4$. Then $f(x) = -3x + 4$, and f is a linear function.
(b) Let $m = 0$ and $b = 8$. Then $f(x) = 0x + 8$, and f is a linear function.
(c) Function f is not linear because its formula contains x^2. The formula for a linear function cannot contain an x with an exponent other than 1.

Now Try Exercises 11, 13, 15

EXAMPLE 2 **Determining linear functions**

Use each table of values to determine whether $f(x)$ could represent a linear function. If f could be linear, write a formula for f in the form $f(x) = mx + b$.

(a)

x	0	1	2	3
$f(x)$	10	15	20	25

(b)

x	-2	0	2	4
$f(x)$	4	2	0	-2

(c)

x	0	1	2	3
$f(x)$	1	2	4	7

(d)

x	-2	0	3	5
$f(x)$	7	7	7	7

Solution

(a) For each unit increase in x, $f(x)$ increases by 5 units, so $f(x)$ could be linear with $m = 5$. Because $f(0) = 10$, $b = 10$. Thus $f(x) = 5x + 10$.
(b) For each 2-unit increase in x, $f(x)$ decreases by 2 units. Equivalently, each unit increase in x results in a 1-unit decrease in $f(x)$, so $f(x)$ could be linear with $m = -1$. Because $f(0) = 2$, $b = 2$. Thus $f(x) = -x + 2$.
(c) Each unit increase in x does not result in a constant change in $f(x)$. Thus $f(x)$ does *not* represent a linear function.
(d) For any change in x, $f(x)$ does *not* change, so $f(x)$ could be linear with $m = 0$. Because $f(0) = 7$, let $b = 7$. Thus $f(x) = 0x + 7$, or $f(x) = 7$. (When $m = 0$, we say that f is a *constant function*. See Example 8.)

Now Try Exercises 23, 25, 27, 31

Representations of Linear Functions

The graph of a linear function is a line. To graph a linear function f we can start by making a table of values and then plotting three or more points. We can then sketch the graph of f by drawing a line through these points, as demonstrated in the next example.

EXAMPLE 3   **Graphing a linear function by hand**

Sketch a graph of $f(x) = x - 1$. Use the graph to evaluate $f(-2)$.

Solution
Begin by making a table of values containing at least three points. Pick convenient values of x, such as $x = -1, 0, 1$.

$$f(-1) = -1 - 1 = -2$$
$$f(0) = 0 - 1 = -1$$
$$f(1) = 1 - 1 = 0$$

Display the results, as shown in Table 8.9.

Plot the points $(-1, -2), (0, -1)$, and $(1, 0)$. Sketch a line through these points to obtain the graph of f. A graph of a line results when *infinitely* many points are plotted, as shown in Figure 8.30.

To evaluate $f(-2)$, first find $x = -2$ on the x-axis. See Figure 8.31. Then move downward to the graph of f. By moving across to the y-axis, we see that the corresponding y-value is -3. Thus $f(-2) = -3$.

TABLE 8.9

x	y
-1	-2
0	-1
1	0

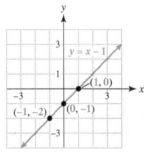

Figure 8.30

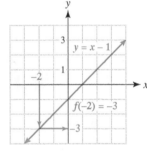

Figure 8.31

Now Try Exercises 39, 57

In the next example a graphing calculator is used to create a graph and table.

EXAMPLE 4   **Using a graphing calculator**

Give numerical and graphical representations of $f(x) = \frac{1}{2}x - 2$.

Solution
Numerical Representation To make a numerical representation, construct the table for $Y_1 = .5X - 2$, starting at $x = -3$ and incrementing by 1, as shown in Figure 8.32(a). (Other tables are possible.)
Graphical Representation Graph Y_1 in the standard viewing rectangle, as shown in Figure 8.32(b). (Other viewing rectangles may be used.)

$[-10, 10, 1]$ by $[-10, 10, 1]$

CALCULATOR HELP

To make a table, see Appendix A (pages AP-2 and AP-3). To make a graph, see Appendix A (page AP-5).

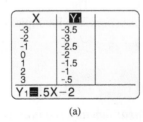

(a)

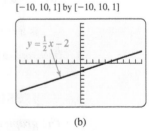

(b)

Figure 8.32

Now Try Exercise 75

CRITICAL THINKING

Two points determine a line. Why is it a good idea to plot at least three points when graphing a linear function by hand?

EXAMPLE 5   **Representing a linear function**

A linear function is given by $f(x) = -3x + 2$.
(a) Give a verbal representation of f.
(b) Make a numerical representation (table) of f by letting $x = -1, 0, 1$.
(c) Plot the points listed in the table from part (b). Then sketch a graph of $y = f(x)$.

Solution
(a) *Verbal Representation* Multiply the input x by -3 and add 2 to obtain the output.

(b) *Numerical Representation* Evaluate the formula $f(x) = -3x + 2$ at $x = -1, 0, 1$, which results in Table 8.10. Note that $f(-1) = 5$, $f(0) = 2$, and $f(1) = -1$.

(c) *Graphical Representation* To make a graph of f by hand without a graphing calculator, plot the points $(-1, 5)$, $(0, 2)$, and $(1, -1)$ from Table 8.10. Then draw a line passing through these points, as shown in Figure 8.33.

TABLE 8.10

x	$f(x)$
-1	5
0	2
1	-1

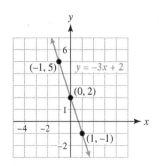

Figure 8.33

Now Try Exercise 71

NOTE: To graph $y = -3x + 2$ in Example 5, we could also graph a line with slope -3 and y-intercept 2.

MAKING CONNECTIONS

Mathematics in Newspapers

Think of the mathematics that you see in newspapers or in online publications. Often, percentages are described *verbally*, numbers are displayed in *tables*, and data are shown in *graphs*. Seldom are *formulas* given, which is an important reason to study verbal, numerical, and graphical representations.

Modeling Data with Linear Functions

▶ **REAL-WORLD CONNECTION** A distinguishing feature of a linear function is that when the input x increases by 1 unit, the output $f(x) = mx + b$ always changes by an amount equal to m. For example, the percentage of wireless households during year x from 2005 to 2010 can be modeled by the linear function

$$f(x) = 4x - 8013,$$

where x is the year. The value of $m = 4$ indicates that the percentage of wireless households has increased, on average, by 4% per year. (*Source*: National Center for Health Statistics.)

The following are other examples of quantities that are modeled by linear functions. Try to determine the value of the constant m.

- The wages earned by an individual working x hours at $8 per hour
- The distance traveled by a jet airliner in x hours if its speed is 500 miles per hour
- The cost of tuition and fees when registering for x credits if each credit costs $200 and the fees are fixed at $300

When we are modeling data with a linear function defined by $f(x) = mx + b$, the following concepts are helpful to determine m and b.

MODELING DATA WITH A LINEAR FUNCTION

The formula $f(x) = mx + b$ may be interpreted as follows.

$$f(x) \quad = \quad mx \quad + \quad b$$

(New amount) = (Change) + (Fixed amount)

When x represents time, *change* equals (rate of change) × (time).

$$f(x) \quad = \quad m \quad \times \quad x \quad + \quad b$$

(Future amount) = (Rate of change) × (Time) + (Initial amount)

▶ **REAL-WORLD CONNECTION** These concepts are applied in the next three examples.

EXAMPLE 6 **Modeling growth of bamboo**

Bamboo is gaining popularity as a *green* building material because of its fast-growing, regenerative characteristics. Under ideal conditions, some species of bamboo grow at an astonishing 2 inches per hour. Suppose a bamboo plant is initially 6 inches tall. (*Source: Cali Bamboo.*)
(a) Find a function H that models the plant's height in inches under ideal conditions after t hours.
(b) Find $H(3)$ and interpret the result.

Solution
(a) The initial height is **6** inches and the rate of change is **2** inches per hour.

$$H(t) \quad = \quad 2 \quad \times \quad t \quad + \quad 6,$$

(Future height) = (Rate of change) × (Time) + (Initial height)

or $H(t) = 2t + 6$.
(b) $H(3) = 2(3) + 6 = 12$. After 3 hours the bamboo plant is 12 inches tall.

Now Try Exercise 117

EXAMPLE 7 **Modeling demand for building green**

Table 8.11 lists estimated sales of green building material in billions of dollars. (Refer to A Look Into Math at the beginning of this section.)

TABLE 8.11 **Green Material Sales ($ billions)**

Year	2010	2011	2012	2013
Sales	65	70	75	80

Source: Freedonia Group, Green Building Material.

(a) Make a scatterplot of the data and sketch the graph of a function f that models these data. Let x represent years after 2010. That is, let $x = 0$ correspond to 2010, $x = 1$ to 2011, and so on.

(b) What were the sales in 2010? What was the annual increase in sales each year?

(c) Find a formula for $f(x)$.

(d) Use your formula to estimate sales in 2014.

Solution

(a) In Figure 8.34 the scatterplot suggests that a linear function models the data. A line has been sketched with the data.

READING CHECK

How can you determine whether data in a table can be modeled by a linear function?

Green Building Material Sales

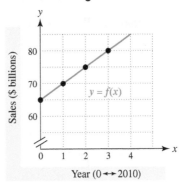

Figure 8.34 A Linear Model

(b) From Table 8.11, sales for green material were $65 billion in 2010, with sales increasing at a *constant rate* of $5 billion per year.

(c) From part (b) initial sales ($x = 0$) were $65 billion, and sales increased by $5 billion per year. Thus

$$f(x) \quad = \quad 5 \quad \times \quad x \quad + \quad 65,$$

(Future sales) = (Rate of change in sales) × (Time) + (Initial sales)

or $f(x) = 5x + 65$.

(d) Because $x = 4$ corresponds to 2014, evaluate $f(4)$.

$$f(4) = 5(4) + 65 = 85$$

This model estimates sales of green building material to be $85 billion in 2014.

Now Try Exercise 119

In the next example, we consider a simple function that models the speed of a car.

EXAMPLE 8 **Modeling with a constant function**

A car travels on a freeway with its speed recorded at regular intervals, as listed in Table 8.12.

TABLE 8.12 **Speed of a Car**

Elapsed Time (hours)	0	1	2	3	4
Speed (miles per hour)	70	70	70	70	70

(a) Discuss the speed of the car during this time interval.
(b) Find a formula for a function f that models these data.
(c) Sketch a graph of f together with the data.

Solution
(a) The speed of the car appears to be constant at 70 miles per hour.
(b) Because the speed is constant, the rate of change is 0. Thus

$$f(x) \quad = \quad 0x \quad + \quad 70$$

(Future speed) = (Change in speed) + (Initial speed)

and $f(x) = 70$. We call f a *constant function*.
(c) Because $y = f(x)$, graph $y = 70$ with the data points

$$(0, 70), (1, 70), (2, 70), (3, 70), \text{ and } (4, 70)$$

to obtain Figure 8.35.

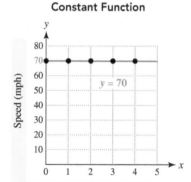

Constant Function

Figure 8.35 Speed of a Car

▌ Now Try Exercise 113

The function defined by $f(x) = 70$ is an example of a *constant function*. A **constant function** *is a linear function* with $m = 0$ and can be written as $f(x) = b$. Regardless of the input, a constant function always outputs the same value, b. Its graph is a horizontal line. Its domain is all real numbers and its range is $R = \{b\}$.

CRITICAL THINKING

Find a formula for a function D that calculates the *distance* traveled by the car in Example 8 after x hours. What is the rate of change for $D(x)$?

▶ **REAL-WORLD CONNECTION** The following are three applications of constant functions.

- A thermostat calculates a constant function regardless of the weather outside by maintaining a set temperature.
- A cruise control in a car calculates a constant function by maintaining a fixed speed, regardless of the type of road or terrain.
- A constant function calculates the 1250-foot height of the Empire State Building.

The Midpoint Formula (Optional)

▶ **REAL-WORLD CONNECTION** A common way to make estimations is to average data items. For example, in 2000 the average tuition and fees at public two-year colleges were about $1700, and in 2010 they were about $2700. (*Source:* The College Board.) To estimate tuition and fees in 2005, we could average the 2000 and 2010 amounts.

$$\frac{1700 + 2700}{2} = \$2200 \quad \text{Finding the average}$$

This technique predicts that tuition and fees were $2200 in 2005 and is referred to as finding the *midpoint*.

MIDPOINT FORMULA ON THE REAL NUMBER LINE The **midpoint** of a line segment is the unique point on the line segment that is an equal distance from the endpoints. For example, in Figure 8.36 the midpoint M of -3 and 5 on the real number line is 1.

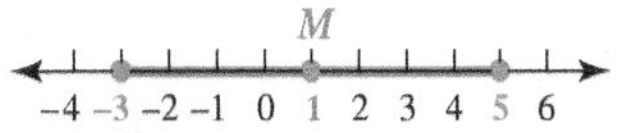

Figure 8.36

We can calculate the value of M as follows.

$$M = \frac{x_1 + x_2}{2} = \frac{-3 + 5}{2} = 1$$

Average the x-values to find the midpoint.

MIDPOINT FORMULA IN THE xy-PLANE The midpoint of a line segment in the xy-plane can be found in a similar way. Figure 8.37(a) shows the midpoint on the line segment connecting the points (x_1, y_1) and (x_2, y_2). The x-coordinate of M is equal to the average of x_1 and x_2, and the y-coordinate of M is equal to the average of y_1 and y_2. For example, the line segment with endpoints $(-2, 1)$ and $(4, -3)$ is shown in Figure 8.37(b). The coordinates of the midpoint are

$$M = \left(\frac{-2 + 4}{2}, \frac{1 + (-3)}{2} \right) = (1, -1).$$

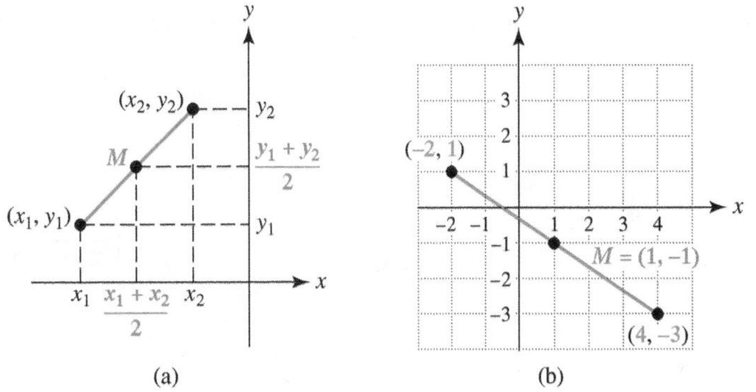

(a)   (b)

Figure 8.37

This discussion is summarized as follows.

MIDPOINT FORMULA IN THE xy-PLANE

The midpoint of the line segment with endpoints (x_1, y_1) and (x_2, y_2) in the xy-plane is

$$\left(\frac{x_1 + x_2}{2}, \frac{y_1 + y_2}{2} \right).$$

EXAMPLE 9 | **Finding the midpoint**

Find the midpoint of the line segment connecting the points $(-3, -2)$ and $(4, 1)$.

Solution
In the midpoint formula let $(-3, -2)$ be (x_1, y_1) and $(4, 1)$ be (x_2, y_2).

$$M = \left(\frac{x_1 + x_2}{2}, \frac{y_1 + y_2}{2} \right) \quad \text{Midpoint formula}$$

$$= \left(\frac{-3 + 4}{2}, \frac{-2 + 1}{2} \right) \quad \text{Substitute.}$$

$$= \left(\frac{1}{2}, -\frac{1}{2} \right) \quad \text{Simplify.}$$

The midpoint of the line segment is $\left(\frac{1}{2}, -\frac{1}{2} \right)$.

Now Try Exercise 93

▶ **REAL-WORLD CONNECTION** In the next example we use the midpoint formula to estimate the divorce rate in the United States in 2005.

EXAMPLE 10 | **Estimating the U.S. divorce rate**

The divorce rate per 1000 people in 2000 was 4.2, and in 2010 it was 3.4. (*Source: Statistical Abstract of the United States.*)
(a) Use the midpoint formula to estimate the divorce rate in 2005.
(b) Could the midpoint formula be used to estimate the divorce rate in 2003? Explain.

Solution
(a) In the midpoint formula, let $(2000, 4.2)$ be (x_1, y_1) and let $(2010, 3.4)$ be (x_2, y_2).

$$M = \left(\frac{x_1 + x_2}{2}, \frac{y_1 + y_2}{2} \right) \quad \text{Midpoint formula}$$

$$= \left(\frac{2000 + 2010}{2}, \frac{4.2 + 3.4}{2} \right) \quad \text{Substitute.}$$

$$= (2005, 3.8) \quad \text{Simplify.}$$

The midpoint formula estimates that the divorce rate was 3.8 per 1000 people in 2005. (Note that the actual rate was 3.6.)
(b) No, the midpoint formula can only be used to estimate data that are exactly halfway between two given data points. Because the year 2003 is not exactly halfway between 2000 and 2010, the midpoint formula cannot be used.

Now Try Exercise 107

NOTE: An estimate obtained from the midpoint formula is equal to an estimate obtained from a linear function whose graph passes through the endpoints of the line segment. This fact is illustrated in the next example.

EXAMPLE 11   **Relating midpoints to linear functions**

The graph of a linear function f shown in Figure 8.38 passes through the points $(-1, 3)$ and $(2, -3)$.

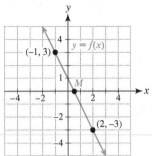

Figure 8.38

(a) Find a formula for $f(x)$.
(b) Evaluate $f\left(\frac{1}{2}\right)$. Does your answer agree with the graph?
(c) Find the midpoint M of the line segment connecting the points $(-1, 3)$ and $(2, -3)$. Comment on your result.

Solution

(a) The graph of f is a line that passes through $(-1, 3)$ and $(2, -3)$. The slope m of the line is

$$m = \frac{-3 - 3}{2 - (-1)} = -\frac{6}{3} = -2,$$

and from the graph, the y-intercept is 1. Thus $f(x) = -2x + 1$.

(b) $f\left(\frac{1}{2}\right) = -2\left(\frac{1}{2}\right) + 1 = 0$. Yes, they agree because the point $\left(\frac{1}{2}, 0\right)$ lies on the graph of $y = f(x)$ in Figure 8.38.

(c) The midpoint of the line segment connecting $(-1, 3)$ and $(2, -3)$ is

$$M = \left(\frac{-1 + 2}{2}, \frac{3 + (-3)}{2}\right) = \left(\frac{1}{2}, 0\right).$$

Finding the midpoint $M = \left(\frac{1}{2}, 0\right)$ of the line segment with endpoints $(-1, 3)$ and $(2, -3)$ is equivalent to evaluating the linear function f, whose graph passes through $(-1, 3)$ and $(2, -3)$, at $x = \frac{1}{2}$.

▌ Now Try Exercise 103

8.2   Putting It All Together

CONCEPT	EXPLANATION	EXAMPLES
Linear Function	Can be represented by $f(x) = mx + b$. Its graph is a line with slope m and y-intercept b.	$f(x) = 2x - 6$, $m = 2$ and $b = -6$ $f(x) = 10$, $m = 0$ and $b = 10$
Constant Function	Can be represented by $f(x) = b$. Its graph is a horizontal line.	$f(x) = -7$, $b = -7$ $f(x) = 22$, $b = 22$
Rate of Change for a Linear Function	The output of a linear function changes by a constant amount for each unit increase in the input.	$f(x) = -3x + 8$ decreases 3 units for each unit increase in x. $f(x) = 5$ neither increases nor decreases. The rate of change is 0.

continued on next page

continued from previous page

CONCEPT	EXPLANATION	EXAMPLES
Midpoint Formula	The midpoint of the line segment connecting (x_1, y_1) and (x_2, y_2) is $$\left(\frac{x_1 + x_2}{2}, \frac{y_1 + y_2}{2}\right).$$	The midpoint of the line segment connecting $(-2, 3)$ and $(4, 5)$ is $$\left(\frac{-2 + 4}{2}, \frac{3 + 5}{2}\right) = (1, 4).$$

REPRESENTATION	COMMENTS	EXAMPLE
Symbolic	Mathematical formula in the form $f(x) = mx + b$	$f(x) = 2x + 1$, where $m = 2$ and $b = 1$
Verbal	Multiply the input x by m and add b.	Multiply the input x by 2 and then add 1 to obtain the output.
Numerical (table of values)	For each unit increase in x in the table, the output of $f(x) = mx + b$ changes by an amount equal to m.	1-unit increase | x	0	1	2
---	---	---	---
$f(x)$	1	3	5	 2-unit increase
Graphical	The graph of a linear function is a line. Plot at least 3 points and then sketch the line. If $f(x) = mx + b$, then the graph of f has slope m and y-intercept b.	*graph of* $y = 2x + 1$

MyMathLab

PRACTICE   WATCH   DOWNLOAD   READ   REVIEW

CONCEPTS AND VOCABULARY

1. The formula for a linear function is $f(x) =$ _____.

2. The formula for a constant function is $f(x) =$ _____.

3. The graph of a linear function is a(n) _____.

4. The graph of a constant function is a(n) _____ line.

5. If $f(x) = 7x + 5$, each time x increases by 1 unit, $f(x)$ increases by _____ units.

6. If $f(x) = 5$, each time x increases by 1 unit, $f(x)$ increases by _____ units.

7. (True or False?) Every constant function is a linear function.

8. (True or False?) Every linear function is a constant function.

9. If $C(x) = 2x$ calculates the cost in dollars of buying x square feet of carpet, what does 2 represent in the formula? Interpret the fact that the point $(10, 20)$ lies on the graph of C.

10. If $G(x) = 100 - 4x$ calculates the number of gallons of water in a tank after x minutes, what does -4 represent in the formula? Interpret the fact that the point $(5, 80)$ lies on the graph of G.

IDENTIFYING LINEAR FUNCTIONS

Exercises 11–18: Determine whether f is a linear function. If f is linear, give values for m and b so that f may be expressed as $f(x) = mx + b$.

11. $f(x) = \dfrac{1}{2}x - 6$

12. $f(x) = x$

13. $f(x) = \dfrac{5}{2} - x^2$

14. $f(x) = \sqrt{x} + 3$

15. $f(x) = -9$

16. $f(x) = 1.5 - 7.3x$

17. $f(x) = -9x$

18. $f(x) = \dfrac{1}{x}$

Exercises 19–22: Determine whether the graph represents a linear function.

19.

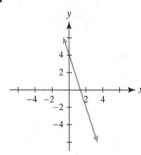

20.

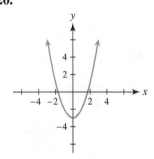

21.

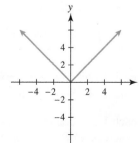

22.

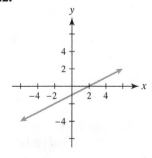

Exercises 23–32: (Refer to Example 2.) Use the table to determine whether $f(x)$ could represent a linear function. If it could, write $f(x)$ in the form $f(x) = mx + b$.

23.

x	0	1	2	3
$f(x)$	-6	-3	0	3

24.

x	0	2	4	6
$f(x)$	-2	2	6	10

25.

x	-2	0	2	4
$f(x)$	6	3	0	-3

26.

x	0	3	6	9
$f(x)$	8	4	2	1

27.

x	-2	-1	0	1
$f(x)$	-5	0	20	40

28.

x	-2	-1	0	1
$f(x)$	6	3	0	-3

29.

x	0	2	3	4
$f(x)$	0	4	6	8

30.

x	1	2	3	4
$f(x)$	0	1	3	7

31.

x	-1	0	1	2
$f(x)$	-4	-4	-4	-4

32.

x	2	5	6	8
$f(x)$	5	5	5	5

EVALUATING LINEAR FUNCTIONS

Exercises 33–38: Evaluate $f(x)$ at the given values of x.

33. $f(x) = 4x$ $\qquad\qquad x = -4, 5$

34. $f(x) = -2x + 1$ $\qquad\quad x = -2, 3$

35. $f(x) = 5 - x$ $\qquad\qquad x = -\frac{2}{3}, 3$

36. $f(x) = \frac{1}{2}x - \frac{1}{4}$ $\qquad\quad x = 0, \frac{1}{2}$

37. $f(x) = -22$ $x = -\frac{3}{4}, 13$

38. $f(x) = 9x - 7$ $x = -1.2, 2.8$

Exercises 39–44: Use the graph of f to evaluate the given expressions.

39. $f(-1)$ and $f(0)$ **40.** $f(-2)$ and $f(2)$

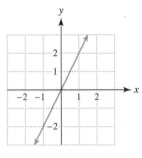 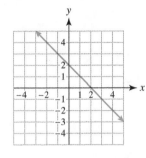

41. $f(-2)$ and $f(4)$ **42.** $f(0)$ and $f(3)$

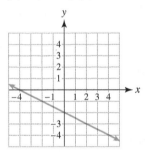 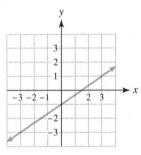

43. $f(-3)$ and $f(1)$ **44.** $f(1.5)$ and $f(0.5\pi)$

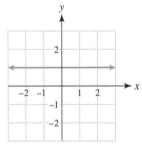 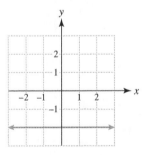

Exercises 45–48: Use the verbal description to write a formula for $f(x)$. Then evaluate $f(3)$.

45. Multiply the input by 6.

46. Multiply the input by -3 and add 7.

47. Divide the input by 6 and subtract $\frac{1}{2}$.

48. Output 8.7 for every input.

REPRESENTING LINEAR FUNCTIONS

Exercises 49–52: Match $f(x)$ with its graph (a.–d.) at the top of the next column.

49. $f(x) = 3x$ **50.** $f(x) = -2x$

51. $f(x) = x - 2$ **52.** $f(x) = 2x + 1$

   a.   **b.**

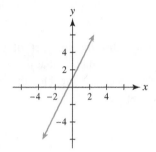 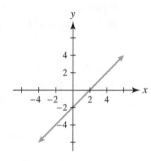

   c.   **d.**

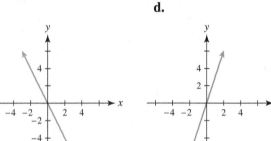

Exercises 53–62: Sketch a graph of $y = f(x)$.

53. $f(x) = 2$ **54.** $f(x) = -1$

55. $f(x) = -\frac{1}{2}x$ **56.** $f(x) = 2x$

57. $f(x) = x + 1$ **58.** $f(x) = x - 2$

59. $f(x) = 3x - 3$ **60.** $f(x) = -2x + 1$

61. $f(x) = 3 - x$ **62.** $f(x) = \frac{1}{4}x + 2$

Exercises 63–68: Write a symbolic representation (formula) for a linear function f that calculates the following.

63. The number of pounds in x ounces

64. The number of dimes in x dollars

65. The distance traveled by a car moving at 65 miles per hour for t hours

66. The long-distance phone bill *in dollars* for calling t minutes at 10 cents per minute and a fixed fee of $4.95

67. The total number of hours in a day during day x

68. The total cost of downhill skiing x times with a $500 season pass

69. Thinking Generally For each 1-unit increase in x with $y = ax + b$ and $a > 0$, y increases by _____ units.

70. Thinking Generally For each 1-unit decrease in x with $y = cx + d$ and $c < 0$, y increases by _____ units.

Exercises 71–74: Do the following.

    (a) *Give a verbal representation of f.*

    (b) *Make a numerical representation (table) of f for*
        $x = -2, 0, 2.$

    (c) *Plot the points listed in the table from part (b),*
        then sketch a graph of f.

71. $f(x) = -2x + 1$ **72.** $f(x) = 1 - x$

73. $f(x) = \frac{1}{2}x - 1$ **74.** $f(x) = \frac{3}{4}x$

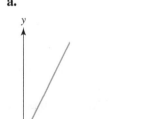 *Exercises 75–78: Do the following.*

    (a) *Make a numerical representation (table) of f for*
        $x = -3, -2, -1, \ldots, 3.$

    (b) *Graph f in the window* $[-6, 6, 1]$ *by* $[-4, 4, 1].$

75. $f(x) = \frac{1}{3}x + \sqrt{2}$ **76.** $f(x) = -\frac{2}{3}x - \sqrt{3}$

77. $f(x) = \dfrac{x + 2}{5}$ **78.** $f(x) = \dfrac{2 - 3x}{7}$

MODELING

Exercises 79–82: Match the situation with the graph
(a.–d.) that models it best, where x-values represent time
from 2000 to 2010.

79. The cost of college tuition

80. The cost of 1 gigabyte of computer memory

81. The distance between Chicago and Denver

82. The total distance traveled by a satellite that is orbit-
ing Earth if the satellite was launched in 2000

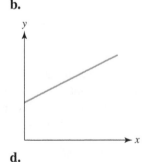

a.   **b.**

c.   **d.**

83. Online Exploration Look up the fuel efficiency
E in miles per gallon for one of your favorite cars.
(Answers will vary.)

    (a) Find a function G that calculates the number of
        gallons required to travel x miles.

    (b) If the cost of gasoline is \$3 per gallon, find func-
        tion C that calculates the cost of fuel to travel x
        miles.

84. Online Exploration Suppose that you would like to
drive to Miami for spring break (if it is possible) in the
car that you chose in Exercise 83. Calculate the gallons of gasoline needed for the trip.

MIDPOINT FORMULA

Exercises 85–92: Find the midpoint of the line segment
shown.

85.

86.

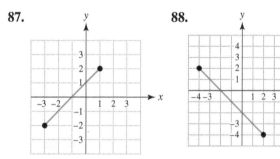

87.   **88.**

89.   **90.**

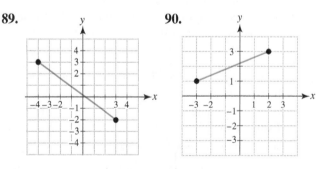

91.   **92.**

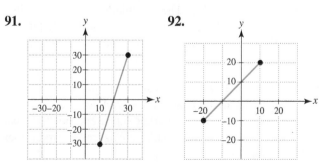

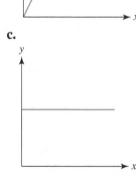

Exercises 93–102: Find the midpoint of the line segment connecting the given points.

93. $(-9, -3), (-7, 1)$ **94.** $(7, -2), (-5, 8)$

95. $\left(\frac{1}{2}, \frac{1}{3}\right), \left(-\frac{5}{2}, -\frac{2}{3}\right)$ **96.** $\left(-\frac{3}{5}, -\frac{1}{4}\right), \left(\frac{1}{10}, \frac{1}{2}\right)$

97. $(-0.3, 0.1), (0.7, 0.4)$

98. $(0.8, -0.4), (0.9, -0.1)$

99. $(2000, 5), (2010, 13)$ **100.** $(2005, 9), (2011, 3)$

101. Thinking Generally $(a, -b), (3a, 5b)$

102. Thinking Generally $(-a, b), (a, -b)$

Exercises 103–106: (Refer to Example 11.) The graph of a linear function f passes through the two given points.

(a) *Find a formula for f(x). Determine f(2).*
(b) *Determine f(2) by finding the midpoint of the line segment connecting the given points.*
(c) *Compare your answers for parts (a) and (b).*

103. $(0, 5), (4, -3)$

104. $(0, 2), (4, 10)$

105. $(-3, -1), (7, 3)$

106. $(-1, 3), (5, -5)$

Exercises 107–112: Use the midpoint formula to make the requested estimation.

107. *U.S. Life Expectancy* The life expectancy of a female born in 1990 was 78.8 years, and the life expectancy of a female born in 2010 rose to 80.8 years. Estimate the life expectancy of a female born in 2000. (*Source:* Centers for Disease Control and Prevention.)

108. *U.S. Life Expectancy* The life expectancy of a male born in 1990 was 71.8 years, and the life expectancy of a male born in 2010 rose to 75.6 years. Estimate the life expectancy of a male born in 2000. (*Source:* Centers for Disease Control and Prevention.)

109. *U.S. Population* The population of the United States in 1970 was 205 million, and in 2010 it was 308 million. Estimate the population in 1990. (*Source:* U.S. Census Bureau.)

110. *Distance Traveled* A car is moving at a constant speed on an interstate highway. After 1 hour the car passes the 103-mile marker and after 5 hours the car passes the 391-mile marker. What mile marker does the car pass after 3 hours?

111. *U.S. Median Income* In 1999 the median family income was \$40,700, and in 2009 it was \$49,800. Estimate the median family income in 2004.

112. *Estimating Fish Populations* In 2008 there were approximately 3200 large-mouth bass in a lake. This number increased to 3800 in 2012. Estimate the number of large-mouth bass in the lake in 2010.

APPLICATIONS

113. *Thermostat* Let $y = f(x)$ describe the temperature y of a room that is kept at $70°$ F for x hours.
   (a) Represent f symbolically and graphically over a 24-hour period for $0 \le x \le 24$.
   (b) Construct a table of f for $x = 0, 4, 8, 12, \ldots, 24$.
   (c) What type of function is f?

114. *Cruise Control* Let $y = f(x)$ describe the speed y of an automobile after x minutes if the cruise control is set at 60 miles per hour.
   (a) Represent f symbolically and graphically over a 15-minute period for $0 \le x \le 15$.
   (b) Construct a table of f for $x = 0, 1, 2, \ldots, 6$.
   (c) What type of function is f?

115. *Distance* A car is initially 50 miles south of the Minnesota–Iowa border, traveling south on Interstate 35. Distances D between the car and the border are recorded in the table for various elapsed times t. Find a linear function D that models these data.

t (hours)	0	2	3	5
D (miles)	50	170	230	350

116. *Estimating the Weight of a Bass* Sometimes the weight of a fish can be estimated by measuring its length. The table lists typical weights of bass having various lengths.

Length (inches)	12	14	16	18	20	22
Weight (pounds)	1.0	1.7	2.5	3.6	5.0	6.6

Source: Minnesota Department of Natural Resources.

   (a) Let x be the length and y be the weight. Make a line graph of the data.
   (b) Could the data be modeled accurately with a linear function? Explain your answer.

117. *Texting* In 2010, the average American under age 18 sent approximately 93 texts per day, whereas the average adult over age 65 sent approximately 1 text per day.

(a) Find a formula for a function K that calculates the number of texts sent in x days by the average person under age 18.

(b) Find a formula for a function A that calculates the number of texts sent in x days by the average person over age 65.

(c) Evaluate $K(365)$ and $A(365)$. Interpret your results.

118. *Rain Forests* Rain forests are forests that grow in regions receiving more than 70 inches of rain per year. The world is losing about 49 million acres of rain forest each year. (*Source: New York Times Almanac.*)

(a) Find a linear function f that calculates the change in the acres of rain forest in millions in x years.

(b) Evaluate $f(7)$ and interpret the result.

119. *Car Sales* The table shows the number of U.S. Toyota vehicles sold in millions for past years.

Year	2000	2001	2002	2003	2004
Vehicles	1.6	1.7	1.8	1.9	2.0

Source: Autodata.

(a) What were the sales in 2000?

(b) What was the annual increase in sales?

(c) Find a linear function f that models these data. Let $x = 0$ correspond to 2000, $x = 1$ to 2001, and so on.

(d) Use f to estimate sales in 2006.

120. *Tuition and Fees* Suppose tuition costs $300 per credit and that student fees are fixed at $100.

(a) Find a formula for a linear function T that models the cost of tuition and fees for x credits.

(b) Evaluate $T(16)$ and interpret the result.

121. *Skype Users* The number of Skype users S in millions x years after 2006 can be modeled by the formula $S(x) = 110x + 123$.

(a) How many users were there in 2010?

(b) What does the number 123 indicate in the formula?

(c) What does the number 110 indicate in the formula?

122. *Temperature and Volume* If a sample of a gas such as helium is heated, it will expand. The formula $V(T) = 0.147T + 40$ calculates the volume V in cubic inches of a sample of gas at temperature T in degrees Celsius.

(a) Evaluate $V(0)$ and interpret the result.

(b) If the temperature increases by $10°C$, by how much does the volume increase?

(c) What is the volume of the gas when the temperature is $100°C$?

123. *Temperature and Volume* (Refer to the preceding exercise.) A sample of gas at $0°C$ has a volume V of 137 cubic centimeters, which increases in volume

by 0.5 cubic centimeter for every $1°C$ increase in temperature T.

(a) Write a formula $V(T) = aT + b$ that gives the volume of the gas at temperature T.

(b) Find the volume of the gas when $T = 50°C$.

124. *Cost* To make a music video it costs $750 to rent a studio plus $5 for each copy produced.

(a) Write a formula $C(x) = ax + b$ that calculates the cost of producing x videos.

(b) Find the cost of producing 2500 videos.

125. *Weight Lifting* Lifting weights can increase a person's muscle mass. Each additional pound of muscle burns an extra 40 calories per day. Write a linear function that models the number of calories burned each day by x pounds of muscle. By burning an extra 3500 calories a person can lose 1 pound of fat. How many pounds of muscle are needed to burn 1 pound of fat in 30 days? (*Source: Runner's World.*)

126. *Wireless Households* The percentage P of wireless households x years after 2005 can be modeled by the formula $P(x) = 4x + 7$, where $0 \leq x \leq 7$.

(a) Evaluate $P(0)$ and $P(3)$. Interpret your results.

(b) Explain the meaning of 4 and 7 in the formula.

127. *Mobile Data Penetration* The table lists the percentage P of people with cell phones who also subscribed to a data package during year x. (For example, with a data package one can surf the Web and check email.)

Year	2007	2008	2009
Percentage	55%	59%	63%

(a) What was this percentage in 2007?

(b) By how much did this percentage change each year?

(c) Write a function P that models these data. Let x be years after 2007.

(d) Estimate this percentage in 2010.

128. *Wal-Mart Sales* The table shows Wal-Mart's share as a percentage of overall U.S. retail sales for past years. (This percentage excludes restaurants and motor vehicles.)

Year	1998	1999	2000	2001	2002
Share (%)	6	6.5	7	7.5	8

Source: Commerce Department, Wal-Mart.

(a) What was Wal-Mart's share in 1998?

(b) By how much (percent) did Wal-Mart's share increase each year?

(c) Find a linear function f that models these data. Let $x = 0$ correspond to 1998.

(d) Use f to estimate Wal-Mart's share in 2005.

WRITING ABOUT MATHEMATICS

129. Explain how you can determine whether a function is linear by using its
  (a) symbolic representation,
  (b) graphical representation, and
  (c) numerical representation.

130. Describe one way to determine whether data can be modeled by a linear function.

SECTIONS 8.1 and 8.2 — Checking Basic Concepts

1. Find a formula and sketch a graph for a function that squares the input x and then subtracts 1.

2. Use the graph of f to do the following.
  (a) Find the domain and range of f.
  (b) Evaluate $f(0)$ and $f(2)$.
  (c) Is f a linear function? Explain.

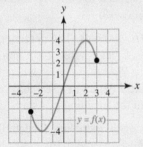

3. Determine whether f is a linear function.
  (a) $f(x) = 4x - 2$
  (b) $f(x) = 2\sqrt{x} - 5$
  (c) $f(x) = -7$
  (d) $f(x) = 9 - 2x + 5x$

4. Graph $f(x) = 4 - 3x$. Evaluate $f(-2)$.

5. Find a formula for a linear function that models the data.

x	0	1	2	3	4
$f(x)$	-1	$-\frac{1}{2}$	0	$\frac{1}{2}$	1

6. The median age in the United States from 1970 to 2010 can be approximated by
$$f(x) = 0.225x + 27.7,$$
where $x = 0$ corresponds to 1970, $x = 1$ to 1971, and so on.
  (a) Evaluate $f(20)$ and interpret the result.
  (b) Interpret the numbers 0.225 and 27.7.

7. Find the midpoint of the line segment connecting the points $(-3, 4)$ and $(5, -6)$.

8.3 Compound Inequalities

Basic Concepts • Symbolic Solutions and Number Lines • Numerical and Graphical Solutions • Interval Notation

A LOOK INTO MATH ▶ A person weighing 143 pounds and needing to purchase a life vest for white-water rafting is not likely to find one designed exactly for this weight. Life vests are manufactured to support a range of body weights. A vest approved for weights between 100 and 160 pounds might be appropriate for this person. In other words, if a person's weight is w, this life vest is safe if $w \geq 100$ *and* $w \leq 160$. This example illustrates the concept of a *compound inequality*.

Basic Concepts

A **compound inequality** consists of two inequalities joined by the words *and* or *or*. The following are two examples of compound inequalities.

1. $2x \geq -3$ **and** $2x < 5$

First compound inequality

2. $x + 2 \geq 3$ **or** $x - 1 < -5$

Second compound inequality

NEW VOCABULARY

- ☐ Compound inequality
- ☐ Intersection
- ☐ Three-part inequality
- ☐ Union
- ☐ Interval notation
- ☐ Infinity
- ☐ Negative infinity

If a compound inequality contains the word *and*, a solution must satisfy *both* inequalities. For example, 1 is a solution to the first compound inequality because

$$2(1) \geq -3 \quad \text{and} \quad 2(1) < 5 \qquad \text{First compound inequality with } x = 1$$
$$\qquad \text{True} \qquad\qquad\quad \text{True}$$

are *both* true statements.

If a compound inequality contains the word *or*, a solution must satisfy *at least one* of the two inequalities. Thus 5 is a solution to the second compound inequality, because the first statement is true.

$$5 + 2 \geq 3 \quad \text{or} \quad 5 - 1 < -5 \qquad \text{Second compound inequality with } x = 5$$
$$\qquad \text{True} \qquad\qquad\quad \text{False}$$

Note that 5 does not need to satisfy both statements for this compound inequality to be true.

EXAMPLE 1 **Determining solutions to compound inequalities**

Determine whether the given *x*-values are solutions to the compound inequalities.
(a) $x + 1 < 9$ and $2x - 1 > 8$ $\qquad x = 5, -5$
(b) $5 - 2x \leq -4$ or $5 - 2x \geq 4$ $\qquad x = 2, -3$

Solution
(a) Substitute $x = 5$ in the compound inequality $x + 1 < 9$ and $2x - 1 > 8$.

$$5 + 1 < 9 \quad \text{and} \quad 2(5) - 1 > 8$$
$$\text{True} \qquad\qquad \text{True}$$

Both inequalities are true, so 5 is a solution. Now substitute $x = -5$.

$$-5 + 1 < 9 \quad \text{and} \quad 2(-5) - 1 > 8$$
$$\text{True} \qquad\qquad \text{False}$$

To be a solution both inequalities must be true, so −5 is *not* a solution.
(b) Substitute $x = 2$ into the compound inequality $5 - 2x \leq -4$ or $5 - 2x \geq 4$.

$$5 - 2(2) \leq -4 \quad \text{or} \quad 5 - 2(2) \geq 4$$
$$\text{False} \qquad\qquad \text{False}$$

Neither inequality is true, so 2 is *not* a solution. Now substitute $x = -3$.

$$5 - 2(-3) \leq -4 \quad \text{or} \quad 5 - 2(-3) \geq 4$$
$$\text{False} \qquad\qquad \text{True}$$

At least one of the two inequalities is true, so −3 is a solution.

Now Try Exercises 7, 9

Symbolic Solutions and Number Lines

We can use a number line to graph solutions to compound inequalities, such as

$$x \leq 6 \quad \text{and} \quad x > -4.$$

The solution set for $x \leq 6$ is shaded to the left of 6, with a bracket placed at $x = 6$, as shown in Figure 8.39 on the next page. The solution set for $x > -4$ can be shown by shading a different number line to the right of −4 and placing a left parenthesis at −4. Because the inequalities are connected by *and*, the solution set consists of all numbers that are shaded on *both* number lines. The final number line represents the intersection of the

STUDY TIP

To review set-builder notation, refer to page 142.

two solution sets. That is, the solution set includes real numbers where the graphs "over-lap." For any two sets A and B, the **intersection** of A and B, denoted $A \cap B$, is defined by

$$A \cap B = \{x \mid x \text{ is an element of } A \text{ and an element of } B\}.$$

Graphing a Compound Inequality

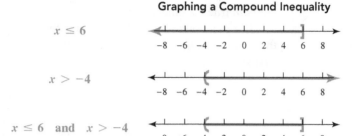

Figure 8.39

NOTE: A bracket, either [or], is used when an inequality contains $\leq$ or $\geq$. A parenthesis, either (or), is used when an inequality contains $<$ or $>$. This notation makes clear whether an endpoint is included in the inequality.

EXAMPLE 2 ▶ **Solving a compound inequality containing "and"**

Solve $2x + 4 > 8$ and $5 - x < 9$. Graph the solution set.

Solution
First solve each linear inequality separately.

$$2x + 4 > 8 \quad \text{and} \quad 5 - x < 9$$
$$2x > 4 \quad \text{and} \quad -x < 4$$
$$x > 2 \quad \text{and} \quad x > -4$$

Graph $x > 2$ and $x > -4$ on two different number lines. On a third number line, shade solutions that appear on both of the first two number lines. As shown in Figure 8.40, the solution set is $\{x \mid x > 2\}$.

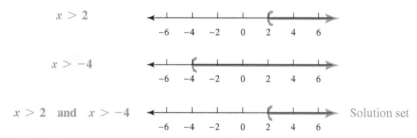

Figure 8.40
Now Try Exercise 43

Sometimes a compound inequality containing the word *and* can be combined into a three-part inequality. For example, rather than writing

$$x > 5 \quad \text{and} \quad x \leq 10,$$

READING CHECK

What is a three-part
inequality?

we could write the **three-part inequality**

$$5 < x \leq 10.$$

This three-part inequality is represented by the number line shown in Figure 8.41.

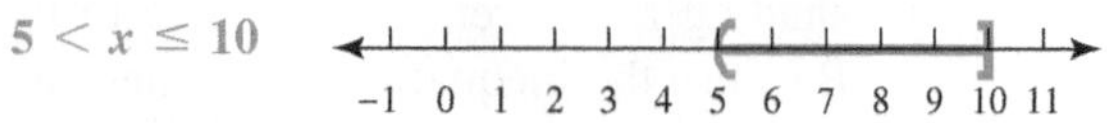

$5 < x \leq 10$ ◄─┼─┼─┼─┼─┼─(┼─┼─┼─┼─]─┼─►
                    -1 0 1 2 3 4 5 6 7 8 9 10 11

Figure 8.41

| EXAMPLE 3 | **Solving three-part inequalities** |

Solve each inequality. Graph each solution set. Write the solution set in set-builder notation. (To review set-builder notation, see page 130.)

(a) $4 < t + 2 \le 8$ **(b)** $-3 \le 3z \le 6$ **(c)** $-\dfrac{5}{2} < \dfrac{1-m}{2} < 4$

Solution

(a) To solve a three-part inequality, isolate the variable by applying properties of inequalities to each part of the inequality.

$$4 < t + 2 \le 8 \qquad \text{Given three-part inequality}$$
$$4 - 2 < t + 2 - 2 \le 8 - 2 \qquad \text{Subtract 2 from each part.}$$
$$2 < t \le 6 \qquad \text{Simplify each part.}$$

The solution set is $\{t \mid 2 < t \le 6\}$. See Figure 8.42.

$2 < t \le 6$

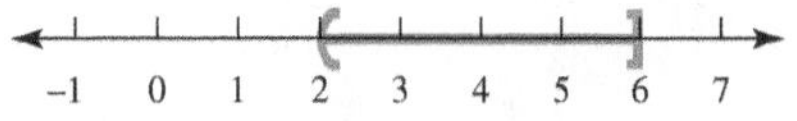

Figure 8.42

Solution set

CRITICAL THINKING

Graph the following inequalities and discuss your results.
1. $x < 2$ and $x > 5$
2. $x > 2$ or $x < 5$

(b) To simplify, divide each part by 3.

$$-3 \le 3z \le 6 \qquad \text{Given three-part inequality}$$
$$\dfrac{-3}{3} \le \dfrac{3z}{3} \le \dfrac{6}{3} \qquad \text{Divide each part by 3.}$$
$$-1 \le z \le 2 \qquad \text{Simplify each part.}$$

The solution set is $\{z \mid -1 \le z \le 2\}$. See Figure 8.43.

$-1 \le z \le 2$

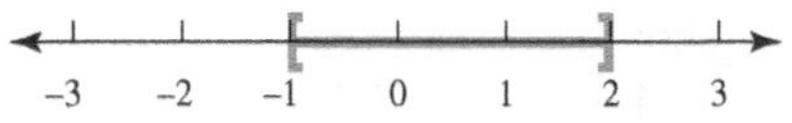

Figure 8.43

Solution set

(c) Multiply each part by 2 to clear (eliminate) fractions.

$$-\dfrac{5}{2} < \dfrac{1-m}{2} < 4 \qquad \text{Given three-part inequality}$$
$$2 \cdot \left(-\dfrac{5}{2}\right) < 2 \cdot \left(\dfrac{1-m}{2}\right) < 2 \cdot 4 \qquad \text{Multiply each part by 2.}$$
$$-5 < 1 - m < 8 \qquad \text{Simplify each part.}$$
$$-5 - 1 < 1 - m - 1 < 8 - 1 \qquad \text{Subtract 1 from each part.}$$
$$-6 < -m < 7 \qquad \text{Simplify each part.}$$
$$-1 \cdot (-6) > -1 \cdot (-m) > -1 \cdot 7 \qquad \text{Multiply each part by } -1; \text{\textit{reverse} inequality symbols.}$$
$$6 > m > -7 \qquad \text{Simplify each part.}$$
$$-7 < m < 6 \qquad \text{Rewrite inequality.}$$

The solution set is $\{m \mid -7 < m < 6\}$. See Figure 8.44.

$-7 < m < 6$

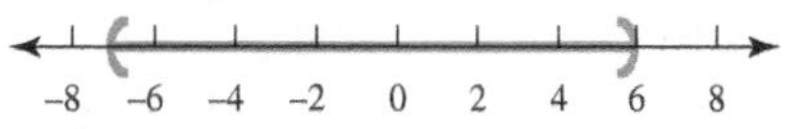

Figure 8.44

Solution set

STUDY TIP

When simplifying a three-part inequality, be sure to perform the same step on each of the three parts.

NOTE: Either $6 > m > -7$ or $-7 < m < 6$ is a correct way to write a three-part inequality. *However*, we usually write the smaller number on the left side and the larger number on the right side.

Now Try Exercises 59, 63, 79

▶ **REAL-WORLD CONNECTION** Three-part inequalities occur frequently in applications. In the next example we find altitudes at which the air temperature is within a certain range.

EXAMPLE 4   **Solving a three-part inequality**

If the ground-level temperature is 80°F, the air temperature x miles above Earth's surface is cooler and can be modeled by $T(x) = 80 - 19x$. Find the altitudes at which the air temperature ranges from 42°F down to 23°F. (*Source:* A. Miller and R. Anthes, *Meteorology.*)

Solution
We write and solve the three-part inequality $23 \le T(x) \le 42$.

$$23 \le 80 - 19x \le 42 \qquad \text{Substitute for } T(x).$$
$$-57 \le -19x \le -38 \qquad \text{Subtract 80 from each part.}$$
$$\frac{-57}{-19} \ge x \ge \frac{-38}{-19} \qquad \text{Divide by } -19; \textit{reverse} \text{ inequality symbols.}$$
$$3 \ge x \ge 2 \qquad \text{Simplify.}$$
$$2 \le x \le 3 \qquad \text{Rewrite inequality.}$$

The air temperature ranges from 42°F to 23°F for altitudes between 2 and 3 miles.

▌ **Now Try Exercise 113**

> **MAKING CONNECTIONS**
>
> **Writing Three-Part Inequalities**
> The inequality $-2 < x < 1$ means that $x > -2$ *and* $x < 1$. A three-part inequality should *not* be used when *or* connects a compound inequality. Writing $x < -2$ or $x > 1$ as $1 < x < -2$ is **incorrect** because it states that x must be both greater than 1 *and* less than -2. It is impossible for any value of x to satisfy this statement.

We can also solve compound inequalities containing the word *or*. To write the solution to such an inequality we sometimes use *union* notation. For any two sets A and B, the **union** of A and B, denoted $A \cup B$, is defined by

$$A \cup B = \{x \mid x \text{ is an element of } A \textit{ or } \text{an element of } B\}.$$

If the solution to an inequality is $\{x \mid x < 1\}$ or $\{x \mid x \ge 3\}$, then it can also be written as

$$\{x \mid x < 1\} \cup \{x \mid x \ge 3\}.$$

That is, we can replace the word *or* with the $\cup$ symbol.

EXAMPLE 5   **Solving a compound inequality containing "or"**

Solve $x + 2 < -1$ or $x + 2 > 1$. Graph the solution set.

Solution
We first solve each linear inequality.

$$x + 2 < -1 \quad \text{or} \quad x + 2 > 1 \qquad \text{Given compound inequality}$$
$$x < -3 \quad \text{or} \quad x > -1 \qquad \text{Subtract 2.}$$

We can graph the simplified inequalities on different number lines, as shown in Figure 8.45. A solution must satisfy at least one of the two inequalities. Thus the solution set for the compound inequality results from taking the *union* of the first two number lines. We can write the solution, using set-builder notation, as $\{x \mid x < -3\} \cup \{x \mid x > -1\}$ or as $\{x \mid x < -3 \text{ or } x > -1\}$.

$x < -3$

$x > -1$

$x < -3 \quad \text{or} \quad x > -1$ Solution set

Figure 8.45

▌ Now Try Exercise 47

CRITICAL THINKING

Carbon dioxide is emitted when human beings breathe. In one study of college students, the amount of carbon dioxide exhaled in grams per hour was measured during both lectures and exams. The average amount exhaled during lectures L satisfied $25.33 \leq L \leq 28.17$, whereas the average amount exhaled during exams E satisfied $36.58 \leq E \leq 40.92$. What do these results indicate? Explain. (*Source:* T. Wang, *ASHRAE Trans.*)

Numerical and Graphical Solutions

Compound inequalities can also be solved graphically and numerically, as illustrated in the next example.

EXAMPLE 6 ▶ **Estimating numbers of Internet users**

The number of U.S. Internet users in millions during year x can be modeled by the formula $f(x) = 11.6(x - 2000) + 124$. Estimate the years when the number of users is expected to be between 240 and 275 million. (*Source:* The Nielsen Company.)

Solution

Numerical Solution Let $y_1 = 11.6(x - 2000) + 124$. Make a table of values, as shown in Figure 8.46(a). In 2010 the number of Internet users was 240 million, and in 2013 this number is about 275 million. Thus from 2010 to about 2013 the number of Internet users is expected to be between 240 million and 275 million.

Graphical Solution The graph of $y_1 = 11.6(x - 2000) + 124$ is shown between the graphs of $y_2 = 240$ and $y_3 = 275$ in Figures 8.46(b) and 8.46(c) from 2010 to about 2013, or when $2010 \leq x \leq 2013$.

CALCULATOR HELP

To find a point of intersection, see Appendix A (page AP-6).

[2006, 2015, 1] by [150, 350, 50]   [2006, 2015, 1] by [150, 300, 50]

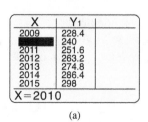

(a)

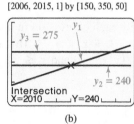

(b)

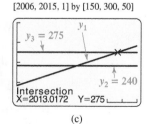

(c)

Figure 8.46

▌ Now Try Exercise 107(a) and (b)

Interval Notation

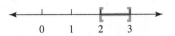

Figure 8.47

The solution set in Example 4 was $\{x \mid 2 \leq x \leq 3\}$. This solution set can be graphed on a number line, as shown in Figure 8.47.

A convenient notation for number line graphs is called **interval notation**. Instead of drawing the entire number line as in Figure 8.47, the solution set can be expressed as [2, 3] in interval notation. Because the solution set includes the endpoints 2 and 3, brackets are used. A solution set that includes all real numbers satisfying $-2 < x < 3$ can be expressed as $(-2, 3)$. Parentheses indicate that the endpoints are *not* included. The interval $0 \leq x < 4$ is represented by $[0, 4)$.

MAKING CONNECTIONS

Points and Intervals

The expression (1, 2) may represent a point in the *xy*-plane or the interval $1 < x < 2$. To alleviate confusion, phrases such as "the point (1, 2)" or "the interval (1, 2)" are used.

Table 8.13 provides examples of interval notation. The symbol ∞ refers to **infinity**, and it does not represent a real number. The interval $(5, \infty)$ represents $x > 5$, which has no maximum *x*-value, so ∞ is used for the right endpoint. The symbol $-\infty$ may be used similarly and denotes **negative infinity**. Real numbers are denoted $(-\infty, \infty)$.

TABLE 8.13 Interval Notation

Inequality	Interval Notation	Number Line Graph
$-1 < x < 3$	$(-1, 3)$	
$-3 < x \leq 2$	$(-3, 2]$	
$-2 \leq x \leq 2$	$[-2, 2]$	
$x < -1 \text{ or } x > 2$	$(-\infty, -1) \cup (2, \infty)$ ($\cup$ is the union symbol.)	
$x > -1$	$(-1, \infty)$	
$x \leq 2$	$(-\infty, 2]$	

EXAMPLE 7 **Writing inequalities in interval notation**

Write each expression in interval notation.
(a) $-2 \leq x < 5$ **(b)** $x \geq 3$ **(c)** $x < -5 \text{ or } x \geq 2$
(d) $\{x \mid x > 0 \text{ and } x \leq 3\}$ **(e)** $\{x \mid x \leq 1 \text{ or } x \geq 3\}$

Solution
(a) $[-2, 5)$ **(b)** $[3, \infty)$ **(c)** $(-\infty, -5) \cup [2, \infty)$
(d) $(0, 3]$ **(e)** $(-\infty, 1] \cup [3, \infty)$

Now Try Exercises 13, 17, 23, 27, 37

EXAMPLE 8   **Solving an inequality**

Solve $2x + 1 \leq -1$ or $2x + 1 \geq 3$. Write the solution set in interval notation.

Solution
First solve each inequality.

$$2x + 1 \leq -1 \quad \text{or} \quad 2x + 1 \geq 3 \qquad \text{Given compound inequality}$$

$$2x \leq -2 \quad \text{or} \qquad 2x \geq 2 \qquad \text{Subtract 1.}$$

$$x \leq -1 \quad \text{or} \qquad x \geq 1 \qquad \text{Divide by 2.}$$

The solution set may be written as $(-\infty, -1] \cup [1, \infty)$.

Now Try Exercise 55

8.3   Putting It All Together

CONCEPT	EXPLANATION	EXAMPLES
Compound Inequality	Two inequalities joined by *and* or *or*	$2x \geq 10$ and $x + 2 < 16$; $x < -1$ or $x > 2$
Three-Part Inequality	Can be used to write some types of compound inequalities involving *and*	$x > -2$ and $x \leq 3$ is equivalent to $-2 < x \leq 3$.
Interval Notation	Notation used to write sets of real numbers rather than using number lines or inequalities	$-2 \leq z \leq 4$ is equivalent to $[-2, 4]$. $x < 4$ is equivalent to $(-\infty, 4)$. $x \leq -2$ or $x > 0$ is equivalent to $(-\infty, -2] \cup (0, \infty)$.

TYPE OF INEQUALITY	METHOD TO SOLVE THE INEQUALITY
Solving a Compound Inequality Containing *and*	**STEP 1:** First solve each inequality individually. **STEP 2:** The solution set includes values that satisfy *both* inequalities from Step 1.
Solving a Compound Inequality Containing *or*	**STEP 1:** First solve each inequality individually. **STEP 2:** The solution set includes values that satisfy *at least one* of the inequalities from Step 1.
Solving a Three-Part Inequality	Work on all three parts at the same time. Be sure to perform the same step on each part. Continue until the variable is isolated in the middle part.

8.3   Exercises

MyMathLab   Math XL PRACTICE   WATCH   DOWNLOAD   READ   REVIEW

CONCEPTS AND VOCABULARY

1. Give an example of a compound inequality containing the word *and*.

2. Give an example of a compound inequality containing the word *or*.

3. Is 1 a solution to $x > 3$ and $x \leq 5$?

4. Is 1 a solution to $x < 3$ or $x \geq 5$?

5. Is the compound inequality $x \geq -5$ and $x \leq 5$ equivalent to $-5 \leq x \leq 5$?

6. Name three ways to solve a compound inequality.

Exercises 7–12: Determine whether the given values of x are solutions to the compound inequality.

7. $x - 1 < 5$ and $2x > 3$ $\qquad$ $x = 2, x = 6$

8. $2x + 1 \geq 4$ and $1 - x \leq 3$ $\qquad$ $x = -2, x = 3$

9. $3x < -5$ or $2x \geq 3$ $\qquad$ $x = 0, x = 3$

10. $x + 1 \leq -4$ or $x + 1 \geq 4$ $\qquad$ $x = -5, x = 2$

11. $2 - x > -5$ and $2 - x \leq 4$ $\qquad$ $x = -3, x = 0$

12. $x + 5 \geq 6$ or $3x \leq 3$ $\qquad$ $x = -1, x = 1$

INTERVAL NOTATION

Exercises 13–38: Write the inequality in interval notation.

13. $2 \leq x \leq 10$

14. $-1 < x < 5$

15. $5 < x \leq 8$

16. $-\frac{1}{2} \leq x \leq \frac{5}{6}$

17. $x < 4$

18. $x \leq -3$

19. $x > -2$

20. $x \geq 6$

21. $x \geq -2$ and $x < 5$

22. $x \leq 6$ and $x \geq 2$

23. $x \leq 8$ and $x > -8$

24. $x \geq -4$ and $x < 3$

25. $x \geq 6$ or $x > 3$

26. $x \leq -4$ or $x < -3$

27. $x \leq -2$ or $x \geq 4$

28. $x \leq -1$ or $x > 6$

29. $x < 1$ or $x \geq 5$

30. $x < -3$ or $x > 3$

31.

32.

33.

34.

35. $\{x \mid x < 4\}$

36. $\{x \mid -1 \leq x < 4\}$

37. $\{x \mid x < 1 \text{ or } x > 2\}$

38. $\{x \mid -\infty < x < \infty\}$

SYMBOLIC SOLUTIONS

Exercises 39–48: Solve the compound inequality. Graph the solution set on a number line.

39. $x \leq 3$ and $x \geq -1$

40. $x \geq 5$ and $x > 6$

41. $2x < 5$ and $2x > -4$

42. $2x + 1 < 3$ and $x - 1 \geq -5$

43. $x + 2 > 5$ and $3 - x < 10$

44. $x + 2 > 5$ or $3 - x < 10$

45. $x \leq -1$ or $x \geq 2$

46. $2x \leq -6$ or $x \geq 6$

47. $5 - x > 1$ or $x + 3 \geq -1$

48. $1 - 2x > 3$ or $2x - 4 \geq 4$

Exercises 49–58: Solve the compound inequality. Write your answer in interval notation.

49. $x - 3 \leq 4$ and $x + 5 \geq -1$

50. $2z \geq -10$ and $z < 8$

51. $3t - 1 > -1$ and $2t - \frac{1}{2} > 6$

52. $2(x + 1) < 8$ and $-2(x - 4) > -2$

53. $x - 4 \geq -3$ or $x - 4 \leq 3$

54. $1 - 3n \geq 6$ or $1 - 3n \leq -4$

55. $-x < 1$ or $5x + 1 < -10$

56. $7x - 6 > 0$ or $-\frac{1}{2}x \leq 6$

57. $1 - 7x < -48$ and $3x + 1 \leq -9$

58. $3x - 4 \leq 8$ or $4x - 1 \leq 13$

Exercises 59–80: Solve the three-part inequality. Write your answer in interval notation.

59. $-2 \leq t + 4 < 5$

60. $5 < t - 7 < 10$

61. $-\frac{5}{8} \leq y - \frac{3}{8} < 1$

62. $-\frac{1}{2} < y - \frac{3}{2} < \frac{1}{2}$

63. $-27 \le 3x \le 9$ **64.** $-4 < 2y < 22$

65. $\frac{1}{2} < -2y \le 8$ **66.** $-16 \le -4x \le 8$

67. $-4 < 5z + 1 \le 6$ **68.** $-3 \le 3z + 6 < 9$

69. $3 \le 4 - n \le 6$ **70.** $-1 < 3 - n \le 1$

71. $-1 < 2z - 1 < 3$ **72.** $2 \le 4z + 5 \le 6$

73. $-2 \le 5 - \frac{1}{3}m < 2$ **74.** $-\frac{3}{2} < 4 - 2m < \frac{7}{2}$

75. $100 \le 10(5x - 2) \le 200$

76. $-15 < 5(x - 1990) < 30$

77. $-3 < \dfrac{3z + 1}{4} < 1$ **78.** $-3 < \dfrac{z - 1}{2} < 5$

79. $-\dfrac{5}{2} \le \dfrac{2 - m}{4} \le \dfrac{1}{2}$

80. $\dfrac{4}{5} \le \dfrac{4 - 2m}{10} \le 2$

NUMERICAL AND GRAPHICAL SOLUTIONS

Exercises 81–84: Use the table to solve the three-part inequality. Write your answer in interval notation.

81. $-3 \le 3x \le 6$ **82.** $-5 \le 2x - 1 \le 1$

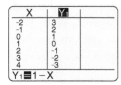

83. $-1 < 1 - x < 2$ **84.** $-2 \le -2x < 4$

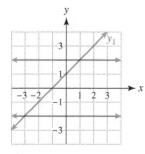
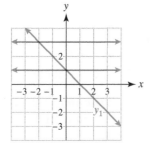

Exercises 85–88: Use the graph to solve the compound inequality. Write your answer in interval notation.

85. $-2 \le y_1 \le 2$ **86.** $1 \le y_1 < 3$

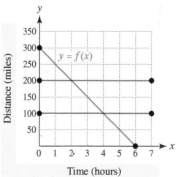

87. $y_1 < -2$ or $y_1 > 2$ **88.** $y_1 \le -2$ or $y_1 \ge 4$

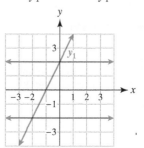
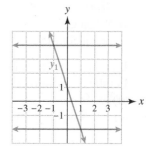

89. *Distance* The function f, shown in the figure, gives the distance y in miles between a car and Omaha, Nebraska, after x hours, where $0 \le x \le 6$.
  (a) Is the car moving toward or away from Omaha? Explain.
  (b) Determine the times when the car is 100 miles or 200 miles from Omaha.
  (c) When is the car from 100 to 200 miles from Omaha?
  (d) When is the car's distance from Omaha greater than or equal to 200 miles?

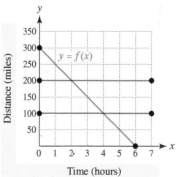

90. *Distance* The function g, shown in the figure, gives the distance y in miles between a train and Seattle after x hours, where $0 \le x \le 5$.

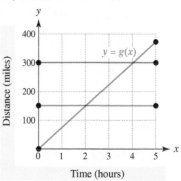

  (a) Is the train moving toward or away from Seattle? Explain.
  (b) Determine the times when the train is 150 miles or 300 miles from Seattle.

(continued on next page)

(c) When is the train from 150 to 300 miles from Seattle?

(d) When is the train's distance from Seattle less than or equal to 150 miles?

91. Use the figure to solve each equation or inequality. Let the domains of y_1, y_2, and y_3 be $0 \le x \le 8$.

(a) $y_1 = y_2$ (b) $y_2 = y_3$

(c) $y_1 \le y_2 \le y_3$ (d) $y_2 < y_1$

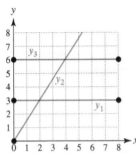

92. Use the figure to solve each equation or inequality. Let the domains of y_1, y_2, and y_3 be $0 \le x \le 5$.

(a) $y_1 = y_2$ (b) $y_2 = y_3$

(c) $y_1 \le y_2 \le y_3$ (d) $y_2 < y_3$

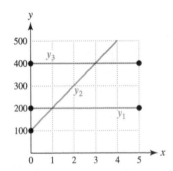

Exercises 93–98: Solve numerically or graphically. Write your answer in interval notation.

93. $-2 \le 2x - 4 \le 4$ **94.** $-1 \le 1 - x \le 3$

95. $x + 1 < -1$ or $x + 1 > 1$

96. $2x - 1 < -3$ or $2x - 1 > 5$

97. $95 \le 25(x - 2000) + 45 \le 295$

98. $42 \le -13(x - 2005) + 120 \le 94$

USING MORE THAN ONE METHOD

Exercises 99–104: Solve symbolically, graphically, and numerically. Write the solution set in interval notation.

99. $4 \le 5x - 1 \le 14$ **100.** $-4 < 2x < 4$

101. $4 - x \ge 1$ or $4 - x < 3$

102. $x + 3 \ge -2$ or $x + 3 \le 1$

103. $2x + 1 < 3$ or $2x + 1 \ge 7$

104. $3 - x \le 4$ or $3 - x > 8$

105. Thinking Generally Solve $c < x + b \le d$ for x.

106. Thinking Generally Solve $c \le ax + b \le d$ for x, if $a < 0$.

APPLICATIONS

107. *Online Betting* Global online betting losses in billions can be modeled by $L(x) = 2.5x - 5000$, where x is a year from 2006 to 2011. Use each method to estimate when losses ranged from \$15 billion to \$20 billion. (*Source:* Christiansen Capital Advisors.)

(a) Numerical

(b) Graphical

(c) Symbolic

108. *College Tuition* From 1980 to 2000, college tuition and fees at private colleges could be modeled by the linear function $f(x) = 575(x - 1980) + 3600$. Use each method to estimate when the average tuition and fees ranged from \$8200 to \$10,500. (*Source:* The College Board.)

(a) Numerical

(b) Graphical

(c) Symbolic

109. *Altitude and Dew Point* If the dew point D on the ground is $60°F$, then the dew point x miles high is given by $D(x) = 60 - 5.8x$. Find the altitudes where the dew point ranges from $57.1°F$ to $51.3°F$. (*Source:* A. Miller.)

110. *Cigarette Consumption* Worldwide cigarette consumption in trillions from 1950 to 2010 can be modeled by $C(x) = 0.09x - 173.8$, where x is the year. Estimate the years when cigarette consumption was between 5.3 and 6.2 trillion. (*Source:* Department of Agriculture.)

111. *Geometry* For what values of x is the perimeter of the rectangle from 40 to 60 feet?

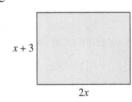

112. *Geometry* A rectangle is three times as long as it is wide. If the perimeter ranges from 100 to 160 inches, what values for the width are possible?

113. *Altitude and Temperature* If the air temperature at ground level is $70°F$, the air temperature x miles high is given by $T(x) = 70 - 19x$. Determine the altitudes at which the air temperature is from $41.5°F$ to $22.5¡$ F. (*Source:* A. Miller and R. Anthes, *Meteorology*.)

114. *Distance* A car's distance in miles from a rest stop after x hours is given by $f(x) = 70x + 50$.
  (a) Make a table for $f(x)$ for $x = 4, 5, 6, \ldots, 10$ and use the table to solve the inequality $470 \le f(x) \le 680$. Explain your result.
  (b) Solve the inequality in part (a) symbolically.

115. *Medicare Costs* In 2000 Medicare cost taxpayers $250 billion, and in 2010 it cost $500 billion. (*Source:* Department of Health and Human Services.)
  (a) Find a linear function M that models these data x years after 2000.
  (b) Estimate when Medicare costs were from $300 billion to $400 billion.

116. *Temperature Conversion* Water freezes at 32° F, or 0° C, and boils at 212° F, or 100° C.
  (a) Find a linear function $C(F)$ that converts Fahrenheit temperature to Celsius temperature.

  (b) The greatest temperature ranges on Earth are recorded in Siberia, where temperature has varied from about –70° C to 35° C. Find this temperature range in Fahrenheit.

WRITING ABOUT MATHEMATICS

117. Suppose that the solution set for a compound inequality can be written as $x < -3$ or $x > 2$. A student writes it as $2 < x < -3$. Is the student's three-part inequality correct? Explain your answer.

118. How can you determine whether an x-value is a solution to a compound inequality containing the word *and*? Give an example. Repeat the question for a compound inequality containing the word *or*.

8.4   Other Functions and Their Properties

Expressing Domain and Range in Interval Notation ● Absolute Value Function ● Polynomial Functions ● Rational Functions (Optional) ● Operations on Functions

A LOOK INTO MATH ▶

Many quantities in applications cannot be modeled with linear functions and equations. If data points do not lie on a line, we say that the data are *nonlinear*. For example, a scatterplot of the *cumulative* number of AIDS deaths from 1981 through 2007 is nonlinear, as shown in Figure 8.48. To model such data, we often use *nonlinear functions*, whose graphs are *not* a line. Because scatterplots of nonlinear data can have a variety of shapes, mathematicians use many different types of nonlinear functions, such as polynomial functions, which we discuss in this section. See Exercise 121. (*Source:* U.S. Department of Health and Human Services.)

NEW VOCABULARY

☐ Absolute value function
☐ Polynomial function of one variable
☐ Linear function
☐ Quadratic function
☐ Cubic function
☐ Rational function

U.S. AIDS Deaths

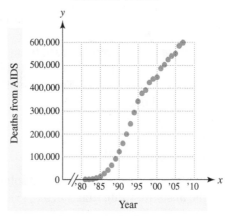

Figure 8.48

Expressing Domain and Range in Interval Notation

The set of all valid inputs for a function is called the *domain*, and the set of all outputs from a function is called the *range*. For example, all real numbers are valid inputs for $f(x) = x^2$. Rather than writing "the set of all real numbers" for the domain of f, we can use *interval notation* to express the domain as $(-\infty, \infty)$. The symbol ∞ represents infinity and is not a real number. Because $x^2 \geq 0$ for every real number x, the output from $f(x) = x^2$ is never negative. Therefore the range of f is $[0, \infty)$, which denotes all nonnegative real numbers, or $x \geq 0$. Note that 0 is in the range of f because $f(0) = 0$, and a bracket "[" is used to indicate that 0 is included in the range of f.

EXAMPLE 1   Writing domains in interval notation

Write the domain for each function in interval notation.
(a) $f(x) = 4x$ (b) $g(t) = \sqrt{t - 1}$ (c) $h(v) = \dfrac{1}{v + 3}$

Solution
(a) The expression $4x$ is defined for all real numbers x. Thus the domain of f is $(-\infty, \infty)$.
(b) The square root $\sqrt{t - 1}$ is defined only when $t - 1$ is *not* negative. Thus the domain of g includes all real numbers satisfying $t - 1 \geq 0$ or $t \geq 1$. In interval notation this inequality is written as $[1, \infty)$.
(c) The expression $\frac{1}{v + 3}$ is defined except when $v + 3 = 0$ or $v = -3$. Thus the domain of h includes all real numbers except -3 and can be written as $(-\infty, -3) \cup (-3, \infty)$. Parentheses are used because -3 is not included in the domain of h.

Now Try Exercises 13, 21, 25

In the next example, we determine the domain and range of a function from its graph. Note that dots placed at each end of a graph indicate that the endpoints are included.

EXAMPLE 2   Writing the domain and range in interval notation

Use the graph of f in Figure 8.49 to write its domain and range in interval notation.

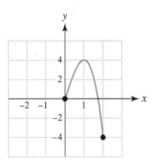

Figure 8.49

Solution
Because dots are placed at $(0, 0)$ and $(2, -4)$, the endpoints are included in the graph of f. Thus the graph in Figure 8.49 includes x-values from $x = 0$ to $x = 2$. In interval notation, the domain of f is $[0, 2]$. The range of f includes y-values from -4 to 4 and can be expressed in interval notation as $[-4, 4]$.

Now Try Exercise 39

Absolute Value Function

In Chapter 1 we discussed the absolute value of a number. We can define a function called the **absolute value function** as $f(x) = |x|$. We evaluate f as follows.

$$f(11) = |11| = 11, \quad f(-4) = |-4| = 4, \quad \text{and} \quad f(-\pi) = |-\pi| = \pi$$

To graph $y = |x|$ we begin by making a table of values, as shown in Table 8.14. Next we plot these points and sketch the graph, as shown in Figure 8.50. Note that the graph is V-shaped and never lies below the x-axis because the absolute value of a number cannot be negative.

TABLE 8.14

x	$|x|$
-2	2
-1	1
0	0
1	1
2	2

Absolute Value Function

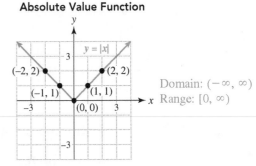

Domain: $(-\infty, \infty)$
Range: $[0, \infty)$

Figure 8.50

Because the input for $f(x) = |x|$ is any real number, the domain of f is all real numbers, or $(-\infty, \infty)$. The graph of the absolute value function shows that the output y (range) is any real number greater than or equal to 0. That is, the range is $[0, \infty)$.

Polynomial Functions

In Chapter 5 we introduced polynomials and defined their degrees. The following expressions are examples of polynomials of one variable.

$$1 - 5x, \quad 3t^2 - 5t + 1, \quad \text{and} \quad z^3 + 5$$

(The exponents on variables in polynomials must be nonnegative integers.) Recall that the *degree* of a polynomial of one variable equals the largest exponent on the variable. Thus the degree of $1 - 5x$ is 1, the degree of $3t^2 - 5t + 1$ is 2, and the degree of $z^3 + 5$ is 3.

The equations

$$f(x) = 1 - 5x, \quad g(t) = 3t^2 - 5t + 1, \quad \text{and} \quad h(z) = z^3 + 5$$

define three **polynomial functions of one variable**. Function f is a **linear function** because it has degree 1, function g is a **quadratic function** because it has degree 2, and function h is a **cubic function** because it has degree 3.

NOTE: The domain of *every* polynomial function is *all* real numbers.

EXAMPLE 3   **Identifying polynomial functions**

Determine whether $f(x)$ represents a polynomial function. If possible, identify the type of polynomial function and its degree.
(a) $f(x) = 5x^3 - x + 10$
(b) $f(x) = x^{-2.5} + 1$
(c) $f(x) = 1 - 2x$
(d) $f(x) = \dfrac{3}{x - 1}$

Solution
(a) The expression $5x^3 - x + 10$ is a cubic polynomial, so $f(x)$ represents a cubic polynomial function. It has degree 3.

(b) $f(x) = x^{-2.5} + 1$ does not represent a polynomial function because the variables in a polynomial must have *nonnegative integer* exponents.

(c) $f(x) = 1 - 2x$ represents a polynomial function that is linear. It has degree 1.

(d) $f(x) = \frac{3}{x-1}$ does not represent a polynomial function because $\frac{3}{x-1}$ is not a polynomial.

Now Try Exercises 43, 45, 47, 51

Frequently, polynomials represent functions or formulas that can be evaluated. This situation is illustrated in the next two examples.

EXAMPLE 4   **Evaluating a polynomial function graphically and symbolically**

A graph of $f(x) = 4x - x^3$ is shown in Figure 8.51, where $y = f(x)$. Evaluate $f(-1)$ graphically and check your result symbolically.

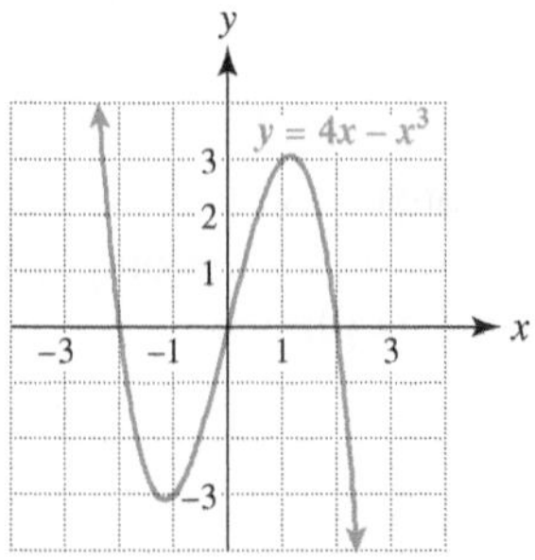

Solution

Graphical Evaluation To evaluate $f(-1)$ graphically, find -1 on the x-axis and move down until the graph of f is reached. Then move horizontally to the y-axis, as shown in Figure 8.52. Thus when $x = -1$, $y = -3$ and $f(-1) = -3$.

Symbolic Evaluation When $x = -1$, evaluation of $f(x) = 4x - x^3$ is performed as follows.

$$f(-1) = 4(-1) - (-1)^3 = -4 - (-1) = -3$$

Evaluating f(−1) = −3

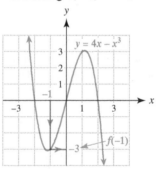

Figure 8.52

Now Try Exercises 59, 73

EXAMPLE 5   **Evaluating a polynomial function symbolically**

Evaluate $f(x)$ at the given value of x.

(a) $f(x) = -3x^4 - 2$, $x = 2$ **(b)** $f(x) = -2x^3 - 4x^2 + 5$, $x = -3$

Solution

(a) Be sure to evaluate exponents before multiplying.

$$f(2) = -3(2)^4 - 2 = -3 \cdot 16 - 2 = -50$$

(b) $f(-3) = -2(-3)^3 - 4(-3)^2 + 5 = -2(-27) - 4(9) + 5 = 23$

Now Try Exercises 61, 63

Figure 8.51

▶ **REAL-WORLD CONNECTION** A well-conditioned athlete's heart rate can reach 200 beats per minute during strenuous physical activity. Upon quitting, a typical heart rate decreases rapidly at first and then more gradually after a few minutes, as illustrated in the next example.

EXAMPLE 6   **Modeling heart rate of an athlete**

Let $P(t) = 1.875t^2 - 30t + 200$ model an athlete's heart rate (or pulse P) in beats per minute (bpm) t minutes after strenuous exercise has stopped, where $0 \le t \le 8$. (*Source: V. Thomas, Science and Sport.*)

(a) What is the initial heart rate when the athlete stops exercising?
(b) What is the heart rate after 8 minutes?
(c) A graph of P is shown in Figure 8.53. Interpret this graph.

Athlete's Heart Rate

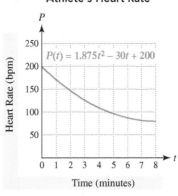

Figure 8.53

Solution
(a) To find the initial heart rate, evaluate $P(t)$ at $t = 0$, or

$$P(0) = 1.875(0)^2 - 30(0) + 200 = 200.$$

When the athlete stops exercising, the heart rate is 200 beats per minute. (This result agrees with the graph.)

(b) $P(8) = 1.875(8)^2 - 30(8) + 200 = 80$ beats per minute.

(c) The heart rate does not drop at a constant rate; rather, it drops rapidly at first and then gradually begins to level off.

▌ Now Try Exercise 115

Rational Functions (Optional)

A rational expression is formed when a polynomial is divided by a polynomial. For example, the expressions

$$\frac{2x - 1}{x}, \quad \frac{5}{x^2 - 1}, \quad \text{and} \quad \frac{2x - 5}{x^2 - 9}$$

are rational expressions. Rational expressions can be used to define *rational functions*.

RATIONAL FUNCTIONS

Let $p(x)$ and $q(x)$ be polynomials. Then a **rational function** is given by

$$f(x) = \frac{p(x)}{q(x)}.$$

The domain of f includes all x-values such that $q(x) \ne 0$.

From this definition, it follows that

$$f(x) = \frac{2x - 1}{x}, \quad g(x) = \frac{5}{x^2 + 1}, \quad \text{and} \quad h(x) = \frac{2x - 5}{x^2 - 9}$$

define rational functions. The domain of f includes all real numbers except 0, the domain of g includes all real numbers because $x^2 + 1 \neq 0$ for any x-value, and the domain of h includes all real numbers except ± 3.

Formulas for linear and polynomial functions are *defined* for all x-values. However, formulas for a rational function are *undefined* for x-values that make the denominator equal to 0. (Division by 0 is undefined.) For example, if $f(x) = \frac{1}{x-2}$, then $f(2) = \frac{1}{2-2} = \frac{1}{0}$ is undefined because the denominator equals 0. A graph of $y = f(x)$ is shown in Figure 8.54. The graph does not cross the dashed vertical line $x = 2$, because $f(x)$ is *undefined* at $x = 2$. The red vertical dashed line $x = 2$ is called a *vertical asymptote*, and is used as an aid for sketching a graph of f. It is not actually part of the graph of the function.

READING CHECK

How can you determine the domain of a rational function?

A Rational Function

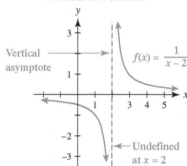

Figure 8.54

EXAMPLE 7   **Identifying the domains of rational functions**

Write the domain of each function in interval notation.

(a) $f(x) = \dfrac{1}{x + 2}$ **(b)** $g(x) = \dfrac{2x}{x^2 - 3x + 2}$ **(c)** $h(t) = \dfrac{4}{t^3 - t}$

Solution

(a) The domain of f includes all x-values except when the denominator equals 0.

$$x + 2 = 0 \qquad \text{Set the denominator equal to 0.}$$
$$x = -2 \qquad \text{Subtract 2.}$$

Thus $f(-2)$ is undefined and -2 must be excluded from the domain of f. In interval notation the domain of f is $(-\infty, -2) \cup (-2, \infty)$.

(b) The domain of g includes all real numbers except when $x^2 - 3x + 2 = 0$.

$$x^2 - 3x + 2 = 0 \qquad \text{Set the denominator equal to 0.}$$
$$(x - 1)(x - 2) = 0 \qquad \text{Factor.}$$
$$x = 1 \quad \text{or} \quad x = 2 \qquad \text{Zero-product property}$$

Because $g(1)$ and $g(2)$ are both undefined, 1 and 2 must be excluded from the domain of g. In interval notation the domain of g is $(-\infty, 1) \cup (1, 2) \cup (2, \infty)$.

(c) The domain of h includes all real numbers except when $t^3 - t = 0$.

$$t^3 - t = 0 \qquad \text{Set the denominator equal to 0.}$$
$$t(t^2 - 1) = 0 \qquad \text{Factor out } t.$$
$$t(t - 1)(t + 1) = 0 \qquad \text{Difference of squares}$$
$$t = 0 \quad \text{or} \quad t = 1 \quad \text{or} \quad t = -1 \qquad \text{Zero-product property}$$

In interval notation the domain of h is $(-\infty, -1) \cup (-1, 0) \cup (0, 1) \cup (1, \infty)$.

Now Try Exercises 27, 33, 35

To graph a rational function by hand, we usually start by making a table of values, as demonstrated in the next example. Because the graphs of rational functions are typically nonlinear, it is a good idea to plot at least 3 points on each side of an x-value where the formula is undefined—that is, where the denominator equals 0.

EXAMPLE 8 **Graphing a rational function**

Graph $f(x) = \dfrac{1}{x}$. State the domain of f.

Solution

Make a table of values for $f(x) = \frac{1}{x}$, as shown in Table 8.15. Notice that $x = 0$ is not in the domain of f, and a dash can be used to denote this undefined value. The domain of f is all real numbers such that $x \neq 0$. Start by picking three x-values on each side of 0.

TABLE 8.15

x	-2	-1	$-\frac{1}{2}$	0	$\frac{1}{2}$	1	2
$\frac{1}{x}$	$-\frac{1}{2}$	-1	-2	—	2	1	$\frac{1}{2}$

↑———— Undefined

Plot the points shown in Table 8.15 and then connect the points with a smooth curve, as shown in Figure 8.55. Because $f(0)$ is undefined, the graph of $f(x) = \frac{1}{x}$ does not cross the line $x = 0$ (the y-axis). The line $x = 0$ is a vertical asymptote.

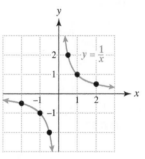

Figure 8.55

▌ Now Try Exercise 89

In the next example we evaluate a rational function in three ways.

EXAMPLE 9 **Evaluating a rational function**

Use Table 8.16, the formula for $f(x)$, and Figure 8.56 to evaluate $f(-1)$, $f(1)$, and $f(2)$.

(a) TABLE 8.16

x	$f(x)$
-3	$\frac{3}{2}$
-2	$\frac{4}{3}$
-1	1
0	0
1	—
2	4
3	3

(b) $f(x) = \dfrac{2x}{x - 1}$

(c)

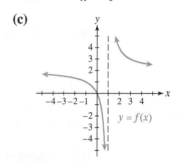

Figure 8.56

**TABLE 8.16
(repeated)**

x	$f(x)$
-3	$\frac{3}{2}$
-2	$\frac{4}{3}$
-1	1
0	0
1	—
2	4
3	3

Solution

(a) Numerical Evaluation Table 8.16 (repeated in the margin) shows that

$$f(-1) = 1, \quad f(1) \text{ is undefined}, \quad \text{and} \quad f(2) = 4.$$

(b) Symbolic Evaluation Let $f(x) = \dfrac{2x}{x-1}$.

$$f(-1) = \frac{2(-1)}{-1-1} = 1$$

$$f(1) = \frac{2(1)}{1-1} = \frac{2}{0}, \text{ which is undefined. Input 1 is } not \text{ in the domain of } f.$$

$$f(2) = \frac{2(2)}{2-1} = 4$$

(c) Graphical Evaluation To evaluate $f(-1)$ graphically, find $x = -1$ on the x-axis and move upward to the graph of f. The y-value is 1 at the point of intersection, so $f(-1) = 1$, as shown in Figure 8.57(a). In Figure 8.57(b) the red, dashed vertical line $x = 1$ is a vertical asymptote. Because the graph of f does not intersect this line, $f(1)$ is undefined. Figure 8.57(c) reveals that $f(2) = 4$.

Evaluating a Rational Function Graphically

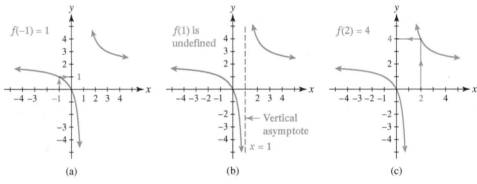

| (a) | (b) | (c) |

Figure 8.57

▍ Now Try Exercises 67, 77, 79

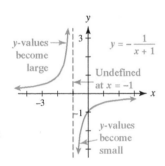

MAKING CONNECTIONS

Asymptotes and Graphs of Rational Functions

A *vertical asymptote* often occurs at x-values in the graph of a rational function $y = f(x)$ where the denominator equals 0. A vertical asymptote can be used as an aid to sketch the graph of a rational function. However, the graph of a rational function *never* crosses a vertical asymptote, so a vertical asymptote is *not* part of the graph of f.

On either side of a vertical asymptote, the y-values on the graph of a rational function typically become either very large (approach ∞) or very small (approach $-\infty$). See the figure in the margin.

▶ **REAL-WORLD CONNECTION** You may have noticed that a relatively small percentage of people do the vast majority of postings on social networks, such as Facebook and Twitter. This phenomenon is called *participation inequality*. That is, a vast majority of the population falls under the category of "lurkers," who are on the network but are not posting material. This characteristic of a social network can be modeled approximately by a rational function, as illustrated in the next example. (*Source:* Wu, Michael, *The Economics of 90-9-1.*)

Modeling social network participation

The rational function given by

$$f(x) = \frac{100}{101 - x}, \quad 5 \leq x \leq 100,$$

models participation inequality in a social network. In this formula, $f(x)$ outputs the percentage of the postings done by the least active (bottom) x percent of the population.
(a) Evaluate $f(95)$. Interpret your answer.
(b) A graph of $y = f(x)$ is shown in Figure 8.58. Interpret the graph.

Participation in a Social Network

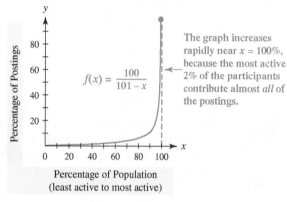

Figure 8.58 Participation Inequality

(c) Solve the rational equation $\frac{100}{101 - x} = 9$. Interpret your answer.

Solution

(a) $f(95) = \dfrac{100}{101 - 95} = \dfrac{100}{6} \approx 16.7\%$ Let $x = 95$.

This means that the least active 95% of the population contributes only 16.7% of the postings, so the most active 5% of the population is responsible for the remaining 83.3% of the postings.

(b) The graph shows participation inequality visually. The graph remains at a relatively low percentage until $x = 90\%$. This means that the bottom 90% of the population does very few postings. For $x \geq 90\%$ the graph rises rapidly because the top 10% contributes a vast majority of the postings.

(c) To solve this equation, we begin by multiplying each side by $(101 - x)$.

$$\frac{100}{101 - x} = 9 \qquad \text{Given equation}$$

$$(101 - x) \cdot \frac{100}{101 - x} = 9(101 - x) \qquad \text{Multiply by } (101 - x).$$

$$100 = 9(101 - x) \qquad \text{Simplify left side.}$$

$$100 = 909 - 9x \qquad \text{Distributive property}$$

$$9x + 100 - 100 = 909 - 100 + 9x - 9x \qquad \text{Add } 9x.\ \text{Subtract } 100.$$

$$9x = 809 \qquad \text{Simplify.}$$

$$x = \frac{809}{9} \approx 90\% \qquad \text{Simplify.}$$

This result indicates that the least active 90% of the population contributes only 9% of the postings.

Now Try Exercise 117

CRITICAL THINKING

Suppose that a social network had *participation equality*, in which every member contributed an equal number of postings. Sketch a graph like Figure 8.58 that describes this social network.

TECHNOLOGY NOTE

Asymptotes, Dot Mode, and Decimal Windows
When a rational function is graphed on a graphing calculator in connected mode, pseudo-asymptotes often occur because the calculator is simply connecting dots to draw a graph. The accompanying figures show the graph of $y = \frac{2}{x-2}$ in connected mode, in dot mode, and with a *decimal*, or *friendly*, window. In dot mode, pixels in the calculator screen are not connected. With dot mode (and sometimes with a decimal window) pseudo-asymptotes do not appear. To learn more about these features, consult your owner's manual.

CALCULATOR HELP

To set a calculator in dot mode or to set a decimal window, see Appendix A (page AP-11).

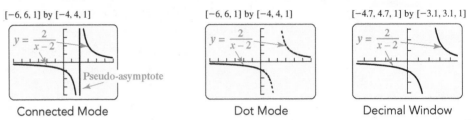

[−6, 6, 1] by [−4, 4, 1]	[−6, 6, 1] by [−4, 4, 1]	[−4.7, 4.7, 1] by [−3.1, 3.1, 1]
Connected Mode	Dot Mode	Decimal Window

Operations on Functions

▶ **REAL-WORLD CONNECTION** A business incurs a *cost* to make its product and then it receives *revenue* from selling this product. For example, suppose a small business reconditions motorcycles. The graphs of its cost and of its revenue for reconditioning and selling x motorcycles are shown in Figure 8.59.

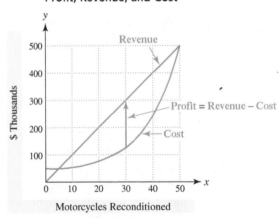

Figure 8.59

In general, *profit equals revenue minus cost.* In Figure 8.59, profit is shown visually as the length of the vertical green arrow between the graphs of revenue and cost. For any x-value, the distance by which revenue is above cost is called the profit for reconditioning and selling x motorcycles. *Maximum profit* for the company occurs at the x-value where the *length of the vertical green arrow is greatest.*

If we let $C(x)$, $R(x)$, and $P(x)$ be functions that calculate the cost, revenue, and profit, respectively, for reconditioning and selling x motorcycles, then

$$P(x) = R(x) - C(x).$$

Profit   *equals*   Revenue   *minus*   Cost.

This example helps explain why we subtract functions in the real world. Functions can be added, multiplied, and divided in a similar manner.

Given two functions f and g, we define the sum $f + g$, difference $f - g$, product fg, and quotient $\frac{f}{g}$, as follows.

OPERATIONS ON FUNCTIONS

If $f(x)$ and $g(x)$ are both defined, then the sum, difference, product, and quotient of two functions f and g are defined by

$$(f + g)(x) = f(x) + g(x) \qquad \text{Sum}$$

$$(f - g)(x) = f(x) - g(x) \qquad \text{Difference}$$

$$(fg)(x) = f(x) \cdot g(x) \qquad \text{Product}$$

$$\left(\frac{f}{g}\right)(x) = \frac{f(x)}{g(x)}, \text{ where } g(x) \neq 0. \quad \text{Quotient}$$

EXAMPLE 11 **Performing arithmetic on functions**

Use $f(x) = x^2$ and $g(x) = 2x - 4$ to evaluate each of the following.

(a) $(f + g)(3)$ **(b)** $(fg)(-1)$ **(c)** $\left(\frac{f}{g}\right)(0)$ **(d)** $(f/g)(2)$

Solution

(a) $(f + g)(3) = f(3) + g(3) = 3^2 + (2 \cdot 3 - 4) = 9 + 2 = 11$

(b) $(fg)(-1) = f(-1) \cdot g(-1) = (-1)^2 \cdot (2 \cdot (-1) - 4) = 1 \cdot (-6) = -6$

(c) $\left(\frac{f}{g}\right)(0) = \frac{f(0)}{g(0)} = \frac{0^2}{2 \cdot 0 - 4} = \frac{0}{-4} = 0$

(d) Note that $(f/g)(2)$ is equivalent to $\left(\frac{f}{g}\right)(2)$.

$$(f/g)(2) = \frac{f(2)}{g(2)} = \frac{2^2}{2 \cdot 2 - 4} = \frac{4}{0},$$

which is not possible because division by 0 is undefined. Thus $(f/g)(2)$ is *undefined*.

Now Try Exercise 101

In the next example, we find the sum, difference, product, and quotient of two functions for a general x.

EXAMPLE 12 **Performing arithmetic on functions**

Use $f(x) = 4x - 5$ and $g(x) = 3x + 1$ to evaluate each of the following.

(a) $(f + g)(x)$ **(b)** $(f - g)(x)$ **(c)** $(fg)(x)$ **(d)** $\left(\frac{f}{g}\right)(x)$

Solution

(a) $(f + g)(x) = f(x) + g(x) = (4x - 5) + (3x + 1) = 7x - 4$

(b) $(f - g)(x) = f(x) - g(x) = (4x - 5) - (3x + 1) = x - 6$

(c) $(fg)(x) = f(x) \cdot g(x) = (4x - 5)(3x + 1) = 12x^2 - 11x - 5$

(d) $\left(\frac{f}{g}\right)(x) = \frac{f(x)}{g(x)} = \frac{4x - 5}{3x + 1}$

Now Try Exercise 105

8.4	**Putting It All Together**

CONCEPT	COMMENTS	EXAMPLES
Writing Domain and Range in Interval Notation	Interval notation can be used to specify the domain and range of a function.	If $f(x) = x^2 + 1$, the domain of f is $(-\infty, \infty)$, and the range of f is $[1, \infty)$.
Absolute Value Function	Defined by $$f(x) = |x|$$ and has a V-shaped graph	$f(-5) = |-5| = 5$ $f(0) = |0| = 0$ $f(4) = |4| = 4$
Polynomial Function of One Variable	Can be defined by a polynomial; its degree equals the largest exponent of the variable.	Because $x^3 - 4x^2 + 6$ is a polynomial with degree 3, $$f(x) = x^3 - 4x^2 + 6$$ defines a polynomial function of degree 3 and is called a cubic function.
Rational Function	A rational function can be written as $$f(x) = \frac{p(x)}{q(x)},$$ where $p(x)$ and $q(x)$ are polynomials. Note that $q(x) \neq 0$.	Because $2x - 3$ and $x + 1$ are polynomials, $$f(x) = \frac{2x - 3}{x + 1}$$ defines a rational function. Because $f(x)$ is undefined at $x = -1$, the domain of f is $(-\infty, -1) \cup (-1, \infty)$.
Operations on Functions	$(f + g)(x) = f(x) + g(x)$ Sum $(f - g)(x) = f(x) - g(x)$ Difference $(fg)(x) = f(x)g(x)$ Product $\left(\dfrac{f}{g}\right)(x) = \dfrac{f(x)}{g(x)}, g(x) \neq 0$ Quotient	Let $f(x) = x^2$ and $g(x) = 1 - x^2$. $(f + g)(x) = f(x) + g(x)$ $\quad\quad = x^2 + (1 - x^2)$ $\quad\quad = 1$ $(f - g)(x) = f(x) - g(x)$ $\quad\quad = x^2 - (1 - x^2)$ $\quad\quad = 2x^2 - 1$ $(fg)(x) = f(x)g(x)$ $\quad\quad = x^2(1 - x^2)$ $\quad\quad = x^2 - x^4$ $\left(\dfrac{f}{g}\right)(x) = \dfrac{f(x)}{g(x)}$ $\quad\quad = \dfrac{x^2}{1 - x^2}, x \neq -1, x \neq 1$

CONCEPTS AND VOCABULARY

1. The set of all valid inputs for a function is called its _____.

2. The set of all outputs for a function is called its _____.

3. The set of all real numbers can be written in interval notation as _____.

4. If the domain of a function includes all real numbers except 5, then its domain can be written in interval notation as _____.

5. The graph of the _____ function is V-shaped.

6. The degree of a polynomial of one variable equals the largest _____ of the variable.

7. A quadratic function has degree _____.

8. If a function is linear, then its degree is _____.

9. If $f(x) = \frac{x}{2x + 1}$, then f is a(n) _____ function.

10. If $f(x) = \frac{x}{2x + 1}$, then the domain of f includes all real numbers except _____.

11. Which of the following expressions (a.–d.) is not a rational function?

    a. $f(x) = \frac{1}{x}$ **b.** $f(x) = x^2 + 1$

    c. $f(x) = \sqrt{x}$ **d.** $f(x) = \frac{2x^2}{x - 1}$

12. Which (a.–d.) is the domain of $f(x) = \frac{2x}{2x - 1}$?

    a. $\{x \mid x \neq \frac{1}{2}\}$ **b.** $\{x \mid x \neq 1\}$

    c. $\{x \mid x \neq 0\}$ **d.** $\{x \mid x = 1\}$

DOMAIN AND RANGE

Exercises 13–24: Write the domain and the range of the function in interval notation. (Hint: You may want to consider the graph of the function.)

13. $f(x) = -2x$ 14. $f(x) = -\frac{1}{4}x + 1$

15. $g(t) = \frac{2}{3}t - 3$ 16. $g(t) = 9t$

17. $h(z) = z^2 + 2$ 18. $h(z) = z^2 - 1$

19. $f(z) = -z^2$ 20. $f(z) = -\frac{1}{4}z^2$

21. $g(x) = \sqrt{x + 1}$ 22. $g(x) = \sqrt{x - 2}$

23. $h(x) = |x - 1|$ 24. $h(x) = |2x|$

Exercises 25–36: Write the domain of the rational function in interval notation.

25. $f(x) = \frac{1}{x - 1}$ 26. $f(x) = \frac{6}{x}$

27. $f(x) = \frac{x}{6 - 3x}$ 28. $f(x) = \frac{3x}{2x - 4}$

29. $g(t) = \frac{2}{t^2 - 4}$ 30. $g(t) = \frac{5}{1 - t^2}$

31. $g(t) = \frac{5t}{t^2 - 2t}$ 32. $g(t) = \frac{-t}{2t^2 - 3t}$

33. $h(z) = \frac{2 - z}{z^3 - 1}$ 34. $h(z) = \frac{z + 1}{z^3 - z^2}$

35. $f(x) = \frac{4}{x^2 - 2x - 3}$

36. $f(x) = \frac{1}{x^2 + 4x - 5}$

Exercises 37–42: A graph of a function is shown. Write the domain and range of the function in interval notation.

37.

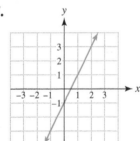

38.

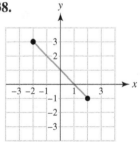

39.

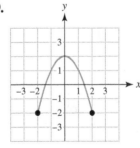

40.

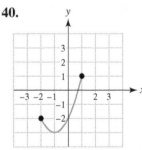

41.

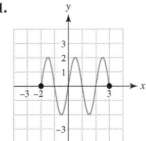

42.

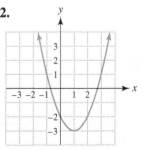

IDENTIFYING POLYNOMIAL FUNCTIONS

Exercises 43–54: Determine whether $f(x)$ represents a polynomial function. If possible, identify the degree and type of polynomial function.

43. $f(x) = 5x - 11$

44. $f(x) = 9 - x$

45. $f(x) = x^3$

46. $f(x) = x^2 + 3$

47. $f(x) = \dfrac{6}{x + 5}$

48. $f(x) = |x|$

49. $f(x) = 1 + 2x - x^2$

50. $f(x) = \frac{1}{4}x^3 - x$

51. $f(x) = 5x^{-2}$

52. $f(x) = x^2 + x^{-1}$

53. $f(x) = x^4 + 2x^2$

54. $f(x) = x^5 - 3x^3$

EVALUATING FUNCTIONS

Exercises 55–70: If possible, evaluate $g(t)$ for the given values of t.

55. $g(t) = |4t|$ $\qquad t = 3, t = 0$

56. $g(t) = |t + 12|$ $\qquad t = 18, t = -15$

57. $g(t) = |t - 2|$ $\qquad t = 1, t = -\frac{3}{4}$

58. $g(t) = |2t + 1|$ $\qquad t = 2, t = -\frac{1}{2}$

59. $g(t) = t^2 - t - 6$ $\qquad t = 3, t = -3$

60. $g(t) = 3t^2 - 2t$ $\qquad t = -2, t = 4$

61. $g(t) = -2t^3 + t$ $\qquad t = 2, t = -2$

62. $g(t) = \frac{1}{3}t^3$ $\qquad t = 1, t = -3$

63. $g(t) = t^2 - 2t - 6$ $\qquad t = 0, t = -3$

64. $g(t) = 2t^3 - t^2 + 4$ $\qquad t = 2, t = -1$

65. $g(t) = \dfrac{1}{t}$ $\qquad t = 11, t = -7$

66. $g(t) = \dfrac{2}{3 - t}$ $\qquad t = 10, t = 3$

67. $g(t) = -\dfrac{t}{t + 1}$ $\qquad t = 5, t = -1$

68. $g(t) = -\dfrac{2 - t}{4t}$ $\qquad t = 4, t = -1$

69. $g(t) = \dfrac{t^2}{t^2 - t}$ $\qquad t = -5, t = 1$

70. $g(t) = \dfrac{t - 3}{t^2 - 3t + 2}$ $\qquad t = -2, t = 1$

Exercises 71–78: If possible, use the graph to evaluate each expression. Then use the formula for $f(x)$ to check your results.

71. $f(0)$ and $f(1)$

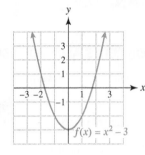

72. $f(-1)$ and $f(2)$

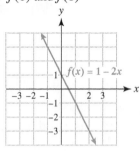

73. $f(-1)$ and $f(2)$

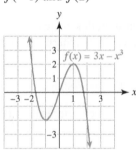

74. $f(0)$ and $f(-2)$

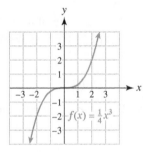

75. $f(-2)$ and $f(2)$

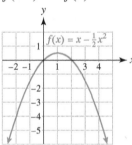

76. $f(-1)$ and $f(0)$

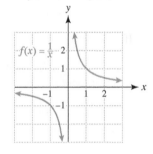

77. $f(-3)$ and $f(-1)$

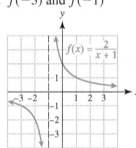

78. $f(0)$ and $f(1)$

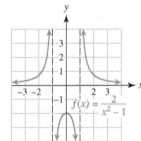

Exercises 79 and 80: Complete the table. Then evaluate $f(1)$.

79.

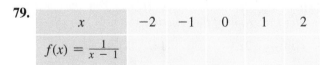

x	-2	-1	0	1	2
$f(x) = \dfrac{1}{x - 1}$					

80.

x	-2	-1	0	1	2
$f(x) = \dfrac{2x}{x + 2}$					

Exercises 81–100: Graph $y = f(x)$.

81. $f(x) = |2x|$

82. $f(x) = \left|\frac{1}{2}x\right|$

83. $f(x) = |x + 2|$ **84.** $f(x) = |x - 2|$

85. $f(x) = 1 - 2x$ **86.** $f(x) = \frac{1}{2}x + 1$

87. $f(x) = \frac{1}{2}x^2$ **88.** $f(x) = x^2 - 2$

89. $f(x) = \dfrac{1}{x - 1}$ **90.** $f(x) = \dfrac{1}{x + 1}$

91. $f(x) = \dfrac{1}{2x}$ **92.** $f(x) = \dfrac{2}{x}$

93. $f(x) = \dfrac{1}{x + 2}$ **94.** $f(x) = \dfrac{1}{x - 2}$

95. $f(x) = \dfrac{4}{x^2 + 1}$ **96.** $f(x) = \dfrac{6}{x^2 + 2}$

97. $f(x) = \dfrac{3}{2x - 3}$ **98.** $f(x) = \dfrac{1}{3x + 2}$

99. $f(x) = \dfrac{1}{x^2 - 1}$ **100.** $f(x) = \dfrac{4}{4 - x^2}$

OPERATIONS ON FUNCTIONS

Exercises 101–104: Use f(x) and g(x) to evaluate each of the following.

   (a) $(f + g)(3)$ **(b)** $(f - g)(-2)$
   (c) $(fg)(5)$ **(d)** $(f/g)(0)$

101. $f(x) = 5x, g(x) = x + 1$

102. $f(x) = x^2 + 2, g(x) = -2x$

103. $f(x) = 2x - 1, g(x) = 4x^2$

104. $f(x) = x^2 - 1, g(x) = x + 2$

Exercises 105–108: Use f(x) and g(x) to find each of the following.

   (a) $(f + g)(x)$ **(b)** $(f - g)(x)$
   (c) $(fg)(x)$ **(d)** $(f/g)(x)$

105. $f(x) = x + 1, g(x) = x + 2$

106. $f(x) = -3x, g(x) = x - 1$

107. $f(x) = 1 - x, g(x) = x^2$

108. $f(x) = x^2 + 4, g(x) = 6x$

109. Thinking Generally If $f(x) = x^2 - 2x$, then it follows that $f(a) = $ _____.

110. Thinking Generally If $f(x) = 2x - 1$, then it follows that $f(a + 2) = $ _____.

APPLICATIONS

Exercises 111–114: Graphical Interpretation Match the physical situation with the graph (a.–d.) of the rational function in the next column that models it best.

111. A population of fish that increases and then levels off

112. An insect population that dies out

113. The length of a ticket line as the rate at which people arrive in line increases

114. The wind speed during a day that is initially calm, becomes windy, and then is calm again

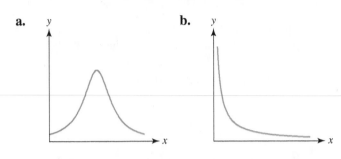

a.   **b.**

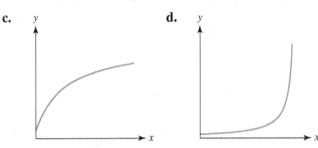

c.   **d.**

115. *Heart Rate of an Athlete* The following table lists the heart rate of an athlete running a 100-meter race. The race lasts 10 seconds.

Time (seconds)	0	2	4	6	8	10
Heart Rate (bpm)	90	100	113	127	143	160

  (a) Does $P(t) = 0.2t^2 + 5t + 90$ model the data in the table exactly? Explain.
  (b) Does P provide a reasonable model for the athlete's heart rate?
  (c) Does $P(12)$ have significance in this situation? What should be the domain of P?

116. *Heart Rate of an Athlete* The following table lists an athlete's heart rate after the athlete finishes exercising strenuously.

Time (minutes)	0	2	4	6
Heart Rate (bpm)	180	137	107	90

  (a) Does $P(t) = \frac{5}{3}t^2 - 25t + 180$ model the data in the table exactly? Explain.
  (b) Does P provide a reasonable model for the athlete's heart rate?
  (c) Does $P(12)$ have significance in this situation? What should be the domain of P?

117. *Time Spent in Line* If a parking lot attendant can wait on 5 vehicles per minute and vehicles are leaving the lot randomly at an average rate of x vehicles per minute, then the average time T in minutes spent waiting in line *and* paying the attendant is given by

$$T(x) = \frac{1}{5 - x},$$

where $x < 5$. (*Source:* N. Garber.)

(a) Evaluate $T(4)$ and interpret the result.

(b) A graph of T is shown in the figure. Interpret the graph as x increases from 0 to 5. Does this result agree with your intuition?

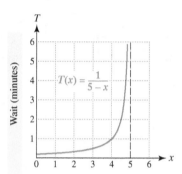

Traffic Rate (vehicles per minute)

(c) Find x if the waiting time is 3 minutes.

118. *People Waiting in Line* At a post office, workers can wait on 50 people per hour. If people arrive randomly at an average rate of x per hour, then the average number of people N waiting in line is given by

$$N(x) = \frac{x^2}{2500 - 50x},$$

where $x < 50$. (*Source:* N. Garber.)

(a) Evaluate $N(30)$ and interpret the result.

(b) A graph of N is shown in the figure. Interpret the graph as x increases from 0 to 50. Does this result agree with your intuition?

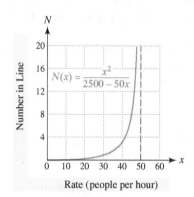

Rate (people per hour)

(c) Find x if $N = 8$.

119. *Uphill Highway Grade* The *grade* x of a hill is a measure of its steepness and corresponds to the slope of the road. For example, if a road rises 10 feet for

every 100 feet of horizontal distance, it has an uphill grade of $x = \frac{10}{100}$, or 10%, as illustrated in the figure.

The braking distance for a car traveling 30 miles per hour on a wet, *uphill* grade x is given by

$$D(x) = \frac{900}{10.5 + 30x}.$$

(*Source:* N. Garber.)

(a) Evaluate $D(0.05)$ and interpret the result.

(b) If the braking distance for this car is 60 feet, find the uphill grade x.

120. *Downhill Highway Grade* (See Exercise 119.) The braking distance for a car traveling 30 miles per hour on a wet, *downhill* grade x is given by

$$S(x) = \frac{900}{10.5 - 30x}.$$

(a) Evaluate $S(0.05)$ and interpret the result.

(b) Make a table for $D(x)$ from Exercise 119 and $S(x)$, starting at $x = 0$ and incrementing by 0.05.

(c) How do the braking distances for uphill and downhill grades compare? Does this result agree with your driving experience?

121. *U.S. AIDS Deaths* The following scatterplot shows the cumulative number of reported AIDS deaths. The data may be modeled x years after 1980 by $f(x) = 2.4x^2 - 14x + 23$, where the output is in thousands of deaths.

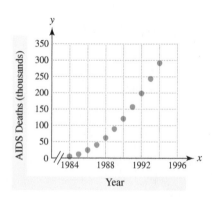

Year

(a) Use $f(x)$ to estimate the cumulative total of AIDS deaths in 1990. Compare it with the actual value of 121.6 thousand.

(b) In 1997 the cumulative number of AIDS deaths was 390 thousand. What estimate does $f(x)$ give? Discuss your result.

122. *A PC for All?* Worldwide sales of computers have climbed as prices have continued to drop. The function $f(x) = 0.29x^2 + 8x + 19$ models the number of personal computers sold in millions during year x, where $x = 0$ corresponds to 1990, $x = 1$ corresponds to 1991, and so on until $x = 25$ corresponds to 2015. Estimate the number of personal computers sold in 2010, using both the graph and the polynomial. (*Source:* eTForcasts.)

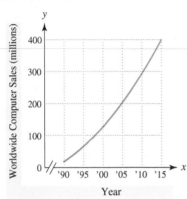

Exercises 123 and 124: Remembering What You Learn
After a test students often forget what they learned. The rational function

$$R(x) = \frac{100}{1.2x + 1}, \quad 0 \le x \le 5,$$

gives an estimate of the percentage of the material a student remembers x days after a test.

123. Evaluate $R(1)$ and $R(3)$. Interpret your results.

124. If a student takes notes in class, these percentages increase by 30% for $1 \le x \le 5$. Write another function $N(x)$ that models this result. Evaluate $N(3)$.

125. *Profit* A company makes and sells notebook computers. The company's cost function in thousands of dollars is $C(x) = 0.3x + 100$, and the revenue function in thousands of dollars is $R(x) = 0.75x$, where x is the number of notebook computers.
  (a) Evaluate and interpret $C(100)$.
  (b) Interpret the y-intercepts on the graphs of C and R.
  (c) Give the profit function $P(x)$.
  (d) How many computers need to be sold to make a profit?

126. *Profit* A company makes and sells sailboats. The company's cost function in thousands of dollars is $C(x) = 2x + 20$, and the revenue function in thousands of dollars is $R(x) = 4x$, where x is the number of sailboats.
  (a) Evaluate and interpret $C(5)$.
  (b) Interpret the y-intercepts on the graphs of C and R.
  (c) Give the profit function $P(x)$.
  (d) How many sailboats need to be sold to break even?

WRITING ABOUT MATHEMATICS

127. Name two functions. Give their formulas, sketch their graphs, and state their domains and ranges.

128. Explain the difference between the domain and the range of a function.

SECTIONS 8.3 and 8.4
Checking Basic Concepts

1. (a) Is 3 a solution to the compound inequality $x + 2 < 4$ or $2x - 1 \ge 3$?
  (b) Is 3 a solution to the compound inequality $x + 2 < 4$ and $2x - 1 \ge 3$?

2. Solve the following compound inequalities. Write your answer in interval notation.
  (a) $-5 \le 2x + 1 \le 3$
  (b) $1 - x \le -2$ or $1 - x \ge 2$
  (c) $-2 < \dfrac{4 - 3x}{2} \le 6$

3. Write the domain of each function in interval notation.
  (a) $f(x) = x^2$
  (b) $g(t) = \dfrac{1}{t - 1}$
  (c) $h(z) = \sqrt{z}$

4. Use the graph of f to do the following.
  (a) Write the domain and range of f in interval notation.
  (b) Evaluate $f(0)$ and $f(-2)$.

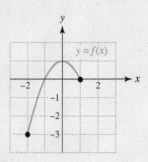

5. Graph $f(x) = |x - 3|$.

CHAPTER 8   Summary

Function A function is a set of ordered pairs (x, y) where each x-value corresponds to exactly one y-value. A function takes a valid input x and computes exactly one output y, forming the ordered pair (x, y).

Domain and Range of a Function The domain D is the set of all valid inputs, or x-values, and the range R is the set of all outputs, or y-values.

Examples: $f = \{(1, 2), (2, 3), (3, 3)\}$ has $D = \{1, 2, 3\}$ and $R = \{2, 3\}$.

$f(x) = x^2$ has domain all real numbers and range $y \geq 0$. (See the graph below.)

Function Notation $y = f(x)$ and is read "y equals f of x."

Example: $f(x) = \frac{2x}{x - 1}$ implies that $f(3) = \frac{2 \cdot 3}{3 - 1} = \frac{6}{2} = 3$. Thus the point $(3, 3)$ is on the graph of f.

Function Representations A function can be represented symbolically, numerically, graphically, or verbally.

Symbolic Representation (Formula) $f(x) = x^2$

Numerical Representation (Table)		**Graphical Representation (Graph)**

x	y
-2	4
-1	1
0	0
1	1
2	4

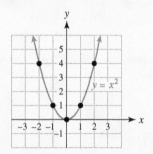

Verbal Representation (Words) f computes the square of the input x.

Vertical Line Test If every vertical line intersects a graph at most once, then the graph represents a function.

Linear Function A linear function can be represented by $f(x) = mx + b$. Its graph is a (straight) line, where m is the slope and b is the y-intercept. For each unit increase in x, $f(x)$ changes by an amount equal to m.

Example: $f(x) = 2x - 1$ represents a linear function with $m = 2$ and $b = -1$.

Numerical Representation	**Graphical Representation**

x	$f(x)$
-1	-3
0	-1
1	1
2	3

1 unit → 2 units
1 unit → 2 units
1 unit → 2 units

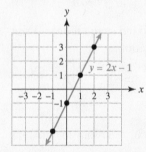

Each 1-unit increase in x results in a 2-unit increase in $f(x)$; thus $m = 2$.

NOTE: A numerical representation is a table of values of $f(x)$.

Modeling Data with Linear Functions When data have a constant rate of change, they can be modeled by $f(x) = mx + b$. The constant m represents the *rate of change*, and the constant b represents the *initial amount* or the value when $x = 0$. That is,

$$f(x) = (\text{Rate of change})x + (\text{Initial amount}).$$

Example: In the following table, the y-values decrease by 3 units for each 1-unit increase in x. When $x = 0$, $y = 4$. Thus the data are modeled by $f(x) = -3x + 4$.

x	-2	-1	0	1	2
y	10	7	4	1	-2

Midpoint Formula The midpoint of the line segment connecting (x_1, y_1) and (x_2, y_2) is

$$\left(\frac{x_1 + x_2}{2}, \frac{y_1 + y_2}{2} \right).$$

Example: The midpoint of the line segment connecting $(-5, 8)$ and $(9, 4)$ is

$$\left(\frac{-5 + 9}{2}, \frac{8 + 4}{2} \right) = (2, 6).$$

SECTION 8.3 ■ COMPOUND INEQUALITIES

Compound Inequality Two inequalities connected by *and* or *or*.

Examples: For $x + 1 < 3$ *or* $x + 1 > 6$, a solution satisfies *at least* one of the inequalities.

For $2x + 1 < 3$ *and* $1 - x > 6$, a solution satisfies *both* inequalities.

Three-Part Inequality A compound inequality in the form $x > a$ *and* $x < b$ can be written as the three-part inequality $a < x < b$.

Example: $1 \le x < 7$ means $x \ge 1$ *and* $x < 7$.

Interval Notation Can be used to identify intervals on the real number line

Examples: $-2 < x \le 3$ is equivalent to $(-2, 3]$.

$x < 5$ is equivalent to $(-\infty, 5)$.

All real numbers are denoted $(-\infty, \infty)$.

SECTION 8.4 ■ OTHER FUNCTIONS AND THEIR PROPERTIES

Domain and Range in Interval Notation The domain and range of a function can often be expressed in interval notation.

Example: The domain of $f(x) = x^2 - 2$ is all real numbers, or $(-\infty, \infty)$, and its range is real numbers greater than or equal to -2, or $[-2, \infty)$.

Absolute Value Function The domain of $f(x) = |x|$ is $(-\infty, \infty)$, and the range is $[0, \infty)$.

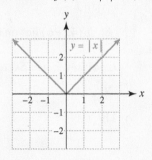

Polynomial Functions The degree of a polynomial function (of one variable) equals the largest exponent of a variable. The graphs of polynomial functions with degree greater than 1 are not lines. The domain of a polynomial function is $(-\infty, \infty)$.

Examples: $f(x) = 4x - 1$ defines a linear function with degree 1.

$g(x) = 4x^2 + x - 4$ defines a quadratic function with degree 2.

$h(x) = x^3 + 0.7x - 1$ defines a cubic function with degree 3.

Rational Functions If $f(x) = \frac{p(x)}{q(x)}$, where $p(x)$ and $q(x)$ are polynomials, f is a rational function. The domain of a rational function includes all real numbers, except x-values that make the denominator 0.

Examples: $f(x) = \frac{1}{x}$ has domain $(-\infty, 0) \cup (0, \infty)$, or $x \neq 0$.

$g(x) = \frac{x}{x^2 - 9}$ has domain $(-\infty, -3) \cup (-3, 3) \cup (3, \infty)$, or $x \neq -3, x \neq 3$.

Operations on Functions If $f(x)$ and $g(x)$ are both defined, then the sum, difference, product, and quotient of two functions f and g are defined by

$$(f + g)(x) = f(x) + g(x) \qquad \text{Sum}$$

$$(f - g)(x) = f(x) - g(x) \qquad \text{Difference}$$

$$(fg)(x) = f(x) \cdot g(x) \qquad \text{Product}$$

$$\left(\frac{f}{g}\right)(x) = \frac{f(x)}{g(x)}, \text{ where } g(x) \neq 0. \quad \text{Quotient}$$

Example: Let $f(x) = x^2 - 1$ and $g(x) = x^2 + 1$.

$$(f + g)(x) = f(x) + g(x) = (x^2 - 1) + (x^2 + 1) = 2x^2$$

$$(f - g)(x) = f(x) - g(x) = (x^2 - 1) - (x^2 + 1) = -2$$

$$(fg)(x) = f(x) \cdot g(x) = (x^2 - 1)(x^2 + 1) = x^4 - 1$$

$$\left(\frac{f}{g}\right)(x) = \frac{f(x)}{g(x)} = \frac{x^2 - 1}{x^2 + 1}$$

CHAPTER 8   Review Exercises

SECTION 8.1

Exercises 1–4: Evaluate $f(x)$ for the given values of x.

1. $f(x) = 3x - 1$ \qquad\qquad $x = -2, \frac{1}{3}$

2. $f(x) = 5 - 3x^2$ \qquad\quad $x = -3, 1$

3. $f(x) = \sqrt{x} - 2$ \qquad\quad $x = 0, 9$

4. $f(x) = 5$ \qquad\qquad\qquad $x = -5, \frac{7}{5}$

Exercises 5 and 6: Do the following.
- (a) *Write a symbolic representation (formula) for the function described.*
- (b) *Evaluate the function for input 5 and interpret the result.*

5. Function P computes the number of pints in q quarts.

6. Function f computes 3 less than 4 times a number x.

7. If $f(3) = -2$, then the point _____ lies on the graph of f.

8. If $(4, -6)$ lies on the graph of f, then $f(\underline{\quad}) = \underline{\quad}$.

Exercises 9–12: Sketch a graph of f.

9. $f(x) = -2x$ \qquad\qquad **10.** $f(x) = \frac{1}{2}x - \frac{3}{2}$

11. $f(x) = x^2 - 1$ \qquad\quad **12.** $f(x) = \sqrt{x + 1}$

Exercises 13 and 14: Use the graph of f to evaluate the given expressions.

13. $f(0)$ and $f(-3)$ **14.** $f(-2)$ and $f(1)$

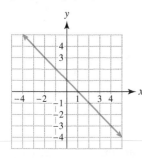
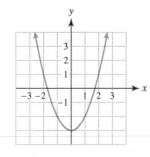

15. Use the table to evaluate $f(-1)$ and $f(3)$.

x	-1	1	3	5
$f(x)$	7	3	-1	-5

16. A function f is represented verbally by "Multiply the input x by 3 and then subtract 2." Give numerical, symbolic, and graphical representations for f. Let $x = -3, -2, -1, \ldots, 3$ in the table of values, and let $-3 \le x \le 3$ for the graph.

Exercises 17 and 18: Use the graph of f to estimate its domain and range.

17.   **18.**

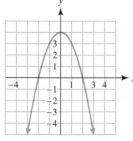
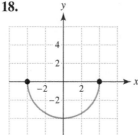

Exercises 19 and 20: Does the graph represent a function?

19.   **20.**

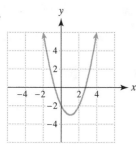
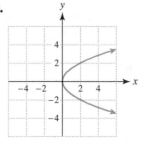

Exercises 21 and 22: Find the domain and range of S. Then state whether S defines a function.

21. $S = \{(-3, 4), (-1, 4), (2, 3), (4, -1)\}$

22. $S = \{(-1, 5), (0, 3), (1, -2), (-1, 2), (2, 4)\}$

Exercises 23–30: Find the domain.

23. $f(x) = -3x + 7$ **24.** $f(x) = \sqrt{x}$

25. $f(x) = \dfrac{3}{x}$ **26.** $f(x) = x^2 + 2$

27. $f(x) = \sqrt{5 - x}$ **28.** $f(x) = \dfrac{x}{x + 2}$

29. $f(x) = |2x + 1|$ **30.** $f(x) = x^3$

SECTION 8.2

Exercises 31 and 32: Does the graph represent a linear function?

31.   **32.**

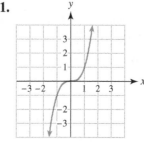
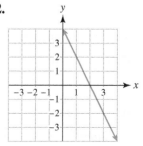

Exercises 33–36: Determine whether f is a linear function. If f is linear, give values for m and b so that f may be expressed as $f(x) = mx + b$.

33. $f(x) = -4x + 5$ **34.** $f(x) = 7 - x$

35. $f(x) = \sqrt{x}$ **36.** $f(x) = 6$

Exercises 37 and 38: Use the table to determine whether $f(x)$ could represent a linear function. If it could, write the formula for f in the form $f(x) = mx + b$.

37.

x	0	2	4	6
$f(x)$	-3	0	3	6

38.

x	-1	0	1	2
$f(x)$	-5	0	10	15

39. Evaluate $f(x) = \frac{1}{2}x + 3$ at $x = -4$.

40. Use the graph to evaluate $f(-2)$ and $f(1)$.

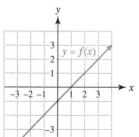

Exercises 41–44: Sketch a graph of $y = f(x)$.

41. $f(x) = x + 1$

42. $f(x) = 1 - 2x$

43. $f(x) = -\frac{1}{3}x$

44. $f(x) = -1$

45. Write a symbolic representation (formula) for a linear function H that calculates the number of hours in x days. Evaluate $H(2)$ and interpret the result.

46. Let $f(x) = \sqrt{x + 2} - x^2$.
  (a) Make a numerical representation (table) for the function f with $x = 1, 2, 3, \ldots, 7$.
  (b) Graph f in the standard window. What is the domain of f?

Exercises 47 and 48: Find the midpoint of the line segment connecting the given points.

47. $(-5, 3), (6, -9)$

48. $\left(\frac{2}{3}, -\frac{3}{4}\right), \left(\frac{1}{6}, \frac{3}{2}\right)$

SECTION 8.3

Use interval notation whenever possible for the remaining exercises.

Exercises 49–52: Solve the compound inequality. Graph the solution set on a number line.

49. $x + 1 \leq 3$ and $x + 1 \geq -1$

50. $2x + 7 < 5$ and $-2x \geq 6$

51. $5x - 1 \leq 3$ or $1 - x < -1$

52. $3x + 1 > -1$ or $3x + 1 < 10$

53. Use the table to solve $-2 \leq 2x + 2 \leq 4$.

x	-3	-2	-1	0	1	2	3
$2x + 2$	-4	-2	0	2	4	6	8

54. Use the following figure to solve each equation or inequality.
  (a) $y_1 = y_2$
  (b) $y_2 = y_3$
  (c) $y_1 \leq y_2 \leq y_3$
  (d) $y_2 < y_3$

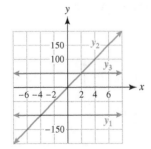

55. The graphs of y_1 and y_2 are shown at the top of the next column. Solve each equation or inequality.

(a) $y_1 = y_2$
(b) $y_1 < y_2$
(c) $y_1 > y_2$

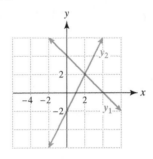

56. The graphs of three linear functions f, g, and h are shown in the following figure. Solve each equation or inequality.
  (a) $f(x) = g(x)$
  (b) $g(x) = h(x)$
  (c) $f(x) < g(x) < h(x)$

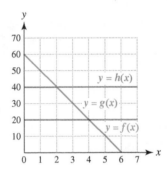

Exercises 57–62: Write the given inequality in interval notation.

57. $-3 \leq x \leq \frac{2}{3}$

58. $-6 < x \leq 45$

59. $x < \frac{7}{2}$

60. $x \geq 1.8$

61. $x > -3$ and $x < 4$

62. $x < 4$ or $x > 10$

Exercises 63–68: Solve the three-part inequality. Write the solution set in interval notation.

63. $-4 < x + 1 < 6$

64. $20 \leq 2x + 4 \leq 60$

65. $-3 < 4 - \frac{1}{3}x < 7$

66. $2 \leq \frac{1}{2}x - 2 \leq 12$

67. $-3 \leq \dfrac{4 - 5x}{3} - 2 < 3$

68. $30 \leq \dfrac{2x - 6}{5} - 4 < 50$

SECTION 8.4

Exercises 69 and 70: Write the domain and the range of the function.

69. $f(t) = \frac{1}{2}t^2$

70. $f(x) = |x + 2|$

71. Write the domain of $f(x) = \frac{x + 1}{2x - 8}$.

72. Write the domain and range of the function shown in the graph.

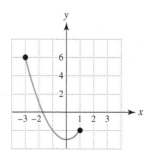

Exercises 73–76: Determine whether f(x) represents a polynomial function. If possible, identify the degree and type of polynomial function.

73. $f(x) = 1 + 2x - 3x^2$

74. $f(x) = 5 + 7x$

75. $f(x) = x^3 + 2x$ **76.** $f(x) = |2x - 1|$

Exercises 77 and 78: If possible, evaluate g(t) for the given values of t.

77. $g(t) = |1 - 4t|$ $t = 3, t = -\frac{1}{4}$

78. $g(t) = \dfrac{4}{4 - t^2}$ $t = 3, t = -2$

Exercises 79–82: Graph y = f(x).

79. $f(x) = |x + 3|$ **80.** $f(x) = x^2 + 1$

81. $f(x) = \dfrac{1}{x}$ **82.** $f(x) = -3x$

83. Use $f(x) = 2x^2 - 3x$ and $g(x) = 2x - 3$ to find each of the following.
(a) $(f + g)(3)$ (b) $(fg)(3)$

84. Use $f(x) = x^2 - 1$ and $g(x) = x - 1$ to find each of the following.
(a) $(f - g)(x)$ (b) $(f/g)(x)$

APPLICATIONS

111. *Age at First Marriage* The median age at the first marriage for men from 1890 to 1960 can be modeled by $f(x) = -0.0492x + 119.1$, where x is the year. (*Source:* National Center of Health Statistics.)
(a) Find the median age in 1910.
(b) Graph f in [1885, 1965, 10] by [22, 26, 1]. What happened to the median age?
(c) What is the slope of the graph of f? Interpret the slope as a rate of change.

112. *Marriages* From 2002 to 2008 the number of U.S. marriages in millions could be modeled by the formula $f(x) = 2.2$, where x is the year.
(a) Estimate the number of marriages in 2006.
(b) What information does f give about the number of marriages from 2002 to 2008?

113. *Fat Grams* A cup of milk contains 8 grams of fat.
(a) Give a formula for $f(x)$ that calculates the number of fat grams in x cups of milk.
(b) What is the slope of the graph of f?
(c) Interpret the slope as a rate of change.

114. *Birth Rate* The U.S. birth rate per 1000 people for selected years is shown in the table.

Year	1950	1970	1990	2010
Birth Rate	24.1	18.4	16.7	13.5

Source: U.S. Census Bureau.

(a) Make a scatterplot of the data.
(b) Model the data with $f(x) = mx + b$, where x is the year. Answers may vary.
(c) Use f to estimate the birth rate in 2000.

115. *Unhealthy Air Quality* The Environmental Protection Agency (EPA) monitors air quality in U.S. cities. The function f gives the annual number of days with unhealthy air quality in Los Angeles, California, for selected years.

x	1995	1999	2000	2003	2007
$f(x)$	113	56	87	88	100

Source: Environmental Protection Agency.

(a) Find $f(1995)$ and interpret your result.
(b) Identify the domain and range of f.
(c) Discuss the trend of air pollution in Los Angeles.

116. *Temperature Scales* The table at the top of the next column shows equivalent temperatures in degrees Celsius and degrees Fahrenheit.

°C	−40	0	15	35	100
°F	−40	32	59	95	212

(a) Plot the data. Let the x-axis correspond to the Celsius temperature and the y-axis correspond to the Fahrenheit temperature. What type of relation exists between the data?
(b) Find $f(x) = mx + b$ so that f receives the Celsius temperature x as input and outputs the

corresponding Fahrenheit temperature. Interpret the slope of the graph of f.

(c) If the temperature is 20°C, what is the equivalent temperature in degrees Fahrenheit?

117. *Distance Between Bicyclists* The following graph shows the distance between two bicyclists traveling toward each other along a straight road after x hours.

(a) After how long did the bicycle riders meet?

(b) When were they 20 miles apart?

(c) Find the times when they were less than 20 miles apart.

(d) Estimate the sum of the speeds of the bicyclists.

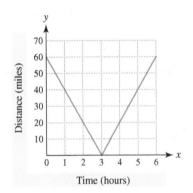

118. *Violent Crimes in the U.S.* The number of violent crimes reported has dropped from 10 million in 1992 to 5 million in 2008.

(a) Find a linear function $f(x) = mx + b$ that models the data x years after 1992.

(b) Use $f(x)$ to estimate the number of violent crimes in 2005.

119. *Average Precipitation* The average rainfall in Houston, Texas, is 3.9 inches per month. Each month's average A is within 1.7 inches of 3.9 inches. (*Source:* J. Williams, *The Weather Almanac 1995.*)

(a) Write an absolute value inequality that models this situation.

(b) Solve the inequality.

120. *Relative Error* If a quantity is measured to be T and the actual value is A, then the relative error in this measurement is $\left|\frac{T - A}{A}\right|$. If $A = 35$ and the relative error is to be less than 0.08 (8%), what values for T are possible?

CHAPTER 8   Extended and Discovery Exercises

1. *Developing a Model* Two identical cylindrical tanks, A and B, each contain 100 gallons of water. Tank A has a pump that begins removing water at a constant rate of 8 gallons per minute. Tank B has a plug removed from its bottom and water begins to flow out—faster at first and then more slowly.

(a) Assuming that the tanks become empty at the same time, sketch a graph that models the amount of water in each tank. Explain your graphs.

(b) Which tank is half empty first? Explain.

2. *Modeling Real Data* Per capita personal incomes in the United States are listed in the following table.

Year	2002	2003	2004
Income	$31,461	$32,271	$33,881

Year	2005	2006	2007
Income	$35,424	$37,698	$39,458

Source: Department of Commerce.

(a) Make a scatterplot of the data.

(b) Find a function f that models the data. Explain your reasoning.

(c) Use f to estimate per capita income in 2000.

3. *Weight of a Small Fish* The graph shows a function f that models the weight in milligrams of a small fish, *Lebistes reticulatus*, during the first 14 weeks of its life. (*Source:* D. Brown and P. Rothery, *Models in Biology.*)

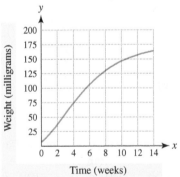

(a) Estimate the weight of the fish when it hatches, at 6 weeks, and at 12 weeks.

(b) If (x_1, y_1) and (x_2, y_2) are points on the graph of a function, the **average rate of change of f from x_1 to x_2** is given by $\frac{y_2 - y_1}{x_2 - x_1}$. Approximate the average rates of change of f from hatching to 6 weeks and from 6 weeks to 12 weeks.

(c) Interpret these rates of change.

(d) During which time period does the fish gain weight the fastest?

4. *Recording Music* A compact disc (CD) can hold approximately 700 million bytes. One million bytes is commonly referred to as a *megabyte* (MB). Recording music requires an enormous amount of memory. The accompanying table lists the megabytes x needed to record y seconds (sec) of music.

x (MB)	0.129	0.231	0.415	0.491
y (sec)	6.010	10.74	19.27	22.83

x (MB)	0.667	1.030	1.160	1.260
y (sec)	31.00	49.00	55.25	60.18

Source: Gateway 2000 System CD.

(a) Make a scatterplot of the data.

(b) What relationship seems to exist between x and y? Why does this relationship seem reasonable?

(c) Find the slope–intercept form of a line that models the data. Interpret the slope of this line as a rate of change. Answers may vary.

(d) Check your answer in part (c) by graphing the line and data in the same graph.

(e) Write a linear equation whose solution gives the megabytes needed to record 120 seconds of music.

(f) Solve the equation in part (e) graphically or symbolically.

10 Radical Expressions and Functions

10.1 Radical Expressions
and Functions

Throughout history, people have created (or discovered) new numbers. Often these new numbers were met with resistance and regarded as being imaginary or unreal. The number 0 was not invented at the same time as the natural numbers. There was no Roman numeral for 0, which is one reason why our calendar started with A.D. 1 and, as a result, the twenty-first century began in 2001. No doubt there were skeptics during the time of the Roman Empire who questioned why anyone needed a number to represent nothing. Negative numbers also met strong resistance. After all, how could anyone possibly have −6 apples?

In this chapter we describe a new number system called *complex numbers*, which involve square roots of negative numbers. The Italian mathematician Cardano (1501–1576) was one of the first mathematicians to work with complex numbers and called them useless. René Descartes (1596–1650) originated the term *imaginary number*, which is associated with complex numbers. Today complex numbers are used in many applications, such as electricity, fiber optics, and the design of airplanes. We are privileged to study in a period of days what took people centuries to discover.

Source: Historical Topics for the Mathematics Classroom, Thirty-first Yearbook, NCTM.

10.1 Radical Expressions and Functions

Radical Notation • The Square Root Function • The Cube Root Function

A LOOK INTO MATH ▶

Suppose you start a summer painting business, and initially you are the only employee. Because business is good, you hire another employee and productivity goes up, more than enough to pay for the new employee. As time goes on, you hire more employees. Eventually, productivity starts to level off because there are too many employees to keep busy. This situation is common in business and can be modeled by using a function involving a square root. (See Example 12.)

Radical Notation

SQUARE ROOTS Recall the definition of the square root of a number a.

NEW VOCABULARY

☐ Radical sign
☐ Radicand
☐ Radical expression
☐ *n*th root
☐ Index
☐ Odd root
☐ Even root
☐ Principal *n*th root
☐ Square root function
☐ Cube root function

> **SQUARE ROOT**
>
> The number b is a *square root* of a if $b^2 = a$.

EXAMPLE 1 **Finding square roots**

Find the square roots of 100.

Solution

The square roots of 100 are 10 *and* -10 because $10^2 = 100$ and $(-10)^2 = 100$.

Now Try Exercise 1

Every positive number a has two square roots: one positive and one negative. Recall that the *positive square root* is called the *principal square root* and is denoted $\sqrt{a}$. The *negative square root* is denoted $-\sqrt{a}$. To identify both square roots, we write $\pm\sqrt{a}$. The symbol $\pm$ is read "plus or minus." The symbol $\sqrt{}$ is called the **radical sign**. The expression under the radical sign is called the **radicand**, and an expression containing a radical sign is called a **radical expression**. Examples of radical expressions include

$$\sqrt{6}, \quad 5 + \sqrt{x+1}, \quad \text{and} \quad \sqrt{\frac{3x}{2x-1}}.$$

MAKING CONNECTIONS

Expressions and Equations

Expressions and equations are *different* mathematical concepts. An expression does not contain an equals sign, whereas an equation *always* contains an equals sign. *An equation is a statement that two expressions are equal.* For example,

$$\sqrt{x+1} \quad \text{and} \quad \sqrt{5-x} \qquad \text{Expressions}$$

are two different expressions, and

$$\sqrt{x+1} = \sqrt{5-x} \qquad \text{Equation}$$

is an equation. We often *solve an equation*, but we *do not solve an expression*. Instead, we *simplify* and *evaluate* expressions.

In the next example we show how to find the principal square root of an expression.

EXAMPLE 2 **Finding principal square roots**

Evaluate each square root.

(a) $\sqrt{25}$ **(b)** $\sqrt{0.49}$ **(c)** $\sqrt{\frac{4}{9}}$ **(d)** $\sqrt{c^2}, c > 0$

Solution
(a) Because $5 \cdot 5 = 25$, the principal, or *positive*, square root of 25 is $\sqrt{25} = 5$.
(b) Because $(0.7)(0.7) = 0.49$, the principal square root of 0.49 is $\sqrt{0.49} = 0.7$.
(c) Because $\frac{2}{3} \cdot \frac{2}{3} = \frac{4}{9}$, the principal square root of $\frac{4}{9}$ is $\sqrt{\frac{4}{9}} = \frac{2}{3}$.
(d) The principal square root of c^2 is $\sqrt{c^2} = c$, as c is positive.

Now Try Exercises 15, 17, 19, 21

The square roots of many real numbers, such as $\sqrt{17}$, $\sqrt{1.2}$, and $\sqrt{\frac{5}{7}}$, cannot be conveniently evaluated (or approximated) by hand. In these cases we sometimes use a calculator to give a decimal *approximation*, as demonstrated in the next example.

EXAMPLE 3 **Approximating a square root**

Approximate $\sqrt{17}$ to the nearest thousandth.

Solution
Figure 10.1 shows that $\sqrt{17} \approx 4.123$, rounded to the nearest thousandth. This result means that $4.123 \times 4.123 \approx 17$.

```
√(17)
           4.123105626
```

Figure 10.1

Now Try Exercise 39

SQUARE ROOTS OF NEGATIVE NUMBERS The square root of a *negative* number is *not* a real number. For example, $\sqrt{-4} \neq 2$ because $2 \cdot 2 \neq -4$ and $\sqrt{-4} \neq -2$ because $(-2)(-2) \neq -4$. (Later in this chapter, we will use the complex numbers to identify square roots of negative numbers.)

READING CHECK

Are square roots of negative numbers real numbers? Explain.

▶ **REAL-WORLD CONNECTION** Have you ever noticed that if you climb up a hill or a tower you can see farther to the horizon? This phenomenon can be described by a formula containing a square root, as demonstrated in the next example.

EXAMPLE 4　**Seeing the horizon**

A formula for calculating the distance d in miles that one can see to the horizon on a clear day is approximated by $d = 1.22\sqrt{x}$, where x is the elevation, in feet, of a person.
(a) Approximate how far a 6-foot-tall person can see to the horizon.
(b) Approximate how far a person can see from an 8000-foot mountain.

Solution
(a) Let $x = 6$ in the formula $d = 1.22\sqrt{x}$.

$$d = 1.22\sqrt{6} \approx 3, \text{ or about 3 miles.}$$

(b) If $x = 8000$, then $d = 1.22\sqrt{8000} \approx 109$, or about 109 miles.

▍ Now Try Exercise 107

CUBE ROOTS The cube root of a number a is denoted $\sqrt[3]{a}$.

CALCULATOR HELP

To calculate a cube root, see Appendix A (page AP-1).

CUBE ROOT

The number b is a *cube root* of a if $b^3 = a$.

Although the square root of a negative number is *not* a real number, the cube root of a negative number is a negative real number. *Every real number has one real cube root.*

EXAMPLE 5　**Finding cube roots**

Evaluate the cube root. Approximate your answer to the nearest hundredth when appropriate.
(a) $\sqrt[3]{8}$　**(b)** $\sqrt[3]{-27}$　**(c)** $\sqrt[3]{\frac{1}{64}}$　**(d)** $\sqrt[3]{d^6}$　**(e)** $\sqrt[3]{16}$

Solution
(a) $\sqrt[3]{8} = 2$ because $2^3 = 2 \cdot 2 \cdot 2 = 8$.
(b) $\sqrt[3]{-27} = -3$ because $(-3)^3 = (-3)(-3)(-3) = -27$.
(c) $\sqrt[3]{\frac{1}{64}} = \frac{1}{4}$ because $\left(\frac{1}{4}\right)^3 = \frac{1}{4} \cdot \frac{1}{4} \cdot \frac{1}{4} = \frac{1}{64}$.
(d) $\sqrt[3]{d^6} = d^2$ because $(d^2)^3 = d^2 \cdot d^2 \cdot d^2 = d^{2+2+2} = d^6$.
(e) $\sqrt[3]{16}$ is not an integer. Figure 10.2 shows that $\sqrt[3]{16} \approx 2.52$.

▍ Now Try Exercises 23, 25, 27, 41

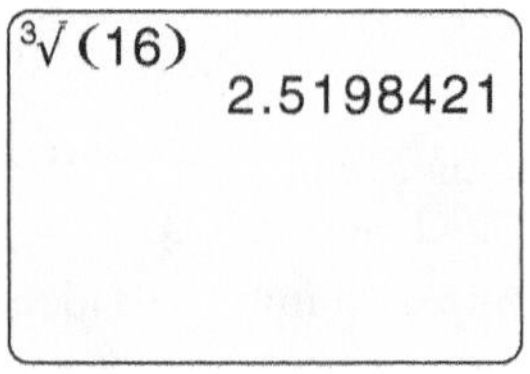

```
³√(16)
           2.5198421
```

Figure 10.2

NOTE: $\sqrt[3]{-b} = -\sqrt[3]{b}$ for any real number b. That is, the cube root of a negative is the negative of the cube root. For example, $\sqrt[3]{-8} = -\sqrt[3]{8} = -2$.

Table 10.1 illustrates how to evaluate both square roots and cube roots. If the radical expression is undefined, a dash is used.

TABLE 10.1 **Radicals**

Expression	$\sqrt{64}$	$-\sqrt{64}$	$\sqrt{-64}$	$\sqrt[3]{64}$	$-\sqrt[3]{64}$	$\sqrt[3]{-64}$
Evaluated	8	-8	—	4	-4	-4

*N*th ROOTS We can generalize square roots and cube roots to include *n*th roots of a number *a*. The number *b* is an **nth root** of *a* if $b^n = a$, where *n* is a positive integer. For example, $2^5 = 32$, so the 5th root of 32 is 2 and can be written as $\sqrt[5]{32} = 2$.

THE NOTATION $\sqrt[n]{a}$

The equation $\sqrt[n]{a} = b$ means that $b^n = a$, where *n* is a natural number called the **index**. If *n* is odd, we are finding an **odd root** and if *n* is even, we are finding an **even root**.

1. If $a > 0$, then $\sqrt[n]{a}$ is a positive number. $\sqrt[4]{16} = 2$ and is positive.
2. If $a < 0$ and
    (a) *n* is odd, then $\sqrt[n]{a}$ is a negative number. $\sqrt[3]{-8} = -2$ and is negative.
    (b) *n* is even, then $\sqrt[n]{a}$ is *not* a real number. $\sqrt[4]{-8}$ is undefined.

If $a > 0$ and *n* is even, then *a* has two real *n*th roots: one positive and one negative. The positive root is denoted $\sqrt[n]{a}$ and called the **principal *n*th root** of *a*. For example, $(-3)^4 = 81$ *and* $3^4 = 81$, but $\sqrt[4]{81} = 3$ in the same way *principal square roots* are calculated.

EXAMPLE 6 ▶ **Finding *n*th roots**

Find each root, if possible.

(a) $\sqrt[4]{16}$ **(b)** $\sqrt[5]{-32}$ **(c)** $\sqrt[4]{-81}$ **(d)** $-\sqrt[4]{81}$

Solution
(a) $\sqrt[4]{16} = 2$ because $2^4 = 2 \cdot 2 \cdot 2 \cdot 2 = 16$.
(b) $\sqrt[5]{-32} = -2$ because $(-2)^5 = (-2)(-2)(-2)(-2)(-2) = -32$.
(c) An *even* root of a *negative* number is *not* a real number.
(d) $-\sqrt[4]{81} = -3$ because $\sqrt[4]{81} = 3$.

Now Try Exercises 33, 35, 37

ABSOLUTE VALUE Consider the calculations

$$\sqrt{3^2} = \sqrt{9} = 3, \quad \sqrt{(-4)^2} = \sqrt{16} = 4, \quad \text{and} \quad \sqrt{(-6)^2} = \sqrt{36} = 6.$$

In general, the expression $\sqrt{x^2}$ equals $|x|$. Graphical support is shown in Figure 10.3, where the graphs of $Y_1 = \sqrt{(X^2)}$ and $Y_2 = \text{abs}(X)$ appear to be identical.

CRITICAL THINKING

Evaluate $\sqrt[6]{(-2)^6}$ and $\sqrt[3]{(-2)^3}$. Now simplify $\sqrt[n]{x^n}$ when *n* is even and when *n* is odd.

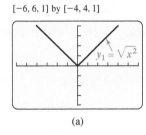

[−6, 6, 1] by [−4, 4, 1]   [−6, 6, 1] by [−4, 4, 1]

$y_1 = \sqrt{x^2}$ $y_2 = |x|$

(a)   (b)

Figure 10.3

THE EXPRESSION $\sqrt{x^2}$

For every real number *x*, $\sqrt{x^2} = |x|$.

EXAMPLE 7   **Simplifying expressions**

Write each expression in terms of an absolute value.

(a) $\sqrt{(-3)^2}$ **(b)** $\sqrt{(x+1)^2}$ **(c)** $\sqrt{z^2 - 4z + 4}$

Solution

(a) $\sqrt{x^2} = |x|$, so $\sqrt{(-3)^2} = |-3|$

(b) $\sqrt{(x+1)^2} = |x+1|$

(c) $\sqrt{z^2 - 4z + 4} = \sqrt{(z-2)^2} = |z-2|$

▮ Now Try Exercises 45, 49, 51

The Square Root Function

The **square root function** is given by $f(x) = \sqrt{x}$. The domain of the square root function is all nonnegative real numbers because we have *not* defined the square root of a negative number. Table 10.2 lists three points that lie on the graph of $f(x) = \sqrt{x}$. In Figure 10.4 these points are plotted and the graph of $y = \sqrt{x}$ has been sketched. The graph does not appear to the left of the origin because $f(x) = \sqrt{x}$ is undefined for negative inputs.

TABLE 10.2

x	$\sqrt{x}$
0	0
1	1
4	2

Square Root Function

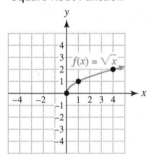

Figure 10.4

TECHNOLOGY NOTE

Square Roots of Negative Numbers
If a table of values for $y_1 = \sqrt{x}$ includes both negative and positive values for x, then many calculators give error messages when x is negative, as shown in the figure in the margin.

X	Y1
-9	ERROR
-4	ERROR
-1	ERROR
0	0
1	1
4	2
9	3

Y1◼√(X)

EXAMPLE 8   **Evaluating functions involving square roots**

If possible, evaluate $f(1)$ and $f(-2)$ for each $f(x)$.

(a) $f(x) = \sqrt{2x - 1}$ **(b)** $f(x) = \sqrt{4 - x^2}$

Solution

(a) $f(1) = \sqrt{2(1) - 1} = \sqrt{1} = 1$

$f(-2) = \sqrt{2(-2) - 1} = \sqrt{-5}$, which does not equal a real number.

(b) $f(1) = \sqrt{4 - (1)^2} = \sqrt{3}$

$f(-2) = \sqrt{4 - (-2)^2} = \sqrt{0} = 0$

▮ Now Try Exercises 61, 63

▶ **REAL-WORLD CONNECTION** A good punter can kick a football so that the ball has a long *hang time*. Hang time is the length of time that the ball is in the air, and a long hang time gives the kicking team time to run down the field and stop the punt return. By using a function involving a square root, we can estimate hang time.

EXAMPLE 9 **Calculating hang time**

If a football is kicked x feet high, then the time T in seconds that the ball is in the air is given by the function

$$T(x) = \frac{1}{2}\sqrt{x}.$$

(a) Find the hang time if the ball is kicked 50 feet into the air.
(b) Does the hang time double if the ball is kicked 100 feet in the air?

Solution
(a) The hang time is $T(50) = \frac{1}{2}\sqrt{50} \approx 3.5$ seconds.
(b) The hang time is $T(100) = \frac{1}{2}\sqrt{100} = 5$ seconds. The time does *not* double when the height doubles.

Now Try Exercise 105

CRITICAL THINKING

How high would a football have to be kicked to have twice the hang time of a football kicked 50 feet into the air?

EXAMPLE 10 **Finding the domain of a square root function**

Let $f(x) = \sqrt{x-1}$.
(a) Find the domain of f. Write your answer in interval notation.
(b) Graph $y = f(x)$ and compare it to the graph of $y = \sqrt{x}$.

Solution
(a) For $f(x)$ to be defined, $x - 1$ cannot be negative. Thus valid inputs for x must satisfy

$$x - 1 \geq 0 \quad \text{or} \quad x \geq 1.$$

The domain is $[1, \infty)$.
(b) Table 10.3 lists points that lie on the graph of $y = \sqrt{x-1}$. Note in Figure 10.5 that the graph appears only when $x \geq 1$. This graph is similar to $y = \sqrt{x}$ (see Figure 10.4) except that it is shifted one unit to the right.

TABLE 10.3

x	$\sqrt{x-1}$
1	0
2	1
5	2

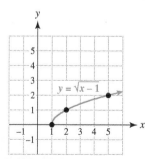

Figure 10.5

Now Try Exercises 75, 89

EXAMPLE 11 **Finding the domains of square root functions**

Find the domain of each function. Write your answer in interval notation.

(a) $f(x) = \sqrt{4 - 2x}$ **(b)** $g(x) = \sqrt{x^2 + 1}$

Solution

(a) To determine when $f(x) = \sqrt{4 - 2x}$ is defined, we must solve $4 - 2x \geq 0$.

$$4 - 2x \geq 0 \quad \text{Inequality to be solved}$$
$$4 \geq 2x \quad \text{Add } 2x \text{ to each side.}$$
$$2 \geq x \quad \text{Divide each side by 2.}$$

The domain is $(-\infty, 2]$.

(b) Regardless of the value of x in $g(x) = \sqrt{x^2 + 1}$, the expression $x^2 + 1$ is always positive because $x^2 \geq 0$. Thus $g(x)$ is defined for all real numbers, and its domain is $(-\infty, \infty)$.

▌ Now Try Exercises 83, 85

MAKING CONNECTIONS

Domains of Functions and Their Graphs

In Example 11, the domains of f and g were found *symbolically*. Notice that the graph of f does not appear to the right of $x = 2$ because the domain of f is $(-\infty, 2]$, whereas the graph of g appears for all values of x because the domain of g is $(-\infty, \infty)$.

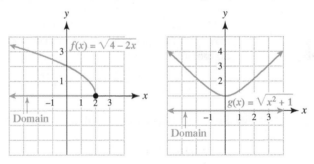

▶ **REAL-WORLD CONNECTION** (Refer to A Look Into Math at the beginning of this section.) In the next example, we analyze the benefit of adding employees to a small business.

EXAMPLE 12 **Increasing productivity with more employees**

The function $R(x) = 108\sqrt{x}$ gives the total revenue per year in thousands of dollars generated by a small business having x employees. A graph of $y = R(x)$ is shown in Figure 10.6.

Revenue as a Function of Employees

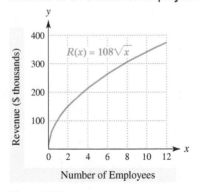

Figure 10.6

(a) Approximate values for $R(4)$, $R(8)$, and $R(12)$ by using both the formula and the graph.
(b) Evaluate $R(12) - R(8)$ and $R(8) - R(4)$ using the formula. Interpret your answer.

Solution
(a) $R(4) = 108\sqrt{4} = \$216$ thousand, $R(8) = 108\sqrt{8} \approx \$305$ thousand, and finally $R(12) = 108\sqrt{12} \approx \$374$ thousand.

We can graphically evaluate $R(4) \approx \$215$ thousand, $R(8) \approx \$305$ thousand, and $R(12) \approx \$375$ thousand, as shown in Figure 10.7.

Revenue as a Function of Employees

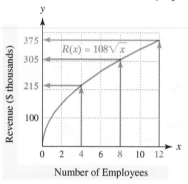

Figure 10.7

(b) $R(8) - R(4) \approx 305 - 216 = \$89$ thousand
$R(12) - R(8) \approx 374 - 305 = \$69$ thousand

There is more revenue gained from 4 to 8 employees than there is from 8 to 12 employees. Because the graph of $R(x) = 108\sqrt{x}$ starts to level off, there is a limited benefit to adding employees.

Now Try Exercise 109

The Cube Root Function

Cube Root Function

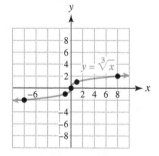

Figure 10.8

We can define the **cube root function** by $f(x) = \sqrt[3]{x}$. Cube roots are defined for both positive and negative numbers, so *the domain of the cube root function includes all real numbers*. Table 10.4 lists points that lie on the graph of the cube root function. Figure 10.8 shows a graph of $y = \sqrt[3]{x}$.

TABLE 10.4 **Cube Root Function**

x	-27	-8	-1	0	1	8	27
$\sqrt[3]{x}$	-3	-2	-1	0	1	2	3

MAKING CONNECTIONS

Domains of the Square Root and Cube Root Functions

$f(x) = \sqrt{x}$ equals a real number for any nonnegative x. Thus $D = [0, \infty)$.
$f(x) = \sqrt[3]{x}$ equals a real number for any x. Thus $D = (-\infty, \infty)$.

Examples: $\sqrt{4} = 2$ but $\sqrt{-4}$ is *not* a real number. $\sqrt[3]{8} = 2$ and $\sqrt[3]{-8} = -2$.

EXAMPLE 13 **Evaluating functions involving cube roots**

Evaluate $f(1)$ and $f(-3)$ for each $f(x)$.

(a) $f(x) = \sqrt[3]{x^2 - 1}$ **(b)** $f(x) = \sqrt[3]{2 - x^2}$

Solution

(a) $f(1) = \sqrt[3]{1^2 - 1} = \sqrt[3]{0} = 0$; $f(-3) = \sqrt[3]{(-3)^2 - 1} = \sqrt[3]{8} = 2$

(b) $f(1) = \sqrt[3]{2 - 1^2} = \sqrt[3]{1} = 1$; $f(-3) = \sqrt[3]{2 - (-3)^2} = \sqrt[3]{-7}$ or $-\sqrt[3]{7}$

Now Try Exercises 65, 69

10.1 Putting It All Together

CONCEPT	EXPLANATION	EXAMPLES
*n*th Root of a Real Number	An *n*th root of a real number a is b if $b^n = a$, and the (principal) *n*th root is denoted $\sqrt[n]{a}$. If $a < 0$ and n is even, $\sqrt[n]{a}$ is not a real number.	The square roots of 25 are 5 and -5. The principal square root is $\sqrt{25} = 5$. $\sqrt[3]{-125} = -5$ because $(-5)^3 = -125$. $\sqrt[4]{-9}$ is not a real number.
Square Root and Cube Root Functions	$f(x) = \sqrt{x}$ and $g(x) = \sqrt[3]{x}$ The cube root function g is defined for all inputs, whereas the square root function f is defined only for nonnegative inputs. **Square Root Function** **Cube Root Function**  Domain: $[0, \infty)$ Domain: $(-\infty, \infty)$	$f(64) = \sqrt{64} = 8$ $f(-64) = \sqrt{-64}$ is *not* a real number. $g(64) = \sqrt[3]{64} = 4$ $g(-64) = \sqrt[3]{-64} = -4$

10.1 Exercises

MyMathLab Math XL PRACTICE WATCH DOWNLOAD READ REVIEW

CONCEPTS AND VOCABULARY

1. What are the square roots of 9?

2. What is the principal square root of 9?

3. What is the cube root of 8?

4. Does every real number have a cube root?

5. If $b^n = a$ and $b > 0$, then $\sqrt[n]{a} =$ _____.

6. What is $\sqrt{x^2}$ equal to?

7. Evaluate $\sqrt{-25}$, if possible.

8. Evaluate $\sqrt[3]{-27}$, if possible.

9. Which of the following (a.–d.) equals -4?
   a. $\sqrt{16}$ b. $\sqrt{-16}$
   c. $-\sqrt[3]{16}$ d. $\sqrt[3]{-64}$

10. Which of the following (a.–d.) equals $|2x + 1|$?
    a. $\sqrt{(2x + 1)^2}$ b. $\sqrt[3]{(2x + 1)^3}$
    c. $\left(\sqrt{2x + 1}\right)^2$ d. $\sqrt{(2x)^2 + 1}$

11. Sketch a graph of the square root function.

12. Sketch a graph of the cube root function.

13. What is the domain of the square root function?

14. What is the domain of the cube root function?

RADICAL EXPRESSIONS

Exercises 15–38: Evaluate the expression by hand, if possible. Variables represent any real number.

15. $\sqrt{9}$ 16. $\sqrt{121}$

17. $\sqrt{0.36}$ 18. $\sqrt{0.64}$

19. $\sqrt{\frac{16}{25}}$ 20. $\sqrt{\frac{9}{49}}$

21. $\sqrt{x^2}, x > 0$ 22. $\sqrt{(x - 1)^2}, x > 1$

23. $\sqrt[3]{27}$ 24. $\sqrt[3]{64}$

25. $\sqrt[3]{-64}$ 26. $-\sqrt[3]{-1}$

27. $\sqrt[3]{\frac{8}{27}}$ 28. $\sqrt[3]{-\frac{1}{125}}$

29. $-\sqrt[3]{x^9}$ 30. $\sqrt[3]{(x + 1)^6}$

31. $\sqrt[3]{(2x)^6}$ 32. $\sqrt[3]{27x^3}$

33. $\sqrt[4]{81}$ 34. $\sqrt[5]{-1}$

35. $\sqrt[5]{-243}$ 36. $\sqrt[4]{625}$

37. $\sqrt[4]{-16}$ 38. $\sqrt[6]{-64}$

Exercises 39–44: Approximate to the nearest hundredth.

39. $-\sqrt{5}$ 40. $\sqrt{11}$

41. $\sqrt[3]{5}$ 42. $\sqrt[3]{-13}$

43. $\sqrt[5]{-7}$ 44. $\sqrt[4]{6}$

Exercises 45–58: Simplify the expression. Assume that all variables are real numbers.

45. $\sqrt{(-4)^2}$ 46. $\sqrt{9^2}$

47. $\sqrt{y^2}$ 48. $\sqrt{z^4}$

49. $\sqrt{(x - 5)^2}$ 50. $\sqrt{(2x - 1)^2}$

51. $\sqrt{x^2 - 2x + 1}$ 52. $\sqrt{4x^2 + 4x + 1}$

53. $\sqrt[4]{y^4}$ 54. $\sqrt[4]{x^8 z^4}$

55. $\sqrt[4]{x^{12}}$ 56. $\sqrt[6]{x^6}$

57. $\sqrt[5]{x^5}$ 58. $\sqrt[5]{32(x + 4)^5}$

SQUARE AND CUBE ROOT FUNCTIONS

Exercises 59–74: If possible, evaluate the function at the given value(s) of the variable.

59. $f(x) = \sqrt{x - 1}$ $x = 10, 0$

60. $f(x) = \sqrt{4 - 3x}$ $x = -4, 1$

61. $f(x) = \sqrt{3 - 3x}$ $x = -1, 5$

62. $f(x) = \sqrt{x - 5}$ $x = -1, 5$

63. $f(x) = \sqrt{x^2 - x}$ $x = -4, 3$

64. $f(x) = \sqrt{2x^2 - 3}$ $x = -1, 2$

65. $f(x) = \sqrt[3]{x^2 - 8}$ $x = -3, 4$

66. $f(x) = \sqrt[3]{2x^2}$ $x = -2, 2$

67. $f(x) = \sqrt[3]{x - 9}$ $x = 1, 10$

68. $f(x) = \sqrt[3]{5x - 2}$ $x = -5, 2$

69. $f(x) = \sqrt[3]{3 - x^2}$ $x = -2, 3$

70. $f(x) = \sqrt[3]{-1 - x^2}$ $x = 0, 3$

71. $T(h) = \frac{1}{2}\sqrt{h}$ $h = 64$

72. $L(k) = 2\sqrt{k + 2}$ $k = 23$

73. $f(x) = \sqrt{x + 5} + \sqrt{x}$ $x = 4$

74. $f(x) = \dfrac{\sqrt{x - 5} - \sqrt{x}}{2}$ $x = 9$

Exercises 75–88: Find the domain of f. Write your answer in interval notation.

75. $f(x) = \sqrt{x + 2}$ 76. $f(x) = \sqrt{x - 1}$

77. $f(x) = \sqrt{x - 2}$ 78. $f(x) = \sqrt{x + 1}$

79. $f(x) = \sqrt{2x - 4}$ 80. $f(x) = \sqrt{4x + 2}$

81. $f(x) = \sqrt{1 - x}$ 82. $f(x) = \sqrt{6 - 3x}$

83. $f(x) = \sqrt{8 - 5x}$ 84. $f(x) = \sqrt{3 - 2x}$

85. $f(x) = \sqrt{3x^2 + 4}$ 86. $f(x) = \sqrt{1 + 2x^2}$

87. $f(x) = \dfrac{1}{\sqrt{2x + 1}}$ 88. $f(x) = \dfrac{1}{\sqrt{x - 1}}$

Exercises 89–94: Graph the equation. Compare the graph to either $y = \sqrt{x}$ or $y = \sqrt[3]{x}$.

89. $y = \sqrt{x} + 2$

90. $y = \sqrt{x} - 1$

91. $y = \sqrt{x + 2}$

92. $y = \sqrt[3]{x} + 2$

93. $y = \sqrt[3]{x + 2}$

94. $y = \sqrt[3]{x} - 1$

REPRESENTATIONS OF ROOT FUNCTIONS

Exercises 95–102: Give symbolic, numerical, and graphical representations for the function f.

95. Function f takes the square root of x and then adds 1 to the result.

96. Function f takes the square root of x and then subtracts 2 from the result.

97. Function f takes the square root of the quantity three times x.

98. Function f takes the square root of the quantity x plus 1.

99. Function f takes the cube root of x and then multiplies the result by 2.

100. Function f takes the cube root of the quantity 4 times x.

101. Function f takes the cube root of the quantity x minus 1.

102. Function f takes the cube root of x and then adds 1.

AREA OF A TRIANGLE

Exercises 103 and 104: Heron's Formula Suppose the lengths of the sides of a triangle are a, b, and c as illustrated in the figure.

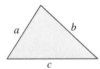

*If the **semiperimeter** (half of the perimeter) of the triangle is $s = \frac{1}{2}(a + b + c)$, then the area of the triangle is*

$$A = \sqrt{s(s - a)(s - b)(s - c)}.$$

Find the area A of the triangle with the given sides.

103. $a = 3, b = 4, c = 5$

104. $a = 5, b = 9, c = 10$

APPLICATIONS

105. *Jumping* (Refer to Example 9.) If a person jumps 4 feet off the ground, estimate how long the person is in the air.

106. *Hang Time* (Refer to Example 9.) Find the hang time for a golf ball hit 80 feet into the air.

107. *Distance to the Horizon* (Refer to Example 4.) Use the formula $d = 1.22\sqrt{x}$ to estimate how many miles a person can see from a jet airliner at 10,000 feet.

108. *Distance to the Horizon* (Refer to Example 4.) Use the formula $d = 1.22\sqrt{x}$ to estimate how many miles a 5-foot-tall person can see standing on the deck of a ship that is 50 feet above the ocean.

109. *Increasing Productivity* (Refer to Example 12.) Use $R(x) = 108\sqrt{x}$ to evaluate $R(16) - R(15)$. If the salary for the sixteenth employee is $25,000, is it a good decision to hire the sixteenth employee?

110. *Increasing Productivity* (Refer to Example 12.) Use $R(x) = 108\sqrt{x}$ to evaluate $R(2) - R(1)$. If the salary for the second employee is $25,000, is it a good decision to hire the second employee?

111. *Productivity of Workers* If workers are given more equipment, or *physical capital*, they are often more productive. For example, a carpenter definitely needs a hammer to be productive, but probably does not need 20 hammers. There is a leveling off in a worker's productivity as more is spent on equipment. The function $P(x) = 400\sqrt{x} + 8000$ approximates the worth of the goods produced by a typical U.S. worker in dollars when x dollars are spent on equipment per worker.
 (a) Evaluate $P(25,000)$ and interpret the result.
 (b) Sketch a graph of $y = P(x)$.
 (c) Use the graph from (b) and the formula to evaluate $P(50,000) - P(25,000)$ and also to evaluate $P(75,000) - P(50,000)$. Interpret the result.

112. *Design of Open Channels* To protect cities from flooding during heavy rains, open channels are sometimes constructed to handle runoff. The rate R at which water flows through the channel is modeled by $R = k\sqrt{m}$, where m is the slope of the channel and k is a constant determined by the shape of the channel. (*Source:* N. Garber and L. Hoel, *Traffic and Highway Design.*)

(a) Suppose that a channel has a slope of $m = 0.01$ (or 1%) and a runoff rate of $R = 340$ cubic feet per second (cfs). Find k.

(b) If the slope of the channel increases to $m = 0.04$ (or 4%), what happens to R? Be specific.

WRITING ABOUT MATHEMATICS

113. Try to calculate $\sqrt{-7}$, $\sqrt[4]{-56}$, and $\sqrt[6]{-10}$ with a calculator. Describe what happens when you evaluate an even root of a negative number. Does the same difficulty occur when you evaluate an odd root of a negative number? Try to evaluate $\sqrt[3]{-7}$, $\sqrt[5]{-56}$, and $\sqrt[7]{-10}$. Explain.

114. Explain the difference between a root and a positive integer power of a number. Give examples.

CHAPTER 10 Summary

SECTION 10.1 ■ RADICAL EXPRESSIONS AND FUNCTIONS

Radicals and Radical Notation

Square Root b is a square root of a if $b^2 = a$.

Principal Square Root $\sqrt{a} = b$ if $b^2 = a$ and $b \geq 0$.

Examples: $\sqrt{16} = 4$, $-\sqrt{9} = -3$, and $\pm\sqrt{36} = \pm 6$

Cube Root b is a cube root of a if $b^3 = a$.

Examples: $\sqrt[3]{27} = 3$, $\sqrt[3]{-8} = -2$

nth Root b is an nth root of a if $b^n = a$.

Example: $\sqrt[4]{16} = 2$ because $2^4 = 16$.

NOTE: An *even* root of a *negative* number is not a real number. Also, $\sqrt[n]{a}$ denotes the *principal* nth root.

Absolute Value   The expressions $|x|$ and $\sqrt{x^2}$ are equivalent.

Example: $\sqrt{(x + y)^2} = |x + y|$

The Square Root Function   The square root function is denoted $f(x) = \sqrt{x}$. Its domain is $\{x \mid x \geq 0\}$ and its graph is shown in the figure.

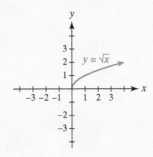

The Cube Root Function The cube root function is denoted $f(x) = \sqrt[3]{x}$. Its domain is all real numbers and its graph is shown in the figure.

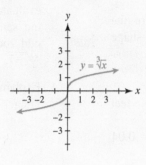

CHAPTER 10 Review Exercises

SECTION 10.1

Exercises 1–12: Simplify the expression.

1. $\sqrt{4}$

2. $\sqrt{36}$

3. $\sqrt{9x^2}$

4. $\sqrt{(x-1)^2}$

5. $\sqrt[3]{-64}$

6. $\sqrt[3]{-125}$

7. $\sqrt[3]{x^6}$

8. $\sqrt[3]{27x^3}$

9. $\sqrt[4]{16}$

10. $\sqrt[5]{-1}$

11. $\sqrt[4]{x^8}$

12. $\sqrt[5]{(x+1)^5}$

CHAPTER 10   Extended and Discovery Exercises

1. *Modeling Wood in a Tree* Forestry services estimate the volume of timber in a given area of forest. To make such estimates, scientists have developed formulas to find the amount of wood contained in a tree with height h in feet and diameter d in inches. One study concluded that the volume V of wood in cubic feet in a tree is given by $V = kh^{1.12}d^{1.98}$, where k is a constant. Note that the diameter is measured 4.5 feet above the ground. (*Source*: B. Ryan, B. Joiner, and T. Ryan, *Minitab Handbook*.)

   (a) A tree with an 11-inch diameter and a 47-foot height has a volume of 11.4 cubic feet. Approximate the constant k.

   (b) Estimate the volume of wood in the same type of tree with $d = 20$ inches and $h = 105$ feet.

2. *Area of Skin* The surface area of the skin covering the human body is a function of more than one variable. Both height and weight influence the surface area of a person's body. Hence a taller person tends to have a larger surface area, as does a heavier person. A formula to determine the area of a person's skin in square inches is $S = 15.7w^{0.425}h^{0.725}$, where w is weight in pounds and h is height in inches. (*Source*: H. Lancaster, *Quantitative Methods in Biological and Medical Sciences*.)

   (a) Use S to estimate the area of a person's skin who is 65 inches tall and weighs 154 pounds.

   (b) If a person's weight doubles, what happens to the area of the person's skin? Explain.

   (c) If a person's height doubles, what happens to the area of the person's skin? Explain.

3. *Minimizing Cost* A natural gas line running along a river is to be connected from point A to a cabin on the other bank located at point D, as illustrated in the figure. The width of the river is 500 feet, and the distance from point A to point C is 1000 feet. The cost of running the pipe along the shoreline is \$30 per foot, and the cost of running it underwater is \$50 per foot. The cost of connecting the gas line from A to D is to be minimized.

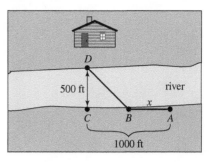

   (a) Write an expression that gives the cost of running the line from A to B if the distance between these points is x feet.

   (b) Find the distance from B to D in terms of x.

   (c) Write an expression that gives the cost of running the line from B to D.

   (d) Use your answer from parts (a) and (c) to write an expression that gives the cost of running the line from A to B to D.

   (e) Graph your expression from part (d) in the window [0, 1000, 100] by [40000, 60000, 5000] to determine the value of x that minimizes the cost of the line going from A to D. What is the minimum cost?

11 Quadratic Functions and Equations

11.1 Quadratic Functions and Their Graphs
11.2 Parabolas and Modeling
11.3 Quadratic Equations
11.4 The Quadratic Formula

There is no branch of mathematics, however abstract, which may not some day be applied to the real world.

—NIKOLAI LOBACHEVSKY

W hat size television should you buy? Should you buy a 32-inch screen or a 50-inch screen? According to a home entertainment article in *Money* magazine, the answer depends on how far you sit from your television. The farther you sit from your television, the larger it should be. For example, if you sit only 6 feet from the screen, then a 32-inch television would be adequate; if you sit 10 feet from the screen, then a 50-inch television is more appropriate.

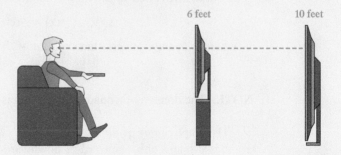

We can use a *quadratic function* to calculate the size S of the television screen needed for a person who sits x feet from the screen. You might want to use S to determine the size of screen that is recommended for you. (See Exercises 97 and 98 in Section 11.1.) Quadratic functions are a special type of polynomial function that occur frequently in applications involving economics, road construction, falling objects, geometry, and modeling real-world data. In this chapter we discuss quadratic functions and equations.

Source: Money, January 2007, p. 107; hdguru.com.

11.1 Quadratic Functions and Their Graphs

Graphs of Quadratic Functions • Min–Max Applications • Basic Transformations of $y = ax^2$ • Transformations of $y = ax^2 + bx + c$ (Optional)

A LOOK INTO MATH ▶

Suppose that a hotel is considering giving a group discount on room rates. The regular price is $80, but for each room rented the price decreases by $2. On the one hand, if the hotel rents one room, it makes only $78. On the other hand, if the hotel rents 40 rooms, the rooms are all free and the hotel makes nothing. Is there an optimal number of rooms between 1 and 40 that should be rented to maximize the revenue from the group?

In Figure 11.1 the hotel's revenue is graphed. From the graph it is apparent that "peak" revenue occurs when 20 rooms are rented. Obviously, this graph is not described by a linear function; rather, in Example 7 we see that it is described by a *quadratic function*.

NEW VOCABULARY

☐ Quadratic function
☐ Vertex
☐ Axis of symmetry
☐ Reflection
☐ Vertical shift

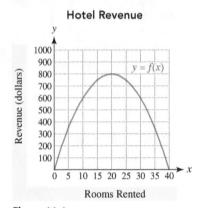

Hotel Revenue

$y = f(x)$

Revenue (dollars)

Rooms Rented

Figure 11.1

Graphs of Quadratic Functions

In Section 8.4 we discussed how a quadratic function could be represented by a polynomial of degree 2. We now give an alternative definition of a quadratic function.

QUADRATIC FUNCTION

A **quadratic function** can be written in the form

$$f(x) = ax^2 + bx + c,$$

where a, b, and c are constants with $a \neq 0$.

NOTE: The domain of a quadratic function is all real numbers.

READING CHECK

How can you identify the vertex and the axis of symmetry on the graph of a parabola?

The graph of *any* quadratic function is a *parabola*. Recall that a parabola is a ∪-shaped graph that opens either upward or downward. The graph of the simple quadratic function $y = x^2$ is a parabola that opens upward, with its *vertex* located at the origin, as shown in Figure 11.2(a). The **vertex** is the *lowest* point on the graph of a parabola that opens upward and the *highest* point on the graph of a parabola that opens downward. A parabola opening downward is shown in Figure 11.2(b). Its vertex is the point $(0, 2)$ and is the highest point on the graph. If we were to fold the xy-plane along the y-axis, or the line $x = 0$, the left and right sides of the graph would match. That is, the graph is symmetric with respect to the line $x = 0$. In this case the line $x = 0$ is the **axis of symmetry** for the graph. Figure 11.2(c) shows a parabola that opens upward with vertex $(2, -1)$ and axis of symmetry $x = 2$.

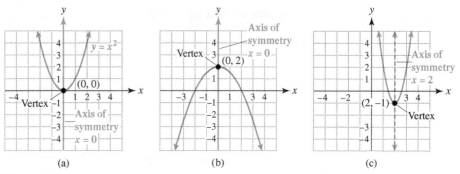

Figure 11.2

EXAMPLE 1 **Identifying the vertex and the axis of symmetry**

Use the graph of the quadratic function to identify the vertex, the axis of symmetry, and whether the parabola opens upward or downward.

(a)

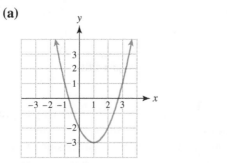

Figure 11.3

(b)

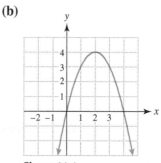

Figure 11.4

Solution

(a) The vertex is the lowest point on the graph shown in Figure 11.3, and its coordinates are $(1, -3)$. The axis of symmetry is the vertical line passing through the vertex, so its equation is $x = 1$. The parabola opens upward.

(b) The vertex is the highest point on the graph shown in Figure 11.4, and its coordinates are $(2, 4)$. The axis of symmetry is the vertical line passing through the vertex, so its equation is $x = 2$. The parabola opens downward.

Now Try Exercises 29, 31

THE VERTEX FORMULA In order to graph a parabola by hand, it is helpful to know the location of the vertex. The following formula can be used to find the coordinates of the vertex for *any* parabola. This formula is derived by *completing the square*, a technique discussed later in the next section.

READING CHECK

How do you use the vertex formula to find the coordinates of the vertex?

VERTEX FORMULA

The x-coordinate of the vertex of the graph of $y = ax^2 + bx + c$, $a \neq 0$, is given by

$$x = -\frac{b}{2a}.$$

To find the y-coordinate of the vertex, substitute this x-value in $y = ax^2 + bx + c$.

NOTE: The equation of the axis of symmetry for $f(x) = ax^2 + bx + c$ is $x = -\frac{b}{2a}$, and the vertex is the point $\left(-\frac{b}{2a}, f\left(-\frac{b}{2a}\right)\right)$.

EXAMPLE 2   **Finding the vertex of a parabola**

Find the vertex for the graph of $f(x) = 2x^2 - 4x + 1$. Support your answer graphically.

Solution

For $f(x) = 2x^2 - 4x + 1$, $a = 2$ and $b = -4$. The x-coordinate of the vertex is

$$x = -\frac{b}{2a} = -\frac{(-4)}{2(2)} = 1. \qquad \text{x-coordinate of vertex}$$

To find the y-coordinate of the vertex, substitute $x = 1$ in the given formula.

$$f(1) = 2(1)^2 - 4(1) + 1 = -1 \qquad \text{y-coordinate of vertex}$$

Thus the vertex is located at $(1, -1)$, which is supported by Figure 11.5.

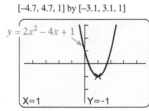

[-4.7, 4.7, 1] by [-3.1, 3.1, 1]

$y = 2x^2 - 4x + 1$

X=1   Y=-1

Figure 11.5

Now Try Exercise 15

GRAPHING QUADRATIC FUNCTIONS One way to graph a quadratic function without a graphing calculator is to first apply the vertex formula. After the vertex is located, a table of values can be made to locate points on either side of the vertex. This technique is used in the next example to graph three quadratic functions.

EXAMPLE 3   **Graphing quadratic functions**

Identify the vertex and axis of symmetry on the graph of $y = f(x)$. Graph $y = f(x)$.
(a) $f(x) = x^2 - 1$ **(b)** $f(x) = -(x + 1)^2$ **(c)** $f(x) = x^2 + 4x + 3$

Solution
(a) Begin by applying the vertex formula with $a = 1$ and $b = 0$ to locate the vertex.

$$x = -\frac{b}{2a} = -\frac{0}{2(1)} = 0 \qquad \text{x-coordinate of vertex}$$

The y-coordinate of the vertex is found by evaluating $f(0)$.

$$y = f(0) = 0^2 - 1 = -1 \qquad \text{y-coordinate of vertex}$$

Thus the coordinates of the vertex are $(0, -1)$. Table 11.1 is made by finding points on either side of the vertex. Plotting these points and connecting a smooth ∪-shaped graph results in Figure 11.6. The axis of symmetry is the vertical line passing through the vertex, so its equation is $x = 0$.

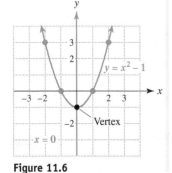

$y = x^2 - 1$

Vertex

$x = 0$

Figure 11.6

TABLE 11.1

x	$y = x^2 - 1$	
-2	3	
-1	0	
Vertex → 0	-1	Equal
1	0	
2	3	

(b) Before we can apply the vertex formula, we need to determine values for a and b by multiplying the expression for $f(x) = -(x + 1)^2$.

$$-(x + 1)^2 = -(x^2 + 2x + 1) \qquad \text{Multiply.}$$
$$= -x^2 - 2x - 1 \qquad \text{Distribute the negative sign.}$$

Substitute $a = -1$ and $b = -2$ into the vertex formula.

$$x = -\frac{b}{2a} = -\frac{(-2)}{2(-1)} = -1 \qquad \textit{x-coordinate of vertex}$$

The y-coordinate of the vertex is found by evaluating $f(-1)$.

$$y = f(-1) = -(-1 + 1)^2 = 0 \qquad \textit{y-coordinate of vertex}$$

Thus the coordinates of the vertex are $(-1, 0)$. Table 11.2 is made by finding points on either side of the vertex. Plotting these points and connecting a smooth ∩-shaped graph results in Figure 11.7. The axis of symmetry is the vertical line passing through the vertex, so its equation is $x = -1$.

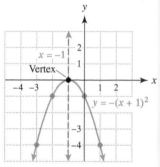

Figure 11.7

TABLE 11.2

	x	$y = -(x + 1)^2$	
	-3	-4	
	-2	-1	
Vertex →	-1	**0**	Equal
	0	-1	
	1	-4	

(c) The graph of $f(x) = x^2 + 4x + 3$ can be found in a manner similar to that used for the graphs in (a) and (b). See Table 11.3 and Figure 11.8. With $a = 1$ and $b = 4$, the vertex formula can be used to show that the vertex is located at $(-2, -1)$. The equation of the axis of symmetry is $x = -2$.

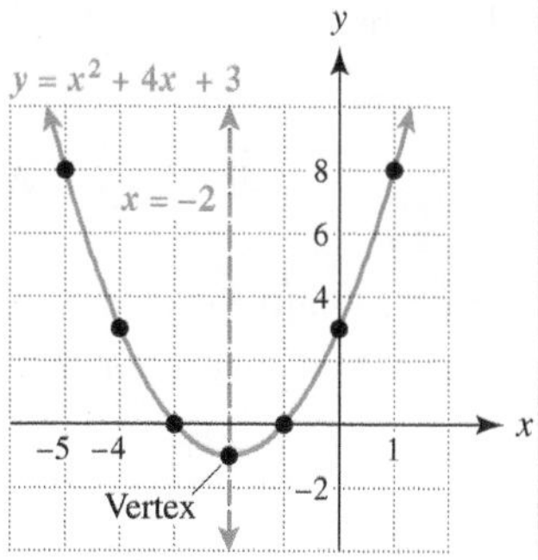

TABLE 11.3

	x	$y = x^2 + 4x + 3$	
	-5	8	
	-4	3	
	-3	0	
Vertex →	-2	**-1**	Equal
	-1	0	
	0	3	
	1	8	

Figure 11.8

Now Try Exercises 35, 41, 43

STUDY TIP

The vertex formula is important to memorize because it is often used when graphing parabolas.

Min–Max Applications

▶ **REAL-WORLD CONNECTION** Have you ever noticed that the first piece of pizza tastes really great and gives a person a lot of satisfaction? The second piece may be almost as good. After a few more pieces, there is often a point where the satisfaction starts to level off, and it can even go down as a person starts to eat too much. Eventually, if a person overeats, he or she might regret eating any pizza at all.

In Figure 11.9 a parabola models the total satisfaction received from eating x slices of pizza. Notice that the satisfaction level increases and then decreases. Although maximum satisfaction would vary with the individual, it always occurs at the vertex. (This is a seemingly simple model, but it is nonetheless used frequently in economics to describe consumer satisfaction from buying x identical items.)

Satisfaction from Eating Pizza

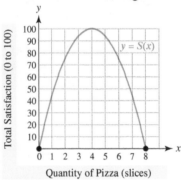

Figure 11.9

EXAMPLE 4   **Finding maximum satisfaction from pizza**

The graph of $S(x) = -6.25x^2 + 50x$ is shown in Figure 11.9. Use the vertex formula to determine the number of slices of pizza that give maximum satisfaction. Does this maximum agree with what is shown in the graph of $y = S(x)$?

Solution
The parabola in Figure 11.9 opens downward, so the greatest y-value occurs at the vertex. To find the x-coordinate of the vertex, we can apply the vertex formula. Substitute $a = -6.25$ and $b = 50$ into the vertex formula.

$$x = -\frac{b}{2a} = -\frac{50}{2(-6.25)} = 4 \qquad \textit{x-coordinate of vertex}$$

Maximum satisfaction on a scale of 1 to 100 occurs when 4 slices of pizza are eaten, which agrees with Figure 11.9. (This number obviously varies from individual to individual.)

┃ Now Try Exercise 81

READING·CHECK

How do you determine if a parabola has a maximum y-value or a minimum y-value?

FINDING MIN–MAX The graph in Figure 11.9 is a parabola that opens downward and whose maximum y-value of 100 occurs at the vertex. When a quadratic function f is used to model real data, the y-coordinate of the vertex represents either a maximum value of $f(x)$ or a minimum value of $f(x)$. For example, Figure 11.10(a) shows a parabola that opens upward. The minimum y-value on this graph is 1 and occurs at the vertex $(2, 1)$. Similarly, Figure 11.10(b) shows a parabola that opens downward. The maximum y-value on this graph is 3 and occurs at the vertex $(-3, 3)$.

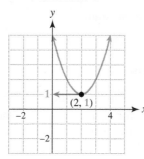

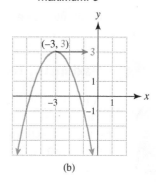

Figure 11.10

EXAMPLE 5 **Finding a minimum y-value**

Find the minimum y-value on the graph of $f(x) = x^2 - 4x + 3$.

Solution

To locate the minimum y-value on a parabola, first apply the vertex formula with $a = 1$ and $b = -4$ to find the x-coordinate of the vertex.

$$x = -\frac{b}{2a} = -\frac{(-4)}{2(1)} = 2 \qquad \text{x-coordinate of vertex}$$

The minimum y-value on the graph is found by evaluating $f(2)$.

$$y = f(2) = 2^2 - 4(2) + 3 = -1 \qquad \text{y-coordinate of vertex}$$

Thus the minimum y-coordinate on the graph of $y = f(x)$ is -1. This result is supported by Figure 11.11.

Locating a Minimum y-Value

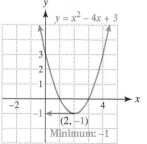

Figure 11.11

Now Try Exercise 53

▶ **REAL-WORLD CONNECTION** In the next example, we demonstrate finding a maximum height reached by a baseball.

EXAMPLE 6 **Finding maximum height**

A baseball is hit into the air, and its height h in feet after t seconds can be calculated by $h(t) = -16t^2 + 96t + 3$.
(a) What is the height of the baseball when it is hit?
(b) Determine the maximum height of the baseball.

Solution

(a) The baseball is hit when $t = 0$, so $h(0) = -16(0)^2 + 96(0) + 3 = 3$ feet.
(b) The graph of h opens downward because $a = -16 < 0$. Thus the maximum height of the baseball occurs at the vertex. To find the vertex, we apply the vertex formula with $a = -16$ and $b = 96$ because $h(t) = -16t^2 + 96t + 3$.

$$t = -\frac{b}{2a} = -\frac{96}{2(-16)} = 3 \text{ seconds}$$

The maximum height of the baseball occurs at $t = 3$ seconds and is

$$h(3) = -16(3)^2 + 96(3) + 3 = 147 \text{ feet}.$$

Now Try Exercise 87

▶ **REAL-WORLD CONNECTION**   In the next example, we answer the question presented in A Look Into Math for this section.

EXAMPLE 7   **Maximizing revenue**

A hotel is considering giving the following group discount on room rates. The regular price for a room is $80, but for each room rented the price decreases by $2. A graph of the revenue received from renting x rooms is shown in Figure 11.12.
  (a) Interpret the graph.
  (b) What is the maximum revenue? How many rooms should be rented to receive the maximum revenue?
  (c) Write a formula for $f(x)$ whose graph is shown in Figure 11.12.
  (d) Use $f(x)$ to determine symbolically the maximum revenue and the number of rooms that should be rented.

Hotel Revenue

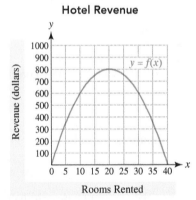

Figure 11.12

TECHNOLOGY NOTE

Locating a Vertex
Graphing calculators can locate a vertex with the MAXIMUM or MINIMUM utility. The maximum in Example 7 is found in the figure.

[0, 50, 10] by [0, 1000, 100]

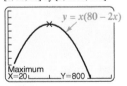

Solution
  (a) The revenue increases at first, reaches a maximum (which corresponds to the vertex), and then decreases.
  (b) In Figure 11.12 the vertex is $(20, 800)$. Thus the maximum revenue of $800 occurs when 20 rooms are rented.
  (c) If x rooms are rented, the price for each room is $80 - 2x$. The revenue equals the number of rooms rented times the price of each room. Thus $f(x) = x(80 - 2x)$.
  (d) First, multiply $x(80 - 2x)$ to obtain $80x - 2x^2$ and then let $f(x) = -2x^2 + 80x$. The x-coordinate of the vertex is

$$x = -\frac{b}{2a} = -\frac{80}{2(-2)} = 20.$$

The y-coordinate is $f(20) = -2(20)^2 + 80(20) = 800$. These calculations verify our results in part (b).

Now Try Exercise 91

Basic Transformations of $y = ax^2$

THE GRAPH OF $y = ax^2$, $a > 0$ First, graph $y_1 = \frac{1}{2}x^2$, $y_2 = x^2$, and $y_3 = 2x^2$, as shown in Figure 11.13(a). Note that $a = \frac{1}{2}$, $a = 1$, and $a = 2$, respectively, and that as a increases, the resulting parabola becomes narrower. The graph of $y_1 = \frac{1}{2}x^2$ is wider than the graph of $y_2 = x^2$, and the graph of $y_3 = 2x^2$ is narrower than the graph of $y_2 = x^2$. In general, the graph of $y = ax^2$ is wider than the graph of $y = x^2$ when $0 < a < 1$ and

CALCULATOR HELP

To find a minimum or maximum, see Appendix A (page AP-11).

narrower than the graph of $y = x^2$ when $a > 1$. When $a > 0$, the graph of $y = ax^2$ opens upward and never lies *below* the x-axis.

THE GRAPH OF $y = ax^2$, $a < 0$ When $a < 0$, the graph of $y = ax^2$ never lies *above* the x-axis because, for any input x, the product $ax^2 \le 0$. The graphs of $y_4 = -\frac{1}{2}x^2$, $y_5 = -x^2$, and $y_6 = -2x^2$ are shown in Figure 11.13(b) and open downward. The graph of $y_4 = -\frac{1}{2}x^2$ is wider than the graph of $y_5 = -x^2$ and the graph of $y_6 = -2x^2$ is narrower than the graph of $y_5 = -x^2$.

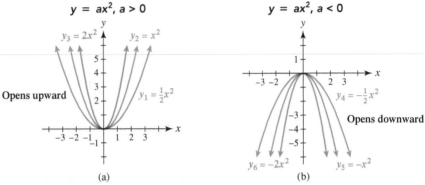

Figure 11.13 The Effect of a on $y = ax^2$

THE GRAPH OF $y = ax^2$

The graph of $y = ax^2$ is a parabola with the following characteristics.

1. The vertex is $(0, 0)$, and the axis of symmetry is given by $x = 0$.
2. It opens upward if $a > 0$ and opens downward if $a < 0$.
3. It is wider than the graph of $y = x^2$, if $0 < |a| < 1$. It is narrower than the graph of $y = x^2$, if $|a| > 1$.

Reflection Across the x-Axis

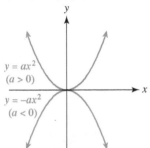

Figure 11.14

REFLECTIONS OF $y = ax^2$ In Figure 11.13 the graph of $y_1 = \frac{1}{2}x^2$ can be *transformed* into the graph of $y_4 = -\frac{1}{2}x^2$ by *reflecting* it across the x-axis. The graph of y_4 is a **reflection** of the graph of y_1 across the x-axis. In general, *the graph of $y = -ax^2$ is a reflection of the graph of $y = ax^2$ across the x-axis*, as shown in Figure 11.14. That is, if we folded the xy-plane along the x-axis the two graphs would match.

EXAMPLE 8   **Graphing $y = ax^2$**

Compare the graph of $g(x) = -3x^2$ to the graph of $f(x) = x^2$. Then graph both functions on the same coordinate axes.

Solution
Both graphs are parabolas. However, the graph of g opens downward and is narrower than the graph of f. These graphs are shown in Figure 11.15.

Now Try Exercise 67

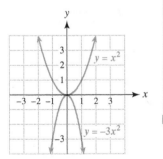

Figure 11.15

Transformations of $y = ax^2 + bx + c$ (Optional)

The graph of a quadratic function is a parabola, and any quadratic function f can be written as $f(x) = ax^2 + bx + c$, where a, b, and c are constants with $a \ne 0$. As a result, the values of a, b, and c determine both the shape and position of the parabola in the xy-plane. In this subsection, we summarize some of the effects that these constants have on the graph of f.

THE EFFECTS OF a The effects of a on the graph of $y = ax^2$ were already discussed, and these effects can be generalized to include the graph of $y = ax^2 + bx + c$.

1. **Width:** The graph of $f(x) = ax^2 + bx + c$ is wider than the graph of $y = x^2$ if $0 < |a| < 1$ and narrower if $|a| > 1$. See Figures 11.16(a) and (b).

2. **Opening:** The graph of $f(x) = ax^2 + bx + c$ opens upward if $a > 0$ and downward if $a < 0$. See Figure 11.16(c).

The Effects of a on $y = ax^2 + bx + c$

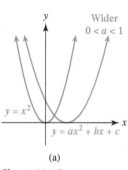 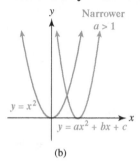 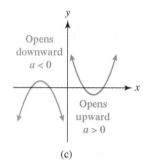

(a)   (b)   (c)

Figure 11.16

THE EFFECTS OF c The value of c affects the vertical placement of the parabola in the xy-plane. This placement is often called **vertical shift**.

1. **y-Intercept:** Because $f(0) = a(0)^2 + b(0) + c = c$, it follows that the y-intercept for the graph of $y = f(x)$ is c. See Figure 11.17(a).

2. **Vertical Shift:** The graph of $f(x) = ax^2 + bx + c$ is shifted vertically c units compared to the graph of $y = ax^2 + bx$. If $c < 0$, the shift is downward; if $c > 0$, the shift is upward. See Figures 11.17(b) and (c). The parabolas in both figures have identical shapes.

The Effects of c on $y = ax^2 + bx + c$

The Combined Effects of a and b

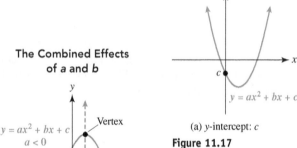

Figure 11.18

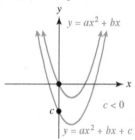 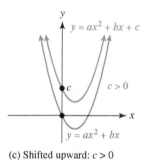

(a) y-intercept: c

(b) Shifted downward: $c < 0$

(c) Shifted upward: $c > 0$

Figure 11.17

THE COMBINED EFFECTS OF a AND b The combined values of a and b determine the x-coordinate of the vertex and the equation of the axis of symmetry.

1. **Vertex:** The x-coordinate of the vertex is $-\frac{b}{2a}$.

2. **Axis of Symmetry:** The axis of symmetry is given by $x = -\frac{b}{2a}$.

Figure 11.18 illustrates these concepts.

EXAMPLE 9   **Analyzing the graph of $y = ax^2 + bx + c$**

Let $f(x) = -\frac{1}{2}x^2 + x + \frac{3}{2}$.

(a) Does the graph of f open upward or downward? Is this graph wider or narrower than the graph of $y = x^2$?

(b) Find the axis of symmetry and the vertex.

(c) Find the y-intercept and any x-intercepts.

(d) Sketch a graph of f.

Solution

(a) If $f(x) = -\frac{1}{2}x^2 + x + \frac{3}{2}$, then $a = -\frac{1}{2}$, $b = 1$, and $c = \frac{3}{2}$. Because $a = -\frac{1}{2} < 0$, the parabola opens downward. Also, because $0 < |a| < 1$, the graph is wider than the graph of $y = x^2$.

(b) The axis of symmetry is $x = -\dfrac{b}{2a} = -\dfrac{1}{2\left(-\frac{1}{2}\right)} = 1$, or $x = 1$. Because

$$f(1) = -\frac{1}{2}(1)^2 + (1) + \frac{3}{2} = -\frac{1}{2} + 1 + \frac{3}{2} = 2,$$

the vertex is $(1, 2)$.

(c) The y-intercept equals c, or $\frac{3}{2}$. To find x-intercepts we let $y = 0$ and solve for x.

$$-\frac{1}{2}x^2 + x + \frac{3}{2} = 0 \quad \text{Equation to be solved}$$

$$x^2 - 2x - 3 = 0 \quad \text{Multiply by } -2; \text{ clear fractions.}$$

$$(x + 1)(x - 3) = 0 \quad \text{Factor.}$$

$$x + 1 = 0 \quad \text{or} \quad x - 3 = 0 \quad \text{Zero-product property}$$

$$x = -1 \quad \text{or} \quad x = 3 \quad \text{Solve.}$$

The x-intercepts are -1 and 3.

(d) Start by plotting the vertex and intercepts, as shown in Figure 11.19. Then sketch a smooth, $\cap$-shaped graph that connects these points.

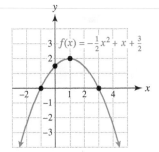

Figure 11.19

❙ **Now Try Exercise 75**

11.1 Putting It All Together

CONCEPT	EXPLANATION	EXAMPLES
Quadratic Function	Can be written as $f(x) = ax^2 + bx + c$, $a \neq 0$	$f(x) = x^2 + x - 2$ and $g(x) = -2x^2 + 4$ ($b = 0$)
Vertex of a Parabola	The x-coordinate of the vertex for the function $f(x) = ax^2 + bx + c$ with $a \neq 0$ is given by $$x = -\frac{b}{2a}.$$ The y-coordinate of the vertex is found by substituting this x-value in the equation. Hence the vertex is $\left(-\frac{b}{2a}, f\left(-\frac{b}{2a}\right)\right)$.	If $f(x) = -2x^2 + 8x - 7$, then $$x = -\frac{8}{2(-2)} = 2$$ and $$f(2) = -2(2)^2 + 8(2) - 7 = 1.$$ The vertex is $(2, 1)$. The graph of f opens downward because $a < 0$.
Graph of a Quadratic Function	Its graph is a parabola that opens upward if $a > 0$ and downward if $a < 0$. The value of $|a|$ affects the width of the parabola. The vertex can be used to determine the maximum or minimum output of a quadratic function.	The graph of $y = -\frac{1}{4}x^2$ opens downward and is wider than the graph of $y = x^2$, as shown in the figure. Each graph has its vertex at $(0, 0)$. 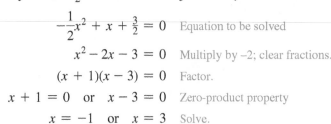

continued on next page

continued from previous page

The following gives symbolic, numerical, and graphical representations for the quadratic function f that *squares the input x and then subtracts 1.*

Symbolic Representation	Numerical Representation	Graphical Representation
$f(x) = x^2 - 1$		

Numerical Representation

x	$f(x) = x^2 - 1$
-2	3
-1	0
Vertex → 0	-1
1	0
2	3

 Equal

Graphical Representation

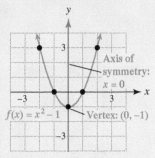

Axis of symmetry: $x = 0$

$f(x) = x^2 - 1$ Vertex: $(0, -1)$

11.1 Exercises

CONCEPTS AND VOCABULARY

1. The graph of a quadratic function is called a(n) _____.

2. If a parabola opens upward, what is the lowest point on the parabola called?

3. If a parabola is symmetric with respect to the y-axis, the y-axis is called the _____.

4. The vertex on the graph of $y = x^2$ is _____.

5. Sketch a parabola that opens downward with a vertex of $(1, 2)$.

6. If $y = ax^2 + bx + c$, the x-coordinate of the vertex is given by $x = $ _____.

7. Compared to the graph of $y = x^2$, the graph of $y = 2x^2$ is (wider/narrower).

8. The graph of $y = -x^2$ is similar to the graph of $y = x^2$ except that it is _____ across the x-axis.

9. Any quadratic function can be written in the form $f(x) = $ _____.

10. If a parabola opens downward, the point with the largest y-value is called the _____.

11. (True or False?) The axis of symmetry for the graph of $y = ax^2 + bx + c$ is given by $x = -\frac{b}{2a}$.

12. (True or False?) If the vertex of a parabola is located at (a, b), then the axis of symmetry is given by $x = b$.

13. (True or False?) If a parabola opens downward and its vertex is (a, b), then the minimum y-value on the parabola is b.

14. (True or False?) The graph of $y = -ax^2$ with $a > 0$ opens downward.

VERTEX FORMULA

Exercises 15–24: Find the vertex of the parabola.

15. $f(x) = x^2 - 4x - 2$

16. $f(x) = 2x^2 + 6x - 3$

17. $f(x) = -\frac{1}{3}x^2 - 2x + 1$

18. $f(x) = 5 - 4x + x^2$

19. $f(x) = 3 - 2x^2$

20. $f(x) = \frac{1}{4}x^2 - 3x - 2$

21. $f(x) = -0.3x^2 + 0.6x + 1.1$

22. $f(x) = 25 - 10x + 20x^2$

23. $f(x) = 6x - x^2$

24. $f(x) = x - \frac{1}{2}x^2$

GRAPHS OF QUADRATIC FUNCTIONS

Exercises 25–28: Use the given graph of f to evaluate the expressions.

25. $f(-2)$ and $f(0)$

26. $f(-2)$ and $f(2)$

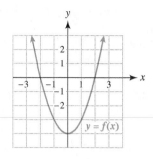
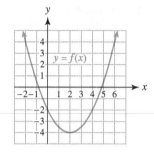

27. $f(-3)$ and $f(1)$

28. $f(-1)$ and $f(2)$

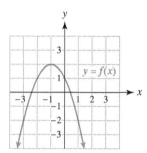
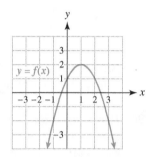

Exercises 29–32: Identify the vertex, axis of symmetry, and whether the parabola opens upward or downward.

29.

30.

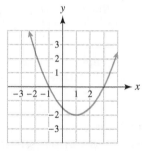
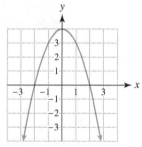

31.

32.

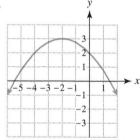
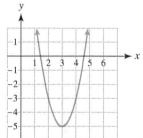

Exercises 33–52: Do the following for the given f(x).
(a) Identify the vertex and axis of symmetry on the graph of $y = f(x)$.
(b) Graph $y = f(x)$.
(c) Evaluate $f(-2)$ and $f(3)$.

33. $f(x) = \frac{1}{2}x^2$

34. $f(x) = -3x^2$

35. $f(x) = x^2 - 2$

36. $f(x) = x^2 - 1$

37. $f(x) = -3x^2 + 1$

38. $f(x) = \frac{1}{2}x^2 + 2$

39. $f(x) = (x - 1)^2$

40. $f(x) = (x + 2)^2$

41. $f(x) = -(x + 2)^2$

42. $f(x) = -(x - 1)^2$

43. $f(x) = x^2 + x - 2$

44. $f(x) = x^2 - 2x + 2$

45. $f(x) = 2x^2 - 3$

46. $f(x) = 1 - 2x^2$

47. $f(x) = 2x - x^2$

48. $f(x) = x^2 + 2x - 8$

49. $f(x) = -2x^2 + 4x - 1$

50. $f(x) = -\frac{1}{2}x^2 + 2x - 3$

51. $f(x) = \frac{1}{4}x^2 - x + 5$

52. $f(x) = 3 - 6x - 4x^2$

MIN–MAX

Exercises 53–58: Find the minimum y-value on the graph of $y = f(x)$.

53. $f(x) = x^2 + 2x - 1$

54. $f(x) = x^2 + 6x + 2$

55. $f(x) = x^2 - 5x$

56. $f(x) = x^2 - 3x$

57. $f(x) = 2x^2 + 2x - 3$

58. $f(x) = 3x^2 - 3x + 7$

Exercises 59–64: Find the maximum y-value on the graph of $y = f(x)$.

59. $f(x) = -x^2 + 2x + 5$

60. $f(x) = -x^2 + 4x - 3$

61. $f(x) = 4x - x^2$

62. $f(x) = 6x - x^2$

63. $f(x) = -2x^2 + x - 5$

64. $f(x) = -5x^2 + 15x - 2$

65. *Numbers* Find two positive numbers whose sum is 20 and whose product is maximum.

66. Thinking Generally Find two positive numbers whose sum is k and whose product is maximum.

TRANSFORMATIONS OF GRAPHS

Exercises 67–74: Graph f(x). Compare the graph of $y = f(x)$ to the graph of $y = x^2$.

67. $f(x) = -x^2$

68. $f(x) = -2x^2$

69. $f(x) = 2x^2$

70. $f(x) = 3x^2$

71. $f(x) = \frac{1}{4}x^2$

72. $f(x) = \frac{1}{2}x^2$

73. $f(x) = -\frac{1}{2}x^2$

74. $f(x) = -\frac{3}{2}x^2$

Exercises 75–80: (Refer to Example 9.) Use the given $f(x)$ to complete the following.

(a) *Does the graph of f open upward or downward? Is this graph wider, narrower, or the same as the graph of $y = x^2$?*

(b) *Find the axis of symmetry and the vertex.*

(c) *Find the y-intercept and any x-intercepts.*

(d) *Sketch a graph of f.*

75. $f(x) = \frac{1}{2}x^2 + x - \frac{3}{2}$ **76.** $f(x) = -x^2 + 4x + 5$

77. $f(x) = 2x - x^2$ **78.** $f(x) = x - 2x^2$

79. $f(x) = 2x^2 + 2x - 4$ **80.** $f(x) = \frac{1}{2}x^2 - \frac{1}{2}x - 1$

APPLICATIONS

Exercises 81 and 82: Eating Pizza (Refer to Example 4.) Let $S(x)$ denote the satisfaction, on a scale from 0 to 100, from eating x pieces of pizza. Find the number of pieces that gives the maximum satisfaction.

81. $S(x) = -\frac{100}{9}x^2 + \frac{200}{3}x$

82. $S(x) = -16x^2 + 80x$

Exercises 83–86: Quadratic Models Match the physical situation with the graph (a.–d.) that models it best.

83. The height y of a stone thrown from ground level after x seconds

84. The number of people attending a popular movie x weeks after its opening

85. The temperature after x hours in a house when the furnace quits and then a repair person fixes it

86. U.S. population from 1800 to the present

a.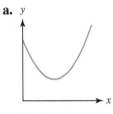

b.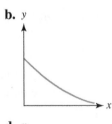

c.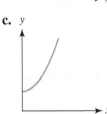

d.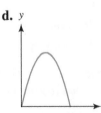

87. *Height Reached by a Baseball* (Refer to Example 6.) A baseball is hit into the air, and its height h in feet after t seconds is given by $h(t) = -16t^2 + 64t + 2$.

(a) What is the height of the baseball when it is hit?

(b) After how many seconds does the baseball reach its maximum height?

(c) Determine the maximum height of the baseball.

88. *Height Reached by a Golf Ball* A golf ball is hit into the air, and its height h in feet after t seconds is given by $h(t) = -16t^2 + 128t$.

(a) What is the height of the golf ball when it is hit?

(b) After how many seconds does the golf ball reach its maximum height?

(c) Determine the maximum height of the golf ball.

89. *Height Reached by a Baseball* Suppose that a baseball is thrown upward with an initial velocity of 66 feet per second (45 miles per hour) and it is released 6 feet above the ground. Its height h after t seconds is given by

$$h(t) = -16t^2 + 66t + 6.$$

After how many seconds does the baseball reach a maximum height? Estimate this height.

90. *Throwing a Baseball on the Moon* (Refer to Exercise 89.) If the same baseball were thrown the same way on the moon, its height h above the moon's surface after t seconds would be

$$h(t) = -2.55t^2 + 66t + 6.$$

Does the baseball go higher on the moon or on Earth? What is the difference in these two heights?

91. *Concert Tickets* (Refer to Example 7.) An agency is promoting concert tickets by offering a group-discount rate. The regular price is $100 and for each ticket bought the price decreases by $1. (One ticket costs $99, two tickets cost $98 *each*, and so on.)

(a) A graph of the revenue received from selling x tickets is shown in the figure. Interpret the graph.

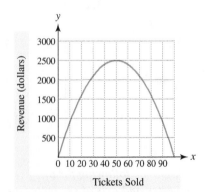

Tickets Sold

(b) What is the maximum revenue? How many tickets should be sold to maximize revenue?

(c) Write a formula for $y = f(x)$ whose graph is shown in the figure.

(d) Use $f(x)$ to determine symbolically the maximum revenue and the number of tickets that should be sold to maximize revenue.

92. *Maximizing Revenue* The regular price for a round-trip ticket to Las Vegas, Nevada, charged by an airline charter company is $300. For a group rate the company will reduce the price of each ticket by $1.50 for every passenger on the flight.

(a) Write a formula $f(x)$ that gives the revenue from selling x tickets.

(b) Determine how many tickets should be sold to maximize the revenue. What is the maximum revenue?

93. *Monthly Facebook Visitors* The number of *unique* monthly Facebook visitors in millions x years after 2006 can be modeled by

$$V(x) = 10.75x^2 - 24x + 35.$$

(a) Evaluate $V(1)$, $V(2)$, $V(3)$, and $V(4)$. Interpret your answer.

(b) Explain why numbers of Facebook visitors can not be modeled by a linear function.

94. *Cell Phone Complexity* Consumers often enjoy having certain features on their cell phones, such as e-mail and the ability to surf the Web. However, as phones become more and more complicated to operate, the benefits from the additional complexity start to decrease. The following parabola models this general situation. Interpret why a parabola is appropriate to model this consumer experience.

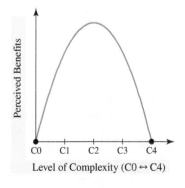

95. *Maximizing Area* A farmer is fencing a rectangular area for cattle and uses a straight portion of a river as one side of the rectangle, as illustrated in the figure. Note that there is no fence along the river. If the farmer has 1200 feet of fence, find the dimensions for the rectangular area that give a maximum area for the cattle.

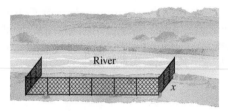

96. *Maximizing Area* A rectangular pen being constructed for a pet requires 60 feet of fence.

(a) Write a formula $f(x)$ that gives the area of the pen if one side of the pen has length x.

(b) Find the dimensions of the pen that give the largest area. What is the largest area?

Exercises 97 and 98: Large-Screen Televisions (Refer to the introduction to this chapter.) Use the formula

$$S(x) = -0.227x^2 + 8.155x - 8.8,$$

where $6 \le x \le 16$, *to estimate the recommended screen size in inches when viewers sit x feet from the screen.*

97. $x = 8$ feet

98. $x = 12$ feet

99. *Carbon Emissions* Past and future carbon emissions in billions of metric tons during year x can be modeled by

$$C(x) = \frac{1}{300}x^2 - \frac{199}{15}x + \frac{39{,}619}{3},$$

where $1990 \le x \le 2020$. (*Source:* U.S. Department of Energy.)

(a) Evaluate $C(1990)$. Interpret your answer.

(b) Find the expected *increase* in carbon emissions from 1990 to 2020.

100. *Seedling Growth* In a study of the effect of temperature on the growth of melon seedlings, the seedlings were grown at different temperatures, and their heights were measured after a fixed period of time. The findings of this study can be modeled by

$$f(x) = -0.095x^2 + 5.4x - 52.2,$$

where x is the temperature in degrees Celsius and the output $f(x)$ gives the resulting average height in centimeters. (*Source:* R. Pearl, "The growth of *Cucumis melo* seedlings at different temperatures.")

(a) Graph f in [20, 40, 5] by [0, 30, 5].
(b) Estimate graphically the temperature that resulted in the greatest height for the melon seedlings.
(c) Solve part (b) symbolically.

WRITING ABOUT MATHEMATICS

101. If $f(x) = ax^2 + bx + c$, explain how the values of a and c affect the graph of f.

102. Suppose that a quantity Q is modeled by the formula $Q(x) = ax^2 + bx + c$ with $a < 0$. Explain how to find the x-value that maximizes $Q(x)$. How do you find the maximum value of $Q(x)$?

11.2 Parabolas and Modeling

Vertical and Horizontal Translations ● Vertex Form ●
Modeling with Quadratic Functions (Optional)

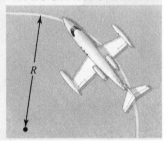

A LOOK INTO MATH ▶

A taxiway used by an airplane to exit a runway often contains curves. A curve that is too sharp for the speed of the plane is a safety hazard. The scatterplot shown in Figure 11.20 gives an appropriate radius R of a curve designed for an airplane taxiing at x miles per hour. The data are nonlinear because they do not lie on a line. In this section we explain how a quadratic function may be used to model such data. First, we discuss translations of parabolas. (*Source:* FAA.)

NEW VOCABULARY

☐ Translations
☐ Vertex form
☐ Completing the square

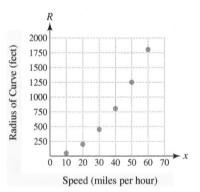

Figure 11.20

Vertical and Horizontal Translations

The graph of $y = x^2$ is a parabola opening upward with vertex $(0, 0)$. Suppose that we graph $y_1 = x^2$, $y_2 = x^2 + 1$, and $y_3 = x^2 - 2$ in the same xy-plane, as calculated in Table 11.4 and shown in Figure 11.21. All three graphs have the same shape. However, compared to the graph of $y_1 = x^2$, the graph of $y_2 = x^2 + 1$ is shifted *upward* 1 unit and the graph of $y_3 = x^2 - 2$ is shifted *downward* 2 units. Such shifts are called **translations** because they do not change the shape of a graph—only its position.

Vertical Shifts of $y = x^2$

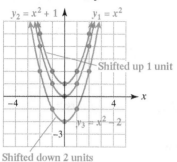

Shifted up 1 unit

Shifted down 2 units

Figure 11.21

TABLE 11.4

x	$y_2 = x^2 + 1$	$y_1 = x^2$	$y_3 = x^2 - 2$
-2	5	4	2
-1	2	1	-1
0	1	0	-2
1	2	1	-1
2	5	4	2

The x-values do NOT change.   Add 1 to find the y-values.   Subtract 2 to find the y-values.

Next, suppose that we graph $y_1 = x^2$ and $y_2 = (x - 1)^2$ in the same xy-plane. Compare Tables 11.5 and 11.6. Note that the y-values are equal when the x-value for y_2 is 1 unit *larger* than the x-value for y_1. For example, $y_1 = 4$ when $x = -2$ and $y_2 = 4$ when $x = -1$. Thus the graph of $y_2 = (x - 1)^2$ has the same shape as the graph of $y_1 = x^2$ except that it is translated *horizontally to the right* 1 unit, as illustrated in Figure 11.22.

Horizontal Shift of $y = x^2$

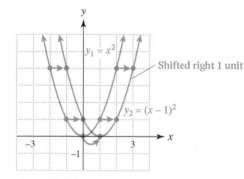

Shifted right 1 unit

Figure 11.22

TABLE 11.5

x	$y_1 = x^2$
-2	4
-1	1
0	0
1	1
2	4

TABLE 11.6

x	$y_2 = (x - 1)^2$
-1	4
0	1
1	0
2	1
3	4

Add 1 to find the x-values.   The y-values do NOT change.

The graphs $y_1 = x^2$ and $y_2 = (x + 2)^2$ are shown in Figure 11.23. Note that Tables 11.7 and 11.8 show their y-values to be equal when the x-value for y_2 is 2 units *smaller* than the x-value for y_1. As a result, the graph of $y_2 = (x + 2)^2$ has the same shape as the graph of $y_1 = x^2$ except that it is translated *horizontally to the left* 2 units.

Horizontal Shift of $y = x^2$

Shifted left 2 units

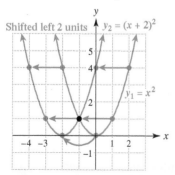

Figure 11.23

TABLE 11.7

x	$y_1 = x^2$
-2	4
-1	1
0	0
1	1
2	4

TABLE 11.8

x	$y_2 = (x + 2)^2$
-4	4
-3	1
-2	0
-1	1
0	4

Subtract 2 to find the x-values.   The y-values do NOT change.

These results are summarized as follows.

VERTICAL AND HORIZONTAL TRANSLATIONS OF PARABOLAS

Let h and k be positive numbers.

To graph	*shift the graph of $y = x^2$ by k units*
$y = x^2 + k$	upward.
$y = x^2 - k$	downward.

To graph	*shift the graph of $y = x^2$ by h units*
$y = (x - h)^2$	right.
$y = (x + h)^2$	left.

EXAMPLE 1 | **Translating the graph $y = x^2$**

Sketch the graph of the equation and identify the vertex.

(a) $y = x^2 + 2$ **(b)** $y = (x + 3)^2$ **(c)** $y = (x - 2)^2 - 3$

Solution

(a) The graph of $y = x^2 + 2$ is similar to the graph of $y = x^2$ except that it has been translated *upward* 2 units, as shown in Figure 11.24(a). The vertex is $(0, 2)$.

(b) The graph of $y = (x + 3)^2$ is similar to the graph of $y = x^2$ except that it has been translated *left* 3 units, as shown in Figure 11.24(b). The vertex is $(-3, 0)$.

NOTE: If you are thinking that the graph should be shifted right (instead of left) 3 units, try graphing $y = (x + 3)^2$ on a graphing calculator.

(c) The graph of $y = (x - 2)^2 - 3$ is similar to the graph of $y = x^2$ except that it has been translated downward 3 units *and* right 2 units, as shown in Figure 11.24(c). The vertex is $(2, -3)$.

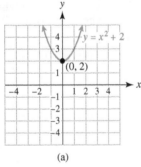 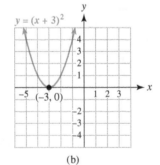 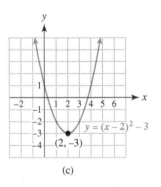

(a)   (b)   (c)

Figure 11.24

Now Try Exercises 15, 19, 27

Vertex Form

The graphs of $y = 2x^2$ and $y = 2x^2 - 12x + 20$ have *exactly* the same shape, as illustrated in Figures 11.25 and 11.26. However, the vertex for $y = 2x^2$ is $(0, 0)$, whereas the vertex for $y = 2x^2 - 12x + 20$ is $(3, 2)$.

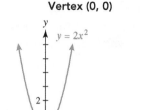

Vertex (0, 0)

Figure 11.25

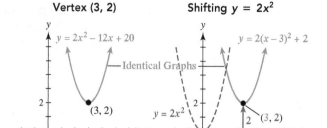

Vertex (3, 2)

Figure 11.26

Shifting $y = 2x^2$

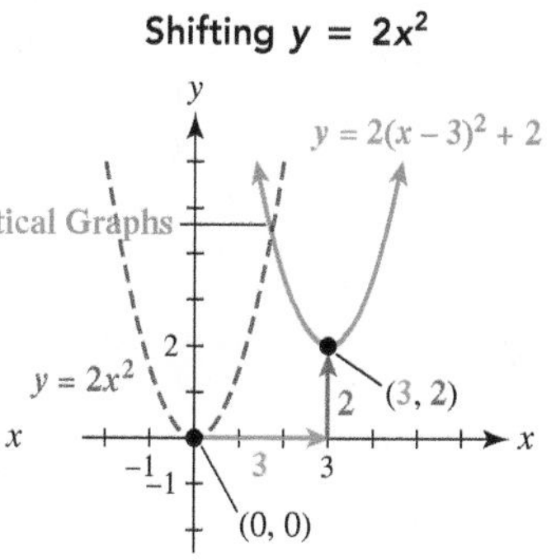

Figure 11.27

When the graph of $y = 2x^2$ (in Figure 11.25) is shifted **3** units right and **2** units upward by graphing the equation

$$y = 2(x - 3)^2 + 2, \quad \text{Vertex form}$$

Shift 2 units upward

Shift 3 units right

CRITICAL THINKING

Expand $y = 2(x - 3)^2 + 2$ and combine like terms. What does it equal?

we get the graph in Figure 11.27, which is identical to the graph of $y = 2x^2 - 12x + 20$ in Figure 11.26. Thus $y = 2(x - 3)^2 + 2$ and $y = 2x^2 - 12x + 20$ are equivalent equations for the same parabola.

In general, the equation for any parabola can be written as either $y = ax^2 + bx + c$ or $y = a(x - h)^2 + k$, where the vertex is (h, k). The second form is sometimes called *vertex form*.

VERTEX FORM

The **vertex form** of the equation of a parabola with vertex (h, k) is

$$y = a(x - h)^2 + k,$$

where $a \neq 0$ is a constant. If $a > 0$, the parabola opens upward; if $a < 0$, the parabola opens downward.

READING CHECK

Give the vertex form. Explain it with an example.

NOTE: Vertex form is sometimes called **standard form for a parabola with a vertical axis**.

In the next three examples, we demonstrate graphing parabolas in vertex form, finding their equations, and writing vertex forms of equations.

EXAMPLE 2 **Graphing parabolas in vertex form**

Compare the graph of $y = f(x)$ to the graph of $y = x^2$. Then sketch a graph of $y = f(x)$ and $y = x^2$ in the same xy-plane.

(a) $f(x) = \frac{1}{2}(x - 5)^2 + 2$ (b) $f(x) = -3(x + 5)^2 - 3$

Solution

(a) Compared to the graph of $y = x^2$, the graph of $y = f(x)$ is *translated 5 units right* and *2 units upward*. The vertex for $f(x)$ is $(5, 2)$, whereas the vertex of $y = x^2$ is $(0, 0)$. Because $a = \frac{1}{2}$, the graph of $y = f(x)$ *opens upward* and is *wider* than the graph of $y = x^2$. These graphs are shown in Figure 11.28(a) on the next page.

(b) Compared to the graph of $y = x^2$, the graph of $y = -3(x + 5)^2 - 3$ is *translated 5 units left* and 3 *units downward*. The vertex for $f(x)$ is $(-5, -3)$. Because $a = -3$, the graph of $y = f(x)$ *opens downward* and is *narrower* than the graph of $y = x^2$. These graphs are shown in Figure 11.28(b).

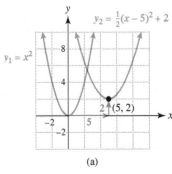

(a)

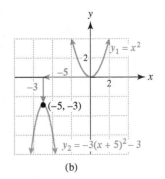

(b)

Figure 11.28

Now Try Exercises 35, 37

EXAMPLE 3   **Finding equations of parabolas**

Write the vertex form of a parabola with $a = 2$ and vertex $(-2, 1)$. Then express this equation in the form $y = ax^2 + bx + c$.

Solution
The vertex form of a parabola is given by $y = a(x - h)^2 + k$, where the vertex is (h, k). For $a = 2, h = -2$, and $k = 1$, the equation becomes

$$y = 2(x - (-2))^2 + 1 \quad \text{or} \quad y = 2(x + 2)^2 + 1.$$

To write $y = 2(x + 2)^2 + 1$ in the form $y = ax^2 + bx + c$, do the following.

$$
\begin{aligned}
y &= 2(x^2 + 4x + 4) + 1 && \text{Multiply } (x + 2)^2 \text{ as } x^2 + 4x + 4. \\
&= 2x^2 + 8x + 8 + 1 && \text{Distributive property} \\
&= 2x^2 + 8x + 9 && \text{Add.}
\end{aligned}
$$

The equivalent equation is $y = 2x^2 + 8x + 9$.

Now Try Exercise 41

In the next example, the vertex formula is used to write the equation of a parabola in vertex form.

EXAMPLE 4   **Using the vertex formula to write vertex form**

Find the vertex on the graph of $y = 3x^2 + 6x + 1$. Write this equation in vertex form.

Solution
We can use the vertex formula, $x = -\frac{b}{2a}$, to find the x-coordinate of the vertex with $a = 3$ and $b = 6$.

$$x = -\frac{b}{2a} = -\frac{6}{2(3)} = -1 \quad \text{x-coordinate of vertex}$$

To find the y-coordinate, let $x = -1$ in $y = 3x^2 + 6x + 1$.

$$y = 3(-1)^2 + 6(-1) + 1 = -2 \quad \text{Let } x = -1.$$

The vertex is $(-1, -2)$. We can now find the vertex form with $a = 3$, $h = -1$, and $k = -2$.

$$y = a(x - h)^2 + k \qquad \text{Vertex form}$$
$$y = 3(x - (-1))^2 - 2 \qquad \text{Substitute.}$$
$$y = 3(x + 1)^2 - 2 \qquad \text{Simplify.}$$

The equations $y = 3x^2 + 6x + 1$ and $y = 3(x + 1)^2 - 2$ are equivalent, and their graphs represent the same parabola with vertex $(-1, -2)$.

| Now Try Exercise 53

Completing the Square

$$x^2 + 4x + 4 = (x + 2)^2$$

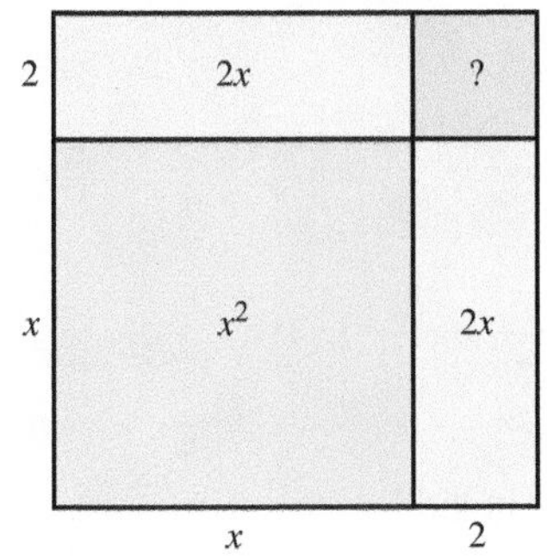

Figure 11.29

COMPLETING THE SQUARE TO FIND THE VERTEX The vertex of a parabola can be found by using a technique called **completing the square**. To complete the square for the expression $x^2 + 4x$, consider Figure 11.29.

Note that the blue and pink areas sum to

$$x^2 + 2x + 2x = x^2 + 4x.$$

The area of the small green square must be $2 \cdot 2 = 4$. Thus to *complete the square* for $x^2 + 4x$, we add 4. That is,

$$x^2 + 4x + 4 = (x + 2)^2.$$

Area of pink rectangles

Area of large square: $A = L \cdot W$

Area of blue square

Area of green square

In the next example, we use the above result to complete the square and find the vertex on the graph of $y = x^2 + 4x$.

EXAMPLE 5   **Writing vertex form by completing the square**

Write the equation $y = x^2 + 4x$ in vertex form by completing the square. Identify the vertex.

Solution
As discussed, we must add 4 to $x^2 + 4x$ to complete the square. Because we are given an equation, we will add 4 *and* subtract 4 from the right side of the equation in order to keep the equation "balanced."

$$y = x^2 + 4x. \qquad \text{Given equation}$$
$$y = x^2 + 4x + 4 - 4 \qquad \text{Add and subtract 4 on the right.}$$
$$y = (x^2 + 4x + 4) - 4 \qquad \text{Associative property}$$
$$y = (x + 2)^2 - 4 \qquad \text{Perfect square trinomial}$$

The vertex form is $y = (x + 2)^2 - 4$, and the vertex is $(-2, -4)$.

| Now Try Exercise 61

NOTE: Adding 4 and subtracting 4 from the right side of the equation in Example 5 is equivalent to adding 0 to the right side, which does not change the equation.

In general, to complete the square for $x^2 + bx$ we must add $\left(\frac{b}{2}\right)^2$, as illustrated in Figure 11.30. This technique is shown in Example 6.

READING CHECK

Use the figure to *complete the square* for $x^2 + 8x$.

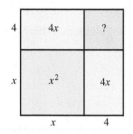

Completing the Square

$$x^2 + bx + \left(\frac{b}{2}\right)^2 = \left(x + \frac{b}{2}\right)^2$$

Figure 11.30

EXAMPLE 6   **Writing vertex form**

Write each equation in vertex form. Identify the vertex.
(a) $y = x^2 - 6x - 1$ **(b)** $y = x^2 + 3x + 4$ **(c)** $y = 2x^2 + 4x - 1$

Solution
(a) Because $\left(\frac{b}{2}\right)^2 = \left(\frac{-6}{2}\right)^2 = 9$, add *and* subtract 9 on the right side.

$$
\begin{aligned}
y &= x^2 - 6x - 1 & \text{Given equation}\\
&= (x^2 - 6x + 9) - 9 - 1 & \text{Add and subtract 9.}\\
&= (x - 3)^2 - 10 & \text{Perfect square trinomial}
\end{aligned}
$$

The vertex is $(3, -10)$.

(b) Because $\left(\frac{b}{2}\right)^2 = \left(\frac{3}{2}\right)^2 = \frac{9}{4}$, add *and* subtract $\frac{9}{4}$ on the right side.

$$
\begin{aligned}
y &= x^2 + 3x + 4 & \text{Given equation}\\
&= \left(x^2 + 3x + \frac{9}{4}\right) - \frac{9}{4} + 4 & \text{Add and subtract } \tfrac{9}{4}.\\
&= \left(x + \frac{3}{2}\right)^2 + \frac{7}{4} & \text{Perfect square trinomial}
\end{aligned}
$$

The vertex is $\left(-\frac{3}{2}, \frac{7}{4}\right)$.

(c) This equation is slightly different because the leading coefficient is 2 rather than 1. Start by factoring 2 from the first two terms on the right side.

$$
\begin{aligned}
y &= 2x^2 + 4x - 1 & \text{Given equation}\\
&= 2(x^2 + 2x) - 1 & \text{Factor out 2.}\\
&= 2(x^2 + 2x + 1 - 1) - 1 & \left(\tfrac{b}{2}\right)^2 = \left(\tfrac{2}{2}\right)^2 = 1\\
&= 2(x^2 + 2x + 1) - 2 - 1 & \text{Distributive property: } 2 \cdot (-1)\\
&= 2(x + 1)^2 - 3 & \text{Perfect square trinomial}
\end{aligned}
$$

The vertex is $(-1, -3)$.

Now Try Exercises 65, 69, 73

Modeling with Quadratic Functions (Optional)

▶ **REAL-WORLD CONNECTION** In A Look Into Math for this section, we discussed airport taxiway curves designed for airplanes. The data previously shown in Figure 11.20 are listed in Table 11.9.

TABLE 11.9 Safe Taxiway Speed

x (mph)	10	20	30	40	50	60
R (ft)	50	200	450	800	1250	1800

Source: Federal Aviation Administration.

A second scatterplot of the data is shown in Figure 11.31. The data may be modeled by $R(x) = ax^2$ for some value a. To illustrate this relation, graph R for different values of a. In Figures 11.32–11.34, R has been graphed for $a = 2$, -1, and $\frac{1}{2}$, respectively. When $a > 0$ the parabola opens upward, and when $a < 0$ the parabola opens downward. Larger values of $|a|$ make a parabola narrower, whereas smaller values of $|a|$ make the parabola wider. Through trial and error, $a = \frac{1}{2}$ gives a good fit to the data, so $R(x) = \frac{1}{2}x^2$ models the data.

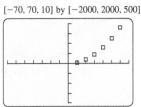

$[-70, 70, 10]$ by $[-2000, 2000, 500]$

Figure 11.31

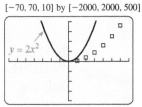

$[-70, 70, 10]$ by $[-2000, 2000, 500]$

$y = 2x^2$

Figure 11.32 $a = 2$

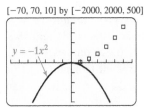

$[-70, 70, 10]$ by $[-2000, 2000, 500]$

$y = -1x^2$

Figure 11.33 $a = -1$

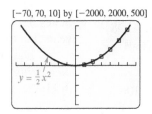

$[-70, 70, 10]$ by $[-2000, 2000, 500]$

$y = \frac{1}{2}x^2$

Figure 11.34 $a = \frac{1}{2}$

CALCULATOR HELP

To make a scatterplot, see Appendix A (pages AP-3 and AP-4).

This value of a can also be found *symbolically*, as demonstrated in the next example.

EXAMPLE 7 **Modeling safe taxiway speed**

Find a value for the constant a so that $R(x) = ax^2$ models the data in Table 11.9. Check your result by making a table of values for $R(x)$.

Solution

From Table 11.9, when $x = 10$ miles per hour, the curve radius is 50 feet. Therefore

$$R(10) = 50 \quad \text{or} \quad a(10)^2 = 50. \qquad R(x) = ax^2$$

Solving for a gives

$$a = \frac{50}{10^2} = \frac{1}{2}.$$

To be sure that $R(x) = \frac{1}{2}x^2$ is correct, make a table, as shown in Figure 11.35. Its values agree with those in Table 11.9.

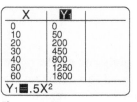

X	Y₁
0	0
10	50
20	200
30	450
40	800
50	1250
60	1800

Y₁■.5X²

Figure 11.35

▌ Now Try Exercise 87

INCREASING AND DECREASING The concept of increasing and decreasing is frequently used when modeling data with functions. Suppose that the graph of the equation $y = x^2$ shown in Figure 11.36 represents a valley. If we walk from *left to right*, the valley "goes down" and then "goes up." Mathematically, we say that the graph of $y = x^2$ is *decreasing* when $x \le 0$ and *increasing* when $x \ge 0$. In Figure 11.33, the graph of $y = -1x^2$ increases when $x \le 0$ and decreases when $x \ge 0$, and in Figure 11.24(c) on page 428 the graph decreases when $x \le 2$ and increases when $x \ge 2$.

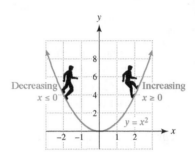

Figure 11.36

NOTE: When determining where a graph is increasing and where it is decreasing, we must "walk" along the graph *from left to right*. (We read English from left to right, which might help you remember.)

TABLE 11.10

Year	U.S. AIDS Cases
1981	425
1984	11,106
1987	71,414
1990	199,608
1993	417,835
1996	609,933

Source: Department of Health and Human Services.

▶ **REAL-WORLD CONNECTION** In 1981, the first cases of AIDS were reported in the United States. Table 11.10 lists the *cumulative* number of AIDS cases in the United States for various years. For example, between 1981 and 1990, a total of 199,608 AIDS cases were reported.

A scatterplot of these data is shown in Figure 11.37. To model these nonlinear and *increasing* data, we want to find (the right half of) a parabola with the shape illustrated in Figure 11.38. We do so in the next example.

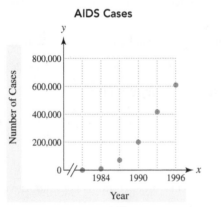

Figure 11.37

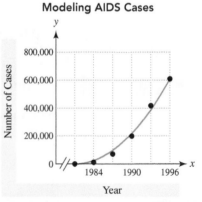

Figure 11.38

NOTE: From 1981 to 1996, the number of AIDS cases grew rapidly and can be modeled by a quadratic function. After 1996, the growth in AIDS cases slowed so a quadratic model is much less accurate. When modeling data with functions, it is important to remember that data can change character over time. As a result, the same modeling function may not be appropriate for every time period.

EXAMPLE 8   **Modeling AIDS cases**

Use the data in Table 11.10 to complete the following.
(a) Make a scatterplot of the data in [1980, 1997, 2] by [−10000, 800000, 100000].
(b) The lowest data point in Table 11.10 is (1981, 425). Let this point be the vertex of a parabola that opens upward. Graph $y = a(x - 1981)^2 + 425$ together with the data by first letting $a = 1000$.
(c) Use trial and error to adjust the value of a until the graph models the data.
(d) Use your final equation to estimate the number of AIDS cases in 1992. Compare it to the known value of 338,786.

Solution
(a) A scatterplot of the data is shown in Figure 11.39.

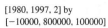

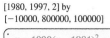

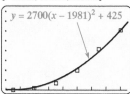

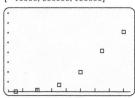

Figure 11.39

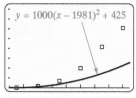

Figure 11.40 $a = 1000$

Figure 11.41 $a = 2700$

STUDY TIP

Sometimes we use only the right half or only the left half of a parabola to model data.

(b) A graph of $y = 1000(x - 1981)^2 + 425$ is shown in Figure 11.40. To have a better fit of the data, a larger value for a is needed.
(c) Figure 11.41 shows the effect of adjusting the value of a to 2700. This value provides a reasonably good fit. (Note that you may decide on a slightly different value for a.)
(d) If $a = 2700$, the modeling equation becomes

$$y = 2700(x - 1981)^2 + 425.$$

To estimate the number of AIDS cases in 1992, substitute $x = 1992$ to obtain

$$y = 2700(1992 - 1981)^2 + 425 = 327{,}125.$$

This number is about 12,000 less than the known value of 338,786.

Now Try Exercise 91

11.2   Putting It All Together

CONCEPT	EXPLANATION	EXAMPLES
Translations of Parabolas	Compared to the graph $y = x^2$, the graph of $y = x^2 + k$ is shifted vertically k units and the graph of $y = (x - h)^2$ is shifted horizontally h units.	Compared to the graph of $y = x^2$, the graph of $y = x^2 - 4$ is shifted *downward* 4 units. Compared to the graph of $y = x^2$, the graph of $y = (x - 4)^2$ is shifted *right* 4 units and the graph of $y = (x + 4)^2$ is shifted *left* 4 units.
Vertex Form	The vertex form of the equation of a parabola with vertex (h, k) is $$y = a(x - h)^2 + k,$$ where $a \neq 0$ is a constant. If $a > 0$, the parabola opens upward; if $a < 0$, the parabola opens downward.	The graph of $y = 3(x + 2)^2 - 7$ has a vertex of $(-2, -7)$ and opens upward because $3 > 0$.

continued on next page

continued from previous page

CONCEPT	EXPLANATION	EXAMPLES
Completing the Square Method	To complete the square to obtain the vertex form, add *and* subtract $\left(\frac{b}{2}\right)^2$ on the right side of the equation $y = x^2 + bx + c$. Then factor the perfect square trinomial.	If $y = x^2 + 10x - 3$, then add *and* subtract $\left(\frac{b}{2}\right)^2 = \left(\frac{10}{2}\right)^2 = 25$ on the right side of this equation. $y = (x^2 + 10x + 25) - 25 - 3$ $\quad = (x + 5)^2 - 28$ The vertex is $(-5, -28)$.

11.2 Exercises

MyMathLab

PRACTICE   WATCH   DOWNLOAD   READ   REVIEW

CONCEPTS AND VOCABULARY

1. Compared to the graph of $y = x^2$, the graph of $y = $ _____ is shifted upward 2 units.

2. Compared to the graph of $y = x^2$, the graph of $y = $ _____ is shifted to the right 2 units.

3. The vertex of $y = (x - 1)^2 + 2$ is _____.

4. The vertex of $y = (x + 1)^2 - 2$ is _____.

5. A quadratic function f may be written either in the form _____ or _____.

6. The vertex form of a parabola is given by _____ and its vertex is _____.

7. The graph of the equation $y = -x^2$ is a parabola that opens _____.

8. The x-coordinate of the vertex of $y = ax^2 + bx + c$ is $x = $ _____.

9. Compared to the graph of $y = x^2$, the graph of $y = x^2 + k$ with $k > 0$ is shifted k units _____.
   a. upward   b. downward
   c. left   d. right

10. Compared to the graph of $y = x^2$, the graph of $y = (x - k)^2$ with $k > 0$ is shifted k units _____.
   a. upward   b. downward
   c. left   d. right

TABLES AND TRANSLATIONS

Exercises 11–14: Complete the table for each translation of $y = x^2$. State what the translation does.

11.

x	-2	-1	0	1	2
$y = x^2$					
$y = x^2 - 3$					

12.

x	-2	-1	0	1	2
$y = x^2$					
$y = x^2 + 5$					

13.

x					
$y = x^2$	4	1	0	1	4

x					
$y = (x - 3)^2$	4	1	0	1	4

14.

x					
$y = x^2$	16	4	0	4	16

x					
$y = (x + 4)^2$	16	4	0	4	16

GRAPHS OF PARABOLAS

Exercises 15–34: Do the following.
  (a) Sketch a graph of the equation.
  (b) Identify the vertex.
  (c) Compare the graph of $y = f(x)$ to the graph of $y = x^2$. (State any transformations used.)

15. $f(x) = x^2 - 4$ **16.** $f(x) = x^2 - 1$

17. $f(x) = 2x^2 + 1$ **18.** $f(x) = \frac{1}{2}x^2 + 1$

19. $f(x) = (x - 3)^2$ **20.** $f(x) = (x + 1)^2$

21. $f(x) = -x^2$ **22.** $f(x) = -(x + 2)^2$

23. $f(x) = 2 - x^2$ **24.** $f(x) = (x - 1)^2$

25. $f(x) = (x + 2)^2$ **26.** $f(x) = (x - 2)^2 - 3$

27. $f(x) = (x + 1)^2 - 2$ **28.** $f(x) = (x - 3)^2 + 1$

29. $f(x) = (x - 1)^2 + 2$

30. $f(x) = \frac{1}{2}(x + 3)^2 - 3$

31. $f(x) = 2(x - 5)^2 - 4$

32. $f(x) = -3(x + 4)^2 + 5$

33. $f(x) = -\frac{1}{2}(x + 3)^2 + 1$

34. $f(x) = 2(x - 5)^2 + 10$

Exercises 35–38: Compare the graph of $y = f(x)$ to the graph of $y = x^2$. Then sketch a graph of $y = f(x)$ and $y = x^2$ in the same xy-plane.

35. $f(x) = \frac{1}{2}(x - 1)^2 - 2$

36. $f(x) = 2(x + 2)^2 - 1$

37. $f(x) = -2(x + 1)^2 + 3$

38. $f(x) = -\frac{1}{2}(x - 2)^2 + 2$

Exercises 39 and 40: Graph the equation in a window that shows the vertex and all intercepts.

39. $f(x) = -0.4x^2 + 6x - 10$

40. $f(x) = 3x^2 - 40x + 50$

VERTEX FORM

Exercises 41–44: (Refer to Example 3.) Write the vertex form of a parabola that satisfies the conditions given. Then write the equation in the form $y = ax^2 + bx + c$.

41. Vertex $(3, 4)$ and $a = 3$

42. Vertex $(-1, 3)$ and $a = -5$

43. Vertex $(5, -2)$ and $a = -\frac{1}{2}$

44. Vertex $(-2, -6)$ and $a = \frac{3}{4}$

Exercises 45–48: Write the vertex form of a parabola that satisfies the conditions given. Assume that $a = \pm 1$.

45. Opens upward, vertex $(1, 2)$

46. Opens downward, vertex $(-1, -2)$

47. Opens downward, vertex $(0, -3)$

48. Opens upward, vertex $(5, -4)$

Exercises 49–52: Write the vertex form of the parabola shown in the graph. Assume that $a = \pm 1$.

49.
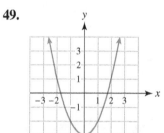

50.
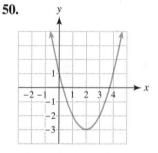

51.
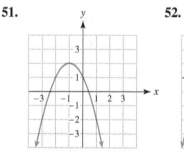

52.
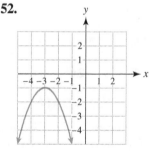

Exercises 53–58: (Refer to Example 4.) Do the following.
(a) Find the vertex on the graph of the equation.
(b) Write the equation in vertex form.

53. $y = 4x^2 - 8x + 5$

54. $y = 3x^2 - 12x + 15$

55. $y = -x^2 - 2x - 3$

56. $y = -x^2 - 4x - 5$

57. $y = -2x^2 - 4x + 1$

58. $y = 2x^2 - 16x + 27$

COMPLETING THE SQUARE

Exercises 59 and 60: Use the given figure to determine what number should be added to the expression to complete the square.

59. $x^2 + 2x$

60. $x^2 + 6x$

Exercises 61–78: (Refer to Example 6.) Write the equation in vertex form. Identify the vertex.

61. $y = x^2 + 2x$

62. $y = x^2 + 6x$

63. $y = x^2 - 4x$

64. $y = x^2 - 8x$

65. $y = x^2 + 2x - 3$

66. $y = x^2 + 4x + 1$

67. $y = x^2 - 4x + 5$

68. $y = x^2 - 8x + 10$

69. $y = x^2 + 3x - 2$

70. $y = x^2 + 5x - 4$

71. $y = x^2 - 7x + 1$

72. $y = x^2 - 3x + 5$

73. $y = 3x^2 + 6x - 1$

74. $y = 2x^2 + 4x - 9$

75. $y = 2x^2 - 3x$

76. $y = 3x^2 - 7x$

77. $y = -2x^2 - 8x + 5$

78. $y = -3x^2 + 6x + 1$

MODELING DATA

Exercises 79–82: Find a value for the constant a so that $f(x) = ax^2$ models the data. If you are uncertain about your value for a, check it by making a table of values.

79.

x	1	2	3
y	2	8	18

80.

x	-2	0	2
y	6	0	6

81.

x	2	4	6	8
y	1.2	4.8	10.8	19.2

82.

x	5	10	15	20
y	17.5	70	157.5	280

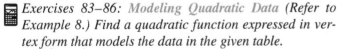 *Exercises 83–86: Modeling Quadratic Data (Refer to Example 8.) Find a quadratic function expressed in vertex form that models the data in the given table.*

83.

x	1	2	3	4
y	-3	-1	5	15

84.

x	-2	-1	0	1	2
y	5	2	-7	-22	-43

85.

x	1980	1990	2000	2010
y	6	55	210	450

86.

x	1990	1995	2000	2005
y	10	60	205	470

87. *Braking Distance* The table lists approximate braking distances D in feet for cars traveling at x miles per hour on dry, level pavement.

x	12	24	36	48
D	12	48	108	192

(a) Make a scatterplot of the data.
(b) Find a function given by $D(x) = ax^2$ that models these data.

88. *Health Care Costs* The table lists approximate *annual* percent increases in the cost of health insurance premiums between 1992 and 2000.

Year	1992	1994	1996	1998	2000
Increase	11%	4%	1%	4%	11%

Source: Kaiser Family Foundation.

(a) Describe what happened to health care costs from 1992 to 2000.
(b) Would a linear function model these data? Explain.
(c) What type of function might model these data? Explain.
(d) What might be a good choice for the vertex? Explain.
(e) Find a quadratic function C expressed in vertex form that models the data. (Answers may vary.)
(f) Graph C and the data.

89. *Sub-Saharan Africa* The table lists actual and projected real gross domestic product (GDP) per capita for selected years in Sub-Saharan Africa.

Year	1980	1995	2010	2025
Real GDP	$1000	$600	$1000	$2200

Source: IMF WEO, Standard Chartered Research.

(a) Describe what happens to the real GDP.
(b) Would a linear function model these data? Explain.
(c) What type of function might model these data? Explain.

(d) What might be a good choice for the vertex? Explain.
(e) Find a quadratic function C expressed in vertex form that models the data. (Answers may vary.)
(f) Graph C and the data.

90. *Tax Theory and Modeling* If a government wants to generate enough revenue from income taxes, then it is important to assess the correct tax rates. On the one hand, if tax rates are too low, then enough revenue may not be generated. On the other hand, if taxes are too high, people may work less and not earn as much money. Again, enough revenue may not be generated. The following parabolic graph illustrates this phenomenon.

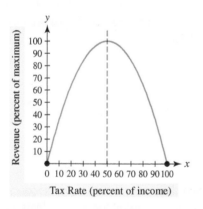

(a) The points $(0, 0)$ and $(100, 0)$ are on this graph. Explain why.
(b) Explain why a linear model is not suitable.
(c) According to *this* graph, what rate maximizes revenue?

91. *U.S. AIDS Deaths* (Refer to Example 8.) The table lists cumulative numbers of AIDS deaths *in thousands* for selected years.

Year	1982	1986	1990	1994
Deaths (thousands)	1	25	123	300

Source: Department of Health and Human Services.

(a) Determine $f(x) = a(x - h)^2 + k$, so that f models these data.
(b) Estimate the number of AIDS deaths in 1992 and compare it to the actual value of 202 thousand.

92. *Head Start Enrollment* The table lists numbers of students *in thousands* enrolled in Head Start for selected years.

Year	1966	1980	1995
Students (thousands)	733	376	750

(a) Determine $f(x) = a(x - h)^2 + k$, so that f models these data.
(b) Estimate Head Start enrollment in 1990 and compare it to the actual value of 541 thousand.

INCREASING AND DECREASING

Exercises 93–96: Use the graph of $y = f(x)$ to determine the intervals where f is increasing and where f is decreasing.

93.

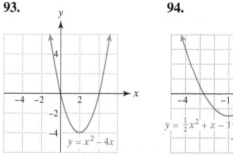

$y = x^2 - 4x$

94.

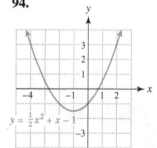

$y = \frac{1}{2}x^2 + x - 1$

95.

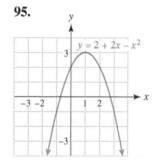

$y = 2 + 2x - x^2$

96.

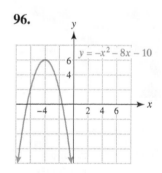

$y = -x^2 - 8x - 10$

Exercises 97–102: Determine the intervals where $y = f(x)$ is increasing and where it is decreasing.

97. $y = 3x^2 - 4x + 1$
98. $y = 2x^2 - 5x - 2$

99. $y = -x^2 - 3x$
100. $y = -2x^2 + 3x - 4$

101. $y = 5 - x - 4x^2$
102. $y = 3 + x + x^2$

WRITING ABOUT MATHEMATICS

103. Explain how to find the vertex of $y = x^2 + bx + c$ by completing the square.

104. If $f(x) = a(x - h)^2 + k$, explain how the values of a, h, and k affect the graph of $y = f(x)$.

Checking Basic Concepts

1. Graph each quadratic function. Identify the vertex and axis of symmetry
   (a) $f(x) = x^2 - 2$
   (b) $f(x) = x^2 - 2x - 2$

2. Compare the graph of $y_1 = 2x^2$ to the graph of $y_2 = -\frac{1}{2}x^2$.

3. Find the maximum y-value on the graph of the equation $y = -3x^2 + 12x - 5$.

4. Sketch a graph of $y = f(x)$. Compare this graph to the graph of $y = x^2$.
   (a) $f(x) = (x - 1)^2 + 2$
   (b) $f(x) = -(x + 3)^2$

5. Write the vertex form for each equation.
   (a) $y = x^2 + 14x - 7$
   (b) $y = 4x^2 + 8x - 2$

11.3 Quadratic Equations

Basics of Quadratic Equations • The Square Root Property • Completing the
Square • Solving an Equation for a Variable • Applications of Quadratic Equations

A LOOK INTO MATH ▶

For many years, MySpace was the largest social network in the United States. However, during 2010 the number of unique monthly visitors fell dramatically from 70 million in January 2010 to 45 million in January 2011. Table 11.11 lists the number of unique visitors V to MySpace in millions x months after January 2010.

TABLE 11.11 Unique MySpace Visitors (millions)

x (months after Jan. 2010)	0	6	12
V (unique monthly visitors)	70	63	45

Source: comScore.

Decreased   Decreased
7 million   18 million

NEW VOCABULARY

☐ Quadratic equation
☐ Square root property

The number of unique visitors to MySpace decreased faster in the second half of 2010 than it did in the first half, so a linear function will *not* model these data. Instead, these data can be modeled by the *quadratic function*

$$V(x) = -\frac{25}{144}x^2 + 70. \qquad \text{Quadratic function}$$

If we want to determine the month when MySpace had **56** million unique visitors, then we could solve the *quadratic equation*

$$-\frac{25}{144}x^2 + 70 = 56. \qquad \text{Quadratic equation}$$

In this section we learn how to solve this and other quadratic equations. See Exercise 125.

Basics of Quadratic Equations

Any quadratic function f can be represented by $f(x) = ax^2 + bx + c$ with $a \neq 0$. Examples of quadratic functions include

$$f(x) = 2x^2 - 1, g(x) = -\frac{1}{3}x^2 + 2x, \text{ and } h(x) = x^2 + 2x - 1. \qquad \text{Quadratic functions}$$

Quadratic functions can be used to write quadratic equations. Examples of quadratic equations include

$$2x^2 - 1 = 0, \quad -\tfrac{1}{3}x^2 + 2x = 0, \quad \text{and} \quad x^2 + 2x - 1 = 0. \quad \text{Quadratic equations}$$

READING CHECK

How can you identify a quadratic equation?

QUADRATIC EQUATION

A **quadratic equation** is an equation that can be written as

$$ax^2 + bx + c = 0,$$

where a, b, and c are constants with $a \neq 0$.

Solutions to the quadratic equation $ax^2 + bx + c = 0$ correspond to x-intercepts of the graph of $y = ax^2 + bx + c$. Because the graph of a quadratic function is either $\cup$-shaped or $\cap$-shaped, it can intersect the x-axis zero, one, or two times, as illustrated in Figure 11.42. Hence a quadratic equation can have zero, one, or two real solutions.

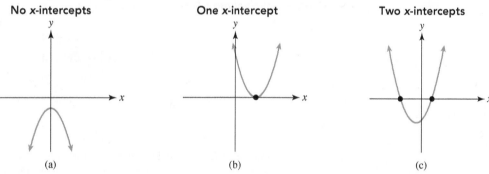

| No x-intercepts | One x-intercept | Two x-intercepts |
| (a) | (b) | (c) |

Figure 11.42

NOTE: Some quadratic equations may not have 0 on the right side of the equation, such as $4x^2 = 1$. To solve this quadratic equation graphically, we will sometimes rewrite it as $4x^2 - 1 = 0$ and graph $y = 4x^2 - 1$. Then solutions are x-intercepts, because $y = 0$ on the x-axis.

We have already solved quadratic equations by factoring, graphing, and constructing tables. In the next example we apply these three techniques to quadratic equations that have no real solutions, one real solution, and two real solutions.

EXAMPLE 1   **Solving quadratic equations**

Solve each quadratic equation. Support your results numerically and graphically.

(a) $2x^2 + 1 = 0$ (No real solutions)

(b) $x^2 + 4 = 4x$ (One real solution)

(c) $x^2 - 6x + 8 = 0$ (Two real solutions)

Solution
(a) Symbolic Solution

$$\begin{aligned}
2x^2 + 1 &= 0 && \text{Given equation} \\
2x^2 &= -1 && \text{Subtract 1 from each side.} \\
x^2 &= -\frac{1}{2} && \text{Divide each side by 2.}
\end{aligned}$$

This equation has no real-number solutions because $x^2 \geq 0$ for all real numbers x.

Numerical and Graphical Solution The points in Table 11.12 for $y = 2x^2 + 1$ are plotted in Figure 11.43 and connected with a parabolic graph. The graph of $y = 2x^2 + 1$ has no x-intercepts, indicating that there are no real solutions.

TABLE 11.12

For all x, $y \neq 0$, so there are no solutions.

x	y
−2	9
−1	3
0	1
1	3
2	9

No Solutions

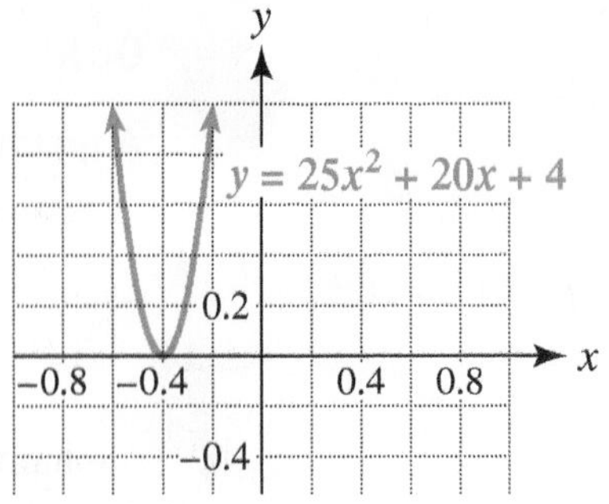

Figure 11.43

(b) Symbolic Solution Next, we solve $x^2 + 4 = 4x$.

$$x^2 + 4 = 4x \qquad \text{Given equation}$$
$$x^2 - 4x + 4 = 0 \qquad \text{Subtract } 4x \text{ from each side.}$$
$$(x - 2)(x - 2) = 0 \qquad \text{Factor.}$$
$$x - 2 = 0 \quad \text{or} \quad x - 2 = 0 \qquad \text{Zero-product property}$$
$$x = 2 \qquad \text{There is one solution.}$$

Numerical and Graphical Solution Because the given quadratic equation is equivalent to $x^2 - 4x + 4 = 0$, we let $y = x^2 - 4x + 4$. The points in Table 11.13 are plotted in Figure 11.44 and connected with a parabolic graph. The graph of $y = x^2 - 4x + 4$ has one x-intercept, 2. Note that in Table 11.13, $y = 0$ when $x = 2$, indicating that the equation has one solution.

TABLE 11.13

x	y
0	4
1	1
2	**0**
3	1
4	4

One solution: 2

One Solution

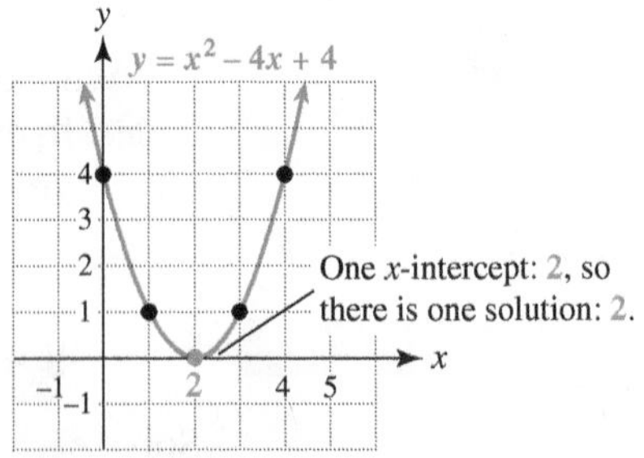

Figure 11.44

(c) Symbolic Solution Next, we solve $x^2 - 6x + 8 = 0$.

$$x^2 - 6x + 8 = 0 \qquad \text{Given equation}$$
$$(x - 2)(x - 4) = 0 \qquad \text{Factor.}$$
$$x - 2 = 0 \quad \text{or} \quad x - 4 = 0 \qquad \text{Zero-product property}$$
$$x = 2 \quad \text{or} \quad x = 4 \qquad \text{There are two solutions.}$$

Numerical and Graphical Solution The points in Table 11.14 for $y = x^2 - 6x + 8$ are plotted in Figure 11.45 and connected with a parabolic graph. The graph of

$y = x^2 - 6x + 8$ has two x-intercepts, **2** and **4**, indicating two solutions. Note that in Table 11.14 $y = \mathbf{0}$ when $x = \mathbf{2}$ or $x = \mathbf{4}$.

TABLE 11.14

x	y
0	8
1	3
2	**0**
3	−1
4	**0**
5	3
6	8

Two solutions: **2** and **4**

Two Solutions

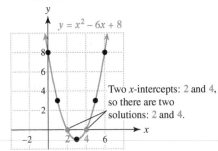

Figure 11.45

Two x-intercepts: **2** and **4**, so there are two solutions: **2** and **4**.

Now Try Exercises 29, 37, 39

READING CHECK

How many solutions can a quadratic equation have?

The Square Root Property

The **square root property** is used to solve quadratic equations that have no x-terms. The following is an example of the square root property.

$$x^2 = 25 \quad \text{is equivalent to} \quad x = \pm 5.$$

The equation $x = \pm 5$ (read "x equals plus or minus 5") indicates that either $x = 5$ or $x = -5$. Each value is a solution because $(5)^2 = 25$ and $(-5)^2 = 25$.

We can derive this result in general for $k \geq 0$.

$$\begin{aligned} x^2 &= k & \text{Given quadratic equation} \\ \sqrt{x^2} &= \sqrt{k} & \text{Take the square root of each side.} \\ |x| &= \sqrt{k} & \sqrt{x^2} = |x| \text{ for all } x. \\ x &= \pm\sqrt{k} & |x| = b \text{ implies } x = \pm b,\, b \geq 0. \end{aligned}$$

This result is summarized by the *square root property*.

SQUARE ROOT PROPERTY

Let k be a nonnegative number. Then the solutions to the equation

$$x^2 = k$$

are given by $x = \pm\sqrt{k}$. If $k < 0$, then this equation has no real solutions.

Before applying the square root property in the next two examples, we review a quotient property of square roots. If a and b are positive numbers, then

$$\sqrt{\frac{a}{b}} = \frac{\sqrt{a}}{\sqrt{b}}.$$

For example, $\sqrt{\frac{25}{36}} = \frac{\sqrt{25}}{\sqrt{36}} = \frac{5}{6}$.

EXAMPLE 2 | **Using the square root property**

Solve each equation.
(a) $x^2 = 7$ (b) $16x^2 - 9 = 0$ (c) $(x - 4)^2 = 25$

Solution

(a) $x^2 = 7$ is equivalent to $x = \pm\sqrt{7}$ by the square root property. The solutions are $\sqrt{7}$ and $-\sqrt{7}$.

(b)

$16x^2 - 9 = 0$	Given equation
$16x^2 = 9$	Add 9 to each side.
$x^2 = \dfrac{9}{16}$	Divide each side by 16.
$x = \pm\sqrt{\dfrac{9}{16}}$	Square root property
$x = \pm\dfrac{3}{4}$	Simplify.

READING CHECK

When do you use the square root property to solve an equation?

The solutions are $\frac{3}{4}$ and $-\frac{3}{4}$.

(c)

$(x - 4)^2 = 25$	Given equation
$(x - 4) = \pm\sqrt{25}$	Square root property
$x - 4 = \pm 5$	Simplify.
$x = 4 \pm 5$	Add 4 to each side.
$x = 9$ or $x = -1$	Evaluate $4 + 5$ and $4 - 5$.

The solutions are 9 and -1.

▌Now Try Exercises 51, 53, 57

▶ **REAL-WORLD CONNECTION** If an object is dropped from a height of h feet, its distance d above the ground after t seconds is given by

$$d(t) = h - 16t^2.$$

This formula can be used to estimate the time it takes for a falling object to hit the ground.

EXAMPLE 3 | **Modeling a falling object**

A toy falls 30 feet from a window. How long does the toy take to hit the ground?

Solution

The height h of the window above the ground is 30 feet, so let $d(t) = 30 - 16t^2$. The toy strikes the ground when the distance d above the ground equals 0.

$30 - 16t^2 = 0$	Equation to solve for t
$-16t^2 = -30$	Subtract 30 from each side.
$t^2 = \dfrac{30}{16}$	Divide each side by -16.
$t = \pm\sqrt{\dfrac{30}{16}}$	Square root property
$t = \pm\dfrac{\sqrt{30}}{4}$	Simplify.

Time cannot be negative in this problem, so the appropriate solution is $t = \frac{\sqrt{30}}{4} \approx 1.4$. The toy hits the ground after about 1.4 seconds.

▌Now Try Exercise 115

Completing the Square

In Section 11.2 we used the *method of completing the square* to find the vertex of a parabola. This method can also be used to solve quadratic equations. Because

$$x^2 + bx + \left(\frac{b}{2}\right)^2 = \left(x + \frac{b}{2}\right)^2,$$

we can solve a quadratic equation in the form $x^2 + bx = d$, where b and d are constants, by adding $\left(\frac{b}{2}\right)^2$ to each side and then factoring the resulting perfect square trinomial.

In the equation $x^2 + 6x = 7$ we have $b = 6$, so we add $\left(\frac{6}{2}\right)^2 = 9$ to each side.

3	$3x$	?
x	x^2	$3x$
	x	3

$x^2 + 6x = 7$	Given equation
$x^2 + 6x + 9 = 7 + 9$	Add 9 to each side.
$(x + 3)^2 = 16$	Perfect square trinomial
$x + 3 = \pm 4$	Square root property
$x = -3 \pm 4$	Add -3 to each side.
$x = 1 \quad \text{or} \quad x = -7$	Simplify $-3 + 4$ and $-3 - 4$.

The solutions are 1 and -7. Note that after completing the square, the left side of the equation is a perfect square trinomial. We show how to create one in the next example.

EXAMPLE 4 **Creating a perfect square trinomial**

Find the term that should be added to $x^2 - 10x$ to form a perfect square trinomial.

Solution

The coefficient of the x-term is -10, so we let $b = -10$. To complete the square we divide b by 2 and then square the result.

$$\left(\frac{b}{2}\right)^2 = \left(\frac{-10}{2}\right)^2 = 25$$

If we add 25 to $x^2 - 10x$, a perfect square trinomial is formed.

$$x^2 - 10x + 25 = (x - 5)^2$$

Now Try Exercise 67

EXAMPLE 5 **Completing the square when the leading coefficient is 1**

Solve the equation $x^2 - 4x + 2 = 0$.

Solution

Start by writing the equation in the form $x^2 + bx = d$.

$x^2 - 4x + 2 = 0$	Given equation
$x^2 - 4x = -2$	Subtract 2.
$x^2 - 4x + 4 = -2 + 4$	Add $\left(\frac{b}{2}\right)^2 = \left(\frac{-4}{2}\right)^2 = 4.$
$(x - 2)^2 = 2$	Perfect square trinomial; add.
$x - 2 = \pm\sqrt{2}$	Square root property
$x = 2 \pm \sqrt{2}$	Add 2.

The solutions are $2 + \sqrt{2} \approx 3.41$ and $2 - \sqrt{2} \approx 0.59$.

Now Try Exercise 73

EXAMPLE 6   **Completing the square when the leading coefficient is not 1**

Solve the equation $2x^2 + 7x - 5 = 0$.

Solution
Start by writing the equation in the form $x^2 + bx = d$. That is, add 5 to each side and then divide each side by 2 so that the leading coefficient of the x^2-term becomes 1.

$$2x^2 + 7x - 5 = 0 \qquad \text{Given equation}$$

$$2x^2 + 7x = 5 \qquad \text{Add 5 to each side.}$$

$$x^2 + \frac{7}{2}x = \frac{5}{2} \qquad \text{Divide each side by 2.}$$

$$x^2 + \frac{7}{2}x + \frac{49}{16} = \frac{5}{2} + \frac{49}{16} \qquad \text{Add } \left(\frac{b}{2}\right)^2 = \left(\frac{7}{4}\right)^2 = \frac{49}{16}.$$

$$\left(x + \frac{7}{4}\right)^2 = \frac{89}{16} \qquad \text{Perfect square trinomial; add.}$$

$$x + \frac{7}{4} = \pm \frac{\sqrt{89}}{4} \qquad \text{Square root property}$$

$$x = -\frac{7}{4} \pm \frac{\sqrt{89}}{4} \qquad \text{Add } -\frac{7}{4}.$$

$$x = \frac{-7 \pm \sqrt{89}}{4} \qquad \text{Combine fractions.}$$

The solutions are $\frac{-7 + \sqrt{89}}{4} \approx 0.61$ and $\frac{-7 - \sqrt{89}}{4} \approx -4.1$.

▌ Now Try Exercise 81

CRITICAL THINKING

What happens if you try to solve
$$2x^2 - 13 = 1$$
by completing the square? What method could you use to solve this problem?

Solving an Equation for a Variable

We often need to solve an equation or formula for a variable. For example, the formula $V = \frac{1}{3}\pi r^2 h$ calculates the volume of the cone shown in Figure 11.46. Let's say that we know the volume V is 120 cubic inches and the height h is 15 inches. We can then find the radius of the cone by solving the equation for r.

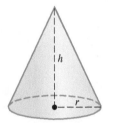

Figure 11.46

$$V = \frac{1}{3}\pi r^2 h \qquad \text{Solve the equation for } r.$$

$$3V = \pi r^2 h \qquad \text{Multiply by 3.}$$

$$\frac{3V}{\pi} = r^2 h \qquad \text{Divide by } \pi.$$

$$\frac{3V}{\pi h} = r^2 \qquad \text{Divide by } h.$$

$$r = \pm \sqrt{\frac{3V}{\pi h}} \qquad \text{Square root property; rewrite.}$$

Because $r \geq 0$, we use the positive or *principal square root*. Thus for $V = 120$ cubic inches and $h = 15$ inches,

$$r = \sqrt{\frac{3(120)}{\pi(15)}} = \sqrt{\frac{24}{\pi}} \approx 2.8 \text{ inches.}$$

EXAMPLE 7   **Solving equations for variables**

Solve each equation for the specified variable.
(a) $s = -\frac{1}{2}gt^2 + h$ for t **(b)** $d^2 = x^2 + y^2$ for y

Solution
(a) Begin by subtracting h from each side of the equation.

$$s = -\frac{1}{2}gt^2 + h \qquad \text{Solve the equation for } t.$$

$$s - h = -\frac{1}{2}gt^2 \qquad \text{Subtract } h.$$

$$-2(s-h) = gt^2 \qquad \text{Multiply by } -2.$$

$$\frac{2h - 2s}{g} = t^2 \qquad \text{Divide by } g; \text{ simplify.}$$

$$t = \pm\sqrt{\frac{2h - 2s}{g}} \qquad \text{Square root property; rewrite.}$$

(b) Begin by subtracting x^2 from each side of the equation.

$$d^2 = x^2 + y^2 \qquad \text{Solve the equation for } y.$$

$$d^2 - x^2 = y^2 \qquad \text{Subtract } x^2.$$

$$y = \pm\sqrt{d^2 - x^2} \qquad \text{Square root property; rewrite.}$$

Now Try Exercises 105, 107

Applications of Quadratic Equations

▶ **REAL-WORLD CONNECTION** In Section 11.2 we modeled curves on airport taxiways by using $R(x) = \frac{1}{2}x^2$. In this formula x represented the airplane's speed in miles per hour, and R represented the radius of the curve in feet. This formula may be used to determine the speed limit for a curve with a radius of **650** feet by solving the *quadratic equation*

$$\frac{1}{2}x^2 = 650.$$

In the next example, we solve this quadratic equation. (*Source:* FAA.)

EXAMPLE 8   **Finding a safe speed limit**

Solve $\frac{1}{2}x^2 = 650$ and interpret any solutions.

Solution
Use the square root property to solve this problem.

$$\frac{1}{2}x^2 = 650 \qquad \text{Given equation}$$

$$x^2 = 1300 \qquad \text{Multiply by 2.}$$

$$x = \pm\sqrt{1300} \qquad \text{Square root property}$$

The solutions are $\sqrt{1300} \approx 36$ and $-\sqrt{1300} \approx -36$. The solution of $x \approx 36$ indicates that a safe speed limit for a curve with a radius of 650 feet is about 36 miles per hour. (The negative solution has no physical meaning in this problem.)

Now Try Exercise 113

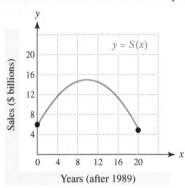

▶ **REAL-WORLD CONNECTION** From 1989 to 2009 there was a dramatic increase in compact disc and tape sales and then a dramatic decrease. Their global music sales S in billions of dollars x years after 1989 are modeled by

$$S(x) = -0.095x^2 + 1.85x + 6.$$

A graph of $S(x) = -0.095x^2 + 1.85x + 6$ is shown in Figure 11.47. (*Source:* RIAA, Bain Analysis.)

Global Music Sales from CDs and Tapes

Figure 11.47

When were sales equal to $12 billion? Because the graph is parabolic, it appears that there are two answers to the question: about 4 years and about 15 years after 1989. In the next example, we use graphical and numerical methods to find these years. In Section 11.4 (Exercise 113), you are asked to answer this question symbolically.

EXAMPLE 9 | **Modeling global CD and tape sales**

Use each method to determine the years when global sales of CDs and tapes were $12 billion.
(a) Graphical   **(b)** Numerical

Solution
(a) *Graphical Solution* Graph $y_1 = -0.095x^2 + 1.85x + 6$ and $y_2 = 12$, as shown in Figures 11.48(a) and (b). Their graphs intersect near the points $(4.11, 12)$ and $(15.36, 12)$. Because x is years *after* 1989, sales were $12 billion dollars in about 1993 (1989 + 4) and about 2004 (1989 + 15).

CALCULATOR HELP

To find a point of intersection, see Appendix A (page AP-6).

Determining When Sales Were $12 Billion

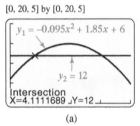

(a)

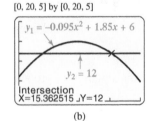

(b)

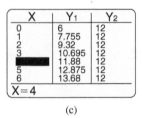

(c)

Figure 11.48

(b) *Numerical Solution* Make a table of $y_1 = -0.095x^2 + 1.85x + 6$ and $y_2 = 12$, as shown in Figure 11.48(c). When $x = 4$, y_1 is approximately 12. Thus sales were $12 billion around 1993. If we were to scroll down in the table further, we would see that sales also equal $12 billion when $x \approx 15$, or in 2004. The graphical and numerical solutions agree.

▍ Now Try Exercise 117

11.3 Putting It All Together

Quadratic equations can have no real solutions, one real solution, or two real solutions. Symbolic techniques for solving quadratic equations include factoring, the square root property, and completing the square. The following table summarizes only the square root property and the method of completing the square.

TECHNIQUE	DESCRIPTION	EXAMPLES
Square Root Property	If $k \geq 0$, the solutions to the equation $x^2 = k$ are $\pm\sqrt{k}$.	$x^2 = 100$ is equivalent to $x = \pm 10$ and $x^2 = 13$ is equivalent to $x = \pm\sqrt{13}$. $x^2 = -2$ has no real solutions.
Method of Completing the Square	To solve an equation in the form $x^2 + bx = d$, add $\left(\frac{b}{2}\right)^2$ to each side of the equation. Factor the resulting perfect square trinomial and solve for x by applying the square root property.	To solve $x^2 + 8x = 3$, add $\left(\frac{8}{2}\right)^2 = 16$ to each side. $x^2 + 8x + 16 = 3 + 16$ Add 16. $(x + 4)^2 = 19$ Perfect square trinomial $x + 4 = \pm\sqrt{19}$ Square root property $x = -4 \pm\sqrt{19}$ Add -4.

11.3 Exercises

MyMathLab   Math XL PRACTICE   WATCH   DOWNLOAD   READ   REVIEW

CONCEPTS AND VOCABULARY

1. Give an example of a quadratic equation. How many real solutions can a quadratic equation have?

2. Is a quadratic equation a linear equation or a nonlinear equation?

3. Name three symbolic methods that can be used to solve a quadratic equation.

4. Sketch a graph of a quadratic function that has two x-intercepts and opens downward.

5. Sketch a graph of a quadratic function that has no x-intercepts and opens upward.

6. If the graph of $y = ax^2 + bx + c$ intersects the x-axis twice, how many solutions does the equation $ax^2 + bx + c = 0$ have? Explain.

7. Solve $x^2 = 64$. What property did you use?

8. To solve $x^2 + bx = 6$ by completing the square, what value should be added to each side of the equation?

Exercises 9–16: Is the given equation quadratic?

9. $x^2 - 3x + 1 = 0$

10. $2x^2 - 3 = 0$

11. $3x + 1 = 0$

12. $x^3 - 3x^2 + x = 0$

13. $-3x^2 + x = 16$

14. $x^2 - 1 = 4x$

15. $x^2 = \sqrt{x} + 1$

16. $\dfrac{1}{x - 1} = 5$

SOLVING QUADRATIC EQUATIONS

Exercises 17–20: Approximate to the nearest hundredth.

17. (a) $1 \pm \sqrt{7}$ (b) $-2 \pm \sqrt{11}$

18. (a) $\pm\dfrac{\sqrt{3}}{2}$ (b) $\pm\dfrac{2\sqrt{5}}{7}$

19. (a) $\dfrac{3 \pm \sqrt{13}}{5}$ (b) $\dfrac{-5 \pm \sqrt{6}}{9}$

20. (a) $\dfrac{2}{5} \pm \dfrac{\sqrt{5}}{5}$ (b) $-\dfrac{3}{7} \pm \dfrac{\sqrt{3}}{7}$

Exercises 21–24: A graph of $y = ax^2 + bx + c$ is given. Use this graph to solve $ax^2 + bx + c = 0$, if possible.

21.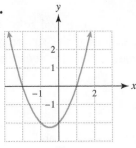

22.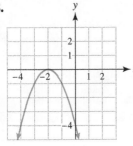

23.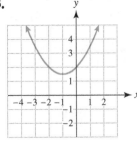

24.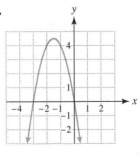

Exercises 25–28: A table of $y = ax^2 + bx + c$ is given. Use this table to solve $ax^2 + bx + c = 0$.

25.

X	Y1
-3	6
-2	0
-1	-6
0	-6
1	-6
2	-4
3	0

Y1 ▤ X^2−X−6

26.

X	Y1
-6	0
-4	-16
-2	-24
0	-24
2	-16
4	0
6	24

Y1 ▤ X^2+2X−24

27.

X	Y1
-2	9
-1.5	4
-1	1
-.5	0
0	1
.5	4
1	9

Y1 ▤ 4X^2+4X+1

28.

X	Y1
-4	-2.5
-3	0
-2	1.5
-1	2
0	1.5
1	0
2	-2.5

Y1 ▤ −X^2/2−X+3/2

Exercises 29–40: Use each method to solve the equation.

(a) *Symbolic* **(b)** *Graphical* **(c)** *Numerical*

29. $x^2 - 4x - 5 = 0$ **30.** $x^2 - x - 6 = 0$

31. $x^2 + 2x = 3$ **32.** $x^2 + 4x = 5$

33. $x^2 = 9$ **34.** $x^2 = 4$

35. $4x^2 - 4x = 3$ **36.** $2x^2 + x = 1$

37. $x^2 + 2x = -1$ **38.** $4x^2 - 4x + 1 = 0$

39. $x^2 + 2 = 0$ **40.** $-4x^2 - 1 = 2$

Exercises 41–50: Solve by factoring.

41. $x^2 + 2x - 35 = 0$ **42.** $2x^2 - 7x + 3 = 0$

43. $6x^2 - x - 1 = 0$ **44.** $x^2 + 4x + 6 = -3x$

45. $4x^2 + 13x + 9 = x$ **46.** $9x^2 + 4 = 12x$

47. $25x^2 - 350 = 125x$ **48.** $20x^2 + 150 = 130x$

49. $2(5x^2 + 9) = 27x$ **50.** $15(3x^2 + x) = 10$

Exercises 51–62: Use the square root property to solve.

51. $x^2 = 144$ **52.** $4x^2 - 5 = 0$

53. $5x^2 - 64 = 0$ **54.** $3x^2 = 7$

55. $(x + 1)^2 = 25$ **56.** $(x + 4)^2 = 9$

57. $(x - 1)^2 = 64$ **58.** $(x - 3)^2 = 0$

59. $(2x - 1)^2 = 5$ **60.** $(5x + 3)^2 = 7$

61. $10(x - 5)^2 = 50$ **62.** $7(3x + 1)^2 = 14$

COMPLETING THE SQUARE

Exercises 63–66: To solve by completing the square, what value should you add to each side of the equation?

63. $x^2 + 4x = -3$ **64.** $x^2 - 6x = 4$

65. $x^2 - 5x = 4$ **66.** $x^2 + 3x = 1$

Exercises 67–70: (Refer to Example 4.) Find the term that should be added to the expression to form a perfect square trinomial. Write the resulting perfect square trinomial in factored form.

67. $x^2 - 8x$ **68.** $x^2 - 5x$

69. $x^2 + 9x$ **70.** $x^2 + x$

Exercises 71–86: Solve by completing the square.

71. $x^2 - 2x = 24$ **72.** $x^2 - 2x + \frac{1}{2} = 0$

73. $x^2 + 6x - 2 = 0$ **74.** $x^2 - 16x = 5$

75. $x^2 - 3x = 5$ **76.** $x^2 + 5x = 2$

77. $x^2 - 5x + 1 = 0$ **78.** $x^2 - 9x + 7 = 0$

79. $x^2 - 4 = 2x$ **80.** $x^2 + 1 = 7x$

81. $2x^2 - 3x = 4$ **82.** $3x^2 + 6x - 5 = 0$

83. $4x^2 - 8x - 7 = 0$ **84.** $25x^2 - 20x - 1 = 0$

85. $36x^2 + 18x + 1 = 0$ **86.** $12x^2 + 8x - 2 = 0$

Exercises 87–96: Solve by any method.

87. $3x^2 + 12x = 36$ **88.** $6x^2 + 9x = 27$

89. $x^2 + 4x = -2$ **90.** $x^2 + 6x + 3 = 0$

91. $3x^2 - 4 = 2$ **92.** $-2x^2 + 3 = 1$

93. $-6x^2 + 70 = 16x$

94. $-15x^2 + 25x + 10 = 0$

95. $-3x(x - 8) = 6$ **96.** $-2x(4 - x) = 8$

Exercises 97 and 98: Thinking Generally *Solve for x. Assume a and c are positive.*

97. $ax^2 - c = 0$ **98.** $ax^2 + bx = 0$

SOLVING EQUATIONS BY MORE
THAN ONE METHOD

Exercises 99–104: Solve the quadratic equation

   (a) symbolically,
   (b) graphically, and
   (c) numerically.

99. $x^2 - 3x - 18 = 0$ **100.** $\frac{1}{2}x^2 + 2x - 6 = 0$

101. $x^2 - 8x + 15 = 0$ **102.** $2x^2 + 3 = 7x$

103. $4(x^2 + 35) = 48x$ **104.** $4x(2 - x) = -5$

SOLVING AN EQUATION FOR A VARIABLE

Exercises 105–112: Solve for the specified variable.

105. $x = y^2 - 1$ for y

106. $x = 9y^2$ for y **107.** $K = \frac{1}{2}mv^2$ for v

108. $c^2 = a^2 + b^2$ for b

109. $E = \frac{k}{r^2}$ for r **110.** $W = I^2R$ for I

111. $LC = \dfrac{1}{(2\pi f)^2}$ for f

112. $F = \dfrac{KmM}{r^2}$ for r

APPLICATIONS

113. *Safe Curve Speed* (Refer to Example 8.) Find a safe speed limit x for an airport taxiway curve with the given radius R by using $R = \frac{1}{2}x^2$.
   (a) $R = 450$ feet   **(b)** $R = 800$ feet

114. *Braking Distance* The braking distance y in feet that it takes for a car to stop on wet, level pavement can be estimated by $y = \frac{1}{9}x^2$, where x is the speed of the car in miles per hour. Find the speed associated with each braking distance. (*Source:* L. Haefner, *Introduction to Transportation Systems.*)
   (a) 25 feet   **(b)** 361 feet   **(c)** 784 feet

115. *Falling Object* (Refer to Example 3.) How long does it take for a toy to hit the ground if it is dropped out of a window 60 feet above the ground? Does it take twice as long as it takes to fall from a window 30 feet above the ground?

116. *Falling Object* If a metal ball is thrown *downward* with an initial velocity of 22 feet per second (15 mph) from a 100-foot water tower, its height h in feet above the ground after t seconds is modeled by

$$h(t) = -16t^2 - 22t + 100.$$

   (a) Determine symbolically when the height of the ball is 62 feet.
   (b) Support your result in part (a) either graphically or numerically.
   (c) If the ball is thrown *upward* at 22 feet per second, then its height is given by

$$h(t) = -16t^2 + 22t + 100.$$

   Determine when the height of the ball is 80 feet.

Exercises 117 and 118: Television Size (Refer to the introduction of this chapter.) The size S of the television screen recommended for a person who sits x feet from the screen ($6 \le x \le 15$) is given by

$$S(x) = -0.227x^2 + 8.155x - 8.8.$$

If a person buys a television set with a size S screen, how far from the screen should the person sit?

117. $S = 42$ inches   **118.** $S = 50$ inches

119. *Distance* Two athletes start jogging at the same time. One jogs north at 6 miles per hour while the second jogs east at 8 miles per hour. After how long are the two athletes 20 miles apart?

120. *Geometry* A triangle has an area of 35 square inches, and its base is 3 inches more than its height. Find the base and height of the triangle.

121. *Construction* A rectangular plot of land has an area of 520 square feet and is 6 feet longer than it is wide.
  (a) Write a quadratic equation in the form $ax^2 + bx + c = 0$, whose solution gives the width of the rectangular plot of land.
  (b) Solve the equation.

122. *Modeling Motion* The height y in feet of a tennis ball after x seconds is shown in the graph. Estimate when the ball was 25 feet above the ground.

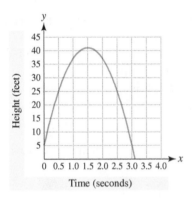

Time (seconds)

123. *Seedling Growth* (Refer to Exercise 100, Section 11.1.) The heights of melon seedlings grown at different temperatures are shown in the following graph. At what temperatures were the heights of the seedlings about 22 centimeters? (*Source:* R. Pearl, "The growth of *Cucumis melo* seedlings at different temperatures.")

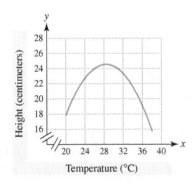

Temperature (°C)

124. *U.S. Population* The three tables show the population of the United States in millions from 1800 through 2010 for selected years.

Year	1800	1820	1840	1860
Population	5	10	17	31

Year	1880	1900	1920	1940
Population	50	76	106	132

Year	1960	1980	2000	2010
Population	179	226	269	308

Source: U.S. Census Bureau.

  (a) Without plotting the data, how do you know that the data are nonlinear?
  (b) These data are modeled (approximately) by

$$f(x) = 0.0066(x - 1800)^2 + 5.$$

  Find the vertex of the graph of f and interpret it.
  (c) Estimate when the U.S. population reached 85 million.

125. *MySpace Visitors* (Refer to A Look Into Math at the beginning of this section.) The number of unique monthly visitors V in millions to MySpace x months after January 2010 can be modeled by

$$V(x) = -\frac{25}{144}x^2 + 70.$$

Determine the month when this number of visitors was 56 million.

126. *Federal Debt* The federal debt D in trillions of dollars held by foreign and international investors x years after 1970 can be modeled by

$$D(x) = \frac{1}{320}x^2 - \frac{3}{80}x,$$

where $15 \leq x \leq 40$.
  (a) Evaluate $D(40)$ and interpret the result.
  (b) Determine the year when the federal debt held by foreign and international investors first reached $500 billion ($0.5 trillion).

WRITING ABOUT MATHEMATICS

127. Suppose that you are asked to solve

$$ax^2 + bx + c = 0.$$

Explain how the graph of $y = ax^2 + bx + c$ can be used to find any real solutions to the equation.

128. Explain why a quadratic equation could not have more than two solutions. (*Hint:* Consider the graph of $y = ax^2 + bx + c$.)

Group Activity   Working With Real Data

Directions: Form a group of 2 to 4 people. Select someone to record the group's responses for this activity. All members of the group should work cooperatively to answer the questions. If your instructor asks for the results, each member of the group should be prepared to respond.

Personal Consumption Although there was an economic downturn in 2008, personal consumption has grown overall. Table 11.15 lists (approximate) personal consumption C in dollars for selected years x.

TABLE 11.15 **Personal Consumption (dollars)**

x	1959	1982	1990	1998	2009
C	$300	$2000	$4000	$6000	$10,000

Source: BEA.

(a) Make a scatterplot of these data. Use the window [1955, 2010, 10] by [0, 12000, 2000].

(b) Find a quadratic function given by

$$C(x) = a(x - 1959)^2 + k$$

that models the data. Graph C and the data. (Answers may vary.)

(c) Estimate when personal consumption was $8000. Compare your answer to the actual value of 2005.

(d) Use your function C to predict consumption in 2020 to the nearest thousand dollars.

11.4   The Quadratic Formula

Solving Quadratic Equations ● The Discriminant ●
Quadratic Equations Having Complex Solutions

A LOOK INTO MATH ▶

NEW VOCABULARY

☐ Quadratic formula
☐ Discriminant

To model the stopping distance of a car, highway engineers compute two quantities. The first quantity is the *reaction distance*, which is the distance a car travels from the time a driver first recognizes a hazard until the brakes are applied. The second quantity is *braking distance*, which is the distance a car travels after a driver applies the brakes. *Stopping distance* equals the sum of the reaction distance and the braking distance. If a car is traveling x miles per hour, highway engineers estimate the reaction distance in feet as $\frac{11}{3}x$ and the braking distance in feet as $\frac{1}{9}x^2$. See Figure 11.49. (*Source*: L. Haefner, *Introduction to Transportation Systems*.)

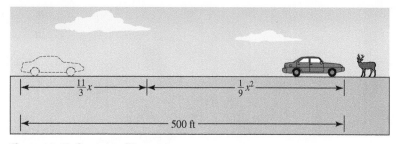

Figure 11.49 Stopping Distance

To estimate the total stopping distance d in feet, add the two expressions to obtain

$$d(x) = \frac{1}{9}x^2 + \frac{11}{3}x.$$

If a car's headlights don't illuminate the road beyond 500 feet, a safe nighttime speed limit x for the car can be determined by solving the quadratic equation

$$\frac{1}{9}x^2 \quad + \quad \frac{11}{3}x \quad = \quad 500. \qquad \text{Quadratic equation}$$

Braking Distance + Reaction Distance = Stopping Distance

In this section we learn how to solve this equation with the quadratic formula. (See Example 4 and Exercises 109–112.)

Solving Quadratic Equations

Thus far, we have solved quadratic equations by factoring, the square root property, and completing the square. In this subsection, we derive a formula that can be used to solve *any* quadratic equation. To do this, we solve the general quadratic equation $ax^2 + bx + c = 0$ for x by completing the square. The resulting formula is called the **quadratic formula**. We assume that $a > 0$ and derive this formula as follows.

$$ax^2 + bx + c = 0 \qquad \text{Quadratic equation}$$

$$ax^2 + bx = -c \qquad \text{Subtract } c.$$

$$x^2 + \frac{b}{a}x = -\frac{c}{a} \qquad \text{Divide by } a.$$

$$x^2 + \frac{b}{a}x + \frac{b^2}{4a^2} = -\frac{c}{a} + \frac{b^2}{4a^2} \qquad \text{Add } \left(\frac{b/a}{2}\right)^2 = \frac{b^2}{4a^2}.$$

$$\left(x + \frac{b}{2a}\right)^2 = -\frac{c}{a} + \frac{b^2}{4a^2} \qquad \text{Perfect square trinomial}$$

$$\left(x + \frac{b}{2a}\right)^2 = -\frac{c \cdot 4a}{a \cdot 4a} + \frac{b^2}{4a^2} \qquad \text{Multiply } -\frac{c}{a} \text{ by } \frac{4a}{4a}.$$

$$\left(x + \frac{b}{2a}\right)^2 = -\frac{4ac}{4a^2} + \frac{b^2}{4a^2} \qquad \text{Simplify.}$$

$$\left(x + \frac{b}{2a}\right)^2 = \frac{-4ac + b^2}{4a^2} \qquad \text{Add fractions.}$$

$$\left(x + \frac{b}{2a}\right)^2 = \frac{b^2 - 4ac}{4a^2} \qquad \text{Rewrite.}$$

$$x + \frac{b}{2a} = \pm\sqrt{\frac{b^2 - 4ac}{4a^2}} \qquad \text{Square root property}$$

$$x = -\frac{b}{2a} \pm \sqrt{\frac{b^2 - 4ac}{4a^2}} \qquad \text{Add } -\frac{b}{2a}.$$

$$x = -\frac{b}{2a} \pm \frac{\sqrt{b^2 - 4ac}}{2a} \qquad \text{Property of square roots}$$

$$x = \frac{-b \pm \sqrt{b^2 - 4ac}}{2a} \qquad \text{Combine fractions.}$$

QUADRATIC FORMULA

The solutions to $ax^2 + bx + c = 0$ with $a \neq 0$ are given by

$$x = \frac{-b \pm \sqrt{b^2 - 4ac}}{2a}.$$

NOTE: The quadratic formula can be used to solve *any* quadratic equation. It always "works."

EXAMPLE 1   Solving a quadratic equation having two solutions

Solve the equation $2x^2 - 3x - 1 = 0$. Support your results graphically.

Solution
Symbolic Solution Let $a = 2$, $b = -3$, and $c = -1$ in $2x^2 - 3x - 1 = 0$.

$$x = \frac{-b \pm \sqrt{b^2 - 4ac}}{2a}$$ Quadratic formula

$$x = \frac{-(-3) \pm \sqrt{(-3)^2 - 4(2)(-1)}}{2(2)}$$ Substitute for a, b, and c.

$$x = \frac{3 \pm \sqrt{17}}{4}$$ Simplify.

The solutions are $\frac{3 + \sqrt{17}}{4} \approx 1.78$ and $\frac{3 - \sqrt{17}}{4} \approx -0.28$.

Graphical Solution The graph of $y = 2x^2 - 3x - 1$ is shown in Figure 11.50. Note that the two x-intercepts correspond to the two solutions for $2x^2 - 3x - 1 = 0$. Estimating from this graph, we see that the solutions are approximately -0.25 and 1.75, which supports our symbolic solution. (You could also use a graphing calculator to find the x-intercepts.)

Two Solutions

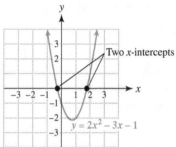

$y = 2x^2 - 3x - 1$

Two x-intercepts

Figure 11.50

Now Try Exercise 9

CRITICAL THINKING

Use the equation and results from Example 1 to evaluate each expression mentally.

$$2\left(\frac{3 + \sqrt{17}}{4}\right)^2 - 3\left(\frac{3 + \sqrt{17}}{4}\right) - 1 \quad \text{and} \quad 2\left(\frac{3 - \sqrt{17}}{4}\right)^2 - 3\left(\frac{3 - \sqrt{17}}{4}\right) - 1$$

EXAMPLE 2   **Solving a quadratic equation having one solution**

Solve the equation $25x^2 + 20x + 4 = 0$. Support your result graphically.

Solution
Symbolic Solution Let $a = 25$, $b = 20$, and $c = 4$ in $25x^2 + 20x + 4 = 0$.

$$x = \frac{-b \pm \sqrt{b^2 - 4ac}}{2a}$$ Quadratic formula

$$= \frac{-20 \pm \sqrt{20^2 - 4(25)(4)}}{2(25)}$$ Substitute for a, b, and c.

$$= \frac{-20 \pm \sqrt{0}}{50}$$ Simplify.

$$= \frac{-20}{50} = -0.4$$ $\sqrt{0} = 0$

There is one solution, -0.4.

Graphical Solution The graph of $y = 25x^2 + 20x + 4$ is shown in Figure 11.51. Note that the one x-intercept, -0.4, corresponds to the solution to $25x^2 + 20x + 4 = 0$.

Now Try Exercise 11

One Solution

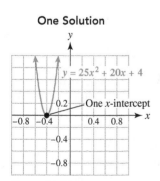

$y = 25x^2 + 20x + 4$

One x-intercept

Figure 11.51

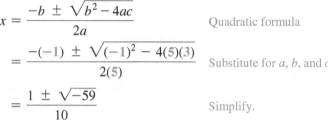

EXAMPLE 3

Recognizing a quadratic equation having no real solutions

Solve the equation $5x^2 - x + 3 = 0$. Support your result graphically.

Solution

Symbolic Solution Let $a = 5$, $b = -1$, and $c = 3$ in $5x^2 - 1x + 3 = 0$.

$$x = \frac{-b \pm \sqrt{b^2 - 4ac}}{2a} \qquad \text{Quadratic formula}$$

$$= \frac{-(-1) \pm \sqrt{(-1)^2 - 4(5)(3)}}{2(5)} \qquad \text{Substitute for } a, b, \text{ and } c.$$

$$= \frac{1 \pm \sqrt{-59}}{10} \qquad \text{Simplify.}$$

No Real Solutions

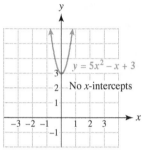

Figure 11.52

There are *no real solutions* to this equation because $\sqrt{-59}$ *is not a real number.* (Later in this section we discuss how to find complex solutions to quadratic equations like this one.)

Graphical Solution The graph of $y = 5x^2 - x + 3$ is shown in Figure 11.52. There are no x-intercepts, indicating that the equation $5x^2 - x + 3 = 0$ has no real solutions.

▌ Now Try Exercise 13

▶ **REAL-WORLD CONNECTION** Earlier in this section we discussed how engineers estimate safe stopping distances for automobiles. In the next example we solve the equation presented in A Look Into Math.

EXAMPLE 4

Modeling stopping distance

If a car's headlights do not illuminate the road beyond 500 feet, estimate a safe nighttime speed limit x for the car by solving $\frac{1}{9}x^2 + \frac{11}{3}x = 500$.

Solution
Begin by subtracting 500 from each side of the given equation.

$$\frac{1}{9}x^2 + \frac{11}{3}x - 500 = 0 \qquad \text{Subtract 500.}$$

To eliminate fractions, multiply each side by the LCD, which is 9. (This step is not necessary, but it makes the problem easier to work.)

$$x^2 + 33x - 4500 = 0 \qquad \text{Multiply by 9.}$$

Now let $a = 1$, $b = 33$, and $c = -4500$ in the quadratic formula.

$$x = \frac{-b \pm \sqrt{b^2 - 4ac}}{2a} \qquad \text{Quadratic formula}$$

$$= \frac{-33 \pm \sqrt{33^2 - 4(1)(-4500)}}{2(1)}$$ Substitute for a, b, and c.

$$= \frac{-33 \pm \sqrt{19{,}089}}{2}$$ Simplify.

The solutions are

$$\frac{-33 + \sqrt{19{,}089}}{2} \approx 52.6 \quad \text{and} \quad \frac{-33 - \sqrt{19{,}089}}{2} \approx -85.6.$$

The negative solution has no physical meaning because negative speeds are not possible. The other solution is 52.6, so an appropriate speed limit might be 50 miles per hour.

Now Try Exercise 109

The Discriminant

The expression $b^2 - 4ac$ in the quadratic formula is called the **discriminant**. It provides information about the number of solutions to a quadratic equation.

READING CHECK

How can you use the discriminant to determine the number of solutions to a quadratic equation?

THE DISCRIMINANT AND QUADRATIC EQUATIONS

To determine the number of solutions to the quadratic equation $ax^2 + bx + c = 0$, evaluate the discriminant $b^2 - 4ac$.

1. If $b^2 - 4ac > 0$, there are two real solutions.
2. If $b^2 - 4ac = 0$, there is one real solution.
3. If $b^2 - 4ac < 0$, there are no real solutions; there are two complex solutions.

GRAPHS AND THE DISCRIMINANT The graph of $y = ax^2 + bx + c$ can be used to determine the sign of the discriminant, $b^2 - 4ac$. Figure 11.53 illustrates several possibilities. For example, in Figure 11.53(a) neither graph with $a > 0$ or $a < 0$ intersects the x-axis. Therefore these graphs indicate that the equation $ax^2 + bx + c = 0$ has no real solutions and that the discriminant must be negative: $b^2 - 4ac < 0$. Figures 11.53(b) and (c) can be done similarly.

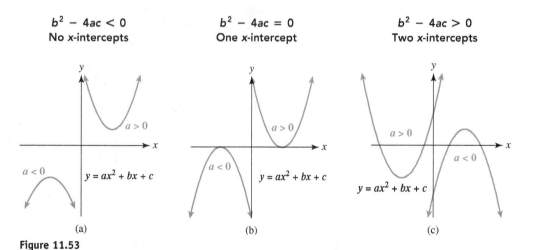

Figure 11.53

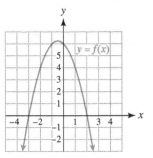

Figure 11.54

EXAMPLE 5 **Analyzing graphs of quadratic functions**

A graph of $f(x) = ax^2 + bx + c$ is shown in Figure 11.54.
(a) State whether $a > 0$ or $a < 0$.
(b) Solve the equation $ax^2 + bx + c = 0$.
(c) Determine whether the discriminant is positive, negative, or zero.

Solution
(a) The parabola opens downward, so $a < 0$.
(b) The graph of $f(x) = ax^2 + bx + c$ intersects the x-axis at -3 and 2. Therefore $f(-3) = 0$ and $f(2) = 0$. The solutions to $ax^2 + bx + c = 0$ are -3 and 2.
(c) There are two solutions, so the discriminant is positive.

Now Try Exercise 33

EXAMPLE 6 **Using the discriminant**

Use the discriminant to determine the number of solutions to $4x^2 + 25 = 20x$. Then solve the equation, using the quadratic formula.

Solution
Write the equation as $4x^2 - 20x + 25 = 0$ so that $a = 4, b = -20$, and $c = 25$. The discriminant evaluates to

$$b^2 - 4ac = (-20)^2 - 4(4)(25) = 0.$$

Thus there is **one real solution**.

$$x = \frac{-b \pm \sqrt{b^2 - 4ac}}{2a} \qquad \text{Quadratic formula}$$

$$= \frac{-(-20) \pm \sqrt{0}}{2(4)} \qquad \text{Substitute.}$$

$$= \frac{20}{8} = 2.5 \qquad \text{Simplify.}$$

The only solution is 2.5.

Now Try Exercise 39(a), (b)

Quadratic Equations Having Complex Solutions

The quadratic equation written as $ax^2 + bx + c = 0$ has no real solutions if the discriminant, $b^2 - 4ac$, is negative. For example, the quadratic equation $x^2 + 4 = 0$ has $a = 1, b = 0$, and $c = 4$. Its discriminant is

$$b^2 - 4ac = 0^2 - 4(1)(4) = -16 < 0,$$

so this equation has no real solutions. However, if we use complex numbers, we can solve this equation as follows.

$$x^2 + 4 = 0 \qquad \text{Given equation}$$

$$x^2 = -4 \qquad \text{Subtract 4.}$$

$$x = \pm\sqrt{-4} \qquad \text{Square root property}$$

$$x = \sqrt{-4} \quad \text{or} \quad x = -\sqrt{-4} \qquad \text{Meaning of } \pm$$

$$x = 2i \quad \text{or} \quad x = -2i \qquad \text{The expression } \sqrt{-a}$$

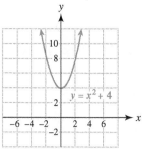

No x-intercepts

Figure 11.55

The solutions are $\pm 2i$. We check each solution to $x^2 + 4 = 0$ as follows.

$$(2i)^2 + 4 = (2)^2 i^2 + 4 = 4(-1) + 4 = 0 \checkmark \quad \text{It checks.}$$
$$(-2i)^2 + 4 = (-2)^2 i^2 + 4 = 4(-1) + 4 = 0 \checkmark \quad \text{It checks.}$$

The fact that the equation $x^2 + 4 = 0$ has only imaginary solutions is apparent from the graph of $y = x^2 + 4$, shown in Figure 11.55. This parabola does not intersect the x-axis, so the equation $x^2 + 4 = 0$ has no real solutions.

These results can be generalized as follows.

> **THE EQUATION $x^2 + k = 0$**
>
> If $k > 0$, the solutions to $x^2 + k = 0$ are given by $x = \pm i\sqrt{k}$.

NOTE: This result is a form of the *square root property* that includes complex solutions.

EXAMPLE 7 Solving a quadratic equation having complex solutions

Solve $x^2 + 5 = 0$.

Solution
The solutions are $\pm i\sqrt{5}$. That is, $x = i\sqrt{5}$ or $x = -i\sqrt{5}$.

Now Try Exercise 57

When $b \neq 0$, the preceding method cannot be used. Consider the quadratic equation $2x^2 + x + 3 = 0$, which has $a = 2$, $b = 1$, and $c = 3$. Its discriminant is negative.

$$b^2 - 4ac = 1^2 - 4(2)(3) = -23 < 0$$

This equation has two complex solutions, as demonstrated in the next example.

EXAMPLE 8 Solving a quadratic equation having complex solutions

Solve $2x^2 + x + 3 = 0$. Write your answer in standard form: $a + bi$.

Solution
Let $a = 2$, $b = 1$, and $c = 3$.

CALCULATOR HELP

To set your calculator in $a + bi$ mode or to access the imaginary unit i, see Appendix A (page AP-7).

$$x = \frac{-b \pm \sqrt{b^2 - 4ac}}{2a} \qquad \text{Quadratic formula}$$

$$= \frac{-1 \pm \sqrt{1^2 - 4(2)(3)}}{2(2)} \qquad \text{Substitute for } a, b, \text{ and } c.$$

$$= \frac{-1 \pm \sqrt{-23}}{4} \qquad \text{Simplify.}$$

$$= \frac{-1 \pm i\sqrt{23}}{4} \qquad \sqrt{-23} = i\sqrt{23}$$

$$= -\frac{1}{4} \pm i\frac{\sqrt{23}}{4} \qquad \text{Property of fractions}$$

The solutions are $-\frac{1}{4} + i\frac{\sqrt{23}}{4}$ and $-\frac{1}{4} - i\frac{\sqrt{23}}{4}$.

Now Try Exercise 73

CRITICAL THINKING

Use the results of Example 8 to evaluate each expression mentally.

$$2\left(-\tfrac{1}{4} + i\tfrac{\sqrt{23}}{4}\right)^2 + \left(-\tfrac{1}{4} + i\tfrac{\sqrt{23}}{4}\right) + 3 \quad \text{and} \quad 2\left(-\tfrac{1}{4} - i\tfrac{\sqrt{23}}{4}\right)^2 + \left(-\tfrac{1}{4} - i\tfrac{\sqrt{23}}{4}\right) + 3$$

Sometimes we can use properties of radicals to simplify a solution to a quadratic equation, as demonstrated in the next example.

EXAMPLE 9 **Solving a quadratic equation having complex solutions**

Solve $\tfrac{3}{4}x^2 + 1 = x$. Write your answer in standard form: $a + bi$.

Solution
Begin by subtracting x from each side of the equation and then multiply by 4 to clear fractions. The resulting equation is $3x^2 - 4x + 4 = 0$. Substitute $a = 3$, $b = -4$, and $c = 4$ in the quadratic formula.

$$
\begin{aligned}
x &= \frac{-b \pm \sqrt{b^2 - 4ac}}{2a} && \text{Quadratic formula} \\[2mm]
&= \frac{-(-4) \pm \sqrt{(-4)^2 - 4(3)(4)}}{2(3)} && \text{Substitute.} \\[2mm]
&= \frac{4 \pm \sqrt{-32}}{6} && \text{Simplify.} \\[2mm]
&= \frac{4 \pm 4i\sqrt{2}}{6} && \sqrt{-32} = i\sqrt{32} = i\sqrt{16}\sqrt{2} = 4i\sqrt{2} \\[2mm]
&= \frac{2}{3} \pm \frac{2}{3}i\sqrt{2} && \text{Property of fractions; simplify.}
\end{aligned}
$$

Now Try Exercise 79

In the next example, we use completing the square to obtain complex solutions.

EXAMPLE 10 **Completing the square to find complex solutions**

Solve $x(x + 2) = -2$ by completing the square.

Solution
After applying the distributive property, we obtain the equation $x^2 + 2x = -2$. Because $b = 2$, add $\left(\tfrac{b}{2}\right)^2 = \left(\tfrac{2}{2}\right)^2 = 1$ to each side of the equation.

$$
\begin{aligned}
x^2 + 2x &= -2 && \text{Equation to be solved} \\
x^2 + 2x + 1 &= -2 + 1 && \text{Add 1 to each side.} \\
(x + 1)^2 &= -1 && \text{Perfect square trinomial; add.} \\
x + 1 &= \pm\sqrt{-1} && \text{Square root property} \\
x + 1 &= \pm i && \sqrt{-1} = i, \text{ the imaginary unit} \\
x &= -1 \pm i && \text{Add } -1 \text{ to each side.}
\end{aligned}
$$

The solutions are $-1 + i$ and $-1 - i$.

Now Try Exercise 91

11.4 Putting It All Together

CONCEPT	EXPLANATION	EXAMPLES
Quadratic Formula	The quadratic formula can be used to solve *any* quadratic equation written as $ax^2 + bx + c = 0$. The solutions are given by $$x = \frac{-b \pm \sqrt{b^2 - 4ac}}{2a}.$$	For the equation $$2x^2 - 3x + 1 = 0$$ with $a = 2$, $b = -3$, and $c = 1$, the solutions are $$\frac{-(-3) \pm \sqrt{(-3)^2 - 4(2)(1)}}{2(2)} = \frac{3 \pm \sqrt{1}}{4} = 1, \frac{1}{2}.$$
The Discriminant	The expression $b^2 - 4ac$ is called the discriminant. 1. $b^2 - 4ac > 0$ indicates two real solutions. 2. $b^2 - 4ac = 0$ indicates one real solution. 3. $b^2 - 4ac < 0$ indicates no real solutions; rather, there are two complex solutions.	For the equation $$x^2 + 4x - 1 = 0$$ with $a = 1$, $b = 4$, and $c = -1$, the discriminant is $$b^2 - 4ac = 4^2 - 4(1)(-1) = 20 > 0,$$ indicating two real solutions.
Quadratic Formula and Complex Solutions	If the discriminant is negative $(b^2 - 4ac < 0)$, the two solutions are complex numbers that are not real numbers. If $k > 0$, the solutions to $x^2 + k = 0$ are given by $x = \pm i\sqrt{k}$.	Solve $2x^2 - x + 3 = 0$. $$x = \frac{-(-1) \pm \sqrt{(-1)^2 - 4(2)(3)}}{2(2)}$$ $$= \frac{1 \pm \sqrt{-23}}{4} = \frac{1}{4} \pm i\frac{\sqrt{23}}{4}$$ $x^2 + 7 = 0$ is equivalent to $x = \pm i\sqrt{7}$.

Three Ways to Solve $x^2 - x - 2 = 0$

Symbolic Solution

Solve $x^2 - x - 2 = 0$.

$$x = \frac{-(-1) \pm \sqrt{(-1)^2 - 4(1)(-2)}}{2(1)}$$

$$x = \frac{1 \pm 3}{2}$$

$$x = 2, -1$$

Solutions are -1 and 2.

Numerical Solution

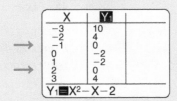

$x^2 - x - 2 = 0$ when
$x = -1$ or 2.

Graphical Solution

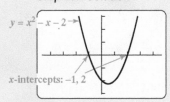

The x-intercepts are -1 and 2.

11.4 Exercises

CONCEPTS AND VOCABULARY

1. What is the quadratic formula used for?

2. What basic algebraic technique is used to derive the quadratic formula?

3. Write the discriminant.

4. If the discriminant evaluates to 0, what does that indicate about the quadratic equation?

5. Name four symbolic techniques for solving a quadratic equation.

6. Does every quadratic equation have at least one real solution? Explain.

7. Solve $x^2 - k = 0$, if $k > 0$.

8. Solve $x^2 + k = 0$, if $k > 0$.

THE QUADRATIC FORMULA

Exercises 9–14: Use the quadratic formula to solve the equation. Support your result graphically. If there are no real solutions, say so.

9. $2x^2 + 11x - 6 = 0$ **10.** $x^2 + 2x - 24 = 0$

11. $-x^2 + 2x - 1 = 0$ **12.** $3x^2 - x + 1 = 0$

13. $-2x^2 + x - 1 = 0$ **14.** $-x^2 + 4x - 4 = 0$

Exercises 15–32: Solve by using the quadratic formula. If there are no real solutions, say so.

15. $x^2 - 6x - 16 = 0$ **16.** $2x^2 - 9x + 7 = 0$

17. $4x^2 - x - 1 = 0$ **18.** $-x^2 + 2x + 1 = 0$

19. $-3x^2 + 2x - 1 = 0$ **20.** $x^2 + x + 3 = 0$

21. $36x^2 - 36x + 9 = 0$ **22.** $4x^2 - 5.6x + 1.96 = 0$

23. $2x(x - 3) = 2$ **24.** $x(x + 1) + x = 5$

25. $(x - 1)(x + 1) + 2 = 4x$

26. $\frac{1}{2}(x - 6) = x^2 + 1$ **27.** $\frac{1}{2}x(x + 1) = 2x^2 - \frac{3}{2}$

28. $\frac{1}{2}x^2 - \frac{1}{4}x + \frac{1}{2} = x$ **29.** $2x(x - 1) = 7$

30. $3x(x - 4) = 4$ **31.** $-3x^2 + 10x - 5 = 0$

32. $-2x^2 + 4x - 1 = 0$

THE DISCRIMINANT

Exercises 33–38: A graph of $y = ax^2 + bx + c$ is shown.
(a) State whether $a > 0$ or $a < 0$.
(b) Solve $ax^2 + bx + c = 0$, if possible.
(c) Determine whether the discriminant is positive, negative, or zero.

33.
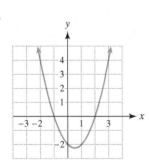

34.
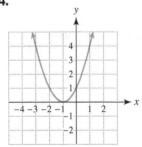

35.
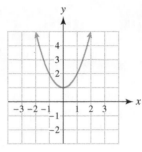

36.
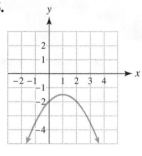

37.
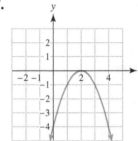

38.
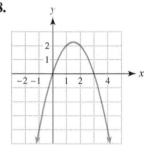

Exercises 39–46: Do the following for the given equation.
(a) Evaluate the discriminant.
(b) How many real solutions are there?
(c) Support your answer for part (b) graphically.

39. $3x^2 + x - 2 = 0$ **40.** $5x^2 - 13x + 6 = 0$

41. $x^2 - 4x + 4 = 0$ **42.** $\frac{1}{4}x^2 + 4 = 2x$

43. $\frac{1}{2}x^2 + \frac{3}{2}x + 2 = 0$ **44.** $x - 3 = 2x^2$

45. $x(x + 3) = 3$

46. $(4x - 1)(x - 3) = -25$

Exercises 47–56: Use the quadratic formula to find any x-intercepts on the graph of the equation.

47. $y = x^2 - 2x - 1$ **48.** $y = x^2 + 3x + 1$

49. $y = -2x^2 - x + 3$ **50.** $y = -3x^2 - x + 4$

51. $y = x^2 + x + 5$ **52.** $y = 3x^2 - 2x + 5$

53. $y = x^2 + 9$ **54.** $y = x^2 + 11$

55. $y = 3x^2 + 4x - 2$ **56.** $y = 4x^2 - 2x - 3$

COMPLEX SOLUTIONS

Exercises 57–88: Solve the equation. Write complex solutions in standard form.

57. $x^2 + 9 = 0$ **58.** $x^2 + 16 = 0$

59. $x^2 + 80 = 0$ **60.** $x^2 + 20 = 0$

61. $x^2 + \frac{1}{4} = 0$ **62.** $x^2 + \frac{9}{4} = 0$

63. $16x^2 + 9 = 0$ **64.** $25x^2 + 36 = 0$

65. $x^2 = -6$ **66.** $x^2 = -75$

67. $x^2 - 3 = 0$ **68.** $x^2 - 8 = 0$

69. $x^2 + 2 = 0$ **70.** $x^2 + 4 = 0$

71. $x^2 - x + 2 = 0$ **72.** $x^2 + 2x + 3 = 0$

73. $2x^2 + 3x + 4 = 0$ **74.** $3x^2 - x = 1$

75. $x^2 + 1 = 4x$ **76.** $3x^2 + 2 = x$

77. $x(x + 1) = -2$ **78.** $x(x - 4) = -8$

79. $5x^2 + 2x + 4 = 0$ **80.** $7x^2 - 2x + 4 = 0$

81. $\frac{1}{2}x^2 + \frac{3}{4}x = -1$ **82.** $-\frac{1}{3}x^2 + x = 2$

83. $x(x + 2) = x - 4$ **84.** $x - 5 = 2x(2x + 1)$

85. $x(2x - 1) = 1 + x$ **86.** $2x = x(3 - 4x)$

87. $x^2 = x(1 - x) - 2$ **88.** $2x^2 = 2x(5 - x) - 8$

COMPLETING THE SQUARE

Exercises 89–94: Solve by completing the square.

89. $x^2 + 2x + 4 = 0$ **90.** $x^2 - 2x + 2 = 0$

91. $x(x + 4) = -5$ **92.** $x(8 - x) = 25$

93. $2x^2 - 4x + 6 = 0$ **94.** $2x^2 + 2x + 1 = 0$

YOU DECIDE THE METHOD

Exercises 95–108: Find exact solutions to the quadratic equation, using a method of your choice. Explain why you chose the method you did. Answers may vary.

95. $x^2 - 3x + 2 = 0$ **96.** $x^2 + 2x + 1 = 0$

97. $0.5x^2 - 1.75x = 1$ **98.** $\frac{3}{5}x^2 + \frac{9}{10}x = \frac{3}{5}$

99. $x^2 - 5x + 2 = 0$ **100.** $2x^2 - x - 4 = 0$

101. $2x^2 + x = -8$ **102.** $4x^2 = 2x - 3$

103. $4x^2 - 1 = 0$ **104.** $3x^2 = 9$

105. $3x^2 + 6 = 0$ **106.** $4x^2 + 7 = 0$

107. $9x^2 + 1 = 6x$ **108.** $10x^2 + 15x = 25$

APPLICATIONS

Exercises 109–112: Modeling Stopping Distance (Refer to Example 4.) Use $d = \frac{1}{9}x^2 + \frac{11}{3}x$ to find a safe speed x for the following stopping distances d.

109. 42 feet

110. 152 feet

111. 390 feet

112. 726 feet

113. *Global Music Sales* (Refer to Example 9, Section 11.3.) From 1989 to 2009, global music sales S of compact discs and tapes in billions of dollars can be modeled by $S(x) = -0.095x^2 + 1.85x + 6$, where x is years after 1989. Estimate symbolically when sales were $12 billion. (*Source: RIAA, Bain Analysis.*)

114. *Monthly Facebook Visitors* The number of *unique* monthly Facebook visitors in millions x years after 2006 can be modeled by

$$V(x) = 10.75x^2 - 24x + 35.$$

Assuming current trends continue, estimate symbolically when this number might reach 530 million.

115. *Groupon's Growth* Groupon negotiates coupons for items discounted 50–90% off by having thousands of subscribers. As a result, it experienced a dramatic increase in value from October 2010 to March 2011. The function

$$G(x) = 0.4x^2 + 1.8x + 6$$

approximates the company's value in billions of dollars x months after October 2010.
(a) Evaluate $G(0)$. Interpret the result.
(b) Determine when Groupon's value was about $15 billion.

116. *Foursquare Users* Foursquare provides a service that allows your friends to know your whereabouts by "checking in." From March 2010 to March 2011, it experienced amazing growth. The function

$$F(x) = \frac{1}{18}x^2 - \frac{1}{12}x + \frac{1}{2}$$

approximates Foursquare users in millions x months after March 2010.
(a) Evaluate $F(3)$. Interpret the result.
(b) Determine symbolically when Foursquare had 4.25 million users.

117. *U.S. AIDS Deaths* The cumulative numbers in thousands of AIDS deaths from 1984 through 1994 may be modeled by

$$f(x) = 2.39x^2 + 5.04x + 5.1,$$

where $x = 0$ corresponds to 1984, $x = 1$ corresponds to 1985, and so on until $x = 10$ corresponds to 1994. See the accompanying graph. Use the formula for $f(x)$ to estimate the year when the total number of AIDS deaths reached 200 thousand. Compare your result with that shown in the graph.

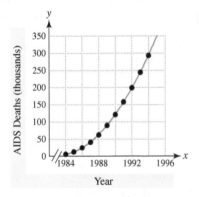

118. *Canoeing* A camper paddles a canoe 2 miles downstream in a river that has a 2-mile-per-hour current. To return to camp, the canoeist travels upstream on a different branch of the river. It is 4 miles long and has a 1-mile-per-hour current. The total trip (both ways) takes 3 hours. Find the average speed of the canoe in still water. (*Hint:* Time equals distance divided by rate.)

119. *Airplane Speed* A pilot flies 500 miles against a 20-mile-per-hour wind. On the next day, the pilot flies back home with a 10-mile-per-hour tail wind. The total trip (both ways) takes 4 hours. Find the speed of the airplane without a wind.

120. *Distance* Two cars leave an intersection, one traveling south and one traveling east, as shown in the figure at the top of the next column. After 1 hour the

two cars are 50 miles apart and the car traveling east has traveled 10 miles farther than the car traveling south. How far did each car travel?

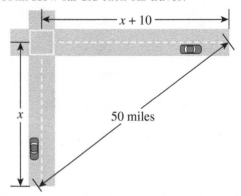

121. *Screen Dimensions* The width of a rectangular computer screen is 3 inches more than its height. If the area of the screen is 154 square inches, find its dimensions
(a) graphically,
(b) numerically, and
(c) symbolically.

122. *Sidewalk Dimension* A rectangular flower garden in a park is 30 feet wide and 40 feet long. A sidewalk around the perimeter of the garden is being planned, as shown in the figure. The gardener has enough money to pour 624 square feet of cement sidewalk. Find the width of the sidewalk.

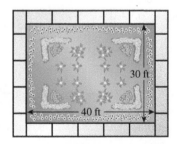

123. *Modeling Water Flow* When water runs out of a hole in a cylindrical container, the height of the water in the container can often be modeled by a quadratic function. The data in the table show the height y in centimeters of water at 30-second intervals in a metal can that has a small hole in it.

Time	0	30	60	90
Height	16	11.9	8.4	5.3

Time	120	150	180
Height	3.1	1.4	0.5

These data are modeled by

$$f(x) = 0.0004x^2 - 0.15x + 16.$$

(a) Explain why a linear function would not be appropriate for modeling these data.

(b) Use the table to estimate the time at which the height was 7 centimeters.

(c) Use the quadratic formula to solve part (b).

124. *Hospitals* The general trend in the number of hospitals in the United States from 1945 through 2000 is shown in the graph and can be modeled by

$$f(x) = -1.38x^2 + 84x + 5865,$$

where $x = 5$ corresponds to 1945, $x = 10$ corresponds to 1950, and so on until $x = 60$ represents 2000.

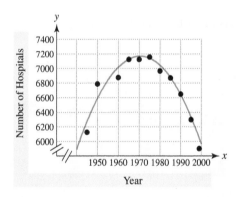

Year

(a) Describe any trends in the numbers of hospitals from 1945 to 2000.

(b) What information does the vertex give?

(c) Use the formula for $f(x)$ to estimate the number of hospitals in 1970. Compare your result with that shown in the graph.

(d) Use the formula for $f(x)$ to estimate the year (or years) when there were 6300 hospitals. Compare your result with that shown in the graph.

WRITING ABOUT MATHEMATICS

125. Explain how the discriminant $b^2 - 4ac$ can be used to determine the number of solutions to a quadratic equation.

126. Let $f(x) = ax^2 + bx + c$ be a quadratic function. If you know the value of $b^2 - 4ac$, what information does this give you about the graph of f? Explain your answer.

SECTIONS 11.3 and 11.4 — Checking Basic Concepts

1. Solve the quadratic equation $2x^2 - 7x + 3 = 0$ symbolically and graphically.

2. Use the square root property to solve $x^2 = 5$.

3. Complete the square to solve $x^2 - 4x + 1 = 0$.

4. Solve the equation $x^2 + y^2 = 1$ for y.

5. Use the quadratic formula to solve each equation.
   (a) $2x^2 = 3x + 1$
   (b) $9x^2 - 24x + 16 = 0$
   (c) $x^2 + x + 2 = 0$

6. Calculate the discriminant for each equation and give the number of *real* solutions.
   (a) $x^2 - 5x + 5 = 0$
   (b) $2x^2 - 5x + 4 = 0$
   (c) $49x^2 - 56x + 16 = 0$

7. Solve each equation.
   (a) $x^2 + 5 = 0$
   (b) $x^2 + x + 3 = 0$

CHAPTER 11   Summary

SECTION 11.1 ■ QUADRATIC FUNCTIONS AND THEIR GRAPHS

Quadratic Function Any quadratic function f can be written as

$$f(x) = ax^2 + bx + c \quad (a \neq 0).$$

Graph of a Quadratic Function Its graph is a parabola that is wider than the graph of $y = x^2$ if $0 < |a| < 1$, and narrower than the graph of $y = x^2$ if $|a| > 1$. The y-intercept is c.

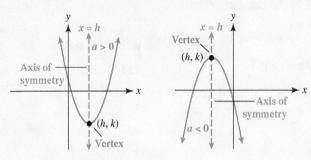

Axis of Symmetry The parabola is symmetric with respect to this vertical line. The axis of symmetry passes through the vertex. Its equation is $x = -\frac{b}{2a}$.

Vertex Formula The x-coordinate of the vertex is $-\frac{b}{2a}$.

Example: Let $y = x^2 - 4x + 1$ with $a = 1$ and $b = -4$.

$$x = -\frac{-4}{2(1)} = 2 \quad \text{and} \quad y = 2^2 - 4(2) + 1 = -3. \text{ The vertex is } (2, -3).$$

SECTION 11.2 ■ PARABOLAS AND MODELING

Vertical and Horizontal Translations Let h and k be positive numbers.

To graph	*shift the graph of $y = x^2$ by k units*
$y = x^2 + k$	upward.
$y = x^2 - k$	downward.

To graph	*shift the graph of $y = x^2$ by h units*
$y = (x - h)^2$	right.
$y = (x + h)^2$	left.

Example: Compared to $y = x^2$, the graph of $y = (x - 1)^2 + 2$ is translated right 1 unit and upward 2 units.

Vertex Form Any quadratic function can be expressed as $f(x) = a(x - h)^2 + k$. In this form the point (h, k) is the vertex. A quadratic function can be put in this form by completing the square or by applying the vertex formula.

Example: $y = x^2 + 10x - 4$ Given equation

$\qquad = (x^2 + 10x + 25) - 25 - 4$ $\left(\frac{b}{2}\right)^2 = \left(\frac{10}{2}\right)^2 = 25$; complete the square.

$\qquad = (x + 5)^2 - 29$ Perfect square trinomial; add.

The vertex is $(-5, -29)$.

SECTION 11.3 ■ QUADRATIC EQUATIONS

Quadratic Equations Any quadratic equation can be written as $ax^2 + bx + c = 0$ and can have no real solutions, one real solution, or two real solutions. These solutions correspond to the x-intercepts for the graph of $y = ax^2 + bx + c$.

Example: $x^2 + x - 2 = 0$
$(x + 2)(x - 1) = 0$
$x = -2$ or $x = 1$

The solutions are -2 and 1.
See the graph to the right.

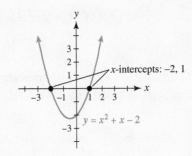

Completing the Square Write the equation in the form $x^2 + bx = d$. Complete the square by adding $\left(\frac{b}{2}\right)^2$ to each side of the equation.

Example: $x^2 - 8x = 3$
$x^2 - 8x + 16 = 3 + 16$ Add $\left(\frac{-8}{2}\right)^2 = 16$ to each side.
$(x - 4)^2 = 19$ Perfect square trinomial
$x - 4 = \pm\sqrt{19}$ Square root property
$x = 4 \pm \sqrt{19}$ Add 4 to each side.

SECTION 11.4 ■ THE QUADRATIC FORMULA

The Quadratic Formula The solutions to $ax^2 + bx + c = 0$ $(a \neq 0)$ are given by

$$x = \frac{-b \pm \sqrt{b^2 - 4ac}}{2a}.$$

Example: Solve $2x^2 + 3x - 1 = 0$ by letting $a = 2$, $b = 3$, and $c = -1$.

$$x = \frac{-3 \pm \sqrt{3^2 - 4(2)(-1)}}{2(2)} = \frac{-3 \pm \sqrt{17}}{4} \approx 0.28, -1.78$$

The Discriminant The expression $b^2 - 4ac$ is called the discriminant. If $b^2 - 4ac > 0$, there are two real solutions; if $b^2 - 4ac = 0$, there is one real solution; and if $b^2 - 4ac < 0$, there are no real solutions—rather there are two complex solutions.

Example: For $2x^2 + 3x - 1 = 0$, the discriminant is

$$b^2 - 4ac = 3^2 - 4(2)(-1) = 17 > 0.$$

There are two real solutions to this quadratic equation, as shown in the previous example.

Quadratic Equations with Complex Solutions A quadratic equation sometimes has no real solutions.

Example: $x^2 + 4 = 0$
$x^2 = -4$ Subtract 4 from each side.
$x = \pm 2i$ Square root property; two complex solutions

CHAPTER 11   Review Exercises

SECTION 11.1

Exercises 1 and 2: Identify the vertex, axis of symmetry, and whether the parabola opens upward or downward.

1.

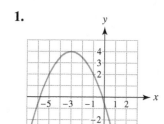

2.

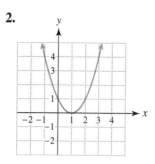

Exercises 3–6: Do the following.
  (a) *Graph f.*
  (b) *Identify the vertex and axis of symmetry.*
  (c) *Evaluate f(x) at the given value of x.*

3. $f(x) = x^2 - 2$, $x = -1$

4. $f(x) = -x^2 + 4x - 3$, $x = 3$

5. $f(x) = -\frac{1}{2}x^2 + x + \frac{3}{2}$, $x = -2$

6. $f(x) = 2x^2 + 8x + 5$, $x = -3$

7. Find the minimum y-value located on the graph of $y = 2x^2 - 6x + 1$.

8. Find the maximum y-value located on the graph of $y = -3x^2 + 2x - 5$.

Exercises 9–12: Find the vertex of the parabola.

9. $f(x) = x^2 - 4x - 2$ **10.** $f(x) = 5 - x^2$

11. $f(x) = -\frac{1}{4}x^2 + x + 1$ **12.** $f(x) = 2 + 2x + x^2$

SECTION 11.2

Exercises 13–18: Do the following.
  (a) *Graph f.*
  (b) *Compare the graph of f with the graph of $y = x^2$.*

13. $f(x) = x^2 + 2$ **14.** $f(x) = 3x^2$

15. $f(x) = (x - 2)^2$ **16.** $f(x) = (x + 1)^2 - 3$

17. $f(x) = \frac{1}{2}(x + 1)^2 + 2$

18. $f(x) = 2(x - 1)^2 - 3$

19. Write the vertex form of a parabola with $a = -4$ and vertex $(2, -5)$.

20. Write the vertex form of a parabola that opens downward with vertex $(-4, 6)$. Assume that $a = \pm 1$.

Exercises 21–24: Write the equation in vertex form. Identify the vertex.

21. $y = x^2 + 4x - 7$ **22.** $y = x^2 - 7x + 1$

23. $y = 2x^2 - 3x - 8$ **24.** $y = 3x^2 + 6x - 2$

Exercises 25 and 26: Find a value for the constant a so that $f(x) = ax^2 - 1$ models the data.

25.

x	1	2	3
$f(x)$	2	11	26

26.

x	-1	0	1
$f(x)$	$-\frac{3}{4}$	-1	$-\frac{3}{4}$

Exercises 27 and 28: Write $f(x)$ in the form given by $f(x) = ax^2 + bx + c$. Identify the y-intercept on the graph of f.

27. $f(x) = -5(x - 3)^2 + 4$

28. $f(x) = 3(x + 2)^2 - 4$

SECTION 11.3

Exercises 29–32: Use the graph of $y = ax^2 + bx + c$ to solve $ax^2 + bx + c = 0$.

29.

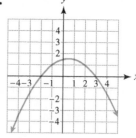

30.

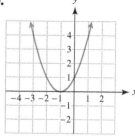

31.

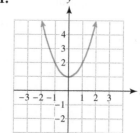

32.

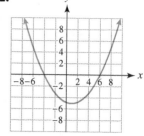

Exercises 33 and 34: A table of $y = ax^2 + bx + c$ is given. Solve $ax^2 + bx + c = 0$.

33.

X	Y1
-20	250
-15	100
-10	0
-5	-50
0	-50
5	0
10	100

Y1▪X^2+5X−50

34.

X	Y1
-.75	2
-.5	0
-.25	-1
0	-1
.25	0
.5	2
.75	5

Y1▪8X^2+2X−1

Exercises 35–38: Solve the quadratic equation
  (a) graphically and
  (b) numerically.

35. $x^2 - 5x - 50 = 0$ **36.** $\frac{1}{2}x^2 + x - \frac{3}{2} = 0$

37. $\frac{1}{4}x^2 + \frac{1}{2}x = 2$ **38.** $\frac{1}{2}x + \frac{3}{4} = \frac{1}{4}x^2$

Exercises 39–42: Solve by factoring.

39. $x^2 + x - 20 = 0$ **40.** $x^2 + 11x + 24 = 0$

41. $15x^2 - 4x - 4 = 0$ **42.** $7x^2 - 25x + 12 = 0$

Exercises 43–46: Use the square root property to solve.

43. $x^2 = 100$ **44.** $3x^2 = \frac{1}{3}$

45. $4x^2 - 6 = 0$ **46.** $5x^2 = x^2 - 4$

Exercises 47–50: Solve by completing the square.

47. $x^2 + 6x = -2$ **48.** $x^2 - 4x = 6$

49. $x^2 - 2x - 5 = 0$ **50.** $2x^2 + 6x - 1 = 0$

Exercises 51 and 52: Solve for the specified variable.

51. $F = \dfrac{k}{(R + r)^2}$ for R **52.** $2x^2 + 3y^2 = 12$ for y

SECTION 11.4

Exercises 53–58: Use the quadratic formula to solve.

53. $x^2 - 9x + 18 = 0$ **54.** $x^2 - 24x + 143 = 0$

55. $6x^2 + x = 1$ **56.** $5x^2 + 1 = 5x$

57. $x(x - 8) = 5$ **58.** $2x(2 - x) = 3 - 2x$

Exercises 59–64: Solve by any method.

59. $x^2 - 4 = 0$ **60.** $4x^2 - 1 = 0$

61. $2x^2 + 15 = 11x$ **62.** $2x^2 + 15 = 13x$

63. $x(5 - x) = 2x + 1$ **64.** $-2x(x - 1) = x - \frac{1}{2}$

Exercises 65–68: A graph of $y = ax^2 + bx + c$ is shown.
  (a) State whether $a > 0$ or $a < 0$.
  (b) Solve $ax^2 + bx + c = 0$.
  (c) Determine whether the discriminant is positive, negative, or zero.

65.

66.

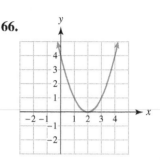

67.

68.

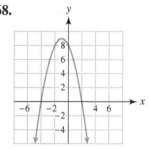

Exercises 69–72: Do the following for the given equation.
  (a) Evaluate the discriminant.
  (b) How many real solutions are there?
  (c) Support your answer for part (b) graphically.

69. $2x^2 - 3x + 1 = 0$ **70.** $7x^2 + 2x - 5 = 0$

71. $3x^2 + x + 2 = 0$

72. $4.41x^2 - 12.6x + 9 = 0$

Exercises 73–76: Solve. Write any complex solutions in standard form.

73. $x^2 + x + 5 = 0$ **74.** $2x^2 + 8 = 0$

75. $2x^2 = x - 1$ **76.** $7x^2 = 2x - 5$

APPLICATIONS

95. *Construction* A rain gutter is being fabricated from a flat sheet of metal so that the cross section of the gutter is a rectangle, as shown in the accompanying figure. The width of the metal sheet is 12 inches.

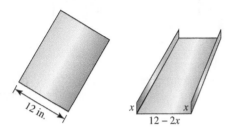

(a) Write a formula $f(x)$ that gives the area of the cross section.

(b) To hold the greatest amount of rainwater, the cross section should have maximum area. Find the dimensions that result in this maximum.

96. *Height of a Stone* Suppose that a stone is thrown upward with an initial velocity of 44 feet per second (30 miles per hour) and is released 4 feet above the ground. Its height h in feet after t seconds is given by

$$h(t) = -16t^2 + 44t + 4.$$

(a) When does the stone reach a height of 32 feet?

(b) After how many seconds does the stone reach maximum height? Estimate this height.

97. *Maximizing Revenue* Suppose that hotel rooms cost $90 per night. However, for a group rate the management is considering reducing the cost of a room by $3 for every room rented.

(a) Write a formula $f(x)$ that gives the revenue from renting x rooms at the group rate.

(b) Graph f in [0, 30, 5] by [0, 800, 100].

(c) How many rooms should be rented to receive revenue of $600?

(d) How many rooms should be rented to maximize revenue?

98. *Numbers* The product of two numbers is 143. One number is 2 more than the other.

(a) Write a quadratic equation whose solution gives the smaller number x.

(b) Solve the equation.

99. *Braking Distance* On dry pavement a safe braking distance d in feet for a car traveling x miles per hour is $d = \frac{x^2}{12}$. For each distance d, find x. (*Source:* F. Mannering, *Principles of Highway Engineering and Traffic Control.*)

(a) $d = 144$ feet   (b) $d = 300$ feet

100. *U.S. Energy Consumption* From 1950 to 1970 per capita consumption of energy in millions of Btu can be modeled by $f(x) = \frac{1}{4}(x - 1950)^2 + 220$, where x is the year. (*Source:* Department of Energy.)

(a) Find and interpret the vertex.

(b) Graph f in [1950, 1970, 5] by [200, 350, 25]. What happened to energy consumption during this time period?

(c) Use f to predict the consumption in 2010. Actual consumption was 321 million Btu. Did f provide a good model for 2010? Explain.

101. *Screens* A square computer screen has an area of 123 square inches. Approximate its dimensions to the nearest tenth of an inch.

102. *Flying a Kite* A kite is being flown, as illustrated in the accompanying figure. If 130 feet of string have been let out, find the value of x.

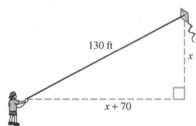

103. *Area* A uniform strip of grass is to be planted around a rectangular swimming pool, as illustrated in the accompanying figure on the next page. The swimming pool is 30 feet wide and 50 feet long. If there is only enough grass seed to cover 250 square feet, estimate the width x that the strip of grass should be.

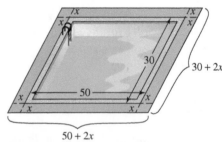

104. *Dimensions of a Cone* The volume V of a cone is given by $V = \frac{1}{3}\pi r^2 h$, where r is its base radius and h is its height. See the accompanying figure. If $h = 20$ inches and the volume of the cone must be between 750 and 1700 cubic inches, inclusively, estimate, to the nearest tenth of an inch, possible values for r.

CHAPTER 11   Extended and Discovery Exercises

MODELING DATA WITH A QUADRATIC FUNCTION

1. *Survival Rate of Birds* The survival rate of sparrow-hawks varies according to their age. The following table summarizes the results of one study by listing the age in years and the percentage of birds that survived the previous year. For example, 52% of sparrowhawks that reached age 6 lived to be 7 years old. (*Source:* D. Brown and P. Rothery, *Models in Biology.*)

Age	1	2	3	4	5
Percent (%)	45	60	71	67	67

Age	6	7	8	9
Percent (%)	61	52	30	25

(a) Try to explain the relationship between age and the likelihood of surviving the next year.

(b) Make a scatterplot of the data. What type of function might model the data? Explain.

(c) Graph each function. Which of the following functions models the data better?

$$f_1(x) = -3.57x + 71.1$$

$$f_2(x) = -2.07x^2 + 17.1x + 33$$

(d) Use one of these functions to estimate the likelihood of a 5.5-year-old sparrowhawk surviving for 1 more year.

2. *Photosynthesis and Temperature* Photosynthesis is the process by which plants turn sunlight into energy. At very cold temperatures photosynthesis may halt even though the sun is shining. In one study the efficiency of photosynthesis for an Antarctic species of grass was investigated. The following table lists results for various temperatures. The temperature x is in degrees Celsius, and the efficiency y is given as a percent. The purpose of the research was to determine the temperature at which photosynthesis is most efficient. (*Source:* D. Brown.)

x (°C)	−1.5	0	2.5	5	7	10	12
y (%)	33	46	55	80	87	93	95

x (°C)	15	17	20	22	25	27	30
y(%)	91	89	77	72	54	46	34

(a) Plot the data.

(b) What type of function might model these data? Explain your reasoning.

(c) Find a function f that models the data.

(d) Use f to estimate the temperature at which photosynthesis is most efficient in this type of grass.

TRANSLATIONS OF PARABOLAS IN COMPUTER GRAPHICS

Exercises 3 and 4: In older video games with two-dimensional graphics, the background is often translated to give the illusion that a character in the game is moving. The simple scene on the left shows a mountain and an airplane. To make it appear that the airplane is flying, the mountain can be translated to the left, as shown in the figure on the right. (*Reference:* C. Pokorny and C. Gerald, *Computer Graphics.*)

3. *Video Games* Suppose that the mountain in the figure on the left is modeled by $f(x) = -0.4x^2 + 4$ and that the airplane is located at the point $(1, 5)$.

(a) Graph f in $[-4, 4, 1]$ by $[0, 6, 1]$, where the units are kilometers. Plot the point $(1, 5)$ to show the location of the airplane.

(b) Assume that the airplane is moving horizontally to the right at 0.2 kilometer per second. To give a video game player the illusion that the airplane is moving, graph the image of the mountain and the position of the airplane after 10 seconds.

4. *Video Games* (Refer to Exercise 3.) Discuss how you could create the illusion of the airplane moving to the left and gaining altitude as it passes over the mountain. Try to perform a translation of this type. Explain your reasoning.

Exercises 5–8: Factoring and the Discriminant If the discriminant of the trinomial $ax^2 + bx + c$ with integer coefficients is a perfect square, then it can be factored. For example, on the one hand, the discriminant of $6x^2 + x - 2$ is

$$1^2 - 4(6)(-2) = 49,$$

which is a perfect square ($7^2 = 49$), so we can factor the trinomial as

$$6x^2 + x - 2 = (2x - 1)(3x + 2).$$

On the other hand, the discriminant for $x^2 + x - 1$ is

$$1^2 - 4(1)(-1) = 5,$$

which is not a perfect square, so we cannot factor this trinomial by using integers as coefficients. Similarly, if the discriminant is negative, the trinomial cannot be factored by using integer coefficients. Use the discriminant to predict whether the trinomial can be factored. Then test your prediction.

5. $10x^2 - x - 3$ **6.** $4x^2 - 3x - 6$

7. $3x^2 + 2x - 2$ **8.** $2x^2 + x + 3$

Exercises 9–14: *Polynomial Inequalities* The solution set for a polynomial inequality can be found by first determining the boundary numbers. For example, to solve $f(x) = x^3 - 4x > 0$ begin by solving $x^3 - 4x = 0$. The solutions (boundary numbers) are $-2, 0$, and 2. The function $f(x) = x^3 - 4x$ is either only positive or only negative on intervals between consecutive zeros. To determine the solution set, we can evaluate test values for each interval as shown below.

Interval	Test Value	$f(x) = x^3 - 4x$
$(-\infty, -2)$	$x = -3$	$f(-3) = -15 < 0$
$(-2, 0)$	$x = -1$	$f(-1) = 3 > 0$
$(0, 2)$	$x = 1$	$f(1) = -3 < 0$
$(2, \infty)$	$x = 3$	$f(3) = 15 > 0$

$[-6, 6, 1]$ by $[-4, 4, 1]$

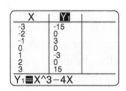
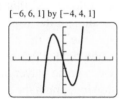

We can see that $f(x) > 0$ for $(-2, 0) \cup (2, \infty)$. These results are also supported graphically in the figure on the right above, where the graph of f is above the x-axis when $-2 < x < 0$ or when $x > 2$.

Use these concepts to solve the polynomial inequality.

9. $x^3 - x^2 - 6x > 0$

10. $x^3 - 3x^2 + 2x < 0$

11. $x^3 - 7x^2 + 14x \leq 8$

12. $9x - x^3 \geq 0$

13. $x^4 - 5x^2 + 4 > 0$

14. $1 < x^4$

Exercises 15–20: *Rational Inequalities* Rational inequalities can be solved using many of the same techniques that are used to solve other types of inequalities. However, there is one important difference. For a rational inequality, the boundary between greater than and less than can be either an x-value where equality occurs or an x-value where a rational expression is undefined. For example, consider the inequality $f(x) = \frac{2 - x}{2x} > 0$. The solution to the equation $\frac{2 - x}{2x} = 0$ is 2. The rational expression $\frac{2 - x}{2x}$ is undefined when $x = 0$. Therefore we select test values on the intervals $(-\infty, 0)$, $(0, 2)$, and $(2, \infty)$. The table in the next column reveals that $f(x) > 0$ for $(0, 2)$.

Interval	Test Value	$f(x) = \dfrac{2 - x}{2x}$
$(-\infty, 0)$	$x = -0.5$	$f(-0.5) = -2.5 < 0$
$(0, 2)$	$x = 1$	$f(1) = 0.5 > 0$
$(2, \infty)$	$x = 2.5$	$f(2.5) = -0.1 < 0$

$[-4.7, 4.7, 1]$ by $[-3.1, 3.1, 1]$

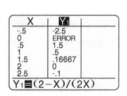
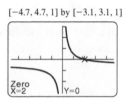

Note that $f(x)$ changes from negative to positive at $x = 0$, where $f(x)$ is undefined. These results are supported graphically in the figure on the right above.

Solve the rational inequality.

15. $\dfrac{3 - x}{3x} \geq 0$ **16.** $\dfrac{x - 2}{x + 2} > 0$

17. $\dfrac{3 - 2x}{1 + x} < 3$ **18.** $\dfrac{x + 1}{4 - 2x} \geq 1$

19. $\dfrac{5}{x^2 - 4} < 0$ **20.** $\dfrac{x}{x^2 - 1} \geq 0$

12

Exponential and Logarithmic Functions

12.2 Exponential Functions

Time is money.

—BENJAMIN FRANKLIN

If you deposit money into a savings account, you might *earn* an interest rate of 0.18%, whereas if you charge purchases on your credit card, you might *pay* an interest rate of 18%. Do interest rates and decimal points really matter? To find out, consider the following.

If $1000 is deposited in a savings account at 0.18% interest per year for 15 years, the final amount would be about $1027.37. However, if the interest rate were a typical credit card rate of 18%, the final amount would be about $14,584.37. Interest rates and decimal points clearly matter! After *doing the math*, it becomes obvious that the best financial decision is to pay off high-interest credit cards first, before putting money into a savings account that pays only 0.18%.

In this chapter we will learn ways to calculate interest on investments by studying a new type of function called an *exponential function*. (See Section 12.2.) Exponential functions are frequently used in business and finance, but they also have many other applications.

12.2 Exponential Functions

Basic Concepts • Graphs of Exponential Functions • Percent Change and Exponential Functions • Compound Interest • Models Involving Exponential Functions • The Natural Exponential Function

A LOOK INTO MATH ▶

Suppose that we deposit $100 into a savings account that pays 2% annual interest. If neither the money nor the interest is withdrawn, then after 1 year the account balance will be $102 and after 2 years the account balance will be $104.04. The extra 4 cents in interest in the second year occurs because we get not only 2% interest on the original $100 but also 2% interest on the $2 interest earned during the first year. In general, when an amount A experiences a constant percent change over each fixed time period, such as a year or a month, then the growth (or possibly decay) in A can be described by an exponential function. In this section we discuss exponential functions and many of their applications, including how to calculate interest.

Basic Concepts

NEW VOCABULARY

☐ Exponential function with base *a* and coefficient *C*
☐ Growth factor
☐ Decay factor
☐ Exponential growth
☐ Exponential decay
☐ Percent change
☐ Compound interest
☐ Base *e*
☐ Natural exponential function
☐ Continuous growth

▶ **REAL-WORLD CONNECTION** Suppose that an insect population (per acre) doubles each week. Table 12.5 shows the size of the population after *x* weeks. Note that, as the population of insects becomes larger, the *increase* in population each week becomes greater. The population is increasing by 100%, or doubling, each week. When a quantity increases by a constant percentage (or constant factor) at regular intervals, its growth is *exponential*.

TABLE 12.5 Insect Population

Week	0	1	2	3	4	5
Population	100	200	400	800	1600	3200

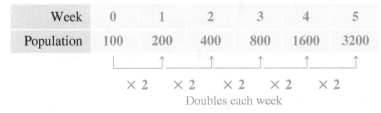

We can model the data in Table 12.5 by using the exponential function

$$f(x) = 100(2)^x.$$

For example,

$$f(0) = 100(2)^0 = 100 \cdot 1 = 100,$$
$$f(1) = 100(2)^1 = 100 \cdot 2 = 200,$$
$$f(2) = 100(2)^2 = 100 \cdot 4 = 400,$$

and so on. Note that the exponential function *f* has a *variable as an exponent*.

EXPONENTIAL FUNCTION

A function represented by

$$f(x) = Ca^x, \quad a > 0 \quad \text{and} \quad a \neq 1,$$

is an **exponential function with base a and coefficient C**. (Unless stated otherwise, we assume that $C > 0$.)

In the formula $f(x) = Ca^x$, a is called the **growth factor** when $a > 1$ and the **decay factor** when $0 < a < 1$. For an exponential function, each time x increases by 1 unit, $f(x)$ increases by a factor of a when $a > 1$ and decreases by a factor of a when $0 < a < 1$. Moreover, because

$$f(0) = Ca^0 = C(1) = C,$$

the value of C equals the value of $f(x)$ when $x = 0$. That is, C is the y-intercept. If x represents time, C represents the initial value of f when time equals 0. Figure 12.14 illustrates **exponential growth** and **exponential decay** for $x > 0$.

Exponential Growth for Positive x

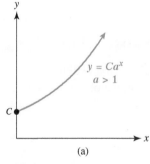

$y = Ca^x$
$a > 1$

(a)

Exponential Decay for Positive x

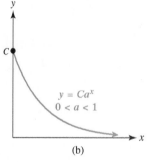

$y = Ca^x$
$0 < a < 1$

(b)

Figure 12.14

The set of valid inputs (domain) for an exponential function includes all real numbers. The set of corresponding outputs (range) includes all positive real numbers.

When evaluating an exponential function, we evaluate exponents *before* we multiply. For example, if $f(x) = 4(3)^x$, then

$$f(2) = 4(3)^2 = 4(9) = 36.$$

Evaluate exponents first.

The next example illustrates how exponential functions are evaluated.

EXAMPLE 1 **Evaluating exponential functions**

Evaluate $f(x)$ for the given value of x.
(a) $f(x) = 10(3)^x \qquad x = 2$ **(b)** $f(x) = 5\left(\frac{1}{2}\right)^x \qquad x = 3$
(c) $f(x) = \frac{1}{3}(2)^x \qquad x = -1$

Solution

(a) $f(2) = 10(3)^2 = 10 \cdot 9 = 90$

(b) $f(3) = 5\left(\frac{1}{2}\right)^3 = 5 \cdot \frac{1}{8} = \frac{5}{8}$

(c) $f(-1) = \frac{1}{3}(2)^{-1} = \frac{1}{3} \cdot \frac{1}{2} = \frac{1}{6}$

NOTE: $f(x)$ is also defined for all *negative* inputs.

Now Try Exercises 11, 13, 15

MAKING CONNECTIONS

The Expressions a^{-x} and $\left(\frac{1}{a}\right)^x$

Using properties of exponents, we can write 2^{-x} as

$$2^{-x} = \frac{1}{2^x} = \left(\frac{1}{2}\right)^x.$$

In general, the expressions a^{-x} and $\left(\frac{1}{a}\right)^x$ are equal for all positive values of a.

Graphs of Exponential Functions

We can graph $f(x) = 2^x$ by first evaluating some points, as in Table 12.6. If we plot these points and sketch the graph, we obtain Figure 12.15.

TABLE 12.6
$f(x) = 2^x$

x	2^x
-2	$\frac{1}{4}$
-1	$\frac{1}{2}$
0	1
1	2
2	4

Graphing $f(x) = 2^x$

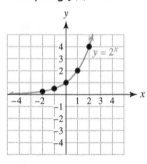

Figure 12.15

- This graph is always above the x-axis.
- The graph passes through the point $(0, 1)$.
- Negative x-values give y-values between 0 and 1.
- Positive x-values give y-values greater than 1.

In Figure 12.16, we investigate the graph of $y = a^x$ for values of a that are greater than 1 by graphing $y = 1.3^x$, $y = 1.7^x$, and $y = 2.5^x$. Graphs of $y = a^x$ where a is between 0 and 1 are shown in Figure 12.17.

Graphing $y = a^x$ for $a > 1$

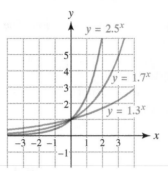

Figure 12.16

- As x increases, the y-values increase.
- Larger values of a ($a > 1$) result in y-values that increase more rapidly.
- The graphs pass through (0, 1) because $C = 1$.
- The graphs are always above the x-axis.

Graphing $y = a^x$ for $0 < a < 1$

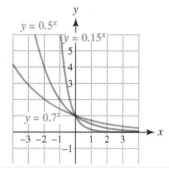

Figure 12.17

- As x increases, the y-values decrease.
- Smaller values of a ($0 < a < 1$) result in y-values that decrease more rapidly.
- The graphs pass through (0, 1) because $C = 1$.
- The graphs are always above the x-axis.

In the next example we show the dramatic difference between the outputs of linear and exponential functions.

EXAMPLE 2 Comparing exponential and linear functions

Compare $f(x) = 3^x$ and $g(x) = 3x$ graphically and numerically for $x \geq 0$.

Solution

Graphical Comparison The graphs of $y_1 = 3^x$ and $y_2 = 3x$ are shown in Figure 12.18. For large values of x, the graph of the exponential function y_1 increases much faster than the graph of the linear function y_2.

Numerical Comparison The tables of $y_1 = 3^x$ and $y_2 = 3x$ are shown in Figure 12.19. For large values of x, the values for y_1 increase much faster than the values for y_2.

Comparing Exponential and Linear Growth

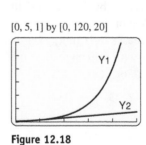

[0, 5, 1] by [0, 120, 20]

Figure 12.18

Exponential growth (Y1) — Linear growth (Y2)

X	Y1	Y2
0	1	0
1	3	3
2	9	6
3	27	9
4	81	12
5	243	15
6	729	18

X=0

Figure 12.19

Now Try Exercise 89

NOTE: The results of Example 2 are true in general: for large enough inputs, exponential functions with $a > 1$ grow far faster than any linear function.

> **MAKING CONNECTIONS**
>
> **Exponential and Polynomial Functions**
>
> The function $f(x) = 2^x$ is an exponential function. The base 2 is a constant and the exponent x is a variable, so $f(3) = 2^3 = 8$.
>
> The function $g(x) = x^2$ is a quadratic (polynomial) function. The base x is a variable and the exponent 2 is a constant, so $g(3) = 3^2 = 9$.
>
> The table clearly shows that the exponential function grows much faster than the quadratic function for large values of x.
>
> | x | 0 | 2 | 4 | 6 | 8 | 10 | 12 | |
> |-----|---|---|----|----|-----|------|------|---|
> | 2^x | 1 | 4 | 16 | 64 | 256 | 1024 | 4096 | ← Exponential growth |
> | x^2 | 0 | 4 | 16 | 36 | 64 | 100 | 144 | ← Quadratic growth |

In the next example, we determine whether a function is linear or exponential.

EXAMPLE 3 **Finding linear and exponential functions**

For each table, determine whether f is a linear function or an exponential function. Find a formula for f.

(a)

x	0	1	2	3	4
$f(x)$	16	8	4	2	1

(b)

x	0	1	2	3	4
$f(x)$	5	7	9	11	13

(c)

x	0	1	2	3	4
$f(x)$	1	3	9	27	81

Solution

(a) Each time x increases by 1 unit, $f(x)$ decreases by a factor of $\frac{1}{2}$. Therefore f is an exponential function with a *decay factor* of $\frac{1}{2}$. Because $f(0) = 16$, $C = 16$, so $f(x) = 16\left(\frac{1}{2}\right)^x$. This formula can also be written as $f(x) = 16(2)^{-x}$.

(b) Each time x increases by 1 unit, $f(x)$ increases by 2 units. Therefore f is a linear function, and the slope of its graph equals 2. The y-intercept is 5, so $f(x) = 2x + 5$.

(c) Each time x increases by 1 unit, $f(x)$ increases by a factor of 3. Therefore f is an exponential function with a *growth factor* of 3. Because $f(0) = 1$, it follows that $C = 1$ and $f(x) = 1(3)^x$, or $f(x) = 3^x$.

Now Try Exercises 45, 47, 49

READING CHECK

How can you distinguish between a linear function and an exponential function?

> **MAKING CONNECTIONS**
>
> **Linear and Exponential Functions**
>
> For a *linear function*, given by $f(x) = ax + b$, each time x increases by 1 unit y increases (or decreases) *by a units*, where a equals the slope of the graph of f.
>
> For an *exponential function*, given by $f(x) = Ca^x$, each time x increases by 1 unit y increases *by a factor of a* when $a > 1$ and decreases by a factor of a when $0 < a < 1$. The constant a equals either the growth factor or the decay factor.

Percent Change and Exponential Functions

PERCENT CHANGE When an amount A changes to a new amount B, then the **percent change** is calculated by

$$\frac{B - A}{A} \times 100. \qquad \text{Percent change formula}$$

We multiply the ratio by 100 to change decimal form to percent form.

EXAMPLE 4 ▶ **Finding percent change**

Complete the following.
(a) Find the percent change if an account balance increases from $500 to $1000.
(b) Find the percent change if an account balance decreases from $1000 to $500.

Solution
(a) Let $A = 500$ and $B = 1000$.

$$\frac{1000 - 500}{500} \times 100 = \frac{500}{500} \times 100 \qquad \frac{B - A}{A} \times 100$$

$$= 1 \times 100 \qquad \text{Simplify.}$$

$$= 100\% \qquad \text{Multiply.}$$

The percent change (increase) is 100%; that is, the account balance doubles.

(b) Let $A = 1000$ and $B = 500$.

$$\frac{500 - 1000}{1000} \times 100 = -\frac{500}{1000} \times 100 \qquad \frac{B - A}{A} \times 100$$

$$= -\frac{1}{2} \times 100 \qquad \text{Simplify.}$$

$$\approx -50\% \qquad \text{Multiply.}$$

The percent change (decrease) is -50%.

▌ Now Try Exercise 51

NOTE: In Example 4, the account did *not* increase by 100% and then decrease by 100% to return the account to its initial value of $500. In part (b) the initial amount is $A = \$1000$ and needs to decrease only by a factor of $\frac{1}{2}$, or 50%, to decrease to $500.

PERCENT CHANGE AND GROWTH FACTOR Suppose a savings account A increases from $200 to $600. The percent change, $R\%$, equals

$$\frac{600 - 200}{200} \times 100 = 2 \times 100 = 200\%.$$

Note that the account balance *tripled* from $200 to 600, but the percent change is 200%, *not* 300%. Also, the *increase* in the account balance A is $400 because $600 - \$200 = \$400$. This $400 increase equals 200% of $200. If we let r represent the percent change as a decimal, then

$$\underbrace{200\% \text{ of } \$200}_{} = \underbrace{2.00 \times \$200}_{} = \underbrace{\$400.}_{} \qquad R\% = 200\%;\ r = 2.00$$

$$\qquad R\% \text{ of } A \qquad = \qquad rA \qquad = \qquad \text{Increase in } A$$

In general, if the *percent increase* in an account balance A is given by r in decimal form, then the *amount of increase* in A is equal to rA and the new balance after the increase is $A + rA$. For example, if \$200 increases by 200%, then $r = 2.00$, $A = \$200$, and

$$rA = 2.00(200) = \$400, \qquad \text{Increase in account balance}$$

so the balance increases by \$400. The new balance for the account is

$$A + rA = \$200 + \$400 = \$600.$$

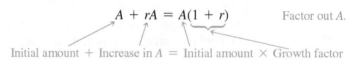

Initial amount + Increase = Final amount

If we factor out A in the expression $A + rA$, we get

$$A + rA = A(1 + r) \qquad \text{Factor out } A.$$

Initial amount + Increase in A = Initial amount $\times$ Growth factor

Thus if an account increases from \$200 to \$600, the increase is \$400 and the percent increase is 200%. In addition, the account balance increased by a growth factor equal to

$$a = 1 + r = 1 + 2.00 = 3, \qquad \text{Growth factor is } a = 3.$$

which means that the account balance tripled.

EXAMPLE 5   **Analyzing the decrease in an account balance**

An account that contains \$2000 decreases in value by 20%.
(a) Find the decrease in value of the account.
(b) Find the final value of the account.
(c) By what factor a did the account decrease?

Solution
(a) Let $A = 2000$ and $r = -0.20$ (-20% in decimal form). The decrease is

$$rA = -0.20(2000) = -400. \qquad \text{Decrease in } A \text{ is } rA.$$

The account decreased in value by \$400.

(b) The final value of the account is

$$A + rA = 2000 + (-400) = \$1600.$$

Initial amount + Decrease = New amount

(c) The account decreased by a factor of

$$a = 1 + r = 1 + (-0.20) = 0.80. \qquad \text{Decay factor is } a = 0.80.$$

The account value decreased to 80% of its original value because 80% of \$2000 is \$1600.

Now Try Exercise 55

NOTE: In general, a positive amount A cannot *decrease* by more than 100% because a 100% decrease would reduce A to 0. However, percent *increases* can be more than 100%.

PERCENT CHANGE AND EXPONENTIAL FUNCTIONS An exponential function results when an *initial value C* is multiplied by a *growth* (or *decay*) *factor a* for each unit increase in x. For example, if the population P of a city is 100,000 people, and the city is growing at 5% per year, then $C = 100,000$ and the growth factor is

$$a = 1 + r = 1 + 0.05 = 1.05. \qquad \text{Growth factor is } r = 0.05$$

Thus the exponential function

$$P(x) = 100,000(1.05)^x \qquad P(x) = Ca^x \text{ with } C = 100,000 \text{ and } a = 1.05.$$

models the city's population after x years. For example,

$$P(6) = 100,000(1.05)^6 \approx 134,000$$

indicates that after 6 years the city's population has grown to about 134,000 people.
These concepts are summarized by the following.

PERCENT CHANGE AND EXPONENTIAL FUNCTIONS

Suppose that an amount A increases or decreases by $R\%$ (or by r expressed in decimal form) for each unit increase in x.

1. If $r > 0$, the *growth factor* is $a = 1 + r$ and $a > 1$.
2. If $-1 < r < 0$, the *decay factor* is $a = 1 + r$ and $0 < a < 1$.
3. If the initial amount is C, the amount A after x-unit increases is given by

$$A(x) = Ca^x \quad \text{or equivalently,} \quad A(x) = C(1 + r)^x.$$

READING CHECK

If your income increases by 200%, what is the growth factor?

EXAMPLE 6   **Analyzing growth of bacteria**

Initially a laboratory culture contains 50,000 bacteria per milliliter and it is increasing in numbers by 20% per hour.
(a) Write the formula for an exponential function B that gives the number of bacteria per milliliter after x hours.
(b) Evaluate $B(3)$ and interpret your result.

Solution
(a) The initial value is $C = 50,000$ and the hourly percent increase is 20%, or $r = 0.20$ in decimal form. Thus the growth factor is

$$a = 1 + r = 1 + 0.20 = 1.20. \qquad \text{Growth factor} = 1.20 \text{ with } r = 0.20.$$

Because the exponential function can be written as $B(x) = Ca^x$, it follows that

$$B(x) = 50,000(1.20)^x.$$

(b) $B(3) = 50,000(1.20)^3 = 50,000(1.728) = 86,400$. Thus after 3 hours, the culture contains 86,400 bacteria per milliliter.

Now Try Exercise 85

Compound Interest

▶ **REAL-WORLD CONNECTION** If $100 is deposited in a savings account paying 10% annual interest, the interest earned after 1 year equals $100 \times 0.10 = 10. The total amount of money in the account after 1 year is $100(1 + 0.10) = 110. Each year the money in the account increases by a growth factor of 1.10, so after x years there will be $100(1.10)^x$ dollars in the account. Thus **compound interest** is an example of exponential growth.

COMPOUND INTEREST

If P dollars is deposited in an account and if interest is paid at the end of each year with an annual rate of interest r, expressed in decimal form, then after t years the account will contain A dollars, where

$$A = P(1 + r)^t.$$

The growth factor is $(1 + r)$.

NOTE: The compound interest formula takes the form of an exponential function with

$$a = 1 + r.$$

EXAMPLE 7 **Calculating compound interest**

A 20-year-old worker deposits $2000 in a retirement account that pays 6% annual interest at the end of each year. How much money will be in the account when the worker is 65 years old? What is the growth factor?

Solution

Here, $P = 2000$, $r = 0.06$, and $t = 45$. The amount in the account after 45 years is

$$A = 2000(1 + 0.06)^{45} \approx \$27,529.22, \quad A = P(1 + r)^t$$

which is supported by Figure 12.20. Each year the amount of money in the account is multiplied by a factor of $(1 + 0.06)$, so the growth factor is 1.06.

```
2000(1+.06)^45
          27529.22165
```

Figure 12.20

Now Try Exercise 65

INTEREST PAID MORE THAN ONCE A YEAR Many times, interest is paid more than once a year. For example, suppose an account gives 8% annual interest that is paid every 3 months, or *quarterly*. It follows that $\frac{1}{4}$ of the annual 8% interest, or 2%, is paid every 3 months. The growth factor is $a = 1 + 0.02 = 1.02$ for each 3-month period. If the initial balance is $1000, then after 5 years, the quarterly 2% interest has been paid $4 \cdot 5 = 20$ times, and the account contains

$$\$1000(1.02)^{20} \approx \$1485.95.$$

In general, if P dollars are deposited in an account paying an *annual* interest rate r (in decimal form) and this interest rate is compounded or paid n times per year, then after t years the account contains A dollars, given by

Amount after t years   Annual interest (decimal)

Number of years

$$A = P\left(1 + \frac{r}{n}\right)^{nt}$$

Initial deposit   Number of times interest is paid per year

EXAMPLE 8

Calculating compound interest

Initially, $1500 is deposited in an account paying 6% annual interest, compounded monthly. What is the account balance after 5 years?

Solution

Let $P = 1500$, $r = 0.06$, $n = 12$, and $t = 5$. The balance after 5 years is

$$A = P\left(1 + \frac{r}{n}\right)^{nt}$$ Interest formula

$$= 1500\left(1 + \frac{0.06}{12}\right)^{(12 \cdot 5)}$$ Substitute.

$$= 1500(1.005)^{60}$$ Evaluate.

$$\approx \$2023.28.$$ Approximate.

Now Try Exercise 73

NOTE: Generally, compounding interest more frequently results in more interest being paid. In Example 8, if the annual 6% interest had been paid only once a year, the growth factor would be larger, $a = 1.06$, but this 6% annual interest would have been paid only 5 times, once each year. The new balance would be $1500(1.06)^5 \approx \$2007.34$, rather than the $2023.28 that resulted from monthly compounding.

Models Involving Exponential Functions

▶ **REAL-WORLD CONNECTION** Apple's path to 2 billion iPhone application downloads occurred over a relatively short period of time. In the next example, we model this exponential growth of iPhone application downloads.

EXAMPLE 9

Modeling iPhone application downloads

In September 2008 about 100 million iPhone applications were downloaded, and the number of iPhone downloads was increasing at a rate of 28.4% per month. (*Source:* Apple Corp.)
(a) What was the monthly growth factor?
(b) Write an exponential function $P(x) = Ca^x$ that models the number of downloads in millions for the iPhone x months after September 2008.
(c) Evaluate $P(12)$ and interpret the result.

Solution

(a) Because $r = 0.284$, the monthly growth factor was $a = 1 + 0.284 = 1.284$.
(b) Let $C = 100$ and $a = 1.284$. Then $P(x) = 100(1.284)^x$.
(c) $P(12) = 100(1.284)^{12} \approx 2000$. In approximately 12 months, from September 2008 to September 2009, iPhone application downloads grew from 100 million to about 2000 million, or 2 billion.

Now Try Exercise 91

▶ **REAL-WORLD CONNECTION** Traffic flow at intersections can be modeled by exponential functions whenever traffic patterns occur randomly. In the next example we model traffic at an intersection by using an exponential function.

EXAMPLE 10   **Modeling traffic flow**

On average, a particular intersection has 360 vehicles arriving randomly each hour. Traffic engineers use $f(x) = (0.905)^x$ to estimate the likelihood, or probability, that *no* vehicle will enter the intersection within an interval of x seconds. (*Source:* F. Mannering and W. Kilareski, *Principles of Highway Engineering and Traffic Analysis*.)

(a) Compute $f(5)$ and interpret the results.

(b) A graph of $y = f(x)$ is shown in Figure 12.21. Discuss this graph.

(c) Is this function an example of exponential growth or decay?

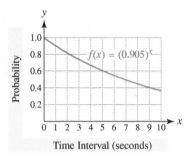

Figure 12.21

Solution

(a) The result $f(5) = (0.905)^5 \approx 0.61$ indicates that there is a 61% chance that no vehicle will enter the intersection during any particular 5-second interval.

(b) The graph decreases, which means that as the interval of time increases there is less chance (likelihood) that a car will *not* enter the intersection.

(c) Because the graph is decreasing and $a = 0.905 < 1$, this function is an example of exponential decay.

Now Try Exercise 97

The Natural Exponential Function

A special type of exponential function is called the *natural exponential function*, expressed as $f(x) = e^x$. The **base** e is a special number in mathematics similar to π. The number π is approximately 3.14, whereas the number e is approximately 2.72. The number e is named for the great Swiss mathematician Leonhard Euler (1707–1783). Most calculators have a special key that can be used to compute the natural exponential function.

NATURAL EXPONENTIAL FUNCTION

The function represented by

$$f(x) = e^x$$

is the **natural exponential function**, where $e \approx 2.71828$.

CALCULATOR HELP

To evaluate the natural exponential function, see Appendix A (page AP-8).

▶ **REAL-WORLD CONNECTION**   The natural exponential function is frequently used to model **continuous growth**. For example, the fact that births and deaths occur throughout the year, not just at one time during the year, must be recognized when population growth is being modeled. If a population P is growing continuously at r percent per year, expressed as a decimal, we can model this population after x years by

$$P = Ce^{rx}, \quad \text{Continuous growth, } r > 0$$

where C is the initial population. To evaluate natural exponential functions, we use a calculator, as demonstrated in the next example.

EXAMPLE 11   **Modeling population**

In 2011 Texas' population was 26 million people and was growing at a continuous rate of 2% per year. This population in millions x years after 2011 can be modeled by

$$f(x) = 26e^{0.02x}.$$

Estimate the population in 2015.

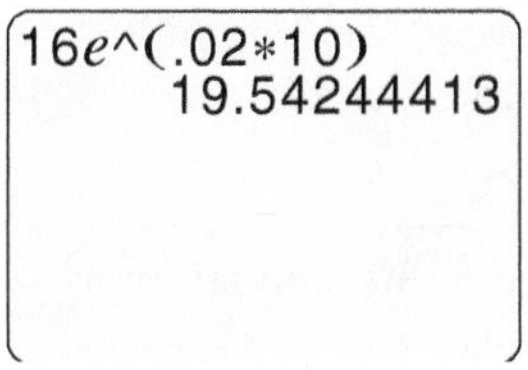

```
16e^(.02*10)
        19.54244413
```

Figure 12.22

Solution

Because 2015 is 4 years after 2011, we evaluate $f(4)$ to obtain

$$f(4) = 26e^{0.02(4)} \approx 28.2,$$

which is supported by Figure 12.22. (Be sure to include parentheses around the exponent of e.) This model estimates the population of Texas to be about 28.2 million in 2015.

Now Try Exercise 99

CRITICAL THINKING

Sketch a graph of $y = 2^x$ and $y = 3^x$ in the same xy-plane. Then use these two graphs to sketch a graph of $y = e^x$. How do these graphs compare?

12.2 Putting It All Together

TOPIC	EXPLANATION	EXAMPLE
Exponential Function	The variable is an exponent. $$f(x) = Ca^x$$ Initial value when $x = 0$ Growth factor (base) Growth: $a > 1$ Decay: $0 < a < 1$	$f(x) = 3(2)^x$ models exponential growth, and $g(x) = 2\left(\frac{1}{3}\right)^x$ models exponential decay.
Graphs of Exponential Functions	• Above the x-axis for all inputs • Increases for $a > 1$ • Decreases for $0 < a < 1$ • y-intercept is C.	Exponential Functions: $f(x) = Ca^x$ 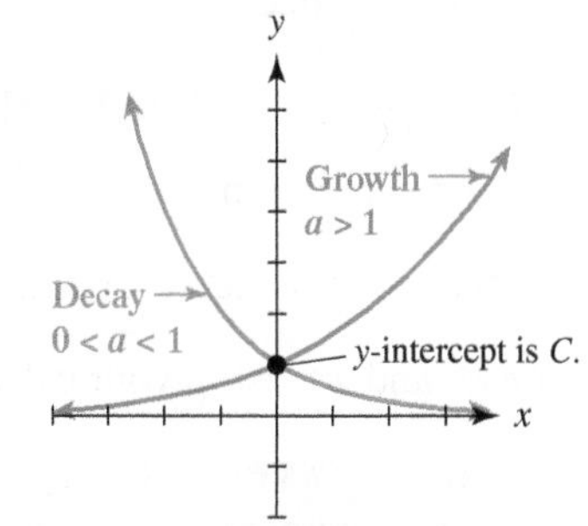
Percent Change	An amount changes from A to B: $$\text{Percent change} = \frac{B - A}{A} \times 100.$$	If \$200 increases to \$300, then $$\frac{300 - 200}{200} \times 100 = 50\%$$ is the percent change.

continued on next page

continued from previous page

TOPIC	EXPLANATION	EXAMPLE
Constant Percent Change and Exponential Functions	Constant percent change (decimal) Time $$f(x) = C(1 + r)^x$$ Initial amount Growth factor	If 3000 bacteria increase in number by 12% daily for x days, then $$f(x) = 3000(1.12)^x$$ models these numbers after x days.
Compound Interest	Compounded annually: $$A = P(1 + r)^t$$ Compounded n times per year: $$A = P\left(1 + \frac{r}{n}\right)^{nt}$$ P: Initial deposit A: Final amount r: Annual interest rate (decimal) n: Interest paid n times per year t: Number of years	If \$1000 is deposited at 3% annual interest for 4 years, then $$A = \$1000(1.03)^4$$ $$\approx 1125.51.$$ If \$1000 is deposited at 3% annual interest compounded monthly for 4 years, then $$A = \$1000\left(1 + \frac{0.03}{12}\right)^{(12\cdot4)}$$ $$\approx \$1127.33.$$
Natural Exponential Function	$$f(x) = e^x$$ Growth factor, or base, is $e \approx 2.72$.	Using a calculator, $$f(2) = e^2 \approx 7.39.$$

12.2 Exercises

CONCEPTS AND VOCABULARY

1. Give a general formula for an exponential function f.

2. Sketch a graph of an exponential function that illustrates exponential decay.

3. Give the domain and range of an exponential function.

4. Evaluate the expressions 2^x and x^2 for $x = 5$.

5. Approximate e to the nearest thousandth.

6. Evaluate e^2 and π^2 using your calculator.

7. If a quantity y grows exponentially, then for each unit increase in x, y increases by a constant _____.

8. If $f(x) = 1.5^x$, what is the growth factor?

9. If a quantity increases from A to B, then the percent change equals _____.

10. If a quantity increases by 35% each year, then the growth factor a is _____.

EVALUATING EXPONENTIAL FUNCTIONS

Exercises 11–22: Evaluate the exponential function for the given values of x by hand when possible. Approximate answers to the nearest hundredth when appropriate.

11. $f(x) = 3^x$ $x = -2, x = 2$

12. $f(x) = 5^x$ $x = -1, x = 3$

13. $f(x) = 5(2^x)$ $x = 0, x = 5$

14. $f(x) = 3(7^x)$ $x = -2, x = 0$

15. $f(x) = \left(\frac{1}{2}\right)^x$ $x = -2, x = 3$

16. $f(x) = \left(\frac{1}{4}\right)^x$ $x = 0, x = 2$

17. $f(x) = 5(3)^{-x}$ $x = -1, x = 2$

18. $f(x) = 4\left(\frac{3}{7}\right)^x$ $x = 1, x = 4$

19. $f(x) = 1.8^x$ $x = -3, x = 1.5$

20. $f(x) = 0.91^x$ $x = 5.1, x = 10$

21. $f(x) = 3(0.6)^x$ $\qquad x = -1, x = 2$

22. $f(x) = 5(4.5)^{-x}$ $\qquad x = -2.1, x = 1.9$

Exercises 23 and 24: Thinking Generally *For the given exponential function, evaluate $f(0)$ and $f(-1)$.*

23. $f(x) = a^x$

24. $f(x) = (1 + r)^{2x}$

GRAPHS OF EXPONENTIAL FUNCTIONS

Exercises 25–28: Match the formula with its graph (a.–d.). Do not use a calculator.

25. $f(x) = 1.5^x$ $\qquad$ **26.** $f(x) = \frac{1}{4}(2^x)$

27. $f(x) = 4\left(\frac{1}{2}\right)^x$ $\qquad$ **28.** $f(x) = \left(\frac{1}{3}\right)^x$

a.

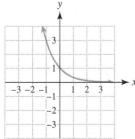

b.

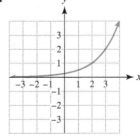

c.

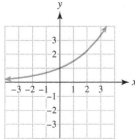

d.

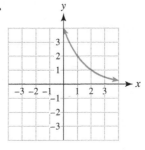

Exercises 29–32: Use the graph of $y = Ca^x$ to determine the constants C and a.

29.

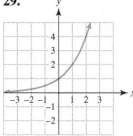

30.

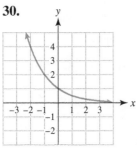

31.

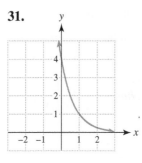

32.

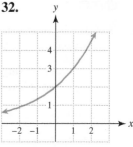

Exercises 33–44: Graph $y = f(x)$. State whether the graph depicts exponential growth or exponential decay.

33. $f(x) = 2^x$ $\qquad$ **34.** $f(x) = 3^x$

35. $f(x) = \left(\frac{1}{4}\right)^x$ $\qquad$ **36.** $f(x) = \left(\frac{1}{2}\right)^x$

37. $f(x) = 2^{-x}$ $\qquad$ **38.** $f(x) = 3^{-x}$

39. $f(x) = 3^x - 1$ $\qquad$ **40.** $f(x) = 2^x + 1$

41. $f(x) = 2^{x-1}$ $\qquad$ **42.** $f(x) = 2^{x+1}$

43. $f(x) = 4\left(\frac{1}{3}\right)^x$ $\qquad$ **44.** $f(x) = 3\left(\frac{1}{2}\right)^x$

LINEAR AND EXPONENTIAL GROWTH

Exercises 45–50: (Refer to Example 3.) A table for a function f is given.

(a) *Determine whether function f represents exponential growth, exponential decay, or linear growth.*
(b) *Find a formula for f.*

45.

x	0	1	2	3	4
$f(x)$	64	16	4	1	$\frac{1}{4}$

46.

x	0	1	2	3	4
$f(x)$	$\frac{1}{2}$	1	2	4	8

47.

x	0	1	2	3	4
$f(x)$	8	11	14	17	20

48.

x	−2	−1	0	1	2
$f(x)$	4	2	1	$\frac{1}{2}$	$\frac{1}{4}$

49.

x	−2	−1	0	1	2
$f(x)$	2.56	3.2	4	5	6.25

50.

x	−2	−1	0	1	2
$f(x)$	−6	−2	2	6	10

PERCENT CHANGE AND EXPONENTIAL FUNCTIONS

Exercises 51–54: For the given amounts A and B, find each of the following.

(a) The percent change if A changes to B
(b) The percent change if B changes to A

51. $A = \$200, B = \$400$

52. $A = \$1.50, B = \$1.00$

53. $A = 150, B = 30$

54. $A = 80, B = 200$

Exercises 55–60: An account contains A dollars and increases or decreases by R%. For each A and R, answer the following.

(a) Find the increase or decrease in the value of the account.
(b) Find the final value of the account.
(c) By what factor did the account value increase or decrease?

55. $A = \$1000, R = 120\%$

56. $A = \$500, R = 230\%$

57. $A = \$650, R = 20\%$

58. $A = \$70, R = 35\%$

59. $A = \$800, R = -10\%$

60. $A = \$950, R = -60\%$

Exercises 61–64: For the given f(x), state the initial value C, the growth or decay factor a, and percent change R for each unit increase in x.

61. $f(x) = 9(1.07)^x$

62. $f(x) = 3(1.351)^x$

63. $f(x) = 1.5(0.45)^x$

64. $f(x) = 0.9^x$

COMPOUND INTEREST

Exercises 65–70: (Refer to Example 7.) If P dollars is deposited in an account paying R percent annual interest, approximate the amount in the account after x years.

65. $P = \$1500 \quad R = 9\% \quad x = 10$ years

66. $P = \$1500 \quad R = 15\% \quad x = 10$ years

67. $P = \$200 \quad R = 20\% \quad x = 50$ years

68. $P = \$5000 \quad R = 8.4\% \quad x = 7$ years

69. $P = \$560 \quad R = 1.4\% \quad x = 25$ years

70. $P = \$750 \quad R = 10\% \quad x = 13$ years

71. Thinking Generally Suppose that $1000 is deposited in an account paying 8% annual interest for 10 years. If $2000 had been deposited instead of $1000, would there be twice the money in the account after 10 years? Explain.

72. Thinking Generally Suppose that $500 is deposited in an account paying 5% annual interest for 10 years. If the interest rate had been 10% instead of 5%, would the total interest earned after 10 years be twice as much? Explain.

Exercises 73–76: (Refer to Example 8.) The amount P is deposited in an account giving R% annual interest compounded n times a year. Find the amount A in the account after t years.

73. $P = \$700, R = 4\%, n = 4, t = 3$

74. $P = \$550, R = 3\%, n = 2, t = 5$

75. $P = \$1200, R = 2.5\%, n = 12, t = 7$

76. $P = \$1500, R = 6.5\%, n = 365, t = 20$

THE NATURAL EXPONENTIAL FUNCTION

Exercises 77–80: Evaluate f(x) for the given value of x. Approximate answers to the nearest hundredth.

77. $f(x) = e^x$ $\qquad\qquad x = 1.2$

78. $f(x) = 2e^x$ $\qquad\qquad x = 2$

79. $f(x) = 1 - e^x$ $\qquad\qquad x = -2$

80. $f(x) = 4e^{-x}$ $\qquad\qquad x = 1.5$

Exercises 81–84: Graph f(x) in [−4, 4, 1] by [0, 8, 1]. State whether the graph illustrates exponential growth or exponential decay.

81. $f(x) = e^{0.5x}$ $\qquad$ **82.** $f(x) = e^x + 1$

83. $f(x) = 1.5e^{-0.32x}$ $\qquad$ **84.** $f(x) = 2e^{-x} + 1$

APPLICATIONS

Exercises 85–88: Exponential Models Write the formula for an exponential function, $f(x) = Ca^x$, that models the situation. Evaluate f(4).

85. A sample of 5000 bacteria decreases in number by 25% per week.

86. A sample of 700 insects increases in number by 200% per day.

87. A sample of 50 birds increases in number by 10% per month.

88. A sample of 137 fish decreases in number by 2% per week.

89. *Salary Growth* Suppose your salary is $50,000 per year. Would you rather have a 20% raise each year or a $20 raise each year?

90. *Salary Growth* Suppose your salary is $35,000 per year. Would you rather have a 10% raise each year or a $4000 raise each year? Assume that you will keep this job for 10 years.

91. *Blood Alcohol* Suppose that a person's peak blood alcohol level is 0.07 (grams per 100 mL) and that this level decreases by 40% each hour. (*Source:* National Institutes of Health.)
  (a) What is the hourly decay factor?
  (b) Write an exponential function $B(x) = Ca^x$ that models the blood alcohol level after x hours.
  (c) Evaluate $B(2)$ and interpret the result.

92. *Apple's Revenue* From 2001 to 2010 Apple's revenue grew at an annual rate of 40%, from $1 billion to about $21 billion. (*Source:* Apple Corp.)
  (a) What is the annual growth factor?
  (b) Write an exponential function $R(x) = Ca^x$ that models the revenue in billions of dollars x years after 2001.
  (c) Evaluate $R(9)$ and interpret the result.

93. *Tweets per Month* From July 2008 to July 2010, the number of tweets T per month increased dramatically and could be modeled in millions by

$$T(x) = 0.5(1.242)^x,$$

where x represents months after July 2008. (*Source:* Silicon Alley.)
  (a) What is the monthly growth factor?
  (b) Interpret the 0.5 in the formula.
  (c) Evaluate $T(24)$ and interpret the result.

94. *Dating Artifacts* Radioactive carbon-14 is found in all living things and is used to date objects containing organic material. Suppose that an object initially contains C grams of carbon-14. After x years it will contain A grams, where

$$A = C(0.99988)^x.$$

  (a) Let $C = 10$ and graph A over a 20,000-year period. Is this function an example of exponential growth or decay?
  (b) If $C = 10$, how many grams are left after 5700 years? What fraction of the carbon-14 is left?

95. *E. coli Bacteria* A strain of bacteria that inhabits the intestines of animals is named *Escherichia coli* (*E. coli*). These bacteria are capable of rapid growth and can be dangerous to humans—particularly children. The table shows the results of one study of the growth of *E. coli* bacteria, where concentrations are listed in *thousands* of bacteria per milliliter.

t (minutes)	0	50	100
Concentration	500	1000	2000

t (minutes)	150	200	250
Concentration	4000	8000	16,000

Source: G. S. Stent, *Molecular Biology of Bacterial Viruses.*

  (a) Find C and a so that $f(t) = Ca^{t/50}$ models these data.
  (b) Use $f(t)$ to estimate the concentration of bacteria after 170 minutes.
  (c) Discuss the growth of this strain of bacteria over a 250-minute time period.

96. *Swimming Pool Maintenance* Chlorine is frequently used to disinfect swimming pools. The chlorine concentration should remain between 1.5 and 2.5 parts per million (ppm). After a warm, sunny day only 80% of the chlorine may remain in the water, with the other 20% dissipating into the air or combining with other chemicals in the water. (*Source:* D. Thomas, *Swimming Pool Operator's Handbook.*)
  (a) Let $f(x) = 3(0.8)^x$ model the concentration of chlorine in parts per million after x days. What is the initial concentration of chlorine in the pool?
  (b) If no more chlorine is added, estimate when the chlorine level drops below 1.6 parts per million.

97. *Modeling Traffic Flow* (Refer to Example 10.) Construct a table of $f(x) = (0.905)^x$, starting at $x = 0$ and incrementing by 10, until $x = 50$.
  (a) Evaluate $f(0)$ and interpret the result.
  (b) For a time interval of what length is there only a 5% chance that no cars will enter the intersection?

98. *Pros and Putts* The percentage of putts P from 3 feet to 25 feet made by professional golfers can be modeled by the exponential function

$$P(x) = 99(0.872)^{x-3},$$

where x is the length of the putt.

(a) Find the percentage of putts made by professionals from 3 feet.
(b) Evaluate $P(8)$ and interpret the results.
(c) What is the decay factor? Interpret the decay factor.

Exercises 99–102: Population Growth (Refer to Example 11.) The population P in 2010 for a state is given along with R%, its annual percentage rate of continuous growth.

(a) *Write the formula $f(x) = Pe^{rx}$, where r is in decimal notation, that models the population in millions x years after 2010.*
(b) *Estimate the population in 2020.*

99. Nevada: $P = 2.7$ million, $R = 1.4\%$

100. North Carolina: $P = 9.4$ million, $R = 1.36\%$

101. California: $P = 38$ million, $R = 1.02\%$

102. Arizona: $P = 6.6$ million, $R = 1.44\%$

103. Online Exploration In many states, landlords are mandated to return a tenant's security deposit plus interest. Go online and look up this interest rate for your state. Answers may vary.
(a) If you are a tenant, calculate the interest you should receive after 1 year. (If you are not, assume the security deposit is $1200.)
(b) Write a function I that calculates the interest that you should receive after x years. (Does your landlord have to pay compound interest?)

104. Online Exploration Go online and determine how long it takes the fastest growing bacteria to double in number.
(a) Suppose that you start with a sample of 4 million such bacteria. Write an exponential function that gives the number N of bacteria in millions after x minutes.
(b) How many bacteria are there after 2 hours?

WRITING ABOUT MATHEMATICS

105. A student evaluates $f(x) = 4(2)^x$ at $x = 3$ and obtains 512. Did the student evaluate the function correctly? What was the student's error?

106. For a set of data, how can you distinguish between linear growth and exponential growth? Give an example of each type of data.

SECTION 12.2 **Checking Basic Concepts**

1. If $f(x) = 2x^2 + 5x - 1$ and $g(x) = x + 1$, find each expression.
   (a) $(g \circ f)(1)$ (b) $(f \circ g)(x)$

2. Sketch a graph of $f(x) = x^2 - 1$.
   (a) Is f a one-to-one function? Explain.
   (b) Does f have an inverse function?

3. If $f(x) = 4x - 3$, find $f^{-1}(x)$.

4. Evaluate $f(-2)$ if $f(x) = 3(2)^x$.

5. Sketch a graph of $f(x) = \left(\frac{1}{3}\right)^x$.

6. Use the graph of $y = Ca^x$ to determine the constants C and a.

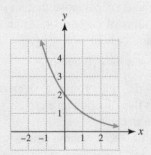

CHAPTER 12   Summary

SECTION 12.2 ■ EXPONENTIAL FUNCTIONS

Exponential Function An exponential function is defined by $f(x) = Ca^x$, where $a > 0$, $C > 0$, and $a \neq 1$. Its domain (set of valid inputs) is all real numbers and its range (outputs) is all positive real numbers. The base is a.

Example: $f(x) = e^x$ is the natural exponential function and $e \approx 2.71828$.

Exponential Growth and Decay When $a > 1$, the graph of $f(x) = Ca^x$ models exponential growth, and when $0 < a < 1$, it models exponential decay. The base a represents either the growth factor or the decay factor. The constant C equals the y-intercept.

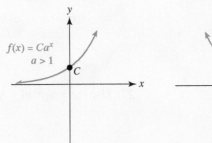

Exponential Growth

Exponential Decay

Example: $f(x) = 1.5(2)^x$ is an exponential function with $a = 2$ and $C = 1.5$. It models exponential growth because $a > 1$. The growth factor is 2 because for each unit increase in x, the output from $f(x)$ increases by a *factor* of 2.

Percent Change If an amount A changes to a new amount B, then the percent change is given by

$$\frac{B - A}{A} \times 100.$$

Example: If \$500 increases to \$700, the percent change is

$$\frac{700 - 500}{500} \times 100 = 40\%.$$

Percent Change and Growth Factor If an initial amount C experiences a constant percent change r (in decimal form) for each x-unit increase in time, then the new amount A is

$$A = C(1 + r)^x,$$

where the growth factor is $a = 1 + r$.

Example: If \$800 increases by 4% each year, then after 5 years the amount is

$$A = 800(1 + 0.04)^5 \approx \$973.32.$$

The growth factor is $a = 1.04$.

Compound Interest If P dollars are deposited in an account paying an *annual* interest rate r (in decimal form) and this interest rate is compounded or paid n times per year, then after t years the account contains A dollars given by the following.

Amount after t years   —Annual interest (decimal)
                           Number of years

$$A = P\left(1 + \frac{r}{n}\right)^{nt}$$

Initial deposit   Number of times interest is paid per year

Example: If \$1200 is deposited at 6% annual interest, compounded quarterly, then after 8 years the account contains

$$A = 1200\left(1 + \frac{0.06}{4}\right)^{(4\,\cdot\,8)} \approx \$1932.39.$$

CHAPTER 12   Review Exercises

SECTION 12.2

Exercises 17–20: Evaluate the exponential function for the given values of x.

17. $f(x) = 6^x$ $x = -1,\quad x = 2$

18. $f(x) = 5(2^{-x})$ $x = 0,\quad x = 3$

19. $f(x) = \left(\frac{1}{3}\right)^x$ $x = -1,\quad x = 4$

20. $f(x) = 3\left(\frac{1}{6}\right)^x$ $x = 0,\quad x = 1$

Exercises 21–24: Graph f. State whether the graph illustrates exponential growth, exponential decay, or logarithmic growth.

21. $f(x) = 2^x$ **22.** $f(x) = \left(\frac{1}{2}\right)^x$

23. $f(x) = \ln(x + 1)$ **24.** $f(x) = 3^{-x}$

Exercises 25 and 26: A table for a function f is given.

    (a) Determine whether f represents linear or exponential growth.
    (b) Find a formula for f.

25.

x	0	1	2	3	4
$f(x)$	5	10	20	40	80

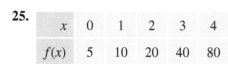

26.

x	0	1	2	3	4
$f(x)$	5	10	15	20	25

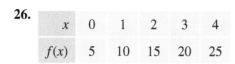

27. Use the graph of $y = Ca^x$ to find C and a.

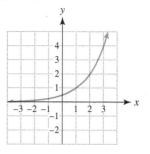

28. Use the graph of $y = k\log_2 x$ to find k.

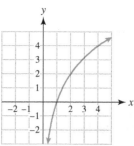

29. Find the percent change if \$150 decreases to \$120.

30. Find the growth factor if \$1500 increases by 7% each year.

Exercises 31 and 32: For the given amounts A and B, find each of the following. Round values to the nearest hundredth of a percent when appropriate.

    (a) The percent change if A changes to B
    (b) The percent change if B changes to A

31. $A = \$600,\ B = \$1200$

32. $A = \$2.20,\ B = \$1.00$

Exercises 33 and 34: An account contains A dollars and increases or decreases by R%. For each A and R, answer the following.

   (a) Find the increase or decrease in value of the account.

   (b) Find the final value of the account.

   (c) By what factor did the account value increase or decrease?

33. $A = \$500$, $R = \$210\%$

34. $A = \$700$, $R = -25\%$

Exercises 35 and 36: Exponential Models Write the formula for an exponential function, $f(x) = Ca^x$, that models the situation. Evaluate $f(2)$.

35. A city's population of 20,000 decreases in number by 5% per year.

36. A sample of 1500 insects increases in number by 300% per day.

Exercises 37 and 38: If P dollars is deposited in an account that pays R percent annual interest at the end of each year, approximate the amount in the account after x years.

37. $P = \$1200$ $R = 10\%$ $x = 9$ years

38. $P = \$900$ $R = 18\%$ $x = 40$ years

Exercises 39–42: Evaluate $f(x)$ for the given value of x. Approximate answers to the nearest hundredth.

39. $f(x) = 2e^x - 1$ $x = 5.3$

40. $f(x) = 0.85^x$ $x = 2.1$

41. $f(x) = 2 \log x$ $x = 55$

42. $f(x) = \ln(2x + 3)$ $x = 23$

CHAPTER 12   Extended and Discovery Exercises

*Exercises 1–4: Radioactive Carbon Dating While an animal is alive, it breathes both carbon dioxide and oxygen. Because a small portion of normal atmospheric carbon dioxide is made up of radioactive carbon-14, a fixed percentage of the animal's body is composed of carbon-14. When the animal dies, it quits breathing and the carbon-14 disintegrates without being replaced. One method used to determine when an animal died is to estimate the percentage of carbon-14 remaining in its bones. The **half-life** of carbon-14 is 5730 years. That is, half the original amount of carbon-14 in bones of a fossil will remain after 5730 years. The percentage P, in decimal form, of carbon-14 remaining after x years is modeled by $P(x) = a^x$. (Because of nuclear testing, radioactive carbon dating is no longer accurate for animals that died after 1950.)*

1. Find the value of a. (*Hint:* $P(5730) = 0.5$.)

2. Calculate the percentage of carbon-14 that remains after 10,000 years.

3. Estimate the age of a fossil with $P = 0.9$.

4. Estimate the age of a fossil with $P = 0.01$.

Exercises 5–8: Modeling Blood Flow in Animals For medical reasons, dyes are injected into the bloodstream to determine the health of internal organs. In one study that involved animals, the dye BSP was injected to assess blood flow in the liver. The results are listed in the accompanying table, where x represents the elapsed time in minutes and y is the concentration of the dye in the bloodstream in milligrams per milliliter (mg/mL). Scientists modeled the data with $f(x) = 0.133(0.878(0.73^x) + 0.122(0.92^x))$.

x (minutes)	1	2	3	4
y (mg/mL)	0.102	0.077	0.057	0.045

x (minutes)	5	7	9	13
y (mg/mL)	0.036	0.023	0.015	0.008

x (minutes)	16	19	22
y (mg/mL)	0.005	0.004	0.003

Source: F. Harrison, "The measurement of liver blood flow in conscious calves."

5. Graph f together with the data. Comment on the fit.

6. Determine the y-intercept and interpret the result.

7. What happens to the concentration of the dye after a long period of time? Explain.

8. Estimate graphically the time at which the concentration of the dye reached 40% of its initial amount. Would you want to solve this problem symbolically? Explain.

Exercises 9 and 10: Acid Rain Air pollutants frequently cause acid rain. An index of acidity is pH, which measures the concentration of the hydrogen ions in a solution, and ranges from 1 to 14. Pure water is neutral and has a pH of 7, acid solutions have a pH less than 7, and alkaline solutions have a pH greater than 7. The pH of a substance can be computed by $f(x) = -\log x$, where x represents the hydrogen ion concentration in moles per liter. Pure water exposed to normal carbon dioxide in the atmosphere has a pH of 5.6. If the pH of a lake drops below this level, it is indicative of an acidic lake. (Source: G. Howells, *Acid Rain and Acid Water.*)

9. In rural areas of Europe, rainwater typically has a hydrogen ion concentration of $x = 10^{-4.7}$. Find its pH. What effect might this rain have on a lake with a pH of 5.6?

10. Seawater has a pH of 8.2. Compared to seawater, how many times greater is the hydrogen ion concentration in rainwater from rural Europe?

Exercises 11 and 12: Investment Account If x dollars are deposited every 2 weeks (26 times per year) in an account paying an annual interest rate r, expressed in decimal form, the amount A in the account after n years can be approximated by the formula

$$A = x\left[\frac{(1 + r/26)^{26n} - 1}{(r/26)}\right].$$

11. If $100 is deposited every 2 weeks in an account paying 9% interest, approximate the amount in the account after 10 years.

12. Suppose that your retirement account pays 12% annual interest. Determine how much you should deposit in this account every 2 weeks, in order to have one million dollars at age 65.

Appendix A
Using the Graphing Calculator

Overview of the Appendix

This appendix provides instruction for the TI-83, TI-83 Plus, and TI-84 Plus graphing calculators that may be used in conjunction with this textbook. It includes specific keystrokes needed to work several examples from the text. Students are advised to consult the *Graphing Calculator Guidebook* provided by the manufacturer.

Entering Mathematical Expressions

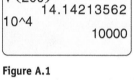

Figure A.1

EVALUATING π To evaluate π, use the following keystrokes, as shown in the first and second lines of Figure A.1. (Do *not* use 3.14 or $\frac{22}{7}$ for π.)

(2nd)(^[π])(ENTER)

EVALUATING A SQUARE ROOT To evaluate a square root, such as $\sqrt{200}$, use the following keystrokes, as shown in the third and fourth lines of Figure A.1.

(2nd)(x²[√])(2)(0)(0)( ))(ENTER)

EVALUATING AN EXPONENTIAL EXPRESSION To evaluate an exponential expression, such as 10^4, use the following keystrokes, as shown in the last two lines of Figure A.1.

(1)(0)(^)(4)(ENTER)

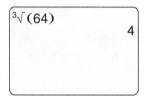

Figure A.2

EVALUATING A CUBE ROOT To evaluate a cube root, such as $\sqrt[3]{64}$, use the following keystrokes, as shown in Figure A.2.

(MATH)(4)(6)(4)( ))(ENTER)

SUMMARY: ENTERING MATHEMATICAL EXPRESSIONS

To access the *number* π, use (2nd)(^[π]).

To evaluate a *square root*, use (2nd)(x²[√]).

To evaluate an *exponential expression*, use the (^) key. To square a number, the (x²) key can also be used.

To evaluate a *cube root*, use (MATH)(4).

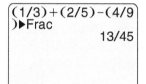

Figure A.3

Expressing Answers as Fractions

To evaluate $\frac{1}{3} + \frac{2}{5} - \frac{4}{9}$ in fraction form, use the following keystrokes, as shown in Figure A.3.

SUMMARY: EXPRESSING ANSWERS AS FRACTIONS

Enter the arithmetic expression. To access the "Frac" feature, use the keystrokes (MATH)(1). Then press (ENTER).

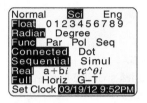

Figure A.4

Displaying Numbers in Scientific Notation

To display numbers in scientific notation, set the graphing calculator in scientific mode (Sci) by using the following keystrokes. See Figure A.4. (These keystrokes assume that the calculator is starting from normal mode.)

(MODE)(▷)(ENTER)(2nd)(MODE [QUIT])

In scientific mode we can display the numbers 5432 and 0.00001234 in scientific notation, as shown in Figure A.5.

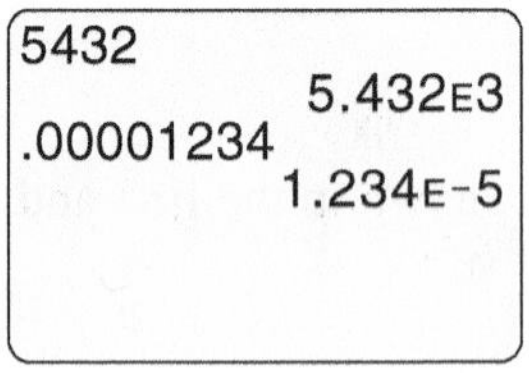

```
5432
            5.432E3
.00001234
            1.234E-5
```

Figure A.5

SUMMARY: SETTING SCIENTIFIC MODE

If your calculator is in normal mode, it can be set in scientific mode by pressing

(MODE)(▷)(ENTER)(2nd)(MODE [QUIT]).

These keystrokes return the graphing calculator to the home screen.

Entering Numbers in Scientific Notation

Numbers can be entered in scientific notation. For example, to enter 4.2×10^{-3} in scientific notation, use the following keystrokes. (Be sure to use the negation key $(-)$ rather than the subtraction key.)

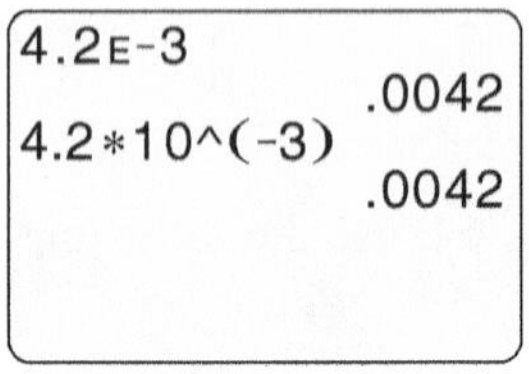

```
4.2E-3
            .0042
4.2*10^(-3)
            .0042
```

Figure A.6

This number can also be entered using the following keystrokes. See Figure A.6.

SUMMARY: ENTERING NUMBERS IN SCIENTIFIC NOTATION

One way to enter a number in scientific notation is to use the keystrokes

(2nd)(,[EE])

to access an exponent (EE) of 10.

```
Plot1  Plot2  Plot3
\Y1=3X+1
\Y2=
\Y3=
\Y4=
\Y5=
\Y6=
\Y7=
```

Figure A.7

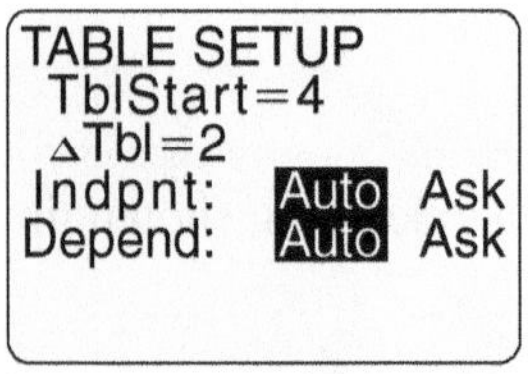

Making a Table

To make a table of values for $y = 3x + 1$ starting at $x = 4$ and incrementing by 2, begin by pressing (Y=) and then entering the formula $Y_1 = 3X + 1$, as shown in Figure A.7. (See Entering a Formula on page AP-4.) To set the table parameters, press the following keys. See Figure A.8.

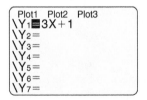

Figure A.8

(2nd)(WINDOW [TBLSET])(4)(ENTER)(2)

X	Y₁	
4	13	
6	19	
8	25	
10	31	
12	37	
14	43	
16	49	
Y₁■3X+1		

Figure A.9

These keystrokes specify a table that starts at $x = 4$ and increments the x-values by 2. Therefore, the values of Y_1 at $x = 4, 6, 8, \ldots$ appear in the table. To create this table, press the following keys.

$$\boxed{\text{2nd}}\ \boxed{\text{GRAPH [TABLE]}}$$

We can scroll through x- and y-values by using the arrow keys. See Figure A.9. Note that there is no first or last x-value in the table.

SUMMARY: MAKING A TABLE

1. Enter the formula for the equation using $\boxed{Y =}$.
2. Press $\boxed{\text{2nd}}\boxed{\text{WINDOW [TBLSET]}}$ to set the starting x-value and the increment between x-values appearing in the table.
3. Create the table by pressing $\boxed{\text{2nd}}\boxed{\text{GRAPH [TABLE]}}$.

Setting the Viewing Rectangle (Window)

ZOOM MEMORY
1:ZBox
2:Zoom In
3:Zoom Out
4:ZDecimal
5:ZSquare
6:ZStandard
7↓ZTrig

Figure A.10

There are at least two ways to set the standard viewing rectangle of $[-10, 10, 1]$ by $[-10, 10, 1]$. The first involves pressing $\boxed{\text{ZOOM}}$ followed by $\boxed{6}$. See Figure A.10. The second method for setting the standard viewing rectangle is to press $\boxed{\text{WINDOW}}$ and enter the following keystrokes. See Figure A.11.

$$\boxed{(-)}\ \boxed{1}\ \boxed{0}\ \boxed{\text{ENTER}}\ \boxed{1}\ \boxed{0}\ \boxed{\text{ENTER}}\ \boxed{1}\ \boxed{\text{ENTER}}$$
$$\boxed{(-)}\ \boxed{1}\ \boxed{0}\ \boxed{\text{ENTER}}\ \boxed{1}\ \boxed{0}\ \boxed{\text{ENTER}}\ \boxed{1}\ \boxed{\text{ENTER}}$$

WINDOW
 Xmin =-10
 Xmax = 10
 Xscl = 1
 Ymin =-10
 Ymax = 10
 Yscl = 1
 Xres = 1

Figure A.11

(Be sure to use the negation key $(-)$ rather than the subtraction key.) Other viewing rectangles can be set in a similar manner by pressing $\boxed{\text{WINDOW}}$ and entering the appropriate values. To see the viewing rectangle, press $\boxed{\text{GRAPH}}$.

SUMMARY: SETTING THE VIEWING RECTANGLE

To set the standard viewing rectangle, press $\boxed{\text{ZOOM}}\ \boxed{6}$. To set any viewing rectangle, press $\boxed{\text{WINDOW}}$ and enter the necessary values. To see the viewing rectangle, press $\boxed{\text{GRAPH}}$.

NOTE: You do not need to change "Xres" from 1.

L1	L2	L3	1
1	4	------	
2	5		
3	6		
------	------		
L1={1, 2, 3}			

Figure A.12

Making a Scatterplot or a Line Graph

To make a scatterplot with the points $(-5, -5)$, $(-2, 3)$, $(1, -7)$, and $(4, 8)$, begin by following these steps.

1. Press $\boxed{\text{STAT}}$ followed by $\boxed{1}$.
2. If list L1 is not empty, use the arrow keys to place the cursor on L1, as shown in Figure A.12. Then press $\boxed{\text{CLEAR}}$ followed by $\boxed{\text{ENTER}}$. This deletes all elements in the list. Similarly, if L2 is not empty, clear the list.
3. Input each x-value into list L1 followed by $\boxed{\text{ENTER}}$. Input each y-value into list L2 followed by $\boxed{\text{ENTER}}$. See Figure A.13.

L1	L2	L3	1
-5	-5	------	
-2	3		
1	-7		
4	8		
-----	------		
L1(5) =			

Figure A.13

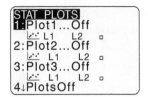

Figure A.14

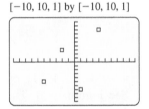

Figure A.15

[−10, 10, 1] by [−10, 10, 1]

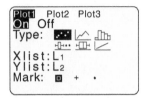

Figure A.16

It is essential that both lists have the same number of values—otherwise, an error message appears when a scatterplot is attempted. Before these four points can be plotted, "STAT PLOT" must be turned on. It is accessed by pressing

$$\boxed{\text{2nd}}\ \boxed{\text{Y =}\ \text{[STAT PLOT]}},$$

as shown in Figure A.14.

There are three possible "STAT PLOTS," numbered 1, 2, and 3. Any one of the three can be selected. The first plot can be selected by pressing $\boxed{1}$. Next, place the cursor over "On" and press $\boxed{\text{ENTER}}$ to turn "Plot1" on. There are six types of plots that can be selected. The first type is a *scatterplot* and the second type is a *line graph*, so place the cursor over the first type of plot and press $\boxed{\text{ENTER}}$ to select a scatterplot. (To make the line graph, place the cursor over the second type of plot and press $\boxed{\text{ENTER}}$.) The *x*-values are stored in list L1, so select L1 for "Xlist" by pressing $\boxed{\text{2nd}}\boxed{1}$. Similarly, press $\boxed{\text{2nd}}\boxed{2}$ for the "Ylist," since the *y*-values are stored in list L2. Finally, there are three styles of marks that can be used to show data points in the graph. We will usually use the first because it is largest and shows up the best. Make the screen appear as in Figure A.15. Before plotting the four data points, be sure to set an appropriate viewing rectangle. Then press $\boxed{\text{GRAPH}}$. The data points appear as in Figure A.16.

REMARK 1: A fast way to set the viewing rectangle for any scatterplot is to select the "ZOOMSTAT" feature by pressing $\boxed{\text{ZOOM}}\boxed{9}$. This feature automatically scales the viewing rectangle so that all data points are shown.

REMARK 2: If an equation has been entered into the $\boxed{\text{Y =}}$ menu and selected, it will be graphed with the data. This feature is used frequently to model data.

SUMMARY: MAKING A SCATTERPLOT OR A LINE GRAPH

The following are basic steps necessary to make either a scatterplot or a line graph.

1. Use $\boxed{\text{STAT}}\boxed{1}$ to access lists L1 and L2.
2. If list L1 is not empty, place the cursor on L1 and press $\boxed{\text{CLEAR}}\boxed{\text{ENTER}}$. Repeat for list L2, if it is not empty.
3. Enter the *x*-values into list L1 and the *y*-values into list L2.
4. Use $\boxed{\text{2nd}}\boxed{\text{Y =}\ \text{[STAT PLOT]}}$ to select appropriate parameters for the scatterplot or line graph.
5. Set an appropriate viewing rectangle. Press $\boxed{\text{GRAPH}}$. Otherwise, press $\boxed{\text{ZOOM}}\boxed{9}$. This feature automatically sets the viewing rectangle and plots the data.

NOTE: $\boxed{\text{ZOOM}}\boxed{9}$ *cannot* be used to set a viewing rectangle for the graph of an equation.

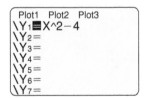

Figure A.17

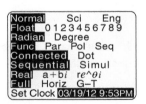

Figure A.18

Entering a Formula

To enter a formula, press $\boxed{\text{Y =}}$. For example, use the following keystrokes after "$Y_1 =$" to enter $y = x^2 - 4$. See Figure A.17.

$$\boxed{\text{Y =}}\ \boxed{\text{CLEAR}}\ \boxed{\text{X, T, }\theta\text{, }n}\ \boxed{\wedge}\ \boxed{2}\ \boxed{-}\ \boxed{4}$$

Note that there is a built-in key to enter the variable X. If "$Y_1 =$" does not appear after pressing $\boxed{\text{Y =}}$, press $\boxed{\text{MODE}}$ and make sure the calculator is set in *function mode*, denoted "Func". See Figure A.18.

SUMMARY: ENTERING A FORMULA

To enter a formula, press Ⓨ=. To delete a formula, press CLEAR.

Graphing an Equation

[−10, 10, 1] by [−10, 10, 1]

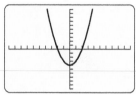

Figure A.19

To graph an equation, such as $y = x^2 - 4$, start by pressing Ⓨ= and enter $Y_1 = X^2 - 4$. If there is an equation already entered, remove it by pressing CLEAR. The equals signs in "$Y_1 =$" should be in reverse video (a dark rectangle surrounding a white equals sign), which indicates that the equation will be graphed. If the equals sign is not in reverse video, place the cursor over it and press ENTER. Set an appropriate viewing rectangle and then press GRAPH. The graph will appear in the specified viewing rectangle. See Figures A.17 and A.19.

SUMMARY: GRAPHING AN EQUATION

1. Use the Ⓨ= menu to enter the formula.
2. Use the WINDOW menu to set an appropriate viewing rectangle.
3. Press GRAPH.

Graphing a Vertical Line

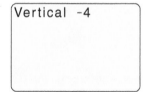

Figure A.20

Set an appropriate window (or viewing rectangle). Then return to the home screen by pressing

$$\text{2nd} \quad \text{MODE [QUIT]}.$$

To graph a vertical line, such as $x = -4$, press

$$\text{2nd} \quad \text{PRGM [DRAW]} \quad 4 \quad (-) \quad 4.$$

See Figure A.20. Pressing ENTER will make the vertical line appear, as shown in Figure A.21.

[−6, 6, 1] by [−6, 6, 1]

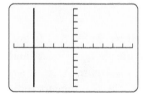

Figure A.21

SUMMARY: GRAPHING THE VERTICAL LINE $x = h$

1. Set an appropriate window by pressing WINDOW.
2. Return to the home screen by pressing 2nd MODE [QUIT].
3. Draw a vertical line by pressing 2nd PRGM [DRAW] 4 h ENTER.

Squaring a Viewing Rectangle

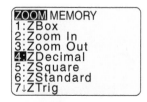

Figure A.22

In a square viewing rectangle the graph of $y = x$ is a line that makes a 45° angle with the positive x-axis, a circle appears circular, and all sides of a square have the same length. An approximate square viewing rectangle can be set if the distance along the x-axis is 1.5 times the distance along the y-axis. Examples of viewing rectangles that are (approximately) square include

$$[-6, 6, 1] \text{ by } [-4, 4, 1] \quad \text{and} \quad [-9, 9, 1] \text{ by } [-6, 6, 1].$$

Square viewing rectangles can be set automatically by pressing either

$$\text{ZOOM} \quad 4 \quad \text{or} \quad \text{ZOOM} \quad 5.$$

ZOOM 4 provides a *decimal window*, which is discussed on page AP-11. See Figure A.22.

Either $\boxed{\text{ZOOM}}\boxed{4}$ or $\boxed{\text{ZOOM}}\boxed{5}$ may be used to produce a square viewing rectangle. An (approximately) square viewing rectangle has the form

$$[-1.5k, 1.5k, 1] \text{ by } [-k, k, 1],$$

where k is a positive number.

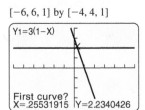

Figure A.23

Locating a Point of Intersection

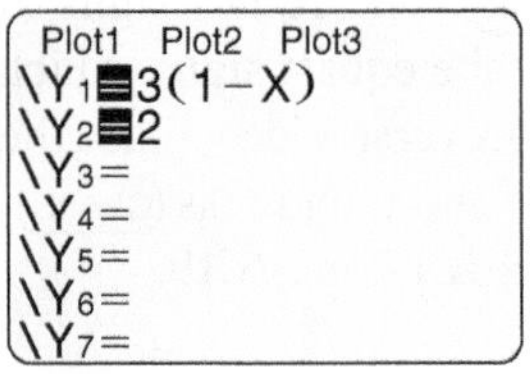

To find the point of intersection for the graphs of

$$y_1 = 3(1 - x) \quad \text{and} \quad y_2 = 2,$$

start by entering Y_1 and Y_2, as shown in Figure A.23. Set the window, and graph both equations. Then press the following keys to find the intersection point.

$$\boxed{\text{2nd}}\boxed{\text{TRACE [CALC]}}\boxed{5}$$

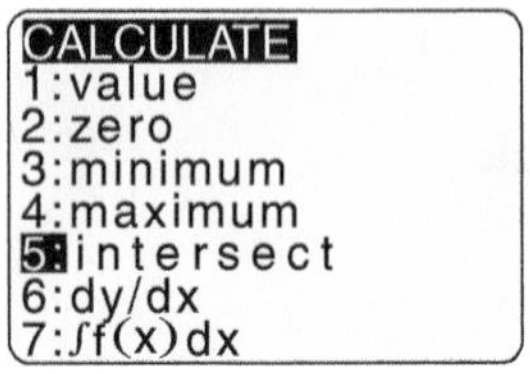

```
CALCULATE
1:value
2:zero
3:minimum
4:maximum
5:intersect
6:dy/dx
7:∫f(x)dx
```

Figure A.24

See Figure A.24, where the "intersect" utility is being selected. The calculator prompts for the first curve, as shown in Figure A.25. Use the arrow keys to locate the cursor near the point of intersection and press $\boxed{\text{ENTER}}$. Repeat these steps for the second curve. Finally we are prompted for a guess. For each of the three prompts, place the free-moving cursor near the point of intersection and press $\boxed{\text{ENTER}}$. The approximate coordinates of the point of intersection will be shown.

$[-6, 6, 1]$ by $[-4, 4, 1]$

```
Y1=3(1-X)




First curve?
X=.25531915  Y=2.2340426
```

Figure A.25

SUMMARY: FINDING A POINT OF INTERSECTION

1. Graph the two equations in an appropriate viewing rectangle.
2. Press $\boxed{\text{2nd}}\boxed{\text{TRACE [CALC]}}\boxed{5}$.
3. Use the arrow keys to select an approximate location for the point of intersection. Press $\boxed{\text{ENTER}}$ to make the three selections for "First curve?", "Second curve?", and "Guess?". (Note that if the cursor is near the point of intersection, you usually do not need to move the cursor for each selection. Just press $\boxed{\text{ENTER}}$ three times.)

Shading Inequalities

To shade the solution set for one or more linear inequalities such as $2x + y \le 5$ and $-2x + y \ge 1$, begin by solving each inequality for y to obtain $y \le 5 - 2x$ and $y \ge 2x + 1$. Then let $Y_1 = 5 - 2X$ and $Y_2 = 2X + 1$, as shown in Figure A.26. Position the cursor to the left of Y_1 and press $\boxed{\text{ENTER}}$ three times. The triangle that appears indicates that the calculator will shade the region below the graph of Y_1. Next locate the cursor to the left of Y_2 and press $\boxed{\text{ENTER}}$ twice. This triangle indicates that the calculator will shade the region above the graph of Y_2. After setting the viewing rectangle to $[-15, 15, 5]$ by $[-10, 10, 5]$, press $\boxed{\text{GRAPH}}$. The result is shown in Figure A.27.

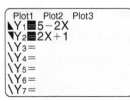

Figure A.26

$[-15, 15, 5]$ by $[-10, 10, 5]$

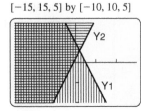

Figure A.27

SUMMARY: SHADING ONE OR MORE INEQUALITIES

1. Solve each inequality for y.
2. Enter each formula as Y_1 and Y_2 in the $\boxed{Y=}$ menu.
3. Locate the cursor to the left of Y_1 and press $\boxed{\text{ENTER}}$ two or three times to shade either above or below the graph of Y_1. Repeat for Y_2.
4. Set an appropriate viewing rectangle.
5. Press $\boxed{\text{GRAPH}}$.

NOTE: The "Shade" utility in the DRAW menu can also be used to shade the region *between* two graphs.

Figure A.28

Setting $a + bi$ Mode

To evaluate expressions containing square roots of negative numbers, such as $\sqrt{-25}$, set your calculator in $a + bi$ mode by using the following keystrokes.

See Figures A.28 and A.29.

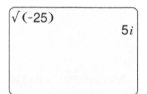

Figure A.29

SUMMARY: SETTING $a + bi$ MODE

1. Press $\boxed{\text{MODE}}$.
2. Move the cursor to the seventh line, highlight $a + bi$, and press $\boxed{\text{ENTER}}$.
3. Press $\boxed{\text{2nd}}$ $\boxed{\text{MODE [QUIT]}}$ and return to the home screen.

Evaluating Complex Arithmetic

Complex arithmetic can be performed much like other arithmetic expressions. This is done by entering

to obtain the imaginary unit i from the home screen. For example, to find the sum $(-2 + 3i) + (4 - 6i)$, perform the following keystrokes on the home screen.

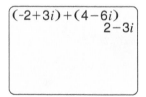

Figure A.30

The result is shown in Figure A.30. Other complex arithmetic operations are done similarly.

SUMMARY: EVALUATING COMPLEX ARITHMETIC

Enter a complex expression in the same way as you would any arithmetic expression. To obtain the complex number i, use $\boxed{\text{2nd}}$ $\boxed{. [i]}$.

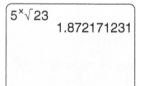

Figure A.31

Other Mathematical Expressions

EVALUATING OTHER ROOTS To evaluate a fifth root, such as $\sqrt[5]{23}$, use the following keystrokes, as shown in Figure A.31.

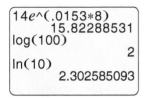

```
14e^(.0153*8)
         15.82288531
log(100)
                    2
ln(10)
          2.302585093
```

Figure A.32

EVALUATING THE NATURAL EXPONENTIAL FUNCTION To evaluate $14e^{0.0153(8)}$, use the following keystrokes, as shown in the first and second lines of Figure A.32.

(1)(4)(2nd)(LN [eˣ])(.)(0)(1)(5)(3)(×)(8)( ))(ENTER)

EVALUATING THE COMMON LOGARITHMIC FUNCTION To evaluate $\log(100)$, use the following keystrokes, as shown in the third and fourth lines of Figure A.32.

(LOG)(1)(0)(0)( ))(ENTER)

EVALUATING THE NATURAL LOGARITHMIC FUNCTION To evaluate ln (10), use the following keystrokes, as shown in the last two lines of Figure A.32.

(LN)(1)(0)( ))(ENTER)

SUMMARY: OTHER MATHEMATICAL EXPRESSIONS

To evaluate a *kth root*, use (k)(MATH)(5).

To access the *natural exponential function*, use (2nd)(LN [eˣ]).

To access the *common logarithmic function*, use (LOG).

To access the *natural logarithmic function*, use (LN).

Accessing the Absolute Value

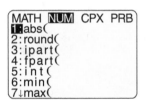

```
MATH NUM CPX PRB
1:abs(
2:round(
3:ipart(
4:fpart(
5:int(
6:min(
7↓max(
```

Figure A.33

To graph $y_1 = |x - 50|$, begin by entering $Y_1 = \text{abs}(X - 50)$. The absolute value (abs) is accessed by pressing

(MATH)(▷)(1).

See Figure A.33.

SUMMARY: ACCESSING THE ABSOLUTE VALUE

1. Press (MATH).
2. Position the cursor over "NUM".
3. Press (1) to select the absolute value.

Entering the Elements of a Matrix

The elements of the augmented matrix A given by

$$A = \begin{bmatrix} 1 & 1 & 2 & | & 1 \\ -1 & 0 & 1 & | & -2 \\ 2 & 1 & 5 & | & -1 \end{bmatrix}$$

can be entered by using the following keystrokes on the TI-83 Plus or TI-84 Plus to define a matrix A with dimension 3×4. (*Note:* On the TI-83 the matrix menu is found by pressing (MATRX).)

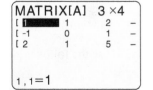

```
MATRIX[A]  3 ×4
[ 1      1      2    –
[ -1     0      1    –
[ 2      1      5    –

1,1=1
```

Figure A.34

(2nd)(x⁻¹ [MATRIX])(▷)(▷)(1)(3)(ENTER)(4)(ENTER)

Input the 12 elements of the matrix A, row by row. Finish each entry by pressing (ENTER). See Figure A.34. After these elements have been entered, press

(2nd)(MODE [QUIT])

```
[A]
   [[ 1   1   2   1 ]
    [-1   0   1  -2]
    [ 2   1   5  -1]]
```

Figure A.35

to return to the home screen. To display the matrix A, press

$$\boxed{2nd}\boxed{x^{-1} \text{ [MATRIX]}}\boxed{1}\boxed{\text{ENTER}}.$$

See Figure A.35.

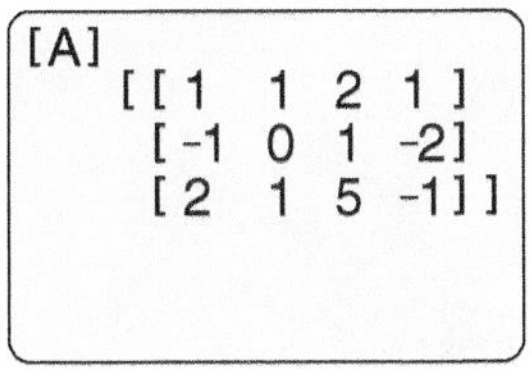

SUMMARY: ENTERING THE ELEMENTS OF A MATRIX A

1. Begin by accessing the matrix A by pressing $\boxed{2nd}\boxed{x^{-1}\text{ [MATRIX]}}\boxed{\triangleright}\boxed{\triangleright}\boxed{1}$.
2. Enter the dimension of A by pressing $\boxed{m}\boxed{\text{ENTER}}\boxed{n}\boxed{\text{ENTER}}$, where the dimension of the matrix is $m \times n$.
3. Input each element of the matrix, row by row. Finish each entry by pressing $\boxed{\text{ENTER}}$. Use $\boxed{2nd}\boxed{\text{MODE [QUIT]}}$ to return to the home screen.

NOTE: On the TI-83, replace the keystrokes $\boxed{2nd}\boxed{x^{-1}\text{ [MATRIX]}}$ with $\boxed{\text{MATRX}}$.

Reduced Row–Echelon Form

To find the reduced row–echelon form of matrix A (entered above in Figure A.35), use the following keystrokes from the home screen on the TI-83 Plus or TI-84 Plus.

$$\boxed{2nd}\boxed{x^{-1}\text{ [MATRIX]}}\boxed{\triangleright}\boxed{\text{ALPHA}}\boxed{\text{APPS [B]}}\boxed{2nd}\boxed{x^{-1}\text{ [MATRIX]}}\boxed{1}\boxed{)}\boxed{\text{ENTER}}$$

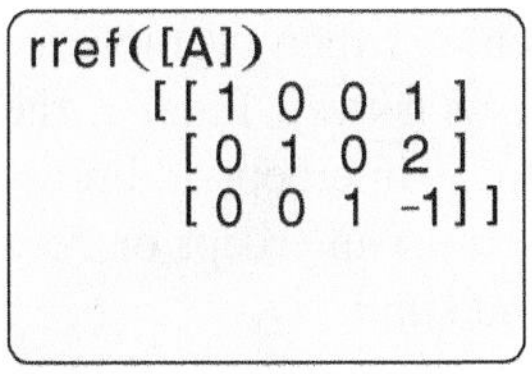

```
rref([A])
   [[1  0  0   1]
    [0  1  0   2]
    [0  0  1  -1]]
```

Figure A.36

The resulting matrix is shown in Figure A.36. On the TI-83 graphing calculator, use the following keystrokes to find the reduced row–echelon form.

$$\boxed{\text{MATRX}}\boxed{\triangleright}\boxed{\text{ALPHA}}\boxed{\text{MATRX [B]}}\boxed{\text{MATRX}}\boxed{1}\boxed{)}\boxed{\text{ENTER}}$$

SUMMARY: FINDING THE REDUCED ROW–ECHELON FORM OF A MATRIX

1. To make rref([A]) appear on the home screen, use the following keystrokes for the TI-83 Plus or TI-84 Plus graphing calculator.

$$\boxed{2nd}\boxed{x^{-1}\text{ [MATRIX]}}\boxed{\triangleright}\boxed{\text{ALPHA}}\boxed{\text{APPS [B]}}\boxed{2nd}\boxed{x^{-1}\text{ [MATRIX]}}\boxed{1}\boxed{)}$$

2. Press $\boxed{\text{ENTER}}$ to calculate the reduced row–echelon form.
3. Use arrow keys to access elements that do not appear on the screen.

NOTE: On the TI-83, replace the keystrokes $\boxed{2nd}\boxed{x^{-1}\text{ [MATRIX]}}$ with $\boxed{\text{MATRX}}$ and $\boxed{\text{APPS [B]}}$ with $\boxed{\text{MATRX [B]}}$.

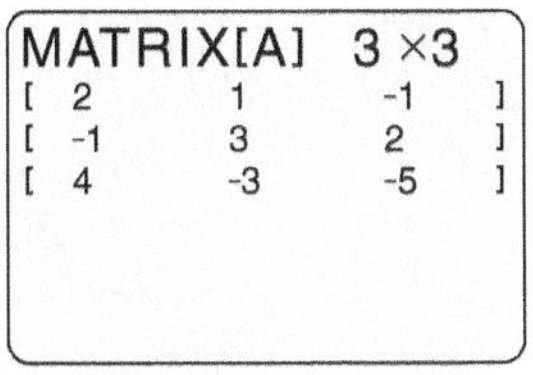

```
MATRIX[A]  3×3
[  2      1     -1   ]
[ -1      3      2   ]
[  4     -3     -5   ]
```

Figure A.37

Evaluating a Determinant

To evaluate the determinant of matrix A given by

$$A = \begin{bmatrix} 2 & 1 & -1 \\ -1 & 3 & 2 \\ 4 & -3 & -5 \end{bmatrix},$$

start by entering the 9 elements of the 3×3 matrix, as shown in Figure A.37. To compute det A, perform the following keystrokes from the home screen.

$$\boxed{2nd}\boxed{x^{-1}\text{ [MATRIX]}}\boxed{\triangleright}\boxed{1}\boxed{2nd}\boxed{x^{-1}\text{ [MATRIX]}}\boxed{1}\boxed{)}\boxed{\text{ENTER}}$$

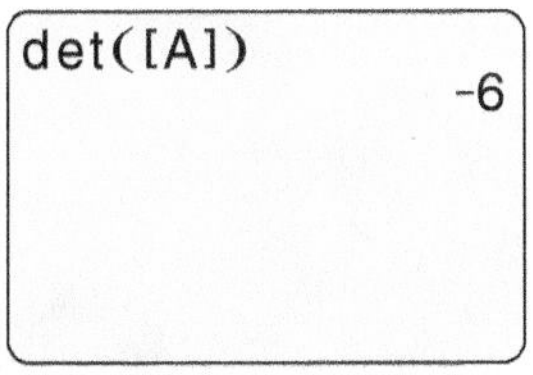

```
det([A])
                -6
```

Figure A.38

The results are shown in Figure A.38.

SUMMARY: EVALUATING A DETERMINANT OF A MATRIX

1. Enter the dimension and elements of the matrix A.
2. Return to the home screen by pressing (2nd)(MODE [QUIT]).
3. On the TI-83 Plus or TI-84 Plus, perform the following keystrokes.

(2nd)(x^{-1} [MATRIX])($\triangleright$)(1)(2nd)(x^{-1} [MATRIX])(1)())(ENTER)

NOTE: On the TI-83, replace the keystrokes (2nd)(x^{-1} [MATRIX]) with (MATRX).

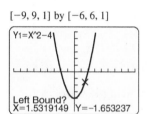

CALCULATE
1:value
2:zero
3:minimum
4:maximum
5:intersect
6:dy/dx
7:∫f(x)dx

Figure A.39

Locating an *x*-Intercept or Zero

To locate an *x*-intercept or *zero* of $f(x) = x^2 - 4$, start by entering $Y_1 = X^2 - 4$ into the (Y=) menu. Set the viewing rectangle to $[-9, 9, 1]$ by $[-6, 6, 1]$ and graph Y_1. Afterwards, press the following keys to invoke the zero finder. See Figure A.39.

(2nd)(TRACE [CALC])(2)

The graphing calculator prompts for a left bound. Use the arrow keys to set the cursor to the left of the *x*-intercept and press (ENTER). The graphing calculator then prompts for a right bound. Set the cursor to the right of the *x*-intercept and press (ENTER). Finally, the graphing calculator prompts for a guess. Set the cursor roughly at the *x*-intercept and press (ENTER). See Figures A.40–A.42. The calculator then approximates the *x*-intercept or zero automatically, as shown in Figure A.43. The zero of -2 can be found similarly.

$[-9, 9, 1]$ by $[-6, 6, 1]$

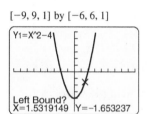

Y1=X^2−4

Left Bound?
X=1.5319149 Y=−1.653237

Figure A.40

$[-9, 9, 1]$ by $[-6, 6, 1]$

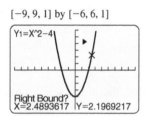

Y1=X^2−4

Right Bound?
X=2.4893617 Y=2.1969217

Figure A.41

$[-9, 9, 1]$ by $[-6, 6, 1]$

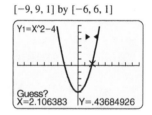

Y1=X^2−4

Guess?
X=2.106383 Y=.43684926

Figure A.42

$[-9, 9, 1]$ by $[-6, 6, 1]$

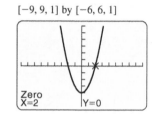

Zero
X=2 Y=0

Figure A.43

SUMMARY: LOCATING AN *x*-INTERCEPT OR ZERO

1. Graph the function in an appropriate viewing rectangle.
2. Press (2nd)(TRACE [CALC])(2).
3. Select the left and right bounds, followed by a guess. Press (ENTER) after each selection. The calculator then approximates the *x*-intercept or zero.

Normal Sci Eng
Float 0123456789
Radian Degree
Func Par Pol Seq
Connected Dot
Sequential Simul
Real a+b*i* re^θ*i*
Full Horiz G-T
Set Clock 03/19/12 9:54PM

Figure A.44

Setting Connected or Dot Mode

To set your graphing calculator in dot mode, press (MODE), position the cursor over "Dot," and press (ENTER). See Figure A.44. Graphs will now appear in dot mode rather than connected mode.

SUMMARY: SETTING CONNECTED OR DOT MODE

1. Press (MODE).
2. Position the cursor over "Connected" or "Dot". Press (ENTER).

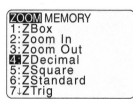

Figure A.45

Setting a Decimal Window

With a decimal window, the cursor stops on convenient x-values. In the decimal window $[-9.4, 9.4, 1]$ by $[-6.2, 6.2, 1]$ the cursor stops on x-values that are multiples of 0.2. If we reduce the viewing rectangle to $[-4.7, 4.7, 1]$ by $[-3.1, 3.1, 1]$, the cursor stops on x-values that are multiples of 0.1. To set this smaller window automatically, press (ZOOM)(4). See Figure A.45. Decimal windows are also useful when graphing rational functions with asymptotes in connected mode.

SUMMARY: SETTING A DECIMAL WINDOW

1. Press (ZOOM)(4) to set the viewing rectangle $[-4.7, 4.7, 1]$ by $[-3.1, 3.1, 1]$.
2. A larger decimal window is $[-9.4, 9.4, 1]$ by $[-6.2, 6.2, 1]$.

Finding Maximum and Minimum Values

To find a minimum y-value (or vertex) on the graph of $f(x) = 1.5x^2 - 6x + 4$, start by entering $Y_1 = 1.5X\verb|^|2 - 6X + 4$ from the (Y =) menu. Set the viewing rectangle and then perform the following keystrokes to find the minimum y-value.

(2nd)(TRACE [CALC])(3)

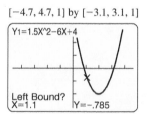

Figure A.46

See Figure A.46.

The calculator prompts for a left bound. Use the arrow keys to position the cursor left of the vertex and press (ENTER). Similarly, position the cursor to the right of the vertex for the right bound and press (ENTER). Finally, the graphing calculator asks for a guess between the left and right bounds. Place the cursor near the vertex and press (ENTER). See Figures A.47–A.49. The minimum value is shown in Figure A.50.

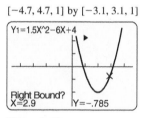

Figure A.47

Figure A.48

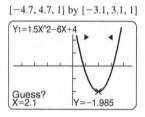

Figure A.49

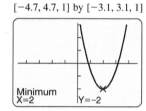

Figure A.50

A maximum of the function f on an interval can be found similarly, except enter

(2nd)(TRACE [CALC])(4).

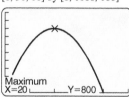

Figure A.51

The calculator prompts for left and right bounds, followed by a guess. Press (ENTER) after the cursor has been located appropriately for each prompt. The graphing calculator will display the maximum y-value. An example is shown in Figure A.51, where $f(x) = x(80 - 2x)$.

SUMMARY: FINDING MAXIMUM AND MINIMUM VALUES

1. Graph the function in an appropriate viewing rectangle.
2. Press (2nd)(TRACE [CALC])(3) to find a minimum y-value.
3. Press (2nd)(TRACE [CALC])(4) to find a maximum y-value.
4. Use the arrow keys to locate the left and right x-bounds, followed by a guess. Press (ENTER) to select each position of the cursor.

Answers to Selected Exercises

SECTION 1.1 (pp. 9–11)

1. natural   **2.** 0   **3.** 1   **4.** composite   **5.** factors
6. formula   **7.** variable   **8.** equals sign   **9.** sum
10. product   **11.** quotient   **12.** difference
13. Composite; $4 = 2 \cdot 2$ **15.** Neither   **17.** Prime
19. Composite; $92 = 2 \cdot 2 \cdot 23$
21. Composite; $225 = 3 \cdot 3 \cdot 5 \cdot 5$ **23.** Prime
25. $6 = 2 \cdot 3$ **27.** $12 = 2 \cdot 2 \cdot 3$
29. $32 = 2 \cdot 2 \cdot 2 \cdot 2 \cdot 2$ **31.** $39 = 3 \cdot 13$
33. $294 = 2 \cdot 3 \cdot 7 \cdot 7$ **35.** $300 = 2 \cdot 2 \cdot 3 \cdot 5 \cdot 5$
37. Yes   **39.** No   **41.** Yes   **43.** No   **45.** 15   **47.** 5   **49.** 4
51. 18   **53.** 4   **55.** 22   **57.** 12   **59.** 9   **61.** 5   **63.** 28
65. 7   **67.** 5   **69.** 0   **71.** 3   **73.** $x + 5$; x is the number.
75. $3s$; s is the cost of soda.   **77.** $n + 5$; n is the number.
79. $p - 200$; p is the population.   **81.** $\frac{z}{6}$; z is the number.
83. st; s is the speed and t is the time.
85. $\frac{x + 7}{y}$; x is one number, y is the other number.
87. $P = 100D$
89.

Yards (y)	1	2	3	4	5	6	7
Feet (F)	3	6	9	12	15	18	21

$F = 3y$
91. $M = 3x$; 108 mi   **93.** $B = 6D$ **95.** $C = 12x$
97. 198 square feet

SECTION 1.2 (pp. 23–26)

1. $\frac{3}{4}$; $\frac{1}{4}$ **2.** 11; 21   **3.** 0   **4.** lowest   **5.** True   **6.** False
7. $\frac{a}{b}$ **8.** multiply   **9.** $\frac{1}{a}$ **10.** $\frac{1}{5}$ **11.** $\frac{ac}{bd}$ **12.** $\frac{ad}{bc}$ **13.** $\frac{a + c}{b}$
14. $\frac{a - c}{b}$ **15.** 4   **17.** 25   **19.** 10   **21.** $\frac{3}{5}$ **23.** $\frac{3}{5}$ **25.** $\frac{1}{2}$
27. $\frac{2}{5}$ **29.** $\frac{1}{3}$ **31.** $\frac{2}{5}$ **33.** $\frac{1}{4}$ **35.** $\frac{3}{20}$ **37.** 1   **39.** $\frac{3}{5}$
41. $\frac{12}{5}$ **43.** $\frac{3}{4}$ **45.** 1   **47.** $\frac{3a}{2b}$ **49.** $\frac{3}{16}$ **51.** 4   **53.** $\frac{1}{3}$
55. (a) $\frac{1}{5}$ (b) $\frac{1}{7}$ (c) $\frac{7}{4}$ (d) $\frac{8}{9}$
57. (a) 2   (b) 9   (c) $\frac{101}{12}$ (d) $\frac{17}{31}$
59. $\frac{3}{2}$ **61.** 6   **63.** 1   **65.** $\frac{4}{3}$ **67.** 12   **69.** $\frac{3}{10}$ **71.** $\frac{a}{2}$
73. 1   **75.** (a) $\frac{1}{2}$ (b) $\frac{1}{3}$ **77.** (a) $\frac{25}{29}$ (b) $\frac{11}{29}$ **79.** 45
81. 15   **83.** 24   **85.** 12   **87.** 24   **89.** $\frac{3}{6}, \frac{4}{6}$ **91.** $\frac{28}{36}, \frac{15}{36}$
93. $\frac{3}{48}, \frac{28}{48}$ **95.** $\frac{4}{12}, \frac{9}{12}, \frac{10}{12}$ **97.** $\frac{13}{16}$ **99.** $\frac{1}{6}$ **101.** $\frac{59}{70}$
103. $\frac{13}{36}$ **105.** $\frac{17}{600}$ **107.** $\frac{9}{8}$ **109.** $4\frac{3}{4}$ ft   **111.** $32\frac{5}{16}$ inches
113. $\frac{5}{8}$ yd^2 **115.** $8\frac{1}{4}$ miles   **117.** $\frac{1}{6250}$ **119.** $\frac{961}{1260}$

CHECKING BASIC CONCEPTS 1.1 & 1.2 (p. 26)

1. (a) Prime   (b) Composite; $28 = 2 \cdot 2 \cdot 7$
(c) Neither   (d) Composite; $180 = 2 \cdot 2 \cdot 3 \cdot 3 \cdot 5$
2. 2   **3.** 30   **4.** $x + 5$ **5.** $I = 12F$ **6.** (a) 3   (b) 8
7. (a) $\frac{5}{7}$ (b) $\frac{2}{3}$ **8.** $\frac{3}{4}$ **9.** (a) $\frac{1}{2}$ (b) $\frac{1}{4}$ (c) $\frac{2}{5}$ (d) $\frac{7}{12}$
10. $3\frac{1}{3}$ cups

SECTION 1.3 (pp. 32–33)

1. multiply   **2.** 2   **3.** base; exponent   **4.** 6^2 **5.** 8^3
6. 17; multiplication; addition   **7.** 2; exponents; subtraction
8. 4; left; right   **9.** False   **10.** False   **11.** 3^4 **13.** 2^5
15. $\left(\frac{1}{2}\right)^4$ **17.** a^5 **19.** $(x + 3)^2$ **21.** (a) 16   (b) 16
23. (a) 6   (b) 1   **25.** (a) 32   (b) 1000   **27.** (a) $\frac{4}{9}$ (b) $\frac{1}{32}$
29. 2^3 **31.** 5^2 **33.** 7^2 **35.** 10^3 **37.** $\left(\frac{1}{2}\right)^4$ **39.** $\left(\frac{2}{3}\right)^5$
41. 29   **43.** 4   **45.** 90   **47.** 3   **49.** 2   **51.** 19   **53.** 32
55. 125   **57.** 3   **59.** 4   **61.** 80   **63.** $\frac{49}{16}$ **65.** $2^3 - 8$; 0
67. $30 - 4 \cdot 3$; 18   **69.** $\frac{4^2}{2^3}$; 2   **71.** $\frac{40}{10} + 2$; 6
73. $100(2 + 3)$; 500   **75.** 536,870,912 bytes
77. (a) $k = 7$ (b) 32   **79.** (a) 8 yr   (b) $80,000

SECTION 1.4 (pp. 42–44)

1. $-b$ **2.** natural   **3.** rational   **4.** real   **5.** irrational
6. True   **7.** True   **8.** $0.\overline{27}$ **9.** 1; 4   **10.** 4   **11.** principal
12. not equal   **13.** approximately equal   **14.** 0   **15.** left
16. origin   **17.** (a) -9 (b) 9   **19.** (a) $-\frac{2}{3}$ (b) $\frac{2}{3}$
21. (a) -8 (b) 8   **23.** (a) $-a$ (b) a **25.** 6   **27.** $\frac{1}{2}$
29. 0.25   **31.** 0.875   **33.** 1.5   **35.** 0.05   **37.** $0.\overline{6}$ **39.** $0.\overline{7}$
41. Natural, whole, integer, and rational
43. Natural, whole, integer, and rational
45. Whole, integer, and rational   **47.** Rational   **49.** 5
51. 7   **53.** 2.646   **55.** Rational   **57.** Rational
59. Irrational   **61.** Natural, integer, and rational
63. Natural, integer, and rational   **65.** Rational
67.

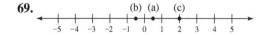

69.

71.

73.

75. 5.23   **77.** 8   **79.** 0   **81.** $\pi - 3$ **83.** $-b$ **85.** $<$
87. $>$ **89.** $>$ **91.** $<$ **93.** $>$ **95.** $<$ **97.** $>$ **99.** $=$
101. $-9, -2^3, -3, 0, 1$ **103.** $-2, -\frac{3}{2}, \frac{1}{3}, \sqrt{5}, \pi$
105. (a) 25.5   **(b)** Answers may vary.
(c) 25.45; answers may vary.

CHECKING BASIC CONCEPTS 1.3 & 1.4 (p. 44)

1. (a) 5^4 **(b)** 7^5 **2. (a)** 8   **(b)** 10,000   **(c)** $\frac{8}{27}$
3. (a) 4^3 **(b)** 2^6 **4. (a)** 26   **(b)** 9   **(c)** 2   **(d)** $\frac{1}{2}$ **(e)** 4
(f) 0   **5.** $5^3 \div 3$, or $\frac{5^3}{3}$ **6. (a)** 17   **(b)** $-a$
7. (a) 0.15   **(b)** 0.625
8. (a) Natural, integer, and rational   **(b)** Integer and rational
(c) Irrational   **(d)** Rational
9.

10. (a) 12   **(b)** 0   **11. (a)** $<$ **(b)** $<$ **(c)** $<$
12. $-7, -1.6, 0, \frac{1}{3}, \sqrt{3}, 3^2$

SECTION 1.5 (pp. 50–51)

1. sum   **2.** zero   **3.** True   **4.** True   **5.** absolute value
6. difference   **7.** addition   **8.** opposite; $(-b)$ **9.** addition
10. subtraction   **11.** $-25; 0$ **13.** $\sqrt{21}; 0$ **15.** $-5.63; 0$
17. 4   **19.** 2   **21.** -3 **23.** 4   **25.** 2   **27.** -1 **29.** 10
31. -150 **33.** 1   **35.** -7 **37.** $\frac{1}{4}$ **39.** $-\frac{9}{14}$ **41.** -1.1
43. 34   **45.** -3 **47.** 7   **49.** $-\frac{1}{14}$ **51.** $\frac{1}{2}$ **53.** 2.9
55. -164 **57.** -9 **59.** 42   **61.** -5 **63.** 50   **65.** 8.8
67. $\frac{1}{2}$ **69.** -1 **71.** $2 + (-5); -3$ **73.** $-5 + 7; 2$
75. $-(2^3); -8$ **77.** $-6 - 7; -13$ **79.** $6 + (-10) - 5; -9$
81. Mt. Whitney: 14,497 ft; Death Valley: -282 ft; 14,779 ft
83. \$230   **85.** 25 yards   **87.** 64,868 feet

SECTION 1.6 (pp. 58–59)

1. product   **2.** negative   **3.** positive   **4.** quotient   **5.** $\frac{1}{a}$
6. reciprocal   **7.** reciprocal, or multiplicative inverse
8. $-a$ **9.** $\frac{1}{b}$ **10.** positive   **11.** negative   **12.** 5; 8
13. -12 **15.** -18 **17.** 0   **19.** 60   **21.** $\frac{1}{4}$ **23.** -1
25. 200   **27.** -50 **29.** 120   **31.** $-\frac{3}{2}$ **33.** Negative
35. 25   **37.** -1 **39.** -16 **41.** 8   **43.** -40 **45.** -2
47. 10   **49.** -4 **51.** -32 **53.** 0   **55.** Undefined
57. $-\frac{1}{22}$ **59.** $\frac{4}{15}$ **61.** $-\frac{15}{16}$ **63.** Undefined   **65.** -1
67. $-\frac{4}{3}$ **69.** 0.5   **71.** 0.1875   **73.** 3.5   **75.** $5.\overline{6}$
77. 1.4375   **79.** 0.875   **81.** $\frac{1}{4}$ **83.** $\frac{4}{25}$ **85.** $\frac{5}{8}$ **87.** $\frac{11}{16}$
89. $2.\overline{3}; \frac{7}{3}$ **91.** $2.1; \frac{21}{10}$ **93.** $-1.8\overline{3}; -\frac{11}{6}$ **95.** $0.8; \frac{4}{5}$
97. About 131 million   **99.** 0.168

CHECKING BASIC CONCEPTS 1.5 & 1.6 (p. 60)

1. (a) 0   **(b)** -19 **2. (a)** $\frac{8}{9}$ **(b)** -3.2
3. (a) $-1 + 5; 4$ **(b)** $4 - (-3); 7$ **4.** 145°F
5. (a) 35   **(b)** $\frac{4}{15}$ **6. (a)** -9 **(b)** -32 **(c)** 25

7. (a) $-\frac{15}{2}$ **(b)** $\frac{15}{32}$ **8.** $-\frac{6}{7}$ **9. (a)** -5 **(b)** -5 **(c)** -5
(d) 5   **10. (a)** 0.6   **(b)** 3.875

SECTION 1.7 (pp. 68–71)

1. commutative; addition   **2.** commutative; multiplication
3. associative; addition   **4.** associative; multiplication
5. True   **6.** False   **7.** distributive   **8.** distributive
9. identity; addition   **10.** identity; multiplication
11. $-a$ **12.** $\frac{1}{a}$ **13.** $10 + (-6)$ **15.** $6 \cdot (-5)$
17. $10 + a$ **19.** $7b$ **21.** $1 + (2 + 3)$ **23.** $(2 \cdot 3) \cdot 4$
25. $a + (5 + c)$ **27.** $x \cdot (3 \cdot 4)$
29. $a + b + c = (a + b) + c$
$= c + (a + b)$
$= c + (b + a)$
$= c + b + a$
31. 20   **33.** $ab - 8a$ **35.** $-4t + 4z$ **37.** $-5 + a$
39. $3a + 15$ **41.** $17 - a$
43. $a \cdot (b + c + d) = a \cdot ((b + c) + d)$
$= a \cdot (b + c) + ad$
$= ab + ac + ad$
45. $11x$ **47.** $-b$ **49.** $2a$ **51.** $-14w$
53. Commutative (multiplication)   **55.** Associative (addition)
57. Distributive   **59.** Distributive, commutative (multiplication)   **61.** Distributive   **63.** Associative (multiplication)
65. Distributive   **67.** Identity (addition)
69. Identity (multiplication)   **71.** Identity (multiplication)
73. Inverse (multiplication)   **75.** Inverse (addition)
77. 30   **79.** 100   **81.** 178   **83.** 79   **85.** 90   **87.** 816
89. 1   **91.** $\frac{1}{6}$ **93. (a)** 410   **(b)** 9970   **(c)** -6300
(d) $-140,000$ **95. (a)** 19,000   **(b)** $-45,100$ **(c)** 60,000
(d) $-7,900,000$ **97. (a)** 1.256   **(b)** 0.96   **(c)** 0.0987
(d) -0.0056 **(e)** 120   **(f)** 457.8
99. Commutative (addition)   **101.** 19.8 miles
103. (a) $13 \cdot (5 \cdot 2)$; multiplying by 10 is easy.
(b) Associative (multiplication)

SECTION 1.8 (pp. 77–78)

1. term   **2.** coefficient   **3.** factors; terms   **4.** like   **5.** like
6. distributive   **7.** Yes; 91   **9.** Yes; -6 **11.** No
13. Yes; 1   **15.** No   **17.** Like   **19.** Like   **21.** Unlike
23. Unlike   **25.** Like   **27.** Unlike   **29.** Like   **31.** $3x$
33. $14y$ **35.** $41a$ **37.** 0   **39.** Not possible
41. Not possible   **43.** $3x^2$ **45.** $-y$ **47.** $3x + 2$
49. $-2z + \frac{1}{2}$ **51.** $11y$ **53.** $4z - 1$ **55.** $12y - 7z$
57. $-3x - 4$ **59.** $-6x - 1$ **61.** $-\frac{1}{3}x + \frac{2}{3}$
63. $\frac{2}{5}x + \frac{3}{5}y + \frac{1}{5}$ **65.** $0.4x^2$ **67.** $7x^2 - 7x$ **69.** $2b$
71. $7x^3 + 2y$ **73.** x **75.** 3   **77.** z **79.** $3x - 2$
81. $2z + 3$ **83.** $5x + 6x; 11x$ **85.** $x^2 + 2x^2; 3x^2$
87. $6x - 4x; 2x$ **89. (a)** $1570w$ **(b)** 65,940 square feet
91. (a) $50x$ **(b)** 2400 cubic feet   **(c)** 24 minutes

CHECKING BASIC CONCEPTS 1.7 & 1.8 (p. 79)

1. (a) $18y$ **(b)** $x + 10$ **2.** $20y$ **3. (a)** $5 - x$
(b) $5x - 35$ **4.** Distributive   **5.** 0   **6. (a)** 60   **(b)** 7
(c) 368   **7. (a)** Unlike   **(b)** Like   **8. (a)** $14z$ **(b)** $-3y + 3$

9. (a) $-3y - 3$ **(b)** $-14y$ **(c)** x **(d)** 35
10. $3x + 5x$; $8x$

CHAPTER 1 REVIEW (pp. 84–87)

1. Prime **2.** Composite; $27 = 3 \cdot 3 \cdot 3$
3. Composite; $108 = 2 \cdot 2 \cdot 3 \cdot 3 \cdot 3$
4. Composite; $91 = 7 \cdot 13$ **5.** Neither **6.** Neither
7. 3 **8.** 5 **9.** 12 **10.** 6 **11.** 7 **12.** 7 **13.** 8
14. 6 **15.** $3^2 + 5$ **16.** $2^3 \div (3 + 1)$
17. $3x$, where x is the number
18. $x - 4$, where x is the number **19.** 5 **20.** 6
21. (a) $\frac{5}{8}$ **(b)** $\frac{3}{4}$ **22. (a)** $\frac{3}{4}$ **(b)** $\frac{3}{5}$ **23.** $\frac{5}{8}$ **24.** $\frac{2}{9}$ **25.** $\frac{3}{5}$
26. $\frac{24}{23}$ **27.** $\frac{5}{2}$ **28.** 6 **29.** 2 **30.** $\frac{3x}{2y}$ **31.** $\frac{3}{35}$
32. (a) $\frac{1}{8}$ **(b)** 1 **(c)** $\frac{19}{5}$ **(d)** $\frac{2}{3}$ **33.** 9 **34.** $\frac{9}{14}$ **35.** 12
36. $\frac{1}{8}$ **37.** $\frac{x}{3}$ **38.** $\frac{20}{27y}$ **39.** 24 **40.** 42 **41.** $\frac{1}{3}$ **42.** $\frac{1}{2}$
43. $\frac{19}{24}$ **44.** $\frac{9}{22}$ **45.** $\frac{5}{12}$ **46.** $\frac{13}{18}$ **47.** 5^6 **48.** $\left(\frac{7}{6}\right)^3$
49. x^5 **50.** 3^4 **51.** $(x + 1)^2$ **52.** $(a - 5)^3$
53. (a) 64 **(b)** 49 **(c)** 8 **54.** 5 **55.** 25 **56.** 7 **57.** 3
58. 25 **59.** 1 **60.** 2 **61.** 0 **62.** 0 **63.** 10 **64.** 1 **65.** 5
66. 19 **67. (a)** 8 **(b)** 3 **68. (a)** $-\frac{3}{7}$ **(b)** $-\frac{2}{5}$
69. (a) 0.8 **(b)** 0.15 **70. (a)** $0.\overline{5}$ **(b)** $0.\overline{63}$
71. Whole, integer, and rational **72.** Rational
73. Integer and rational **74.** Irrational **75.** Irrational
76. Rational
77.

78. (a) 5 **(b)** π **(c)** 0 **79. (a)** $<$ **(b)** $>$ **(c)** $<$ **(d)** $>$
80. $-3, -\frac{2}{3}, \sqrt{3}, \pi - 1, 3$ **81.** 4 **82.** -3 **83.** 1
84. -5 **85.** 1 **86.** -2 **87.** -44 **88.** 40 **89.** $-\frac{11}{4}$
90. -7 **91.** $-\frac{2}{9}$ **92.** $-\frac{5}{4}$ **93.** $\frac{2}{7}$ **94.** $-\frac{4}{35}$ **95.** 4
96. $-\frac{3}{4}$ **97.** $3 + (-5)$; -2 **98.** $2 - (-4)$; 6 **99.** $0.\overline{7}$
100. 2.2 **101.** $\frac{3}{5}$ **102.** $\frac{3}{8}$ **103.** $16 + 3$ **104.** $-x \cdot 14$
105. $(-4 + 1) + 3$ **106.** $x \cdot (y \cdot 5)$ **107.** $5x + 60$
108. $-a + 3$ **109.** Identity (addition)
110. Identity (multiplication) **111.** Inverse (multiplication)
112. Inverse (addition) **113.** Commutative (multiplication)
114. Associative (addition) **115.** Distributive
116. Commutative (addition) **117.** Identity (multiplication)
118. Associative (multiplication) **119.** Distributive
120. Identity (addition) **121.** Inverse (addition)
122. Inverse (multiplication) **123.** 40 **124.** 301
125. 2475 **126.** 6580 **127.** 549.8 **128.** 43.56
129. Yes; 55 **130.** Yes; -1 **131.** No **132.** No
133. $-6x$ **134.** $15z$ **135.** $4x^2$ **136.** $3x + 1$
137. $\frac{1}{2}z + 2$ **138.** $x - 18$ **139.** $9x^2 - 6$ **140.** 0
141. 5 **142.** c **143.** $3y + 2$ **144.** $2x - 5$
145. (a) $7x$ **(b)** 420 square feet **(c)** 24 minutes
146. 16 square feet
147.

Gallons (G)	1	2	3	4	5	6
Pints (P)	8	16	24	32	40	48

$P = 8G$

148. $C = 0.05x$ **149.** $\frac{3}{20}$ **150.** \$200,000 **151.** $1\frac{3}{20}$ feet
152. $15\frac{3}{8}$ miles **153.** \$1101 **154.** 124°F
155. About 129 million

---

2   Linear Equations and Inequalities

SECTION 2.1 (pp. 97–99)

1. solution **2.** true **3.** false **4.** solution set **5.** solutions
6. equivalent **7.** $b + c$ **8.** subtraction **9.** bc
10. division **11.** equivalent **12.** given **13.** 22 **15.** 3
17. -5 **19.** 9 **21.** 17 **23.** $\frac{17}{10}$ **25.** 5.1 **27.** -3 **29.** $\frac{2}{3}$
31. a **33.** $\frac{1}{5}$ **35.** 6 **37.** 3 **39.** 0 **41.** 7 **43.** -6
45. 3 **47.** $\frac{5}{4}$ **49.** 7 **51.** -8.5 **53.** a
55. (a)

Hours (x)	0	1	2	3	4	5	6
Rainfall (R)	3	3.5	4	4.5	5	5.5	6

(b) $R = 0.5x + 3$ **(c)** 4.5 inches; yes **(d)** 4.125 inches
57. (a) $L = 300x$ **(b)** $870 = 300x$ **(c)** 2.9 **59.** 50 days
61. (a) 50° N **(b)** 5.7 **63.** \$25,000

SECTION 2.2 (pp. 108–110)

1. constant **2.** $ax + b = 0$ **3.** Exactly one
4. numerically **5.** Addition, multiplication **6.** LCD
7. None **8.** Infinitely many **9.** Yes; $a = 3, b = -7$
11. Yes; $a = \frac{1}{2}, b = 0$ **13.** No **15.** No **17.** Yes;
$a = 1.1, b = -0.9$ **19.** Yes; $a = 2, b = -6$ **21.** No
23.

x	-1	0	1	2	3
$x - 3$	-4	-3	-2	-1	0

2

25.

x	0	1	2	3	4
$-3x + 7$	7	4	1	-2	-5

2

27.

x	-2	-1	0	1	2
$4 - 2x$	8	6	4	2	0

-1

29. $\frac{3}{11}$ **31.** 23 **33.** 28 **35.** $-\frac{11}{5}$ **37.** $-\frac{7}{2}$ **39.** 3 **41.** $\frac{9}{4}$
43. $-\frac{5}{2}$ **45.** $\frac{10}{3}$ **47.** $\frac{9}{8}$ **49.** 1 **51.** -0.055 **53.** 8 **55.** $\frac{1}{3}$
57. 1 **59.** $-\frac{b}{a}$ **61.** No solutions **63.** One solution **65.** No
solutions **67.** Infinitely many solutions **69.** No solutions
71. (a)

Hours (x)	0	1	2	3	4
Distance (D)	4	12	20	28	36

(b) $D = 8x + 4$ **(c)** 28 miles; yes **(d)** 2.25 hours; the
bicyclist is 22 miles from home after 2 hours and 15 minutes.
73. 2009 **75.** 2004 **77.** 2008

CHECKING BASIC CONCEPTS 2.1 & 2.2 (p. 111)

1. (a) No **(b)** Yes
2.

x	3	3.5	4	4.5	5
$4x - 3$	9	11	13	15	17

4

3. (a) 18 **(b)** $\frac{1}{6}$ **(c)** $2.\overline{6}$ or $\frac{8}{3}$ **(d)** 3 **4. (a)** One solution
(b) Infinitely many solutions **(c)** No solutions
5. (a) $D = 300 - 75x$ **(b)** $0 = 300 - 75x$ **(c)** 4 hours

SECTION 2.4 (pp. 121–123)

1. formula **2.** lw **3.** $\frac{1}{2}bh$ **4.** $\frac{1}{360}$ **5.** 360 **6.** 180
7. lwh **8.** $2lw + 2wh + 2lh$ **9.** $2\pi r$ **10.** πr^2
11. $\pi r^2 h$ **12.** $\frac{1}{2}(a + b)h$ **13.** 18 ft^2 **15.** 9 in^2
17. $16\pi \approx 50.3$ cm^2 **19.** 11 mm^2 **21.** 91 in^2
23. 105 ft^2 or $\frac{35}{3}$ yd^2 **25.** $8\pi \approx 25.1$ in. **27.** 4602 ft^2

29. 65° **31.** 81° **33.** 36° **35.** 36°, 36°, 108°
37. $C = 12\pi \approx 37.7$ in.; $A = 36\pi \approx 113.1$ in^2
39. $r = 1$ in.; $A = \pi \approx 3.14$ in^2
41. $V = 2640$ in^3; $S = 1208$ in^2
43. $V = 2$ ft^3; $S = \frac{32}{3}$ ft^2 **45.** 20π in^3 **47.** 600π in^3
49. (a) $\frac{45}{32}\pi \approx 4.4$ in^3 **(b)** About 2.4 fl oz
51. $y = -3x + 2$ **53.** $y = -\frac{4}{3}x + 4$ **55.** $w = \frac{A}{l}$
57. $h = \frac{V}{\pi r^2}$ **59.** $a = \frac{2A}{h} - b$ **61.** $w = \frac{V}{lh}$
63. $b = 2s - a - c$ **65.** $b = a - c$ **67.** $a = \frac{cd}{b - d}$
69. 15 in. **71.** 2.98 **73.** 2.24 **75.** 77°F **77.** −40°F
79. −5°C **81.** −20°C **83.** 11 mpg **85.** 2.4 mi

CHECKING BASIC CONCEPTS 2.4 (p. 123)

1. (a) $3x = 36$; 12 **(b)** $35 - x = 43$; −8
2. −32, −31, −30 **3.** 0.095 **4.** 125%
5. About 75,747 **6.** 6.5 hr **7.** $5000 at 6%; $3000
at 7% **8.** 18 gal **9.** 12 in.
10. $A = 9\pi \approx 28.3$ ft^2; $C = 6\pi \approx 18.8$ ft **11.** 30°
12. $l = \frac{A - \pi r^2}{\pi r}$

SECTION 2.5 (pp. 134–136)

1. $<, \leq, >, \geq$ **2.** greater than; less than **3.** solution
4. equivalent **5.** True **6.** True **7.** number line **8.** >
9. < **10.** >

11.

13.

15.

17.

19. $x < 0$ **21.** $x \leq 3$ **23.** $x \geq 10$ **25.** $[6, \infty)$
27. $(-2, \infty)$ **29.** $(-\infty, 7]$ **31.** Yes **33.** No **35.** Yes
37. No **39.** $x > -2$ **41.** $x < 1$

43.

x	1	2	3	4	5
$-2x + 6$	4	2	0	−2	−4

$x \geq 3$

45.

x	−3	−2	−1	0	1
$5 - x$	8	7	6	5	4
$x + 7$	4	5	6	7	8

$x < -1$

47. $x > 3$;

49. $y \geq -2$;

51. $z > 8$;

53. $t \leq -5$;

55. $x < 5$;

57. $t \leq -2$;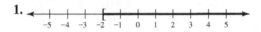

59. $y > -\frac{3}{20}$;

61. $z \geq -\frac{14}{3}$;

63. $\{x \mid x > 1\}$ **65.** $\{x \mid x \geq -7\}$ **67.** $\{x \mid x < 6\}$
69. $x < 7$ **71.** $x \leq -\frac{4}{3}$ **73.** $x > -\frac{39}{2}$ **75.** $x \leq \frac{3}{2}$
77. $x > \frac{1}{2}$ **79.** $x \leq \frac{5}{4}$ **81.** $x > -\frac{8}{3}$ **83.** $x \leq -\frac{1}{3}$
85. $x < 5$ **87.** $x \leq -\frac{3}{2}$ **89.** $x > -\frac{9}{8}$ **91.** $x \leq \frac{4}{7}$
93. $x < \frac{21}{11}$ **95.** $x > 60$ **97.** $x \geq 21$ **99.** $x > 40,000$
101. $x \leq 70$ **103.** Less than 10 feet
105. 86 or more **107.** 4.5 hours **109.** 4 days
111. (a) $C = 1.5x + 2000$ **(b)** $R = 12x$
(c) $P = 10.5x - 2000$ **(d)** 191 or more compact discs
113. (a) After 48 minutes **(b)** After more than 48 minutes
115. Altitudes more than 4.5 miles

CHECKING BASIC CONCEPTS 2.5 (p. 137)

1.

2. $x < 1$ **3.** Yes

4.

x	−2	−1	0	1	2
$5 - 2x$	9	7	5	3	1

; $x \geq -1$

5. (a) $x > 3$ **(b)** $x \geq -35$ **(c)** $x \leq -1$
6. $x \leq 12$ **7.** More than 13 inches

CHAPTER 2 REVIEW (pp. 140–142)

1. −6 **2.** 2 **3.** $\frac{9}{4}$ **4.** $-\frac{1}{2}$ **5.** 3 **6.** $-\frac{7}{3}$ **7.** −2.5 **8.** $-\frac{7}{2}$
9. Yes; $a = -4, b = 1$ **10.** No **11.** 2 **12.** 22 **13.** $\frac{27}{5}$
14. 7 **15.** −7 **16.** $-\frac{2}{3}$ **17.** $\frac{9}{4}$ **18.** 0 **19.** $\frac{7}{8}$ **20.** $\frac{11}{4}$
21. No solutions **22.** Infinitely many solutions
23. Infinitely many solutions **24.** One solution
25.

x	0.5	1.0	1.5	2.0	2.5
$-2x + 3$	2	1	0	−1	−2

1.5

26.

x	−2	−1	0	1	2
$-(x + 1) + 3$	4	3	2	1	0

0

45. 7.5 m^2 **46.** $36\pi \approx 113.1$ ft^2 **47.** 864 in^2, or 6 ft^2
48. 40 in. **49.** $18\pi \approx 56.5$ ft **50.** $25\pi \approx 78.5$ in^2
51. 50° **52.** 22.5° **53.** $625\pi \approx 1963.5$ in^3
54. 1620 in^2, or 11.25 ft^2 **55.** 174 in^2 **56.** About 60.6 ft^2
57. $y = 3x - 5$ **58.** $y = -x + 8$ **59.** $y = \frac{z}{2x}$
60. $b = 3S - a - c$ **61.** $b = \frac{12T - 4a}{3}$
62. $c = \frac{ab}{d - b}$ **63.** 2.82 **64.** 3.12 **65.** 59°F **66.** 45°C
67.

68.

69.

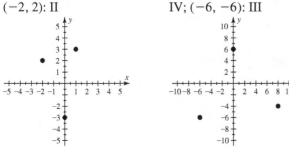

70.

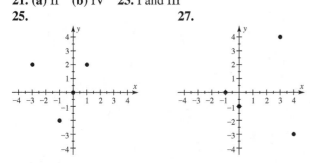

71. $x < 3$ **72.** $x \geq -1$ **73.** Yes   **74.** No

75.

x	0	1	2	3	4
$5 - x$	5	4	3	2	1

$x < 2$

76.

x	1	1.5	2	2.5	3
$2x - 5$	-3	-2	-1	0	1

$x \leq 2.5$

77. $x > 3$ **78.** $x \geq -5$ **79.** $x \leq -1$ **80.** $x < \frac{23}{3}$
81. $x \leq \frac{1}{9}$ **82.** $x \geq \frac{9}{4}$ **83.** $x < 50$ **84.** $x \leq 45,000$
85. $x \geq 16$ **86.** $x < 1995$ or $x \leq 1994$
87. (a)

Time	12:00	1:00	2:00	3:00	4:00	5:00
Rainfall (R)	2	2.75	3.5	4.25	5	5.75

(b) $R = \frac{3}{4}x + 2$ **(c)** $\frac{23}{4} = 5\frac{3}{4}$ in.; yes   **(d)** $\frac{77}{16} = 4\frac{13}{16}$ in.
88. \$2125
89. (a)

Hours (x)	1	2	3	4	5
Distance (D)	40	30	20	10	0

(b) $D = 50 - 10x$ **(c)** 20 miles; yes   **(d)** 3 hours or less
or from noon to 3:00 P.M.
90. About 33.4%   **91.** $\frac{1}{6}$ hr, or 10 min   **92.** 33 in. by 23 in.
93. 50 mL   **94.** \$500 at 3%; \$800 at 5%   **95.** 25 inches or
less   **96.** 74 or more   **97.** 6 hr   **98. (a)** $C = 85x + 150,000$
(b) $R = 225x$ **(c)** $P = 140x - 150,000$ **(d)** 1071 or
fewer

3   Graphing Equations

SECTION 3.1 (pp. 151–154)

1. xy-plane   **2.** origin   **3.** $(0, 0)$ **4.** 4   **5.** False   **6.** x; y
7. scatterplot   **8.** line   **9.** $(-2, -2), (-2, 2), (0, 0), (2, 2)$
11. $(-1, 0), (0, -3), (0, 2), (2, 0)$

13. $(1, 3)$: I; $(0, -3)$: None;   **15.** $(0, 6)$: None; $(8, -4)$:
$(-2, 2)$: II   IV; $(-6, -6)$: III

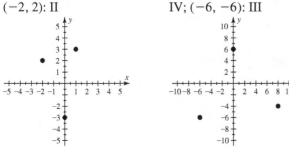

17. (a) I   **(b)** III   **19. (a)** None   **(b)** I
21. (a) II   **(b)** IV   **23.** I and III
25.   **27.**

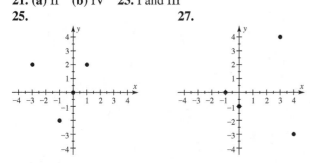

29.

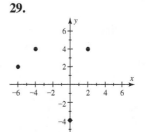

31.

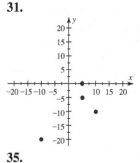

33.

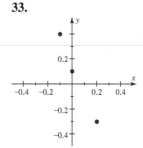

35.

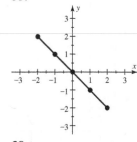

37.

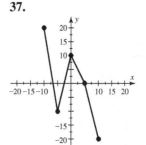

39.

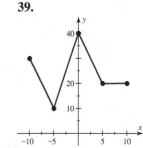

41. $(1960, 484), (1980, 632), (2000, 430), (2010, 325)$;
in 1960 there were 484 billion cigarettes consumed in the
United States (answers may vary slightly).

43. (a)

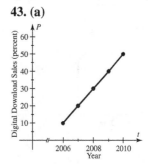

45. (a)

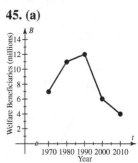

(b) The percentage of digital   **(b)** The number of welfare
download sales increased.   beneficiaries increased and
                                then decreased.

47. (a)

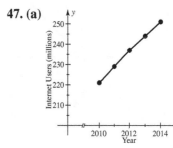

(b) The number of Internet users is increasing.

49. (a) The rate decreased.   **(b)** 9   **(c)** About -70%

SECTION 3.2 (pp. 161–163)

1. True   **2.** False   **3.** ordered pair   **4.** linear   **5.** False
6. True   **7.** graph   **8.** line   **9.** False   **10.** False   **11.** Yes
13. No   **15.** No   **17.** Yes   **19.** No

21.

x	-2	-1	0	1	2
y	-8	-4	0	4	8

23.

x	6	3	0	-3	-9
y	-2	0	2	4	8

25.

x	y
-8	-4
-4	0
0	4
4	8
8	12

27.

x	y
-6	-4
0	-2
6	0
12	2
18	4

29.

x	-3	0	3	6
y	-9	0	9	18

31.

x	8	6	4	2
y	-2	0	2	4

33.

x	y
-8	-2
-4	0
0	2
4	4

35.

x	y
$-\frac{1}{2}$	-2
$-\frac{1}{4}$	-1
0	0
$\frac{1}{4}$	1

37. They must be multiples of 5.

39.

x	-1	0	1
y	2	0	-2

Table values may vary.

41.

x	0	1	2
y	3	2	1

Table values may vary.

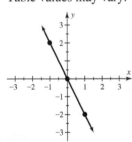

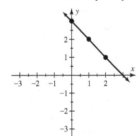

43.

x	-2	0	2
y	3	2	1

Table values may vary.

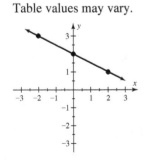

45.

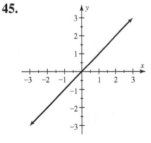

47.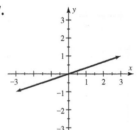

49.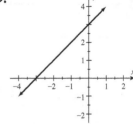

51.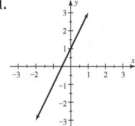

53.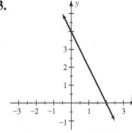

55.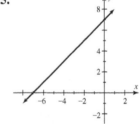

57.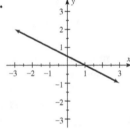

59.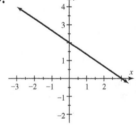

61.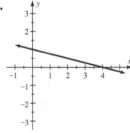

63.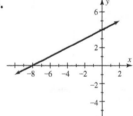

65.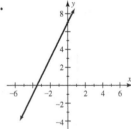

67.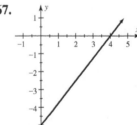

69.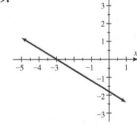

71. (a)

t	2010	2020	2030	2040	2050
P	13.2	15.0	16.7	18.5	20.3

(b) 2030

73. (a)

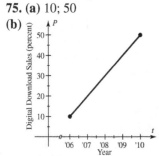

(b) About 37 days

75. (a) 10; 50

(b)

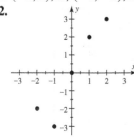

(c) 2008

CHECKING BASIC CONCEPTS 3.1 & 3.2 (p. 164)

1. $(-2, 2)$, II; $(-1, -2)$, III; $(1, 3)$, I; $(3, 0)$, none

2.

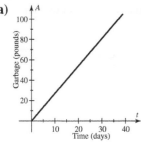

3.

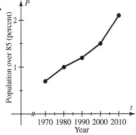

The percentage increased.

4. Yes

5.

x	-2	-1	0	1	2
y	5	3	1	-1	-3

6. (a)

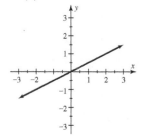

(b)

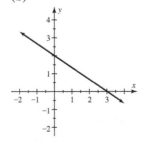

7. (a) In 1990, receipts were \$0.47 trillion; in 2010, receipts were \$2.17 trillion.

(b)

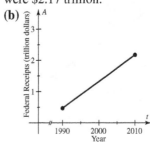

(c) 2006

SECTION 3.3 (pp. 172–175)

1. x-intercept   **2.** 0   **3.** y-intercept   **4.** 0   **5.** horizontal
6. $y = b$ **7.** vertical   **8.** $x = k$ **9.** 3; -2
11. 0; 0   **13.** -2 and 2; 4   **15.** 1; 1

17.

x	-2	-1	0	1	2
y	0	1	2	3	4

-2; 2

19.

x	-4	-2	0	2	4
y	-6	-4	-2	0	2

2; -2

21. x-int: 3; y-int: -2

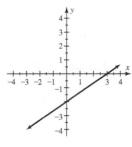

23. x-int: 6; y-int: -2

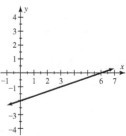

25. x-int: -1; y-int: 6

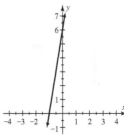

27. x-int: 7; y-int: 3

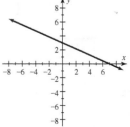

29. x-int: 4; y-int: -3

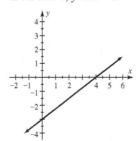

31. x-int: 4; y-int: -2

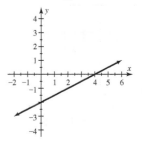

33. x-int: -4; y-int: 3

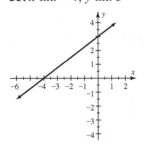

35. x-int: 3; y-int: 2

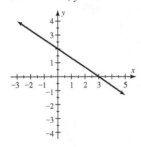

37. x-int: -2; y-int: 5

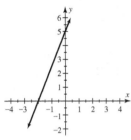

39. x-int: $\frac{C}{A}$; y-int: $\frac{C}{B}$ **41.** $y = 1$ **43.** $x = -6$

45. (a)   **(b)**

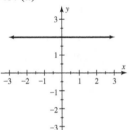
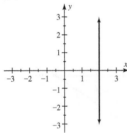

47. (a)   **(b)**

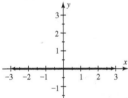
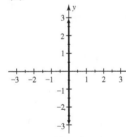

49. (a)   **(b)**

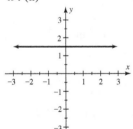
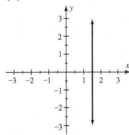

51. $y = 4$ **53.** $x = -1$ **55.** $y = -6$ **57.** $x = 5$
59. $y = 2$; $x = 1$ **61.** $y = -45$; $x = 20$

63. $y = 5$; $x = 0$ **65.** $x = -1$ **67.** $y = -\frac{5}{6}$
69. $x = 4$ **71.** $x = -\frac{2}{3}$ **73.** $y = 0$
75. (a) y-int: 200; x-int: 4   **(b)** The driver was initially
200 miles from home; the driver arrived home after 4 hours.
77. (a) v-int: 128; t-int: 4

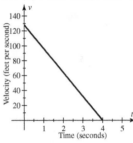

(b) The initial velocity was 128 ft/sec; the velocity after
4 seconds was 0.
79. (a) y-int: 2000; x-int: 4   **(b)** The pool initially contained
2000 gallons; the pool was empty after 4 hours.

SECTION 3.4 (pp. 184–189)

1. True   **2.** True   **3.** rise; run   **4.** horizontal   **5.** vertical
6. $\frac{y_2 - y_1}{x_2 - x_1}$ **7.** positive   **8.** negative   **9.** rate   **10.** Toward
11. Positive   **13.** Zero   **15.** Negative   **17.** Undefined
19. 0; the rise always equals 0.
21. 1; the graph rises 1 unit for each unit of run.
23. 2; the graph rises 2 units for each unit of run.
25. Undefined; the run always equals 0.
27. $-\frac{3}{2}$; the graph falls 3 units for each 2 units of run.
29. -1; the graph falls 1 unit for each unit of run.
31. 2;   **33.** Undefined;

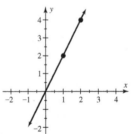
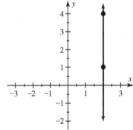

35. $-\frac{2}{3}$;   **37.** 0;

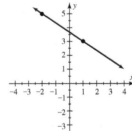
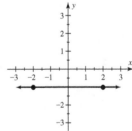

39. 1   **41.** $-\frac{6}{7}$ **43.** 0   **45.** Undefined   **47.** $\frac{13}{20}$
49. $\frac{9}{100}$ **51.** $-\frac{5}{7}$ **53.** 49

55.

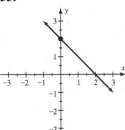

57.

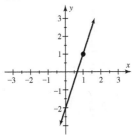

59.

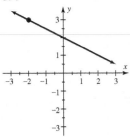

61.

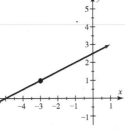

63.

x	0	1	2	3
y	−4	−2	0	2

65.

x	1	2	3	4
y	4	1	−2	−5

67.

x	−4	−2	0	2
y	0	3	6	9

69. c. **71.** b. **73. (a)** $m_1 = 1000$; $m_2 = -1000$
(b) $m_1 = 1000$: Water is being added to the pool at a rate of 1000 gallons per hour. $m_2 = -1000$: Water is being removed from the pool at a rate of 1000 gallons per hour. **(c)** Initially the pool contained 2000 gallons of water. Over the first 3 hours, water was pumped into the pool at a rate of 1000 gallons per hour. For the next 2 hours, water was pumped out of the pool at a rate of 1000 gallons per hour.
75. (a) $m_1 = 50$; $m_2 = 0$; $m_3 = -50$ **(b)** $m_1 = 50$: The car is moving away from home at a rate of 50 mph. $m_2 = 0$: The car is not moving. $m_3 = -50$: The car is moving toward home at a rate of 50 mph. **(c)** Initially the car is at home. Over the first 2 hours, the car travels away from home at a rate of 50 mph. Then the car is parked for 1 hour. Finally, the car travels toward home at a rate of 50 mph.
77. m³ /min

79.

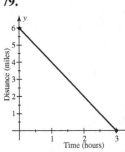

81.

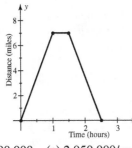

83. (a) 76,000,000 **(b)** 281,000,000 **(c)** 2,050,000/yr
85. (a) 40,800 **(b)** The celebrity gained 40,800 followers each year, on average.

87. (a) 25 **(b)** The revenue is $25 per flash drive.
89. (a)

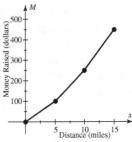

(b) $m_1 = 20$; $m_2 = 30$; $m_3 = 40$ **(c)** $m_1 = 20$: Each mile between 0 and 5 miles is worth $20 per mile. $m_2 = 30$: Each mile between 5 and 10 miles is worth $30 per mile. $m_3 = 40$: Each mile between 10 and 15 miles is worth $40 per mile.
91. (a) 1000 **(b)** Median family income increased on average by $1000 per year over this time period. **(c)** $56,000
93. (a) Toward **(b)** 10 ft **(c)** 2 ft/min **(d)** 5

CHECKING BASIC CONCEPTS 3.3 & 3.4
(pp. 189–190)

1. −2; 3
2.

x	−2	−1	0	1	2
y	−6	−4	−2	0	2

1; −2

3. (a) x-int: 6; y-int: −3 **(b)** y-int: 2

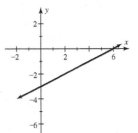

(c) x-int: −1

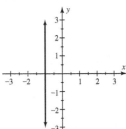

4. $y = 4$; $x = -2$ **5. (a)** $\frac{3}{4}$ **(b)** 0 **(c)** Undefined
6. $-\frac{1}{2}$
7.

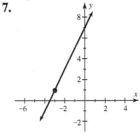

8. (a) $m_1 = 0$; $m_2 = 2$; $m_3 = -\frac{2}{3}$ **(b)** $m_1 = 0$: The depth is not changing. $m_2 = 2$: The depth increased at a rate of 2 feet per hour. $m_3 = -\frac{2}{3}$: The depth decreased at a rate of $\frac{2}{3}$ foot per hour.   **(c)** Initially the pond had a depth of 5 feet. For the first hour, there was no change in the depth of the pond. For the next hour, the depth of the pond increased at a rate of 2 feet per hour to a depth of 7 feet. Finally, the depth of the pond decreased for 3 hours at a rate of $\frac{2}{3}$ foot per hour until it was 5 feet deep.

SECTION 3.5 (pp. 197–199)

1. $y = mx + b$ **2.** slope **3.** y-intercept **4.** origin
5. parallel **6.** slope **7.** perpendicular **8.** reciprocals
9. f. **10.** d. **11.** a. **12.** b. **13.** e. **14.** c.
15. $y = x - 1$ **17.** $y = -2x + 1$ **19.** $y = -2x$
21. $y = \frac{3}{4}x + 2$

23. $y = x + 2$

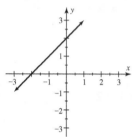

25. $y = 2x - 1$

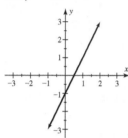

27. $y = -\frac{1}{2}x - 2$

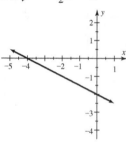

29. $y = \frac{1}{3}x$

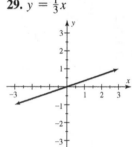

31. $y = 3$

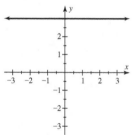

33. (a) $y = -x + 4$ **(b)** $-1; 4$
35. (a) $y = -2x + 4$ **(b)** $-2; 4$
37. (a) $y = \frac{1}{2}x + 2$ **(b)** $\frac{1}{2}; 2$
39. (a) $y = \frac{2}{3}x - 2$ **(b)** $\frac{2}{3}; -2$
41. (a) $y = \frac{1}{4}x + \frac{3}{2}$ **(b)** $\frac{1}{4}; \frac{3}{2}$
43. (a) $y = -\frac{1}{3}x + \frac{2}{3}$ **(b)** $-\frac{1}{3}; \frac{2}{3}$

45.

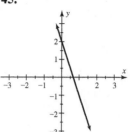

47.

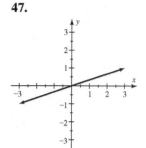

49.

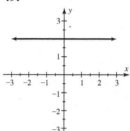

51.

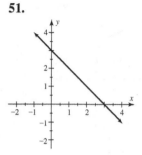

53.

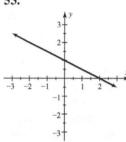

55.

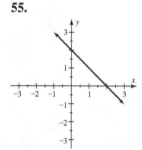

57. $y = 2x + 2$ **59.** $y = x - 2$ **61.** $y = \frac{4}{7}x + 3$
63. $y = 3x$ **65.** $y = -\frac{1}{2}x + \frac{5}{2}$ **67.** $y = 2x$
69. $y = \frac{1}{3}x + \frac{1}{3}$ **71. (a)** \$25 **(b)** 25 cents **(c)** 25; the fixed cost of renting the car **(d)** 0.25; the cost per mile of driving the car **73. (a)** \$7.45 **(b)** $C = 0.07x + 3.95$
(c) 67 min **75. (a)** $m = 0.35; b = 164.3$
(b) The fixed cost of owning the car for one month

SECTION 3.6 (pp. 207–210)

1. True **2.** True **3.** $y = mx + b$
4. $y - y_1 = m(x - x_1)$ or $y = m(x - x_1) + y_1$
5. 1; 3 **6.** distributive **7.** Yes; every nonvertical line has exactly one slope and one y-intercept. **8.** No; it depends on the point used. **9.** No **11.** Yes **13.** $y - 3 = -2(x + 2)$
15. $y - 2 = \frac{3}{4}(x - 1)$ **17.** $y + 1 = -\frac{1}{2}(x - 3)$
19. $y - 1 = 4(x + 3)$ **21.** $y + 3 = \frac{1}{2}(x + 5)$
23. $y - 30 = 1.5(x - 2010)$ **25.** $y - 4 = \frac{7}{3}(x - 2)$
27. $y = \frac{3}{5}(x - 5)$ **29.** $y - 15 = 5(x - 2003)$
31. $y = 3x - 2$ **33.** $y = \frac{1}{3}x$ **35.** $y = \frac{2}{3}x + \frac{1}{12}$
37. $y = -2x + 9$ **39.** $y = \frac{3}{5}x - 2$ **41.** $y = -16x - 19$
43. $y = -2x + 5$ **45.** $y = -x + 1$ **47.** $y = -\frac{1}{9}x + \frac{1}{3}$
49. $y = 2x - 7$ **51.** $y = 2x - 15$ **53.** $y = -2x - 1$
55. $y = \frac{1}{2}x - \frac{5}{2}$ **57.** $-mx_1 + y_1$

59. (a) $-5°F$ per hour   **(b)** $T = -5x + 45$; the temperature is decreasing at a rate of $5°F$ per hour.
(c) 9; at 9 A.M. the temperature was $0°F$.
(d)

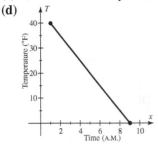

(e) At 4 A.M. the temperature was $25°F$.
61. (a) Entering; 300 gallons   **(b)** 100; initially the tank contains 100 gallons.   **(c)** $y = 50x + 100$; the amount of water is increasing at a rate of 50 gallons per minute.
(d) 8 minutes   **63. (a)** Toward   **(b)** After 1 hour the person is 250 miles from home. After 4 hours the person is 100 miles from home.   **(c)** 50 mph   **(d)** $y = -50x + 300$; the car is traveling toward home at 50 mph.
65. (a) In 2002, average home size was 2334 square feet.
(b) $y - 2334 = 34(x - 2002)$
(c) About 2500 square feet; 2504 square feet
(d) Home size increased, on average, by 34 square feet per year.
67. (a) $y - 731 = 515(x - 2006)$ **(b)** 1761
69. Cigarette consumption decreased on average by 10.33 billion cigarettes per year.
71. (a) $y = 2.7x - 5391.3$ **(b)** 41.1 million

CHECKING BASIC CONCEPTS 3.5 & 3.6 (pp. 210–211)

1. $y = -3x + 1$ **2.** $y = \frac{4}{5}x - 4; \frac{4}{5}; -4$
3.

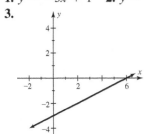

4. (a) $y = 3x - 2$ **(b)** $y = -\frac{3}{2}x$ **(c)** $y = -\frac{7}{3}x - \frac{5}{3}$
5. $y - 3 = -2(x + 1)$ **6.** $y = -2x + 1$
7. $y = 2x + 3$ **8. (a)** $y = -12x + 48$ **(b)** 12 mph
(c) 4 P.M.   **(d)** 48 miles   **9. (a)** 5 inches   **(b)** 2 inches per hour   **(c)** 5; total inches of snow that fell before noon
(d) 2; the rate of snowfall was 2 inches per hour.

SECTION 3.7 (pp. 216–218)

1. linear   **2.** exact   **3.** approximate   **4.** constant
5. constant rate of change   **6.** initial amount   **7.** f.   **8.** d.
9. a.   **10.** c.   **11.** e.   **12.** b.   **13.** Yes   **15.** No   **17.** No
19. Exact; $y = 2x - 2$ **21.** Approximate; $y = 2x + 2$

23. Approximate; $y = 2$ **25.** $y = 5x + 40$
27. $y = -20x - 5$ **29.** $y = 8$
31. (a) Yes   **(b)**

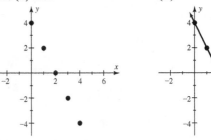

(c) $y = -2x + 4$
33. (a) No   **(b)**

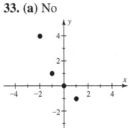

(c) $y = -2x$
35. (a) Yes   **(b)**

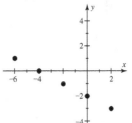

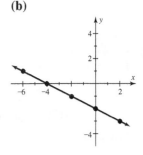

(c) $y = -\frac{1}{2}x - 2$
37. (a) No   **(b)**

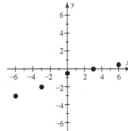

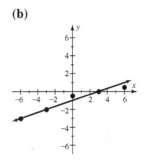

(c) $y = \frac{1}{3}x - 1$
39. $g = 5t + 200$, where g represents gallons of water and t represents time in minutes.
41. $d = 6t + 5$, where d represents distance in miles and t represents time in hours.
43. $p = 8t + 200$, where p represents total pay in dollars and t represents time in hours.
45. $r = t + 5$, where r represents total number of roofs shingled and t represents time in days.
47. (a) $-\frac{2}{45}$ acre per year   **(b)** $A = -\frac{2}{45}t + 5$
49. (a) $y = 6x - 11,846$ **(b)** About 232,000

51. (a)   **(b)**

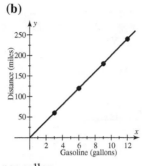   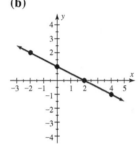

(c) 20; the mileage is 20 miles per gallon.
(d) $y = 20x$ **(e)** 140 miles

CHECKING BASIC CONCEPTS 3.7 (p. 218)

1. Yes   **2.** Approximate; $y = x - 1$
3. (a) $y = 10x + 50$ **(b)** $y = -2x + 200$
4. (a)   **(b)**

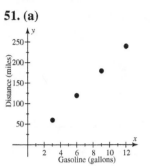   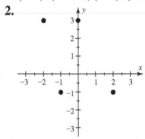

(c) $y = -\frac{1}{2}x + 1$
5. (a) $T = 0.075x$ **(b)** 5.1°F

CHAPTER 3 REVIEW (pp. 223–227)

1. $(-2, 0)$: none; $(-1, 2)$: II; $(0, 0)$: none; $(1, -2)$: IV; $(1, 3)$: I
2.

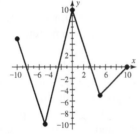

3. (a) II   **(b)** IV   **4. (a)** None   **(b)** III
5.   **6.**

5. (graph)   6. (graph)

7. Yes   **8.** No   **9.** No   **10.** Yes
11.

x	-2	-1	0	1	2
y	6	3	0	-3	-6

12.

x	4	3	2.5	2	1
y	-3	-1	0	1	3

13.

x	-2	0	2	4
y	-4	2	8	14

14.

x	1	2	3	4
y	6	5	4	3

15.

x	-0.5	0	0.5	1
y	-1	0	1	2

16.

x	-1	-3	-5	-7
y	1	2	3	4

17.   **18.**

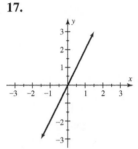   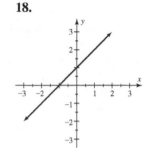

19.   **20.**

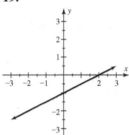   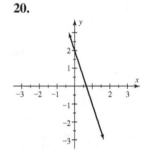

21.   **22.**

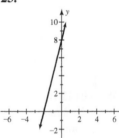   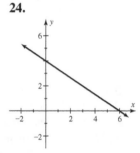

23.   **24.**

23. (graph)   24. (graph)

25. 3; -2   **26.** -2 and 2; -4
27.

x	-2	-1	0	1	2
y	4	3	2	1	0

2; 2

28.

x	-4	-2	0	2	4
y	-4	-3	-2	-1	0

4; -2

29. *x*-int: 3;   *y*-int: −2

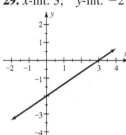

30. *x*-int: 1;   *y*-int: −5

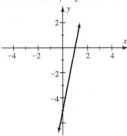

51.

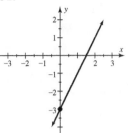

52.

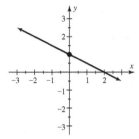

31. *x*-int: 4;   *y*-int: −2

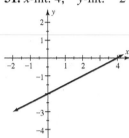

32. *x*-int: 2;   *y*-int: 3

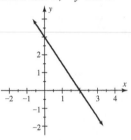

53.

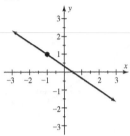

54.

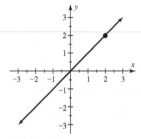

33. $y = 1$ **34.** $x = 3$
35. (a)

(b)

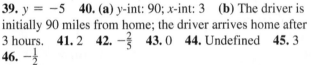

55.

x	0	1	2	3
y	1	$\frac{3}{2}$	2	$\frac{5}{2}$

56. Positive

57. $y = x + 1$ **58.** $y = -2x + 2$
59. $y = 2x - 2$

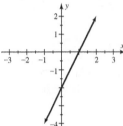

60. $y = -\frac{3}{4}x + 3$

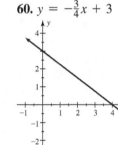

36. $x = -1; y = 1$ **37.** $y = 3; x = -2$ **38.** $x = 4$
39. $y = -5$ **40. (a)** *y*-int: 90; *x*-int: 3   **(b)** The driver is initially 90 miles from home; the driver arrives home after 3 hours.   **41.** 2   **42.** $-\frac{2}{5}$ **43.** 0   **44.** Undefined   **45.** 3
46. $-\frac{1}{2}$

47. (a)

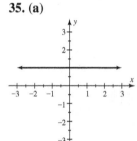

48. (a)

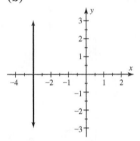

61. (a) $y = -x + 3$ **(b)** −1; 3
62. (a) $y = \frac{3}{2}x - 3$ **(b)** $\frac{3}{2}$; −3
63. (a) $y = 2x - 20$ **(b)** 2; −20
64. (a) $y = \frac{5}{6}x - 5$ **(b)** $\frac{5}{6}$; −5
65.

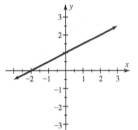

66.

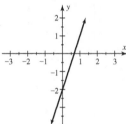

(b) −2; 0

(b) 1; −1

67.

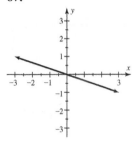

68.

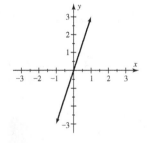

49. (a)

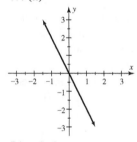

50. (a)

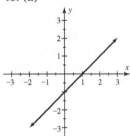

(b) $-\frac{1}{2}$; 2

(b) $\frac{2}{3}$; 2

69.

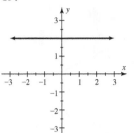

70.

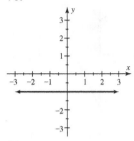

71.

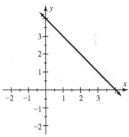

72.

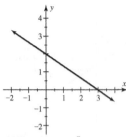

73. $y = 5x - 5$ **74.** $y = -2x$ **75.** $y = -\frac{5}{6}x + 2$
76. $y = -2x - 3$ **77.** $y = \frac{2}{3}x - 2$ **78.** $y = -\frac{1}{5}x - 2$
79. Yes   **80.** No   **81.** $y - 2 = 5(x - 1)$
82. $y + 5 = 20(x - 3)$ **83.** $y - 1 = -\frac{2}{3}(x + 2)$
84. $y + 30 = 3(x - 20)$ **85.** $y = \frac{4}{3}(x - 3)$
86. $y = 2\left(x - \frac{1}{2}\right)$ **87.** $y - 7 = 2(x - 5)$
88. $y = -\frac{2}{3}(x + 1)$ **89.** $y = 3x + 5$ **90.** $y = \frac{1}{3}x + 7$
91. $y = 2x + 11$ **92.** $y = -\frac{1}{4}x + 3$ **93.** No
94. Approximate; $y = -x + 5$ **95.** $y = -2x + 40$
96. $y = 20x + 200$ **97.** $y = 50$ **98.** $y = 5x - 20$

99. (a) Yes

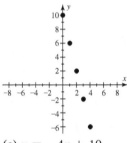

(b)

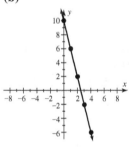

(c) $y = -4x + 10$

100. (a) No

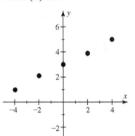

(b)

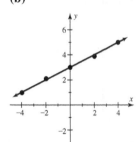

(c) $y = \frac{1}{2}x + 3$

101. (a)

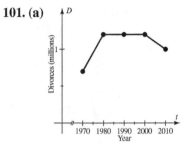

(b) The number of divorces increased significantly between 1970 and 1980, remained unchanged from 1980 to 2000, and then decreased.

102. (a) $G = 100t$

(b)

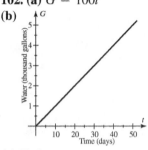

(c) 50 days

103. (a)

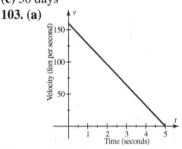

(b) v-int: 160; t-int: 5; the initial velocity was 160 ft/sec, and the velocity after 5 seconds was 0.

104. (a) $m_1 = 0$; $m_2 = -1500$; $m_3 = 500$ **(b)** $m_1 = 0$: The population remained unchanged. $m_2 = -1500$: The population decreased at a rate of 1500 insects per week. $m_3 = 500$: The population increased at a rate of 500 insects per week.   **(c)** For the first week the population did not change from its initial value of 4000. Over the next two weeks the population decreased at a rate of 1500 insects per week until it reached 1000. Finally, the population increased at a rate of 500 per week for two weeks, reaching 2000.

105.

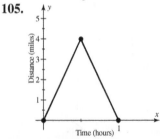

106. (a) -120 **(b)** The number of nursing homes decreased at an average rate of 120 per year.

107. (a) \$35   **(b)** 20¢   **(c)** 35; the fixed cost of renting the car   **(d)** 0.2; the cost for each mile driven
108. (a) Toward; the slope is negative.   **(b)** After 1 hour the car is 200 miles from home; after 3 hours the car is 100 miles from home.   **(c)** $y = -50x + 250$; the car is moving toward home at 50 mph.   **(d)** 150 miles; 150 miles
109. (a)

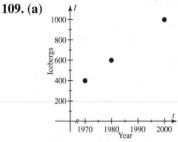

(b) $I = 20t - 39{,}000$; the number of icebergs increased at an average rate of 20 per year.   **(c)** Yes   **(d)** 1100 icebergs
110. (a)   **(b)**

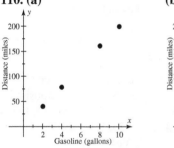 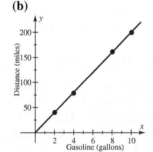

(c) 20; the mileage is 20 miles per gallon.
(d) $y = 20x$; no   **(e)** About 180 miles

4   Systems of Linear Equations in Two Variables

SECTION 4.1 (pp. 238–241)

1. ordered   **2.** intersection-of-graphs   **3.** no solutions; one solution; infinitely many   **4.** consistent   **5.** inconsistent
6. independent   **7.** dependent   **8.** table   **9.** the same
10. intercepts   **11.** 1   **13.** 2   **15.** −2   **17.** 2
19. One; consistent; independent   **21.** Infinitely many; consistent; dependent   **23.** None; inconsistent   **25.** (1, 1)
27. (2, −3)   **29.** (2, 0)   **31.** (2, 1)   **33.** (3, 2)
35. (−1, 1)   **37.** (2, 4)   **39.** (3, 1)
41. (1, 3);

x	0	1	2	3
$y = x + 2$	2	3	4	5
$y = 4 - x$	4	3	2	1

43. (a) (−1, 1)   **(b)** (−1, 1)   **45. (a)** (3, 1)   **(b)** (3, 1)
47. (a) (1, 3)   **(b)** (1, 3)   **49.** (−1, −2)   **51.** (1, −1)
53. (1, 2)   **55.** (3, 2)   **57.** (3, 1)   **59.** (1, 2)
61. (a) $x + y = 4$, $x - y = 0$ **(b)** 2, 2
63. (a) $2x + y = 7$, $x - y = 2$ **(b)** 3, 1
65. (a) $x = 3y$, $x - y = 4$ **(b)** 6, 2

67. (a) $C = 0.5x + 50$ **(b)** 60 mi   **(c)** 60 mi
69. (a) $x + y = 42$; $x = 2y$ **(b)** (28, 14)
71. (a) $x - y = 4$; $2x + 2y = 28$ where x is length, y is width   **(b)** (9, 5); the rectangle is 9 in. × 5 in.

SECTION 4.2 (pp. 247–249)

1. exact   **2.** parentheses   **3.** It has infinitely many solutions.
4. It has no solutions.   **5.** (3, 6)   **7.** (2, 1)   **9.** (−1, 0)
11. (3, 0)   **13.** $\left(\frac{1}{2}, 0\right)$ **15.** (0, 4)   **17.** (1, 2)
19. (6, −4)   **21.** (4, −3)   **23.** $\left(1, -\frac{1}{2}\right)$ **25.** (1, 3)
27. (0, −2)   **29.** (2, 2)   **31.** (−3, 5)   **33.** No solutions
35. Infinitely many   **37.** (3, 1)   **39.** Infinitely many
41. No solutions   **43.** $\left(-\frac{4}{3}, \frac{11}{9}\right)$ **45.** (0, 0)
47. No solutions   **49.** No solutions   **51.** They are a single line.
53. (a) $L - W = 10$, $2L + 2W = 72$ **(b)** (23, 13)
55. (a) $x = \frac{1}{2}y$; $x + y = 90$ **(b)** (30, 60)   **(c)** (30, 60)
57. (a) $x - y = 21$; $y = 0.86x$ **(b)** (150, 129)
59. 94 ft × 50 ft   **61.** 17 and 53   **63.** 10 mph; 2 mph
65. $3.\overline{3}$ L of 20% solution, $6.\overline{6}$ L of 50% solution
67. Superior: 32,000 mi^2; Michigan: 22,000 mi^2

CHECKING BASIC CONCEPTS 4.1 & 4.2 (p. 249)

1. (a) −2   **(b)** 6   **2.** (4, 2)   **3.** (2, 1)   **4. (a)** No solutions
(b) (1, −1)   **(c)** Infinitely many solutions
5. (a) $x + y = 300$, $150x + 200y = 55{,}000$ **(b)** (100, 200)

SECTION 4.3 (pp. 257–259)

1. Substitution; elimination   **2.** addition   **3.** =   **4.** =
5. It has infinitely many solutions.   **6.** It has no solutions.
7. (1, 1)   **9.** (−2, 1)   **11.** No solutions   **13.** Infinitely many   **15.** (6, 1)   **17.** (−1, 4)   **19.** (2, 4)   **21.** (2, 1)
23. (4, −1)   **25.** (−4, 1)   **27.** $\left(\frac{4}{5}, 1\right)$ **29.** (−2, −5)
31. (1, 0)   **33.** (2, 2)   **35.** $\left(\frac{4}{5}, \frac{9}{5}\right)$ **37.** (3, 2)   **39.** (0, 1)
41. (2, 1)   **43.** (4, −3)   **45.** (1, 0)
47. Infinitely many;   **49.** One;

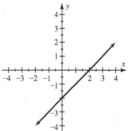 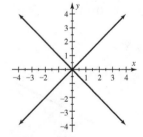

51. No solutions;   **53.** No solutions;

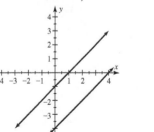 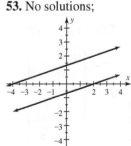

55. Infinitely many;

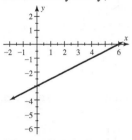

57. Men: 39,000; women: 29,000 **59.** Bicycle:18 min; stair climber: 12 min **61.** Current: 2 mph; boat: 6 mph **63.** $2000 at 3%; $3000 at 5% **65.** −43, 26 **67. (a)** 20 in. × 40 in. **(b)** 20 in. × 40 in.

CHAPTER 4 REVIEW (pp. 262–264)

1. 3 **2.** 2 **3. (a)** None **(b)** Inconsistent **4. (a)** One **(b)** Consistent; independent **5. (a)** Infinitely many **(b)** Consistent; dependent **6. (a)** None **(b)** Inconsistent **7.** (1, 2) **8.** (5, 2) **9.** (4, 3) **10.** (2, −4) **11.** (2, 2) **12.** (1, 2) **13.** (2, 6) **14.** (1, 1) **15.** (4, −3) **16.** (1, 2) **17.** (1, 1) **18.** (1, 2) **19.** (1, 1) **20.** (−2, −1) **21.** (2, 6) **22.** (2, −10) **23.** (−2, 1) **24.** (−4, −4) **25.** No solutions **26.** No solutions **27.** Infinitely many **28.** (1, 1) **29.** (2, 1) **30.** (−1, 2) **31.** (11, −1) **32.** (1, 0) **33.** $\left(\frac{9}{4}, \frac{7}{4}\right)$ **34.** $\left(\frac{5}{2}, 1\right)$ **35.** (5, −7) **36.** (8, 2) **37.** (−2, 3) **38.** (1, 0) **39.** (1, 3) **40.** (2, −1) **41.** Infinitely many **42.** Infinitely many **43.** No solutions **44.** One **67.** 3100 deaths in 1912; 37,200 deaths in 2008 **68.** Men: 40,000 cases; women: 34,000 cases **69. (a)** $C = 0.2x + 40$ **(b)** 250 mi **(c)** 250 mi **70.** 75°, 105° **71. (a)** $2x + y = 180, 2x − y = 40$ **(b)** (55, 70) **(c)** (55, 70) **72.** 20 ft × 24 ft **73. (a)** $x + y = 10, 80x + 120y = 920$; x is $80 rooms, y is $120 rooms. **(b)** (7, 3) **74.** 7 lb of $2 candy; 11 lb of $3 candy **75.** Bicycle: 35 min; stair climber: 25 min **76.** 2 mph **77. (a)** 16 ft × 24 ft (answers may vary slightly) **(b)** 16 ft × 24 ft **78.**

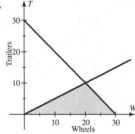

79. (a) 136 bpm; 108 bpm **(b)**

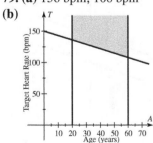

(c) Target heart rates above 70% of the maximum heart rate for ages 20 to 60

5 Polynomials and Exponents

SECTION 5.1 (pp. 275–276)

1. base; exponent **2.** 1 **3.** a^{m+n} **4.** a^{mn} **5.** $a^n b^n$ **6.** $\frac{a^n}{b^n}$ **7.** 64 **9.** −8 **11.** −8 **13.** 1 **15.** 11 **17.** $\frac{1}{2}$ **19.** 3^3 or 27 **21.** 4^8 or 65,536 **23.** x^9 **25.** x^6 **27.** $20x^7$ **29.** $-3x^3y^4$ **31.** 2^6 or 64 **33.** n^{12} **35.** x^7 **37.** $49b^2$ **39.** a^3b^3 **41.** 1 **43.** $-64b^6$ **45.** $x^{14}y^{21}$ **47.** $x^{12}y^9$ **49.** $a^{10}b^8$ **51.** $\frac{1}{27}$ **53.** $\frac{a^5}{b^5}$ **55.** $\frac{(x-y)^3}{27}$ **57.** $\frac{25}{(a+b)^2}$ **59.** $\frac{8x^3}{125}$ **61.** $\frac{27x^6}{125y^{12}}$ **63.** $(x + y)^4$ **65.** $(a + b)^5$ **67.** 6 **69.** $a^3 + 2ab^2$ **71.** $12a^5 + 6a^3b$ **73.** $r^2t + rt^2$ **75.** $a = 3, b = 1, m = 1, n = 0$ (answers may vary) **77.** $10x^4$ **79.** $9\pi x^4$ **81.** $8x^3$ **83.** $1157.63 **85. (a)** 3^2 **(b)** $72,000

SECTION 5.2 (pp. 284–286)

1. monomial **2.** polynomial **3.** degree **4.** degree **5.** binomial **6.** trinomial **7.** like **8.** like **9.** opposite **10.** vertically **11.** 2; 3 **13.** 2; −1 **15.** 2; −5 **17.** 0; 6 **19.** Yes; 1; 1; 1 **21.** Yes; 3; 1; 2 **23.** No **25.** No **27.** Yes; 1; 3; 6 **29.** Yes; x **31.** Yes; $-5x^3$ **33.** No **35.** Yes; $2ab$ **37.** $-x + 9$ **39.** $4x^2 + 8x + 1$ **41.** $4y^3 + 3y^2 + 4y − 9$ **43.** $4xy + 1$ **45.** $2a^2b^3$ **47.** $9x^2 + x − 6$ **49.** $x^2 − 7x − 1$ **51.** $-5x^2$ **53.** $-3a^2 + a − 4$ **55.** $2t^2 + 3t − 4$ **57.** $4x − 2$ **59.** $-3x^2 + 5x + 2$ **61.** $z^3 − 6z^2 − 6z − 1$ **63.** $3xy + 2x^2y^2$ **65.** $-a^3b$ **67.** $-x^2 − 5x − 4$ **69.** $-2x^3 − 6x − 2$ **71. (a)** 200 bpm **(b)** 100 bpm **(c)** It decreases quickly at first, then more slowly. **73.** $2z^2$; 200 in^2 **75.** $2x^2 + x^2$ or $3x^2$; 108 ft^2 **77.** $\pi x^2 + \pi y^2$; 13π ft^2 **79. (a)** $m_1 \approx 0.077; m_2 \approx 0.083; m_3 \approx 0.077$. A line is reasonable but not exact. **(b)** For the given years, its estimates are reasonable.

CHECKING BASIC CONCEPTS 5.1 & 5.2 (p. 286)

1. (a) −25 **(b)** 1 **2. (a)** 10^8 **(b)** $-12x^7$ **(c)** a^6b^2 **(d)** $\frac{x^4}{z^{12}}$ **3. (a)** 1 **(b)** $9x^{14}$ **(c)** $10a^5 − 14a^2$ **4.** 3; 2; 4 **5. (a)** $2w^2h$ **(b)** 2880 in^3 **6. (a)** $3a^2 + 6$ **(b)** $2z^3 + 7z − 8$ **(c)** $4xy$

SECTION 5.3 (pp. 292–294)

1. The product rule **2.** Distributive **3.** term; term **4.** vertically **5.** x^7 **7.** $-12a^2$ **9.** $20x^5$ **11.** $4x^2y^3$ **13.** $-12x^3y^3$ **15.** $3x + 12$ **17.** $-45x − 5$ **19.** $4z − z^2$ **21.** $-5y − 3y^2$ **23.** $15x^3 − 12x$ **25.** $6x^3 − 6x^2$ **27.** $-32t^2 − 8t − 8$ **29.** $-5n^4 + n^3 − 2n^2$ **31.** $x^2y + xy^2$ **33.** $x^4y − x^3y^2$ **35.** $-a^4b + 2ab^4$ **37.** $x^2 + 3x$ **39.** $x^2 + 4x + 4$ **41.** $x^2 + 9x + 18$ **43.** $x^2 + 8x + 15$ **45.** $x^2 − 17x + 72$

47. $6z^2 - 19z + 10$ **49.** $64b^2 - 1$ **51.** $10y^2 - 3y - 7$
53. $5 - 13a + 6a^2$ **55.** $1 - 9x^2$ **57.** $x^3 - x^2 + x - 1$
59. $4x^3 - 3x^2 + 16x - 12$ **61.** $2n^3 + n^2 + 6n + 3$
63. $m^3 + 4m^2 + 4m + 1$ **65.** $6x^3 - 7x^2 + 14x - 8$
67. $x^3 + 1$ **69.** $4b^4 + 3b^3 + 19b^2 + 9b + 21$
71. $x^3 - x^2 - 5x + 2$ **73.** $a^3 - 8$
75. $6x^4 - 2x^3 + 5x^2 - x + 1$ **77.** $m \cdot n$
79. (a) $h^3 - 2h^2 - 8h$ (b) 14,175 in^3
81. (a) $50x - x^2$ (b) 625   **83.** $6x^2 + 12x + 6$
85. (a) $64t - 16t^2$ (b) 64; 64   (c) Yes; yes

SECTION 5.5 (pp. 303–305)

1. $\frac{1}{a^n}$ **2.** a^n **3.** a^{m-n} **4.** $\frac{b^m}{a^n}$ **5.** $\left(\frac{b}{a}\right)^n$ **6.** $1 \le b < 10$
7. (a) $\frac{1}{4}$ (b) 9   **9.** (a) 2   (b) $\frac{1}{1000}$ **11.** (a) $\frac{1}{81}$ (b) $\frac{1}{8}$
13. (a) $\frac{1}{576}$ (b) 64   **15.** (a) 1   (b) 64   **17.** (a) 25   (b) $\frac{49}{4}$
19. (a) $\frac{1}{x}$ (b) $\frac{1}{a^4}$ **21.** (a) $\frac{1}{x^2}$ (b) $\frac{1}{a^8}$ **23.** (a) $\frac{y^3}{x^3}$ (b) $\frac{1}{x^3 y^3}$
25. (a) $\frac{1}{16t^4}$ (b) $\frac{1}{(x+1)^7}$ **27.** (a) a^8 (b) $\frac{1}{r^2 t^6}$
29. (a) $\frac{b^2}{a^4}$ (b) x^2 **31.** (a) a^{13} (b) $\frac{2}{z^3}$ **33.** (a) $-\frac{2y^3}{3x^2}$ (b) $\frac{1}{x^3}$
35. (a) $2b$ (b) $\frac{a^3}{b^3}$ **37.** (a) $\frac{x^7}{3y^8}$ (b) $\frac{4a^5}{b^6}$ **39.** (a) y^5 (b) $2t^3$
41. (a) $\frac{3a^{10}}{8}$ (b) $\frac{1}{32b^9}$ **43.** (a) $x^2 y^2$ (b) $a^6 b^3$
45. (a) $\frac{n^4}{72m^{11}}$ (b) $\frac{16x^{11}}{y^{13}}$ **47.** (a) $\frac{b^2}{a^2}$ (b) $\frac{4v}{u}$
49. (a) $\frac{4}{9a^6 b^6}$ (b) $\frac{16m^{14}}{25n^2}$ **51.** $\frac{a^n}{a^m} = a^{n-m} = a^{-(m-n)} = \frac{1}{a^{m-n}}$
53. Thousand   **55.** Billion   **57.** Hundredth   **59.** 2000
61. 45,000   **63.** 0.008   **65.** 0.000456   **67.** 39,000,000
69. $-500,000$ **71.** 2×10^3 **73.** 5.67×10^2
75. 1.2×10^7 **77.** 4×10^{-3} **79.** 8.95×10^{-4}
81. -5×10^{-2} **83.** 1,500,000   **85.** -1.5 **87.** 2000
89. 0.002   **91.** (a) About 5.859×10^{12} mi
(b) About 2.5×10^{13} mi   **93.** About 9.2×10^9 mi
95. 1×10^{100} **97.** (a) 1.246×10^{13} (b) About \$41,812

SECTION 5.6 (pp. 311–312)

1. $\frac{a}{d} + \frac{b}{d}$ **2.** $\frac{a}{d} + \frac{b}{d} - \frac{c}{d}$ **3.** term   **4.** False   **5.** False
6. 9; 4; 1   **7.** $x + 1$; $2x^2 - 2x + 1$; 4   **8.** $0x^2$ **9.** $2x$
11. $z^3 + z^2$ **13.** $\frac{a^2}{2} - 3$ **15.** $\frac{1}{3y^2} + \frac{2}{y}$ **17.** $\frac{4}{x} - 7x^2$
19. $\frac{2}{y} + \frac{1}{y^2}$ **21.** $3x^3 - 1 + \frac{2}{x}$ **23.** $4y^2 - 1 + \frac{2}{y}$
25. $3m^2 - 2m + 4$ **27.** $2x + 1 + \frac{3}{x-2}$ **29.** $x + 1$
31. $x^2 + 1 + \frac{-1}{x-1}$ **33.** $x^2 + 3x - 1$
35. $x^2 - x + 2 + \frac{1}{4x+1}$ **37.** $x^2 + 2x + 3 + \frac{8}{x-2}$
39. $3x^2 + 3x + 3 + \frac{5}{x-1}$ **41.** $x + 3 + \frac{-x-2}{x^2+1}$
43. $x + 1$ **45.** $x^2 - 2x + 4$ **47.** They are the same.
49. $4x$
51. $x + 2$;

CHECKING BASIC CONCEPTS 5.5 & 5.6 (p. 312)

1. (a) $\frac{1}{81}$ (b) $\frac{1}{2x^7}$ (c) $\frac{b^8}{16a^2}$ **2.** (a) z^5 (b) $\frac{y^6}{x^3}$ (c) $\frac{x^6}{27}$
3. (a) 4.5×10^4 (b) 2.34×10^{-4} (c) 1×10^{-2}
4. (a) 47,100   (b) 0.006   **5.** $5a - 3$ **6.** $3x + 2$; R: -2
7. $x^2 + 2x + 1$; R: $x + 1$ **8.** (a) 9.3×10^7
(b) 500 sec (8 min 20 sec)

CHAPTER 5 REVIEW (pp. 316–318)

1. 125   **2.** -81 **3.** 4   **4.** 11   **5.** -5 **6.** 1   **7.** 6^5
8. 10^{12} **9.** z^9 **10.** y^6 **11.** $30x^9$ **12.** $a^4 b^4$ **13.** 2^{10}
14. m^{20} **15.** $a^3 b^3$ **16.** $x^8 y^{12}$ **17.** $x^7 y^{11}$ **18.** 1
19. $(r - t)^9$ **20.** $(a + b)^6$ **21.** $\frac{9}{(x-y)^2}$ **22.** $\frac{(x+y)^3}{8}$
23. $6x^3 - 10x^2$ **24.** $12x^2 + 3x^4$ **25.** 7; 6   **26.** 5; -1
27. Yes; 1; 1; 1   **28.** Yes; 4; 1; 3   **29.** Yes; 3; 2; 2   **30.** No
31. $5x^2 - x + 3$ **32.** $-6x^2 + 3x + 7$ **33.** $3x + 4$
34. $-2x^2 - 13$ **35.** $-2x^2 + 9x + 5$ **36.** $3x^2 - 2x - 6$
37. $2a^3 - a^2 + 7a$ **38.** $-2x + 12$ **39.** $5y^2 - 3xy$
40. $4xy$ **41.** $-x^5$ **42.** $-r^3 t^4$ **43.** $-6t + 15$
44. $2y - 12y^2$ **45.** $18x^5 + 30x^4$ **46.** $-x^3 + 2x^2 - 9x$
47. $-a^3 b + 2a^2 b^2 - ab^3$ **48.** $a^2 + 3a - 10$
49. $8x^2 + 13x - 6$ **50.** $-2x^2 + 3x - 1$
51. $2y^3 + y^2 + 2y + 1$ **52.** $2y^4 - y^2 - 1$ **53.** $z^3 + 1$
54. $4z^3 - 15z^2 + 13z - 3$ **55.** $z^2 + z$ **56.** $2x^2 + 4x$
75. $\frac{9}{9}$ **76.** $\frac{1}{9}$ **77.** 4   **78.** $\frac{1}{1000}$ **79.** 36   **80.** $\frac{1}{25}$
81. $\frac{9}{16}$ **82.** 1   **83.** $\frac{1}{z^2}$ **84.** $\frac{1}{y^4}$ **85.** $\frac{1}{a^2}$ **86.** $\frac{1}{x^3}$
87. $\frac{1}{4t^2}$ **88.** $\frac{1}{a^3 b^6}$ **89.** $\frac{1}{y^3}$ **90.** x^4 **91.** $\frac{2}{x^3}$ **92.** $\frac{2x^4}{3y^3}$ **93.** $\frac{a^5}{b^5}$
94. $4t^4$ **95.** $\frac{n^7}{72m^{12}}$ **96.** $\frac{9x^{10}}{y^{10}}$ **97.** $\frac{y^2}{x^2}$ **98.** $\frac{2v}{3u}$ **99.** 600
100. 52,400   **101.** 0.0037   **102.** 0.06234   **103.** 1×10^4
104. 5.61×10^7 **105.** 5.4×10^{-5} **106.** 1×10^{-3}
107. 24,000,000   **108.** 0.2   **109.** $\frac{5x}{3} + 1$
110. $3b^2 - 2 + \frac{1}{b^2}$ **111.** $3x + 2 + \frac{4}{x-1}$
112. $3x - 4 + \frac{6}{3x+2}$ **113.** $x^2 - 3x - 1$
114. $x^2 + \frac{-1}{2x-1}$ **115.** $x - 1 + \frac{-2x+2}{x^2+1}$
116. $x^2 + 2x + 5$ **117.** (a) 60 bpm   (b) 110 bpm
(c) It increases.   **118.** $6xy$; 72 ft^2
119. $10z^2 + 25z$; 510 in^2 **120.** $x^4 y^2$ **121.** \$833.71
122. $\frac{4}{3}\pi x^3 + 8\pi x^2 + 16\pi x + \frac{32}{3}\pi$ **123.** (a) $96t - 16t^2$
(b) 128; after 2 seconds the ball is 128 ft high.
124. (a) $600L - L^2$ (b) 27,500; a rectangular building
with a perimeter of 1200 ft and a side of length 50 ft has
an area of 27,500 ft^2.
125. (a) $x^2 + 10x + 25$ (b) $x^2 + 10x + 25$
126. (a) $16x$ (b) 1600   **127.** About \$8795 per person
128. About 552,090,000 gal or 5.5209×10^8 gal

8 Introduction to Functions

SECTION 8.1 (pp. 335–340)

1. function **2.** y equals f of x **3.** symbolic **4.** numerical
5. domain **6.** range **7.** one **8.** False **9.** True
10. $(3, 4); 3; 6$ **11.** (a, b) **12.** d **13.** 1 **14.** equal
15. Yes **16.** Yes **17.** No **18.** No **19.** Yes **20.** No
21. $-6; -2$ **23.** $0; \frac{3}{2}$ **25.** $25; \frac{9}{4}$ **27.** $3; 3$ **29.** $13; -22$
31. $-\frac{1}{2}; \frac{2}{5}$ **33.** (a) $I(x) = 36x$ (b) $I(10) = 360$; There are
360 inches in 10 yards. **35.** (a) $M(x) = \frac{x}{5280}$
(b) $M(10) = \frac{10}{5280} \approx 0.0019$; There is $\frac{10}{5280}$ mile in
10 feet. **37.** (a) $A(x) = 43{,}560x$ (b) $A(10) = 435{,}600$;
There are 435,600 square feet in 10 acres.
39. $f = \{(1, 3), (2, -4), (3, 0)\}$;
$D = \{1, 2, 3\}; R = \{-4, 0, 3\}$
41. $f = \{(a, b), (c, d), (e, a), (d, b)\}$;
$D = \{a, c, d, e\}; R = \{a, b, d\}$

43.
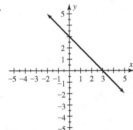

45.
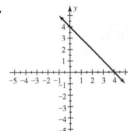

47.
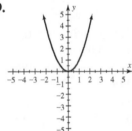

49.
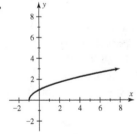

51.

53. $3; -1$ **55.** $0; 2$ **57.** $-4; -3$ **59.** $5.5; 3.7$
61. 26.9; in 1990 average fuel efficiency was **26.9** mpg.
63. Numerical:

x	-3	-2	-1	0	1	2	3
$y = f(x)$	2	3	4	5	6	7	8

Graphical:

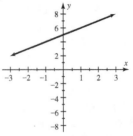

Symbolic: $y = x + 5$

65. Numerical:

x	-3	-2	-1	0	1	2	3
$y = f(x)$	-17	-12	-7	-2	3	8	13

Graphical:

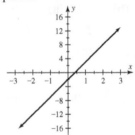

Symbolic: $y = 5x - 2$

67. Subtract $\frac{1}{2}$ from the input x to obtain the output y.
69. Divide the input x by 3 to obtain the output y.
71. Subtract 1 from the input x and then take the square root
to obtain the output y.
73. $f(x) = 0.50x$

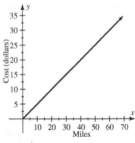

Miles	10	20	30	40	50	60	70
Cost	$5	$10	$15	$20	$25	$30	$35

75. 1825; in 2011 there were 1825 billion, or 1.825 trillion,
World Wide Web searches.
77. D: $-2 \le x \le 2$; R: $0 \le y \le 2$
79. D: $-2 \le x \le 4$; R: $-2 \le y \le 2$
81. D: All real numbers; R: $y \ge -1$
83. D: $-3 \le x \le 3$; R: $-3 \le y \le 2$
85. $D = \{1, 2, 3, 4\}$; $R = \{5, 6, 7\}$
87. All real numbers **89.** All real numbers **91.** $x \ne 5$
93. All real numbers **95.** $x \ge 1$ **97.** All real numbers

99. $x \neq 0$ **101. (a)** 1726; 1726 whales were sighted in 2008.   **(b)** $D = \{2005, 2006, 2007, 2008, 2009\}$, $R = \{649, 1265, 959, 1726, 1010\}$ **(c)** Increased every other year   **103.** $D = \{1, 2, 3, \ldots, 20\}$; $R = \{200, 400, 600, \ldots, 4000\}$ **105.** No   **107.** Yes
109. (a) 0.2   (b) Yes. Each month has one average amount of precipitation.   **(c)** 2, 3, 7, 11   **111.** Yes. D: All real numbers; R: All real numbers   **113.** No
115. Yes. D: $-4 \leq x \leq 4$; R: $0 \leq y \leq 4$
117. Yes. D: All real numbers; R: $y = 3$ **119.** No
121. It does. $D = \{-6, -4, 2, 4\}$; $R = \{-4, 2\}$ **123.** Yes
125. No   **127.** The person walks away from home, then turns around and walks back a little slower.

129.

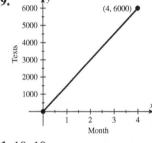

131. 10; 10
[−10, 10, 1] by [−10, 10, 1]

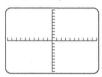

133. 10; 5
[0, 100, 10] by [−50, 50, 10]

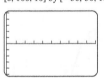

135. 16; 5
[1980, 1995, 1] by
[12000, 16000, 1000]

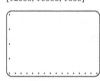

137.
[−6, 6, 1] by [−6, 6, 1]

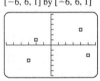

139. [−30, 30, 5] by
[−50, 50, 5]

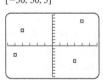

141. [−200, 200, 50] by
[−250, 250, 50]

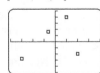

143. Numerical

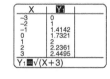

Graphical
[−10, 10, 1] by [−10, 10, 1]

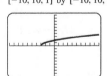

145. Numerical

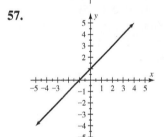

Graphical (Dot Mode)
[−10, 10, 1] by [−10, 10, 1]

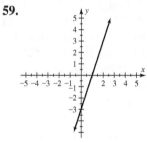

SECTION 8.2 (pp. 352–358)

1. $mx + b$ **2.** b **3.** line   **4.** horizontal   **5.** 7   **6.** 0
7. True   **8.** False   **9.** Carpet costs $2 per square foot. Ten square feet of carpet costs $20.   **10.** The rate at which water is leaving the tank is 4 gallons per minute. After 5 minutes the tank contains 80 gallons of water.
11. Yes; $m = \frac{1}{2}, b = -6$ **13.** No
15. Yes; $m = 0, b = -9$ **17.** Yes; $m = -9, b = 0$
19. Yes   **21.** No   **23.** Yes; $f(x) = 3x - 6$ **25.** Yes; $f(x) = -\frac{3}{2}x + 3$ **27.** No   **29.** Yes; $f(x) = 2x$
31. Yes; $f(x) = -4$ **33.** -16; 20   **35.** $\frac{17}{3}$; 2
37. -22; -22 **39.** -2; 0   **41.** -1; -4 **43.** 1; 1
45. $f(x) = 6x$; 18   **47.** $f(x) = \frac{x}{6} - \frac{1}{2}$; 0   **49.** d.   **51.** b.
53.

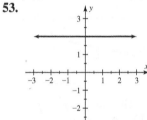

55.

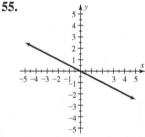

57.

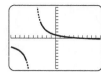

59.

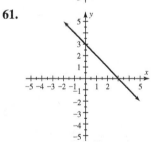

61.

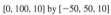

63. $f(x) = \frac{1}{16}x$ **65.** $f(t) = 65t$ **67.** $f(x) = 24$ **69.** a

71. (a) f multiplies the input x by -2 and then adds 1 to obtain the output y.

(b)

x	-2	0	2
$y = f(x)$	5	1	-3

(c)

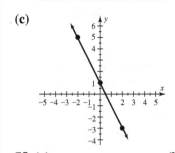

73. (a) f multiplies the input x by $\frac{1}{2}$ and then subtracts 1 to obtain the output y.

(b)

x	-2	0	2
$y = f(x)$	-2	-1	0

(c)

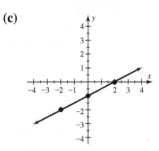

75. (a)

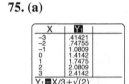

$Y_1 \blacksquare X/3 + \sqrt{}(2)$

(b) $[-6, 6, 1]$ by $[-4, 4, 1]$

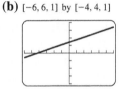

77. (a)

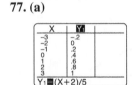

$Y_1 \blacksquare (X+2)/5$

(b) $[-6, 6, 1]$ by $[-4, 4, 1]$

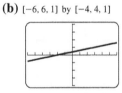

79. b.   **81.** c.   **83. (a)** $G(x) = \frac{X}{E}$ **(b)** $C(x) = \frac{3x}{E}$
85. -1 **87.** $(-1, 0)$ **89.** $\left(-\frac{1}{2}, \frac{1}{2}\right)$ **91.** $(20, 0)$
93. $(-8, -1)$ **95.** $\left(-1, -\frac{1}{6}\right)$ **97.** $(0.2, 0.25)$
99. $(2005, 9)$ **101.** $(2a, 2b)$ **103. (a)** $f(x) = -2x + 5; 1$
(b) 1   **(c)** Equal   **105. (a)** $f(x) = \frac{2}{5}x + \frac{1}{5}; 1$
(b) 1   **(c)** Equal   **107.** 79.8 years
109. 256.5 million   **111.** \$45,250
113. (a) Symbolic: $f(x) = 70$
Graphical:

(b)

Hours	0	4	8	12	16	20	24
Temp. (°F)	70	70	70	70	70	70	70

(c) Constant
115. $D(t) = 60t + 50$ **117. (a)** $K(x) = 93x$
(b) $A(x) = x$ **(c)** 33,945; 365; On average, someone under 18 sends 33,945 texts in 1 year while someone over 65 sends 365 texts.
119. (a) 1.6 million   **(b)** 0.1 million
(c) $f(x) = 0.1x + 1.6$ **(d)** 2.2 million

121. (a) 563 million   **(b)** In 2006, there were about 123 million users.   **(c)** Users increased, on average, by 110 million per year.   **123. (a)** $V(T) = 0.5T + 137$
(b) 162 cm^3 **125.** $f(x) = 40x$; about 2.92 pounds
127. (a) 55%   **(b)** 4%   **(c)** $P(x) = 4x + 55$ **(d)** 67%

CHECKING BASIC CONCEPTS 8.1 & 8.2 (p. 358)

1. Symbolic: $f(x) = x^2 - 1$
Graphical:

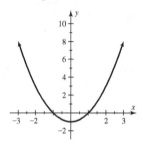

2. (a) D: $-3 \le x \le 3$; R: $-4 \le y \le 4$ **(b)** 0; 4
(c) No. The graph is not a line.
3. (a) Yes   **(b)** No   **(c)** Yes   **(d)** Yes
4. $f(-2) = 10$

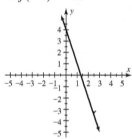

5. $f(x) = \frac{1}{2}x - 1$ **6. (a)** 32.2: In 1990 the median age was about 32 years.   **(b)** 0.225: The median age is increasing by 0.225 year each year. 27.7: In 1970 the median age was 27.7 years.   **7.** $(1, -1)$

SECTION 8.3 (pp. 366–369)

1. $x > 1$ and $x \le 7$ (answers may vary)
2. $x \le 3$ or $x > 5$ (answers may vary)   **3.** No   **4.** Yes
5. Yes   **6.** Numerically, graphically, symbolically
7. Yes, no   **8.** No, yes   **9.** No, yes   **10.** Yes, no
11. No, yes   **12.** Yes, yes   **13.** $[2, 10]$ **15.** $(5, 8]$
17. $(-\infty, 4)$ **19.** $(-2, \infty)$ **21.** $[-2, 5)$ **23.** $(-8, 8]$
25. $(3, \infty)$ **27.** $(-\infty, -2] \cup [4, \infty)$
29. $(-\infty, 1) \cup [5, \infty)$ **31.** $(-3, 5]$ **33.** $(-\infty, -2)$
35. $(-\infty, 4)$ **37.** $(-\infty, 1) \cup (2, \infty)$
39. $\{x \mid -1 \le x \le 3\}$

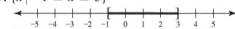

41. $\{x \mid -2 < x < 2.5\}$

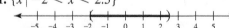

43. $\{x \mid x > 3\}$

45. $\{x \mid x \le -1 \text{ or } x \ge 2\}$

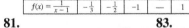

47. All real numbers

49. $[-6, 7]$　**51.** $\left(\frac{13}{4}, \infty\right)$　**53.** $(-\infty, \infty)$
55. $\left(-\infty, -\frac{11}{5}\right) \cup (-1, \infty)$　**57.** No solutions
59. $[-6, 1)$　**61.** $\left[-\frac{1}{4}, \frac{11}{8}\right)$　**63.** $[-9, 3]$
65. $\left[-4, -\frac{1}{4}\right)$　**67.** $(-1, 1]$　**69.** $[-2, 1]$　**71.** $(0, 2)$
73. $(9, 21]$　**75.** $\left[\frac{12}{5}, \frac{22}{5}\right]$　**77.** $\left(-\frac{13}{3}, 1\right)$　**79.** $[0, 12]$
81. $[-1, 2]$　**83.** $(-1, 2)$　**85.** $[-3, 1]$
87. $(-\infty, -2) \cup (0, \infty)$
89. (a) Toward, because distance is decreasing
(b) 4 hours, 2 hours　**(c)** From 2 to 4 hours　**(d)** During the
first 2 hours　**91. (a)** 2　**(b)** 4　**(c)** $\{x \mid 2 \le x \le 4\}$
(d) $\{x \mid 0 \le x < 2\}$　**93.** $[1, 4]$　**95.** $(-\infty, -2) \cup (0, \infty)$
97. $[2002, 2010]$　**99.** $[1, 3]$　**101.** $(-\infty, \infty)$
103. $(-\infty, 1) \cup [3, \infty)$　**105.** $(c - b, d - b]$
107. (a) From 2006 to 2008　**(b)** From 2006 to 2008
(c) From 2006 to 2008　**109.** From 0.5 to 1.5 miles
111. From $5.\overline{6}$ to 9 feet　**113.** From 1.5 to 2.5 miles
115. (a) $M(x) = 25x + 250$　**(b)** From 2002 to 2006

SECTION 8.4 (pp. 381–385)

1. domain　**2.** range　**3.** $(-\infty, \infty)$
4. $(-\infty, 5) \cup (5, \infty)$　**5.** absolute value
6. exponent　**7.** 2　**8.** 1　**9.** rational　**10.** $-\frac{1}{2}$　**11.** c.
12. a.　**13.** $D: (-\infty, \infty); R: (-\infty, \infty)$
15. $D: (-\infty, \infty); R: (-\infty, \infty)$
17. $D: (-\infty, \infty); R: [2, \infty)$
19. $D: (-\infty, \infty); R: (-\infty, 0]$
21. $D: [-1, \infty); R: [0, \infty)$
23. $D: (-\infty, \infty); R: [0, \infty)$
25. $(-\infty, 1) \cup (1, \infty)$　**27.** $(-\infty, 2) \cup (2, \infty)$
29. $(-\infty, -2) \cup (-2, 2) \cup (2, \infty)$
31. $(-\infty, 0) \cup (0, 2) \cup (2, \infty)$　**33.** $(-\infty, 1) \cup (1, \infty)$
35. $(-\infty, -1) \cup (-1, 3) \cup (3, \infty)$
37. $D: (-\infty, \infty); R: (-\infty, \infty)$
39. $D: [-2, 2]; R: [-2, 2]$
41. $D: [-2, 3]; R: [-2, 2]$　**43.** Yes; 1; linear
45. Yes; 3; cubic　**47.** No　**49.** Yes; 2; quadratic
51. No　**53.** Yes; 4; fourth degree　**55.** 12; 0　**57.** 1; $\frac{11}{4}$
59. 0; 6　**61.** -14; 14　**63.** -6; 9　**65.** $\frac{1}{11}$; $-\frac{1}{7}$
67. $-\frac{5}{6}$; undefined　**69.** $\frac{5}{6}$; undefined　**71.** 1; -1
73. -2; -2　**75.** -4; 0　**77.** -1; undefined
79.

x	-2	-1	0	1	2
$f(x) = \frac{1}{x-1}$	$-\frac{1}{3}$	$-\frac{1}{2}$	-1	—	1

81.　　　　　　**83.**

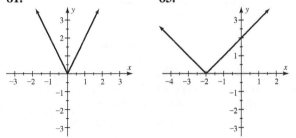

85.　　　　　**87.**

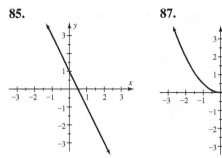

89.　　　　　**91.**

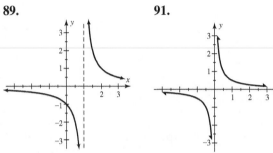

93.　　　　　**95.**

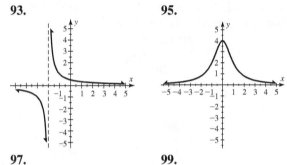

97.　　　　　**99.**

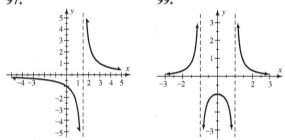

101. (a) 19　**(b)** -9　**(c)** 150　**(d)** 0
103. (a) 41　**(b)** -21　**(c)** 900　**(d)** Undefined
105. (a) $2x + 3$　**(b)** -1　**(c)** $x^2 + 3x + 2$　**(d)** $\frac{x + 1}{x + 2}$
107. (a) $x^2 - x + 1$　**(b)** $1 - x - x^2$　**(c)** $x^2 - x^3$
(d) $\frac{1 - x}{x^2}$　**109.** $a^2 - 2a$　**111.** c.　**113.** d.　**115. (a)** No;
answers may vary.　**(b)** Yes　**(c)** No; $0 \le t \le 10$
117. (a) 1; when cars are leaving the lot at a rate of
4 vehicles per minute, the average wait is 1 minute.　**(b)** As
more cars try to exit, the waiting time increases; yes.　**(c)**
$4.\overline{6}$ vehicles per minute　**119. (a)** 75; the braking distance
is 75 feet when the uphill grade is 0.05.　**(b)** 0.15　**121.**
(a) 123 thousand, which is close to the actual value.　**(b)**
478.6 thousand, which is too high; AIDS deaths did not continue to rise as rapidly as the model predicts.　**123.** About
45% and 22%; after 1 day (3 days) students remember 45%
(22%) of what they have learned.　**125. (a)** 130; it costs
$130 thousand to make 100 notebook computers.　**(b)** The
y-intercept for C is 100. The company has $100 thousand
in fixed costs even if it makes 0 computers. The y-intercept

for R is 0. If the company sells 0 computers, its revenue is $0.   **(c)** $P(x) = 0.45x - 100$ **(d)** 223 or more

CHECKING BASIC CONCEPTS 8.3 & 8.4 (p. 385)

1. (a) Yes   **(b)** No   **2. (a)** $[-3, 1]$
(b) $(-\infty, -1] \cup [3, \infty)$ **(c)** $\left[-\frac{8}{3}, \frac{8}{3}\right)$
3. (a) $(-\infty, \infty)$ **(b)** $(-\infty, 1) \cup (1, \infty)$ **(c)** $[0, \infty)$
4. (a) D: $[-2, 1]$; R: $[-3, 1]$ **(b)** 1; -3
5.

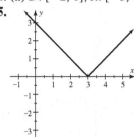

CHAPTER 8 REVIEW (pp. 388–392)

1. -7; 0   **2.** -22; 2   **3.** -2; 1   **4.** 5; 5   **5. (a)** $P(q) = 2q$
(b) $P(5) = 10$; there are 10 pints in 5 quarts.
6. (a) $f(x) = 4x - 3$ **(b)** $f(5) = 17$; three less than
four times 5 is 17.   **7.** $(3, -2)$ **8.** 4; -6
9.   **10.**

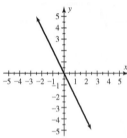   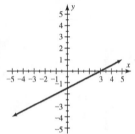

11.   **12.**

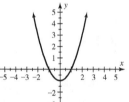   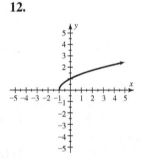

13. 1; 4   **14.** 1; -2 **15.** 7; -1
16. Numerical:

x	-3	-2	-1	0	1	2	3
$y = f(x)$	-11	-8	-5	-2	1	4	7

Symbolic: $f(x) = 3x - 2$
Graphical:

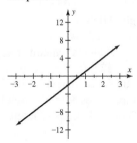

17. D: All real numbers; R: $y \le 4$ **18.** D: $-4 \le x \le 4$;
R: $-4 \le y \le 0$ **19.** Yes   **20.** No
21. $D = \{-3, -1, 2, 4\}$; $R = \{-1, 3, 4\}$; yes
22. $D = \{-1, 0, 1, 2\}$; $R = \{-2, 2, 3, 4, 5\}$; no
23. All real numbers   **24.** $x \ge 0$ **25.** $x \ne 0$
26. All real numbers   **27.** $x \le 5$ **28.** $x \ne -2$
29. All real numbers   **30.** All real numbers   **31.** No
32. Yes   **33.** Yes; $m = -4$, $b = 5$ **34.** Yes;
$m = -1$, $b = 7$ **35.** No   **36.** Yes; $m = 0$, $b = 6$
37. Yes; $f(x) = \frac{3}{2}x - 3$ **38.** No   **39.** 1
40. $f(-2) = -3$; $f(1) = 0$
41.   **42.**

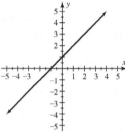   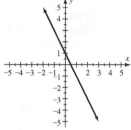

43.   **44.**

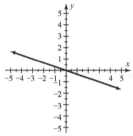   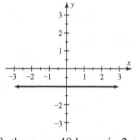

45. $H(x) = 24x$; $H(2) = 48$, there are 48 hours in 2 days.
46. (a)   **(b)** Domain: $x \ge -2$

$[-10, 10, 1]$ by $[-10, 10, 1]$

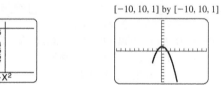

47. $(0.5, -3)$ **48.** $\left(\frac{5}{12}, \frac{3}{8}\right)$
49. $[-2, 2]$

50. $(-\infty, -3]$

51. $\left(-\infty, \frac{4}{5}\right] \cup (2, \infty)$

52. $(-\infty, \infty)$

53. $[-2, 1]$ **54. (a)** -4 **(b)** 2   **(c)** $[-4, 2]$ **(d)** $(-\infty, 2)$
55. (a) 2   **(b)** $(2, \infty)$ **(c)** $(-\infty, 2)$ **56. (a)** 4   **(b)** 2
(c) $(2, 4)$ **57.** $\left[-3, \frac{2}{3}\right]$ **58.** $(-6, 45]$ **59.** $\left(-\infty, \frac{7}{2}\right)$
60. $[1.8, \infty)$ **61.** $(-3, 4)$ **62.** $(-\infty, 4) \cup (10, \infty)$

63. $(-5, 5)$ **64.** $[8, 28]$ **65.** $(-9, 21)$ **66.** $[8, 28]$
67. $\left(-\frac{11}{5}, \frac{7}{5}\right]$ **68.** $[88, 138)$
69. $D = (-\infty, \infty); R = [0, \infty)$
70. $D = (-\infty, \infty); R = [0, \infty)$
71. $(-\infty, 4) \cup (4, \infty)$ **72.** $D = [-3, 1]; R = [-3, 6]$
73. Yes; 2; quadratic   **74.** Yes; 1; linear   **75.** Yes; 3;
cubic   **76.** No   **77.** 11; 2   **78.** $-\frac{4}{5}$; undefined
79.   **80.**

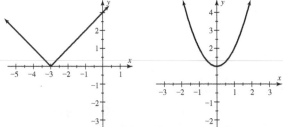

81.   **82.**

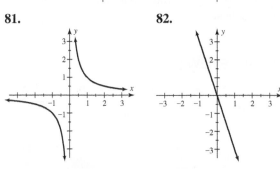

83. (a) 12   **(b)** 27   **84. (a)** $x^2 - x$ **(b)** $x + 1$
111. (a) About 25.1
(b) Decreased
[1885, 1965, 10] by [22, 26, 1]

(c) -0.0492; the median age decreased by about 0.0492
year per year.
112. (a) 2.2 million   **(b)** The number of marriages each
year did not change.   **113. (a)** $f(x) = 8x$ **(b)** 8
(c) The total fat increases at the rate of 8 grams per cup.
114. (a)

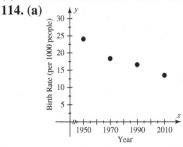

(b) $f(x) = -0.1675x + 350$ **(c)** About 15 per
1000 people (answers may vary)
115. (a) 113; in 1995, there were 113 unhealthy
days.   **(b)** $D = \{1995, 1999, 2000, 2003, 2007\}$
$R = \{56, 87, 88, 100, 113\}$ **(c)** It decreased and then
increased.

116. (a) Linear

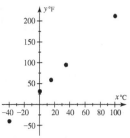

(b) $f(x) = \frac{9}{5}x + 32$; a 1°C change equals $\frac{9}{5}$°F change.
(c) 68°F   **117. (a)** 3 hours   **(b)** 2 hours and 4 hours
(c) Between 2 and 4 hours, exclusive   **(d)** 20 miles
per hour   **118. (a)** $f(x) = -0.3125x + 10$
(b) About 5.9 million   **119. (a)** $|A - 3.9| \le 1.7$
(b) $2.2 \le A \le 5.6$
120. Values between 32.2 and 37.8, exclusive

10   Radical Expressions and Functions

SECTION 10.1 (pp. 404–407)

1. ± 3 **2.** 3   **3.** 2   **4.** Yes   **5.** b   **6.** $|x|$ **7.** Undefined   **8.** -3 **9.** d.
10. a.
11.   **12.**

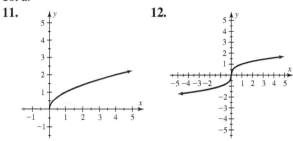

13. $\{x|x \ge 0\}$ **14.** All real numbers   **15.** 3   **17.** 0.6
19. $\frac{4}{5}$ **21.** x **23.** 3   **25.** -4 **27.** $\frac{2}{3}$ **29.** $-x^3$ **31.** $4x^2$ **33.** 3
35. -3 **37.** Not possible   **39.** -2.24 **41.** 1.71
43. -1.48 **45.** 4   **47.** $|y|$ **49.** $|x - 5|$ **51.** $|x - 1|$ **53.** $|y|$
55. $|x^3|$ **57.** x **59.** 3, not possible   **61.** $\sqrt{6}$, not possible
63. $\sqrt{20}$ or $2\sqrt{5}$, $\sqrt[3]{6}$ **65.** 1, 2   **67.** $-2, 1$ **69.** $-1, \sqrt[3]{-6}$ or
$-\sqrt[3]{6}$ **71.** 4   **73.** 5   **75.** $[-2, \infty)$ **77.** $[2, \infty)$ **79.** $[2, \infty)$
81. $(-\infty, 1]$ **83.** $\left(-\infty, \frac{8}{5}\right]$ **85.** $(-\infty, \infty)$ **87.** $\left(-\frac{1}{2}, \infty\right)$
89.   **91.**

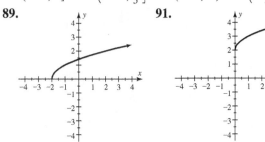

Shifted 2 units left   Shifted 2 units upward

93.

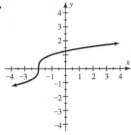

Shifted 2 units left

95.

x	$\sqrt{x}+1$
−1	—
0	1
1	2
4	3
9	4

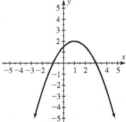

$f(x) = \sqrt{x}+1$

97.

x	$\sqrt{3x}$
−1	—
0	0
$\frac{1}{3}$	1
$\frac{4}{3}$	2
3	3

$f(x) = \sqrt{3x}$

99.

x	$2\sqrt[3]{x}$
−8	−4
−1	−2
0	0
1	2
8	4

$f(x) = 2\sqrt[3]{x}$

101.

x	$\sqrt[3]{x-1}$
−7	−2
0	−1
1	0
2	1
9	2

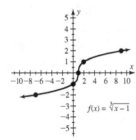

$f(x) = \sqrt[3]{x-1}$

103. $A = 6$ **105.** 1 sec   **107.** 122 mi
109. About $14 thousand; no
111. (a) $P(25,000) = \$71,246$; if \$25,000 is spent on equipment per worker, each worker will produce about \$71,246 worth of goods.
(b)

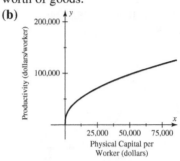

(c) \$26,197; \$20,102; an additional \$25,000 is spent on equipment per worker, but productivity levels off. There is a point where the business starts to lose money.

CHAPTER 10 REVIEW (p. 408)

1. 2   **2.** 6   **3.** $3|x|$ **4.** $|x-1|$ **5.** −4   **6.** −5   **7.** x^2
8. $3x$ **9.** 2   **10.** −1   **11.** x^2 **12.** $x+1$

---

11   Quadratic Functions and Equations

SECTION 11.1 (pp. 422–426)

1. parabola   **2.** The vertex   **3.** axis of symmetry   **4.** (0, 0)
5.

6. $-\frac{b}{2a}$ **7.** narrower   **8.** reflected   **9.** $ax^2 + bx + c$ with $a \neq 0$ **10.** vertex   **11.** True   **12.** False
13. False   **14.** True   **15.** (2, −6)   **17.** (−3, 4)
19. (0, 3)   **21.** (1, 1.4)   **23.** (3, 9)   **25.** 0, −4
27. −2, −2   **29.** (1, −2); $x = 1$; upward
31. (−2, 3); $x = -2$; downward

33. (b)

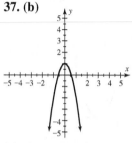

(a) $(0, 0)$; $x = 0$
(c) 2; 4.5

35. (b)

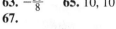

(a) $(0, -2)$; $x = 0$
(c) 2; 7

37. (b)

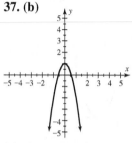

(a) $(0, 1)$; $x = 0$
(c) -11; -26

39. (b)

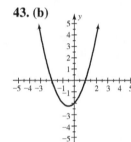

(a) $(1, 0)$; $x = 1$
(c) 9; 4

41. (b)

(a) $(-2, 0)$; $x = -2$
(c) 0; -25

43. (b)

(a) $(-0.5, -2.25)$; $x = -0.5$
(c) 0; 10

45. (b)

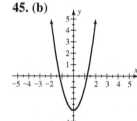

(a) $(0, -3)$; $x = 0$
(c) 5; 15

47. (b)

(a) $(1, 1)$; $x = 1$
(c) -8; -3

49. (b)

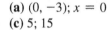

(a) $(1, 1)$; $x = 1$
(c) -17; -7

51. (b)

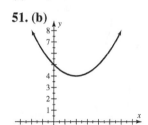

(a) $(2, 4)$; $x = 2$
(c) 8; 4.25

53. -2 **55.** $-\frac{25}{4}$ **57.** $-\frac{7}{2}$ **59.** 6   **61.** 4
63. $-\frac{39}{8}$ **65.** 10, 10

67.

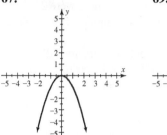

69.

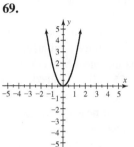

Reflected across the x-axis   Narrower

71.

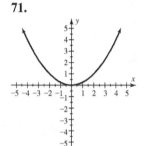

73.

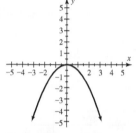

Wider   Reflected across the x-axis
and wider

75. (a) Upward; wider
(b) $x = -1$; $(-1, -2)$
(c) y-int: $-\frac{3}{2}$; x-int: $-3, 1$
(d)

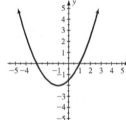

77. (a) Downward; the same
(b) $x = 1$; $(1, 1)$
(c) y-int: 0; x-int: 0, 2
(d)

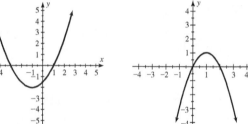

79. (a) Upward; narrower **(b)** $x = -\frac{1}{2}$; $\left(-\frac{1}{2}, -\frac{9}{2}\right)$
(c) y-int: -4; x-int: $-2, 1$
(d)

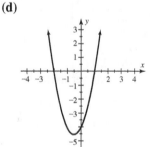

81. 3 slices   **83.** d.   **85.** a.   **87. (a)** 2 feet   **(b)** 2 seconds
(c) 66 feet   **89.** $\frac{66}{32} \approx 2$ seconds; about 74 feet

91. (a) The revenue increases at first up to 50 tickets and then it decreases.   **(b)** $2500; 50 **(c)** $f(x) = x(100 - x)$
(d) $2500; 50   **93. (a)** $V(1) = 21.75$, $V(2) = 30$,
$V(3) = 59.75$, and $V(4) = 111$; in 2007 there were 21.75 million unique Facebook visitors in one month. Other values can be interpreted similarly.
(b) The increases between consecutive years are 8.25 million, 29.75 million, and 51.25 million. A linear function does not model the data because these three increases are not equal (or nearly equal).
95. 300 feet by 600 feet   **97.** 42 in.
99. (a) In 1990, emissions were 6 billion metric tons.
(b) 3 billion metric tons.

SECTION 11.2 (pp. 436–439)

1. $x^2 + 2$ **2.** $(x - 2)^2$ **3.** $(1, 2)$ **4.** $(-1, -2)$
5. $f(x) = ax^2 + bx + c; f(x) = a(x - h)^2 + k$
6. $y = a(x - h)^2 + k; (h, k)$ **7.** downward   **8.** $-\frac{b}{2a}$
9. a.   **10.** d.

11.

x	-2	-1	0	1	2
$y = x^2$	4	1	0	1	4
$y = x^2 - 3$	1	-2	-3	-2	1

Shifted 3 units downward

13.

x	-2	-1	0	1	2
$y = x^2$	4	1	0	1	4

x	1	2	3	4	5
$y = (x - 3)^2$	4	1	0	1	4

Shifted 3 units right

15. (a)

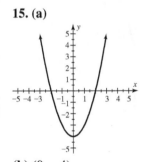

(b) $(0, -4)$
(c) Down 4 units

17. (a)

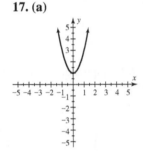

(b) $(0, 1)$
(c) Narrower and up 1 unit

19. (a)

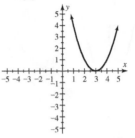

(b) $(3, 0)$
(c) Right 3 units

21. (a)

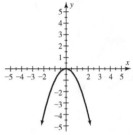

(b) $(0, 0)$
(c) Reflected across the
    x-axis

23. (a)

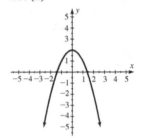

(b) $(0, 2)$
(c) Reflected across the
x-axis and up 2 units

25. (a)

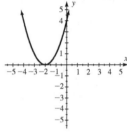

(b) $(-2, 0)$
(c) Left 2 units

27. (a)

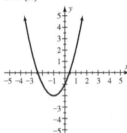

(b) $(-1, -2)$
(c) Left 1 unit and down
2 units

29. (a)

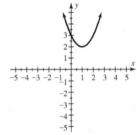

(b) $(1, 2)$
(c) Right 1 unit and up
2 units

31. (a)

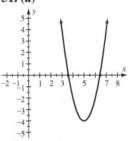

(b) $(5, -4)$
(c) Narrower, right 5 units
and down 4 units

33. (a)

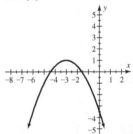

(b) $(-3, 1)$
(c) Wider, reflected
across the x-axis, left
3 units and up 1 unit

35. Translated 1 unit right, 2 units downward, and is wider

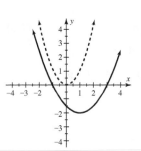

37. Translated 1 unit left, 3 units upward, opens downward, and is narrower

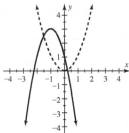

39. [−20, 20, 2] by [−20, 20, 2]

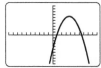

41. $y = 3(x - 3)^2 + 4$; $y = 3x^2 - 18x + 31$
43. $y = -\frac{1}{2}(x - 5)^2 - 2$; $y = -\frac{1}{2}x^2 + 5x - \frac{29}{2}$
45. $y = (x - 1)^2 + 2$ **47.** $y = -(x - 0)^2 - 3$
49. $y = (x - 0)^2 - 3$ **51.** $y = -(x + 1)^2 + 2$
53. (a) $(1, 1)$ **(b)** $y = 4(x - 1)^2 + 1$ **55. (a)** $(-1, -2)$
(b) $y = -(x + 1)^2 - 2$ **57. (a)** $(-1, 3)$
(b) $y = -2(x + 1)^2 + 3$ **59.** 1
61. $y = (x + 1)^2 - 1$; $(-1, -1)$
63. $y = (x - 2)^2 - 4$; $(2, -4)$
65. $y = (x + 1)^2 - 4$; $(-1, -4)$
67. $y = (x - 2)^2 + 1$; $(2, 1)$
69. $y = \left(x + \frac{3}{2}\right)^2 - \frac{17}{4}$; $\left(-\frac{3}{2}, -\frac{17}{4}\right)$
71. $y = \left(x - \frac{7}{2}\right)^2 - \frac{45}{4}$; $\left(\frac{7}{2}, -\frac{45}{4}\right)$
73. $y = 3(x + 1)^2 - 4$; $(-1, -4)$
75. $y = 2\left(x - \frac{3}{4}\right)^2 - \frac{9}{8}$; $\left(\frac{3}{4}, -\frac{9}{8}\right)$
77. $y = -2(x + 2)^2 + 13$; $(-2, 13)$ **79.** $a = 2$
81. $a = 0.3$ **83.** $y = 2(x - 1)^2 - 3$
85. $y = 0.5(x - 1980)^2 + 6$
87. (a)   **(b)** $D(x) = \frac{1}{12}x^2$

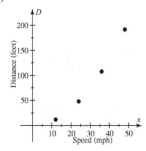

89. (a) Decreases and then increases
(b) No, because the data decrease and then increase
(c) Quadratic; it can model data that decrease and increase.
(d) (1995, 600); it has the minimum y-value.
(e) $C(x) = 1.8(x - 1995)^2 + 600$
(f) [1970, 2030, 10] by [0, 2500, 500]

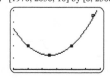

91. (a) $f(x) = 2(x - 1982)^2 + 1$ (answers may vary)
(b) 201 thousand (answers may vary)   **93.** incr: $x \geq 2$,
decr: $x \leq 2$ **95.** incr: $x \leq 1$, decr: $x \geq 1$
97. incr: $x \geq \frac{2}{3}$, decr: $x \leq \frac{2}{3}$ **99.** incr: $x \leq -\frac{3}{2}$,
decr: $x \geq -\frac{3}{2}$ **101.** incr: $x \leq -\frac{1}{8}$, decr: $x \geq -\frac{1}{8}$

CHECKING BASIC CONCEPTS 11.1 & 11.2 (p. 440)

1. (a)   **(b)**

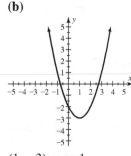

$(0, -2)$; $x = 0$ $(1, -3)$; $x = 1$
2. y_1 opens upward, whereas y_2 opens downward, y_1 is narrower than y_2.   **3.** 7

4. (a)   **(b)**

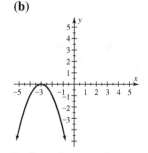

1 unit right, 2 units up   Reflected across the
                                    x-axis, 3 units left
5. (a) $y = (x + 7)^2 - 56$ **(b)** $y = 4(x + 1)^2 - 6$

SECTION 11.3 (pp. 449–452)

1. $x^2 + 3x - 2 = 0$ (answers may vary); it can have 0, 1, or 2 solutions   **2.** Nonlinear   **3.** Factoring, square root property, completing the square

4.   **5.**

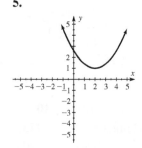

(answers may vary)   (answers may vary)

6. Two; the solutions are the x-intercepts.   **7.** ± 8; the square root property (answers may vary)   **8.** $\left(\frac{b}{2}\right)^2$
9. Yes   **10.** Yes   **11.** No   **12.** No   **13.** Yes   **14.** Yes
15. No   **16.** No   **17. (a)** 3.65, −1.65 **(b)** 1.32, −5.32
19. (a) 1.32, −0.12 **(b)** −0.28, −0.83   **21.** −2, 1
23. No real solutions   **25.** −2, 3   **27.** −0.5   **29.** −1, 5
31. −3, 1   **33.** −3, 3   **35.** $-\frac{1}{2}, \frac{3}{2}$ **37.** −1   **39.** No real
solutions   **41.** −7, 5   **43.** $-\frac{1}{3}, \frac{1}{2}$ **45.** $-\frac{3}{2}$ **47.** −2, 7

49. $\frac{6}{5}, \frac{3}{2}$ **51.** ± 12 **53.** $\pm \frac{8}{\sqrt{5}}$ or $\pm \frac{8\sqrt{5}}{5}$ **55.** $-6, 4$

57. $-7, 9$ **59.** $\frac{1 \pm \sqrt{5}}{2}$ **61.** $5 \pm \sqrt{5}$ **63.** 4 **65.** $\frac{25}{4}$

67. $16; (x - 4)^2$ **69.** $\frac{81}{4}; \left(x + \frac{9}{2}\right)^2$ **71.** $-4, 6$

73. $-3 \pm \sqrt{11}$ **75.** $\frac{3 \pm \sqrt{29}}{2}$ **77.** $\frac{5 \pm \sqrt{21}}{2}$

79. $1 \pm \sqrt{5}$ **81.** $\frac{3 \pm \sqrt{41}}{4}$ **83.** $\frac{2 \pm \sqrt{11}}{2}$

85. $\frac{-3 \pm \sqrt{5}}{12}$ **87.** $-6, 2$ **89.** $-2 \pm \sqrt{2}$

91. $\pm \sqrt{2}$ **93.** $-5, \frac{7}{3}$ **95.** $4 \pm \sqrt{14}$ **97.** $\pm \sqrt{\frac{c}{a}}$

99. $-3, 6$ **101.** $3, 5$ **103.** $5, 7$

105. $y = \pm \sqrt{x + 1}$ **107.** $v = \pm \sqrt{\frac{2K}{m}}$

109. $r = \pm \sqrt{\frac{k}{E}}$ **111.** $f = \pm \frac{1}{2\pi\sqrt{LC}}$ **113. (a)** 30 miles

per hour **(b)** 40 miles per hour **115.** About 1.9 seconds; no **117.** About 8 feet **119.** 2 hours **121. (a)** $x^2 + 6x - 520 = 0$ **(b)** -26 or 20; 20 feet **123.** About 23°C and 34°C **125.** October 2010

SECTION 11.4 (pp. 461–465)

1. To solve quadratic equations that are written in the form $ax^2 + bx + c = 0$ **2.** Completing the square **3.** $b^2 - 4ac$ **4.** One solution **5.** Factoring, square root property, completing the square, and the quadratic formula **6.** No; not when $b^2 - 4ac < 0$ **7.** $\pm\sqrt{k}$ **8.** $\pm i \sqrt{k}$ **9.** $-6, \frac{1}{2}$ **11.** 1 **13.** No real solutions **15.** $-2, 8$ **17.** $\frac{1 \pm \sqrt{17}}{8}$ **19.** No real solutions **21.** $\frac{1}{2}$ **23.** $\frac{3 \pm \sqrt{13}}{2}$ **25.** $2 \pm \sqrt{3}$ **27.** $\frac{1 \pm \sqrt{37}}{6}$ **29.** $\frac{1 \pm \sqrt{15}}{2}$ **31.** $\frac{5 \pm \sqrt{10}}{3}$ **33. (a)** $a > 0$ **(b)** $-1, 2$ **(c)** Positive **35. (a)** $a > 0$ **(b)** No real solutions **(c)** Negative **37. (a)** $a < 0$ **(b)** 2 **(c)** Zero **39. (a)** 25 **(b)** 2 **41. (a)** 0 **(b)** 1 **43. (a)** $-\frac{7}{4}$ **(b)** 0 **45. (a)** 21 **(b)** 2 **47.** $1 \pm \sqrt{2}$ **49.** $-\frac{3}{2}, 1$ **51.** None **53.** None **55.** $\frac{-2 \pm \sqrt{10}}{3}$ **57.** $\pm 3i$ **59.** $\pm 4i\sqrt{5}$ **61.** $\pm \frac{1}{2}i$ **63.** $\pm \frac{3}{4}i$ **65.** $\pm i\sqrt{6}$ **67.** $\pm \sqrt{3}$ **69.** $\pm i\sqrt{2}$ **71.** $\frac{1}{2} \pm i \frac{\sqrt{7}}{2}$ **73.** $-\frac{3}{4} \pm i \frac{\sqrt{23}}{4}$ **75.** $2 \pm \sqrt{3}$ **77.** $-\frac{1}{2} \pm i \frac{\sqrt{7}}{2}$ **79.** $-\frac{1}{5} \pm i \frac{\sqrt{19}}{5}$ **81.** $-\frac{3}{4} \pm i \frac{\sqrt{23}}{4}$ **83.** $-\frac{1}{2} \pm i \frac{\sqrt{15}}{2}$ **85.** $\frac{1 \pm \sqrt{3}}{2}$ **87.** $\frac{1}{4} \pm i \frac{\sqrt{15}}{4}$ **89.** $-1 \pm i\sqrt{3}$ **91.** $-2 \pm i$ **93.** $1 \pm i\sqrt{2}$ **95.** $1, 2$ **97.** $-\frac{1}{2}, 4$ **99.** $\frac{5 \pm \sqrt{17}}{2}$ **101.** $-\frac{1}{4} \pm \frac{3}{4}i\sqrt{7}$ **103.** $\pm \frac{1}{2}$ **105.** $\pm i\sqrt{2}$ **107.** $\frac{1}{3}$ **109.** 9 miles per hour **111.** 45 miles per hour **113.** About 1993 and 2004 ($x \approx 4.11, 15.36$) **115. (a)** 6; in Oct. 2010 Groupon's value was $6 billion. **(b)** Jan. 2011 **117.** $x \approx 8.04$, or about 1992; this agrees with the graph.

119. $130 + 5\sqrt{634} \approx 256$ mph **121. (a)–(c)** 11 in. by 14 in. **123. (a)** The rate of change is not constant. **(b)** 75 seconds (answers may vary) **(c)** 75 seconds

CHECKING BASIC CONCEPTS 11.3 & 11.4 (p. 465)

1. $\frac{1}{2}, 3$ **2.** $\pm \sqrt{5}$ **3.** $2 \pm \sqrt{3}$ **4.** $y = \pm\sqrt{1 - x^2}$ **5. (a)** $\frac{3 \pm \sqrt{17}}{4}$ **(b)** $\frac{4}{3}$ **(c)** $-\frac{1}{2} \pm i \frac{\sqrt{7}}{2}$ **6. (a)** 5; two real solutions **(b)** -7; no real solutions **(c)** 0; one real solution **7. (a)** $\pm i\sqrt{5}$ **(b)** $-\frac{1}{2} \pm i \frac{\sqrt{11}}{2}$

CHAPTER 11 REVIEW (pp. 468–470)

1. $(-3, 4); x = -3$; downward **2.** $(1, 0); x = 1$; upward

3. (a) 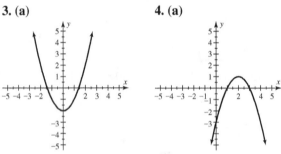 **4. (a)**

(b) $(0, -2); x = 0$ **(b)** $(2, 1); x = 2$
(c) -1 **(c)** 0

5. (a) 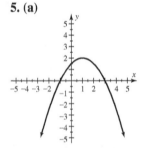 **6. (a)**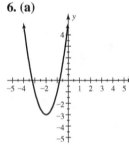

(b) $(1, 2); x = 1$ **(b)** $(-2, -3); x = -2$
(c) -2.5 **(c)** -1

7. $-\frac{7}{2}$ **8.** $-\frac{14}{3}$ **9.** $(2, -6)$ **10.** $(0, 5)$ **11.** $(2, 2)$
12. $(-1, 1)$

13. (a) 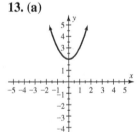 **14. (a)**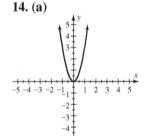

(b) Up 2 units **(b)** Narrower

15. (a)

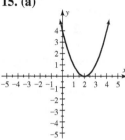

(b) Right 2 units

17. (a)

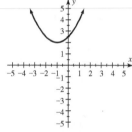

(b) Wider, left 1 unit, up 2 units

16. (a)

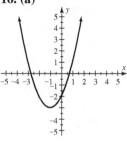

(b) Left 1 unit, down 3 units

18. (a)

(b) Narrower, right 1 unit, down 3 units

19. $y = -4(x - 2)^2 - 5$ **20.** $y = -(x + 4)^2 + 6$

21. $y = (x + 2)^2 - 11; (-2, -11)$

22. $y = \left(x - \frac{7}{2}\right)^2 - \frac{45}{4}; \left(\frac{7}{2}, -\frac{45}{4}\right)$

23. $y = 2\left(x - \frac{3}{4}\right)^2 - \frac{73}{8}; \left(\frac{3}{4}, -\frac{73}{8}\right)$

24. $y = 3(x + 1)^2 - 5; (-1, -5)$ **25.** $a = 3$

26. $a = \frac{1}{4}$ **27.** $f(x) = -5x^2 + 30x - 41; -41$

28. $f(x) = 3x^2 + 12x + 8; 8$ **29.** $-2, 3$ **30.** -1

31. No real solutions   **32.** $-4, 6$ **33.** $-10, 5$

34. $-0.5, 0.25$ **35.** $-5, 10$ **36.** $-3, 1$ **37.** $-4, 2$

38. $-1, 3$ **39.** $-5, 4$ **40.** $-8, -3$ **41.** $-\frac{2}{5}, \frac{2}{3}$

42. $\frac{4}{7}, 3$ **43.** ± 10 **44.** $\pm \frac{1}{3}$ **45.** $\pm \frac{\sqrt{6}}{2}$ **46.** No real

solutions   **47.** $-3 \pm \sqrt{7}$ **48.** $2 \pm \sqrt{10}$

49. $1 \pm \sqrt{6}$ **50.** $\frac{-3 \pm \sqrt{11}}{2}$ **51.** $R = -r \pm \sqrt{\frac{k}{F}}$

52. $y = \pm \sqrt{\frac{12 - 2x^2}{3}}$ **53.** $3, 6$ **54.** $11, 13$ **55.** $-\frac{1}{2}, \frac{1}{3}$

56. $\frac{5 \pm \sqrt{5}}{10}$ **57.** $4 \pm \sqrt{21}$ **58.** $\frac{3 \pm \sqrt{3}}{2}$

59. ± 2 **60.** $\pm \frac{1}{2}$ **61.** $\frac{5}{2}, 3$ **62.** $\frac{3}{2}, 5$ **63.** $\frac{3 \pm \sqrt{5}}{2}$

64. $\frac{1 \pm \sqrt{5}}{4}$ **65. (a)** $a > 0$ **(b)** $-2, 3$ **(c)** Positive

66. (a) $a > 0$ **(b)** 2   **(c)** Zero   **67. (a)** $a < 0$

(b) No real solutions   **(c)** Negative   **68. (a)** $a < 0$

(b) $-4, 2$ **(c)** Positive   **69. (a)** 1   **(b)** 2   **70. (a)** 144

(b) 2   **71. (a)** -23 **(b)** 0   **72. (a)** 0   **(b)** 1

73. $-\frac{1}{2} \pm i\frac{\sqrt{19}}{2}$ **74.** $\pm 2i$ **75.** $\frac{1}{4} \pm i\frac{\sqrt{7}}{4}$ **76.** $\frac{1}{7} \pm i\frac{\sqrt{34}}{7}$

95. (a) $f(x) = x(12 - 2x)$ **(b)** 6 inches by 3 inches

96. (a) After 1 second and 1.75 seconds   **(b)** 1.375 seconds;

34.25 feet   **97. (a)** $f(x) = x(90 - 3x)$

(b) [0, 30, 5] by [0, 800, 100]

(c) 10 or 20 rooms   **(d)** 15 rooms

98. (a) $x(x + 2) = 143$ **(b)** $x = -13$ or $x = 11$; the numbers are -13 and -11 or 11 and 13.

99. (a) $\sqrt{1728} \approx 41.6$ miles per hour   **(b)** 60 miles per hour

100. (a) (1950, 220); in 1950, the per capita consumption was at a low of 220 million Btu.

(b) [1950, 1970, 5] by [200, 350, 25]

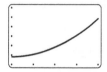

It increased.

(c) $f(2010) = 1120$; no; the trend represented by this model did not continue after 1970.   **101.** About 11.1 inches by 11.1 inches   **102.** 50 feet   **103.** About 1.5 feet

104. About 6.0 to 9.0 inches

---

12   **Exponential and Logarithmic Functions**

SECTION 12.2 (pp. 486–490)

1. $f(x) = Ca^x$

2.

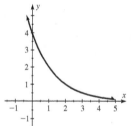

3. D: all real numbers; R: all positive real numbers

4. 32; 25   **5.** 2.718   **6.** 7.389; 9.870 (approximately)

7. factor   **8.** 1.5   **9.** $\frac{B - A}{A} \times 100$ **10.** 1.35

11. $\frac{1}{9}; 9$ **13.** 5; 160   **15.** 4; $\frac{1}{8}$ **17.** 15; $\frac{5}{9}$

19. 0.17; 2.41   **21.** 5; 1.08   **23.** 1; $\frac{1}{a}$ **25.** c.   **27.** d.

29. $C = 1, a = 2$ **31.** $C = 4, a = \frac{1}{4}$

33.

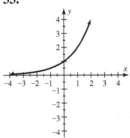

Growth

35.

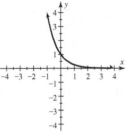

Decay

37.

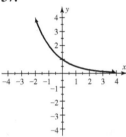

Decay

39.

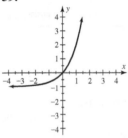

Growth

41.

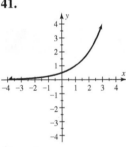

Growth

43.

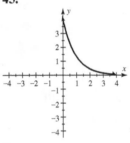

Decay

45. (a) Exponential decay **(b)** $f(x) = 64\left(\frac{1}{4}\right)^x$
47. (a) Linear growth **(b)** $f(x) = 3x + 8$
49. (a) Exponential growth **(b)** $f(x) = 4(1.25)^x$
51. (a) 100% **(b)** −50%
53. (a) −80% **(b)** 400%
55. (a) $1200 **(b)** $2200 **(c)** 2.2
57. (a) $130 **(b)** $780 **(c)** 1.2
59. (a) −$80 **(b)** $720 **(c)** 0.9
61. $C = 9, a = 1.07, R = 7\%$
63. $C = 1.5, a = 0.45, R = -55\%$ **65.** $3551.05
67. $1,820,087.63 **69.** $792.75 **71.** Yes; this is equivalent to having two accounts, each containing $1000 initially.
73. $788.78 **75.** $1429.24 **77.** 3.32 **79.** 0.86

81. [−4, 4, 1] by [0, 8, 1]

Growth

83. [−4, 4, 1] by [0, 8, 1]

Decay

85. $f(x) = 5000(0.75)^x$; $f(4) \approx 1582$

87. $f(x) = 50(1.1)^x$; $f(4) \approx 73$ **89.** 20% is much better
91. (a) 0.6 **(b)** $B(x) = 0.07(0.6)^x$ **(c)** 0.0252; after 2 hours blood alcohol is 0.0252 g/100 mL **93. (a)** 1.242
(b) In July 2008 there were about 0.5 million tweets per month.
(c) About 90.8; after 24 months, there were 90.8 million tweets per month. **95. (a)** $C = 500, a = 2$ **(b)** About 5278 thousand per milliliter **(c)** The growth is exponential and doubles every 50 seconds.

97.

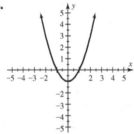

X	Y₁
0	1
10	.36854
20	.13582
30	.05006
40	.01845
50	.0068
60	.00251

Y₁■(0.905)^X

(a) 1; the probability that no vehicle will enter the intersection during a period of 0 seconds is 1 or 100%.
(b) About 30 seconds
99. (a) $f(x) = 2.7e^{0.014x}$ **(b)** 3.1 million
101. (a) $f(x) = 38e^{0.0102x}$ **(b)** 42 million
103. Answers may vary.

CHECKING BASIC CONCEPTS 12.2 (p. 490)

1. (a) 7 **(b)** $(f \circ g)(x) = 2x^2 + 9x + 6$

2.

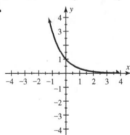

(a) No, it does not pass the horizontal line test. **(b)** No
3. $f^{-1}(x) = \frac{x+3}{4}$ **4.** $\frac{3}{4}$

5.

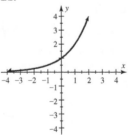

6. $C = 2; a = \frac{1}{2}$

CHAPTER 12 REVIEW (pp. 492–493)

17. $\frac{1}{6}$; 36 **18.** 5; $\frac{5}{8}$ **19.** 3; $\frac{1}{81}$ **20.** 3; $\frac{1}{2}$
21.

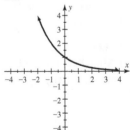

Exponential growth

22.

Exponential decay

23.

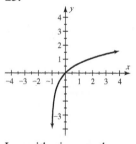

Logarithmic growth

24.

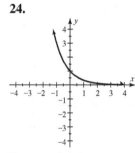

Exponential decay

25. (a) Exponential growth   **(b)** $f(x) = 5(2)^x$
26. (a) Linear growth   **(b)** $f(x) = 5x + 5$
27. $C = \frac{1}{2}, a = 2$ **28.** $k = 2$ **29.** -20% **30.** 1.07
31. (a) 100%   **(b)** -50% **32. (a)** $-54.\overline{54}\%$ **(b)** 120%
33. (a) \$1050   **(b)** \$1550   **(c)** 3.1   **34. (a)** $-\$175$
(b) \$525   **(c)** 0.75   **35.** $f(x) = 20{,}000(0.95)^x$;
$f(2) = 18{,}050$ **36.** $f(x) = 1500(4)^x$; $f(2) = 24{,}000$
37. \$2829.54   **38.** \$675,340.51   **39.** 399.67   **40.** 0.71
41. 3.48   **42.** 3.89

Glossary

absolute value A nonnegative number, written $|a|$, that is equal to the distance of a from the origin on the number line.

absolute value equation An equation that contains an absolute value.

absolute value function The function defined by $f(x) = |x|$.

absolute value inequality An inequality that contains an absolute value.

addends In an addition problem, the two numbers that are added.

addition property of equality If a, b, and c are real numbers, then $a = b$ is equivalent to $a + c = b + c$.

additive identity The number 0.

additive inverse (opposite) The additive inverse, or opposite, of a number a is $-a$.

adjacency matrix A matrix used to represent a map showing distances between cities or a social network.

algebraic expression An expression consisting of numbers, variables, operation symbols, such as $+$, $-$, $\times$, and $\div$, and grouping symbols, such as parentheses.

annuity A sum of money from which regular payments are made.

approximately equal The symbol $\approx$ indicates that two quantities are nearly equal.

arithmetic sequence A linear function given by $a_n = dn + c$ whose domain is the set of natural numbers.

arithmetic series The sum of the terms of an arithmetic sequence.

associative property for addition For any real numbers a, b, and c, $(a + b) + c = a + (b + c)$.

associative property for multiplication For any real numbers a, b, and c, $(a \cdot b) \cdot c = a \cdot (b \cdot c)$.

asymptotes of a hyperbola The two lines determined by the diagonals of the hyperbola's fundamental rectangle.

augmented matrix A matrix used to represent a system of linear equations; a vertical line is positioned in the matrix where the equals signs occur in the system of equations.

average The result of adding up the numbers of a set and then dividing the sum by the number of elements in the set.

axis of symmetry of a parabola The line passing through the vertex of the parabola that divides the parabola into two symmetric parts.

base The value of b in the expression b^n.

base e If the base of an exponential expression is e (approximately 2.72), then we say this expression has base e.

basic complex fraction A complex fraction where both the numerator and denominator are single fractions.

basic principle of fractions When simplifying fractions, the principle that states $\frac{a \cdot c}{b \cdot c} = \frac{a}{b}$.

basic rational equation A rational equation that has a single rational expression on each side of the equals sign.

binary operation An operation that requires two numbers to calculate an answer.

binomial A polynomial with two terms.

binomial coefficient The expression $_nC_r = n!/((n - r)!r!)$, where n and r are nonnegative integers, $n \geq r$, that can be used to calculate the numbers in Pascal's triangle.

binomial theorem A theorem that provides a formula to expand expressions of the form $(a + b)^n$.

braces { }, used to enclose the elements of a set.

branches A hyperbola has two branches, a left branch and a right branch, or an upper branch and a lower branch.

byte A unit of computer memory, capable of storing one letter of the alphabet.

center of a circle The point that is a fixed distance from all the points on a circle.

center of an ellipse The midpoint of the major axis.

change of base formula A formula used to evaluate a logarithm of one base by using a logarithm of a different base and given by $\log_a x = \frac{\log x}{\log a}$ or $\log_a x = \frac{\ln x}{\ln a}$.

circle The set of points in a plane that are the same distance from a fixed point.

circumference The perimeter of a circle.

coefficient The numeric constant of a term.

coefficient of a monomial The number in a monomial.

common difference The value of d in an arithmetic sequence, $a_n = dn + c$.

common logarithmic function The function given by $f(x) = \log x$.

common logarithm of a positive number x Denoted $\log x$, it may be calculated as follows: If x is expressed as $x = 10^k$, then $\log x = k$, where k is a real number. That is, $\log 10^k = k$.

common ratio The value of r in a geometric sequence, $a_n = a_1(r)^{n-1}$.

commutative property for addition For any real numbers a and b, $a + b = b + a$.

commutative property for multiplication For any real numbers a and b, $a \cdot b = b \cdot a$.

complement The set containing all elements in the universal set that are not in A, denoted A'.

completing the square method An important technique in mathematics that involves adding a constant to a binomial so that a perfect square trinomial results.

complex conjugate The complex conjugate of $a + bi$ is $a - bi$.

complex fraction A rational expression that contains fractions in its numerator, denominator, or both.

complex number A complex number can be written in standard form as $a + bi$, where a and b are real numbers and i is the imaginary unit.

composite function If f and g are functions, then g of f, or the composition of g and f, is defined by $(g \circ f)(x) = g(f(x))$ and is read "g of f of x."

composite number A natural number greater than 1 that is not a prime number.

composition Replacing a variable with an algebraic expression in function notation is called composition of functions; when functions are applied to a variable in sequence.

compound inequality Two inequalities joined by the word *and* or the word *or*.

compound interest A type of interest paid at the end of each year using the formula $A = P(1 + r)^t$, where P is the amount deposited, r is the annual interest rate in decimal form, and t is the number of years for the account to contain A dollars.

conic section The curve formed by the intersection of a plane and a cone.

conjugate The conjugate of $a + b$ is $a - b$.

consistent system with dependent equations A system of linear equations with infinitely many solutions.

consistent system with independent equations A system of linear equations with exactly one solution.

constant function A linear function with $m = 0$ that can be written as $f(x) = b$.

constant of proportionality (constant of variation) In the equation $y = kx$, the nonzero number k.

constraint In linear programming, an inequality which limits the objective function.

continuous growth Growth in a quantity that is directly proportional to the amount present.

contradiction An equation that is always false regardless of the values of any variables.

Cramer's rule A method that uses determinants to solve linear systems of equations.

cube root The number b is a cube root of a if $b^3 = a$.

cube root function The function defined by $f(x) = \sqrt[3]{x}$.

cubic function A function f of degree 3 represented by $f(x) = ax^3 + bx^2 + cx + d$, where a, b, c, and d are constants and $a \neq 0$.

decay factor The value of a in an exponential function, $f(x) = Ca^x$, when $0 < a < 1$.

degree A degree (°) is 1/360 of a revolution.

degree of a monomial The sum of the exponents of the variables.

degree of a polynomial The degree of the term (or monomial) with highest degree.

dependent equations Equations in a linear system that have infinitely many solutions.

dependent variable The variable that represents the output of a function.

determinant A real number associated with a square matrix.

diagrammatic representation A function represented by a diagram.

difference The answer to a subtraction problem.

difference of two cubes Expression in the form $a^3 - b^3$, which can be factored as $(a - b)(a^2 + ab + b^2)$.

difference of two squares Expression in the form $a^2 - b^2$, which can be factored as $(a - b)(a + b)$.

dimension of a matrix The size expressed in number of rows and columns. For example, if a matrix has m rows and n columns, its dimension is $m \times n$ (m by n).

directly proportional A quantity y is directly proportional to x if there is a nonzero number k such that $y = kx$.

discriminant The expression $b^2 - 4ac$ in the quadratic formula.

distance The distance d between the points (x_1, y_1) and (x_2, y_2) in the xy-plane is $d = \sqrt{(x_2 - x_1)^2 + (y_2 - y_1)^2}$.

distributive properties For any real numbers a, b, and c, $a(b + c) = ab + ac$ and $a(b - c) = ab - ac$.

dividend In a division problem, the number being divided.

divisor In a division problem, the number being divided *into* the dividend.

domain The set of all x-values of the ordered pairs in a function.

element of a matrix Each number in a matrix.

elements of a set The members of a set.

elimination method A symbolic method used to solve a system of equations that is based on the property that if "equals are added to equals the results are equal."

ellipse The set of points in a plane the sum of whose distances from two fixed points is constant.

empty set (null set) A set that contains no elements.

equal sets If every element in a set A is in set B and every element in set B is in set A, then A and B are equal sets, denoted $A = B$.

equation A mathematical statement that two algebraic expressions are equal.

equation of a line Point-slope form and slope-intercept form are examples of an equation of a line.

equivalent equations Equations that have the same solution set.

even root The nth root, $\sqrt[n]{a}$, where n is even.

expansion of a determinant by minors A method of finding a 3×3 determinant by using determinants of 2×2 matrices.

exponent The value of n in the expression b^n.

exponential decay When $0 < a < 1$, the graph of $f(x) = Ca^x$ models exponential decay.

exponential equation An equation that has a variable as an exponent.

exponential expression An expression that has an exponent.

exponential function with base a and coefficient C A function represented by $f(x) = Ca^x$, where $a > 0$, $C > 0$, and $a \neq 1$.

exponential growth When $a > 1$, the graph of $f(x) = Ca^x$ models exponential growth.

extraneous solution A solution that does not satisfy the given equation.

factorial notation $n! = 1 \cdot 2 \cdot 3 \cdot \cdots \cdot n$ for any positive integer.

factoring a polynomial The process of writing a polynomial as a product of lower degree polynomials.

factoring by grouping A technique that uses the associative and distributive properties by grouping four terms of a polynomial in such a way that the polynomial can be factored even though its greatest common factor is 1.

factors In a multiplication problem, the two numbers multiplied.

feasible solutions In linear programming, the set of solutions that satisfy the constraints.

finite sequence A function with domain $D = \{1, 2, 3, \ldots, n\}$ for some fixed natural number n.

finite series A series that contains a finite number of terms, and that can be expressed in the form $a_1 + a_2 + a_3 + \cdots + a_n$ for some n.

finite set A set whose elements can be listed explicitly.

focus (plural: **foci**) A fixed point used to determine the points that form a parabola, an ellipse, or a hyperbola.

FOIL A method for multiplying two binomials $(A + B)$ and $(C + D)$. Multiply **F**irst terms AC, **O**utside terms AD, **I**nside terms BC, and **L**ast terms BD; then combine like terms.

formula A special type of equation used to calculate one quantity from given values of other quantities.

function A set of ordered pairs (x, y), where each x-value corresponds to exactly one y-value.

function notation The notation $y = f(x)$, where the input x produces output y.

fundamental rectangle The rectangle of a hyperbola whose four vertices are determined by either $(\pm a, \pm b)$ or $(\pm b, \pm a)$, where $\frac{x^2}{a^2} - \frac{y^2}{b^2} = 1$ or $\frac{y^2}{a^2} - \frac{x^2}{b^2} = 1$.

Gauss–Jordan elimination A method used to solve a linear system in which matrix row transformations are applied to an augmented matrix.

general term (nth term) of a sequence a_n, where n is a natural number in the domain of a sequence $a_n = f(n)$.

geometric sequence An exponential function given by $a_n = a_1(r)^{n-1}$, where n is a natural number and $r \neq 0$ or 1.

geometric series The sum of the terms of a geometric sequence.

graphical representation A graph of a function.

graphical solution A solution to an equation obtained by graphing.

greater than If a real number b is located to the right of a real number a on the number line, we say that b is greater than a, and write $b > a$.

greater than or equal to If a real number a is greater than or equal to b, denoted $a \geq b$, then either $a > b$ or $a = b$ is true.

greatest common factor (GCF) of a polynomial The term with the highest degree and greatest coefficient that is a factor of all terms in the polynomial.

growth factor The value of a in the exponential function, $f(x) = Ca^x$, when $a > 1$.

half-life The time it takes for a radioactive sample to decay to half its original amount.

horizontal line test If every horizontal line intersects the graph of a function f at most once, then f is a one-to-one function.

hyperbola The set of points in a plane the difference of whose distances from two fixed points is constant.

identity An equation that is always true regardless of the values of any variables.

identity property of 1 If any number a is multiplied by 1, the result is a, that is, $a \cdot 1 = 1 \cdot a = a$.

identity property of 0 If 0 is added to any real number a, the result is a, that is, $a + 0 = 0 + a = a$.

imaginary number A complex number $a + bi$ with $b \neq 0$.

imaginary part The value of b in the complex number $a + bi$.

imaginary unit A number denoted i whose properties are $i = \sqrt{-1}$ and $i^2 = -1$.

improper fraction A fraction whose numerator is greater than or equal to its denominator in absolute value.

inconsistent system A system of linear equations that has no solution.

independent equations Equations in a linear system that have different graphs.

independent variable The variable that represents the input of a function.

index The value of n in the expression $\sqrt[n]{a}$.

index of summation The variable k in the expression $\sum_{k=1}^{n}$.

inequality When the equals sign in an equation is replaced with any one of the symbols $<, \leq, >$, or $\geq$, an inequality results.

infinite sequence A function whose domain is the set of natural numbers.

infinite set A set with infinitely many elements.

infinity Values that increase without bound.

input An element of the domain of a function.

integers A set of numbers including natural numbers, their opposites, and 0, or $\ldots, -3, -2, -1, 0, 1, 2, 3, \ldots$.

intercept form A linear equation in the form $x/a + y/b = 1$.

intersection The set containing elements that belong to *both A and B*, denoted $A \cap B$ and read "*A* intersect *B*."

intersection-of-graphs method A graphical technique for solving two equations.

interval notation A notation for number line graphs that eliminates the need to draw the entire line.

inverse function If f is a one-to-one function, then f^{-1} is the inverse function of f, if $(f^{-1} \circ f)(x) = f^{-1}(f(x)) = x$ for every x in the domain of f, and $(f \circ f^{-1})(x) = f(f^{-1}(x)) = x$ for every x in the domain of f^{-1}.

inversely proportional A quantity y is inversely proportional to x if there is a nonzero number k such that $y = k/x$.

irrational numbers Real numbers that cannot be expressed as fractions, such as π or $\sqrt{2}$.

joint variation A quantity z varies jointly with x and y if there is a nonzero number k such that $z = kxy$.

leading coefficient In a polynomial of one variable, the coefficient of the monomial with highest degree.

least common denominator (LCD) The common denominator with the fewest factors.

least common multiple (LCM) The smallest number that two or more numbers will divide into evenly.

less than If a real number a is located to the left of a real number b on the number line, we say that a is less than b and write $a < b$.

less than or equal to If a real number a is less than or equal to b, denoted $a \leq b$, then either $a < b$ or $a = b$ is true.

like radicals Radicals that have the same index and the same radicand.

like terms Two terms, or monomials, that contain the same variables raised to the same powers.

linear equation An equation that can be written in the form $ax + b = 0$, where $a \neq 0$.

linear equation in two variables An equation that can be written in the form $Ax + By = C$, where A, B, and C are fixed numbers and A and B are not both equal to 0.

linear function A function f represented by $f(x) = mx + b$, where m and b are constants.

linear inequality A linear inequality results whenever the equals sign in a linear equation is replaced with any one of the symbols $<$, $\leq$, $>$, or $\geq$.

linear inequality in two variables When the equals sign in a linear equation in two variables is replaced with $<$, $\leq$, $>$, or $\geq$, a linear inequality in two variables results.

linear polynomial A polynomial of degree 1 that can be written as $ax + b$, where $a \neq 0$.

linear programming problem A problem consisting of an objective function and a system of linear inequalities called constraints.

linear system in three variables A system of three equations in which each equation can be written in the form $ax + by + cz = d$; an ordered triple (x, y, z) is a solution to the system of equations if the values for x, y, and z make *all three* equations true.

line graph The resulting graph when consecutive data points in a scatterplot are connected with straight line segments.

logarithm with base a of a positive number x Denoted $\log_a x$, it may be calculated as follows: If x can be expressed as $x = a^k$, then $\log_a x = k$, where $a > 0$, $a \neq 1$, and k is a real number. That is, $\log_a a^k = k$.

logarithmic function with base a The function represented by $f(x) = \log_a x$.

logistic function A function used to model growth of a population.

lower limit In summation notation, the number representing the subscript of the first term of the series.

lowest terms A fraction is in lowest terms if its numerator and denominator have no factors in common.

main diagonal In an augmented matrix, the diagonal set of numbers from the upper left of the matrix to the lower right.

major axis The longer axis of an ellipse, which connects the vertices.

matrix A rectangular array of numbers.

matrix row transformations Operations performed on rows of an augmented matrix that result in an equivalent system of linear equations.

method of substitution A symbolic method for solving a system of equations in which one equation is solved for one of the variables and then the result is substituted into the other equation.

minor axis The shorter axis of an ellipse.

minors The 2×2 matrices that are used to find a determinant of a 3×3 matrix.

monomial A number, a variable, or a product of numbers and variables raised to natural number powers.

multiplication property of equality If a, b, and c are real numbers with $c \neq 0$, then $a = b$ is equivalent to $ac = bc$.

multiplicative identity The number 1.

multiplicative inverse (reciprocal) The multiplicative inverse of a nonzero number a is $1/a$.

name of function In the function given by $f(x)$, we call the function f.

natural exponential function The function represented by $f(x) = e^x$, where $e \approx 2.71828$.

natural logarithm The base-e logarithm, denoted either $\log_e x$ or $\ln x$.

natural numbers The set of (counting) numbers expressed as $1, 2, 3, 4, 5, 6, \ldots$.

negative infinity Values that decrease without bound.

negative reciprocals Slopes of two lines satisfy $m_1 = -\frac{1}{m_2}$, or $m_1 \cdot m_2 = -1$. These lines are perpendicular.

negative slope On a graph, the slope of a line that falls from left to right.

negative square root of a Denoted $-\sqrt{a}$.

nonlinear data If data points do not lie on a (straight) line, the data are nonlinear.

nonlinear function A function that is *not* a linear function; its graph is not a line.

nonlinear system of equations Two or more equations at least one of which is nonlinear.

nonlinear system of inequalities Two or more inequalities at least one of which is nonlinear.

nth root The number b is an nth root of a if $b^n = a$, where n is a positive integer.

nth term (general term) of a sequence See general term (nth term) of a sequence.

null set (empty set) A set that contains no elements.

numerical representation A table of values for a function.

numerical solution A solution often obtained by using a table of values.

objective function The given function to be optimized in a linear programming problem.

odd root The nth root, $\sqrt[n]{a}$, where n is odd.

one-to-one function A function f in which for any c and d in the domain of f, $c \neq d$ implies that $f(c) \neq f(d)$. That is, different inputs always result in different outputs.

opposite (additive inverse) The opposite, or additive inverse, of a number a is $-a$.

opposite of a polynomial The polynomial obtained by negating each term in a given polynomial.

optimal value In linear programming, the value that maximizes or minimizes the objective function.

ordered pair A pair of numbers written in parentheses (x, y), in which the order of the numbers is important.

ordered triple Can be expressed as (x, y, z), where x, y, and z are numbers and represent a solution to a linear system in three variables.

origin On the number line, the point associated with the real number 0; in the xy-plane, the point where the axes intersect, $(0, 0)$.

output An element of the range of a function.

parabola The $\cup$-shaped graph of a quadratic function that opens either upward or downward.

parallel lines Two or more lines in the same plane that never intersect; they have the same slope.

Pascal's triangle A triangle made up of numbers in which there are 1s along the sides and each element inside the triangle is the sum of the two numbers above it.

percent change If a quantity changes from x to y, then the percent change is $[(y - x)/x] \times 100$.

perfect cube An integer with an integer cube root.

perfect nth power The value of a if there exists an integer b such that $b^n = a$.

perfect square An integer with an integer square root.

perfect square trinomial A trinomial that can be factored as the square of a binomial, for example, $a^2 + 2ab + b^2 = (a + b)^2$.

perpendicular lines Two lines in a plane that intersect to form a right ($90°$) angle.

point–slope form The line with slope m passing through the point (x_1, y_1), given by the equation $y - y_1 = m(x - x_1)$ or, equivalently, $y = m(x - x_1) + y_1$.

polynomial The sum of one or more monomials.

polynomial functions in one variable Functions that are defined by a polynomial in one variable.

polynomials in one variable Polynomials that contain one variable.

positive slope On a graph, the slope of a line that rises from left to right.

power function A function that can be represented by $f(x) = x^p$, where p is a rational number.

prime factorization A number written as a product of prime numbers.

prime number A natural number greater than 1 that has *only* itself and 1 as natural number factors.

prime polynomial A polynomial with integer coefficients that cannot be factored by using integer coefficients.

principal nth root of a Denoted $\sqrt[n]{a}$.

principal square root The square root of a that is nonnegative, denoted $\sqrt{a}$.

probability A real number between 0 and 1, inclusive. A probability of 0 indicates that an event is impossible, whereas a probability of 1 indicates that an event is certain.

product The answer to a multiplication problem.

proportion A statement that two ratios are equal.

pure imaginary number A complex number $a + bi$ with $a = 0$ and $b \neq 0$.

Pythagorean theorem If a right triangle has legs a and b with hypotenuse c, then $a^2 + b^2 = c^2$.

quadrants The four regions determined by the xy-plane.

quadratic equation An equation that can be written in the form $ax^2 + bx + c = 0$, where a, b, and c are constants, with $a \neq 0$.

quadratic formula The solutions to the quadratic equation, $ax^2 + bx + c = 0$, $a \neq 0$, are $(-b \pm \sqrt{b^2 - 4ac})/(2a)$.

quadratic function A function f represented by the equation $f(x) = ax^2 + bx + c$, where a, b, and c are constants, with $a \neq 0$.

quadratic inequality If the equals sign in a quadratic equation is replaced with $>$, $\geq$, $<$, or $\leq$, a quadratic inequality results.

quadratic polynomial A polynomial of degree 2 that can be written as $ax^2 + bx + c$, with $a \neq 0$.

quotient The answer to a division problem.

radical expression An expression that contains a radical sign.

radical sign The symbol $\sqrt{}$ or $\sqrt[n]{}$ for some positive integer n.

radicand The expression under the radical sign.

radius The fixed distance between the center and any point on a circle.

range The set of all y-values of the ordered pairs in a function.

rate of change Slope can be interpreted as a rate of change. It indicates how fast the graph of a line is changing.

ratio A comparison of two quantities, expressed as a quotient.

rational equation An equation that contains one or more rational expressions.

rational expression A polynomial divided by a nonzero polynomial.

rational function A function defined by $f(x) = p(x)/q(x)$, where $p(x)$ and $q(x)$ are polynomials and the domain of f includes all x-values such that $q(x) \neq 0$.

rational number Any number that can be expressed as the ratio of two integers p/q, where $q \neq 0$; a fraction.

rationalizing the denominator The process of removing radicals from a denominator so that the denominator contains only rational numbers.

real numbers All rational and irrational numbers; any number that can be represented by decimal numbers.

real part The value of a in the complex number $a + bi$.

reciprocal (multiplicative inverse) The reciprocal of a nonzero number a is $1/a$.

rectangular coordinate system (xy-plane) The xy-plane used to plot points and graph data.

reduced row–echelon form A matrix form for representing a system of linear equations in which there are 1s on the main diagonal with 0s above and below each 1.

reflection If the point (x, y) is on the graph of a function, then $(x, -y)$ is on the graph of its reflection across the x-axis.

relation A set of ordered pairs.

rise The change in y between two points on a line, that is, $y_2 - y_1$.

root function In the power function $f(x) = x^p$, if $p = 1/n$, where $n \geq 2$ is an integer, then f is also a root function, which is given by $f(x) = \sqrt[n]{x}$.

run The change in x between two points on a line, that is, $x_2 - x_1$.

scatterplot A graph of distinct points plotted in the xy-plane.

scientific notation A real number a written as $b \times 10^n$, where $1 \leq |b| < 10$ and n is an integer.

set A collection of things.

set-builder notation Notation to describe a set of numbers without having to list all of the elements. For example, $\{x | x > 5\}$ is read as "the set of all real numbers x such that x is greater than 5."

slope The ratio of the change in y (rise) to the change in x (run) along a line. The slope m of a line passing through the points (x_1, y_1) and (x_2, y_2) is $m = (y_2 - y_1)/(x_2 - x_1)$, where $x_1 \neq x_2$.

slope–intercept form The line with slope m and y-intercept b is given by $y = mx + b$.

solution Each value of the variable that makes the equation true.

solution set The set of all solutions to an equation.

solution to a system In a system of two equations in two variables, an ordered pair, (x, y), that makes *both* equations true.

square matrix A matrix in which the number of rows and the number of columns are equal.

square root The number b is a square root of a number a if $b^2 = a$.

square root function The function given by $f(x) = \sqrt{x}$, where $x \geq 0$.

square root property If k is a nonnegative number, then the solutions to the equation $x^2 = k$ are given by $x = \pm \sqrt{k}$. If $k < 0$, then this equation has no real solutions.

standard equation of a circle The standard equation of a circle with center (h, k) and radius r is $(x - h)^2 + (y - k)^2 = r^2$.

standard form (of a linear equation in two variables) The form $Ax + By = C$, where A, B, and C are constants, with A and B not both 0.

standard form of a complex number $a + bi$, where a and b are real numbers.

standard form of a quadratic equation The equation given by $ax^2 + bx + c = 0$, where $a \neq 0$.

standard viewing rectangle of a graphing calculator $\text{Xmin} = -10$, $\text{Xmax} = 10$, $\text{Xscl} = 1$, $\text{Ymin} = -10$, $\text{Ymax} = 10$, and $\text{Yscl} = 1$, denoted $[-10, 10, 1]$ by $[-10, 10, 1]$.

subscript The symbol x_1 has a subscript of 1 and is read "x sub one" or "x one".

subset If every element in a set B is contained in a set A, then we say that B is a subset of A, denoted $B \subseteq A$.

sum The answer to an addition problem.

sum of the first n terms of an arithmetic sequence Denoted S_n, is found by averaging the first and nth terms and then multiplying by n.

sum of the first n terms of a geometric sequence Given by $S_n = a_1(1 - r^n)/(1 - r)$, if its first term is a_1 and its common ratio is r, provided $r \neq 1$.

sum of two cubes Expression in the form $a^3 + b^3$, which can be factored as $(a + b)(a^2 - ab + b^2)$.

summation notation Notation in which the uppercase Greek letter sigma represents the sum, for example,

$$\sum_{k=1}^{n} a_k = a_1 + a_2 + a_3 + \cdots + a_n.$$

symbolic representation Representing a function with a formula; for example, $f(x) = x^2 - 2x$.

symbolic solution A solution to an equation obtained by using properties of equations; the resulting solution set is exact.

synthetic division A shortcut that can be used to divide $x - k$, where k is a number, into a polynomial.

system of linear equations in two variables A system of equations in which each equation can be written as $Ax + By = C$.

system of linear inequalities in two variables Two or more linear inequalities to be solved at the same time, the solution to which must satisfy each inequality.

table of values An organized way to display the inputs and outputs of a function; a numerical representation.

term A number, a variable, or a product of numbers and variables raised to powers.

terms of a sequence $a_1, a_2, a_3, \ldots a_n, \ldots$ where the first term is $a_1 = f(1)$, the second term is $a_2 = f(2)$, and so on.

test point When graphing the solution set to an inequality, a point chosen to determine which region of the xy-plane to include in the solution set.

test value A real number chosen to determine the solution set to an inequality.

three-part inequality A compound inequality written in the form $a < x < b$, where $\leq$ may replace $<$.

translation The shifting of a graph upward, downward, to the right, or to the left in such a way that the shape of the graph stays the same.

transverse axis In a hyperbola, the line segment that connects the vertices.

trinomial A polynomial with three terms.

unary operation An operation that requires only one number.

undefined slope The slope of a line that is vertical.

union Denoted $A \cup B$ and read "A union B," it is the set containing any element that can be found in *either A or B*.

universal set A set that contains all elements under consideration.

upper limit In summation notation, the number representing the subscript of the last term of the series.

variable A symbol, such as x, y, or z, used to represent any unknown quantity.

varies directly A quantity y varies directly with x if there is a non-zero number k such that $y = kx$.

varies inversely A quantity y varies inversely with x if there is a nonzero number k such that $y = k/x$.

varies jointly A quantity z varies jointly with x and y if there is a nonzero number k such that $z = kxy$.

Venn diagrams Diagrams used to depict relationships between sets.

verbal representation A description, in words, of what a function computes.

vertex The lowest point on the graph of a parabola that opens upward or the highest point on the graph of a parabola that opens downward.

vertex form of a parabola The vertex form of a parabola with vertex (h, k) is $y = a(x - h)^2 + k$, where $a \neq 0$ is a constant.

vertical asymptote A vertical asymptote typically occurs in the graph of a rational function when the denominator of a rational expression equals 0 but the numerator does not equal 0; it can be represented by a vertical line in the graph of a rational function.

vertical line test If every vertical line intersects a graph at no more than one point, then the graph represents a function.

vertical shift A translation of a graph upward or downward.

vertices of an ellipse The endpoints of the major axis.

vertices of a hyperbola The endpoints of the transverse axis.

viewing rectangle (window) On a graphing calculator, the window that determines the x- and y-values shown in the graph.

whole numbers The set of numbers 0, 1, 2, 3, 4, 5, ...

x-axis The horizontal axis in the xy-plane.

x-coordinate The first value in an ordered pair.

x-intercept The x-coordinate of a point where a graph intersects the x-axis.

Xmax Regarding the viewing rectangle of a graphing calculator, Xmax is the maximum x-value along the x-axis.

Xmin Regarding the viewing rectangle of a graphing calculator, Xmin is the minimum x-value along the x-axis.

Xscl Regarding the viewing rectangle of a graphing calculator, the distance between consecutive tick marks on the x-axis.

xy-plane (rectangular coordinate system) The system used to plot points and graph data.

y-axis The vertical axis in the xy-plane.

y-coordinate The second value in an ordered pair.

y-intercept The y-coordinate of a point where a graph intersects the y-axis.

Ymax Regarding the viewing rectangle of a graphing calculator, Ymax is the maximum y-value along the y-axis.

Ymin Regarding the viewing rectangle of a graphing calculator, Ymin is the minimum y-value along the y-axis.

Yscl Regarding the viewing rectangle of a graphing calculator, the distance between consecutive tick marks on the y-axis.

zero of a polynomial An x-value that results in 0 when it is substituted into a polynomial; for example, the zeros of $x^2 - 4$ are 2 and -2.

zero-product property If the product of two numbers is 0, then at least one of the numbers must be 0, that is, $ab = 0$ implies $a = 0$ or $b = 0$ (or both).

zero slope The slope of a line that is horizontal.

Photo Credits

1, NASA/Arena Creative/Shutterstock 2, Kirsz Marcin/Shutterstock 11, Haveseen/Shutterstock 26, Dmitriy Shironosov/Shutterstock 34, Markrhiggins/Shutterstock 45, Jupiterimages/Brand X Pictures/Thinkstock 51, Digital Vision/Thinkstock 57, Deklofenak/Shutterstock 60, Matka Wariatka/Shutterstock 70, Johns Hopkins University Applied Physics Laboratory/Southwest Research Institute/Goddard Space Flight Center/NASA 71, Docent/Shutterstock 89, Socrates/Shutterstock 90, Edobric/Shutterstock 99, Vartanov Anatoly/Shutterstock 111, Knktucker/Dreamstime 124, Ginae McDonald/Shutterstock 127, Christa DeRidder/Shutterstock 144, Andy Dean Photography/Shutterstock 145, Photosani/Shutterstock 154, Jupiterimages/Comstock/Thinkstock 164, Tupungato/Shutterstock 176, Comstock/Thinkstock 190, Morgan Lane Photography/Shutterstock 200, Walleyelj/Dreamstime 211, National Oceanic and Atmospheric Administration (NOAA) 217, Graeme Shannon/Shutterstock 229, Iofoto/Fotolia 230, Dan Morar/Shutterstock 240, Digital Vision/Thinkstock 241, Monkey Business/Fotolia 249, Maksym Dykha/Fotolia 264, Jupiterimages/Comstock/Thinkstock 267 top, Tom Wang/Shutterstock 267 bottom, National Space Science Data Center/Goddard Space Flight Center/NASA 268, Graeme Dawes/Shutterstock 276, Duncan Smith/Photodisc/Getty Images 286, Kmiragaya/Fotolia 295, Hubble Space Telescope/NASA 305, Viktar Malyshchyts/Shutterstock 306, Library of Congress Prints and Photographs Division [LC-USZ62-95308] 320, Photosani/Shutterstock 321, Jermvut Kitchaichank/Fotolia 325, BananaStock/Thinkstock 332, Zahradales/Shutterstock 337, Comstock/Thinkstock 340, Elena Elisseeva/Shutterstock 345, Dmitry Nikolaev/Shutterstock 346 top, Michael Jung/Shutterstock 346 bottom, Carroteater/Shutterstock 347, Tlorna/Shutterstock 355, Gallimaufry/Shutterstock 358, Monkey Business Images/Shutterstock 369, Liquidlibrary/Thinkstock 373, Comstock/Thinkstock 377, James Thew/Fotolia 378, Ljupco Smokovski/Shutterstock 395, Andrey Yurlov/Shutterstock 396, Robepco/Fotolia 397, Djgis/Shutterstock 401, Hkratky/Dreamstime 406, Pixland/Thinkstock 411, Rodolfo Clix/Fotolia 412, Levent Konuk/Shutterstock 416, Jason Stitt/Shutterstock 418, Dutourdumonde/Shutterstock 425 left, Savcoco/Dreamstime 425 right, BananaStock/Thinkstock 433, Scion/Shutterstock 439, Vladimir Melnik/Shutterstock 440, Sebcz/Dreamstime 444, Olly/Shutterstock 447, Vinicius Tupinamba/Shutterstock 448, Diego Cervo/Shutterstock 453, Peter Polak/Shutterstock 463, John Kwan/Shutterstock 473, Evok20/Dreamstime 483, JBK Photography/Dreamstime 484, Brian Erickson/Shutterstock 490, Holbox/Shutterstock

Bibliography

Baase, S. *Computer Algorithms: Introduction to Design and Analysis.* 2nd ed. Reading, Mass.: Addison-Wesley Publishing Company, 1988.

Beckmann, P. *A History of Pi.* New York: Barnes and Noble, Inc., 1993.

Brown, D., and P. Rothery. *Models in Biology: Mathematics, Statistics and Computing.* West Sussex, England: John Wiley and Sons Ltd, 1993.

Burden, R., and J. Faires. *Numerical Analysis.* 5th ed. Boston: PWS-KENT Publishing Company, 1993.

Callas, D. *Snapshots of Applications in Mathematics.* Delhi, New York: State University College of Technology, 1994.

Conquering the Sciences. Sharp Electronics Corporation, 1986.

Eves, H. *An Introduction to the History of Mathematics.* 5th ed. Philadelphia: Saunders College Publishing, 1983.

Freedman, B. *Environmental Ecology: The Ecological Effects of Pollution, Disturbance, and Other Stresses.* 2nd ed. San Diego: Academic Press, 1995.

Garber, N., and L. Hoel. *Traffic and Highway Engineering.* Boston, Mass.: PWS Publishing Co., 1997.

Greenspan, A. *The Economic Importance of Improving Math-Science Education*, Speech before the Committee on Education and the Workforce, U.S. House of Representatives, September 2000.

Grigg, D. *The World Food Problem.* Oxford: Blackwell Publishers, 1993.

Haefner, L. *Introduction to Transportation Systems.* New York: Holt, Rinehart and Winston, 1986.

Harrison, F., F. Hills, J. Paterson, and R. Saunders. "The measurement of liver blood flow in conscious calves." *Quarterly Journal of Experimental Physiology* 71: 235–247.

Historical Topics for the Mathematics Classroom, Thirty-first Yearbook. National Council of Teachers of Mathematics, 1969.

Howells, G. *Acid Rain and Acid Waters.* 2nd ed. New York: Ellis Horwood, 1995.

Kraljic, M. *The Greenhouse Effect.* New York: The H. W. Wilson Company, 1992.

Lack, D. *The Life of a Robin.* London: Collins, 1965.

Lancaster, H. *Quantitative Methods in Biological and Medical Sciences: A Historical Essay.* New York: Springer-Verlag, 1994.

Mannering, F., and W. Kilareski. *Principles of Highway Engineering and Traffic Analysis.* New York: John Wiley and Sons, 1990.

Mar, J., and H. Liebowitz. *Structure Technology for Large Radio and Radar Telescope Systems.* Cambridge, Mass.: The MIT Press, 1969.

Meadows, D. *Beyond the Limits.* Post Mills, Vermont: Chelsea Green Publishing Co., 1992.

Miller, A., and R. Anthes. *Meteorology.* 5th ed. Columbus, Ohio: Charles E. Merrill Publishing Company, 1985.

Miller, A., and J. Thompson. *Elements of Meteorology.* 2nd ed. Columbus, Ohio: Charles E. Merrill Publishing Company, 1975.

Paetsch, M. *Mobile Communications in the U.S. and Europe: Regulation, Technology, and Markets.* Norwood, Mass.: Artech House, Inc., 1993.

Pearl, R., T. Edwards, and J. Miner. "The growth of *Cucumis melo* seedlings at different temperatures." *J. Gen. Physiol.* 17: 687–700.

Pennycuick, C. *Newton Rules Biology.* New York: Oxford University Press, 1992.

Pokorny, C., and C. Gerald. *Computer Graphics: The Principles behind the Art and Science.* Irvine, Calif.: Franklin, Beedle, and Associates, 1989.

Ronan, C. *The Natural History of the Universe.* New York: MacMillan Publishing Company, 1991.

Ryan, B., B. Joiner, and T. Ryan. *Minitab Handbook.* Boston: Duxbury Press, 1985.

Smith, C. *Practical Cellular and PCS Design.* New York: McGraw-Hill, 1998.

Thomas, D. *Swimming Pool Operators Handbook.* National Swimming Pool Foundation of Washington, D.C., 1972.

Thomas, V. *Science and Sport.* London: Faber and Faber, 1970.

Thomson, W. *Introduction to Space Dynamics.* New York: John Wiley and Sons, 1961.

Triola, M. *Elementary Statistics.* 7th ed. Reading, Mass.: Addison-Wesley Publishing Company, 1998.

Tucker, A., A. Bernat, W. Bradley, R. Cupper, and G. Scragg. *Fundamentals of Computing I: Logic, Problem Solving, Programs, and Computers.* New York: McGraw-Hill, 1995.

Turner, R. K., D. Pierce, and I. Bateman. *Environmental Economics, An Elementary Approach.* Baltimore: The Johns Hopkins University Press, 1993.

Van Sickle, J. *GPS for Land Surveyors.* Chelsey, Mich.: Ann Arbor Press, 1996.

Varley, G., and G. Gradwell. "Population models for the winter moth." *Symposium of the Royal Entomological Society of London* 4: 132–142.

Wang, T. *ASHRAE Trans.* 81, Part 1 (1975): 32.

Weidner, R., and R. Sells. *Elementary Classical Physics,* Vol. 2. Boston: Allyn and Bacon, Inc., 1965.

Williams, J. *The Weather Almanac 1995.* New York: Vintage Books, 1994.

Wright, J. *The New York Times Almanac 1999.* New York: Penguin Group, 1998.

Zeilik, M., S. Gregory, and D. Smith. *Introductory Astronomy and Astrophysics.* 3rd ed. Philadelphia: Saunders College Publishers, 1992.

The reading material in the following Section PA is taken from

Prealgebra, Seventh Edition, by Elayn Martin-Gay

Section PA Contents

5.7   Decimal Applications: Mean, Median, and Mode   **497**

6.4   Square Roots and the Pythagorean Theorem   **504**

8.1   Reading Pictographs, Bar Graphs, Histograms, and Line Graphs   **512**
8.2   Reading Circle Graphs   **525**

9.2   Perimeter   **532**
9.3   Area, Volume, and Surface Area   **542**
9.4   Linear Measurement   **559**
9.7   Temperature and Conversions Between the U.S. and Metric Systems   **572**

Chapter 9 Highlights   583

Appendix D   Geometric Formulas   585

Answers to Selected Exercises   587

Photo Credits   591

5.7 Decimal Applications: Mean, Median, and Mode

Objective A Finding the Mean

Sometimes we want to summarize data by displaying them in a graph, but sometimes it is also desirable to be able to describe a set of data, or a set of numbers, by a single "middle" number. Three such **measures of central tendency** are the **mean,** the **median,** and the **mode.**

The most common measure of central tendency is the mean (sometimes called the "arithmetic mean" or the "average").

Objectives

A Find the Mean of a List of Numbers.

B Find the Median of a List of Numbers.

C Find the Mode of a List of Numbers.

The **mean (average)** of a set of numbered items is the sum of the items divided by the number of items.

$$\text{mean} = \frac{\text{sum of items}}{\text{number of items}}$$

Example 1 Finding the Mean Time in an Experiment

Seven students in a psychology class conducted an experiment on mazes. Each student was given a pencil and asked to successfully complete the same maze. The timed results are below:

Student	Ann	Thanh	Carlos	Jesse	Melinda	Ramzi	Dayni
Time (Seconds)	13.2	11.8	10.7	16.2	15.9	13.8	18.5

a. Who completed the maze in the shortest time? Who completed the maze in the longest time?

b. Find the mean time.

c. How many students took longer than the mean time? How many students took shorter than the mean time?

Solution:

a. Carlos completed the maze in 10.7 seconds, the shortest time. Dayni completed the maze in 18.5 seconds, the longest time.

b. To find the mean (or average), we find the sum of the items and divide by 7, the number of items.

$$\text{mean} = \frac{13.2 + 11.8 + 10.7 + 16.2 + 15.9 + 13.8 + 18.5}{7}$$
$$= \frac{100.1}{7} = 14.3$$

c. Three students, Jesse, Melinda, and Dayni, had times longer than the mean time. Four students, Ann, Thanh, Carlos, and Ramzi, had times shorter than the mean time.

■ Work Practice 1

✓**Concept Check** Estimate the mean of the following set of data:

5, 10, 10, 10, 10, 15

Often in college, the calculation of a **grade point average** (GPA) is a **weighted mean** and is calculated as shown in Example 2.

Practice 1

Find the mean of the following test scores: 87, 75, 96, 91, and 78.

Answer
1. 85.4

✓**Concept Check Answer**
10

497

Practice 2

Find the grade point average if the following grades were earned in one semester.

Grade	Credit Hours
A	2
B	4
C	5
D	2
A	2

Example 2 Calculating Grade Point Average (GPA)

The following grades were earned by a student during one semester. Find the student's grade point average.

Course	Grade	Credit Hours
College mathematics	A	3
Biology	B	3
English	A	3
PE	C	1
Social studies	D	2

Solution: To calculate the grade point average, we need to know the point values for the different possible grades. The point values of grades commonly used in colleges and universities are given below:

A: 4, B: 3, C: 2, D: 1, F: 0

Now, to find the grade point average, we multiply the number of credit hours for each course by the point value of each grade. The grade point average is the sum of these products divided by the sum of the credit hours.

Course	Grade	Point Value of Grade	Credit Hours	Point Value of Credit Hours
College mathematics	A	4	3	12
Biology	B	3	3	9
English	A	4	3	12
PE	C	2	1	2
Social studies	D	1	2	2
		Totals:	12	37

$$\text{grade point average} = \frac{37}{12} \approx 3.08 \text{ rounded to two decimal places}$$

The student earned a grade point average of 3.08.

■ Work Practice 2

Objective B Finding the Median

You may have noticed that a very low number or a very high number can affect the mean of a list of numbers. Because of this, you may sometimes want to use another measure of central tendency. A second measure of central tendency is called the **median.** The median of a list of numbers is not affected by a low or high number in the list.

> The **median** of a set of numbers in numerical order is the middle number. If the number of items is odd, the median is the middle number. If the number of items is even, the median is the mean of the two middle numbers.

Practice 3

Find the median of the list of numbers: 5, 11, 14, 23, 24, 35, 38, 41, 43

Example 3 Find the median of the following list of numbers:

25, 54, 56, 57, 60, 71, 98

Solution: Because this list is in numerical order, the median is the middle number, 57.

■ Work Practice 3

Answers

2. 2.67   **3.** 24

Example 4 Find the median of the following list of scores: 67, 91, 75, 86, 55, 91

Solution: First we list the scores in numerical order and then we find the middle number.

55, 67, 75, 86, 91, 91

Since there is an even number of scores, there are two middle numbers, 75 and 86. The median is the mean of the two middle numbers.

$$\text{median} = \frac{75 + 86}{2} = 80.5$$

The median is 80.5.

Helpful Hint
Don't forget to write the numbers in order from smallest to largest before finding the median.

■ Work Practice 4

Practice 4
Find the median of the list of scores:
36, 91, 78, 65, 95, 95, 88, 71

Objective C Finding the Mode

The last common measure of central tendency is called the **mode.**

The **mode** of a set of numbers is the number that occurs most often. (It is possible for a set of numbers to have more than one mode or to have no mode.)

Example 5 Find the mode of the list of numbers:

11, 14, 14, 16, 31, 56, 65, 77, 77, 78, 79

Solution: There are two numbers that occur the most often. They are 14 and 77. This list of numbers has two modes, 14 and 77.

■ Work Practice 5

Practice 5
Find the mode of the list of numbers:
14, 10, 10, 13, 15, 15, 15, 17, 18, 18, 20

Example 6 Find the median and the mode of the following set of numbers. These numbers were high temperatures for 14 consecutive days in a city in Montana.

76, 80, 85, 86, 89, 87, 82, 77, 76, 79, 82, 89, 89, 92

Solution: First we write the numbers in numerical order.

76, 76, 77, 79, 80, 82, 82, 85, 86, 87, 89, 89, 89, 92

Since there is an even number of items, the median is the mean of the two middle numbers, 82 and 85.

$$\text{median} = \frac{82 + 85}{2} = 83.5$$

The mode is 89, since 89 occurs most often.

■ Work Practice 6

Practice 6
Find the median and the mode of the list of numbers:
26, 31, 15, 15, 26, 30, 16, 18, 15, 35

Answers
4. 83 **5.** 15 **6.** median: 22; mode: 15

✓**Concept Check** True or false? Every set of numbers *must* have a mean, median, and mode. Explain your answer.

✓**Concept Check Answer**
false; a set of numbers may have no mode

> **Helpful Hint**
>
> Don't forget that it is possible for a list of numbers to have no mode. For example, the list
>
>   2, 4, 5, 6, 8, 9
>
> has no mode. There is no number or numbers that occur more often than the others.

Vocabulary, Readiness & Video Check

Use the choices below to fill in each blank. Some choices may be used more than once.

mean   mode   grade point average

median   average

1. Another word for "mean" is _____.

2. The number that occurs most often in a set of numbers is called the _____.

3. The _____ of a set of number items is $\dfrac{\text{sum of items}}{\text{number of items}}$.

4. The _____ of a set of numbers is the middle number. If the number of numbers is even, it is the _____ of the two middle numbers.

5. An example of weighted mean is a calculation of _____.

Martin-Gay Interactive Videos   *Watch the section lecture video and answer the following questions.*

Objective A 6. Why is the ≈ symbol used in ▱ Example 1? ▶

Objective B 7. From ▱ Example 3, what is always the first step when finding the median of a set of data numbers? ▶

Objective C 8. From ▱ Example 4, why do you think it is helpful to have data numbers in numerical order when finding the mode? ▶

See Video 5.7 ●

See video answer section.

5.7 **Exercise Set** MyMathLab® ▶

Objectives A B C Mixed Practice *For each set of numbers, find the mean, median, and mode. If necessary, round the mean to one decimal place. See Examples 1 and 3 through 6.*

1. 15, 23, 24, 18, 25

2. 45, 36, 28, 46, 52

▶ **3.** 7.6, 8.2, 8.2, 9.6, 5.7, 9.1

4. 4.9, 7.1, 6.8, 6.8, 5.3, 4.9

5. 0.5, 0.2, 0.2, 0.6, 0.3, 1.3, 0.8, 0.1, 0.5

6. 0.6, 0.6, 0.8, 0.4, 0.5, 0.3, 0.7, 0.8, 0.1

7. 231, 543, 601, 293, 588, 109, 334, 268

8. 451, 356, 478, 776, 892, 500, 467, 780

The ten tallest buildings in the world, completed as of the start of 2012, are listed in the following table. Use this table to answer Exercises 9 through 14. If necessary, round results to one decimal place. See Examples 1 and 3 through 6.

9. Find the mean height of the five tallest buildings.

Building	Height (in feet)
Burj Khalifa, Dubai	2717
Makkah Royal Clock Tower Hotel, Saudi Arabia	1972
Taipei 101	1667
Shanghai World Financial Center	1614
International Commerce Centre, Hong Kong	1588
Petronas Tower 1, Kuala Lumpur	1483
Petronas Tower 2, Kuala Lumpur	1483
Zifeng Tower, China	1476
Willis Tower, Chicago	1451
KK 100 Development, China	1449
(*Source:* Council on Tall Buildings and Urban Habitat)	

10. Find the median height of the five tallest buildings.

11. Find the median height of the eight tallest buildings.

12. Find the mean height of the eight tallest buildings.

13. Given the building heights, explain how you know, without calculating, that the answer to Exercise **10** is greater than the answer to Exercise **11**.

14. Given the building heights, explain how you know, without calculating, that the answer to Exercise **12** is less than the answer to Exercise **9**.

For Exercises 15 through 18, the grades are given for a student for a particular semester. Find the grade point average. If necessary, round the grade point average to the nearest hundredth. See Example 2.

15.

Grade	Credit Hours
B	3
C	3
A	4
C	4

16.

Grade	Credit Hours
D	1
F	1
C	4
B	5

17.

Grade	Credit Hours
A	3
A	3
A	4
B	3
C	1

18.

Grade	Credit Hours
B	2
B	2
C	3
A	3
B	3

During an experiment, the following times (in seconds) were recorded:

7.8, 6.9, 7.5, 4.7, 6.9, 7.0.

19. Find the mean. Round to the nearest tenth.

20. Find the median.

21. Find the mode.

In a mathematics class, the following test scores were recorded for a student: 93, 85, 89, 79, 88, 91.

22. Find the mean. Round to the nearest hundredth.

23. Find the median.

24. Find the mode.

The following pulse rates were recorded for a group of 15 students:

    78, 80, 66, 68, 71, 64, 82, 71, 70, 65, 70, 75, 77, 86, 72.

25. Find the mean.

26. Find the median.

27. Find the mode.

28. How many pulse rates were higher than the mean?

29. How many pulse rates were lower than the mean?

Review

Write each fraction in simplest form.

30. $\dfrac{12}{20}$

31. $\dfrac{6}{18}$

32. $\dfrac{4x}{36}$

33. $\dfrac{18}{30y}$

34. $\dfrac{35a^3}{100a^2}$

35. $\dfrac{55y^2}{75y^2}$

Concept Extensions

Find the missing numbers in each set of numbers.

36. 16, 18, _____, _____, _____. The mode is 21. The median is 20.

37. _____, _____, _____, 40, _____. The mode is 35. The median is 37. The mean is 38.

38. Write a list of numbers for which you feel the median would be a better measure of central tendency than the mean.

39. Without making any computations, decide whether the median of the following list of numbers will be a whole number. Explain your reasoning.

    36, 77, 29, 58, 43

Chapter 5 Group Activity

Maintaining a Checking Account

This activity may be completed by working in groups or individually.

A checking account is a convenient way of handling money and paying bills. To open a checking account, the bank or savings and loan association requires a customer to make a deposit. Then the customer receives a checkbook that contains checks, deposit slips, and a register for recording checks written and deposits made. It is important to record all payments and deposits that affect the account. It is also important to keep the checkbook balance current by subtracting checks written and adding deposits made.

About once a month, checking customers receive a statement from the bank listing all activity that the account has had in the last month. The statement lists a beginning balance, all checks and deposits, any service charges made against the account, and an ending balance. Because it may take several days for checks that a customer has written to clear the banking system, the check register may list checks that do not appear on the monthly bank statement. These checks are called **outstanding checks.** Deposits that are recorded in the check register but do not appear on the statement are called **deposits in transit.** Because of these differences, it is important to balance, or reconcile, the checkbook against the monthly statement. The steps for doing so are listed below.

Balancing or Reconciling a Checkbook

Step 1: Place a check mark in the checkbook register next to each check and deposit listed on the monthly bank statement. Any entries in the register without a check mark are outstanding checks or deposits in transit.

Step 2: Find the ending checkbook register balance and add to it any outstanding checks and any interest paid on the account.

Step 3: From the total in Step 2, subtract any deposits in transit and any service charges.

Step 4: Compare the amount found in Step 3 with the ending balance listed on the bank statement. If they are the same, the checkbook balances with the bank statement. Be sure to update the check register with service charges and interest.

Step 5: If the checkbook does not balance, recheck the balancing process. Next, make sure that the running checkbook register balance was calculated correctly. Finally, compare the checkbook register with the statement to make sure that each check was recorded for the correct amount.

For the checkbook register and monthly bank statement given:

a. *update the checkbook register*　　　**b.** *list the outstanding checks and their total, and deposits in transit*

c. *balance the checkbook—be sure to update the register with any interest or service fees*

		Checkbook Register					
							Balance
#	Date	Description	Payment	✓	Deposit		**425.86**
114	4/1	Market Basket	30.27				
115	4/3	May's Texaco	8.50				
	4/4	Cash at ATM	50.00				
116	4/6	UNO Bookstore	121.38				
	4/7	Deposit			100.00		
117	4/9	MasterCard	84.16				
118	4/10	Redbox	6.12				
119	4/12	Kroger	18.72				
120	4/14	Parking sticker	18.50				
	4/15	Direct deposit			294.36		
121	4/20	Rent	395.00				
122	4/25	Student fees	20.00				
	4/28	Deposit			75.00		

First National Bank Monthly Statement 4/30		
BEGINNING BALANCE:		425.86
Date	Number	Amount
CHECKS AND ATM WITHDRAWALS		
4/3	114	30.27
4/4	ATM	50.00
4/11	117	84.16
4/13	115	8.50
4/15	119	18.72
4/22	121	395.00
DEPOSITS		
4/7		100.00
4/15	Direct deposit	294.36
SERVICE CHARGES		
Low balance fee		7.50
INTEREST		
Credited 4/30		1.15
ENDING BALANCE:		227.22

△ 6.4 Square Roots and the Pythagorean Theorem

Objectives

A Find the Square Root of a Number. ▶

B Approximate Square Roots. ▶

C Use the Pythagorean Theorem. ▶

Now that we know how to write ratios and solve proportions, we use proportions to help us find unknown sides of similar triangles. In this section, we prepare for work on triangles by studying right triangles and their applications.

First, let's practice finding square roots.

Objective A Finding Square Roots ▶

The **square** of a number is the number times itself. For example,

The square of 5 is 25 because 5^2 or $5 \cdot 5 = 25$.
The square of -5 is also 25 because $(-5)^2$ or $(-5)(-5) = 25$.

The reverse process of squaring is finding a **square root.** For example,

A square root of 25 is 5 because $5 \cdot 5$ or $5^2 = 25$.
A square root of 25 is also -5 because $(-5)(-5)$ or $(-5)^2 = 25$.

Every positive number has two square roots. We see on the previous page that the square roots of 25 are 5 and -5.

We use the symbol $\sqrt{}$, called a **radical sign,** to indicate the positive square root of a nonnegative number. For example,

$\sqrt{25} = 5$ because $5^2 = 25$ and 5 is positive.
$\sqrt{9} = 3$ because $3^2 = 9$ and 3 is positive.

Square Root of a Number

The square root, $\sqrt{}$, of a positive number a is the positive number b whose square is a. In symbols,

$$\sqrt{a} = b, \quad \text{if } b^2 = a$$

Also, $\sqrt{0} = 0$.

Helpful Hint

Remember that the radical sign $\sqrt{}$ is used to indicate the **positive** (or principal) **square root** of a nonnegative number.

Practice 1–6

Find each square root.
1. $\sqrt{100}$ 2. $\sqrt{64}$
3. $\sqrt{169}$ 4. $\sqrt{0}$
5. $\sqrt{\dfrac{1}{4}}$ 6. $\sqrt{\dfrac{9}{16}}$

Examples Find each square root.

1. $\sqrt{49} = 7$ because $7^2 = 49$.
2. $\sqrt{36} = 6$ because $6^2 = 36$.
3. $\sqrt{1} = 1$ because $1^2 = 1$.
4. $\sqrt{81} = 9$ because $9^2 = 81$.
5. $\sqrt{\dfrac{1}{36}} = \dfrac{1}{6}$ because $\left(\dfrac{1}{6}\right)^2$ or $\dfrac{1}{6} \cdot \dfrac{1}{6} = \dfrac{1}{36}$.
6. $\sqrt{\dfrac{4}{25}} = \dfrac{2}{5}$ because $\left(\dfrac{2}{5}\right)^2$ or $\dfrac{2}{5} \cdot \dfrac{2}{5} = \dfrac{4}{25}$.

■ Work Practice 1–6

Answers

1. 10   **2.** 8   **3.** 13   **4.** 0   **5.** $\dfrac{1}{2}$ **6.** $\dfrac{3}{4}$

Objective B Approximating Square Roots

Thus far, we have found square roots of perfect squares. Numbers like $\frac{1}{4}$, 36, $\frac{4}{25}$, and 1 are called **perfect squares** because their square root is a whole number or a fraction. A square root such as $\sqrt{5}$ cannot be written as a whole number or a fraction since 5 is not a perfect square.

Although $\sqrt{5}$ cannot be written as a whole number or a fraction, it can be approximated by estimating, by using a table (as in the appendix), or by using a calculator.

Example 7 Use Appendix A.4 or a calculator to approximate each square root to the nearest thousandth.

a. $\sqrt{43} \approx 6.557$ is approximately

b. $\sqrt{80} \approx 8.944$

▪ Work Practice 7

Practice 7

Use Appendix A.4 or a calculator to approximate each square root to the nearest thousandth.
a. $\sqrt{10}$ b. $\sqrt{62}$

Helpful Hint

$\sqrt{80}$, on the previous page, is *approximately* 8.944. This means that if we multiply 8.944 by 8.944, the product is *close* to 80.

$8.944 \times 8.944 \approx 79.995$

It is possible to approximate a square root to the nearest whole number without the use of a calculator or table. To do so, study the number line below and look for patterns.

$$\sqrt{25} \quad \sqrt{31}\ \sqrt{36}\ \sqrt{40} \quad \sqrt{49} \quad \sqrt{59}\ \sqrt{64}\ \ \sqrt{72}\ \ \sqrt{81}$$

$$5 \qquad\quad 6 \qquad\quad 7 \qquad\quad 8 \qquad\quad 9$$

Above the number line, notice that as the numbers under the radical signs increase, their value, and thus their placement on the number line, increase also.

Example 8 Without a calculator or table:

a. Determine which two whole numbers $\sqrt{78}$ is between.

b. Use part **a** to approximate $\sqrt{78}$ to the nearest whole.

Solution:

a. Review perfect squares and recall that $\sqrt{64} = 8$ and $\sqrt{81} = 9$. Since 78 is between 64 and 81, $\sqrt{78}$ is between $\sqrt{64}$ (or 8) and $\sqrt{81}$ (or 9).

Thus, $\sqrt{78}$ is between 8 and 9.

b. Since $\sqrt{78}$ is closer to $\sqrt{81}$ (or 9) than $\sqrt{64}$ (or 8), then (as our number line shows) $\sqrt{78}$ approximate to the nearest whole is 9.

▪ Work Practice 8

Practice 8

Without a calculator or table, approximate $\sqrt{62}$ to the nearest whole.

Answers

7. a. 3.162   **b.** 7.874   **8.** 8

Objective C Using the Pythagorean Theorem

One important application of square roots has to do with right triangles. Recall that a **right triangle** is a triangle in which one of the angles is a right angle, or measures 90° (degrees). The **hypotenuse** of a right triangle is the side opposite the right angle. The **legs** of a right triangle are the other two sides. These are shown in the following figure. The right angle in the triangle is indicated by the small square drawn in that angle.

The following theorem is true for all right triangles.

Pythagorean Theorem

If a and b are the lengths of the legs of a right triangle and c is the length of the hypotenuse, then

$$a^2 + b^2 = c^2$$

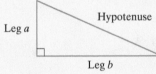

In other words, $(\text{leg})^2 + (\text{other leg})^2 = (\text{hypotenuse})^2$.

Practice 9

Find the length of the hypotenuse of the given right triangle.

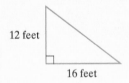

Example 9

Find the length of the hypotenuse of the given right triangle.

Solution: Let $a = 6$ and $b = 8$. According to the Pythagorean theorem,

$$a^2 + b^2 = c^2$$
$$6^2 + 8^2 = c^2 \quad \text{Let } a = 6 \text{ and } b = 8.$$
$$36 + 64 = c^2 \quad \text{Evaluate } 6^2 \text{ and } 8^2.$$
$$100 = c^2 \quad \text{Add.}$$

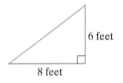

In the equation $c^2 = 100$, the solutions of c are the square roots of 100. Since $10 \cdot 10 = 100$ and $(-10)(-10) = 100$, both 10 and -10 are square roots of 100. Since c represents a length, we are only interested in the positive square root of c^2.

$$c = \sqrt{100}$$
$$= 10$$

The hypotenuse is 10 feet long.

■ Work Practice 9

Practice 10

Approximate the length of the hypotenuse of the given right triangle. Round to the nearest whole unit.

Example 10

Approximate the length of the hypotenuse of the given right triangle. Round the length to the nearest whole unit.

Solution: Let $a = 17$ and $b = 10$.

$$a^2 + b^2 = c^2$$
$$17^2 + 10^2 = c^2$$
$$289 + 100 = c^2$$
$$389 = c^2$$
$$\sqrt{389} = c \text{ or } c \approx 20 \quad \text{From Appendix A.4 or a calculator}$$

The hypotenuse is exactly $\sqrt{389}$ meters, which is approximately 20 meters.

■ Work Practice 10

Answers

9. 20 feet **10.** 11 kilometers

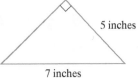

△ **Example 11**   Find the length of the leg in the given right triangle. Give the exact length and a two-decimal-place approximation.

5 inches

7 inches

Solution: Notice that the hypotenuse measures 7 inches and that the length of one leg measures 5 inches. Thus, let $c = 7$ and a or b be 5. We will let $a = 5$.

$$a^2 + b^2 = c^2$$
$$5^2 + b^2 = 7^2 \qquad \text{Let } a = 5 \text{ and } c = 7.$$
$$25 + b^2 = 49 \qquad \text{Evaluate } 5^2 \text{ and } 7^2.$$
$$b^2 = 24 \qquad \text{Subtract 25 from both sides.}$$
$$b = \sqrt{24} \approx 4.90$$

The length of the leg is exactly $\sqrt{24}$ inches and approximately 4.90 inches.

■ Work Practice 11

✓**Concept Check** The following lists are the lengths of the sides of two triangles. Which set forms a right triangle?

a. 8, 15, 17   **b.** 24, 30, 40

△ **Example 12**   Finding the Dimensions of a Park

An inner-city park is in the shape of a square that measures 300 feet on a side. A sidewalk is to be constructed along the diagonal of the park. Find the length of the sidewalk rounded to the nearest whole foot.

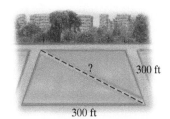

?   300 ft

300 ft

Solution: The diagonal is the hypotenuse of a right triangle, which we label c.

$$a^2 + b^2 = c^2$$
$$300^2 + 300^2 = c^2 \qquad \text{Let } a = 300 \text{ and } b = 300.$$
$$90{,}000 + 90{,}000 = c^2 \qquad \text{Evaluate } (300)^2.$$
$$180{,}000 = c^2 \qquad \text{Add.}$$
$$\sqrt{180{,}000} = c \text{ or } c \approx 424$$

The length of the sidewalk is approximately 424 feet.

■ Work Practice 12

Practice 11

Find the length of the leg in the given right triangle. Give the exact length and a two-decimal-place approximation.

13 feet

7 feet

Practice 12

A football field is a rectangle measuring 100 yards by 53 yards. Draw a diagram and find the length of the diagonal of a football field to the nearest yard.

Answers
11. $\sqrt{120}$ feet ≈ 10.95 feet
12. 113 yards

✓**Concept Check Answer**
a

Calculator Explorations Finding and Approximating Square Roots

To simplify or approximate square roots using a calculator, locate the key marked $\boxed{\sqrt{\ }}$.

    To simplify $\sqrt{64}$, for example, press the keys

$\boxed{64}$ $\boxed{\sqrt{\ }}$ or $\boxed{\sqrt{\ }}$ $\boxed{64}$

The display should read $\boxed{\qquad 8}$. Then

$\sqrt{64} = 8$

    To *approximate* $\sqrt{10}$, press the keys

$\boxed{10}$ $\boxed{\sqrt{\ }}$ or $\boxed{\sqrt{\ }}$ $\boxed{10}$

The display should read $\boxed{3.16227766}$. This is an *approximation* for $\sqrt{10}$. A three-decimal-place approximation is

$\sqrt{10} \approx 3.162$

Is this answer reasonable? Since 10 is between the perfect squares 9 and 16, $\sqrt{10}$ is between $\sqrt{9} = 3$ and $\sqrt{16} = 4$. Our answer is reasonable since 3.162 is between 3 and 4.

Simplify.

1. $\sqrt{1024}$

2. $\sqrt{676}$

Approximate each square root. Round each answer to the nearest thousandth.

3. $\sqrt{15}$

4. $\sqrt{19}$

5. $\sqrt{97}$

6. $\sqrt{56}$

Vocabulary, Readiness & Video Check

Use the choices below to fill in each blank. Some choices will be used more than once.

    squaring   Pythagorean theorem   radical -10 leg

    hypotenuse   perfect squares   10 c^2 b^2

1. The square roots of 100 are _____ and _____ because $10 \cdot 10 = 100$ and
    $(-10)(-10) = 100$.

2. $\sqrt{100} =$ _____ because $10 \cdot 10 = 100$ and 10 is positive.

3. The _____ sign is used to denote the positive square root of a nonnegative number.

4. The reverse process of _____ a number is finding a square root of a number.

5. The numbers $9, 1$, and $\dfrac{1}{25}$ are called _____.

6. Label the parts of the right triangle.

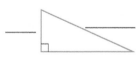

7. In the given triangle, $a^2 +$ _____ $=$ _____.

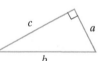

8. The _____ can be used for right triangles.

Martin-Gay Interactive Videos   *Watch the section lecture video and answer the following questions.*

Objective A 9. From the lecture before ▣ Example 1, list the square root(s) of 49. How is this different from finding √49? ▶

Objective B 10. In ▣ Example 5, how do we know √15 is closer to 4 than to 3? ▶

Objective C 11. From ▣ Example 6, how do we know which side of a right triangle is the hypotenuse? ▶

See Video 6.4

6.4 Exercise Set MyMathLab® ▶

Objective A *Find each square root. See Examples 1 through 6.*

▶ **1.** $\sqrt{4}$ **2.** $\sqrt{9}$ ▶ **3.** $\sqrt{121}$ **4.** $\sqrt{144}$

▶ **5.** $\sqrt{\dfrac{1}{81}}$ **6.** $\sqrt{\dfrac{1}{64}}$ **7.** $\sqrt{\dfrac{16}{64}}$ **8.** $\sqrt{\dfrac{36}{81}}$

Objective B *Use Appendix A.4 or a calculator to approximate each square root. Round the square root to the nearest thousandth. See Example 7.*

9. $\sqrt{3}$ **10.** $\sqrt{5}$ ▶ **11.** $\sqrt{15}$ **12.** $\sqrt{17}$

13. $\sqrt{31}$ **14.** $\sqrt{85}$ **15.** $\sqrt{26}$ **16.** $\sqrt{35}$

Determine what two whole numbers each square root is between without using a calculator or table. Then use a calculator or Appendix A.4 to check. See Example 8.

▶ **17.** $\sqrt{38}$ **18.** $\sqrt{27}$ **19.** $\sqrt{101}$ **20.** $\sqrt{85}$

Objectives A B **Mixed Practice** *Find each square root. If necessary, round the square root to the nearest thousandth. See Examples 1 through 8.*

21. $\sqrt{256}$ **22.** $\sqrt{625}$ **23.** $\sqrt{92}$ **24.** $\sqrt{18}$

25. $\sqrt{\dfrac{49}{144}}$ **26.** $\sqrt{\dfrac{121}{169}}$ **27.** $\sqrt{71}$ **28.** $\sqrt{62}$

Objective C *Find the unknown length in each right triangle. If necessary, approximate the length to the nearest thousandth. See Examples 9 through 12.*

▶ **29.**   **30.**   **31.**

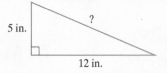

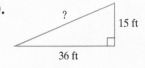

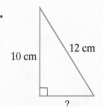

32.

3 yd   9 yd
?

33. 22 m

48 m

?

34.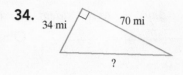

34 mi   70 mi

?

35.

?

108 mm

45 mm

36.   ?

27 km

36 km

Sketch each right triangle and find the length of the side not given. If necessary, approximate the length to the nearest thousandth. (Each length is in units.) See Examples 9 through 12.

37. leg = 3, leg = 4

38. leg = 9, leg = 12

39. leg = 5, hypotenuse = 13

40. leg = 6, hypotenuse = 10

41. leg = 10, leg = 14

42. leg = 2, leg = 16

43. leg = 35, leg = 28

44. leg = 30, leg = 15

45. leg = 30, leg = 30

46. leg = 21, leg = 21

▶ **47.** hypotenuse = 2, leg = 1

48. hypotenuse = 9, leg = 8

49. leg = 7.5, leg = 4

50. leg = 12, leg = 22.5

Solve. See Example 12.

51. A standard city block is a square with each side measuring 100 yards. Find the length of the diagonal of a city block to the nearest hundredth yard.

52. A section of land is a square with each side measuring 1 mile. Find the length of the diagonal of the section of land to the nearest thousandth mile.

53. Find the height of the tree. Round the height to one decimal place.

?   32 feet

20 feet

54. Find the height of the antenna. Round the height to one decimal place.

168 ft   ?

60 ft

55. The playing field for football is a rectangle that is 300 feet long by 160 feet wide. Find the length of a straight-line run that started at one corner and went diagonally to end at the opposite corner. Round to the nearest foot, if necessary.

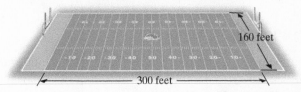

56. A soccer field is in the shape of a rectangle and its dimensions depend on the age of the players. The dimensions of the soccer field below are the minimum dimensions for international play. Find the length of the diagonal of this rectangle. Round the answer to the nearest tenth of a yard.

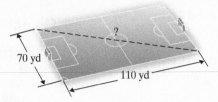

Review

Write each fraction in simplest form.

57. $\dfrac{10}{12}$

58. $\dfrac{10}{15}$

59. $\dfrac{2x}{60}$

60. $\dfrac{35}{75y}$

Perform the indicated operations.

61. $\dfrac{9}{13y} + \dfrac{12}{13y}$

62. $\dfrac{3x}{9} - \dfrac{5}{9}$

63. $\dfrac{9}{8} \cdot \dfrac{x}{8}$

64. $\dfrac{7x}{11} \div \dfrac{8x}{11}$

Concept Extensions

*Use the results of Exercises **17–20** and approximate each square root to the nearest whole without using a calculator or table. Then use a calculator to check. See Example 8.*

65. $\sqrt{38}$

66. $\sqrt{27}$

67. $\sqrt{101}$

68. $\sqrt{85}$

69. Without using a calculator, explain how you know that $\sqrt{105}$ is *not* approximately 9.875.

70. Without using a calculator, explain how you know that $\sqrt{27}$ is *not* approximately 3.296.

Does the set form the lengths of the sides of a right triangle? See the Concept Check in this section.

71. 25, 60, 65

72. 20, 45, 50

△**73.** Find the exact length of x. Then give a two-decimal-place approximation.

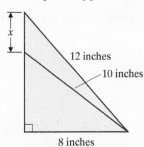

Reading Pictographs, Bar Graphs, Histograms, and Line Graphs

Copyright 2015 Pearson Education, Inc.

Objectives

A Read Pictographs.

B Read and Construct Bar Graphs.

C Read and Construct Histograms.

D Read Line Graphs.

Often data are presented visually in a graph. In this section, we practice reading several kinds of graphs including pictographs, bar graphs, and line graphs.

Objective A Reading Pictographs

A **pictograph** such as the one below is a graph in which pictures or symbols are used. This type of graph contains a key that explains the meaning of the symbol used. An advantage of using a pictograph to display information is that comparisons can easily be made. A disadvantage of using a pictograph is that it is often hard to tell what fractional part of a symbol is shown. For example, in the pictograph below, Arabic shows a part of a symbol, but it's hard to read with any accuracy what fractional part of a symbol is shown.

Practice 1

Use the pictograph shown in Example 1 to answer the following questions:

a. Approximate the number of people who primarily speak Spanish.

b. Approximate how many more people primarily speak Spanish than Arabic.

Example 1 Calculating Languages Spoken

The following pictograph shows the top eight most-spoken (primary) languages. Use this pictograph to answer the questions.

Top 8 Most-Spoken (Primary) Languages

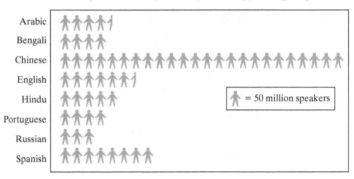

Source: www.ethnologue.com

a. Approximate the number of people who primarily speak Russian.

b. Approximate how many more people primarily speak English than Russian.

Solution:

a. Russian corresponds to 3 symbols, and each symbol represents 50 million speakers. This means that the number of people who primarily speak Russian is approximately 3 · (50 million) or 150 million people.

b. English shows $3\frac{1}{2}$ more symbols than Russian. This means that $3\frac{1}{2}$ · (50 million) or 175 million more people primarily speak English than Russian.

Work Practice 1

Answers

1. a. 400 million people
b. 175 million people

Objective B Reading and Constructing Bar Graphs

Another way to visually present data is with a **bar graph.** Bar graphs can appear with vertical bars or horizontal bars. Although we have studied bar graphs in previous sections, we now practice reading the height or length of the bars contained in a bar graph. An advantage to using bar graphs is that a scale is usually included for greater accuracy. Care must be taken when reading bar graphs, as well as other types of graphs—they may be misleading, as shown later in this section.

Example 2 Finding the Number of Endangered Species

The following bar graph shows the number of endangered species in the United States in 2013. Use this graph to answer the questions.

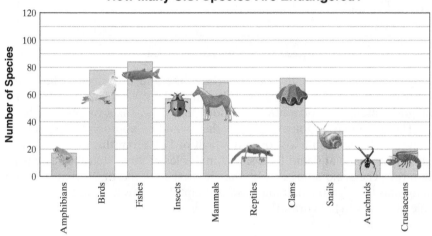

How Many U.S. Species Are Endangered?

Source: U.S. Fish and Wildlife Service

a. Approximate the number of endangered species that are clams.

b. Which category has the most endangered species?

Solution:

a. To approximate the number of endangered species that are clams, we go to the top of the bar that represents clams. From the top of this bar, we move horizontally to the left until the scale is reached. We read the height of the bar on the scale as approximately 72. There are approximately 72 clam species that are endangered, as shown.

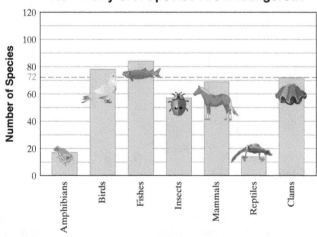

How Many U.S. Species Are Endangered?

Source: U.S. Fish and Wildlife Service

b. The most endangered species is represented by the tallest (longest) bar. The tallest bar corresponds to fishes.

■ Work Practice 2

Practice 2

Use the bar graph in Example 2 to answer the following questions:

a. Approximate the number of endangered species that are birds.

b. Which category shows the fewest endangered species?

Answers
2. a. 78 **b.** arachnids

Practice 3

Draw a vertical bar graph using the information in the table about electoral votes for selected states.

Total Electoral Votes by Selected States

State	Electoral Votes
Texas	34
California	55
Florida	27
Nebraska	5
Indiana	11
Georgia	15

(*Source: World Almanac* 2013)

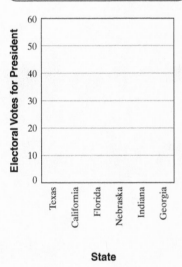

Answer

3.

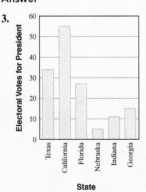

Next, we practice constructing a bar graph.

Example 3 Draw a vertical bar graph using the information in the table below, which gives the caffeine content of selected foods.

Average Caffeine Content of Selected Foods

Food	Milligrams	Food	Milligrams
Brewed coffee (percolator, 8 ounces)	124	Instant coffee (8 ounces)	104
Brewed decaffeinated coffee (8 ounces)	3	Brewed tea (U.S. brands, 8 ounces)	64
Coca-Cola Classic (8 ounces)	31	Mr. Pibb (8 ounces)	27
Dark chocolate (semisweet, $1\frac{1}{2}$ ounces)	30	Milk chocolate (8 ounces)	9

(*Sources:* International Food Information Council and the Coca-Cola Company)

Solution: We draw and label a vertical line and a horizontal line as shown below on the left. These lines are also called axes. We place the different food categories along the horizontal axis. Along the vertical axis, we place a scale.

There are many choices of scales that would be appropriate. Notice that the milligrams range from a low of 3 to a high of 124. From this information, we use a scale that starts at 0 and then shows multiples of 20 so that the scale is not too cluttered. The scale stops at 140, the smallest multiple of 20 that will allow all milligrams to be graphed. It may also be helpful to draw horizontal lines along the scale markings to help draw the vertical bars at the correct height. The finished bar graph is shown below on the right.

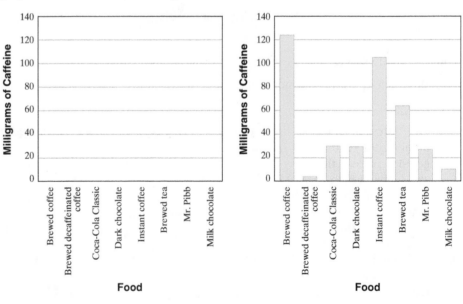

■ Work Practice 3

As mentioned previously, graphs can be misleading. Both graphs on the next page show the same information, but with different scales. Special care should be taken when forming conclusions from the appearance of a graph.

Notice the ⟩ symbol on each vertical scale on the graphs below. This symbol alerts us that numbers are missing from that scale

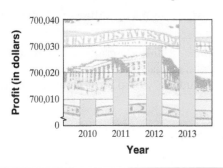

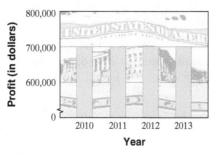

Are profits shown in the graphs above greatly increasing, or are they remaining about the same?

Objective C Reading and Constructing Histograms

Suppose that the test scores of 36 students are summarized in the table below:

Student Scores	Frequency (Number of Students)
40–49	1
50–59	3
60–69	2
70–79	10
80–89	12
90–99	8

The results in the table can be displayed in a histogram. A **histogram** is a special bar graph. The width of each bar represents a range of numbers called a **class interval.** The height of each bar corresponds to how many times a number in the class interval occurs and is called the **class frequency.** The bars in a histogram lie side by side with no space between them.

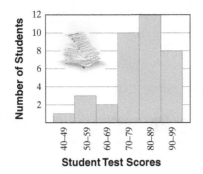

Example 4 Reading a Histogram on Student Test Scores

Use the preceding histogram to determine how many students scored 50–59 on the test.

Solution: We find the bar representing 50–59. The height of this bar is 3, which means 3 students scored 50–59 on the test.

▩ Work Practice 4

Practice 4

Use the histogram above Example 4 to determine how many students scored 80–89 on the test.

Answer
4. 12

Practice 5

Use the histogram above Example 4 to determine how many students scored less than 80 on the test.

Practice 6

Complete the frequency distribution table for the data below. Each number represents a credit card owner's unpaid balance for one month.

0	53	89	125
265	161	37	76
62	201	136	42

Class Intervals (Credit Card Balances)	Tally	Class Frequency (Number of Months)
$0–$49	_____	_____
$50–$99	_____	_____
$100–$149	_____	_____
$150–$199	_____	_____
$200–$249	_____	_____
$250–$299	_____	_____

Practice 7

Construct a histogram from the frequency distribution table for Practice 6.

Example 5 Reading a Histogram on Student Test Scores

Use the histogram above Example 4 to determine how many students scored 80 or above on the test.

Solution: We see that two different bars fit this description. There are 12 students who scored 80–89 and 8 students who scored 90–99. The sum of these two categories is 12 + 8 or 20 students. Thus, 20 students scored 80 or above on the test.

■ Work Practice 5

Now we will look at a way to construct histograms.

The daily high temperatures for 1 month in New Orleans, Louisiana, are recorded in the following list:

85°	90°	95°	89°	88°	94°
87°	90°	95°	92°	95°	94°
82°	92°	96°	91°	94°	92°
89°	89°	90°	93°	95°	91°
88°	90°	88°	86°	93°	89°

The data in this list have not been organized and can be hard to interpret. One way to organize the data is to place them in a **frequency distribution table.** We will do this in Example 6.

Example 6 Completing a Frequency Distribution on Temperature

Complete the frequency distribution table for the preceding temperature data.

Solution: Go through the data and place a tally mark in the second column of the table next to the class interval. Then count the tally marks and write each total in the third column of the table.

Class Intervals (Temperatures)	Tally	Class Frequency (Number of Days)
82°–84°	I	1
85°–87°	III	3
88°–90°	‖‖ ‖‖ I	11
91°–93°	‖‖ II	7
94°–96°	‖‖ III	8

■ Work Practice 6

Example 7 Constructing a Histogram

Construct a histogram from the frequency distribution table in Example 6.

Solution:

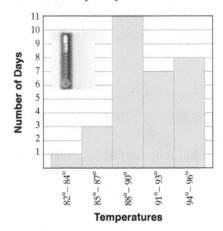

■ Work Practice 7

Answers

5. 16

6.

Tally	Class Frequency (Number Months)	Tally	Class Frequency (Number Months)
III	3	I	1
IIII	4	I	1
II	2	I	1

7.

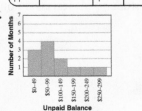

✓Concept Check Which of the following sets of data is better suited to representation by a histogram? Explain.

Set 1		Set 2	
Grade on Final	# of Students	Section Number	Avg. Grade on Final
51–60	12	150	78
61–70	18	151	83
71–80	29	152	87
81–90	23	153	73
91–100	25		

Objective D Reading Line Graphs

Another common way to display information with a graph is by using a **line graph.** An advantage of a line graph is that it can be used to visualize relationships between two quantities. A line graph can also be very useful in showing changes over time.

Example 8 Reading Temperatures from a Line Graph

The following line graph shows the average daily temperature for each month in Omaha, Nebraska. Use this graph to answer the questions below.

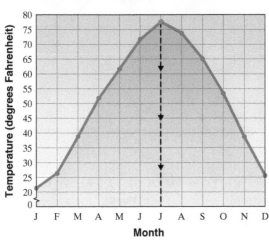

Average Daily Temperature for Omaha, Nebraska

Source: National Climatic Data Center

a. During what month is the average daily temperature the highest?

b. During what month, from July through December, is the average daily temperature 65°F?

c. During what months is the average daily temperature less than 30°F?

Solution:

a. The month with the highest temperature corresponds to the highest point. This is the red point shown on the graph above. We follow this highest point downward to the horizontal month scale and see that this point corresponds to July.

(Continued on next page)

Practice 8

Use the temperature graph in Example 8 to answer the following questions:

a. During what month is the average daily temperature the lowest?

b. During what month is the average daily temperature 25°F?

c. During what months is the average daily temperature greater than 70°F?

Answers

8. a. January **b.** December

c. June, July, and August

✓**Concept Check Answer**

Set 1; the grades are arranged in ranges of scores.

b. The months July through December correspond to the right side of the graph. We find the 65°F mark on the vertical temperature scale and move to the right until a point on the right side of the graph is reached. From that point, we move downward to the horizontal month scale and read the corresponding month. During the month of September, the average daily temperature is 65°F.

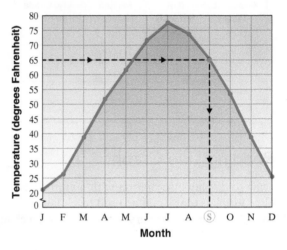

Source: National Climatic Data Center

c. To see what months the temperature is less than 30°F, we find what months correspond to points that fall below the 30°F mark on the vertical scale. These months are January, February, and December.

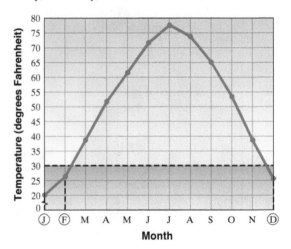

Source: National Climatic Data Center

■ Work Practice 8

Vocabulary, Readiness & Video Check

Fill in each blank with one of the choices below.

pictograph	bar	class frequency
histogram	line	class interval

1. A _____ graph presents data using vertical or horizontal bars.

2. A _____ is a graph in which pictures or symbols are used to visually present data.

3. A _____ graph displays information with a line that connects data points.

4. A _____ is a special bar graph in which the width of each bar represents a _____ and the height of each bar represents the _____ .

Martin-Gay Interactive Videos Watch the section lecture video and answer the following questions.

See Video 8.1

Objective A 5. From the pictograph in Example 1, how would you approximate the number of wildfires for any given year?

Objective B 6. What is one advantage of displaying data in a bar graph?

Objective C 7. Complete this statement based on the lecture before Example 6: A histogram is a special kind of _____.

Objective D 8. From the line graph in Examples 10–13, what year averaged the greatest number of goals per game average and what was this average?

8.1 Exercise Set MyMathLab®

Objective A *The following pictograph shows the number of acres devoted to wheat production in selected states. Use this graph to answer Exercises 1 through 8. See Example 1. (Source: U.S. Department of Agriculture)*

1. Which state plants the greatest quantity of acreage in wheat?

2. Which of the states shown plant the least amount of wheat acreage?

3. Approximate the number of acres of wheat planted in Oklahoma.

4. Approximate the number of acres of wheat planted in Kansas.

5. Which state plants about 6,000,000 acres of wheat?

6. Which state plants about 2,000,000 acres of wheat?

7. Which two states together plant about the same acreage of wheat as North Dakota?

8. Which two states together plant about the same acreage of wheat as Kansas?

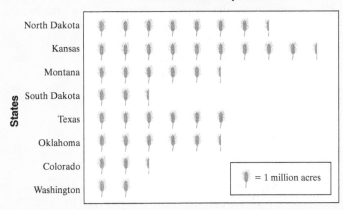

Annual Wheat Acreage in Selected Top States

= 1 million acres

The following pictograph shows the average number of wildfires in the United States between 2006 and 2012. Use this graph to answer Exercises 9 through 16. See Example 1. (Source: National Interagency Fire Center)

9. Approximate the number of wildfires in 2008.

10. Approximately how many wildfires were there in 2012?

11. Which year, of the years shown, had the most wildfires?

12. In what years were the number of wildfires greater than 72,000?

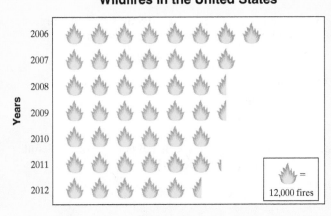

Wildfires in the United States

= 12,000 fires

13. What was the amount of decrease in wildfires from 2006 to 2012?

14. What was the amount of decrease in wildfires from 2010 to 2012?

15. What was the average annual number of wildfires from 2006 to 2008? (*Hint:* How do you calculate the average?)

16. Give a possible explanation for the overall decrease in the number of wildfires since 2006.

Objective B *The National Weather Service has exacting definitions for hurricanes; they are tropical storms with winds in excess of 74 mph. The following bar graph shows the number of hurricanes, by month, that have made landfall on the mainland United States between 1851 and 2012. Use this graph to answer Exercises 17 through 22. See Example 2. (Source: National Weather Service: National Hurricane Center)*

17. In which month did the most hurricanes make landfall in the United States?

18. In which month did the fewest hurricanes make landfall in the United States?

19. Approximate the number of hurricanes that made landfall in the United States during the month of August.

20. Approximate the number of hurricanes that made landfall in the United States in September.

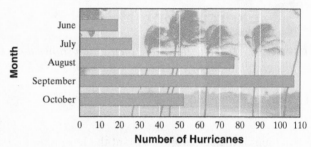

Hurricanes Making Landfall in the United States, by Month, 1851–2012

21. In 2008 alone, two hurricanes made landfall during the month of August. What fraction of all the 77 hurricanes that made landfall during August is this?

22. In 2007, only one hurricane made landfall on the United States during the entire season, in the month of September. If there have been 107 hurricanes to make landfall in the month of September since 1851, approximately what percent of these arrived in 2007?

The following horizontal bar graph shows the approximate 2012 population of the world's largest cities (including their suburbs). Use this graph to answer Exercises 23 through 28. See Example 2. (Source: CityPopulation)

23. Name the city with the largest population, and estimate its population.

24. Name the cities whose population is between 19 million and 22 million.

25. Name the city in the United States with the largest population, and estimate its population.

26. Name the two cities that have approximately the same population.

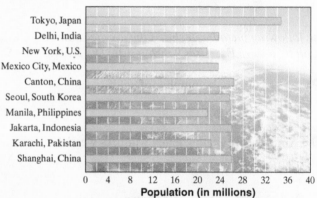

World's Largest Cities (including Suburbs)

27. How much larger (in terms of population) is Seoul, South Korea, than Delhi, India?

28. How much larger (in terms of population) is, Shanghai, China, than Mexico City, Mexico?

Use the information given to draw a vertical bar graph. Clearly label the bars. See Example 3.

29.

Fiber Content of Selected Foods

Food	Grams of Total Fiber
Kidney beans $\left(\frac{1}{2}\text{ c}\right)$	4.5
Oatmeal, cooked $\left(\frac{3}{4}\text{ c}\right)$	3.0
Peanut butter, chunky (2 tbsp)	1.5
Popcorn (1 c)	1.0
Potato, baked with skin (1 med)	4.0
Whole wheat bread (1 slice)	2.5

(*Sources:* American Dietetic Association and National Center for Nutrition and Dietetics)

Fiber Content of Selected Foods

Grams of Total Fiber

Food

30.

U.S. Annual Food Sales

Year	Sales in Billions of Dollars
2009	1086
2010	1139
2011	1274
2012	1357

(*Source:* U.S. Department of Agriculture)

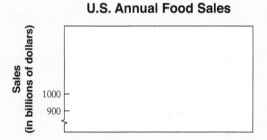

U.S. Annual Food Sales

Sales (in billions of dollars)

1000
900

Year

31.

Best-Selling Albums of All Time (U.S. Sales)

Album	Estimated Sales (in millions)
Pink Floyd: *The Wall* (1979)	23
Michael Jackson: *Thriller* (1982)	29
Billy Joel: *Greatest Hits Volumes I - II* (1985)	23
Eagles: *Their Greatest Hits* (1976)	29
Led Zeppelin: *Led Zeppelin IV* (1971)	23

(*Source:* Recording Industry Association of America)

Best-Selling Albums of All Time
(U.S. sales)

Estimated Sales (in millions)

Album

32.

Selected Worldwide Commercial Space Launches

Location or Name	Total Commercial Space Launches 1990–2012
United States	156
Europe	153
Russia	141
China	23
Sea Launch[*]	39

[*]Sea Launch is an international venture involving 4 countries that uses its own launch facility outside national borders.

Source: Bureau of Transportation Statistics

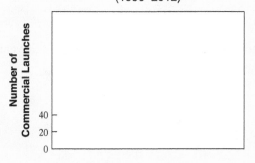

Selected Worldwide Commercial Space Launches
(1990–2012)

Number of Commercial Launches

40
20
0

Location or Name

Objective **C** *The following histogram shows the number of miles that each adult, from a survey of 100 adults, drives per week. Use this histogram to answer Exercises 33 through 42. See Examples 4 and 5.*

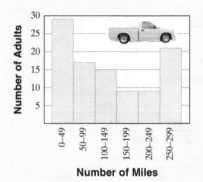

33. How many adults drive 100–149 miles per week?

34. How many adults drive 200–249 miles per week?

▷ 35. How many adults drive fewer than 150 miles per week?

36. How many adults drive 200 miles or more per week?

37. How many adults drive 100–199 miles per week?

38. How many adults drive 150–249 miles per week?

▷ 39. How many more adults drive 250–299 miles per week than 200–249 miles per week?

40. How many more adults drive 0–49 miles per week than 50–99 miles per week?

41. What is the ratio of adults who drive 150–199 miles per week to the total number of adults surveyed?

42. What is the ratio of adults who drive 50–99 miles per week to the total number of adults surveyed?

The following histogram shows the ages of householders for the year 2010. Use this histogram to answer Exercises 43 through 50. For Exercises 45 through 50, estimate to the nearest whole million. See Examples 4 and 5.

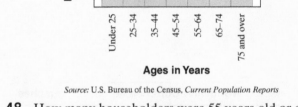

Source: U.S. Bureau of the Census, *Current Population Reports*

43. The most householders were in what age range?

44. The least number of householders were in what age range?

45. How many householders were 55–64 years old?

46. How many householders were 35–44 years old?

47. How many householders were 44 years old or younger?

48. How many householders were 55 years old or older?

49. How many more householders were 45–54 years old than 55–64 years old?

50. How many more householders were 45–54 years old than 75 and over?

The following list shows the golf scores for an amateur golfer. Use this list to complete the frequency distribution table to the right. See Example 6.

78	84	91	93	97
97	95	85	95	96
101	89	92	89	100

	Class Intervals (Scores)	Tally	Class Frequency (Number of Games)
▶ **51.**	70–79		
▶ **52.**	80–89		
▶ **53.**	90–99		
▶ **54.**	100–109		

Twenty-five people in a survey were asked to give their current checking account balances. Use the balances shown in the following list to complete the frequency distribution table to the right. See Example 6.

$53	$105	$162	$443	$109
$468	$47	$259	$316	$228
$207	$357	$15	$301	$75
$86	$77	$512	$219	$100
$192	$288	$352	$166	$292

	Class Intervals (Account Balances)	Tally	Class Frequency (Number of People)
55.	$0–$99		
56.	$100–$199		
57.	$200–$299		
58.	$300–$399		
59.	$400–$499		
60.	$500–$599		

▶ **61.** Use the frequency distribution table from Exercises **51** through **54** to construct a histogram. See Example 7.

Golf Scores

62. Use the frequency distribution table from Exercises **55** through **60** to construct a histogram. See Example 7.

Account Balances

Objective D *Beach Soccer World Cup is now held every two years. The following line graph shows the World Cup goals per game average for beach soccer during the years shown. Use this graph to answer Exercises 63 through 70. See Example 8.*

▶ **63.** Find the average number of goals per game in 2011.

64. Find the average number of goals per game in 2009.

▶ **65.** During what year shown was the average number of goals per game the highest?

66. During what year shown was the average number of goals per game the lowest?

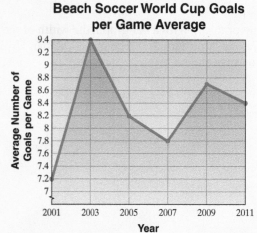

Beach Soccer World Cup Goals per Game Average

Source: Wikipedia

67. From 2007 to 2009, did the average number of goals per game increase or decrease?

68. From 2009 to 2011, did the average number of goals per game increase or decrease?

69. During what year(s) shown were the average goals per game less than 8?

70. During what year(s) shown were the average goals per game greater than 8?

Review

Find each percent.

71. 30% of 12

72. 45% of 120

73. 10% of 62

74. 95% of 50

Write each fraction as a percent.

75. $\frac{1}{4}$

76. $\frac{2}{5}$

77. $\frac{17}{50}$

78. $\frac{9}{10}$

Concept Extensions

The following double line graph shows temperature highs and lows for a week. Use this graph to answer Exercises 79 through 84.

79. What was the high temperature reading on Thursday?

80. What was the low temperature reading on Thursday?

81. What day was the temperature the lowest? What was this low temperature?

82. What day of the week was the temperature the highest? What was this high temperature?

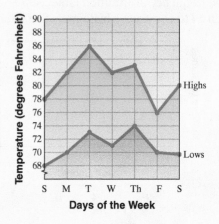

83. On what day of the week was the difference between the high temperature and the low temperature the greatest? What was this difference in temperature?

84. On what day of the week was the difference between the high temperature and the low temperature the least? What was this difference in temperature?

85. True or false? With a bar graph, the width of the bar is just as important as the height of the bar. Explain your answer.

86. Kansas plants about 17% of the wheat acreage in the United States. About how many acres of wheat are planted in the United States, according to the pictograph for Exercises **1** through **8**? Round to the nearest million acre.

8.2 Reading Circle Graphs

Objective A Reading Circle Graphs

Objectives

A Read Circle Graphs.

B Draw Circle Graphs.

In Exercise Set 7.1, the following **circle graph** was shown. This particular graph shows the favorite sport for 100 adults.

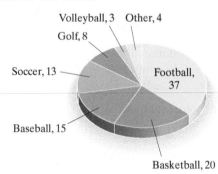

Volleyball, 3   Other, 4
Golf, 8
Soccer, 13
Football, 37
Baseball, 15
Basketball, 20

Each sector of the graph (shaped like a piece of pie) shows a category and the relative size of the category. In other words, the most popular sport is football, and it is represented by the largest sector.

Example 1 Find the ratio of adults preferring basketball to total adults. Write the ratio as a fraction in simplest form.

Solution: The ratio is

$$\frac{\text{people preferring basketball}}{\text{total adults}} = \frac{20}{100} = \frac{1}{5}$$

■ Work Practice 1

Practice 1

Find the ratio of adults preferring golf to total adults. Write the ratio as a fraction in simplest form.

A circle graph is often used to show percents in different categories, with the whole circle representing 100%.

Example 2 Using a Circle Graph

The following graph shows the percent of visitors to the United States in a recent year by various regions. Using the circle graph shown, determine the percent of visitors who came to the United States from Mexico or Canada.

Solution: To find this percent, we add the percents corresponding to Mexico and Canada. The percent of visitors to the United States that came from Mexico or Canada is

$$34\% + 21\% = 55\%$$

■ Work Practice 2

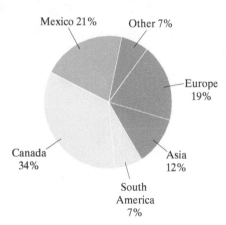

Visitors to U.S. by Region

Mexico 21%   Other 7%

Europe 19%

Canada 34%

Asia 12%

South America 7%

Source: Office of Travel and Tourism Industries, 2012

Practice 2

Using the circle graph shown in Example 2, determine the percent of visitors to the United States that came from Europe, Asia, or South America.

Answers

1. $\frac{2}{25}$ **2.** 38%

Helpful Hint

Since a circle graph represents a whole, the percents should add to 100% or 1. Notice this is true for Example 2.

Practice 3

Use the information in Example 3 and the circle graph from Example 2 to predict the number of tourists from Mexico in 2017.

Example 3 Finding Percent of Population

The U.S. Department of Commerce forecasts 81 million international visitors to the United States in 2017. Use the circle graph from Example 2 and predict the number of tourists that might be from Europe.

Solution: We use the percent equation.

amount = percent · base

amount = 0.19 · 81,000,000

= 0.19(81,000,000)

= 15,390,000

Thus, 15,390,000 tourists might come from Europe in 2017.

■ Work Practice 3

✓**Concept Check** Can the following data be represented by a circle graph? Why or why not?

Responses to the Question, "In Which Activities Are You Involved?"	
Intramural sports	60%
On-campus job	42%
Fraternity/sorority	27%
Academic clubs	21%
Music programs	14%

Objective B Drawing Circle Graphs

To draw a circle graph, we use the fact that a whole circle contains 360° (degrees).

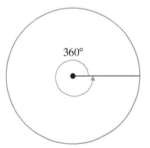

Answer

3. 17,010,000 tourists from Mexico

✓**Concept Check Answer**

no; the percents add up to more than 100%

Example 4 Drawing a Circle Graph for U.S. Armed Forces Personnel

The following table shows the percent of U.S. armed forces personnel that were in each branch of service in 2008. (*Source:* U.S. Department of Defense)

Branch of Service	Percent
Army	40
Navy	23
Marine Corps	15
Air Force	22
(Note: The Coast Guard is now under the Department of Homeland Security.)	

Draw a circle graph showing this data.

Solution: First we find the number of degrees in each sector representing each branch of service. Remember that the whole circle contains 360°. (We will round degrees to the nearest whole.)

Sector	Degrees in Each Sector
Army	$40\% \times 360° = 0.40 \times 360° = 144°$
Navy	$23\% \times 360° = 0.23 \times 360° = 82.8° \approx 83°$
Marine Corps	$15\% \times 360° = 0.15 \times 360° = 54°$
Air Force	$22\% \times 360° = 0.22 \times 360° = 79.2° \approx 79°$

Helpful Hint

Check your calculations by finding the sum of the degrees.

$$144° + 83° + 54° + 79° = 360°$$

The sum should be 360°. (It may vary only slightly because of rounding.)

Next we draw a circle and mark its center. Then we draw a line from the center of the circle to the circle itself.

To construct the sectors, we will use a **protractor.** A protractor measures the number of degrees in an angle. We place the hole in the protractor over the center of the circle. Then we adjust the protractor so that 0° on the protractor is aligned with the line that we drew.

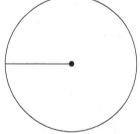

It makes no difference which sector we draw first. To construct the "Army" sector, we find 144° on the protractor and mark our circle. Then we remove the protractor and use this mark to draw a second line from the center to the circle itself.

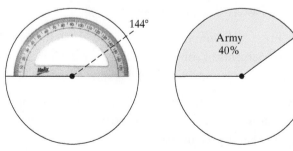

(Continued on next page)

(Continued on next page)

Practice 4

Use the data shown to draw a circle graph.

Freshmen	30%
Sophomores	27%
Juniors	25%
Seniors	18%

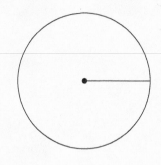

Answer

4.

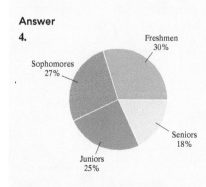

To construct the "Navy" sector, we follow the same procedure as above, except that we line up 0° with the second line we drew and mark the protractor at 83°.

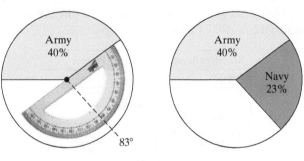

We continue in this manner until the circle graph is complete.

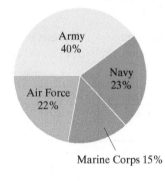

Army 40%
Navy 23%
Air Force 22%
Marine Corps 15%

■ Work Practice 4

✓ Concept Check True or false? The larger a sector in a circle graph, the larger the percent of the total it represents. Explain your answer.

Vocabulary, Readiness & Video Check

Use the choices below to fill in each blank.

sector   circle   100   360

1. In a _____ graph, each section (shaped like a piece of pie) shows a category and the relative size of the category.
2. A circle graph contains pie-shaped sections, each called a _____.
3. The number of degrees in a whole circle is _____.
4. If a circle graph has percent labels, the percents should add up to _____.

Martin-Gay Interactive Videos

See Video 8.2 🍒

See video answer section.

Watch the section lecture video and answer the following questions.

Objective A 5. From ▣ Example 3, when a circle graph shows different parts or percents of some whole category, what is the sum of the percents in the whole circle graph? ▶

Objective B 6. From ▣ Example 6, when looking at the sector degree measures of a circle graph, the whole circle graph corresponds to what degree measure? ▶

8.2 **Exercise Set** MyMathLab®

Objective **A** *The following circle graph is a result of surveying 700 college students. They were asked where they live while attending college. Use this graph to answer Exercises 1 through 6. Write all ratios as fractions in simplest form. See Example 1.*

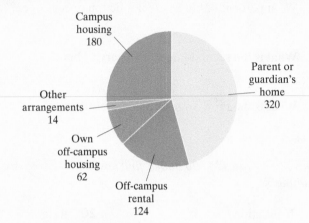

1. Where do most of these college students live?

2. Besides the category "Other arrangements," where do the fewest of these college students live?

3. Find the ratio of students living in campus housing to total students.

4. Find the ratio of students living in off-campus rentals to total students.

5. Find the ratio of students living in campus housing to students living in a parent or guardian's home.

6. Find the ratio of students living in off-campus rentals to students living in a parent or guardian's home.

The following circle graph shows the percent of the land area of the continents of Earth. Use this graph for Exercises 7 through 14. See Example 2.

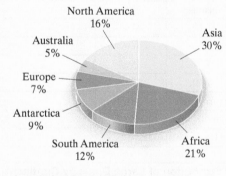

7. Which continent is the largest?

8. Which continent is the smallest?

9. What percent of the land on Earth is accounted for by Asia and Europe together?

10. What percent of the land on Earth is accounted for by North and South America?

Source: National Geographic Society

The total amount of land from the continents is approximately 57,000,000 square miles. Use the graph to find the area of the continents given in Exercises 11 through 14. See Example 3.

11. Asia   **12.** South America   **13.** Australia   **14.** Europe

The following circle graph shows the percent of the types of books available at Midway Memorial Library. Use this graph for Exercises 15 through 24. See Example 2.

15. What percent of books are classified as some type of fiction?

16. What percent of books are nonfiction or reference?

17. What is the second-largest category of books?

18. What is the third-largest category of books?

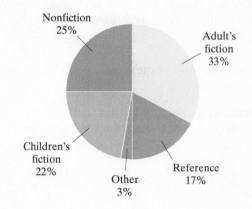

If this library has 125,600 books, find how many books are in each category given in Exercises 19 through 24. See Example 3.

19. Nonfiction

20. Reference

21. Children's fiction

22. Adult's fiction

23. Reference or other

24. Nonfiction or other

Objective B *Fill in the table. Round to the nearest degree. Then draw a circle graph to represent the information given in each table. (Remember: The total of "Degrees in Sector" column should equal 360° or very close to 360° because of rounding.) See Example 4.*

25.

Types of Apples Grown in Washington State		
Type of Apple	**Percent**	**Degrees in Sector**
Red Delicious	37%	
Golden Delicious	13%	
Fuji	14%	
Gala	15%	
Granny Smith	12%	
Other varieties	6%	
Braeburn	3%	
(*Source:* U.S. Apple Association)		

26.

Color Distribution of M&M's Milk Chocolate		
Color	**Percent**	**Degrees in Sector**
Blue	24%	
Orange	20%	
Green	16%	
Yellow	14%	
Red	13%	
Brown	13%	
(*Source:* M&M Mars)		

27.

Distribution of Large Dams by Continent		
Continent	**Percent**	**Degrees in Sector**
Europe	19%	
North America	32%	
South America	3%	
Asia	39%	
Africa	5%	
Australia	2%	
(*Source:* International Commission on Large Dams)		

28.

2010 Hybrid Sales by Make of Car		
Company	**Percent**	**Degrees in Sector**
Toyota	69%	
Ford	13%	
Honda	12%	
GM	3%	
Nissan	2%	
Other	1%	
(*Source:* U.S. Department of Energy, 2010 Data)		

Review

Write the prime factorization of each number.

29. 20

30. 25

31. 40

32. 16

33. 85

34. 105

Concept Extensions

The following circle graph shows the relative sizes of the great oceans.

35. Without calculating, determine which ocean is the largest. How can you answer this question by looking at the circle graph?

36. Without calculating, determine which ocean is the smallest. How can you answer this question by looking at the circle graph?

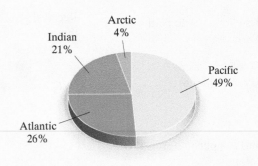

Source: Philip's World Atlas

These oceans together make up 264,489,800 square kilometers of Earth's surface. Find the square kilometers for each ocean.

37. Pacific Ocean   **38.** Atlantic Ocean   **39.** Indian Ocean   **40.** Arctic Ocean

The following circle graph summarizes the results of online spending in America. Let's use these results to make predictions about the online spending behavior of a community of 2800 Internet users age 18 and over. Use this graph for Exercises 41 through 46. Round to the nearest whole. (Note: Because of rounding, these percents do not have a sum of 100%.)

41. How many of the survey respondents said that they spend $0 online each month?

42. How many of the survey repondents said that they spend $1–$100 online each month?

43. How many of the survey respondents said that they spend $0 to $100 online each month?

44. How many of the survey respondents said that they spend $1 to $1000 online each month?

Online Spending per Month

Source: The Digital Future Report, 2013

45. Find the ratio of *number* of respondents who spend $0 online to *number* of respondents who spend $1–$100 online. Write the ratio as a fraction. Simplify the fraction if possible.

46. Find the ratio of *percent* of respondents who spend $101–$1000 online to *percent* of those who spend $1–$100. Write the ratio as a fraction with integers in the numerator and denominator. Simplify the fraction if possible.

See the Concept Checks in this section.

47. Can the data below be represented by a circle graph? Why or why not?

Responses to the Question, "What Classes Are You Taking?"	
Math	80%
English	72%
History	37%
Biology	21%
Chemistry	14%

48. True or false? The smaller a sector in a circle graph, the smaller the percent of the total it represents. Explain why.

Objectives

A Use Formulas to Find Perimeters. ▷

B Use Formulas to Find Circumferences. ▷

Objective A Using Formulas to Find Perimeters ▷

Recall that the perimeter of a polygon is the distance around the polygon. This means that the perimeter of a polygon is the sum of the lengths of its sides.

Example 1 Find the perimeter of the rectangle below.

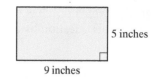

5 inches

9 inches

Solution:

perimeter = 9 inches + 9 inches + 5 inches + 5 inches

= 28 inches

■ Work Practice 1

Practice 1

a. Find the perimeter of the rectangle.

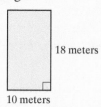

18 meters

10 meters

b. Find the perimeter of the rectangular lot shown below:

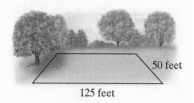

50 feet

125 feet

Notice that the perimeter of the rectangle in Example 1 can be written as $2 \cdot (9 \text{ inches}) + 2 \cdot (5 \text{ inches})$.

↑ length   ↑ width

In general, we can say that the perimeter of a rectangle is always

$2 \cdot \text{length} + 2 \cdot \text{width}$

As we have just seen, the perimeters of some special figures such as rectangles form patterns. These patterns are given as **formulas.** The formula for the perimeter of a rectangle is shown next:

Perimeter of a Rectangle

Perimeter = 2 · length + 2 · width

In symbols, this can be written as

$P = 2l + 2w$

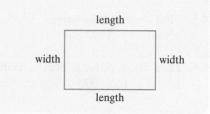

length

width   width

length

Practice 2

Find the perimeter of a rectangle with a length of 32 centimeters and a width of 15 centimeters.

Example 2 Find the perimeter of a rectangle with a length of 11 inches and a width of 3 inches.

11 in.

3 in.

Solution: We use the formula for perimeter and replace the letters by their known lengths.

$P = 2l + 2w$

$= 2 \cdot 11 \text{ in.} + 2 \cdot 3 \text{ in.}$ Replace *l* with 11 in. and *w* with 3 in.

$= 22 \text{ in.} + 6 \text{ in.}$

$= 28 \text{ in.}$

The perimeter is 28 inches.

■ Work Practice 2

Answers

1. a. 56 m   **b.** 350 ft   **2.** 94 cm

Recall that a square is a special rectangle with all four sides the same length. The formula for the perimeter of a square is shown next:

Perimeter of a Square

$$\mathbf{P}\text{erimeter} = \text{side} + \text{side} + \text{side} + \text{side}$$
$$= 4 \cdot \text{side}$$

In symbols,

$$P = 4s$$

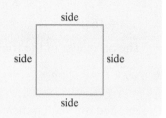

Example 3 Finding the Perimeter of a Field

How much fencing is needed to enclose a square field 50 yards on a side?

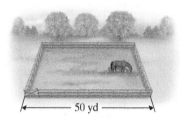

50 yd

Solution: To find the amount of fencing needed, we find the distance around, or perimeter. The formula for the perimeter of a square is $P = 4s$. We use this formula and replace s by 50 yards.

$$P = 4s$$
$$= 4 \cdot 50 \text{ yd}$$
$$= 200 \text{ yd}$$

The amount of fencing needed is 200 yards.

■ Work Practice 3

The formula for the perimeter of a triangle with sides of lengths a, b, and c is given next:

Perimeter of a Triangle

$$\mathbf{P}\text{erimeter} = \text{side } \mathbf{a} + \text{side } \mathbf{b} + \text{side } \mathbf{c}$$

In symbols,

$$P = a + b + c$$

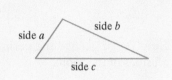

side a side b

side c

Example 4 Find the perimeter of a triangle if the sides are 3 inches, 7 inches, and 6 inches.

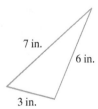

7 in.

6 in.

3 in.

(*Continued on next page*)

Practice 3

Find the perimeter of a square tabletop if each side is 4 feet long.

4 feet

4 feet

Practice 4

Find the perimeter of a triangle if the sides are 6 centimeters, 10 centimeters, and 8 centimeters in length.

Answers

3. 16 ft   **4.** 24 cm

Solution: The formula for the perimeter is $P = a + b + c$, where a, b, and c are the lengths of the sides. Thus,

$$P = a + b + c$$
$$= 3 \text{ in.} + 7 \text{ in.} + 6 \text{ in.}$$
$$= 16 \text{ in.}$$

The perimeter of the triangle is 16 inches.

▶ Work Practice 4

The method for finding the perimeter of any polygon is given next:

Perimeter of a Polygon

The perimeter of a polygon is the sum of the lengths of its sides.

Practice 5

Find the perimeter of the trapezoid shown.

6 km
4 km   4 km
9 km

Example 5

Find the perimeter of the trapezoid shown below:

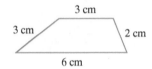

3 cm
3 cm   2 cm
6 cm

Solution: To find the perimeter, we find the sum of the lengths of its sides.

$$\text{perimeter} = 3 \text{ cm} + 2 \text{ cm} + 6 \text{ cm} + 3 \text{ cm} = 14 \text{ cm}$$

The perimeter is 14 centimeters.

▶ Work Practice 5

Practice 6

Find the perimeter of the room shown.

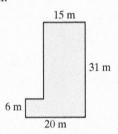

15 m
31 m
6 m
20 m

Example 6 Finding the Perimeter of a Room

Find the perimeter of the room shown below:

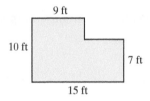

9 ft
10 ft
7 ft
15 ft

Solution: To find the perimeter of the room, we first need to find the lengths of all sides of the room.

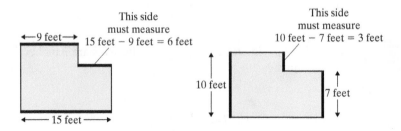

This side must measure
9 feet
15 feet − 9 feet = 6 feet

This side must measure
10 feet − 7 feet = 3 feet

10 feet

15 feet

7 feet

Now that we know the measures of all sides of the room, we can add the measures to find the perimeter.

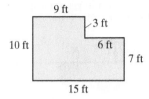

9 ft
3 ft
10 ft
6 ft
7 ft
15 ft

perimeter = 10 ft + 9 ft + 3 ft + 6 ft + 7 ft + 15 ft
= 50 ft

The perimeter of the room is 50 feet.

🟦 Work Practice 6

Example 7   Calculating the Cost of Wallpaper Border

A rectangular room measures 10 feet by 12 feet. Find the cost to hang a wallpaper border on the walls close to the ceiling if the cost of the wallpaper border is $1.09 per foot.

Solution: First we find the perimeter of the room.

$P = 2l + 2w$
$= 2 \cdot 12$ ft $+ 2 \cdot 10$ ft   Replace l with 12 feet and w with 10 feet.
$= 24$ ft $+ 20$ ft
$= 44$ ft

The cost of the wallpaper is

cost $= \$1.09 \cdot 44$ ft $= 47.96$

The cost of the wallpaper is $47.96.

🟦 Work Practice 7

Practice 7

A rectangular lot measures 60 feet by 120 feet. Find the cost to install fencing around the lot if the cost of fencing is $1.90 per foot.

Objective B Using Formulas to Find Circumferences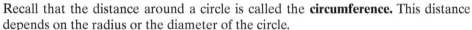

Recall that the distance around a circle is called the **circumference.** This distance depends on the radius or the diameter of the circle.

The formulas for circumference are shown next:

Circumference of a Circle

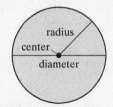

radius
center
diameter

Circumference $= 2 \cdot \pi \cdot$ **r**adius or Circumference $= \pi \cdot$ **d**iameter

In symbols,

$C = 2\pi r$ or $C = \pi d$

where $\pi \approx 3.14$ or $\pi \approx \dfrac{22}{7}$.

Answer

7. $684

To better understand circumference and π (pi), try the following experiment. Take any can and measure its circumference and its diameter.

The can in the figure above has a circumference of 23.5 centimeters and a diameter of 7.5 centimeters. Now divide the circumference by the diameter.

$$\frac{\text{circumference}}{\text{diameter}} = \frac{23.5 \text{ cm}}{7.5 \text{ cm}} \approx 3.13$$

Try this with other sizes of cylinders and circles—you should always get a number close to 3.1. The exact ratio of circumference to diameter is π. (Recall that $\pi \approx 3.14$ or $\approx \frac{22}{7}$.)

Practice 8

An irrigation device waters a circular region with a diameter of 20 yards. Find the exact circumference of the watered region, then use $\pi \approx 3.14$ to give an approximation.

Example 8 Finding Circumference of a Circular Spa

A homeowner plans to install a border of new tiling around the circumference of her circular spa. If her spa has a diameter of 14 feet, find its exact circumference. Then use the approximation 3.14 for π to approximate the circumference.

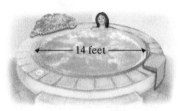

Solution: Because we are given the diameter, we use the formula $C = \pi d$.

$C = \pi d$

$\quad = \pi \cdot 14 \text{ ft}$ Replace d with 14 feet.

$\quad = 14\pi \text{ ft}$

The circumference of the spa is *exactly* 14π feet. By replacing π with the *approximation* 3.14, we find that the circumference is *approximately* 14 feet $\cdot$ 3.14 = 43.96 feet.

▩ Work Practice 8

Answer

8. exactly 20π yd ≈ 62.8 yd

✓ **Concept Check Answer**

a square with side length 5 in.

✓**Concept Check** The distance around which figure is greater: a square with side length 5 inches or a circle with radius 3 inches?

Vocabulary, Readiness & Video Check

Use the choices below to fill in each blank.

circumference	radius	π	$\dfrac{22}{7}$
diameter	perimeter	3.14	

1. The _____ of a polygon is the sum of the lengths of its sides.

2. The distance around a circle is called the _____.

3. The exact ratio of circumference to diameter is _____.

4. The diameter of a circle is double its _____.

5. Both _____ and _____ are approximations for π.

6. The radius of a circle is half its _____.

Martin-Gay Interactive Videos Watch the section lecture video and answer the following questions.

Objective A 7. In ⊟ Example 1, how can the perimeter be found if we forget the formula? ▶

Objective B 8. From the lecture before ⊟ Example 6, circumference is a special name for what? ▶

See Video 9.2

See video answer section.

9.2 Exercise Set MyMathLab® ▶

Objective A *Find the perimeter of each figure. (See Appendix A.1 for any unknown geometric figures.) See Examples 1 through 6.*

▶ 1.
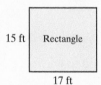
15 ft Rectangle
17 ft

2.
Rectangle 14 m
5 m

3.

Parallelogram 25 cm
35 cm

4.
Parallelogram
3 yd
2 yd

▶ 5.
5 in. 7 in.
9 in.

6.
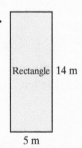
5 units 11 units
10 units

▶ 7.
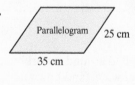
10 ft 8 ft
7 ft 8 ft
15 ft

8.
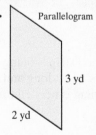
10 m 4 m
10 m
13 m
9 m
20 m

Find the perimeter of each regular polygon. (The sides of a regular polygon have the same length.)

9. 14 inches

10. 50 m

11. 31 cm

12. 15 yd

Solve. See Examples 1 through 7.

13. A polygon has sides of length 5 feet, 3 feet, 2 feet, 7 feet, and 4 feet. Find its perimeter.

14. A triangle has sides of length 8 inches, 12 inches, and 10 inches. Find its perimeter.

15. A line-marking machine lays down lime powder to mark both foul lines on a baseball field. If each foul line for this field measures 312 feet, how many feet of lime powder will be deposited?

16. A baseball diamond has 4 sides, with each side length 90 feet. If a baseball player hits a home run, how far does the player run (home plate, around the bases, then back to home plate)?

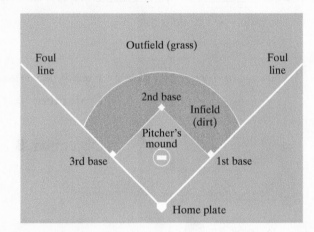

17. If a football field is 53 yards wide and 120 yards long, what is the perimeter?

18. A stop sign has eight equal sides of length 12 inches. Find its perimeter.

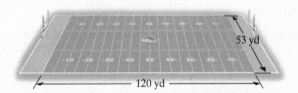

19. A metal strip is being installed around a workbench that is 8 feet long and 3 feet wide. Find how much stripping is needed for this project.

20. Find how much fencing is needed to enclose a rectangular garden 70 feet by 21 feet.

21. If the stripping in Exercise **19** costs $2.50 per foot, find the total cost of the stripping.

22. If the fencing in Exercise **20** costs $2 per foot, find the total cost of the fencing.

23. A regular octagon has a side length of 9 inches.
    a. How many sides does an octagon have?
    b. Find its perimeter.

24. A regular pentagon has a side length of 14 meters.
    a. How many sides does a pentagon have?
    b. Find its perimeter.

25. Find the perimeter of the top of a square compact disc case if the length of one side is 7 inches.

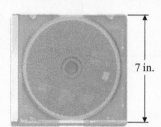

7 in.

26. Find the perimeter of a square ceramic tile with a side of length 3 inches.

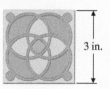

3 in.

27. A rectangular room measures 10 feet by 11 feet. Find the cost of installing a strip of wallpaper around the room if the wallpaper costs $0.86 per foot.

28. A rectangular house measures 85 feet by 70 feet. Find the cost of installing gutters around the house if the cost is $2.36 per foot.

Find the perimeter of each figure. See Example 6.

29.

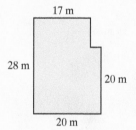

17 m
28 m
20 m
20 m

30.

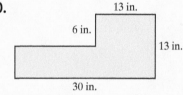

13 in.
6 in.
13 in.
30 in.

31.

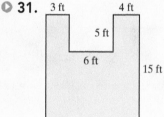

3 ft   4 ft
5 ft
6 ft
15 ft

32.

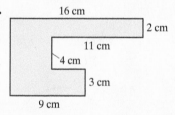

16 cm
2 cm
11 cm
4 cm
3 cm
9 cm

33.

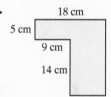

18 cm
5 cm
9 cm
14 cm

34.

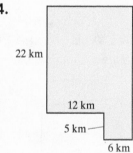

22 km
12 km
5 km
6 km

Objective B *Find the circumference of each circle. Give the exact circumference and then an approximation. Use π ≈ 3.14. See Example 8.*

35.

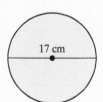

17 cm

36.

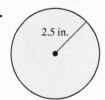

2.5 in.

37.

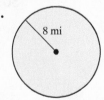

8 mi

38.

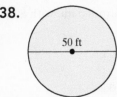

50 ft

39.

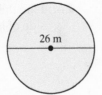

26 m

40.

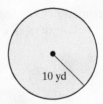

10 yd

41. Wyley Robinson just bought a trampoline for his children to use. The trampoline has a diameter of 15 feet. If Wyley wishes to buy netting to go around the outside of the trampoline, how many feet of netting does he need?

42. The largest round barn in the world is located at the Marshfield Fairgrounds in Wisconsin. The barn has a diameter of 150 ft. What is the circumference of the barn? (*Source: The Milwaukee Journal Sentinel*)

43. Meteor Crater, near Winslow, Arizona, is 4000 feet in diameter. Approximate the distance around the crater. Use 3.14 for π. (*Source: The Handy Science Answer Book*)

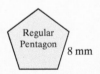

44. The *Pearl of Lao-tze* has a diameter of $5\frac{1}{2}$ inches. Approximate the distance around the pearl. Use $\frac{22}{7}$ for π. (*Source: The Guinness World Records*)

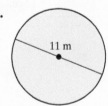

$5\frac{1}{2}$ in.

Objectives A B Mixed Practice *Find the distance around each figure. For circles, give the exact circumference and then an approximation. Use $\pi \approx 3.14$. See Examples 1 through 8.*

45.

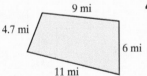

9 mi
4.7 mi
6 mi
11 mi

46.

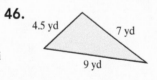

4.5 yd
7 yd
9 yd

47.

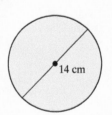

14 cm

48.

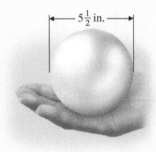

11 m

49.

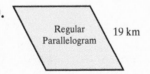

Regular Pentagon
8 mm

50.

Regular Parallelogram
19 km

51.

7 ft
8 ft
22 ft
20 ft

52.

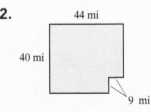

44 mi
40 mi
9 mi

Review

Simplify.

53. $5 + 6 \cdot 3$

54. $25 - 3 \cdot 7$

55. $(20 - 16) \div 4$

56. $6 \cdot (8 + 2)$

57. $72 \div (2 \cdot 6)$

58. $(72 \div 2) \cdot 6$

59. $(18 + 8) - (12 + 4)$

60. $4^1 \cdot (2^3 - 8)$

Concept Extensions

There are a number of factors that determine the dimensions of a rectangular soccer field. Use the table below to answer Exercises 61 and 62.

Soccer Field Width and Length		
Age	**Width Min–Max**	**Length Min–Max**
Under 6/7:	15–20 yards	25–30 yards
Under 8:	20–25 yards	30–40 yards
Under 9:	30–35 yards	40–50 yards
Under 10:	40–50 yards	60–70 yards
Under 11:	40–50 yards	70–80 yards
Under 12:	40–55 yards	100–105 yards
Under 13:	50–60 yards	100–110 yards
International:	70–80 yards	110–120 yards

61. a. Find the minimum length and width of a soccer field for 8-year-old children. (Carefully consider the age.)

 b. Find the perimeter of this field.

62. a. Find the maximum length and width of a soccer field for 12-year-old children.

 b. Find the perimeter of this field.

Solve. See the Concept Check in this section. Choose the figure that has the greater distance around.

63. a. A square with side length 3 inches

 b. A circle with diameter 4 inches

64. a. A circle with diameter 7 inches

 b. A square with side length 7 inches

65. a. Find the circumference of each circle. Approximate the circumference by using 3.14 for π.

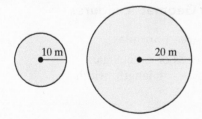

 b. If the radius of a circle is doubled, is its corresponding circumference doubled?

66. a. Find the circumference of each circle. Approximate the circumference by using 3.14 for π.

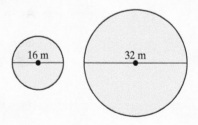

 b. If the diameter of a circle is doubled, is its corresponding circumference doubled?

67. In your own words, explain how to find the perimeter of any polygon.

68. In your own words, explain how perimeter and circumference are the same and how they are different.

Find the perimeter. Round your results to the nearest tenth.

69.

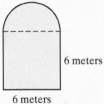

6 meters

6 meters

70.

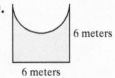

6 meters

6 meters

71.

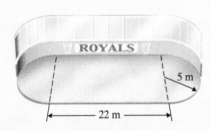

ROYALS

5 m

22 m

72.

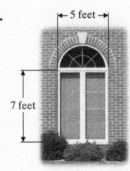

5 feet

7 feet

9.3 **Area, Volume, and Surface Area**

Objectives

A Find the Area of Plane Regions.

B Find the Volume and Surface Area of Solids.

Objective A Finding Area of Plane Regions

Recall that area measures the number of square units that cover the surface of a plane region; that is, a region that lies in a plane. Thus far, we know how to find the areas of a rectangle and a square. These formulas, as well as formulas for finding the areas of other common geometric figures, are given next.

Area Formulas of Common Geometric Figures

Geometric Figure	Area Formula
RECTANGLE	Area of a rectangle: **Area = length · width** $A = lw$
width / length	
SQUARE	Area of a square: **Area = side · side** $A = s \cdot s = s^2$
side / side	

Geometric Figure	Area Formula
TRIANGLE 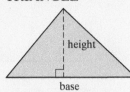	Area of a triangle: $\mathbf{Area} = \dfrac{1}{2} \cdot \mathbf{base} \cdot \mathbf{height}$ $A = \dfrac{1}{2}bh$
PARALLELOGRAM 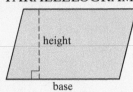	Area of a parallelogram: $\mathbf{Area} = \mathbf{base} \cdot \mathbf{height}$ $A = bh$
TRAPEZOID 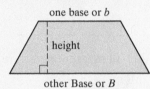	Area of a trapezoid: $\mathbf{Area} = \dfrac{1}{2} \cdot (\text{one } \mathbf{base} + \text{other } \mathbf{Base}) \cdot \mathbf{height}$ $A = \dfrac{1}{2}(b + B)h$

Use these formulas for the following examples.

Helpful Hint

Area is always measured in square units.

Example 1 Find the area of the triangle.

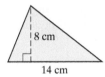

8 cm

14 cm

Solution:

$A = \dfrac{1}{2}bh$

$= \dfrac{1}{2} \cdot 14 \text{ cm} \cdot 8 \text{ cm}$ Replace b, base, with 14 cm and h, height, with 8 cm.

$= \dfrac{\overset{1}{2} \cdot 7 \cdot 8}{\underset{1}{2}}$ square centimeters   Write 14 as $2 \cdot 7$.

$= 56$ square centimeters

The area is 56 square centimeters.

Work Practice 1

Practice 1

Find the area of the triangle.

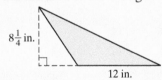

$8\dfrac{1}{4}$ in.

12 in.

Answer

1. $49\dfrac{1}{2}$ sq in.

Practice 2

Find the area of the trapezoid.

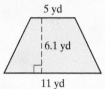

Example 2   Find the area of the parallelogram.

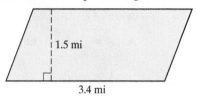

Solution:

$$A = bh$$
$$= 3.4 \text{ miles} \cdot 1.5 \text{ miles}$$ Replace b, base, with 3.4 miles and h, height, with 1.5 miles.
$$= 5.1 \text{ square miles}$$

The area is 5.1 square miles.

▪ **Work Practice 2**

Helpful Hint

When finding the area of figures, check to make sure that all measurements are in the same units before calculations are made.

Practice 3

Find the area of the figure.

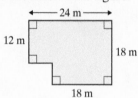

Example 3   Find the area of the figure.

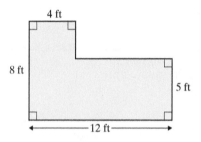

Solution: Split the figure into two rectangles. To find the area of the figure, we find the sum of the areas of the two rectangles.

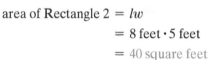

area of Rectangle 1 $= lw$
$$= 8 \text{ feet} \cdot 4 \text{ feet}$$
$$= 32 \text{ square feet}$$

Notice that the length of Rectangle 2 is 12 feet − 4 feet or 8 feet.

area of Rectangle 2 $= lw$
$$= 8 \text{ feet} \cdot 5 \text{ feet}$$
$$= 40 \text{ square feet}$$

area of the figure $=$ area of Rectangle 1 $+$ area of Rectangle 2
$$= 32 \text{ square feet} + 40 \text{ square feet}$$
$$= 72 \text{ square feet}$$

▪ **Work Practice 3**

Answers

2. 48.8 sq yd   **3.** 396 sq m

Helpful Hint

The figure in Example 3 could also be split into two rectangles as shown.

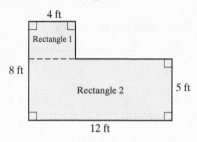

To better understand the formula for area of a circle, try the following. Cut a circle into many pieces, as shown.

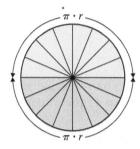

The circumference of a circle is $2\pi r$. This means that the circumference of half a circle is half of $2\pi r$, or πr.

Then unfold the two halves of the circle and place them together, as shown.

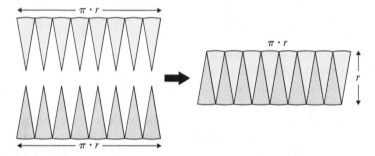

The figure on the right is almost a parallelogram with a base of πr and a height of r. The area is

$$A = \text{base} \cdot \text{height}$$
$$= (\pi r) \cdot r$$
$$= \pi r^2$$

This is the formula for the area of a circle.

Area Formula of a Circle

Circle

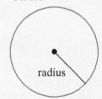

Area of a circle

Area $= \pi \cdot (\text{radius})^2$

$A = \pi r^2$

(A fraction approximation for π is $\dfrac{22}{7}$.)

(A decimal approximation for π is 3.14.)

Practice 4

Find the area of the given circle. Find the exact area and an approximation. Use 3.14 as an approximation for π.

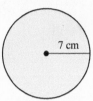

7 cm

Example 4 Find the area of a circle with a radius of 3 feet. Find the exact area and an approximation. Use 3.14 as an approximation for π.

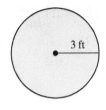

3 ft

Solution: We let $r = 3$ feet and use the formula

$$A = \pi r^2$$
$$= \pi \cdot (3 \text{ feet})^2 \qquad \text{Replace } r \text{ with 3 feet.}$$
$$= 9 \cdot \pi \text{ square feet} \qquad \text{Replace } (3 \text{ feet})^2 \text{ with 9 sq ft.}$$

To approximate this area, we substitute 3.14 for π.

$$9 \cdot \pi \text{ square feet} \approx 9 \cdot 3.14 \text{ square feet}$$
$$= 28.26 \text{ square feet}$$

The *exact* area of the circle is 9π square feet, which is *approximately* 28.26 square feet.

■ Work Practice 4

✔**Concept Check** Use estimation to decide which figure would have a larger area: a circle of diameter 10 in. or a square 10 in. long on each side.

Objective B Finding Volume and Surface Area of Solids

A **convex solid** is a set of points, S, not all in one plane, such that for any two points A and B in S, all points between A and B are also in S. In this section, we will find the volume and surface area of special types of solids called polyhedrons. A solid formed by the intersection of a finite number of planes is called a **polyhedron.** The box to the right is an example of a polyhedron.

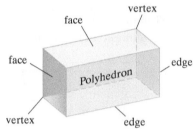

face   vertex

face

Polyhedron   edge

vertex   edge

   Each of the plane regions of a polyhedron is called a **face** of the polyhedron. If the intersection of two faces is a line segment, this line segment is an **edge** of the polyhedron. The intersections of the edges are the **vertices** of the polyhedron.

   Volume is a measure of the space of a region. The volume of a box or can, for example, is the amount of space inside. Volume can be used to describe the amount of juice in a pitcher or the amount of concrete needed to pour a foundation for a house.

   The volume of a solid is the number of **cubic units** in the solid. A cubic centimeter and a cubic inch are illustrated.

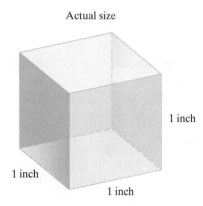

Actual size

Actual size

1 cm

1 cm   1 cm

1 cubic centimeter

1 inch

1 inch

1 inch   1 inch

1 cubic inch

Answer

4. 49π sq cm ≈ 153.86 sq cm

✔**Concept Check Answer**

A square 10 in. long on each side would have a larger area.

The **surface area** of a polyhedron is the sum of the areas of the faces of the polyhedron. For example, each face of the cube to the left on the previous page has an area of 1 square centimeter. Since there are 6 faces of the cube, the sum of the areas of the faces is 6 square centimeters. Surface area can be used to describe the amount of material needed to cover a solid. Surface area is measured in square units.

Formulas for finding the volumes, V, and surface areas, SA, of some common solids are given next. (Note: Spheres, circular cylinders, and cones are not polyhedrons, but they are solids and we will calculate surface areas and volumes of these solids.)

Volume and Surface Area Formulas of Common Solids	
Solid	**Formulas**
RECTANGULAR SOLID height width length	$V = lwh$ $SA = 2lh + 2wh + 2lw$ where h = height, w = width, l = length
CUBE side side side	$V = s^3$ $SA = 6s^2$ where s = side
SPHERE radius	$V = \dfrac{4}{3}\pi r^3$ $SA = 4\pi r^2$ where r = radius
CIRCULAR CYLINDER height radius	$V = \pi r^2 h$ $SA = 2\pi rh + 2\pi r^2$ where h = height, r = radius
CONE height radius	$V = \dfrac{1}{3}\pi r^2 h$ $SA = \pi r\sqrt{r^2 + h^2} + \pi r^2$ where h = height, r = radius
SQUARE-BASED PYRAMID slant height height side	$V = \dfrac{1}{3}s^2 h$ $SA = B + \dfrac{1}{2}pl$ where B = area of base, p = perimeter of base, h = height, s = side, l = slant height

Practice 5

Find the volume and surface area of a rectangular box that is 7 feet long, 3 feet wide, and 4 feet high.

Example 5 Find the volume and surface area of a rectangular box that is 12 inches long, 6 inches wide, and 3 inches high.

3 in.

6 in.   12 in.

Solution: Let $h = 3$ in., $l = 12$ in., and $w = 6$ in.

$$V = lwh$$
$$V = 12 \text{ inches} \cdot 6 \text{ inches} \cdot 3 \text{ inches} = 216 \text{ cubic inches}$$

The volume of the rectangular box is 216 cubic inches.

$$SA = 2lh + 2wh + 2lw$$
$$= 2(12 \text{ in.})(3 \text{ in.}) + 2(6 \text{ in.})(3 \text{ in.}) + 2(12 \text{ in.})(6 \text{ in.})$$
$$= 72 \text{ sq in.} + 36 \text{ sq in.} + 144 \text{ sq in.}$$
$$= 252 \text{ sq in.}$$

The surface area of the rectangular box is 252 square inches.

■ Work Practice 5

✓**Concept Check** Juan is calculating the volume of the following rectangular solid. Find the error in his calculation.

$$\text{Volume} = l + w + h$$
$$= 14 \text{ cm} + 8 \text{ cm} + 5 \text{ cm}$$
$$= 27 \text{ cu cm}$$

5 cm

8 cm   14 cm

Practice 6

Find the volume and surface area of a ball of radius $\frac{1}{2}$ centimeter. Give the exact volume and surface area. Then use $\frac{22}{7}$ for π and approximate the values.

Example 6 Find the volume and surface area of a ball of radius 2 inches. Give the exact volume and surface area. Then use the approximation $\frac{22}{7}$ for π.

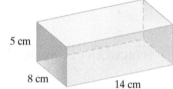

2 in.

Solution:

$$V = \frac{4}{3}\pi r^3 \qquad \text{Formula for volume of a sphere}$$

$$V = \frac{4}{3} \cdot \pi (2 \text{ in.})^3 \qquad \text{Let } r = 2 \text{ inches.}$$

$$= \frac{32}{3}\pi \text{ cu in.} \qquad \text{Exact volume}$$

$$\approx \frac{32}{3} \cdot \frac{22}{7} \text{ cu in.} \qquad \text{Approximate } \pi \text{ with } \frac{22}{7}.$$

$$= \frac{704}{21} \text{ or } 33\frac{11}{21} \text{ cu in.} \qquad \text{Approximate volume}$$

Answers

5. $V = 84$ cu ft; $SA = 122$ sq ft

6. $V = \frac{1}{6}\pi$ cu cm $\approx \frac{11}{21}$ cu cm;

$SA = \pi$ sq cm $\approx 3\frac{1}{7}$ sq cm

✓ **Concept Check Answer**

Volume $= lwh$

$= 14 \text{ cm} \cdot 8 \text{ cm} \cdot 5 \text{ cm}$

$= 560$ cu cm

The volume of the sphere is exactly $\frac{32}{3}\pi$ cubic inches or approximately $33\frac{11}{21}$ cubic inches.

$$SA = 4\pi r^2 \qquad \text{Formula for surface area}$$
$$SA = 4 \cdot \pi (2\,\text{in.})^2 \qquad \text{Let } r = 2 \text{ inches.}$$
$$= 16\pi \text{ sq in.} \qquad \text{Exact surface area}$$
$$\approx 16 \cdot \frac{22}{7} \text{ sq in.} \qquad \text{Approximate } \pi \text{ with } \frac{22}{7}.$$
$$= \frac{352}{7} \text{ or } 50\frac{2}{7} \text{ sq in.} \qquad \text{Approximate surface area}$$

The surface area of the sphere is exactly 16π square inches or approximately $50\frac{2}{7}$ square inches.

■ Work Practice 6

Example 7 Find the volume of a can that has a $3\frac{1}{2}$-inch radius and a height of 6 inches. Give an exact volume and an approximate volume. Use $\frac{22}{7}$ for π.

$3\frac{1}{2}$ in.

6 in.

Practice 7

Find the volume of a cylinder of radius 5 inches and height 9 inches. Give an exact answer and an approximate answer. Use 3.14 for π.

Solution: Using the formula for a circular cylinder, we have

$$V = \pi \cdot r^2 \cdot h \qquad 3\frac{1}{2} = \frac{7}{2}$$

$$= \pi \cdot \left(\frac{7}{2}\,\text{in.}\right)^2 \cdot 6\,\text{in.}$$

$$= \pi \cdot \frac{49}{4} \text{ sq in.} \cdot 6\,\text{in.}$$

$$= \frac{\pi \cdot 49 \cdot \overset{1}{2} \cdot 3}{\underset{1}{2} \cdot 2} \text{ cu in.}$$

$$= 73\frac{1}{2}\pi \text{ cu in. or } 73.5\pi \text{ cu in.}$$

This is the exact volume. To approximate the volume, use the approximation $\frac{22}{7}$ for π.

$$V = 73\frac{1}{2}\pi \text{ or } \frac{147}{2} \cdot \frac{22}{7} \text{ cu in.} \qquad \text{Replace } \pi \text{ with } \frac{22}{7}.$$

$$= \frac{21 \cdot \overset{1}{7} \cdot \overset{1}{2} \cdot 11}{\underset{1}{2} \cdot \underset{1}{7}} \text{ cu in.}$$

$$= 231 \text{ cu in.}$$

The volume is approximately 231 cubic inches.

■ Work Practice 7

Answer

7. 225π cu in. ≈ 706.5 cu in.

Practice 8

Find the volume of a square-based pyramid that has a 3-meter side and a height of 5.1 meters.

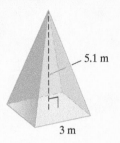

5.1 m

3 m

Example 8   Find the volume of a cone that has a height of 14 centimeters and a radius of 3 centimeters. Give an exact answer and an approximate answer. Use 3.14 for π.

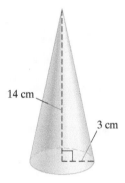

14 cm

3 cm

Solution: Using the formula for volume of a cone, we have

$$V = \frac{1}{3} \cdot \pi \cdot r^2 \cdot h$$

$$= \frac{1}{3} \cdot \pi \cdot (3 \text{ cm})^2 \cdot 14 \text{ cm} \quad \text{Replace } r \text{ with 3 cm and } h \text{ with 14 cm.}$$

$$= 42\pi \text{ cu cm}$$

Thus, 42π cubic centimeters is the exact volume. To approximate the volume, use the approximation 3.14 for π.

$$V \approx 42 \cdot 3.14 \text{ cu cm} \quad \text{Replace } \pi \text{ with 3.14.}$$

$$= 131.88 \text{ cu cm}$$

The volume is approximately 131.88 cubic centimeters.

Answer

8. 15.3 cu m

■ Work Practice 8

Vocabulary, Readiness & Video Check

Use the choices below to fill in each blank. Some choices may be used more than once.

area   surface area   cubic

volume   square

1. The _____ of a polyhedron is the sum of the areas of its faces.

2. The measure of the amount of space inside a solid is its _____.

3. _____ measures the amount of surface enclosed by a region.

4. Volume is measured in_____ units.

5. Area is measured in _____ units.

6. Surface area is measured in _____ units.

Martin-Gay Interactive Videos   Watch the section lecture video and answer the following questions.

Objective A 7. Explain why we need to use a formula twice to solve ⊞ Example 3. ▶

Objective B 8. In ⊞ Examples 7 and 8, explain the difference in the two volume answers found for each. ▶

See Video 9.3 🫐

See video answer section.

9.3 **Exercise Set** MyMathLab® ▶

Objective A *Find the area of each geometric figure. If the figure is a circle, give an exact area and then use the given approximation for π to approximate the area. See Examples 1 through 4.*

1.

2 m | Rectangle
3.5 m

2.

1.2 ft | Rectangle
3.5 ft

3.

3 yd
$6\frac{1}{2}$ yd

4.

5 ft
$4\frac{1}{2}$ ft

5.

6 yd
5 yd

6.

5 ft   7 ft

7. Use 3.14 for π.

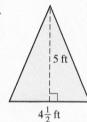

d = 3 in.

8. Use $\frac{22}{7}$ for π.

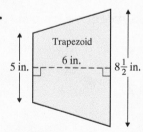

r = 5 cm

9.

Parallelogram
5.25 ft
7 ft

10.

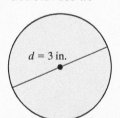

Parallelogram
4.25 cm
3 cm

11.

5 m
Trapezoid
4 m
9 m

12.

Trapezoid
5 in.   6 in. $8\frac{1}{2}$ in.

13.

4 yd
4 yd | Trapezoid
7 yd

14.

10 ft
3 ft | Trapezoid
5 ft

15.

7 ft
Parallelogram
$5\frac{1}{4}$ ft

16.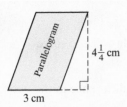

$4\frac{1}{4}$ cm

3 cm

17.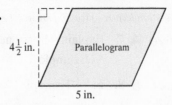

$4\frac{1}{2}$ in.

Parallelogram

5 in.

18.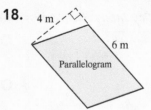

4 m

6 m

Parallelogram

19.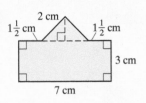

2 cm

$1\frac{1}{2}$ cm $1\frac{1}{2}$ cm

3 cm

7 cm

20.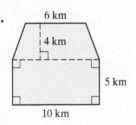

6 km

4 km

5 km

10 km

21.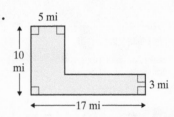

5 mi

10 mi

3 mi

17 mi

22.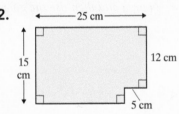

25 cm

15 cm

12 cm

5 cm

23.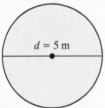

5 cm

3 cm

24.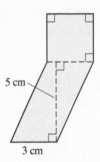

4 in.

5 in.

25. Use $\frac{22}{7}$ for π.

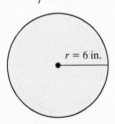

r = 6 in.

26. Use 3.14 for π.

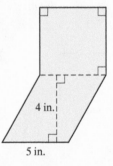

d = 5 m

Objective B *Find the volume and surface area of each solid. See Examples 5 through 8. For formulas containing π, give an exact answer and then approximate using $\frac{22}{7}$ for π.*

27.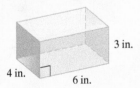

3 in.

4 in.   6 in.

28.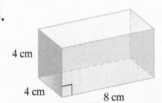

4 cm

4 cm   8 cm

29.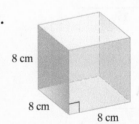

8 cm

8 cm

8 cm   8 cm

30.

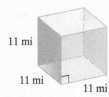

11 mi

11 mi   11 mi

31. For surface area, use $\pi = 3.14$ and round to the nearest hundredth.

3 yd

2 yd

32. For surface area, use $\pi = 3.14$ and round to the nearest hundredth.

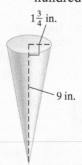

$1\frac{3}{4}$ in.

9 in.

▶ **33.**

10 in.

34.

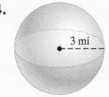

3 mi

▶ **35.** Find the volume only.

2 in.

9 in.

36. Find the volume only.

10 ft

6 ft

37. Find the volume only.

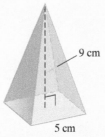

9 cm

5 cm

38. Find the volume only.

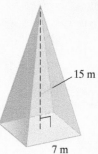

15 m

7 m

Objectives A B Mixed Practice *Solve. See Examples 1 through 8.*

39. Find the volume of a cube with edges of $1\frac{1}{3}$ inches.

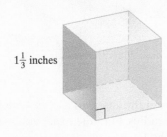

$1\frac{1}{3}$ inches

40. A water storage tank is in the shape of a cone with the pointed end down. If the radius is 14 ft and the depth of the tank is 15 ft, approximate the volume of the tank in cubic feet. Use $\frac{22}{7}$ for π.

14 ft

15 ft

41. Find the volume and surface area of a rectangular box 2 ft by 1.4 ft by 3 ft.

42. Find the volume and surface area of a box in the shape of a cube that is 5 ft on each side.

43. The largest American flag measures 505 feet by 225 feet. It's the U.S. "Super flag" owned by "Ski" Demski of Long Beach, California. Find its area. (*Source: Guinness World Records*)

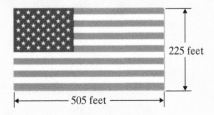

225 feet

← 505 feet →

44. The largest indoor illuminated sign is a billboard at Dubai Airport. It measures 28 meters by 6.2 meters. Find its area. (*Source: The Guinness Book of World Records*)

45. A drapery panel measures 6 ft by 7 ft. Find how many square feet of material are needed for *four* panels.

46. A page in this book measures 27.6 cm by 21.5 cm. Find its area.

47. A paperweight is in the shape of a square-based pyramid 20 centimeters tall. If an edge of the base is 12 centimeters, find the volume of the paperweight.

48. A birdbath is made in the shape of a hemisphere (half-sphere). If its radius is 10 inches, approximate its volume. Use $\frac{22}{7}$ for π.

10 in.

49. Find how many square feet of land are in the following plot:

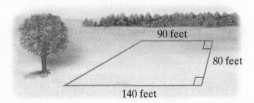

90 feet

80 feet

140 feet

50. For Gerald Gomez to determine how much grass seed he needs to buy, he must know the size of his yard. Use the drawing to determine how many square feet are in his yard.

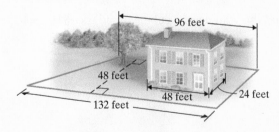

← 96 feet →

48 feet

48 feet   24 feet

← 132 feet →

51. Find the exact volume and surface area of a sphere with a radius of 7 inches.

52. A tank is in the shape of a cylinder 8 feet tall and 3 feet in radius. Find the exact volume and surface area of the tank.

53. The outlined part of the roof shown is in the shape of a trapezoid and needs to be shingled. The number of shingles to buy depends on the area.

   a. Use the dimensions given to find the area of the outlined part of the roof to the nearest whole square foot.

b. Shingles are packaged in a unit called a "square." If a "square" covers 100 square feet, how many whole squares need to be purchased to shingle this part of the roof?

54. The entire side of the building shaded in the drawing is to be bricked. The number of bricks to buy depends on the area.

   a. Find the area.

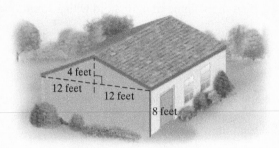

b. If the side area of each brick (including mortar room) is $\frac{1}{6}$ square ft, find the number of bricks that are needed to brick the end of the building.

55. Find the exact volume of a waffle ice cream cone with a 3-in. diameter and a height of 7 inches.

56. A snow globe has a diameter of 6 inches. Find its exact volume. Then approximate its volume using 3.14 for π.

57. Paul Revere's Pizza in the USA will bake and deliver a round pizza with a 4-foot diameter. This pizza is called the "Ultimate Party Pizza" and its current price is $99.99. Find the exact area of the top of the pizza and an approximation. Use 3.14 as an approximation for π.

58. The face of a circular watch has a diameter of 2 centimeters. What is its area? Find the exact area and an approximation. Use 3.14 as an approximation for π.

59. Zorbing is an extreme sport invented by two New Zealanders who joke that they were looking for a way to walk on water. A Zorb is a large sphere inside a second sphere with the space between the spheres pumped full of air. There is a tunnel-like opening so a person can crawl into the inner sphere. You are strapped in and sent down a Zorbing hill. A standard Zorb is approximately 3 m in diameter. Find the exact volume of a Zorb, and approximate the volume using 3.14 for π.

60. Mount Fuji, in Japan, is considered the most beautiful composite volcano in the world. The mountain is in the shape of a cone whose height is about 3.5 kilometers and whose base radius is about 3 kilometers. Approximate the volume of Mt. Fuji in cubic kilometers. Use $\frac{22}{7}$ for π.

61. A $10\frac{1}{2}$-foot by 16-foot concrete wall is to be built using concrete blocks. Find the area of the wall.

62. The floor of Terry's attic is 24 feet by 35 feet. Find how many square feet of insulation are needed to cover the attic floor.

63. Find the volume of a pyramid with a square base 5 inches on a side and a height of $1\frac{3}{10}$ inches.

64. Approximate to the nearest hundredth the volume of a sphere with a radius of 2 centimeters. Use 3.14 for π.

The Space Cube is supposed to be the world's smallest computer, with dimensions of 2 inches by 2 inches by 2.2 inches.

65. Find the volume of the Space Cube.

66. Find the surface area of the Space Cube.

Review

Evaluate.

67. 5^2

68. 7^2

69. 3^2

70. 20^2

71. $1^2 + 2^2$

72. $5^2 + 3^2$

73. $4^2 + 2^2$

74. $1^2 + 6^2$

Concept Extensions

Given the following situations, tell whether you are more likely to be concerned with area or perimeter.

75. ordering fencing to fence a yard

76. ordering grass seed to plant in a yard

77. buying carpet to install in a room

78. buying gutters to install on a house

79. ordering paint to paint a wall

80. ordering baseboards to install in a room

81. buying a wallpaper border to go on the walls around a room

82. buying fertilizer for your yard

Solve.

83. A pizza restaurant recently advertised two specials. The first special was a 12-inch pizza for $10. The second special was two 8-inch pizzas for $9. Determine the better buy. (*Hint:* First compare the areas of the two specials and then find a price per square inch for both specials.)

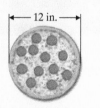
← 12 in. →

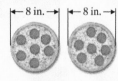
← 8 in. → ← 8 in. →

84. Find the approximate area of the state of Utah.

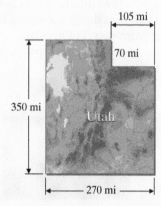
105 mi
70 mi
350 mi
270 mi
Utah

85. The Hayden Planetarium, at the Museum of Natural History in New York City, boasts a dome that has a diameter of 20 m. The dome is a hemisphere, or half a sphere. What is the volume enclosed by the dome at the Hayden Planetarium? Use 3.14 for π and round to the nearest hundredth. (*Source:* Hayden Planetarium)

diameter

hemisphere

86. The Adler Museum in Chicago has a planetarium, its StarRider Theater, that has a diameter of 55 feet. Find the surface area of its hemispheric (half a sphere) dome. Use 3.14 for π. (*Source:* The Adler Museum)

87. Can you compute the volume of a rectangle? Why or why not?

88. In your own words, explain why perimeter is measured in units and area is measured in square units.

89. Find the area of the shaded region. Use the approximation 3.14 for π.

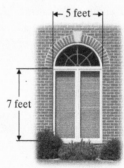

6 in.

90. The largest pumpkin pie on record was made in New Breman, Ohio, by the New Breman Giant Pumpkin Growers, in September 2010. The pie had a diameter of 240 inches. Find the exact area of the top of the pie and an approximation. Use $\pi \approx 3.14$. (*Source:* World Record Academy)

Find the area of each figure. If needed, use $\pi \approx 3.14$ and round results to the nearest tenth.

91. Find the skating area.

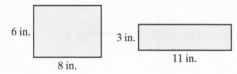

ROYALS

5 m

22 m

92.

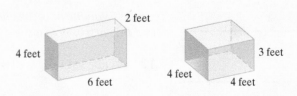

5 feet

7 feet

93. Do two rectangles with the same perimeter have the same area? To see, find the perimeter and the area of each rectangle.

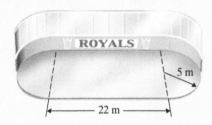

6 in.

8 in.

3 in.

11 in.

94. Do two rectangular solids with the same volume have the same surface area? To see, find the volume and surface area of each rectangular solid.

2 feet

4 feet

6 feet

3 feet

4 feet

4 feet

Answers

Geometry Concepts

1. _____

1. Find the supplement and the complement of a 27° angle.

Find the measures of angles x, y, and z in each figure in Exercises 2 and 3.

2. _____

3. _____

2.

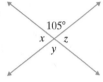

3. $m \| n$

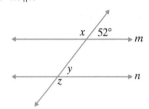

4. Find the measure of ∠x. (*Hint:* The sum of the angle measures of a triangle is 180°.)

4. _____

5. _____

5. Find the diameter.

2.3 in.

6. Find the radius.

$8\frac{1}{2}$ in.

6. _____

7. _____

8. _____

For Exercises 7 through 11, find the perimeter (or circumference) and area of each figure. For the circle, give an exact circumference and area. Then use $\pi \approx 3.14$ to approximate each. Don't forget to attach correct units.

9. _____

7.

Square 5 m

8.

4 ft
3 ft   5 ft

9.

5 cm

10.

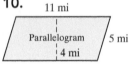

11 mi
Parallelogram 5 mi
4 mi

10. _____

11. _____

11.

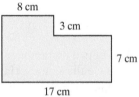

8 cm
3 cm
7 cm
17 cm

12. The smallest cathedral is in Highlandville, Missouri. The rectangular floor of the cathedral measures 14 feet by 17 feet. Find its perimeter and its area. (*Source: The Guinness Book of World Records*)

12. _____

13. _____

Find the volume of each solid. Don't forget to attach correct units. For Exercises 13 and 14, find the surface area also.

14. _____

13. A cube with edges of 4 inches each

14. A rectangular box 2 feet by 3 feet by 5.1 feet

15. _____

15. A pyramid with a square base 10 centimeters on a side and a height of 12 centimeters

16. A sphere with a diameter of 3 miles. Give the exact volume and then use $\pi \approx \frac{22}{7}$ to approximate.

16. _____

9.4 Linear Measurement

Objective A Defining and Converting U.S. System Units of Length

In the United States, two systems of measurement are commonly used. They are the **United States (U.S.), or English, measurement system** and the **metric system.** The U.S. measurement system is familiar to most Americans. Units such as feet, miles, ounces, and gallons are used. However, the metric system is also commonly used in fields such as medicine, sports, international marketing, and certain physical sciences. We are accustomed to buying 2-liter bottles of soft drinks, watching televised coverage of the 100-meter dash at the Olympic Games, or taking a 200-milligram dose of pain reliever.

The U.S. system of measurement uses the **inch, foot, yard,** and **mile** to measure **length.** The following is a summary of equivalencies between units of length:

Objectives

A Define U.S. Units of Length and Convert from One Unit to Another.

B Use Mixed U.S. Units of Length.

C Perform Arithmetic Operations on U.S. Units of Length.

D Define Metric Units of Length and Convert from One Unit to Another.

E Perform Arithmetic Operations on Metric Units of Length.

U.S. Units of Length

12 inches (in.) = 1 foot (ft)

3 feet = 1 yard (yd)

36 inches = 1 yard

5280 feet = 1 mile (mi)

To convert from one unit of length to another, we will use **unit fractions.** We define a unit fraction to be a fraction that is equivalent to 1. Examples of unit fractions are as follows:

Unit Fractions

$\dfrac{12 \text{ in.}}{1 \text{ ft}} = 1$ or $\dfrac{1 \text{ ft}}{12 \text{ in.}} = 1$ (since 12 in. = 1 ft)

$\dfrac{3 \text{ ft}}{1 \text{ yd}} = 1$ or $\dfrac{1 \text{ yd}}{3 \text{ ft}} = 1$ (since 3 ft = 1 yd)

$\dfrac{5280 \text{ ft}}{1 \text{ mi}} = 1$ or $\dfrac{1 \text{ mi}}{5280 \text{ ft}} = 1$ (since 5280 ft = 1 mi)

Remember that multiplying a number by 1 does not change the value of the number.

Example 1 Convert 8 feet to inches.

Solution: We multiply 8 feet by a unit fraction that uses the equality 12 inches = 1 foot. The unit fraction should be in the form $\dfrac{\text{units to convert to}}{\text{original units}}$ or, in this case, $\dfrac{12 \text{ inches}}{1 \text{ foot}}$. We do this so that like units will divide out to 1, as shown.

$8 \text{ ft} = \dfrac{8 \text{ ft}}{1} \cdot 1$ Multiply by 1 in the form of $\dfrac{12 \text{ in.}}{1 \text{ ft}}$.

$= \dfrac{8 \cancel{\text{ ft}}}{1} \cdot \dfrac{12 \text{ in.}}{1 \cancel{\text{ ft}}}$

$= 8 \cdot 12 \text{ in.}$

$= 96 \text{ in.}$ Multiply.

(*Continued on next page*)

Practice 1

Convert 6 feet to inches.

Answer

1. 72 in.

559

Thus, 8 ft = 96 in., as shown in the diagram:

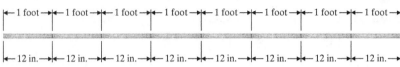

8 feet = 96 inches

■ Work Practice 1

Practice 2

Convert 8 yards to feet.

Example 2 Convert 7 feet to yards.

Solution: We multiply by a unit fraction that compares 1 yard to 3 feet.

$$7\text{ ft} = \frac{7\text{ ft}}{1} \cdot 1$$

$$= \frac{7\text{ ft}}{1} \cdot \frac{1\text{ yd}}{3\text{ ft}} \quad \leftarrow \text{Units to convert to}$$
$$\leftarrow \text{Original units}$$

$$= \frac{7}{3}\text{ yd}$$

$$= 2\frac{1}{3}\text{ yd} \qquad \text{Divide.}$$

Helpful Hint When converting from one unit to another, select a unit fraction with the properties below:

$$\frac{\text{units you are converting to}}{\text{original units}}$$

By using this unit fraction, the original units will divide out, as wanted.

Thus, 7 ft = $2\frac{1}{3}$ yd, as shown in the diagram.

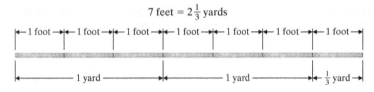

7 feet = $2\frac{1}{3}$ yards

■ Work Practice 2

Practice 3

Suppose the pelican's bill in the photo measures 18 inches. Convert 18 inches to feet, using decimals.

Example 3 Finding the Length of a Pelican's Bill

The Australian pelican has the longest bill, measuring from 13 to 18.5 inches long. The pelican in the photo has a 15-inch bill. Convert 15 inches to feet, using decimals in your final answer.

Solution:

$$15\text{ in.} = \frac{15\text{ in.}}{1} \cdot \frac{1\text{ ft}}{12\text{ in.}} \quad \leftarrow \text{Units to convert to}$$
$$\leftarrow \text{Original units}$$

$$= \frac{15}{12}\text{ ft}$$

$$= \frac{5}{4}\text{ ft} \qquad \text{Simplify } \frac{15}{12}.$$

$$= 1.25\text{ ft} \qquad \text{Divide.}$$

Thus, 15 in. = 1.25 ft, as shown in the diagram.

15 inches = 1.25 ft

1 ft $\frac{1}{4}$ or 0.25 ft

■ Work Practice 3

Objective B Using Mixed U.S. System Units of Length ▶

Sometimes it is more meaningful to express a measurement of length with mixed units such as 1 ft and 5 in. We usually condense this and write 1 ft 5 in.

In Example 2, we found that 7 feet is the same as $2\frac{1}{3}$ yards. The measurement can also be written as a mixture of yards and feet. That is,

7 ft = _____ yd _____ ft

Because 3 ft = 1 yd, we divide 3 into 7 to see how many whole yards are in 7 feet. The quotient is the number of yards, and the remainder is the number of feet.

$$
\begin{array}{r}
2 \text{ yd } 1 \text{ ft} \\
3\overline{)7} \\
-6 \\
\hline
1
\end{array}
$$

Thus, 7 ft = 2 yd 1 ft, as seen in the diagram:

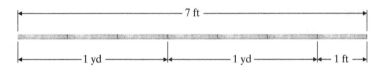

Example 4 | Convert: 134 in. = _____ ft _____ in.

Solution: Because 12 in. = 1 ft, we divide 12 into 134. The quotient is the number of feet. The remainder is the number of inches. To see why we divide 12 into 134, notice that

$$
134 \text{ in.} = \frac{134 \text{ in.}}{1} \cdot \frac{1 \text{ ft}}{12 \text{ in.}} = \frac{134}{12} \text{ ft}
$$

$$
\begin{array}{r}
11 \text{ ft } 2 \text{ in.} \\
12\overline{)134} \\
-12 \\
\hline
14 \\
-12 \\
\hline
2
\end{array}
$$

Thus, 134 in. = 11 ft 2 in.

■ Work Practice 4

Example 5 | Convert 3 feet 7 inches to inches.

Solution: First, we convert 3 feet to inches. Then we add 7 inches.

$$
3 \text{ ft} = \frac{3 \text{ ft}}{1} \cdot \frac{12 \text{ in.}}{1 \text{ ft}} = 36 \text{ in.}
$$

Then

$$
3 \text{ ft } 7 \text{ in.} = 36 \text{ in.} + 7 \text{ in.} = 43 \text{ in.}
$$

■ Work Practice 5

Practice 4

Convert: 68 in. = _____ ft _____ in.

Practice 5

Convert 5 yards 2 feet to feet.

Answers

4. 5 ft 8 in. **5.** 17 ft

Objective C Performing Operations on U.S. System Units of Length ▶

Finding sums or differences of measurements often involves converting units, as shown in the next example. Just remember that, as usual, only like units can be added or subtracted.

Practice 6

Add 4 ft 8 in. to 8 ft 11 in.

Example 6 Add 3 ft 2 in. and 5 ft 11 in.

Solution: To add, we line up the similar units.

$$
\begin{array}{r}
3\ \text{ft}\ \ 2\ \text{in.} \\
+\ 5\ \text{ft}\ 11\ \text{in.} \\
\hline
8\ \text{ft}\ 13\ \text{in.}
\end{array}
$$

Since 13 inches is the same as 1 ft 1 in., we have

$$8\ \text{ft}\ 13\ \text{in.} = 8\ \text{ft} + 1\ \text{ft}\ 1\ \text{in.}$$
$$= 9\ \text{ft}\ 1\ \text{in.}$$

■ Work Practice 6

✓**Concept Check** How could you estimate the following sum?

$$
\begin{array}{r}
7\ \text{yd}\ \ 4\ \text{in.} \\
+\ 3\ \text{yd}\ 27\ \text{in.}
\end{array}
$$

Practice 7

Multiply 4 ft 7 in. by 4.

Example 7 Multiply 8 ft 9 in. by 3.

Solution: By the distributive property, we multiply 8 ft by 3 and 9 in. by 3.

$$
\begin{array}{r}
8\ \text{ft}\ \ 9\ \text{in.} \\
\times\ \ \ \ \ \ \ \ 3 \\
\hline
24\ \text{ft}\ 27\ \text{in.}
\end{array}
$$

Since 27 in. is the same as 2 ft 3 in., we simplify the product as

$$24\ \text{ft}\ 27\ \text{in.} = 24\ \text{ft} + 2\ \text{ft}\ 3\ \text{in.}$$
$$= 26\ \text{ft}\ 3\ \text{in.}$$

■ Work Practice 7

We divide in a similar manner as above.

Practice 8

A carpenter cuts 1 ft 9 in. from a board of length 5 ft 8 in. Find the remaining length of the board.

Answers

6. 13 ft 7 in. **7.** 18 ft 4 in.
8. 3 ft 11 in.

✓**Concept Check Answer**
round each to the nearest yard:
7 yd + 4 yd = 11 yd

Example 8 Finding the Length of a Piece of Rope

A rope of length 6 yd 1 ft has 2 yd 2 ft cut from one end. Find the length of the remaining rope.

Solution: Subtract 2 yd 2 ft from 6 yd 1 ft.

$$
\begin{array}{r}
\text{beginning length} \ \rightarrow \ \ \ \ 6\ \text{yd}\ 1\ \text{ft} \\
-\ \ \ \text{amount cut} \ \rightarrow \ -2\ \text{yd}\ 2\ \text{ft} \\
\hline
\text{remaining length}
\end{array}
$$

We cannot subtract 2 ft from 1 ft, so we borrow 1 yd from the 6 yd. One yard is converted to 3 ft and combined with the 1 ft already there.

Borrow 1 yd = 3 ft

5 yd + (1 yd)(3 ft)

$$
\begin{array}{rcl}
6 \text{ yd } 1 \text{ ft} & = & 5 \text{ yd } 4 \text{ ft} \\
-2 \text{ yd } 2 \text{ ft} & = & -2 \text{ yd } 2 \text{ ft} \\
\hline
& & 3 \text{ yd } 2 \text{ ft}
\end{array}
$$

The remaining rope is 3 yd 2 ft long.

■ Work Practice 8

Objective D Defining and Converting Metric System Units of Length ▶

The basic unit of length in the metric system is the **meter.** A meter is slightly longer than a yard. It is approximately 39.37 inches long. Recall that a yard is 36 inches long.

1 yard = 36 inches

1 meter ≈ 39.37 inches

All units of length in the metric system are based on the meter. The following is a summary of the prefixes used in the metric system. Also shown are equivalencies between units of length. Like the decimal system, the metric system uses powers of 10 to define units.

Metric Units of Length
1 kilometer (km) = 1000 meters (m)
1 hectometer (hm) = 100 m
1 dekameter (dam) = 10 m
1 meter (m) = 1 m
1 decimeter (dm) = 1/10 m or 0.1 m
1 centimeter (cm) = 1/100 m or 0.01 m
1 millimeter (mm) = 1/1000 m or 0.001 m

The figure below will help you with decimeters, centimeters, and millimeters.

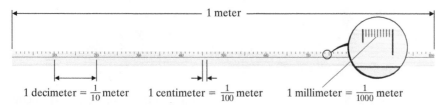

1 decimeter = $\frac{1}{10}$ meter   1 centimeter = $\frac{1}{100}$ meter   1 millimeter = $\frac{1}{1000}$ meter

Helpful Hint

Study the figure above for other equivalencies between metric units of length.

10 decimeters = 1 meter   10 millimeters = 1 centimeter

100 centimeters = 1 meter   10 centimeters = 1 decimeter

1000 millimeters = 1 meter

These same prefixes are used in the metric system for mass and capacity. The most commonly used measurements of length in the metric system are the **meter, millimeter, centimeter,** and **kilometer.**

✓**Concept Check** Is this statement reasonable? "The screen of a home television set has a 30-meter diagonal." Why or why not?

Being comfortable with the metric units of length means gaining a "feeling" for metric lengths, just as you have a "feeling" for the lengths of an inch, a foot, and a mile. To help you accomplish this, study the following examples:

- A millimeter is about the thickness of a large paper clip.

- A centimeter is about the width of a large paper clip.

- A meter is slightly longer than a yard.

- A kilometer is about two-thirds of a mile.

- The width of this book is approximately 21.5 centimeters.

- The distance between New York City and Philadelphia is about 160 kilometers.

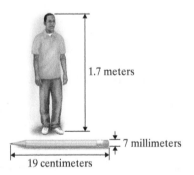

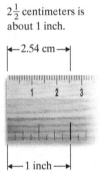

As with the U.S. system of measurement, unit fractions may be used to convert from one unit of length to another. For example, let's convert 1200 meters to kilometers. To do so, we will multiply by 1 in the form of the unit fraction

$$\frac{1 \text{ km}}{1000 \text{ m}} \quad \begin{array}{l} \leftarrow \text{Units to convert to} \\ \leftarrow \text{Original units} \end{array}$$

Unit fraction

$$1200 \text{ m} = \frac{1200 \text{ m}}{1} \cdot 1 = \frac{1200 \text{ m}}{1} \cdot \frac{1 \text{ km}}{1000 \text{ m}} = \frac{1200 \text{ km}}{1000} = 1.2 \text{ km}$$

The metric system does, however, have a distinct advantage over the U.S. system of measurement: the ease of converting from one unit of length to another. Since all units of length are powers of 10 of the meter, converting from one unit of length to another is as simple as moving the decimal point. Listing units of length in

✓**Concept Check Answer**

no; answers may vary

order from largest to smallest helps to keep track of how many places to move the decimal point when converting.

Let's again convert 1200 meters to kilometers. This time, to convert from meters to kilometers, we move along the chart shown, 3 units to the left, from meters to kilometers. This means that we move the decimal point 3 places to the left.

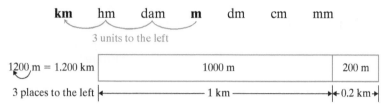

| **km** | hm | dam | **m** | dm | cm | mm |

3 units to the left

| 1200 m = 1.200 km | 1000 m | 200 m |

3 places to the left ◄——————— 1 km ———————► ◄—0.2 km—►

Thus, 1200 m = 1.2 km, as shown in the diagram.

Example 9   Convert 2.3 m to centimeters.

Solution: First we will convert by using a unit fraction.

$$2.3 \text{ m} = \frac{2.3 \text{ m}}{1} \cdot \frac{100 \text{ cm}}{1 \text{ m}} = 230 \text{ cm}$$

(Unit fraction)

Now we will convert by listing the units of length in order from left to right and moving from meters to centimeters.

| km | hm | dam | m | dm | cm | mm |

2 units to the right

2.30 m = 230. cm

2 places to the right

With either method, we get 230 cm.

■ Work Practice 9

Example 10   Convert 450,000 mm to meters.

Solution: We list the units of length in order from left to right and move from millimeters to meters.

| km | hm | dam | m | dm | cm | mm |

3 units to the left

Thus, move the decimal point 3 places to the left.

450,000 mm = 450.000 m or 450 m

■ Work Practice 10

✓**Concept Check** What is wrong with the following conversion of 150 cm to meters?

150.00 cm = 15,000 m

Objective E Performing Operations on Metric System Units of Length ▷

To add, subtract, multiply, or divide with metric measurements of length, we write all numbers using the same unit of length and then add, subtract, multiply, or divide as with decimals.

Practice 9
Convert 2.5 m to millimeters.

Practice 10
Convert 3500 m to kilometers.

Answers
9. 2500 mm   **10.** 3.5 km

✓**Concept Check Answer**
decimal point should be moved two places to the left: 1.5 m

Practice 11

Subtract 640 m from 2.1 km.

Example 11 Subtract 430 m from 1.3 km.

Solution: First we convert both measurements to kilometers or both to meters.

430 m = 0.43 km ⌐   or   1.3 km = 1300 m ⌐

$$\begin{array}{r} 1.30 \text{ km} \\ -0.43 \text{ km} \\ \hline 0.87 \text{ km} \end{array} \qquad \begin{array}{r} 1300 \text{ m} \\ -430 \text{ m} \\ \hline 870 \text{ m} \end{array}$$

The difference is 0.87 km or 870 m.

◾ Work Practice 11

Practice 12

Multiply 18.3 hm by 5.

Example 12 Multiply 5.7 mm by 4.

Solution: Here we simply multiply the two numbers. Note that the unit of measurement remains the same.

$$\begin{array}{r} 5.7 \text{ mm} \\ \times \quad 4 \\ \hline 22.8 \text{ mm} \end{array}$$

◾ Work Practice 12

Practice 13

Doris Blackwell is knitting a scarf that is currently 0.8 meter long. If she knits an additional 45 centimeters, how long will the scarf be?

Answers

11. 1.46 km or 1460 m   **12.** 91.5 hm
13. 125 cm or 1.25 m

Example 13 Finding a Person's Height

Fritz Martinson was 1.2 meters tall on his last birthday. Since then, he has grown 14 centimeters. Find his current height in meters.

Solution:

$$\begin{array}{rcl} \text{original height} & \rightarrow & 1.20 \text{ m} \\ + \text{ height grown} & \rightarrow & + 0.14 \text{ m} \quad \text{(Since 14 cm} = 0.14 \text{ m)} \\ \hline \text{current height} & & 1.34 \text{ m} \end{array}$$

Fritz is now 1.34 meters tall.

◾ Work Practice 13

Vocabulary, Readiness & Video Check

Use the choices below to fill in each blank. Some choices may be used more than once.

inches   yard   unit fraction

feet   meter

1. The basic unit of length in the metric system is the _____.

2. The expression $\dfrac{1 \text{ foot}}{12 \text{ inches}}$ is an example of a(n) _____.

3. A meter is slightly longer than a(n) _____.

4. One foot equals 12 _____.

5. One yard equals 3 _____.

6. One yard equals 36 _____.

7. One mile equals 5280 _____.

Martin-Gay Interactive Videos

See Video 9.4

Watch the section lecture video and answer the following questions.

Objective A   **8.** In ▱ Example 3, what units are used in the denominator of the unit fraction and why was this decided? ▶

Objective B   **9.** In ▱ Example 4, how is a mixed unit similar to a mixed number? Use examples in your answer. ▶

Objective C   **10.** In ▱ Example 5, why is the sum of the addition problem not the final answer? Reference the sum in your answer. ▶

Objective D   **11.** In the lecture before ▱ Example 6, why is it easier to convert metric units than U.S. units? ▶

Objective E   **12.** What two answers did we get for ▱ Example 8? Explain why both answers are correct. ▶

9.4 Exercise Set MyMathLab®

Objective A *Convert each measurement as indicated. See Examples 1 through 3.*

▶ **1.** 60 in. to feet

2. 84 in. to feet

3. 12 yd to feet

4. 18 yd to feet

5. 42,240 ft to miles

6. 36,960 ft to miles

▶ **7.** $8\frac{1}{2}$ ft to inches

8. $12\frac{1}{2}$ ft to inches

▶ **9.** 10 ft to yards

10. 25 ft to yards

11. 6.4 mi to feet

12. 3.8 mi to feet

13. 162 in. to yd (Write answer as a decimal.)

14. 7216 yd to mi (Write answer as a decimal.)

15. 3 in. to ft (Write answer as a decimal.)

16. 129 in. to ft (Write answer as a decimal.)

Objective B *Convert each measurement as indicated. See Examples 4 and 5.*

17. 40 ft = _____ yd _____ ft

18. 100 ft = _____ yd _____ ft

19. 85 in. = _____ ft _____ in.

20. 59 in. = _____ ft _____ in.

21. 10,000 ft = _____ mi _____ ft

22. 25,000 ft = _____ mi _____ ft

▶ **23.** 5 ft 2 in. = _____ in.

24. 4 ft 11 in. = _____ in.

25. 8 yd 2 ft = _____ ft

26. 4 yd 1 ft = _____ ft

27. 2 yd 1 ft = _____ in.

28. 1 yd 2 ft = _____ in.

Objective C *Perform each indicated operation. Simplify the result if possible. See Examples 6 through 8.*

29. 3 ft 10 in. + 7 ft 4 in.

30. 12 ft 7 in. + 9 ft 11 in.

31. 12 yd 2 ft + 9 yd 2 ft

32. 16 yd 2 ft + 8 yd 2 ft

33. 22 ft 8 in. − 16 ft 3 in.

34. 15 ft 5 in. − 8 ft 2 in.

35. 18 ft 3 in. − 10 ft 9 in.

36. 14 ft 8 in. − 3 ft 11 in.

37. 28 ft 8 in. ÷ 2

38. 34 ft 6 in. ÷ 2

39. 16 yd 2 ft × 5

40. 15 yd 1 ft × 8

Objective D *Convert as indicated. See Examples 9 and 10.*

41. 60 m to centimeters

42. 46 m to centimeters

43. 40 mm to centimeters

44. 14 mm to centimeters

45. 500 m to kilometers

46. 400 m to kilometers

47. 1700 mm to meters

48. 6400 mm to meters

49. 1500 cm to meters

50. 6400 cm to meters

51. 0.42 km to centimeters

52. 0.95 km to centimeters

53. 7 km to meters

54. 5 km to meters

55. 8.3 cm to millimeters

56. 4.6 cm to millimeters

57. 20.1 mm to decimeters

58. 140.2 mm to decimeters

59. 0.04 m to millimeters

60. 0.2 m to millimeters

Objective E *Perform each indicated operation. Remember to insert units when writing your answers. See Examples 11 through 13.*

61. 8.6 m + 0.34 m

62. 14.1 cm + 3.96 cm

63. 2.9 m + 40 mm

64. 30 cm + 8.9 m

65. 24.8 mm − 1.19 cm

66. 45.3 m − 2.16 dam

67. 15 km − 2360 m

68. 14 cm − 15 mm

69. 18.3 m × 3

70. 14.1 m × 4

71. 6.2 km ÷ 4

72. 9.6 m ÷ 5

Objectives A C D E **Mixed Practice** *Solve. Remember to insert units when writing your answers. For Exercises 73 through 82, complete the charts. See Examples 1 through 13.*

		Yards	Feet	Inches
73.	Chrysler Building in New York City		1046	
74.	4-story building			792
75.	Python length		35	
76.	Ostrich height			108

		Meters	Millimeters	Kilometers	Centimeters
77.	Length of elephant	5			
78.	Height of grizzly bear	3			
79.	Tennis ball diameter				6.5
80.	Golf ball diameter				4.6
81.	Distance from London to Paris			342	
82.	Distance from Houston to Dallas			396	

83. The National Zoo maintains a small patch of bamboo, which it grows as a food supply for its pandas. Two weeks ago, the bamboo was 6 ft 10 in. tall. Since then, the bamboo has grown 3 ft 8 in. How tall is the bamboo now?

84. While exploring in the Marianas Trench, a submarine probe was lowered to a point 1 mile 1400 feet below the ocean's surface. Later it was lowered an additional 1 mile 4000 feet below this point. How far was the probe below the surface of the Pacific?

85. At its deepest point, the Grand Canyon of the Colorado River in Arizona is about 6000 ft. The Grand Canyon of the Yellowstone River, which is in Yellowstone National Park in Wyoming, is at most 900 feet deep. How much deeper is the Grand Canyon of the Colorado River than the Grand Canyon of the Yellowstone River? (*Source:* National Park Service)

86. The Grand Canyon of the Gunnison River, in Colorado, is often called the Black Canyon of the Gunnison because it is so steep that light rarely penetrates the depth of the canyon. The Black Canyon of the Gunnison is only 1150 ft wide at its narrowest point. At its narrowest, the Grand Canyon of the Yellowstone is $\frac{1}{2}$ mile wide. Find the difference in width between the Grand Canyon of the Yellowstone and the Black Canyon of the Gunnison. (*Note:* Notice that the dimensions are different.) (*Source:* National Park Service)

87. The tallest man in the world is recorded as Robert Pershing Wadlow of Alton, Illinois. Born in 1918, he measured 8 ft 11 in. at his tallest. The shortest man in the world is Chandra Bahadur Dangi of Nepal, who measures 21.5 in. How many times taller than Chandra is Robert? Round to one decimal place. (*Source: Guinness World Records*)

88. A 3.4-m rope is attached to a 5.8-m rope. However, when the ropes are tied, 8 cm of length is lost to form the knot. What is the length of the tied ropes?

89. The ice on a pond is 5.33 cm thick. For safe skating, the owner of the pond insists that it be 80 mm thick. How much thicker must the ice be before skating is allowed?

90. The sediment on the bottom of the Towamencin Creek is normally 14 cm thick, but a recent flood washed away 22 mm of sediment. How thick is it now?

91. The Amana Corporation stacks up its microwave ovens in a distribution warehouse. Each stack is 1 ft 9 in. wide. How far from the wall would 9 of these stacks extend?

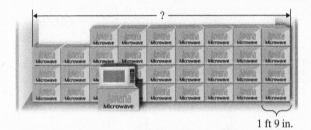

1 ft 9 in.

92. The highway commission is installing concrete sound barriers along a highway. Each barrier is 1 yd 2 ft long. Find the total length of 25 barriers placed end to end.

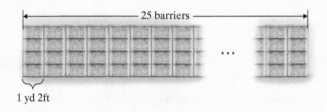

1 yd 2ft

93. A logging firm needs to cut a 67-m-long redwood log into 20 equal pieces before loading it onto a truck for shipment. How long will each piece be?

94. A 112.5-foot-tall dead pinewood tree is removed by starting at the top and cutting off 9-foot-long sections. How many whole sections are removed?

95. The longest truck in the world is operated by Gould Transport in Australia, and is the 182-ft Road Train. How many *yards* long are 2 of these trucks? (*Source: Guinness World Records*)

96. The large Coca-Cola sign in the Tokyo Ginza shopping district is in the shape of a rectangle whose length is 31 yards and whose width is 49 feet. Find the area of the sign in square feet. (*Source:* Coca-Cola Company) (*Hint:* Recall that the area of a rectangle is the product length times width.)

Review

Write each decimal as a fraction and each fraction as a decimal.

97. 0.21

98. 0.86

99. $\dfrac{13}{100}$

100. $\frac{47}{100}$ **101.** $\frac{1}{4}$ **102.** $\frac{3}{20}$

Concept Extensions

Determine whether the measurement in each statement is reasonable.

103. The width of a twin-size bed is 20 meters.

104. A window measures 1 meter by 0.5 meter.

105. A drinking glass is made of glass 2 millimeters thick.

106. A paper clip is 4 kilometers long.

107. The distance across the Colorado River is 50 kilometers.

108. A model's hair is 30 centimeters long.

Estimate each sum or difference. See the first Concept Check in this section.

109. $\begin{array}{r} 5 \text{ yd} \quad 2 \text{ in.} \\ + 7 \text{ yd} \; 30 \text{ in.} \\ \hline \end{array}$

110. $\begin{array}{r} 45 \text{ ft} \quad 1 \text{ in.} \\ - 10 \text{ ft} \; 11 \text{ in.} \\ \hline \end{array}$

111. Using a unit other than the foot, write a length that is equivalent to 4 feet. (*Hint:* There are many possibilities.)

112. Using a unit other than the meter, write a length that is equivalent to 7 meters. (*Hint:* There are many possibilities.)

113. To convert from meters to centimeters, the decimal point is moved two places to the right. Explain how this relates to the fact that the prefix *centi* means $\frac{1}{100}$.

114. Explain why conversions in the metric system are easier to make than conversions in the U.S. system of measurement.

115. An advertisement sign outside Fenway Park in Boston measures 18.3 m by 18.3 m. What is the area of this sign?

9.7 Temperature and Conversions Between the U.S. and Metric Systems

Objectives

A Convert Between the U.S. and Metric Systems.

B Convert Temperatures from Degrees Celsius to Degrees Fahrenheit.

C Convert Temperatures from Degrees Fahrenheit to Degrees Celsius.

Objective A Converting Between the U.S. and Metric Systems

The metric system probably had its beginnings in France in the 1600s, but it was the Metric Act of 1866 that made the use of this system legal (although not mandatory) in the United States. Other laws have followed that allow for a slow, but deliberate, transfer to the modernized metric system. In April 2001, for example, the U.S. Stock Exchanges completed their change to decimal trading instead of fractions. By the end of 2009, all products sold in Europe (with some exceptions) were required to have only metric units on their labels. (*Source:* U.S. Metric Association and National Institute of Standards and Technology)

You may be surprised at the number of everyday items we use that are already manufactured in metric units. We easily recognize 1 L and 2 L soda bottles, but what about the following?

- Pencil leads (0.5 mm or 0.7 mm)
- Camera film (35 mm)
- Sporting events (5-km or 10-km races)
- Medicines (500-mg capsules)
- Labels on retail goods (dual-labeled since 1994)

Since the United States has not completely converted to the metric system, we need to practice converting from one system to the other. Below is a table of mostly approximate conversions.

1 yard
1 meter

1 quart   1 liter

1 pound   1 kilogram

Length:		Capacity:		Weight (mass):	
Metric	U.S. System	Metric	U.S. System	Metric	U.S. System
1 m ≈ 1.09 yd		1 L ≈ 1.06 qt		1 kg ≈ 2.20 lb	
1 m ≈ 3.28 ft		1 L ≈ 0.26 gal		1 g ≈ 0.04 oz	
1 km ≈ 0.62 mi		3.79 L ≈ 1 gal		0.45 kg ≈ 1 lb	
2.54 cm = 1 in.		0.95 L ≈ 1 qt		28.35 g ≈ 1 oz	
0.30 m ≈ 1 ft		29.57 ml ≈ 1 fl oz			
1.61 km ≈ 1 mi					

There are many ways to perform these metric-to-U.S. conversions. We will do so by using unit fractions.

Practice 1

The center hole of a standard-sized compact disc is 1.5 centimeters in diameter. Convert this length to inches. Round the result to 2 decimal places.

Example 1   Compact Discs

Standard-sized compact discs are 12 centimeters in diameter. Convert this length to inches. Round the result to two decimal places.

Solution: From our length conversion table, we know that 2.54 cm = 1 in. This fact gives us two unit fractions:

$\dfrac{2.54 \text{ cm}}{1 \text{ in.}}$ and $\dfrac{1 \text{ in.}}{2.54 \text{ cm}}$. We use the unit fraction with cm in the denominator so that these units divide out.

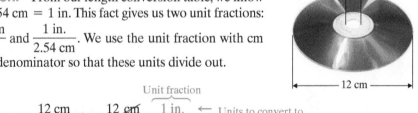

$$12 \text{ cm} = \frac{12 \text{ cm}}{1} \cdot 1 = \frac{12 \text{ cm}}{1} \cdot \frac{1 \text{ in.}}{2.54 \text{ cm}}$$

Unit fraction ⟶ 1 in.
← Units to convert to
2.54 cm ← Original units

$$= \frac{12 \text{ in.}}{2.54}$$

$$\approx 4.72 \text{ in.} \quad \text{Divide.}$$

Answers

1. 0.59 in.

Thus, the diameter of a standard compact disc is exactly 12 cm or approximately 4.72 inches. For a dimension this size, you can use a ruler to check. Another method is to approximate. Our result, 4.72 in., is close to 5 inches. Since 1 in. is about 2.5 cm, then 5 in. is about $5(2.5 \text{ cm}) = 12.5 \text{ cm}$, which is close to 12 cm.

■ Work Practice 1

Example 2 Liver

The liver is your largest internal organ. It weighs about 3.5 pounds in a grown man. Convert this weight to kilograms. Round to the nearest tenth. (*Source: Some Body!* by Dr. Pete Rowan)

Solution:
$$3.5 \text{ lb} \approx \frac{3.5 \text{ lb}}{1} \cdot \overbrace{\frac{0.45 \text{ kg}}{1 \text{ lb}}}^{\text{Unit fraction}} = 3.5(0.45 \text{ kg}) \approx 1.6 \text{ kg}$$

Thus 3.5 pounds is approximately 1.6 kilograms. From the table of conversions, we know that $1 \text{ kg} \approx 2.2 \text{ lb}$. So that means $0.5 \text{ kg} \approx 1.1 \text{ lb}$ and after adding, we have $1.5 \text{ kg} \approx 3.3 \text{ lb}$. Our result is reasonable.

■ Work Practice 2

Practice 2

A full-grown human heart weighs about 8 ounces. Convert this weight to grams. If necessary, round your result to the nearest tenth of a gram.

Example 3 Postage Stamp

Australia converted to the metric system in 1973. In that year, four postage stamps were issued to publicize this conversion. One such stamp is shown. Let's check the mathematics on the stamp by converting 7 fluid ounces to milliliters. Round to the nearest hundred.

Solution:
$$7 \text{ fl oz} \approx \frac{7 \text{ fl oz}}{1} \cdot \overbrace{\frac{29.57 \text{ ml}}{1 \text{ fl oz}}}^{\text{Unit fraction}} = 7(29.57 \text{ ml}) = 206.99 \text{ ml}$$

Rounded to the nearest hundred, $7 \text{ fl oz} \approx 200 \text{ ml}$.

■ Work Practice 3

Practice 3

Convert 237 ml to fluid ounces. Round to the nearest whole fluid ounce.

Now that we have practiced converting between two measurement systems, let's practice converting between two temperature scales.

Temperature When Gabriel Fahrenheit and Anders Celsius independently established units for temperature scales, each based his unit on the heat of water the moment it boils compared to the moment it freezes. One degree Celsius is $\frac{1}{100}$ of the difference in heat. One degree Fahrenheit is $\frac{1}{180}$ of the difference in heat. Celsius arbitrarily labeled the temperature at the freezing point at 0°C, making the boiling point 100°C; Fahrenheit labeled the freezing point 32°F, making the boiling point 212°F. Water boils at 212°F or 100°C.

By comparing the two scales in the figure, we see that a 20°C day is as warm as a 68°F day. Similarly, a sweltering 104°F day in the Mojave desert corresponds to a 40°C day.

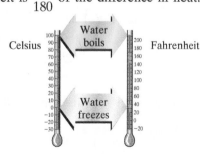

✓**Concept Check** Which of the following statements is correct? Explain.

a. 6°C is below the freezing point of water.

b. 6°F is below the freezing point of water.

Objective B Converting Degrees Celsius to Degrees Fahrenheit ▶

To convert from Celsius temperatures to Fahrenheit temperatures, see the box below. In this box, we use the symbol F to represent degrees Fahrenheit and the symbol C to represent degrees Celsius.

> **Converting Celsius to Fahrenheit**
>
> $$F = \frac{9}{5}C + 32 \qquad \text{or} \qquad F = 1.8C + 32$$
>
> (To convert to Fahrenheit temperature, multiply the Celsius temperature by $\frac{9}{5}$ or 1.8, and then add 32.)

Practice 4

Convert 60°C to degrees Fahrenheit.

Example 4 Convert 15°C to degrees Fahrenheit.

Solution:

$$F = \frac{9}{5}C + 32$$

$$= \frac{9}{5} \cdot 15 + 32 \quad \text{Replace C with 15.}$$

$$= 27 + 32 \quad \text{Simplify.}$$

$$= 59 \quad \text{Add.}$$

Thus, 15°C is equivalent to 59°F.

■ Work Practice 4

Practice 5

Convert 32°C to degrees Fahrenheit.

Example 5 Convert 29°C to degrees Fahrenheit.

Solution:

$$F = 1.8\,C + 32$$

$$= 1.8 \cdot 29 + 32 \quad \text{Replace C with 29.}$$

$$= 52.2 + 32 \quad \text{Multiply 1.8 by 29.}$$

$$= 84.2 \quad \text{Add.}$$

Therefore, 29°C is the same as 84.2°F.

■ Work Practice 5

Answers

4. 140°F **5.** 89.6°F

✓**Concept Check Answer**

b

Objective C Converting Degrees Fahrenheit to Degrees Celsius ▶

To convert from Fahrenheit temperatures to Celsius temperatures, see the box below. The symbol C represents degrees Celsius and the symbol F represents degrees Fahrenheit.

Converting Fahrenheit to Celsius

$$C = \frac{5}{9}(F - 32)$$

(To convert to Celsius temperature, subtract 32 from the Fahrenheit temperature, and then multiply by $\frac{5}{9}$.)

Example 6 Convert 59°F to degrees Celsius.

Solution: We evaluate the formula $C = \frac{5}{9}(F - 32)$ when F is 59.

$$C = \frac{5}{9}(F - 32)$$

$$= \frac{5}{9} \cdot (59 - 32) \quad \text{Replace F with 59.}$$

$$= \frac{5}{9} \cdot (27) \quad \text{Subtract inside parentheses.}$$

$$= 15 \quad \text{Multiply.}$$

Therefore, 59°F is the same temperature as 15°C.

▣ **Work Practice 6**

Example 7 Convert 114°F to degrees Celsius. If necessary, round to the nearest tenth of a degree.

Solution: $C = \frac{5}{9}(F - 32)$

$$= \frac{5}{9}(114 - 32) \quad \text{Replace F with 114.}$$

$$= \frac{5}{9} \cdot (82) \quad \text{Subtract inside parentheses.}$$

$$\approx 45.6 \quad \text{Multiply.}$$

Therefore, 114°F is approximately 45.6°C.

▣ **Work Practice 7**

Practice 6

Convert 68°F to degrees Celsius.

Practice 7

Convert 113°F to degrees Celsius. If necessary, round to the nearest tenth of a degree.

Answers
6. 20°C **7.** 45°C

Practice 8

During a bout with the flu, Albert's temperature reaches 102.8°F. What is his temperature measured in degrees Celsius? Round to the nearest tenth of a degree.

Example 8 Body Temperature

Normal body temperature is 98.6°F. What is this temperature in degrees Celsius?

Solution: We evaluate the formula $C = \dfrac{5}{9}(F - 32)$ when F is 98.6.

$$C = \frac{5}{9}(F - 32)$$

$$= \frac{5}{9}(98.6 - 32) \quad \text{Replace F with 98.6.}$$

$$= \frac{5}{9} \cdot (66.6) \quad\quad \text{Subtract inside parentheses.}$$

$$= 37 \quad\quad\quad\quad \text{Multiply.}$$

Therefore, normal body temperature is 37°C.

Work Practice 8

✓**Concept Check** Clarissa must convert 40°F to degrees Celsius. What is wrong with her work shown below?

$$F = 1.8 \cdot C + 32$$
$$F = 1.8 \cdot 40 + 32$$
$$F = 72 + 32$$
$$F = 104$$

Answers

8. 39.3°C

✓**Concept Check Answer**

She used the conversion for Celsius to Fahrenheit instead of Fahrenheit to Celsius.

Vocabulary, Readiness & Video Check

Martin-Gay Interactive Videos

See Video 9.7

See video answer section.

Watch the section lecture video and answer the following questions.

Objective A 1. Write two conversions that may be used to solve ⊞ Example 2. ▶

2. Why isn't 0.1125 kg the final answer to ⊞ Example 3? ▶

Objective B 3. Which version of the formula is used to solve ⊞ Example 4? What is the replacement value for C? ▶

Objective C 4. In ⊞ Example 5, what is the replacement value for F? What is the final conversion? ▶

9.7 Exercise Set MyMathLab®

Note: Because approximations are used, your answers may vary slightly from the answers given in the back of the book.

Objective A *Convert as indicated. If necessary, round answers to two decimal places. See Examples 1 through 3.*

1. 756 milliliters to fluid ounces

2. 18 liters to quarts

3. 86 inches to centimeters

4. 86 miles to kilometers

5. 1000 grams to ounces

6. 100 kilograms to pounds

7. 93 kilometers to miles

8. 9.8 meters to feet

9. 14.5 liters to gallons

10. 150 milliliters to fluid ounces

11. 30 pounds to kilograms

12. 15 ounces to grams

Fill in the chart. Give exact answers or round to one decimal place. See Examples 1 through 3.

		Meters	Yards	Centimeters	Feet	Inches
13.	The height of a woman				5	
14.	Statue of Liberty length of nose	1.37				
15.	Leaning Tower of Pisa		60			
16.	Blue whale		36			

Solve. If necessary, round answers to two decimal places. See Examples 1 through 3.

17. The balance beam for female gymnasts is 10 centimeters wide. Convert this width to inches.

18. In men's gymnastics, the rings are 250 centimeters from the floor. Convert this height to inches, then to feet.

19. In many states, the maximum speed limit for recreational vehicles is 50 miles per hour. Convert this to kilometers per hour.

20. In some states, the speed limit is 70 miles per hour. Convert this to kilometers per hour.

21. Ibuprofen comes in 200-milligram tablets. Convert this to ounces. (Round your answer to this exercise to 3 decimal places.)

22. Vitamin C tablets come in 500-milligram caplets. Convert this to ounces.

The 70-meter-diameter antenna is the largest and most sensitive Deep Space Network antenna. See the Chapter Opener and answer Exercises 23–26.

70-Meter Antenna

23. Convert 70 meters to feet.

24. The Deep Space Network sites also have a 26-meter antenna. Convert 26 meters to feet.

25. The 70-meter-diameter antenna can track a spacecraft traveling more than 16 billion kilometers from Earth. Convert this distance to miles.

26. The dish reflector and the mount atop the concrete pedestal of the 70-meter antenna weigh nearly 2.7 million kilograms. Convert this number to tons.

27. A stone is a unit in the British customary system. Use the conversion 14 pounds = 1 stone to check the equivalencies in this 1973 Australian stamp. Is 100 kilograms approximately 15 stone 10 pounds?

28. Convert 5 feet 11 inches to centimeters and check the conversion on this 1973 Australian stamp. Is it correct?

29. The Monarch butterfly migrates annually between the northern United States and central Mexico. The trip is about 4500 km long. Convert this to miles.

30. There is a species of African termite that builds nests up to 18 ft high. Convert this to meters.

31. A $3\frac{1}{2}$-inch diskette is not really $3\frac{1}{2}$ inches. To find its actual width, convert this measurement to centimeters, then to millimeters. Round the result to the nearest ten.

32. The average two-year-old is 84 centimeters tall. Convert this to feet and inches.

33. For an average adult, the weight of the right lung is greater than the weight of the left lung. If the right lung weighs 1.5 pounds and the left lung weighs 1.25 pounds, find the difference in grams. (*Source: Some Body!*)

34. The skin of an average adult weighs 9 pounds and is the heaviest organ. Find the weight in grams. (*Source: Some Body!*)

35. A fast sneeze has been clocked at about 167 kilometers per hour. Convert this to miles per hour. Round to the nearest whole.

36. A Boeing 747 has a cruising speed of about 980 kilometers per hour. Convert this to miles per hour. Round to the nearest whole.

37. The General Sherman giant sequoia tree has a diameter of about 8 meters at its base. Convert this to feet. (*Source: Fantastic Book of Comparisons*)

38. The largest crater on the near side of the moon is Billy Crater. It has a diameter of 303 kilometers. Convert this to miles. (*Source: Fantastic Book of Comparisons*)

39. The total length of the track on a CD is about 4.5 kilometers. Convert this to miles. Round to the nearest whole mile.

40. The distance between Mackinaw City, Michigan, and Cheyenne, Wyoming, is 2079 kilometers. Convert this to miles. Round to the nearest whole mile.

41. A doctor orders a dosage of 5 ml of medicine every 4 hours for 1 week. How many fluid ounces of medicine should be purchased? Round up to the next whole fluid ounce.

42. A doctor orders a dosage of 12 ml of medicine every 6 hours for 10 days. How many fluid ounces of medicine should be purchased? Round up to the next whole fluid ounce.

Without actually converting, choose the most reasonable answer.

43. This math book has a height of about_____.
 a. 28 mm   b. 28 cm
 c. 28 m   d. 28 km

44. A mile is _____ a kilometer.
 a. shorter than   b. longer than
 c. the same length as

45. A liter has _____ capacity than a quart.
 a. less   b. greater
 c. the same

46. A foot is _____ a meter.
 a. shorter than   b. longer than
 c. the same length as

47. A kilogram weighs _____ a pound.
 a. the same as   b. less than
 c. greater than

48. A football field is 100 yards, which is about_____.
 a. 9 m   b. 90 m
 c. 900 m   d. 9000 m

49. An $8\frac{1}{2}$-ounce glass of water has a capacity of about _____.
 a. 250 L   b. 25 L
 c. 2.5 L   d. 250 ml

50. A 5-gallon gasoline can has a capacity of about _____.
 a. 19 L   b. 1.9 L
 c. 19 ml   d. 1.9 ml

51. The weight of an average man is about _____.
 a. 700 kg   b. 7 kg
 c. 0.7 kg   d. 70 kg

52. The weight of a pill is about _____.
 a. 200 kg   b. 20 kg
 c. 2 kg   d. 200 mg

Objectives B C Mixed Practice *Convert as indicated. When necessary, round to the nearest tenth of a degree. See Examples 4 through 8.*

53. 77°F to degrees Celsius

54. 86°F to degrees Celsius

55. 104°F to degrees Celsius

56. 140°F to degrees Celsius

57. 50°C to degrees Fahrenheit

58. 80°C to degrees Fahrenheit

59. 115°C to degrees Fahrenheit

60. 225°C to degrees Fahrenheit

61. 20°F to degrees Celsius

62. 26°F to degrees Celsius

63. 142.1°F to degrees Celsius

64. 43.4°F to degrees Celsius

65. 92°C to degrees Fahrenheit

66. 75°C to degrees Fahrenheit

67. 12.4°C to degrees Fahrenheit

68. 48.6°C to degrees Fahrenheit

69. The hottest temperature ever recorded in the United States, in Death Valley, was 134°F. Convert this temperature to degrees Celsius. (*Source:* National Climatic Data Center)

70. The hottest temperature ever recorded in the United States in January was 95°F in Los Angeles. Convert this temperature to degrees Celsius. (*Source:* National Climatic Data Center)

▶ **71.** A weather forecaster in Caracas predicts a high temperature of 27°C. Find this measurement in degrees Fahrenheit.

72. While driving to work, Alan Olda notices a temperature of 18°C flash on the local bank's temperature display. Find the corresponding temperature in degrees Fahrenheit.

73. At Mack Trucks' headquarters, the room temperature is to be set at 70°F, but the thermostat is calibrated in degrees Celsius. Find the temperature to be set.

74. The computer room at Merck, Sharp, and Dohm is normally cooled to 66°F. Find the corresponding temperature in degrees Celsius.

75. In a European cookbook, a recipe requires the ingredients for caramels to be heated to 118°C, but the cook has access only to a Fahrenheit thermometer. Find the temperature in degrees Fahrenheit that should be used to make the caramels.

76. The ingredients for divinity should be heated to 127°C, but the candy thermometer that Myung Kim has is calibrated to degrees Fahrenheit. Find how hot he should heat the ingredients.

77. The temperature of Earth's core is estimated to be 4000°C. Find the corresponding temperature in degrees Fahrenheit.

78. In 2012, the average temperature of Earth's surface was 58.3°F. Convert this temperature to degrees Celsius. (*Source:* NASA)

Review

Perform the indicated operations.

79. $6 \cdot 4 + 5 \div 1$ **80.** $10 \div 2 + 9(8)$ **81.** $3[(1 + 5) \cdot (8 - 6)]$ **82.** $5[(18 - 8) - 9]$

Concept Extensions

Determine whether the measurement in each statement is reasonable.

83. A 72°F room feels comfortable.

84. Water heated to 110°F will boil.

85. Josiah has a fever if a thermometer shows his temperature to be 40°F.

86. An air temperature of 20°F on a Vermont ski slope can be expected in the winter.

87. When the temperature is 30°C outside, an overcoat is needed.

88. An air-conditioned room at 60°C feels quite chilly.

89. Barbara has a fever when a thermometer records her temperature at 40°C.

90. Water cooled to 32°C will freeze.

Body surface area (BSA) is often used to calculate dosages for some drugs. BSA is calculated in square meters using a person's weight and height.

$$BSA = \sqrt{\frac{(\text{weight in kg}) \times (\text{height in cm})}{3600}}$$

For Exercises 91 through 96, calculate the BSA for each person. Round to the nearest hundredth. You will need to use the square root key on your calculator.

91. An adult whose height is 182 cm and weight is 90 kg

92. An adult whose height is 157 cm and weight is 63 kg

93. A child whose height is 40 in. and weight is 50 kg (*Hint:* Don't forget to first convert inches to centimeters.)

94. A child whose height is 26 in. and weight is 13 kg (*Hint:* Don't forget to first convert inches to centimeters.)

95. An adult whose height is 60 in. and weight is 150 lb

96. An adult whose height is 69 in. and weight is 172 lb

97. In February 2010, at the Brookhaven National Laboratory in Long Island, NY, the highest temperature produced in a laboratory was achieved. This temperature was 7,200,000,000°F. Convert this temperature to degrees Celsius. Round your answer to the nearest million degrees. (*Source: Guinness World Records*)

98. The hottest-burning substance known is carbon sub-nitride. Its flame at one atmospheric pressure reaches 9010°F. Convert this temperature to degrees Celsius. (*Source: Guinness World Records*)

99. In your own words, describe how to convert from degrees Celsius to degrees Fahrenheit.

100. In your own words, describe how to convert from degrees Fahrenheit to degrees Celsius.

Chapter 9 Group Activity

Map Reading

Sections 9.4 and 9.7

Materials:

- ruler
- string
- calculator

This activity may be completed by working in groups or individually.

Investigate the route you would take from Santa Rosa, New Mexico, to San Antonio, New Mexico. Use the map in the figure to answer the following questions. You may find that using string to match the roads on the map is useful when measuring distances.

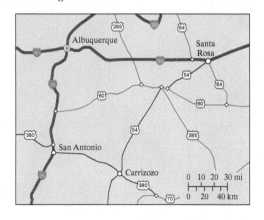

1. How many miles is it from Santa Rosa to San Antonio via Interstate 40 and Interstate 25? Convert this distance to kilometers.

2. How many miles is it from Santa Rosa to San Antonio via U.S. 54 and U.S. 380? Convert this distance to kilometers.

3. Assume that the speed limit on Interstates 40 and 25 is 65 miles per hour. How long would the trip take if you took this route and traveled 65 miles per hour the entire trip?

4. At what average speed would you have to travel on the U.S. routes to make the trip from Santa Rosa to San Antonio in the same amount of time that it would take on the interstate routes? Do you think this speed is reasonable on this route? Explain your reasoning.

5. Discuss in general the factors that might affect your decision between the different routes.

6. Explain which route you would choose in this case and why.

Chapter 9 Vocabulary Check

Fill in each blank with one of the words or phrases listed below.

transversal	line segment	obtuse	straight	adjacent	right	volume	area
acute	perimeter	vertical	supplementary	ray	angle	line	complementary
vertex	mass	unit fractions	gram	weight	meter	liter	surface area

1. _____ is a measure of the pull of gravity.
2. _____ is a measure of the amount of substance in an object. This measure does not change.
3. The basic unit of length in the metric system is the _____.
4. To convert from one unit of length to another, _____ may be used.
5. The _____ is the basic unit of mass in the metric system.
6. The _____ is the basic unit of capacity in the metric system.
7. A(n) _____ is a piece of a line with two endpoints.
8. Two angles that have a sum of 90° are called _____ angles.
9. A(n) _____ is a set of points extending indefinitely in two directions.
10. The _____ of a polygon is the distance around the polygon.
11. A(n) _____ is made up of two rays that share the same endpoint. The common endpoint is called the _____ vertex _____.
12. _____ measures the amount of surface of a region.
13. A(n) _____ is a part of a line with one endpoint. A ray extends indefinitely in one direction.
14. A line that intersects two or more lines at different points is called a(n) _____.
15. An angle that measures 180° is called a(n) _____ angle.
16. The measure of the space of a solid is called its _____.
17. When two lines intersect, four angles are formed. Two of these angles that are opposite each other are called _____ angles.
18. Two of the angles from Exercise **17** that share a common side are called _____ angles.
19. An angle whose measure is between 90° and 180° is called a(n) _____ angle.
20. An angle that measures 90° is called a(n) _____ angle.
21. An angle whose measure is between 0° and 90° is called a(n) _____ angle.
22. Two angles that have a sum of 180° are called _____ angles.
23. The _____ of a polyhedron is the sum of the areas of the faces of the polyhedron.

9 Chapter Highlights

Definitions and Concepts	Examples

Section 9.2 Perimeter

Perimeter Formulas

Rectangle: $P = 2l + 2w$

Square: $P = 4s$

Triangle: $P = a + b + c$

Circumference of a Circle: $C = 2\pi r$ or $C = \pi d$

where $\pi \approx 3.14$ or $\pi \approx \dfrac{22}{7}$

Find the perimeter of the rectangle.

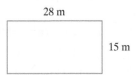

28 m

15 m

$P = 2l + 2w$
$\quad = 2 \cdot 28 \text{ meters} + 2 \cdot 15 \text{ meters}$
$\quad = 56 \text{ meters} + 30 \text{ meters}$
$\quad = 86 \text{ meters}$

The perimeter is 86 meters.

Section 9.3   Area, Volume, and Surface Area

Area Formulas

Rectangle: $A = lw$

Square: $A = s^2$

Triangle: $A = \dfrac{1}{2}bh$

Parallelogram: $A = bh$

Trapezoid: $A = \dfrac{1}{2}(b + B)h$

Circle: $A = \pi r^2$

Volume Formulas

Rectangular Solid: $V = lwh$

Cube: $V = s^3$

Sphere: $V = \dfrac{4}{3}\pi r^3$

Right Circular Cylinder: $V = \pi r^2 h$

Cone: $V = \dfrac{1}{3}\pi r^2 h$

Square-Based Pyramid: $V = \dfrac{1}{3}s^2 h$

Surface Area Formulas: See page 547.

Find the area of the square.

8 cm

$A = s^2$
$\quad = (8 \text{ centimeters})^2$
$\quad = 64 \text{ square centimeters}$

The area of the square is 64 square centimeters.

Find the volume of the sphere. Use $\dfrac{22}{7}$ for π.

4 in.

$V = \dfrac{4}{3}\pi r^3$

$\quad \approx \dfrac{4}{3} \cdot \dfrac{22}{7} \cdot (4 \text{ inches})^3$

$\quad = \dfrac{4 \cdot 22 \cdot 64}{3 \cdot 7} \text{ cubic inches}$

$\quad = \dfrac{5632}{21}$ or $268\dfrac{4}{21}$ cubic inches

Definitions and Concepts	Examples
Section 9.4 Linear Measurement	

Definitions and Concepts	Examples
To convert from one unit of length to another, multiply by a **unit fraction** in the form $$\frac{\text{units to convert to}}{\text{original units}}$$ **Length: U.S. System of Measurement** $$12 \text{ inches (in.)} = 1 \text{ foot (ft)}$$ $$3 \text{ feet} = 1 \text{ yard (yd)}$$ $$5280 \text{ feet} = 1 \text{ mile (mi)}$$ **Length: Metric System of Measurement** The basic unit of length in the metric system is the **meter.** A meter is slightly longer than a yard.	$$\frac{12 \text{ inches}}{1 \text{ foot}}, \frac{1 \text{ foot}}{12 \text{ inches}}, \frac{3 \text{ feet}}{1 \text{ yard}}$$ Convert 6 feet to inches. $$6 \text{ ft} = \frac{6 \text{ ft}}{1} \cdot 1$$ $$= \frac{6 \text{ ft}}{1} \cdot \frac{12 \text{ in.}}{1 \text{ ft}} \begin{array}{l} \leftarrow \text{ units to convert to} \\ \leftarrow \text{ original units} \end{array}$$ $$= 6 \cdot 12 \text{ in.}$$ $$= 72 \text{ in.}$$ Convert 3650 centimeters to meters. $$3650 \text{ cm} = 3650 \text{ cm} \cdot 1$$ $$= \frac{3650 \text{ cm}}{1} \cdot \frac{0.01 \text{ m}}{1 \text{ cm}} = 36.5 \text{ m}$$

Metric Units of Length

1 **kilo**meter (km) = 1000 meters (m)
1 **hecto**meter (hm) = 100 m
1 **deka**meter (dam) = 10 m
1 meter (m) = 1 m
1 **deci**meter (dm) = 1/10 m or 0.1 m
1 **centi**meter (cm) = 1/100 m or 0.01 m
1 **milli**meter (mm) = 1/1000 m or 0.001 m

or

$$\text{km} \quad \text{hm} \quad \text{dam} \quad \text{m} \quad \underbrace{\text{dm} \quad \text{cm}}_{\text{2 units to the left}} \quad \text{mm}$$

$$\underbrace{3650 \text{ cm}}_{\text{2 places to the left}} = 36.5 \text{ m}$$

Definitions and Concepts	Examples
Section 9.7 Temperature and Conversions Between the U.S. and Metric Systems	

Definitions and Concepts	Examples
To convert between systems, use approximate unit fractions. See page 572.	Convert 7 feet to meters. $$7 \text{ ft} \approx \frac{7 \text{ ft}}{1} \cdot \frac{0.30 \text{ m}}{1 \text{ ft}} = 2.1 \text{ m}$$ Convert 8 liters to quarts. $$8 \text{ L} \approx \frac{8 \text{ L}}{1} \cdot \frac{1.06 \text{ qt}}{1 \text{ L}} = 8.48 \text{ qt}$$ Convert 363 grams to ounces. $$363 \text{ g} \approx \frac{363 \text{ g}}{1} \cdot \frac{0.04 \text{ oz}}{1 \text{ g}} = 14.52 \text{ oz}$$
Celsius to Fahrenheit $$F = \frac{9}{5}C + 32 \quad \text{or} \quad F = 1.8C + 32$$	Convert 35°C to degrees Fahrenheit. $$F = \frac{9}{5} \cdot 35 + 32 = 63 + 32 = 95$$ $$35°C = 95°F$$
Fahrenheit to Celsius $$C = \frac{5}{9}(F - 32)$$	Convert 50°F to degrees Celsius. $$C = \frac{5}{9} \cdot (50 - 32) = \frac{5}{9} \cdot (18) = 10$$ $$50°F = 10°C$$

Geometric Formulas

Rectangle

Perimeter: $P = 2l + 2w$
Area: $A = lw$

Square

Perimeter: $P = 4s$
Area: $A = s^2$

Triangle

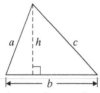

Perimeter: $P = a + b + c$
Area: $A = \frac{1}{2}bh$

Sum of Angles of Triangle

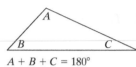

$A + B + C = 180°$

The sum of the measures of
the three angles is 180.

Pythagorean Theorem (for right triangles)

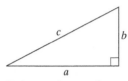

Perimeter: $P = a + b + c$
Area: $A = \frac{1}{2}ab$

One 90° (right) angle

Isosceles Triangle

Triangle has:
two equal sides and
two equal angles.

Equilateral Triangle

Triangle has:
three equal sides and
three equal angles.
Measure of each angle is 60°.

Trapezoid

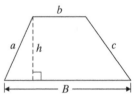

Perimeter: $P = a + b + c + B$
Area: $A = \frac{1}{2}h(B + b)$

Parallelogram

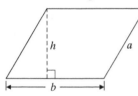

Perimeter: $P = 2a + 2b$
Area: $A = bh$

Circle

Circumference: $C = \pi d$
$C = 2\pi r$
Area: $A = \pi r^2$

Rectangular Solid

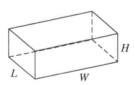

Volume: $V = LWH$
Surface Area:
$S = 2LW + 2HL + 2HW$

Cube

Volume: $V = s^3$
Surface Area: $S = 6s^2$

Cone

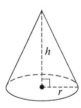

Volume: $V = \frac{1}{3}\pi r^2 h$
Lateral Surface Area:
$S = \pi r\sqrt{r^2 + h^2}$

Right Circular Cylinder

Volume: $V = \pi r^2 h$
Surface Area: $S = 2\pi r^2 + 2\pi rh$

Sphere

Volume: $V = \frac{4}{3}\pi r^3$
Surface Area: $S = 4\pi r^2$

Square-Based Pyramid

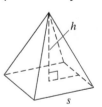

Volume: $V = a \cdot s^2 \cdot h$

Answers to Selected Exercises

Chapter 5 Decimals
Section 5.7

Vocabulary, Readiness & Video Check **1.** average **3.** mean (or average) **5.** grade point average **7.** Place the data numbers in numerical order (or verify that they already are)

Exercise Set 5.7 **1.** mean: 21; median: 23; no mode **3.** mean: 8.1; median: 8.2; mode: 8.2 **5.** mean: 0.5; median: 0.5; mode: 0.2 and 0.5 **7.** mean: 370.9; median: 313.5; no mode **9.** 1911.6 ft **11.** 1601 ft **13.** answers may vary **15.** 2.79 **17.** 3.64 **19.** 6.8 **21.** 6.9 **23.** 88.5 **25.** 73 **27.** 70 and 71 **29.** 9 rates **31.** $\frac{1}{3}$ **33.** $\frac{3}{5y}$ **35.** $\frac{11}{15}$ **37.** 35, 35, 37, 43 **39.** yes; answers may vary

Chapter 6 Ratio, Proportion, and Triangle Applications
Section 6.4

Calculator Explorations **1.** 32 **3.** 3.873 **5.** 9.849

Vocabulary, Readiness & Video Check **1.** 10; −10 **3.** radical **5.** perfect squares **7.** c^2; b^2 **9.** The square roots of 49 are 7 and −7 since $7^2 = 49$ and $(-7)^2 = 49$. The radical sign means the positive square root only, so $\sqrt{49} = 7$. **11.** The hypotenuse is the side across from the right angle.

Exercise Set 6.4 **1.** 2 **3.** 11 **5.** $\frac{1}{9}$ **7.** $\frac{4}{8} = \frac{1}{2}$ **9.** 1.732 **11.** 3.873 **13.** 5.568 **15.** 5.099 **17.** 6, 7 **19.** 10, 11 **21.** 16 **23.** 9.592 **25.** $\frac{7}{12}$ **27.** 8.426 **29.** 13 in. **31.** 6.633 cm **33.** 52.802 m **35.** 117 mm **37.** 5 **39.** 12 **41.** 17.205 **43.** 44.822 **45.** 42.426 **47.** 1.732 **49.** 8.5 **51.** 141.42 yd **53.** 25.0 ft **55.** 340 ft **57.** $\frac{5}{6}$ **59.** $\frac{x}{30}$ **61.** $\frac{21}{13y}$ **63.** $\frac{9x}{64}$ **65.** 6 **67.** 10 **69.** answers may vary **71.** yes **73.** $\sqrt{80} - 6 \approx 2.94$ in.

Chapter 8 Graphing and Introduction to Statistics
Section 8.1

Vocabulary, Readiness & Video Check **1.** bar **3.** line **5.** Count the number of symbols and multiply this number by how much each symbol stands for (from the key). **7.** bar graph

Exercise Set 8.1 **1.** Kansas **3.** 5.5 million or 5,500,000 acres **5.** Texas **7.** Montana (or Oklahoma) and Washington **9.** 78,000 **11.** 2006 **13.** 30,000 **15.** 86,000 wildfires/year **17.** September **19.** 77 **21.** $\frac{2}{77}$ **23.** Tokyo, Japan; about 34.7 million or 34,700,000 **25.** New York; 21.6 million or 21,600,000 **27.** approximately 2 million

29.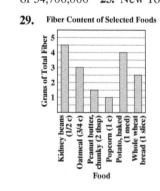

31.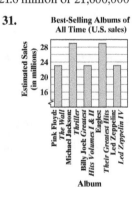

33. 15 adults **35.** 61 adults **37.** 24 adults **39.** 12 adults **41.** $\frac{9}{100}$

43. 45–54 **45.** 21 million households **47.** 44 million households **49.** 4 million households **51.** |; 1 **53.** ⊬⊬ |||; 8 **55.** ⊬⊬ |; 6 **57.** ⊬⊬ |; 6 **59.** ||; 2

61.

63. 8.4 goals/game **65.** 2003 **67.** increase **69.** 2001, 2007 **71.** 3.6 **73.** 6.2 **75.** 25% **77.** 34% **79.** 83°F **81.** Sunday; 68°F **83.** Tuesday; 13°F **85.** answers may vary

Section 8.2

Vocabulary, Readiness & Video Check   **1.** circle   **3.** 360   **5.** 100%

Exercise Set 8.2   **1.** parent or guardian's home   **3.** $\frac{9}{35}$ **5.** $\frac{9}{16}$ **7.** Asia   **9.** 37%   **11.** 17,100,000 sq mi   **13.** 2,850,000 sq mi

15. 55%   **17.** nonfiction   **19.** 31,400 books   **21.** 27,632 books   **23.** 25,120 books

25. 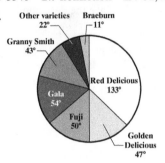   **27.** 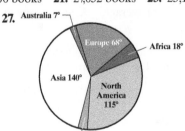   **29.** $2^2 \times 5$ **31.** $2^3 \times 5$ **33.** 5×17 **35.** answers may vary
37. 129,600,002 sq km   **39.** 55,542,858 sq km
41. 672 respondents   **43.** 2408 respondents
45. $\frac{12}{31}$ **47.** no; answers may vary

Chapter 9   Geometry and Measurement

Section 9.2

Vocabulary, Readiness & Video Check   **1.** perimeter   **3.** π **5.** $\frac{22}{7}$ (or 3.14); $3.14\left(\text{or }\frac{22}{7}\right)$ **7.** Opposite sides of a rectangle have the same measure, so we can just find the sum of the measures of all four sides.

Exercise Set 9.2   **1.** 64 ft   **3.** 120 cm   **5.** 21 in.   **7.** 48 ft   **9.** 42 in.   **11.** 155 cm   **13.** 21 ft   **15.** 624 ft   **17.** 346 yd   **19.** 22 ft
21. $55   **23. a.** 8   **b.** 72 in.   **25.** 28 in.   **27.** $36.12   **29.** 96 m   **31.** 66 ft   **33.** 74 cm   **35.** 17π cm; 53.38 cm   **37.** 16π mi; 50.24 mi
39. 26π m; 81.64 m   **41.** 15π ft; 47.1 ft   **43.** 12,560 ft   **45.** 30.7 mi   **47.** 14π cm $\approx$ 43.96 cm   **49.** 40 mm   **51.** 84 ft   **53.** 23
55. 1   **57.** 6   **59.** 10   **61. a.** width: 30 yd; length: 40 yd   **b.** 140 yd   **63.** b   **65. a.** 62.8 m; 125.6 m   **b.** yes   **67.** answers may vary
69. 27.4 m   **71.** 75.4 m

Section 9.3

Vocabulary, Readiness & Video Check   **1.** surface area   **3.** Area   **5.** square   **7.** We don't have a formula for an L-shaped figure, so we divide it into two rectangles, use the formula to find the area of each, and then add these two areas.

Exercise Set 9.3   **1.** 7 sq m   **3.** $9\frac{3}{4}$ sq yd   **5.** 15 sq yd   **7.** 2.25π sq in. $\approx$ 7.065 sq in.   **9.** 36.75 sq ft   **11.** 28 sq m   **13.** 22 sq yd

15. $36\frac{3}{4}$ sq ft   **17.** $22\frac{1}{2}$ sq in.   **19.** 25 sq cm   **21.** 86 sq mi   **23.** 24 sq cm   **25.** 36π sq in. $\approx 113\frac{1}{7}$ sq in.   **27.** $V = 72$ cu in.;

$SA = 108$ sq in.   **29.** $V = 512$ cu cm; $SA = 384$ sq cm   **31.** $V = 4\pi$ cu yd $\approx 12\frac{4}{7}$ cu yd; $SA = (2\pi\sqrt{13} + 4\pi)$ sq yd ≈ 35.20 sq yd

33. $V = \frac{500}{3}\pi$ cu in. $\approx 523\frac{17}{21}$ cu in.; $SA = 100\pi$ sq in. $\approx 314\frac{2}{7}$ sq in.   **35.** $V = 9\pi$ cu in. $\approx 28\frac{2}{7}$ cu in.   **37.** $V = 75$ cu cm

39. $2\frac{10}{27}$ cu in.   **41.** $V = 8.4$ cu ft; $SA = 26$ sq ft   **43.** 113,625 sq ft   **45.** 168 sq ft   **47.** 960 cu cm   **49.** 9200 sq ft

51. $V = \frac{1372}{3}\pi$ cu in. or $457\frac{1}{3}\pi$ cu in.; $SA = 196\pi$ sq in.   **53. a.** 381 sq ft   **b.** 4 squares   **55.** $V = 5.25\pi$ cu in.

57. 4π sq ft $\approx$ 12.56 sq ft   **59.** $V = 4.5\pi$ cu m; 14.13 cu m   **61.** 168 sq ft   **63.** $10\frac{5}{6}$ cu in.   **65.** 8.8 cu in.   **67.** 25   **69.** 9

71. 5   **73.** 20   **75.** perimeter   **77.** area   **79.** area   **81.** perimeter   **83.** 12-in. pizza   **85.** 2093.33 cu m   **87.** no; answers may vary
89. 7.74 sq in.   **91.** 298.5 sq m   **93.** no; answers may vary

Integrated Review   **1.** 153°; 63°   **2.** $m\angle x = 75°$; $m\angle y = 105°$; $m\angle z = 75°$ **3.** $m\angle x = 128°$; $m\angle y = 52°$; $m\angle z = 128°$

4. $m\angle x = 52°$ **5.** 4.6 in.   **6.** $4\frac{1}{4}$ in.   **7.** 20 m; 25 sq m   **8.** 12 ft; 6 sq ft   **9.** 10π cm $\approx$ 31.4 cm; 25π sq cm $\approx$ 78.5 sq cm

10. 32 mi; 44 sq mi   **11.** 54 cm; 143 sq cm   **12.** 62 ft; 238 sq ft   **13.** $V = 64$ cu in.; $SA = 96$ sq in.   **14.** $V = 30.6$ cu ft; $SA = 63$ sq ft

15. $V = 400$ cu cm   **16.** $V = 4\frac{1}{2}\pi$ cu mi $\approx 14\frac{1}{7}$ cu mi

Section 9.4

Vocabulary, Readiness & Video Check **1.** meter **3.** yard **5.** feet **7.** feet **9.** Both mean addition; $5\frac{2}{5} = 5 + \frac{2}{5}$ and

5 ft 2 in. = 5 ft + 2 in. **11.** Since the metric system is based on base 10, we just need to move the decimal point to convert from one unit to another.

Exercise Set 9.4 **1.** 5 ft **3.** 36 ft **5.** 8 mi **7.** 102 in. **9.** $3\frac{1}{3}$ yd **11.** 33,792 ft **13.** 4.5 yd **15.** 0.25 ft **17.** 13 yd 1 ft **19.** 7 ft 1 in.

21. 1 mi 4720 ft **23.** 62 in. **25.** 26 ft **27.** 84 in. **29.** 11 ft 2 in. **31.** 22 yd 1 ft **33.** 6 ft 5 in. **35.** 7 ft 6 in. **37.** 14 ft 4 in.

39. 83 yd 1 ft **41.** 6000 cm **43.** 4 cm **45.** 0.5 km **47.** 1.7 m **49.** 15 m **51.** 42,000 cm **53.** 7000 m **55.** 83 mm **57.** 0.201 dm

59. 40 mm **61.** 8.94 m **63.** 2.94 m or 2940 mm **65.** 1.29 cm or 12.9 mm **67.** 12.64 km or 12,640 m **69.** 54.9 m **71.** 1.55 km

73. $348\frac{2}{3}$; 12,552 **75.** $11\frac{2}{3}$; 420 **77.** 5000; 0.005; 500 **79.** 0.065; 65; 0.000065 **81.** 342,000; 342,000,000; 34,200,000 **83.** 10 ft 6 in.

85. 5100 ft **87.** 5.0 times **89.** 26.7 mm **91.** 15 ft 9 in. **93.** 3.35 m **95.** $121\frac{1}{3}$ yd **97.** $\frac{21}{100}$ **99.** 0.13 **101.** 0.25 **103.** no **105.** yes

107. no **109.** Estimate: 13 yd **111.** answers may vary; for example, $1\frac{1}{3}$ yd or 48 in. **113.** answers may vary **115.** 334.89 sq m

Section 9.7

Vocabulary, Readiness & Video Check **1.** 1 L ≈ 0.26 gal or 3.79 L ≈ 1 gal **3.** F = 1.8C + 32; 27

Exercise Set 9.7 **1.** 25.57 fl oz **3.** 218.44 cm **5.** 40 oz **7.** 57.66 mi **9.** 3.77 gal **11.** 13.5 kg **13.** 1.5; $1\frac{2}{3}$; 150; 60 **15.** 55; 5500;

180; 2160 **17.** 3.94 in. **19.** 80.5 kph **21.** 0.008 oz **23.** 229.6 ft **25.** 9.92 billion mi **27.** yes **29.** 2790 mi **31.** 90 mm **33.** 112.5 g

35. 104 mph **37.** 26.24 ft **39.** 3 mi **41.** 8 fl oz **43.** b **45.** b **47.** c **49.** d **51.** d **53.** 25°C **55.** 40°C **57.** 122°F **59.** 239°F

61. −6.7°C **63.** 61.2°C **65.** 197.6°F **67.** 54.3°F **69.** 56.7°C **71.** 80.6°F **73.** 21.1°C **75.** 244.4°F **77.** 7232°F **79.** 29 **81.** 36

83. yes **85.** no **87.** no **89.** yes **91.** 2.13 sq m **93.** 1.19 sq m **95.** 1.69 sq m **97.** 4,000,000,000°C **99.** answers may vary

Chapter 9 Vocabulary Check **1.** Weight **2.** Mass **3.** meter **4.** unit fractions **5.** gram **6.** liter **7.** line segment **8.** complementary **9.** line **10.** perimeter **11.** angle; vertex **12.** Area **13.** ray **14.** transversal **15.** straight **16.** volume **17.** vertical **18.** adjacent **19.** obtuse **20.** right **21.** acute **22.** supplementary **23.** surface area

Photo Credits

The reading material in the following Section IA is taken from

Intermediate Algebra: A Graphing Approach, Fifth Edition,
by Elayn Martin-Gay and Margaret Greene

Section IA Contents

2.6   Interpreting Data: Linear Models   597
Vocabulary, Readiness & Video Check   604

2.7   Graphing Piecewise-Defined Functions and Shifting and Reflecting Graphs of Functions   608
Vocabulary, Readiness, & Video Check   613

8.7   Interpreting Data: Linear and Quadratic Models   616
Vocabulary, Readiness, & Video Check   622

Appendix E   Graphing Stat Plots and Regression Equations   626

Answers to Selected Exercises   A1

2.6 Interpreting Data: Linear Models

OBJECTIVE

1 Use a Graphing Utility to Find a Linear Equation That Models Data.

The graph below shows the number of passengers who rode public transportation such as a train, bus, or subway during the years shown.

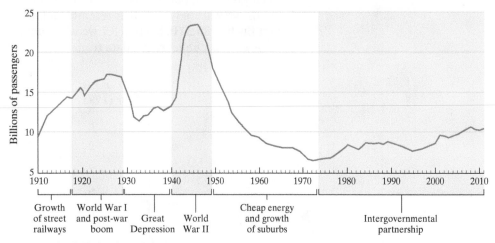

Source: American Public Transit Association

We see that different periods of history affect the number of passengers. For this complex graph there is not one model that best describes the number of passengers. Instead, we can take different periods of time and model each period to study it more closely. Once we get an equation (function) that best models a period of time, we can further study trends by evaluating the function within that period of time, or domain. It is important to remember that if a model is used to predict results outside its domain, this prediction is accurate only if the trend continues in the same manner. For example, if we had modeled the data from 1910 to 1925 and used it to predict the number of passengers for the next decade, we would have expected the number to continue to increase rapidly. Instead, the Great Depression occurred and our prediction would have been very inaccurate.

The following table shows different periods of time for our graph above and possible types of models.

Period of Time	Approximate Shape of Graph	Type of Model (Equation)
1910–1925	Line	Linear
1929–1945	Upward parabola	Quadratic
1940–1950	Downward parabola	Quadratic
1995–2011	Line	Linear

OBJECTIVE

1 Using Graphing Utilities to Find Linear Equations

Regression analysis is the process of fitting a line or a curve to a set of data points. The equation of this line or curve can then be used to further study the graph itself or to predict something in the future. Your calculator has many regression equations to choose from, but in this section we will concentrate on **linear regression.** In other words, we will study data that resemble a line and model it with a linear equation that best fits the data. (In Section 8.7 we will study another regression equation.)

Below is public transit data from the years 1995–2011.

x-List Year (1995 = 0)	y-List Billions of Riders
0	7.8
2	8.4
4	9.2
6	9.7
8	9.4
10	9.7
12	10.3
14	10.3
16	10.4

First we will draw a scatter plot of the ordered pairs and examine it. A scatter plot is a quick way to visually see if there is a relationship, perhaps linear, between the two sets of data.

Plotting the Data

To plot the data, see the steps below.

> **Helpful Hint**
> It is a good idea to first clear or deselect any equations in the Y= editor so that only the plotted data points are graphed.

1. Enter the data. To do so, use the EDIT menu found in the STAT feature. Enter years as L1 and billions of passengers as L2.

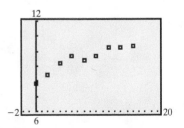

*First two data pairs not shown.

2. Use Stat Plot feature to indicate the type of graph as shown in the screens to the right.

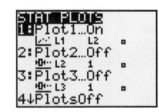 

3. Find an appropriate window. In this case $0 \le x \le 16$, so we choose $[-2, 20, 1]$ for the x-window; and $7.8 \le y \le 10.4$, so we choose $[6, 12, 1]$ for the y-window. You can choose various windows. Just make sure the domain and range are both included in your choice. Press GRAPH to see the individual points plotted.

Fitting a Line to the Data

Since this data resemble a line, let's model it with a linear equation. Your calculator will use a method beyond the scope of this course to find a line that best fits this data. Under the Stat Calc menu select LinReg $(ax + b)$. On the home screen indicate the x-list (L1), y-list (L2), and the Y= position where you want the regression equation to be stored (Y1). (See the second screen.)

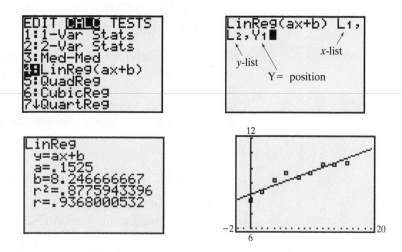

Notice in the above left screen that the calculator gives the slope, a, and the y-intercept, b, for the linear equation of the form $y = ax + b$. It is up to us to insert these values in this form. Thus, the linear regression equation is $y = 0.1525x + 8.246666667$ where x is the number of years since 1995 and y is the number of passengers in the billions.

The r-value shown in the third screen is called the **correlation coefficient.** The values r and r^2 indicate how well the regression equation fits the data. If the diagnostic feature of your calculator is turned on, these values are shown. Check with your instructor to see whether you are to make use of this feature.

EXAMPLE 1 **Using a Linear Regression Equation**

Use the equation $y = 0.1525x + 8.246666667$ from the above data and estimate the number of passengers in the year 2010.

Solution Trace on the above graph of the regression equation to evaluate the function at $x = 15$. Another alternative method is to evaluate the function in Y1 for 15 as shown next.

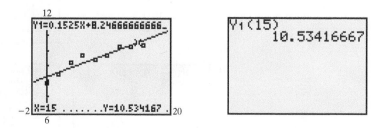

Using either method, the estimate of the number of passengers in 2010 is approximately 10.53 billion. □

PRACTICE

1 Use the equation in Example 1 and estimate the number of passengers in 2020.

You may want to use the following steps to find a linear regression model.

Finding a Linear Regression Model

1. Enter the given data into lists.
2. Draw a scatter plot of the ordered pairs to see if the data appear linear.
3. Find the linear regression equation.
4. Graph the linear regression equation and use it to answer questions.

According to emerging technology research, the number of media tablets is rapidly increasing. The table in the next example shows the average number of media tablets shipped worldwide during the years 2010–2012. It also represents the predicted number of tablets shipped during the years 2013–2015. The prediction is made on the assumption that the number sold continues to increase at the same rate. How do we find this rate?

EXAMPLE 2   Worldwide Media Tablets Usage on the Rise

The number of media tablets in use during the years 2010–2012 along with the projected number for the years 2013–2015 is represented in the table below.

Years after 2010 (x)	0	1	2	3	4	5
Number of Media Tablets Shipped (Millions) (y)	17.61	69.08	114.58	169.73	235.69	318.32

a. Plot the data points

b. Use linear regression to fit a line to the data.

c. What does the slope of this line indicate in this situation?

d. If the number of media tablets continues to increase at the same rate, predict the number shipped in the year 2024.

Solution

a. Enter the data in L1 and L2. Turn the Stat Plot on and graph in an appropriate window. We used the window $[-1, 15, 1]$ by $[-33, 370, 50]$.

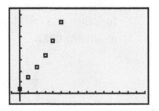

b.

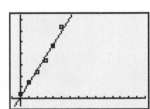

If a and b are rounded to two decimal places, the linear regression equation is $y = 58.82x + 7.13$.

c. The slope, 58.82, indicates that the average rate of increase in the number of media tablets shipped worldwide is 59 million per year.

d. Since the equation is stored in Y1 we evaluate the equation for the year 2024 as
Y1(14).

If the trend continues to increase at the rate of 58.82 tablets per year, we predict
831 million media tablets to be shipped worldwide in the year 2024.   ☐

PRACTICE

2   For the years 2010–2015, the number of sales of tablet PCs in the United
States is listed in the table below. If the trend continues at the same rate, predict the
number of sales in the year 2020. Write a sentence explaining the meaning of slope in
this situation.

Years after 2010 (x)	0	1	2	3	4	5
Number of Tablet PC Sales in the U.S. (*millions*) (*y*)	10.3	24.1	35.1	39.8	42.3	44

EXAMPLE 3   Number of Injured Workers Decreases

The number of cases of injuries and sickness suffered in the workplace continues to
decrease according to the Bureau of Labor and Statistics.

Year	1998	2000	2002	2006	2010	2012
Injuries and Sickness per 100 Workers	6.5	6.1	5.3	4.1	2.8	2.2

a. Plot the data points. (Let $x = 0$ represent the number of years since 1990.)

b. Find the regression equation that best fits the data. Then indicate whether the line is
increasing or decreasing.

c. What is the rate at which the number of sick or injured workers is increasing or
decreasing?

d. If the trend continues at the same rate, predict the number of sick or injured
workers out of 100 to expect in the year 2018.

Solution

a. Enter the years in L1 with 1990 represented by $x = 0$ and the corresponding
number of cases per 100 workers in L2. Find an appropriate window. We choose
$[7, 24, 1]$ by $[1, 8, 1]$.

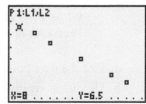

b.

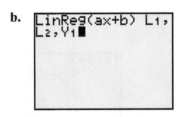 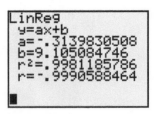

If a and b are rounded to three decimal places, the linear regression equation is $y = -0.314x + 9.105$. Since the slope is negative (-0.314), the line is decreasing.

c.

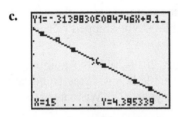

The number of injured or sick workers is decreasing at the rate of 0.314 per 100 workers per year.

d. Since the equation is stored in Y1, we evaluate the equation for the year 2018 by finding Y1(28).

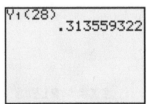

Y1(28) is approximately 0.31, so approximately 0.31 worker per 100 in the year 2018. □

PRACTICE

3   The safety committee of a large construction company is studying the increase in the number of injuries and sickness for their company.

Year	1999	2001	2003	2005	2007	2009	2011
Injuries and Sickness per 100 Workers	4.7	4.9	5.6	5.7	6.8	7.0	7.5

Answer Example 3, parts b, c, and d. (Let $x = 0$ represent the number of years since 1990.)

....

EXAMPLE 4   **A Linear Model for Predicting Selling Price**

The following houses were sold in an Orange Park neighborhood in the past month. Listed below are each house's selling price and the number of square feet of living area in the house.

Total Square Feet	2150	2273	2474	2516	3000
Selling Price in Thousands of Dollars	240	235	258	280	350

a. Plot the data points.

b. Use linear regression to fit a line to the data.

c. Predict the approximate selling price for a house in the same neighborhood that has 2800 square feet of living area.

Solution

a. Enter the total number of square feet in a first list, L1, and the corresponding selling price in a second list, L2. Find an appropriate window and graph as shown.

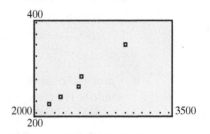

b.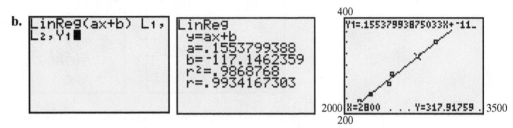

If *a* and *b* are rounded to 2 decimal places, the linear regression equation is $y = 0.16x - 117.15$.

c. Since this equation is stored in Y1, we evaluate the equation for 2800 square feet, or Y1 (2800).

We predict the selling price for a house in the same neighborhood that has 2800 square feet of living area to be $317,918.   □

PRACTICE

4   The table below shows houses that were sold in two adjoining subdivisions.

Total Square Feet (living area)	1750	1810	1536	1975
Selling Price (in dollars)	420,000	405,000	315,000	399,000

a. Use linear regression to fit a line to the data. Round numbers to two decimal places.

b. Use part *a* to predict the selling price for a house with 1662 square feet of living area.

EXAMPLE 5   **Adults Working Longer**

The percent of adults who are 55 and older who are still working has risen since 1990. The table below shows the percent of the workforce ages 55 and older for the years shown. (Note: Some years are projected.)

Year	2011	2012	2013	2014	2015	2016
% 55 or older	40.8%	41.2%	41.6%	42%	42.4%	42.7%

a. Let $x = 0$ represent the number of years since 2000. Use linear regression to fit a line to the data. Round decimals to three places.

b. Find the rate at which the number of workers ages 55 and older is increasing. Round to 2 decimal places.

c. If the trend continues to increase at the same linear rate, find the percent of workers ages 55 and older in the year 2020. Round to 2 decimal places.

Solution

a. Enter the data into L1 and L2. Turn the Stat Plot on and graph in an appropriate window. We chose the window [10, 20, 1] by [40, 45, 1]. The linear regression equation is $y = 0.386x + 36.576$.

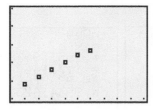 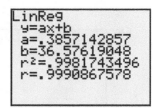 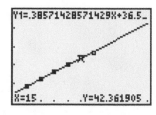

b. The number of workers ages 55 and older is increasing at the rate of 0.386% per year.

c. We stored the equation in Y1, thus we evaluate the equation for the year 2020 by finding Y1(20).

If the trend continues we can expect to see about 44.29% of the workforce being ages 55 and older in the year 2020. □

PRACTICE

5 If the trend given in Example 5 continues, find the number of workers ages 55 and older expected in the year 2025. Round to 2 decimal places.

Vocabulary, Readiness & Video Check

Use the choices below to fill in each blank.

| domain | regression analysis | linear regression equation | Stat Plot |
| data | scatter plot | range | lists |

1. _____ is the process of fitting a line or a curve to a set of data points.

2. Enter the _____ into the calculator using _____.

3. Use the _____ feature to indicate the _____ as the type of graph.

4. When finding an appropriate window, make sure the _____ and _____ are both included in your choice.

5. Use a _____ to find the line of best fit.

Martin-Gay Interactive Videos   Watch the section lecture video and answer the following questions.

OBJECTIVE

1   **6.** Based on Example 2, why was the linear regression equation evaluated for $x = 43$ to predict the cost of a ticket in the year 2013?

See Video 2.6

2.6   Exercise Set   MyMathLab®

Solve. See Examples 1 through 5.

1. Use the function $f(x) = 2.602x - 5178$ to predict the amount of money that will be spent by the Pharmaceutical Manufacturers Association on research and development in 2015. (*Hint:* x corresponds to the year and $f(x)$ represents amount of money in billions of dollars.)

2. Use the function from Exercise 1 to predict the year that $34.9 billion was spent on research and development. (*Hint:* x corresponds to the year and $f(x)$ represents amount of money in billions of dollars.)

3. The adult one-day pass price $f(x)$ for Disney World is given by $f(x) = 2.7x + 38.64$ where x is the number of years since 1996. Find what year the price was approximately $50.

4. Using the function in Exercise 3, find the price of a one-day pass to Disney World in 2013.

MIXED PRACTICE

Solve. Round the values in each linear regression equation to three decimal places. Predictions using linear regression equations may differ slightly depending on different rounding of the coefficients in the equation. See Examples 1 through 5.

5. The number of smartphones shipped or predicted to be shipped worldwide during the years 2010–2015 is shown in the table below.

Year	2010	2011	2012	2013	2014	2015
Smartphones shipped world-wide (millions)	270.93	362.45	458.01	561.42	677.18	775.79

Let x = the number of years since 2000.

a. Use linear regression to fit a line to the data. Round your answer to three decimal places.

b. Find the rate at which the number of smartphones shipped worldwide is increasing.

c. If the trend continues to increase at this rate, find the expected amount to be shipped in the year 2018.

6. The number of smartphones shipped or predicted to be shipped in the U.S. during the years 2010–2015 is shown in the table below.

Year	2010	2011	2012	2013	2014	2015
Smartphones shipped in U.S. (millions)	62.2	93.1	115.8	137.5	176.3	192.4

Let x = the number of years since 2000.

a. Use linear regression to fit a line to the data. Round your answer to three decimal places.

b. Find the rate at which the number of smartphones shipped in the U.S. is increasing.

c. If the trend continues to increase at this rate, find the expected amount to be shipped in the year 2018.

7. The percent of male smokers 18 years and older has decreased from 1965 to 2010.

a. Use linear regression to fit a line to the data in the table.

Years since 1960	5	11	25	30	35	40	50
Percent of Male Smokers	51.9	43.1	32.6	28.4	27	25.7	17.1

b. Predict the percent of male smokers in the year 2020 if the trend continues to decrease at the same rate. Round to the nearest tenth of a percent.

c. Predict the percent at which male smokers are decreasing per year.

8. The percent of female smokers 18 years and older has decreased from 1965 to 2010.

a. Use linear regression to fit a line to the data in the table.

Years since 1960	5	11	25	30	35	40	50
Percent of Female Smokers	33.9	32.1	27.9	22.8	22.6	21	16.5

b. Predict the percent of female smokers in the year 2020 if the trend continues to decrease at the same rate. Round to the nearest tenth of a percent.

c. Predict the percent at which female smokers are decreasing per year.

9. The number of sentenced male prisoners in state and federal prisons rose from 1980 to 2010.

a. Using the data in the table, find the linear regression equation that best fits the data.

Years since 1980	0	5	10	15	20	30
Number of Male Prisoners (in thousands)	304	459	699	1021	1246	1662

b. Predict the number of male prisoners in the year 2020 if the trend continues to increase at the same rate. Round to the nearest thousand.

c. Predict the rate at which male prisoners are increasing. Round to the nearest thousand.

10. The number of sentenced female prisoners in state and federal prisons rose from 1980 to 2010.

a. Using the data in the table, find the regression equation that best fits the data.

Years since 1980	0	5	10	15	20	30
Number of Female Prisoners (in thousands)	12	21	41	64	85	119

b. Predict the number of female prisoners in the year 2020 if the trend continues to increase at the same rate. Round to the nearest thousand.

c. Predict the rate at which female prisoners are increasing. Round to the nearest thousand.

11. The percent of adults in the labor force ages 65 and older who are still working has risen since 1990. The table below shows the data from 1990 to 2010.

Year	1990	1995	2000	2005	2010
% of Labor Force	12.2%	13%	14%	15.2%	16.4%

Let $x =$ the number of years since 1990.

a. Plot the data points.

b. Find the linear regression equation of the line of best fit for the data.

c. What does the slope of this line indicate in this situation?

d. If the number continues to increase at the same rate, predict the percent of the labor force that is 65 and older in the year 2020.

12. The number of high school girls softball teams since Title IX was enacted has grown rapidly. From 1972 to 1974, the number of teams rose from 373 to 6000. Since 1974, the growth of the number of teams has been more steady. The table below shows the increase between 1974 and 2004.

a. Plot the data in the table and find the linear regression equation that best fits the data. (Let $x = 0$ represent the number of years since 1970.)

Year	1974	1984	1990	1994	2001	2004
No. of Teams	6000	8700	8200	12,000	13,001	14,493

b. Predict the number of girls softball teams in 2015 if this trend continues. Round to the nearest whole.

c. Find the rate at which the number of teams is rising annually.

Given the following data for four houses sold in comparable neighborhoods and their corresponding number of square feet, draw a scatter plot and find a linear regression equation representing a relationship between the number of square feet and the selling price of the house.

▶ **13.**

Square Feet	1519	2593	3005	3016
Selling Price	$91,238	$220,000	$254,000	$269,000

14.

Square Feet	1754	2151	2587	2671
Selling Price	$91,238	$130,000	$155,000	$172,500

▶ **15.** Use the equation found in Exercise 13 to predict the selling price of a house with 2200 square feet.

16. Use the equation found in Exercise 14 to predict the selling price of a house with 2400 square feet.

A salesperson's salary depends on the amount of sales for the week. Given the following amounts of sales and the corresponding weekly salaries, plot the data points and find a linear regression equation that describes the salary in terms of the amount of sales.

17.

Sales (in dollars)	1000	3000	5000	8000
Salary (in dollars)	780	940	1100	1340

18.

Sales (in dollars)	5000	10,000	25,000	30,000
Salary (in dollars)	550	800	1550	1800

19. Life expectancy at birth of males was rising in the U.S. between 1900 and 2010 according to the table below.

Year	1900	1930	1950	1970	1990	2000	2010
Life Expectancy	46.3	57.5	65.6	67.1	71.8	74.9	77.6

a. Using the data in the table, find the regression equation that best fits this data. (Let $x = 0$ represent the number of years since 1900.)

b. What is the rate at which the life expectancy at birth of males is rising per year?

c. Predict the life expectancy of a male born in the year 2018 if this trend continues.

20. Life expectancy at birth of females was rising in the U.S. between 1900 and 2010 according to the table below.

Year	1900	1930	1950	1970	1990	2000	2010
Life Expectancy	48.3	59.8	71.1	74.7	78.8	81.5	84.5

a. Using the data in the table, find the regression equation that best fits this data. (Let $x = 0$ represent the number of years since 1900.)

b. What is the rate at which the life expectancy at birth of females is rising?

c. Predict the life expectancy of a female born in the year 2018 if the trend continues.

21. The number of people receiving care in PPOs has increased between the years of 1992 and 2001 according to the American Association of Health Plans.

Year	1992	1994	1996	2001	2010
Number of PPO Members (in millions)	50.4	79.2	96.1	127.8	205.4

a. Using the data in the table, find the regression equation that best fits the data. (Let $x = 0$ represent the number of years since 1990.)

b. Predict the number of people receiving care in PPOs in the year 2020 if the trend continues to increase at the same rate.

c. If this trend continues, predict the year that there will be over 240 million members.

d. What does the slope of the linear regression equation represent?

22. The number of people receiving care in HMOs has increased between the years of 1988 and 2004 according to the American Association of Health Plans.

Year	1988	1990	1992	1994	1996	2012
Number of HMO Members (in millions)	32.7	36.5	41.4	51.1	61.8	90.8

a. Using the data in the table, find the regression equation that best fits the data. (Let $x = 0$ represent the number of years since 1980.)

b. Predict the number of people receiving care in HMOs in the year 2020 if the trend continues to increase at the same rate.

c. If this trend continues, predict the year that there will be over 100 million members.

d. What does the slope of the linear regression equation represent?

▶ 23. The average top ticket price for Broadway musicals increased dramatically between 1975 and 2010.

Year	1975	1985	1998	2000	2010
Average Ticket Price	13.76	45.26	73.03	118.89	146.30

a. Using the data in the table, find the regression equation that best fits the data. (Let $x = 0$ represent the number of years since 1970.)

b. Predict the average top ticket price for Broadway musicals in the year 2020 if the trend continues to increase at the same rate.

c. Find the rate at which the cost is rising.

24. The average top ticket price for Broadway plays increased dramatically between 1975 and 2010.

Year	1975	1985	1998	2000	2010
Average Ticket Price	10.76	35.29	56.35	91.35	112.31

a. Using the data in the table, find the regression equation that best fits the data. (Let $x = 0$ represent the number of years since 1970.)

b. Predict the average top ticket price for Broadway plays in the year 2020 if the trend continues to increase at the same rate.

c. Find the rate at which the cost is rising.

25. **Super Bowl Commercials.** The Super Bowl is the most widely watched event on television. The table below gives the average cost for a 30-second commercial for the years 1991 through 2007.

Years since 1990	1	3	5	7	9	11	13	15	17
Super Bowl Commercial Cost (in millions of dollars)	0.8	0.85	1	1.2	1.6	2.05	2.1	2.4	2.6

Source: Advertising Age

a. Plot the data points.

b. Use a linear regression to fit a line to the data.

c. Find the rate at which the cost of a 30-second commercial during the Super Bowl is increasing per year.

d. If the rate continues to increase in the same manner, use the approximate equation in part **b** and predict the cost of a 30-second commercial during the Super Bowl in the year 2013.

26. **Academy Award Commercials.** The Academy Awards is one of the most watched television shows. The table below gives the average cost of a 30-second commercial slot for the years 1997 through 2007.

Years since 1990	7	9	11	13	15	17
Academy Award Commercial Cost (in millions of dollars)	0.85	1.0	1.45	1.35	1.5	1.67

a. Plot the data points.

b. Use a linear regression to fit a line to the data.

c. Find the rate at which the cost of a 30-second commercial on the Academy Awards presentation is increasing per year.

d. If the rate continues to increase in the same manner, use the approximate equation in part **b** and predict the cost of a 30-second commercial in the year 2014.

REVIEW AND PREVIEW

Solve each equation algebraically. See Section 1.5.

27. $7x + 2 = 9x - 14$

28. $5(x - 2) = 4(x + 7)$

29. $\dfrac{y}{7} + \dfrac{y}{3} = \dfrac{1}{21}$

30. $y + 0.8 = 0.3(y - 2)$

CONCEPT EXTENSIONS

31. In the United States, the revenue (money taken in from sales) at a "full service" restaurant is increasing at a faster rate than the revenue at a "fast food" restaurant. The data represent the annual revenue in billions of dollars for each type of restaurant.

Year	1995	1999	2000	2001	2002	2003	2004
Full Service	99	126	134	141	148	155	164
Fast Food	103	120	128	133	138	147	159

Source: U.S. Census Bureau

Let $x = 0$ represent the number of years since 1990.

a. Write a linear regression equation for "full service" and one for "fast food." Round the coefficients to three decimal places.

b. Use the equations and their graphs to approximate the year that the revenue from the two types of restaurants was the same. Round up to the nearest whole year.

2.7 Graphing Piecewise-Defined Functions and Shifting and Reflecting Graphs of Functions

OBJECTIVES

1 Graph Piecewise-Defined Functions.

2 Vertical and Horizontal Shifts.

3 Reflect Graphs.

OBJECTIVE

1 Graphing Piecewise-Defined Functions

Throughout Chapter 2, we have graphed functions. There are many special functions. In this objective, we study functions defined by two or more expressions. The expression used to complete the function varies with, and depends upon, the value of x. Before we actually graph these piecewise-defined functions, let's practice finding function values. (For this objective, the graphing utility is not mentioned, although it is possible to use it to check separate pieces of your graph.)

EXAMPLE 1 Evaluate $f(2), f(-6)$, and $f(0)$ for the function

$$f(x) = \begin{cases} 2x + 3 & \text{if } x \le 0 \\ -x - 1 & \text{if } x > 0 \end{cases}$$

Then write your results in ordered pair form.

Solution Take a moment and study this function. It is a single function defined by two expressions depending on the value of x. From above, if $x \le 0$, use $f(x) = 2x + 3$. If $x > 0$, use $f(x) = -x - 1$. Thus

$f(2) = -(2) - 1$
$\quad = -3 \quad \text{since } 2 > 0$
$f(2) = -3$
Ordered pairs: $(2, -3)$

$f(-6) = 2(-6) + 3$
$\quad = -9 \quad \text{since } -6 \le 0$
$f(-6) = -9$
$\quad (-6, -9)$

$f(0) = 2(0) + 3$
$\quad = 3 \quad \text{since } 0 \le 0$
$f(0) = 3$
$\quad (0, 3)$ □

PRACTICE

1 Evaluate $f(4), f(-2)$, and $f(0)$ for the function

$$f(x) = \begin{cases} -4x - 2 & \text{if } x \le 0 \\ x + 1 & \text{if } x > 0 \end{cases}$$

Now, let's graph a piecewise-defined function.

EXAMPLE 2   Graph $f(x) = \begin{cases} 2x + 3 & \text{if } x \le 0 \\ -x - 1 & \text{if } x > 0 \end{cases}$

Solution   Let's graph each piece.

If $x \le 0$,
$f(x) = 2x + 3$

If $x > 0$,
$f(x) = -x - 1$

Values ≤ 0

x	$f(x) = 2x + 3$
0	3 Closed circle
−1	1
−2	−1

Values > 0

x	$f(x) = -x - 1$
1	−2
2	−3
3	−4

The graph of the first part of $f(x)$ listed will look like a ray with a closed-circle end point at $(0, 3)$. The graph of the second part of $f(x)$ listed will look like a ray with an open-circle end point. To find the exact location of the open-circle end point, use $f(x) = -x - 1$ and find $f(0)$. Since $f(0) = -0 - 1 = -1$, we graph values from the second table and place an open circle at $(0, -1)$.

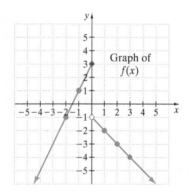

Graph of $f(x)$

Notice that this graph is the graph of a function because it passes the vertical line test. The domain of this function is all real numbers and the range is $\{y \mid y \le 3\}$.   □

PRACTICE
2   Graph

$$f(x) = \begin{cases} -4x - 2 & \text{if } x \le 0 \\ x + 1 & \text{if } x > 0 \end{cases}$$

OBJECTIVE
2   **Vertical and Horizontal Shifting**

Review of Common Graphs

We now take common graphs and learn how more complicated graphs are actually formed by shifting and reflecting these common graphs. These shifts and reflections are called transformations, and it is possible to combine transformations. A knowledge of these transformations will help you simplify future graphs.

Let's begin with a review of the graphs of three common functions.

Common Graphs

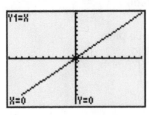
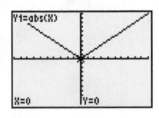
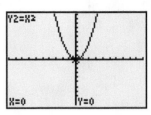

Standard Window

Basic Linear Equation
$y = x$

Absolute Value Equation
$y = |x|$

Quadratic Equation (Parabola)
$y = x^2$

Let's graph by hand a fourth common function, $f(x) = \sqrt{x}$ or $y = \sqrt{x}$. For this graph, you need to recall basic facts about square roots and use your calculator to approximate some square roots to help locate points. Recall also that the square root of a negative number is not a real number, so be careful when finding your domain.

Now **let's graph the square root function $f(x) = \sqrt{x}$, or $y = \sqrt{x}$.**

To graph, we identify the domain, evaluate the function for several values of x, plot the resulting points, and connect the points with a smooth curve. Since $\sqrt{x}$ represents the nonnegative square root of x, the domain of this function is the set of all nonnegative numbers, $\{x \mid x \geq 0\}$. We have approximated $\sqrt{3}$ below to help us locate the point corresponding to $(3, \sqrt{3})$.

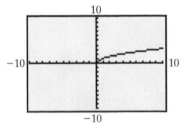

A calculator check: square root equation $y = \sqrt{x}$

If $x = 0$, then $y = \sqrt{0}$, or 0.

If $x = 1$, then $y = \sqrt{1}$, or 1.

If $x = 3$, then $y = \sqrt{3}$, or 1.7.

If $x = 4$, then $y = \sqrt{4}$, or 2.

If $x = 9$, then $y = \sqrt{9}$, or 3.

x	$f(x) = \sqrt{x}$
0	0
1	1
3	$\sqrt{3} \approx 1.7$
4	2

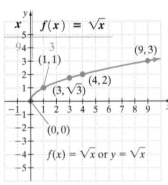

Notice that the graph of this function also passes the vertical line test, as expected.

Take a moment and review all four common graphs. Your success in the rest of this section depends on your knowledge of these graphs. Although we have studied some simple vertical transformations in earlier sections, we now formally study vertical, horizontal, and other transformations. These graphs are hand-drawn, but feel free to check your work with your calculator.

Your knowledge of the slope–intercept form, $f(x) = mx + b$, will help you understand simple shifting of transformations such as vertical shifts. For example, what is the difference between the graphs of $f(x) = x$ and $g(x) = x + 3$?

$f(x) = x$

slope, $m = 1$

y-intercept is $(0, 0)$

$g(x) = x + 3$

slope, $m = 1$

y-intercept is $(0, 3)$

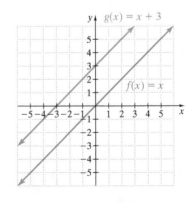

Notice that the graph of $g(x) = x + 3$ is the same as the graph of $f(x) = x$, but moved upward 3 units. This is an example of a **vertical shift** and is true for graphs in general.

Vertical Shifts (Upward and Downward)
Let *k* be a Positive Number

Graph of	Same As	Moved
$g(x) = f(x) + k$	$f(x)$	k units upward
$g(x) = f(x) - k$	$f(x)$	k units downward

EXAMPLES   Without plotting points, sketch the graph of each pair of functions on the same set of axes.

3. $f(x) = x^2$ and $g(x) = x^2 + 2$

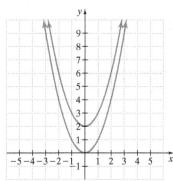

4. $f(x) = \sqrt{x}$ and $g(x) = \sqrt{x} - 3$

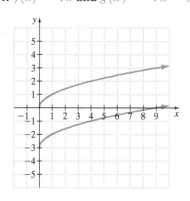

PRACTICE

3-4   Without plotting points, sketch the graphs of each pair of functions on the same set of axes.

3. $f(x) = x^2$ and $g(x) = x^2 - 3$ **4.** $f(x) = \sqrt{x}$ and $g(x) = \sqrt{x} + 1$

A horizontal shift to the left or right may be slightly more difficult to understand. Let's graph $g(x) = |x - 2|$ and compare it with $f(x) = |x|$.

EXAMPLE 5   Sketch the graphs of $f(x) = |x|$ and $g(x) = |x - 2|$ on the same set of axes.

Solution   Study the table to the left to understand the placement of both graphs.

x	$f(x) = |x|$	$g(x) = |x - 2|$
-3	3	5
-2	2	4
-1	1	3
0	0	2
1	1	1
2	2	0
3	3	1

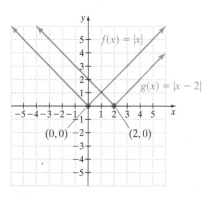

PRACTICE

5   Sketch the graphs of $f(x) = |x|$ and $g(x) = |x - 3|$ on the same set of axes.

The graph of $g(x) = |x - 2|$ is the same as the graph of $f(x) = |x|$, but moved 2 units to the right. This is an example of a **horizontal shift** and is true for graphs in general.

Horizontal Shift (To the Left or Right)
Let h Be a Positive Number

Graph of	Same as	Moved
$g(x) = f(x - h)$	$f(x)$	h units to the right
$g(x) = f(x + h)$	$f(x)$	h units to the left

▶ Helpful Hint
Notice that $f(x - h)$ corresponds to a shift to the right and $f(x + h)$ corresponds to a shift to the left.

Vertical and horizontal shifts can be combined.

EXAMPLE 6 Sketch the graphs of $f(x) = x^2$ and $g(x) = (x - 2)^2 + 1$ on the same set of axes.

Solution The graph of $g(x)$ is the same as the graph of $f(x)$ shifted 2 units to the right and 1 unit up.

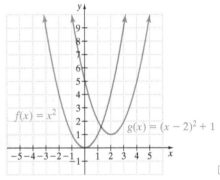

$f(x) = x^2$

$g(x) = (x - 2)^2 + 1$

PRACTICE

6 Sketch the graphs of $f(x) = |x|$ and $g(x) = |x - 2| + 3$ on the same set of axes.

OBJECTIVE

3 Reflecting Graphs ▶

Another type of transformation is called a **reflection**. In this section, we will study reflections (mirror images) about the x-axis only. For example, take a moment and study these two graphs. The graph of $g(x) = -x^2$ can be verified, as usual, by plotting points.

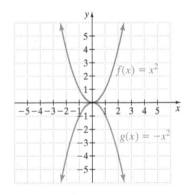

$f(x) = x^2$

$g(x) = -x^2$

Reflection about the x-axis

The graph of $g(x) = -f(x)$ is the graph of $f(x)$ reflected about the x-axis.

EXAMPLE 7   Sketch the graph of $h(x) = -|x - 3| + 2$.

Solution The graph of $h(x) = -|x - 3| + 2$ is the same as the graph of $f(x) = |x|$ reflected about the x-axis, then moved three units to the right and two units upward.

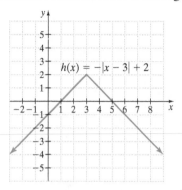

$h(x) = -|x - 3| + 2$

PRACTICE
7   Sketch the graph of $h(x) = -(x + 2)^2 - 1$.

There are other transformations, such as stretching, that won't be covered in this section.

Vocabulary, Readiness & Video Check

Match each equation with its graph.

1. $y = \sqrt{x}$ **2.** $y = x^2$ **3.** $y = x$ **4.** $y = |x|$

A   B   C   D

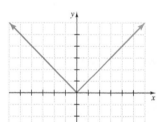

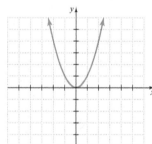

Watch the section lecture video and answer the following questions.

OBJECTIVE
1   **5.** In ▱ Example 1, only one piece of the function is defined for the value $x = -1$. Why do we find $f(-1)$ for $f(x) = x + 3$?

OBJECTIVE
2   **6.** For ▱ Examples 2–8, why is it helpful to be familiar with common graphs and their basic shapes?

OBJECTIVE
3   **7.** Based on the lecture before ▱ Example 9, complete the following statement. The graph of $f(x) = -\sqrt{x} + 6$ has the same shape as the graph of $f(x) = \sqrt{x} + 6$ but it is reflected about the _____.

2.7 Exercise Set

MyMathLab®

Graph each piecewise-defined function. See Examples 1 and 2.

1. $f(x) = \begin{cases} 2x & \text{if } x < 0 \\ x + 1 & \text{if } x \geq 0 \end{cases}$

2. $f(x) = \begin{cases} 3x & \text{if } x < 0 \\ x + 2 & \text{if } x \geq 0 \end{cases}$

3. $f(x) = \begin{cases} 4x + 5 & \text{if } x \leq 0 \\ \frac{1}{4}x + 2 & \text{if } x > 0 \end{cases}$

4. $f(x) = \begin{cases} 5x + 4 & \text{if } x \leq 0 \\ \frac{1}{3}x - 1 & \text{if } x > 0 \end{cases}$

5. $g(x) = \begin{cases} -x & \text{if } x \leq 1 \\ 2x + 1 & \text{if } x > 1 \end{cases}$

6. $g(x) = \begin{cases} 3x - 1 & \text{if } x \leq 2 \\ -x & \text{if } x > 2 \end{cases}$

7. $f(x) = \begin{cases} 5 & \text{if } x < -2 \\ 3 & \text{if } x \geq -2 \end{cases}$

8. $f(x) = \begin{cases} 4 & \text{if } x < -3 \\ -2 & \text{if } x \geq -3 \end{cases}$

MIXED PRACTICE

(Section 2.7) Graph each piecewise-defined function. Use the graph to determine the domain and range of the function. See Examples 1 and 2.

9. $f(x) = \begin{cases} -2x & \text{if } x \leq 0 \\ 2x + 1 & \text{if } x > 0 \end{cases}$

10. $g(x) = \begin{cases} -3x & \text{if } x \leq 0 \\ 3x + 2 & \text{if } x > 0 \end{cases}$

11. $h(x) = \begin{cases} 5x - 5 & \text{if } x < 2 \\ -x + 3 & \text{if } x \geq 2 \end{cases}$

12. $f(x) = \begin{cases} 4x - 4 & \text{if } x < 2 \\ -x + 1 & \text{if } x \geq 2 \end{cases}$

13. $f(x) = \begin{cases} x + 3 & \text{if } x < -1 \\ -2x + 4 & \text{if } x \geq -1 \end{cases}$

14. $h(x) = \begin{cases} x + 2 & \text{if } x < 1 \\ 2x + 1 & \text{if } x \geq 1 \end{cases}$

15. $g(x) = \begin{cases} -2 & \text{if } x \leq 0 \\ -4 & \text{if } x \geq 1 \end{cases}$

16. $f(x) = \begin{cases} -1 & \text{if } x \leq 0 \\ -3 & \text{if } x \geq 2 \end{cases}$

For Exercises 17 through 20, match each equation to its graph.

17. $f(x) = |x| + 3$

18. $f(x) = |x| - 2$

19. $f(x) = \sqrt{x} - 2$

20. $f(x) = \sqrt{x} + 3$

A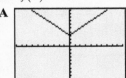

B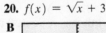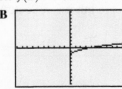

C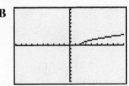

D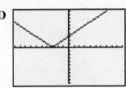

For Exercises 21 through 24, match each equation to its graph.

21. $f(x) = |x - 4|$

22. $f(x) = |x + 3|$

23. $f(x) = \sqrt{x + 2}$

24. $f(x) = \sqrt{x - 2}$

A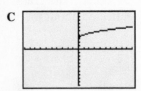

B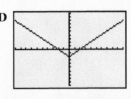

C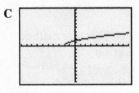

D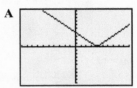

Sketch the graph of function. See Examples 3 through 6.

25. $y = (x - 4)^2$

26. $y = (x + 4)^2$

27. $f(x) = x^2 + 4$

28. $f(x) = x^2 - 4$

29. $f(x) = \sqrt{x - 2} + 3$

30. $f(x) = \sqrt{x - 1} + 3$

31. $f(x) = |x - 1| + 5$

32. $f(x) = |x - 3| + 2$

33. $f(x) = \sqrt{x + 1} + 1$

34. $f(x) = \sqrt{x + 3} + 2$

35. $f(x) = |x + 3| - 1$

36. $f(x) = |x + 1| - 4$

37. $g(x) = (x - 1)^2 - 1$

38. $h(x) = (x + 2)^2 + 2$

39. $f(x) = (x + 3)^2 - 2$

40. $f(x) = (x + 2)^2 + 4$

Sketch the graph of each function. See Examples 3 through 7.

41. $f(x) = -(x - 1)^2$

42. $g(x) = -(x + 2)^2$

43. $h(x) = -\sqrt{x} + 3$

44. $f(x) = -\sqrt{x + 3}$

45. $h(x) = -|x + 2| + 3$

46. $g(x) = -|x + 1| + 1$

47. $f(x) = (x - 3) + 2$

48. $f(x) = (x - 1) + 4$

REVIEW AND PREVIEW

Match each equation with its graph.

49. $y = -1$

50. $x = -1$

51. $x = 3$

52. $y = 3$

A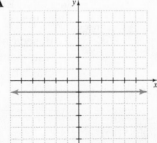

B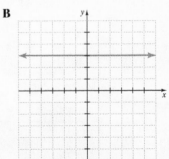

C 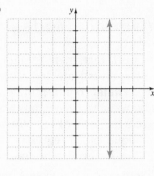 **D**

CONCEPT EXTENSIONS

53. Draw a graph whose domain is $\{x \mid x \leq 5\}$ and whose range is $\{y \mid y \geq 2\}$.

54. In your own words, describe how to graph a piecewise-defined function.

55. Graph: $f(x) = \begin{cases} -\dfrac{1}{2}x & \text{if } x \leq 0 \\ x + 1 & \text{if } 0 < x \leq 2 \\ 2x - 1 & \text{if } x > 2 \end{cases}$

56. Graph: $f(x) = \begin{cases} -\dfrac{1}{3}x & \text{if } x \leq 0 \\ x + 2 & \text{if } 0 < x \leq 4 \\ 3x - 4 & \text{if } x > 4 \end{cases}$

Write the domain and range of the following exercises.

57. Exercise 29

58. Exercise 30

59. Exercise 45

60. Exercise 46

Without graphing, find the domain of each function.

61. $f(x) = 5\sqrt{x - 20} + 1$

62. $g(x) = -3\sqrt{x + 5}$

63. $h(x) = 5|x - 20| + 1$

64. $f(x) = -3|x + 5.7|$

65. $g(x) = 9 - \sqrt{x + 103}$

66. $h(x) = \sqrt{x - 17} - 3$

Sketch the graph of each piecewise-defined function. Write the domain and range of each function.

67. $f(x) = \begin{cases} |x| & \text{if } x \leq 0 \\ x^2 & \text{if } x > 0 \end{cases}$

68. $f(x) = \begin{cases} x^2 & \text{if } x < 0 \\ \sqrt{x} & \text{if } x \geq 0 \end{cases}$

69. $g(x) = \begin{cases} |x - 2| & \text{if } x < 0 \\ -x^2 & \text{if } x \geq 0 \end{cases}$

70. $g(x) = \begin{cases} -|x + 1| - 1 & \text{if } x < -2 \\ \sqrt{x + 2} - 4 & \text{if } x \geq -2 \end{cases}$

8.7 Interpreting Data: Linear and Quadratic Models

As we have seen thus far in our text, many situations arise that involve two related quantities. We saw that we can investigate and record certain facts about these situations, and that these are called **data.** To *model* the data means to find an equation that describes the relationship between the given data quantities. Visually, the graph of the *best fit equation* should have a majority of the plotted ordered pair data points on the graph or close to it. A technique called **regression** is used to determine an equation that best fits two-quantity data. In this text, we concentrate on modeling ordered pair data points with an equation that visually appears to best fit the data points. In this section, we will also check the r^2 or R^2 numbers, called coefficients of determination. The best fit occurs when r^2 or R^2 is close to 1.

Recall that an equation that best fits a set of ordered pair data points is called a regression equation. Keep in mind that no model, or equation, may fit the data exactly, but a model should fit the data closely enough so that useful predictions may be made using it. Most importantly, know that when we use an equation to make predictions in the future, we are assuming that future data is also modeled by the equation.

An important caution should be made about regression equations and using such equations for predictions.

Just because an r^2 or R^2 coefficient of determination is closer to 1, it absolutely does *not* mean that this equation will be a better predictor of future trends. Often, companies model past and present data using many regression equations. Predictions are then made based on R^2 values, the economy, and other restrictions and data.

OBJECTIVE

1   Plotting Data Points and Using a Linear or Quadratic Model

In this section, we concentrate on two models, linear and quadratic. These models are shown below for your review.

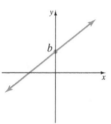

Linear Model
$y = mx + b$
slope: m
y-intercept: (0, b)

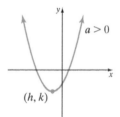

Quadratic Model
$y = ax^2 + bx + c$
$a > 0$, *parabola opens upward*
$a < 0$, *parabola opens downward*

vertex: (h, k) where $h = \dfrac{-b}{2a}$

EXAMPLE 1   **Determining the Better Model for the Cost of a U.S. First-Class Postage Stamp**

The cost of U.S. first-class postage stamps has risen over the years between 1917 and 2012.

Years since 1900	17	19	32	58	63	68	71	74	75	78	81
Cost	3	2	3	4	5	6	8	10	13	18	20

Years since 1900	85	88	91	101	102	106	107	108	109	112
Cost	22	25	29	34	37	39	41	42	44	45

a. Graph the data in the table. Let $x = 0$ represent the year 1900.

b. Find a linear regression equation that models the data.

c. Find a quadratic equation that models the data.

d. Find which regression equation is the better fit by looking at the R^2 values and the graphs of each equation. Use that equation to predict the cost of a first-class stamp in the year 2020 if the trend continues.

Solution

a. Enter the number of years since 1900 in List 1 and the cost of the stamp in List 2. Draw a scatter plot as shown to the left below.

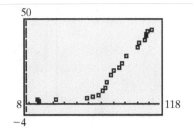 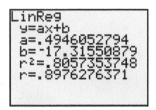

b. The linear regression equation is $y = 0.495x - 17.316$, as shown to the right above. (This equation was stored in Y_1.)

c.

The quadratic regression equation is $y = 0.008x^2 - 0.536x + 9.815$, as shown above. (This equation was stored in Y_2.)

d. From looking at both regression equations' R^2 values, we see that the quadratic equation appears to be the better fit, since its R^2 value is closer to 1. The graph of the two equations with the data confirms that the quadratic equation $y = 0.008x^2 - 0.536x + 9.815$ is the better fit.

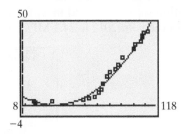 

If the trend continues to rise at the same rate, we can predict the cost of a U.S. first-class postage stamp in the year 2020 to be approximately 57 cents.   □

PRACTICE

1   Use the Example 1 data from the years 1971 and later. Answer parts **b, c,** and **d** from Example 1. For part **d,** use the regression equation whose r^2 or R^2 value is closer to 1.

....

EXAMPLE 2   Models for Fuel Consumption

The table on the next page shows the average miles per gallon (MPG) for U.S. cars in the years shown. (*Source:* U.S. Federal Highway Administration)

Year	2000	2001	2002	2003	2004	2005	2006	2007	2008	2009	2010
Average MPG	22.9	23.0	23.1	23.2	23.1	23.5	23.3	23.4	23.7	23.8	23.5

a. Graph the data points. Let x represent the number of years since 2000.

b. Find and graph a linear regression equation that models the data.

c. Use the equation to predict the average MPG for U.S. cars in the year 2017.

Solution

a. List the years in L_1 and the average MPG in L_2. (For L_1, enter the number of years past 2000.) Then draw a scatter plot as shown below.

Notice that for the most part, the graph resembles the graph of a line.

b. To find and graph the linear regression equation that models this data, select LinReg $(ax + b)$ from the Stat Calc menu. Enter L_1, L_2, Y_1 so that the screen reads LinReg $(ax + b)$ L_1, L_2, Y_1. This instructs the calculator to use L_1 and L_2 as x and y lists and enters the regression equation in the $Y =$ editor as Y_1.

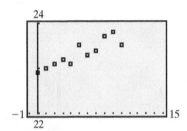

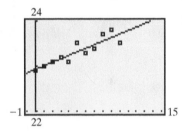

The linear regression equation is $y = 0.078x + 22.927$, where a and b values are rounded to three decimal places.

c. To predict the average MPG for the year 2017, we evaluate the linear regression equation we have stored in Y_1 for 17 $(2017 - 2000 = 17)$. The predicted MPG for cars in the year 2017 is 24.3 MPG rounded to the nearest tenth.

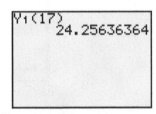

Technology Note

When predicting values of x that lie outside of the chosen window, it is easier to look at a table or evaluate the function $Y_1(x)$.

PRACTICE

2   Use the data in Example 2 for the years 2002, 2004, 2006, 2010.

a. Find a linear regression equation that models the data.

b. Find a quadratic regression equation that models the data.

c. Use both equations to predict the average MPG for the year 2017.

d. Discuss the R^2 value for part **a** and why it is now closer to 1 as compared to Example 2.

For the next example, we study the increase in sport utility vehicle (SUV) sales.

EXAMPLE 3   **Models for SUV Sales**

The table below represents the retail sales in millions of sport utility vehicles (SUVs) for selected years 1996 through 2012.

Year	SUV Sales (in millions)
1996	2
1998	2.9
2000	3.5
2002	4.2
2004	4.7
2006	4.5
2010	4.1
2012	3.8

(*Source:* American Automobile Manufacturer's Assoc.)

a. Let x = the number of years since 1990 and graph the data points. Use the graph to visually identify the type of function that best fits the data.

b. Find the corresponding regression equation for the data and then graph the results.

c. If the sales trend continues in the same manner, predict the number of SUVs that we would expect to sell in the year 2018.

Solution

a. List the years in L_1 and the SUV sales in L_2. (For L_1, enter the number of years past 1990.) Then draw a scatter plot as shown below.

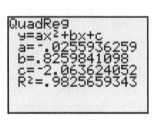

Since a quadratic function appears to best fit the data, we will model the data with a quadratic regression equation.

b. Select QuadReg from the Stat Calc menu. Enter L_1, L_2, Y_1, so that the screen reads QuadReg L_1, L_2, Y_1. This instructs the calculator to use L_1 and L_2 as x and y lists and enters the regression equation in the Y = editor as Y_1.

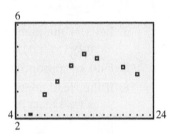

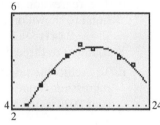

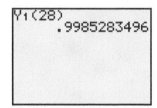

Quadratic regression equation.

Graph of quadratic regression equation.

Projected SUV sales in 2018.

The quadratic regression equation is

$$y = -0.026x^2 + 0.826x - 2.064$$

with a, b, and c values rounded to 3 decimal places.

c. To predict SUV sales for the year 2018, we evaluate the quadratic regression equation we have stored in Y_1 for 2018. The predicted SUV sales for the year 2018 is 1.0 million SUVs, rounded to the nearest tenth of a million.   □

3 The table shows yearly truck sales for a local dealership.

Year	2000	2003	2006	2009	2012
Trucks Sold	362	390	407	433	457

Let x = the number of years since 2000 and answer Example 3 questions **a** and **b**. For part **c**, predict the truck sales in 2019.

For Example 4 below, we see how using different years (including prediction years) can greatly affect future predictions. Be very careful when making predictions with regression equations—especially with quadratic regressions.

The number of broadband connections in the U.S. represents the total number of Internet connections with a speed of more than 200 kilobits per second (includes households and businesses with broadband connections).

EXAMPLE 4 Broadband Connection Growth

The table below shows the number of U.S. broadband connections in millions—some are predictions.

Year	2009	2011	2013	2015	2017
Broadband Connections (in millions)	124.0	206.6	263.3	303.9	326.2

(*Source:* Federal Communications Commission)

a. Let x = the number of years since 2000. Plot the data points and use the graph to identify the type of function that appears to best fit the data.

b. Find an appropriate regression equation for the data and then graph the results.

c. If the trend continues in the same pattern, find the number of broadband connections we expect in 2020.

Solution

a. Enter the data in L_1 (years since 2000) and L_2 (number of broadband connections) and draw a scatter plot.

The graph resembles a part of a parabola so we will model the data with a quadratic regression equation.

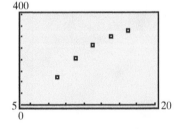

Graphed data points.

b. The regression results and the graph of the equation are shown on the screens below. The equation is $y = -2.441x^2 + 88.553x - 474.318$ with a, b, and c rounded to three decimal places.

c. To predict the number of broadband connections in 2020, we evaluate the quadratic regression equation we stored in Y_1 for $x = 20$. The projected connections for the year 2020 is 320.3 rounded to the nearest tenth of a million.

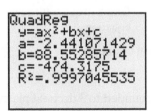

Quadratic regression equation

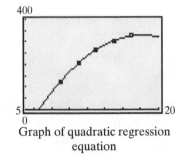

Graph of quadratic regression equation

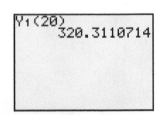

Predicted number of broadband connections for 2020 in millions

PRACTICE

4   Use the table below for data in Example 4. Let $x =$ the number of years since the year 2000 and answer Example 4, parts **b** and **c**.

Year	2010	2012	2014	2016	2018
Broadband Connections (in millions)	159.2	237.2	287.8	316.7	336.0

EXAMPLE 5   The value of each year's diamond production has not decreased for the years shown. Use the table below, which gives the value in billions of dollars for the corresponding year. Let $x = 0$ be the number of years since the year 2000.

Year	2005	2006	2007	2008	2011	2012
Value (in billions of dollars)	11.6	12.1	12.1	12.7	14.4	15.9

a. Find the curve of best fit.

b. Use the regression equation to predict the value in billions of dollars in the year 2019.

Solution

a. Graph a scatter plot of the data in a [5, 15, 1] by [11, 20, 1] window. We see that the graph appears to be quadratic and from the data, we can see that the value is increasing and we expect it to continue to increase over time.

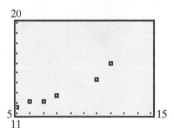

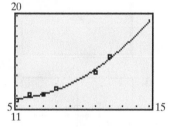

The linear regression equation is $y = 0.070x^2 - 0.634x + 13.155$.

b. Using the equation we can see that we should expect $26.5 billion in the year 2019.   □

PRACTICE

5   The data below shows the average cinema ticket price for the U.S.

Year	2002	2004	2006	2008	2010	2012
Average ticket price	5.81	6.21	6.55	7.18	7.89	8.12*

Source: Motion Picture Association of America *preliminary

a. Let x represent the number of years since 2000. Find a linear or quadratic equation of best fit.

b. Use the results of part **a** to predict the average ticket price in 2019.

In this section, we concentrated on linear and quadratic regression equations only. There are many other types of regression equations that can be used as models and there are advantages and disadvantages of each. Proceed with regression equations carefully and know that we have only looked at the tip of the regression analysis iceberg.

Vocabulary, Readiness & Video Check

Martin-Gay Interactive Videos

See Video 8.7

Watch the section lecture video and answer the following questions.

OBJECTIVE
1

1. Based on Example 3, how can you determine if a linear or a quadratic regression equation would best represent a data set?

8.7 Exercise Set

MyMathLab®

Solve. Predictions using regression equations may differ slightly depending on the rounding of coefficients in the equation to different place values. Given the following graphs of data points, tell whether the graph is likely to be best represented by a linear model, a quadratic model, or neither. See Examples 1 through 5.

1.
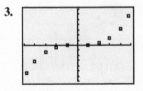

2.
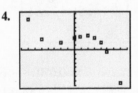

3.
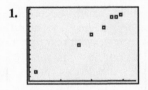

4.
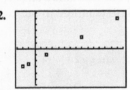

5.
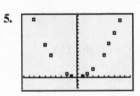

6.
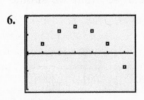

7.
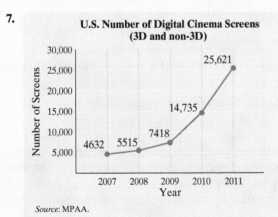

U.S. Number of Digital Cinema Screens (3D and non-3D)

4632 5515 7418 14,735 25,621

Year

Source: MPAA.

8.
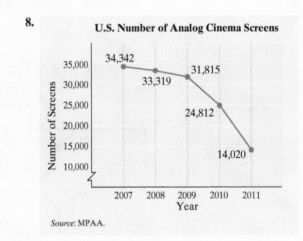

U.S. Number of Analog Cinema Screens

34,342 33,319 31,815 24,812 14,020

Year

Source: MPAA.

MIXED PRACTICE

For each exercise tell whether the graph is likely to be best represented by a linear model, a quadratic model, or neither. If linear or quadratic, find a linear or quadratic regression equation that models the given data. Round the coefficients to three decimal places. Then use the equation to answer the question. Let x = the number of years since 2000. If the graphed data do not appear linear or quadratic, write "not linear or quadratic" and you are through with that exercise. See Examples 1 through 5.

9. The table below shows the number of U.S. wildfires in the odd years 2001–2011. If there is a trend, predict the number of U.S. wildfires in 2016.

Year	2001	2003	2005	2007	2009	2011
No. of Wildfires (in thousands)	84.1	57.6	66.6	85.7	78.8	73.5

10. The table below shows the Canon, Inc., net sales (in billions of yen) for the years 2007–2012.* If there is a trend, predict the net sales in the year 2017.

Year	2007	2008	2009	2010	2011	2012*
Net Sales (in billions of yen)	4481	4094	3209	3707	3557	3532

Hint: No need to convert from yen. (*Source*: Canon, Inc. 2012* projected)

11. The table below shows the median weekly earnings of full-time wage and salary workers 25 years and older with some years of college. If this trend continues, predict the median weekly earnings in 2017. For this exercise, find a linear and a quadratic regression equation and use both to predict the earnings in 2017.

Year	2002	2004	2006	2008	2010
Weekly Earnings (in dollars)	571	580	620	626	621

12. In order to see the value of attaining a bachelor's degree, study the following data from the U.S. Bureau of Labor Statistics. This table shows mean weekly earnings of full-time wage and salary workers 25 years and older with a bachelor's degree. If there is a trend, predict the mean weekly earnings in 2017.

Year	2002	2004	2006	2008	2010
Weekly Earnings (in dollars)	985	992	1092	1127	1089

13. Use the data in Exercise 7 to write a quadratic regression equation. Then predict the number of digital cinema screens in 2015. Let x = the number of years since 2000.

14. Use the data in Exercise 8 to write a regression equation. Then predict the number of U.S. analog cinemas in the year 2012. Let x = the number of years since 2000.

15. Suppose your regression equation predicts a population of 500,000,000 U.S. citizens in 2014. Discuss the limitations of such a regression equation.

16. Suppose your regression equation predicts a population of 10 billion in 2014. Discuss the limitations of such a regression equation.

17. The table shows the number of cell sites in the U.S.

Year	2000	2002	2004	2006	2008	2010	2012
Cell Sites (in thousands)	96	131	174	198	220	252	286

Let x = the number of years since 2000. Round regression coefficients to 3 decimal places.
   a. Write a linear regression equation.
   b. Write a quadratic regression equation.
   c. Use each regression equation to predict the number of cell sites in the year 2018. Round to the nearest whole thousand.
   d. Choose a prediction from part **c** that you think is the better prediction and explain why.

18. The table shows the estimated wireless subscribers in the U.S.

Year	2000	2002	2004	2006	2008	2010	2012
Wireless Subscribers (in millions)	97	135	169	220	263	293	322

Let x = the number of years since 2000. Round regression coefficients to 3 decimal places.
   a. Write a linear regression equation.
   b. Write a quadratic regression equation.
   c. Use each regression equation to predict the number of wireless subscribers in the U.S. in 2017. Round to the nearest whole million. (A person may subscribe to more than one wireless service.)
   d. Choose a prediction from part **c** that you think is the better prediction and explain why.

19. A tennis shoe manufacturer is studying the suggested selling price of a certain brand of tennis shoe. The suggested selling price cannot be too low or the cost of manufacturing the shoes will not be covered, and it cannot be too high or people will not purchase the shoes. Below are data collected for selling tennis shoes at various prices and the corresponding profit.

Price (in dollars)	39	49	65	75	85	95	105
Profit (in dollars)	9500	16,750	19,600	19,500	15,475	7500	1500

   a. Plot the data points and use the graph to determine whether a linear or quadratic regression equation would best represent the data.
   b. Find a regression equation for this data, where x is price of the tennis shoes and y is profit.
   c. Using the model, find the projected profit if the shoes are sold for $80 and for $60.
   d. Use the table to find the profit if the shoes are sold for $105. Is this a good selling price? Why or why not?
   e. Using the model, find the selling price, to the nearest dollar, that will yield the maximum profit.

20. Below are data collected for selling men's and women's flip flop shoes.

Price (in dollars)	5	15	25	35	45	55
Profit (in dollars)	2750	5816	6225	5611	4527	3199

Answer Exercise 19, **a., b., e.**

Given the following data for four houses sold in comparable neighborhoods and their corresponding number of square feet, draw a scatter plot and find a linear regression equation that best fits the relationship between the number of square feet and the selling price of the house.

21.

Square Feet	1754	2151	2587	2671
Selling Price	$90,900	$130,000	$155,000	$172,500

22.

Square Feet	1519	2593	3005	3016
Selling Price	$91,238	$220,000	$254,000	$269,000

23. Use the equation found in Exercise 21 to predict the selling price of a house with 2400 square feet.

24. Use the equation found in Exercise 22 to predict the selling price of a house with 2200 square feet.

25. Find a quadratic equation that models the decline in physical recorded music revenue (not digital). Let x = number of years since 2000 and y be the physical recorded music revenue in millions of dollars. Use this model to fill in the predicted physical revenue below and compare with the actual given data.

x (year)	Actual Physical Music Revenue (in millions of dollars)	Predicted Revenue (in millions of dollars)	Difference between Actual and Predicted
2008	5540		
2009	4432		
2010	3656		
2011	3108		
2012	2673		
2013	2325		
2014	2046		

26. Find a quadratic equation that models the global annual consumption of cigarettes per person, where x = number of years since 1960 and y is the number of cigarettes. Use this model to fill in the predicted consumption of cigarettes below and compare with the actual given data.

x (year)	Actual Consumption (per person)	Predicted Consumption (per person)	Difference between Actual and Predicted
1960	707		
1970	880		
1980	1000		
1990	1010		
2000	939		
2009	870		

Plot the following points and then find a regression equation that best models the data. Let x = 3 represent March, x = 4 represent April, and so on. For each exercise, explain the limitation of the regression equation that you found.

27. The table below shows the average temperature in Wellington, New Zealand, for the months of March through October.

March	April	May	June	July	August	Sept	Oct
60	57	52	49	47	48	51	54

28. The table below shows the average temperature in Louisville, Kentucky, for the months of March through October.

March	April	May	June	July	August	Sept	Oct
45	57	65	74	78	76	70	58

State whether the relationship described can best be modeled by a linear function or a quadratic function.

29. The area of a square *and* the length of one side.

30. A salary of $300 per week plus 5% commission on sales *and* weekly sales.

31. A number of calculators sold each week at a store *and* their cost, plus tax.

32. The area of a circle *and* the radius of the circle

33. The average temperature of Cleveland, Ohio, *and* the months of March through October.

34. An oven is turned on and set to reach 400 degrees. After it reaches the desired temperature, it is shut off. Temperatures are recorded every 2 minutes, from the time the oven is turned on until it cools to room temperature.

35. The number of bacteria present in a person with respect to time when he is coming down with the flu, has the flu, and then recovers.

36. The distance traveled during a recent trip with respect to the amount of time elapsed.

REVIEW AND PREVIEW

Solve each of the following equations. See Sections 1.5 and 5.8.

37. $(x + 3)(x - 5) = 0$

38. $(x - 1)(x + 19) = 0$

39. $2x^2 - 7x - 15 = 0$

40. $6x^2 + 13x - 5 = 0$

41. $3(x - 4) + 2 = 5(x - 6)$

42. $4(2x + 7) = 2(x - 4)$

Find the y-intercept of the graph of each function. See Section 2.3.

43. $f(x) = x^3 + 3x^2 - 5x - 8$

44. $f(x) = 2x^3 + x^2 - 7x + 12$

45. $g(x) = x^2 - 3x + 5$

46. $g(x) = 3x^2 - 5x - 10$

Appendix E

Graphing Stat Plots and Regression Equations

To review graphing Stat Plots and Regressions Equations, we will use a linear model, but the procedure is the same if the data is modeled by a quadratic, cubic, exponential, or any other equation. (For any additional help, consult your graphing utility manual.)

1. **Collect the data.** The table below shows the number of two-income families, which has risen since 1970. For this table,

   $x = 0$ represents the number of years since 1970 and the y-values are the number of two-income families (in millions).

   Calculate a linear regression and use this equation to predict the number of two-income families in 2015.

Year (x)	0	5	10	15	20	30	35	37
Number of Couples (y)	15.3	16.5	20.1	21.5	24	26.4	30.6	31.2

▶ Helpful Hint

Before entering the data in Lists, know that Lists (L1, L2, L3, etc.) often get deleted and/or rearranged as you use them. To arrange back in numerical order, go to the Stat, Edit menu. Choose SetupEditor and press Enter twice. Make sure you see Done on the Home Screen. (See the below left screen.)

2. **Enter the data in Lists** by pressing Stat, Edit, Enter. Next, to enter the data in two

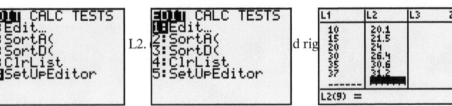

3. **To Create a Stat Plot of this data,** go to Plot1 by pressing 2nd, Y=, Enter. (See the below left screen.)

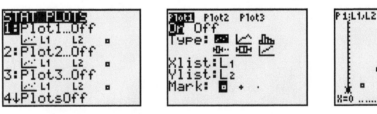

Use this screen (see above middle screen) to indicate that the Type of graph you want is a scatter plot, the XList is in L1, the YList in L2, and we choose a square as the plotting mark. Next choose an appropriate window that will contain all the data points. (Pressing Zoom, ZoomStat will instruct the calculator to automatically choose a window to fit the data.) (See the above right screen.)

4. **Now calculate the linear regression equation** and paste it in Y1. Press Stat, Calc, LinReg(ax + b). We next indicate that the *x*-list is found in L1 and the *y*-list is found in L2, and paste the linear regression equation in Y1. (See the below left screen.) Press Enter and the regression equation is calculated and pasted in Y1. (See the below right screen.)

 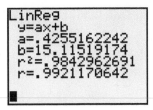

When you press the Y = editor, you can see that the equation is automatically entered into Y1. (See the below left screen.) Press graph and you will see the graph of Y1 along with the plotted data. (See the below middle screen.)

 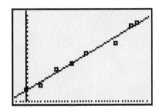 

5. **Make the prediction.** If the trend continues to rise at the same rate, let's predict the number of two-income families by the year 2015. The regression equation is in Y1, so first return to the home screen. To paste Y1 on the home screen, press VARS, Y-VARS, FUNCTION, Y1. To calculate Y1 for the year 2015, remember that *x* = 0 represents the number of years since 1970, so we calculate Y1 for 45 (2015–1970.) (See the above right screen.)

If the trend continues, we can expect to see approximately 34.263 million two-income families in the year 2015.

Answers to Selected Exercises

CHAPTER 2 GRAPHS AND FUNCTIONS

Section 2.6

Practice Exercises

1. ≈ 12.06 billion   **2.** 81.4 tablet PC sales in 2020; the average increase in the number of sales of tablet PCs in the USA between 2010 and 2015 is 6.5 per year.   **3. b.** $y = 0.25x + 2.33$; increasing line, slope is positive   **c.** The number of sick or injured workers is increasing at a rate of 0.25 per 100 workers per year.   **d.** 9.33 per 100 workers in the year 2018   **4. a.** $y = 195.91x + 38,438.48$ **b.** $364,040.90   **5.** 46.22%

Vocabulary, Readiness & Video Check 2.6

1. Regression analysis   **3.** Stat Plot; scatter plot   **5.** linear regression equation

Exercise Set 2.6

1. 65.03 billion dollars   **3.** 2000   **5. a.** $y = 102.054x - 758.049$ **b.** 102.054 million per year   **c.** 1078.923 million or 1.078923 billion
7. a. $y = -0.725x + 52.56$ **b.** 9.0%   **c.** 0.725%   **9. a.** $y = 47.143x + 269.929$ **b.** 2156 thousand or 2,156,000 male prisoners
c. 47 thousand or 47,000 per year   **11. a.** 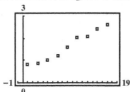   **b.** $y = 0.212x + 12.04$ **c.** The number of workers over 65 is increasing at the rate of 0.212% per year.   **d.** We can expect to see about 18.4% of our workforce over 65 by the year 2020.

13. $y = 114.453x - 81,378.675$ **15.** $170,418   **17.** $y = 0.08x + 700$ **19. a.** $y = 0.268x + 48.587$ **b.** The life expectancy at birth of males is increasing at the rate of 0.268 year annually.   **c.** 80.2 years old   **21. a.** $y = 8.212x + 41.160$ **b.** 287.51 million members   **c.** 2014
d. The number of PPO members is increasing at the rate of 8.212 million per year.   **23. a.** $y = 3.786x - 9.899$ **b.** $179.40 per ticket
c. $3.79 per year   **25. a.** 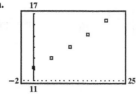   **b.** $y = 0.124x + 0.505$ **c.** The cost is increasing at the rate of 0.124 million, or $124,000 per year.   **d.** $3.357 million or $3,357,000   **27.** 8   **29.** $\dfrac{1}{10}$

31. a. full service: $y = 7.157x + 62.484$; fast food: $y = 5.971x + 69.452$ **b.** 1996

Section 2.7

Practice Exercises

1. $f(4) = 5; f(-2) = 6; f(0) = -2$ **2.**   **3.**   **4.**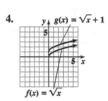

5. 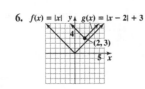   **6.**   **7.**

Vocabulary, Readiness & Video Check 2.7

1. C   **3.** D   **5.** Although $f(x) = x + 3$ isn't defined for $x = -1$, we need to clearly indicate the point where this piece of the graph ends. Therefore, we find this point and graph it as an open circle.   **7.** x-axis

Exercise Set 2.7

1.   **3.**   **5.**   **7.**   **9.**   domain: all real numbers; range: $\{y | y \geq 0\}$:

A1

11. domain: all real numbers; range: $\{y|y < 5\}$

13. domain: all real numbers; range: $\{y|y \leq 6\}$

15. domain: $\{x|x \leq 0 \text{ or } x \geq 1\}$; range: $\{-4, -2\}$

17. A   **19.** B   **21.** A   **23.** C   **25.**   **27.**   **29.**

31.   **33.**   **35.**   **37.**   **39.**

41.   **43.**   **45.**   **47.**   **49.** A   **51.** D   **53.** answers may vary

55.

57. domain: $\{x|x \geq 2\}$; range: $\{y|y \geq 3\}$ **59.** domain: all real numbers; range: $\{y|y \leq 3\}$ **61.** $\{x|x \geq 20\}$ **63.** all real numbers

65. $\{x|x \geq -103\}$ **67.** domain: all real numbers; range: $\{y|y \geq 0\}$ **69.** domain: all real numbers; range: $\{y|y \leq 0 \text{ or } y > 2\}$

CHAPTER 8 QUADRATIC EQUATIONS AND FUNCTIONS

Section 8.7

Practice Exercises

1. b. $y = 0.874x - 52.438$ **c.** $y = -0.004x^2 + 1.656x - 87.469$ **d.** quadratic regression equation; 50¢   **2. a.** $y = 0.054x + 22.951$
b. $y = 0.002x^2 + 0.026x + 23.016$ **c.** linear model: 23.9 MPG; quadratic model: 24.1 MPG   **d.** answers may vary   **3. a.** linear   **b.** $y = 7.767x + 363.2$
c. 511 truck sales in 2019   **4. b.** $y = -2.484x^2 + 91.205x - 502.769$ **c.** 327.8 million connections   **5. a.** $y = 0.003x^2 + 0.207x + 5.343$ **b.** $10.28

Vocabulary, Readiness & Video Check 8.7

1. Create a scatter plot of the data. If the data points appear to form a line, then a linear regression equation would be best; if they appear to form a parabola, then a quadratic regression equation would be best.

Exercise Set 8.7

1. linear   **3.** neither   **5.** quadratic   **7.** quadratic   **9.** not linear or quadratic   **11.** $y = 7.3x + 559.8$; $684;
$y = -1.107x^2 + 20.586x + 528.8$; $559   **13.** quadratic; $y = 1815.714x^2 - 27,563.057x + 108,947.429$; 104,037 theaters   **15.** answers may vary
17. a. $y = 15.321x + 101.929$ **b.** $y = -0.190x^2 + 17.607x + 98.119$ **c.** linear: 378 thousand sites in 2018; quadratic: 353 thousand sites in
2018   **d.** answers may vary   **19. a.** quadratic   **b.** $y = -13.010x^2 + 1727.626x - 37,489.948$ **c.** $17,457 profit at $80; $19,332 profit at $60
d. $1500; no; answers may vary   **e.** $66   **21.** $y = 82.509x - 51,908.333$ **23.** $146,113
25.

Predicted Revenue (in millions of dollars)	Difference Between Actual and Predicted Revenue (in millions of dollars)
5465	75
4517	−85
3725	−69
3087	21
2605	68
2277	48
2105	−59

27. $y = 0.75x^2 - 10.774x + 86.655$; answers may vary

29. quadratic   **31.** linear   **33.** quadratic   **35.** quadratic

37. $-3, 5$ **39.** $-\dfrac{3}{2}, 5$ **41.** 10   **43.** $(0, -8)$ **45.** $(0, 5)$

Index

Absolute value, 40, 42, 81, 397, 399
Absolute value function, 370–371,
    380, 387
Abstraction, model as, 211
Addends, 45
Addition
    associative property for, 62, 68
    commutative property for, 60–61, 68
    of fractions, 18–22
    of opposites, 82
    of polynomials, 278–280, 283, 314
    of real numbers, 45–47, 49, 82
    words associated with, 48
Addition property
    of equality, 91–93, 97, 137
    of inequalities, 127–128, 133, 139
Additive identity, 65–66
Additive inverse, 34–35, 66, 68, 81, 280
Algebraic expression, 4, 8, 79
    evaluating, with one variable, 5
    evaluating, with two variables, 5
    simplifying and writing, 71–76, 83
Angles, measuring, 113–114, 119,
    138–139
Approximately equal, 37
Area
    of boxes, 115–116
    calculating, 113
    of circle, 114, 120, 139, 545–546, 583
    of parallelogram, 543, 544, 583
    of rectangle, 7, 112, 119, 138–139,
        542, 583
    of square, 27, 542, 583
    of trapezoid, 115, 120, 139, 543, 583
    of triangle, 112, 119, 138–139, 543,
        544, 583
Associative properties
    for addition, 62, 68
    for multiplication, 62, 68
    of real numbers, 83
Associativity of operations, 63
Asymptotes, 376, 378
Average (mean), 497–498
Average number, 38–39, 41, 81
Axis of symmetry, 412–413, 466

Bar graphs, 513–515
Base of an exponential expression, 27, 28,
    31, 313
Bases, exponents and, 268–269, 274
Basic principle of fractions, 12, 13

Binomials, 277, 313
    multiplication of, 289, 290
Boxes
    surface area of, 115, 139
    volume of, 115–116, 120, 139
Braces, 91
Bytes, 29

Celsius, converting to/from Fahrenheit,
    572–574, 584
Centimeter, 564
Checking a result, 137, 307, 311
Circle graphs, 525–528
Circles
    area of, 114, 120, 139, 545–546, 583
    finding circumference of, 114, 120,
        536–537, 583
Circular cylinder
    surface area of, 547, 549
    volume of, 547, 549, 583
Circumference, 114, 120, 138–139,
    535–536, 583
Class frequency, 515
Class interval, 515
Coefficient
    of monomial, 277
    of a term, 71–72, 76, 83
Common denominators
    addition and subtraction of fractions
        with, 19
    least common denominator (LCD),
        19–21
Common factors, 12
    greatest. See Greatest common factor
        (GCF)
    smallest common prime factor, 13
Commutative properties
    for addition, 60–61, 68
    for multiplication, 60–61, 68
    of real numbers, 83
Completing the square method
    to find complex solutions, 460
    to solve quadratic equations, 445–446,
        449, 467
    writing vertex form by, 431–432, 436
Complex solutions, 458–460, 467
Composite numbers, 3–4, 8, 79
Compound inequalities
    basic concepts, 358–359
    interval notation, 364–365, 387
    numerical and graphical solutions, 363

symbolic solutions and number lines,
    359–363
Compound interest, 481–483, 486, 491
Cone
    surface area of, 547, 550
    volume of, 547, 550, 582
Consistent system, 233, 237
Constant function, 348, 351
Continuous growth, 484
Contradiction, 107
Conversions
    between decimals and fractions, 55,
        58, 83
    between inches and feet, 4
    between temperature scales, 34,
        118–119, 121
Convex solid, 546–550
Coordinates, 148–150
Correlation coefficient, 599
Cost, 378
Counting numbers, 8
Cube
    surface area of, 548
    volume of, 548, 582
Cube root function, 403–404, 408
Cube roots, 397, 398
Cubed, 27
Cubic function, 371
Cubic units, 546
Cylinders, volume of, 116, 120, 139

Data
    fitting line to, 599
    plotting, 598
    plotting points using linear or quadratic
        model, 616–621
    working with, 34
Decay factor, 475
Decimal places, 37
Decimal windows, 378
Decimals
    clearing, 105–106, 138
    converting to/from fractions, 55, 58, 83
    mean, 497–498
    median, 498–499
    mode, 499
    repeating, 36
    terminating, 36, 58
Decreasing, 434
Degree
    of angles, 113–114

Degree *(continued)*
  measuring, 138–139
  of monomial, 277
  of polynomials, 277
Denominator, 11–12, 80. *See also* Least
  common denominator (LCD)
Dependent equations, 233, 237
Dependent variable, 321, 334
Diagrammatic representation (diagram), 324
Diameter, 114
Difference, 6, 47
Discriminant, 457–458, 467
Distributive properties
  polynomials and, 278, 292, 314
  of real numbers, 63–65, 68, 83
  review of, 287
  to solve linear equations, 104–105, 138
Dividend, 53, 82
Division
  checking a result, 307, 311
  of fractions, 14–18, 80
  by monomials, 306–308, 310
  of polynomials, 306–311, 315
  of real numbers, 53–56, 58, 82–83
Divisor, 53, 82
Domain
  of cube root function, 403
  of function, 327–329, 334, 386
  in interval notation, 370, 380, 387
  of square root function, 401–402, 403
Dot (·), to indicate multiplication, 4
Dot mode, 378
Double negative rule, 35

Edge, of polyhedron, 547
Einstein, Albert, 395
Elimination, solving systems of linear
  equations by, 249–257, 261–262
English measurement system
  converting between Celsius and
    Fahrenheit, 574–575
  converting between metric system and,
    572–574
  defining and converting, 560–561
  performing operations on units of
    length, 563–564, 584
  using mixed units of length, 562
Equality
  addition property of, 91–93, 97, 137
  multiplication property of, 94–96,
    97, 137
Equations, 4, 5, 8, 79, 137
  equivalent, 91, 96
  identifying types of, 234
  of a line, 201
  linear. *See* Linear equations
  for linear regression, 599
  quadratic. *See* Quadratic equations
  solving for variable, 446–447
  in two variables, 161
  using table to solve, 101–102
Equivalent equations, 91, 96, 137

Even root, 399
Exponent, 27, 28, 31
Exponential decay, 475, 491
Exponential expression, 27, 31, 80, 313
Exponential functions
  basic concepts, 474–476
  compound interest, 481–483, 486, 491
  graphs of, 476–478, 485
  linear functions and, 478
  models involving, 483–484
  natural, 484–485, 486
  percent change and, 479–481, 485,
    486, 491
  polynomial functions and, 478
Exponential growth, 475, 491
Exponential notation, 28–29
Exponents
  bases and, 268–269, 274, 313
  natural number, 26–29
  negative integers as, 295–297, 315
  other rules for, 298–299
  power rules, 271–274
  the product rule, 270–271, 274
  zero, 269–270, 274
Expressions
  simplifying, 73–76
  translating words to, 6–7
  writing, 75–76

Face, of polyhedron, 547
Factor trees, 3
Factorization, prime, 3
Factor(s)
  greatest common. *See* Greatest
    common factor (GCF)
  product and, 3, 8, 51, 72, 79, 82
  smallest common prime, 13
Fahrenheit, converting to/from Celsius,
    572–574, 584
FOIL process, 289, 290
Foot, 559
Formulas, 4, 5, 8, 80, 138
  evaluating, 6
  to find area of figures, 543–551
  to find perimeters, 533–537
  of function, 322, 334
  from geometry, 112–116, 138–139
  of linear function, 341
  midpoint, 349–351
  solving for variable, 116–118,
    446–447
  for surface area of solid object, 547
  translating words to, 7
  for volume of solid object, 547
Fractions, 22, 80
  addition and subtraction of, 18–22, 80
  basic concepts, 11–12
  basic principle of, 12, 13
  clearing, 105–106, 138
  converting to decimals, 55, 58, 83
  improper, 18
  least common denominator, 19–21

multiplication and division of, 14–18,
    23, 80
  simplifying, 14, 23, 80
  simplifying to lowest terms, 12–14
Franklin, Benjamin, 473
Frequency distribution table, 516
Function notation, 321, 386
Function representations, 386
Function(s), 334, 386
  absolute value, 370–371, 380
  basic concepts, 321–322
  compound inequalities, 358–365
  cubic, 371
  definition of, 327–329
  exponential. *See* Exponential functions
  expressing domain and range in
    interval notation, 370
  graphing calculators, 331–333
  identifying, 329–331
  linear. *See* Linear functions
  name of, 321
  operations on, 379, 380, 387
  piecewise-defined, 608–609
  polynomial, 371–373
  quadratic, 371. *See also* Quadratic
    function
  rational, 373–378, 380
  representations of, 322–326
Geometry, formulas, 112–116
Grade point average (GPA), 118, 120,
    139, 497–498
Graphical representation
  of function, 322–323, 334, 386
  of linear function, 341, 352
Graphs and graphing
  bar graphs, 513–515
  circle, 525–528
  for compound inequalities, 363
  the discriminant and, 457–458
  exponential functions, 476–478, 485
  finding intercepts, 164–167
  histograms, 515–517
  horizontal lines, 167–168
  intercepts, 219–220
  line graphs, 149–150, 151, 158,
    517–518
  linear equations in two variables, 219
  modeling, 211–215
  pictographs, 512
  piecewise-defined functions, 608–609
  point-slope form, 200–207
  for quadratic equations, 442–443
  quadratic functions, 412–415,
    421–422, 466
  rectangular coordinate system,
    145–147, 219
  reflecting, 612–613
  scatterplots and, 148–150
  slope and rates of change, 176–184
  slope-intercept form, 190–197
  solution to system of equations, 235, 237

to solve systems of linear equations, 230–238
tables and, 145
vertical and horizontal shifting, 609–612
vertical lines, 169–171
of $y = ax^2$, 418–419
Greater than or equal to symbol, 40–41, 124
Greater than symbol, 40–41, 124
Greatest common factor (GCF), 12–14, 23
Growth factor, 475, 479–480, 491

Histograms, 515–517
Horizontal lines, 167–168, 172, 220
Horizontal shift, 612
Horizontal translations, 426–428, 466
Hypotenuse, 505–507

Identity, 107
Identity property
    of one, 65–66, 68
    of real numbers, 83
    of zero, 65–66, 68
Improper fractions, 18
Inch, 560
Inconsistent system, 233, 237
Increasing, 434
Increment, 148
Independent equations, 233, 237
Independent variable, 321, 334
Index, 399
Inequalities, compound. *See* Compound inequalities
Inequality, 40–41, 42, 82
Inequality symbols, 124, 131
Input, 321
Integer exponents, rules for, 299
Integers, 35–36, 41, 81
    negative, as exponents, 295–297
Interest, compound, 481–483
Intersection, 360
Intersection-of-graphs method, 230–231
Interval notation, 125–126, 364–365, 370, 380, 387
Inverse property, of real numbers, 66–67, 68, 83
Irrational numbers, 37–39, 41, 81

Keller, Helen, 229
Kilometer, 564

Least common denominator (LCD), 19–21, 23
Legs, of triangle, 505–507
Length
    metric measurement of, 563–566
    U.S. (English) measurement of, 561–563
Less than or equal to symbol, 40–41, 124
Less than symbol, 40–41, 124
Levchin, Max, 320

Like denominators, 18–19, 23, 80
Like terms
    combining, 72–73, 76, 83
    polynomials and, 278, 283, 314
Line graphs, 149–150, 151, 158, 517–518
Linear equations, 137
    addition property of equality, 91–93
    applying the distributive property, 104–105
    basic concepts, 90, 99–101
    clearing fractions and decimals, 105–106
    graphing utilities for, 598–604
    multiplication property of equality, 94–96
    with no solutions or infinitely many solutions, 106–107, 108
    in one variable, 100–101
    solutions and, 90–91
    solving, 101–104
    solving numerically, 138
    system of, 260–261
    in two variables, 154–161
    using symbols to solve, 102–104, 108, 138
    using table to solve, 108
Linear functions, 386
    basic concepts, 341–343
    exponential functions and, 478
    midpoint formula, 349–351, 387
    modeling data with, 346–348, 387
    representations of, 343–345
Linear inequalities
    addition property of, 127–128, 133, 139
    applications, 131–132
    multiplication property of, 128–131, 133, 139
    solutions and number line graphs, 124–126, 139
Linear measurement, 584
    metric system, 563–566
    U.S. measurement system, 561–563
Linear models
    interpreting data, 597
    plotting data points, 616–621
Linear regression, 598
Lines
    equation of, 201
    finding slope of, 176–180
    horizontal, 167–168, 172
    parallel, 194
    perpendicular, 195–196
    vertical, 169–171, 172
Lobachevsky, Nikolai, 411
Lowest terms, 12–14, 22, 80

Mean, 497–498
Measures of central tendency, 497–499
Median, 498–499
Meter, 564, 584
Method of substitution, 241–246, 261

Metric system
    converting between Celsius and Fahrenheit, 574–575
    converting between U.S. (English) system and, 572–574
    defining and converting, 563–565
    performing operations on units of length, 565–566, 584
Midpoint formula, 349–351, 352, 387
Mile, 559
Millimeter, 564
Min-max applications, 416–418
Mode, 499
Modeling
    data, with linear functions, 346–348, 387
    involving exponential functions, 483–484
    of linear data, 211–215
    with linear equation, 222
    linear or quadratic, plotting data points using, 616–621
    for linear regression, 600–604
    mathematical, 222
    parabolas and, 466
    with quadratic functions, 433–435
Monomials, 283, 313
    division by, 306–308, 310
    multiplication of, 287, 288, 314
    polynomials and, 277–278
    writing and evaluating, 282
Multiplication, 57. *See also* Product(s)
    associative property for, 62, 68
    commutative property for, 60–61, 68
    dot ($\cdot$) to indicate, 4
    of fractions, 14–18, 80
    of monomial, 314
    of polynomials, 286–292, 314
    of real numbers, 51–53, 82–83
Multiplication property
    of equality, 94–96, 97, 137
    of inequalities, 128–131, 133, 139
Multiplicative identity, 65–66
Multiplicative inverse, 16, 23, 53, 66, 68, 80

Name of the function, 321
Natural exponential function, 484–485, 486
Natural number exponents, 26–29
Natural numbers, 2, 8, 79
Negative infinity, 364
Negative integers, as exponents, 295–297, 302, 315
Negative numbers, square roots of, 397
Negative reciprocals, 195
Negative slope, 178
Negative square root, 396
Nonlinear functions, 329
nth roots, 397, 399, 404
Number line
    adding integers on, 47

Number line *(continued)*
    compound inequalities and, 359–363
    graphing inequalities on, 125, 133
    midpoint formula on, 349
    real numbers on, 39, 41, 81
    solution and, 124–126
Number line graphs, 139
Numbers
    average, 38–39
    classifying, 4
    composite, 3–4, 8, 79
    counting, 8
    irrational, 37–39, 41, 81
    natural, 2, 8, 79
    opposite of, 34–35
    prime, 3–4, 8, 79
    rational, 35–36, 41, 81
    real. *See* Real numbers
    sets of, 81
    signed, 34–35
    whole, 2, 8, 79
Numerator, 11–12
Numerical representation (table of
      values), 386
    of function, 322, 334
    of linear function, 341, 352
Numerical solution, 231, 237
    for compound inequalities, 363
    for quadratic equations, 442–443

Odd root, 399
One real solution, 458
Operations, associativity of, 63
Operations on functions, 379, 380, 387
Opposite
    of a number, 34–35, 66, 81
    of polynomials, 280, 283
Order of operations, 29–31, 32, 81
Ordered pair, 146, 151, 327
Origin, 39, 145–146
Osborn, Ronald E., 1
Output, 321

Parabola
    quadratic functions and, 412–415, 421
    vertical and horizontal translations of,
      426–428, 435, 466
Parallel lines, slope and, 194, 197, 221
Parallelogram, area of, 543, 544, 583
Parentheses, when using the distributive
      property, 64
Participation inequality, 376
Percent change, 479–481, 485, 486, 491
Perfect square trinomial, 445
Perfect squares, 505
Perimeter
    of polygons, 534–535
    of rectangle, 112, 119, 138–139, 533, 583
    of square, 533, 583
    of triangles, 533–534, 583

Perpendicular lines, slope and, 195–196,
      197, 221
Pictographs, 512
Piecewise-defined functions, graphing,
      608–609
Plautus, 267
Plotting points, 146–147
Point-slope form, 200, 222
    applications, 205–206
    derivation of, 201
    finding, 201–205
Polygons, finding perimeter of, 534–535
Polyhedron, 546
Polynomial functions, exponential
      functions and, 478
Polynomial functions of one variable, 371,
      380, 387
Polynomials
    addition of, 278–280, 283, 314
    division of, 306–311, 315
    evaluating expressions, 281–283
    functions, 371–373
    monomials and, 277–278
    multiplication of, 286–292, 314
    in one variable, 277
    related terms, 313–314
    subtraction of, 280–281, 283, 314
Positive slope, 178
Positive square root, 396, 504
Power rules, 271–274, 313
Prime factorization, 3, 8, 79
Prime numbers, 3–4, 8, 79
Principal nth root, 399
Principal square roots, 37, 396, 397, 407,
      446, 504
Product rule, 270–271, 274, 296, 313
Product(s). *See also* Multiplication
    factors and, 3–4, 6, 8, 51–52, 79, 82
    raising, to a power, 272, 274
Profit, 378
Protractor, 527–528
Pythagorean Theorem, 505–507

Quadrants, 146
Quadratic equations, 466–467
    applications of, 447–448
    basics of, 440–443
    completing the square, 445–446, 467
    with complex solutions, 458–460
    solving, 441–443
    solving an equation for a variable,
      446–447
    square root property, 443–444
    that have complex solutions, 461
Quadratic formula
    complex solutions and, 458–460,
      461, 467
    the discriminant, 457–458, 467
    solving quadratic equations,
      454–457

Quadratic function
    basic transformations of $y = ax^2$,
      418–419
    graphs of, 412–415, 421–422, 466
    min-max applications, 416–418
    parabolas and modeling, 426–436, 466
    polynomials functions and, 371
    transformations of $y = ax^2 + bx + c$,
      419–421
Quadratic model, plotting data points,
      616–621
Quotient, 6, 53, 82
    raising, to a power, 272–273, 274
Quotient rule, 297–298, 303, 315

Radical expression, 396
Radical notation
    absolute value, 399–400, 407
    cube root, 398, 407
    cube root function, 403–404, 408
    nth root, 399, 407
    principal square root, 396, 397, 407
    square root, 396–398, 407
    square root function, 400–403, 407
Radical sign, 396, 504–505
Radicand, 396
Radius, 114, 546
Range
    of function, 327–329, 334, 386
    in interval notation, 370, 380, 387
Rate of change, 176, 181–183, 184, 221,
      342, 351
Rational functions, 373–378, 380, 387
Rational numbers, 35–36, 41, 81
Real numbers, 81
    absolute value, 40
    addition of, 45–47, 82
    associative properties, 61–63, 83
    commutative properties, 60–61, 83
    distributive properties, 63–65, 83
    division of, 53–56, 82–83
    with exponents, evaluating, 53
    identity properties, 65–66, 83
    inequality, 40–41
    integers and rational numbers,
      35–36
    inverse properties, 65–66, 83
    irrational numbers and, 37–39
    multiplication of, 51–53, 82–83
    number line, 39
    signed numbers, 34–35
    square roots, 37
    subtraction of, 47–48, 82
Reciprocal, 16, 23, 53, 66, 80
Rectangles
    area of, 7, 112, 119, 138–139, 543, 583
    perimeter of, 112, 119, 138–139,
      532, 583
Rectangular coordinate system, 145–147,
      151, 219

Rectangular solid
    surface area of, 547, 548
    volume of, 547, 548, 583
Reflection, 612–613
    of a graph, 419
Regression, 616–621
Regression analysis, 598
Relation, 327
Repeating decimals, 36
Revenue, 378
Right triangle, 505–507
Rise, 176–177, 180, 183
Run, 176–177, 180, 183

Scatterplots, 148–150, 151, 332–333
Scientific notation, 300–302, 303, 315
Set of all solutions, 91
Set-builder notation, 130, 133
Signed numbers, 34–35
Simplification, 307
Simplifying expressions, 73–75
Slope
    of a line, 176–180
    negative, 178–179
    positive, 178–179
    as rate of change, 181–183, 184, 220, 221
    undefined, 178–179
    zero, 178–179
Slope-intercept form, 221
    basic concepts, 190
    finding, 191–194
    parallel lines, 194
    perpendicular lines, 195–196
Smallest common prime factor, 13, 20
Solution
    to an equation, 90–91, 96
    to inequality, 124–126, 133
Solution set
    of an equation, 91, 96, 137
    to inequality, 124–125, 133
Solution to a system, 233, 237
Solutions
    complex, 458–460
    for compound inequalities, 359–363
    to equations, 137
    to inequality, 139
    tables of, 156–157
Sphere
    surface area of, 547, 549
    volume of, 547, 548–549, 583
Square
    area of, 27, 542, 583
    finding perimeter of, 533, 583
Square root function, 400–403, 404, 407, 610
Square root property, 443–444, 449
Square roots, 37, 396–398, 407, 504–505
Square-based pyramid
    surface area of, 547
    volume of, 547, 583

Squared, 27
Standard form
    decimal notation and, 300
    of equation in two variables, 158
    for a parabola with vertical axis, 429
Standard viewing rectangle, 332
Subscript, 177
Substitution, solving systems of linear
    equations by, 241–246
Subtraction
    of fractions, 18–22
    of polynomials, 280–281, 283, 314
    of real numbers, 47–48, 49, 82
    words associated with, 48
Sum, 6, 45
Surface area
    of boxes, 139
    of solid object, 546, 547
Symbolic representation (formula)
    of function, 322, 334, 386
    of linear function, 341, 352
    for quadratic equations, 441–443
System of two equations in two variables,
    232–233
Systems of linear equations in two
    variables
    solving by elimination, 249–257
    solving by substitution, 241–246
    solving graphically and numerically,
        229, 230–238

Table, to find slope-intercept form,
    204–205
Table of solutions, 156–157, 161
Table of values
    completing, 180
    of function, 322, 334, 386
    intersection of graphs and, 231
    of linear function, 341, 352
Temperature, conversions between U.S.
    and metric system, 139, 572–574
Terminating decimals, 36
    converting to fractions, 58
Terms
    of an equation, 71–72, 76, 83
    like. See Like terms
Three-part inequality, 360–362,
    365, 387
Translations, vertical and horizontal,
    426–428, 435
Trapezoids, area of, 115, 120, 139,
    543, 583
Triangles
    area of, 112, 138–139, 543, 544, 583
    finding degrees in, 114, 119
    finding perimeter of, 533–534, 583
Trinomials, 277, 313

Undefined slope, 178
Unit fractions, 559–560, 584

United States (U.S.) measurement system
    converting between Celsius and
        Fahrenheit, 574–575
    converting between metric system and,
        572–574
    defining and converting, 559–560
    performing operations on units of
        length, 562–563, 584
    using mixed units of length, 561
Unlike denominators, 19, 21–22, 80

Values, table of, 180
Variable(s)
    dependent, 321, 334
    formulas and, 116–118
    independent, 321, 334
    one, evaluating algebraic expressions
        with, 5
    one, linear equation in, 100–101
    to represent unknown quantity, 4, 8, 79
    solving equation or formula for,
        446–447
    two, evaluating algebraic expressions
        with, 5
    two, linear equations in, 154–161, 219
Verbal representation (words)
    of function, 322, 334, 386
    of linear function, 341, 352
Vertex, of parabola, 412–413, 421
Vertex form, 428–432, 435, 466
Vertex formula, 413–414, 466
Vertical asymptote, 376
Vertical line test, 330–331, 334, 386
Vertical lines, 169–171, 172, 220
Vertical shift, 420, 611
Vertical translations, 426–428, 466
Vertices, of polyhedron, 547
Viewing rectangle, 331–332
Volume
    of boxes, 115, 120, 139
    of circular cylinder, 583
    of cone, 583
    of cube, 583
    of cylinder, 116, 120, 139
    of rectangular solid, 583
    of solid object, 546, 547
    of sphere, 583
    of square-based pyramid, 583

Weighted mean, 497–498
Whole numbers, 2, 8, 79
Window, 331–332
Wonder, Stevie, 144
Words. See also Verbal representation
    (words)
    translating to expressions, 6–7
    translating to inequalities, 131

x-axis, 145–147
x-coordinate, 148

x-intercept, 164–167, 171, 219–220
Xmax, 332
Xmin, 332
Xscl, 332
xy-plane
    for graphing, 145–147, 151
    midpoint formula in, 349

Yard, 559
y-axis, 145–147
y-coordinate, 148
Yeats, William Butler, 89
y-intercept, 164–167, 171, 219–220
Ymax, 332

Ymin, 332
Yscl, 332

Zero exponents, 269–270, 274, 313
Zero slope, 178